BOOK 3

# Math Matters

**Authors**

FRANK EBOS, Senior Author
Faculty of Education
University of Toronto

PAUL ZOLIS
Coordinator of Mathematics
Scarborough Board of Education

**Reviewer Consultants**

DONNA CHANASYK
Paul Kane High School
St. Albert, Alberta

SHARON CUTCLIFFE
Moscrop Junior Secondary School
Burnaby, British Columbia

LARRY M. ELCHUCK
Pictou District School Board
New Glasgow, Nova Scotia

PAUL W. HIETALA
Seneca College
North York, Ontario

JIM HOGER
Treherne Collegiate Institute
Treherne, Manitoba

HUGH McKNIGHT
St. Stephen High School
St. Stephen, New Brunswick

STEVE WIEBE
Mount Royal Collegiate
Saskatoon, Saskatchewan

**NELSON** CANADA

Published in 1987 by
Nelson Canada,
A Division of International Thomson Limited
1120 Birchmount Road
Scarborough, Ontario M1K 5G4

ISBN 0-17-601794-1

Printed and bound in Canada.
34567890 BP 8943210987

Technical Art: Frank Zsigo
Cover Design: Rob McPhail, Don Gauthier

Printing and Binding: The Bryant Press Limited

PHOTO CREDITS:

Apple Canada–355; Athlete Information Bureau–252, 323; Bank of Montreal–177; BIC–418; Camerique–7; Canapress-cover, 68, 155, 237, 293, 298, 380, 387, 395; Canadian Armed Forces-cover, 399, 429; Cedric Pearson/SSC—Photocentre–120; City T.V., Toronto–7; Dennis Broughton–369;Dep't of Defense–142; Dep't of Fisheries Office–456; Dep't of Health and Human Sciences, USA–39; Dep't of Tourism and Recreation, Manitoba–141; Dr. N.G. Dengler, Dep't of Botany, U. of T.–40; Donald Eldon–74, 77, 96, 134, 157, 164, 187, 228, 274, 384, 389, 409; Federal Dep't of Communications–273; Ford Motor Co.–374, 429; Frank Ebos–20, 128, 153, 154, 155, 276, 297, 303, 386; Global Television Network–277; Gridwork–148; Hitachi–259; I.B.M.–375; Imperial Oil Ltd.–163; Italian Government Travel Office–146; John Deere Co.–167; Kim Brown–173; Metro Toronto Zoo–292; Metropolitan Toronto and Region Conservation Authority–251; Miller Services–132, /American Stock Photo–399, /Camerique–7, /Grant Heilman–62, /H. Armstrong Roberts-cover, 22, 107, 247, 335, 364, 369, 429, 450, /Harold M. Lambert–8, 32, 350, /Malak–135, /Stock Colour Masters–149; Ministry of Industry, Trade and Technology–150; Ministry of Natural Resources–399; Ministry of Tourism and Recreation–141, 195; Ministry of Transportation and Communications–273, 378, 381, 443; NASA–399; NFB–11; Nova Scotia Dep't of Government Services–73; North York Board of Education–141; Office of Sports for the Physically Disabled–146; Ontario Archives–173; Ontario Hydro–33, 369; Ontario Ministry of Agriculture and Food–7; Ontario Ministry of Energy–51; Panasonic–234; Public Archives Canada–304; Roy Thompson Hall–141; Smithsonian Institute–119; T. Edward S. Matchette-396; Toronto Stock Exchange–267; Tourism New Brunswick–15; The Globe and Mail–119; Tracy Walker–415; Transport Canada–335; Walter Cavanaugh–249; Winnipeg Mint, Government of Manitoba–243; Xerox–429.

**Cdn. Cataloguing in Publication Data**

Ebos, Frank, 1939–
Math matters, book 3

Includes index.
ISBN 0-17-601794-1
1. Mathematics—1961–
I. Zolis, Paul. II. Title.

QA39.2.E2 1986 510 C86-093023-8

The authors wish to express special thanks to Maggie Cheverie, Managing Editor.

The authors wish to express their thanks to Anthony Rodrigues, Peter Gardiner, Andrew Clowes, Sharon Kerr, Frank Zsigo, Bill Allan, Geoffrey Hull, Barbara De Carlo, Lesley Ebos, Michael Ebos, Lynda Lou Gourlie, Les Dow, Walt Elliott, Reg Kerford, Don Mason, Danny Crowther and Judy Chapman.

The authors gratefully acknowledge the advice, assistance and contribution of RoseMary Ebos.

# Contents

## 12. Working with Straight Lines



## 13. Applications: Ratio, Rates and Variations



## 14. Exploring with Geometry: Skills and Applications



## 15. Essentials of Trigonometry

# Using Math Matters Book 3

This page explains how the text is organized.

### Lesson Features

Each section follows a general pattern.

- The lesson topic is introduced with new terms in **bold type**.
  Then the particular skill is demonstrated in *Examples* and their *Solutions*.
- Hints and explanatory notes are in red.

## 11.6 Drawing Graphs

The Cartesian plane provides a very useful tool for showing relationships between two variables. The horizontal axis is used to represent the first variable, and the vertical axis is used to represent the second variable. The two variables used most often are $x$ and $y$.

**Example 1**
Use the equation $y = 3x - 1$. Construct a table of values and graph the relation between $x$ and $y$.

**Solution**
*Step 1*: To construct a table of values, choose values for $x$ and use the given formula to find each corresponding value for $y$.

| x | y |
|---|---|
| 2 | 5 |
| 1 | 2 |

$y = 3x - 1$
$= 3(2) - 1$
$= 6 - 1$
$= 5$

### Exercise Features

- The *Try These* are introductory exercises, designed to identify key skills in preparation for the *Written Exercises*. Most *Try These* sections can be done mentally.
- The *Written Exercises* provide practice and application of the skills. The exercises are organized into an A-B-C format. Section A provides skills practise, section B may involve a combination of skills in problems and applications, while section C has challenging problems, activities etc.
- The *Applications* sections are clusters of theme-related problems which apply or extend the topic in interesting, real-world situations.

**Try These**

1 What are the products?
(a) $(m + 2)(m - 2)$
(b) $(p + 3)(p - 3)$
(c) $(n - 10)(n + 10)$
(d) $(1 - a)(1 + a)$

2 What are the products?
(a) $(a - 2b)(a + 2b)$
(b) $(2m + 3)(2m - 3)$
(c) $(p - 2q)(p + 2q)$

3 What are th
(a) $a^2 - 9 =$
(b) $p^2 - 25 =$
(c) $m^2 - 49$
(d) $1 - n^2 =$

**Written Exercises**

**A** Remember: First write each term of a difference of squares in the form
$a^2 - b^2 = (a)^2 - (b)^2$.

1 An important skill is to recognize squares. Which of the following are squares?
(a) $9k^2$ (b) $25x^2$ (c) $16m^2$ (d) $48x^2$
(e) $4t^2$ (f) $36m^4$ (g) $18m^2$ (h) $100k$
(i) $x^2y^2$ (j) $4ab$ (k) $49R^2$ (l) $26n$

3 Find the missing parts.
(a) $49 - 36p^2 = (?)^2 - (?)^2$
(b) $4m^2 - 81n^2 = (?)^2 - (?)^2$
(c) $16x^2 - 36y^2 = (?)^2 - (?)^2$

4 (a) Find the missing parts.
$x^2 - 16y^2 = (?)^2 - (?)^2$
(b) Write the factors of the e

5 (a) Find the missing parts

**Applications: Cost of Depreciation**

Another factor that can affect your decision on whether to buy a particular car is depreciation. Most cars lose value quickly. As soon as you drive your new car it loses up to 20% of the price you paid for it! The rate at which cars depreciate does vary according to the type of car. The chart shows the average depreciation of a medium-priced North American car.

| Time | Depreciation (Percent of previous year's value) |
|---|---|
| First year | 30% |
| Second year | 15% |
| Third year | 15% |
| Fourth year | 10% |
| Fifth year | 8% |

For example, if you buy a new car for $14 000, its value 2 years will decrease as shown

**Career Tip**

Technicians often need to translate technical and scientific ideas into products and services. They provide a vital link between scientists and engineers and the production workers. They perform tests, solve problems and write up their results to assist scientists and engineers.
• Explo

### Extra Features

- Each chapter ends with a *Review: Practice and Problems* and *A Practice Test.*
- An *Update: A Cumulative Review* occurs after every 4 chapters.
- Extension features are found in appropriate contexts throughout the book.
  ▶ Calculator Tip ▶ Computer Tip
  ▶ Career Tip ▶ Consumer Tip
  ▶ Math Tip

# 1 Inventory: Foundation Skills

using steps in mathematics, working with calculators, numbers and charts, skills with estimation, fractions, and decimals, problem-solving, integers and calculators, using percent, organizing information, solving problems and applications

## Introduction

Mathematics has many parts. Some parts you can directly use in your everyday activities. Some parts are needed to do problems in other subjects. Some parts are applied to solve problems that occur in many careers. For each photo, what skills in mathematics do you think are needed by each person?

- a landscaper

- a technician

- a farmer

- a business person

# 1.1 Steps in Mathematics

In flying a modern jet liner, pilots have many responsibilities.

- ▶ They must understand the precise use of all the controls.
- ▶ They must carefully follow a checklist to ensure the safety of the passengers.
- ▶ They must obey very strict safety rules to avoid mishaps in the air.

Whether you play sports, fly a jet, or drive a car, you must understand the meanings of the words used and follow the rules to be successful.

To be a pilot, you undergo a lot of training in reading dials, as well as in interpreting the effect on your aircraft as the readings of the dials change. To obtain a pilot's licence you must pass many tests, many based on skills in mathematics.

To use mathematics, you must also follow very important steps.

- ▶ *The first step* is to understand the words of mathematics. You must know the precise meaning of words used to do mathematics. This step is important not only in doing mathematics, but in other subjects as well. You need to know the vocabulary so that you are able to follow instructions in applying mathematics to solve problems.
- ▶ *The second step* is to learn the rules of mathematics. In so doing, you will learn skills in mathematics that allow you to continue to solve "important problems in many fields such as surveying, business, construction, and social work to name a few. As well, your study in mathematics will enable you to make better decisions when making personal purchases, saving money, and so on.

Throughout any advanced work in mathematics, you need to continually do computations with numbers. In so doing, you need to follow a precise rule for the order in which you do the operations. The table at the right lists the rules. If you follow these rules your answers and procedures will be consistent each time.

**Rules For The Order of Operations**

- Do all calculations in brackets first.
- Multiply and divide in the order they appear, from left to right.
- Add and subtract in the order they appear, from left to right.

## Example 1

(a) $55 \div (8 + 3) - 7 \times 2$ (b) $\dfrac{4 + 18 + 36 \div 9}{12 + 30 \div 5}$

## Solution

(a)
$$\begin{aligned} & 55 \div (8 + 3) - 7 \times 2 && \text{Do the calculations in the brackets} \\ &= 55 \div 11 - 7 \times 2 && \text{Do multiplication before subtracting} \\ &= 5 - 7 \times 2 \\ &= 5 - 14 \\ &= -9 \end{aligned}$$

(b)
$$\begin{aligned} \frac{4 + 18 + 36 \div 9}{12 + 30 \div 5} &= \frac{4 + 18 + 4}{12 + 6} \\ &= \frac{26}{18} \\ &= \frac{13}{9} \text{ or } 1\frac{4}{9} \end{aligned}$$

In doing mathematics, variables are used to represent numbers in many situations.

- in formulas
  $P = 2(l + w)$  $d = r \times t$
  $i = Prt$
- in expressions
  $x + 3y$  $2a + 3b + 5c$
  $2.5p + 3.6j + 2.9k$
- in equations
  $2x - 3 = 6$
  $x^2 - 6x - 27 = 0$

You again apply the rules for the order of operations when working with variables, such as evaluating an expression. To evaluate an expression you substitute number values represented by the variable, as shown in the next example.

**Example 2**

Evaluate each expression for $x = -2$ and $y = 3$.

(a) $3x - y(y - x)$  (b) $\frac{4xy}{5y} + y - x$

**Solution**

(a)
$$\begin{aligned} & 3x - y(y - x) \\ &= 3(-2) - 3(3 - (-2)) \\ &= -6 - 3(3 + 2) \\ &= -6 - 3(5) \\ &= -6 - 15 \\ &= -21 \end{aligned}$$

(b)
$$\begin{aligned} \frac{4xy}{5y} + y - x &= \frac{4(-2)(3)}{5(3)} + 3 - (-2) \\ &= -\frac{8}{5} + 3 + 2 \\ &= -\frac{8}{5} + 5 \\ &= \frac{17}{5} \end{aligned}$$

## Try These

1 Calculate.
(a) $10 \times 4 - 7$  (b) $45 - 3 \times 5$
(c) $(12 + 3) \div 5$
(d) $16 - 8 - 4 \times 5 \div 4 + 9$
(e) $24 - 3 \times 5 + 12$
(f) $6 + 32 - 13 - 24 \div 6$

2 Evaluate each expression. Use $a = 3$, $b = 2$.
(a) $3ab$  (b) $2a + 3b$  (c) $2a - 3b$
(d) $3a - 2b$  (e) $2(a + b)$  (f) $2(2a - b)$

## Written Exercises

**A** 1 Simplify.
(a) $5 \times 8 + 7$  (b) $[6(5 + 9)] + 3 \times 12$
(c) $\frac{3(5 \times 2)}{15} + (4 \times 7) \div 14$
(d) $6 + \frac{3(9 - 7)}{2}$

2 Simplify.
(a) $4 \times 5 + \frac{27}{6} - \frac{5 \times 8 + 23}{21}$
(b) $17 + 14 - 8 \times \frac{1}{2}$
(c) $9 - [6 - 2(7 - 1)] - 36 \div 4$

3 Evaluate the expression $\frac{a(b+4c)}{2d}$ for the given values.
(a) $a = 2$, $b = -1$, $c = 3$, $d = -2$
(b) $a = -3$, $b = 4$, $c = 5$, $d = -1$
(c) $a = -5$, $b = -3$, $c = 4$, $d = 4$

4 Evaluate the following expressions for $x = 2$, $y = -1$, $z = 3$, $w = 0$.
(a) $x(2y - wz)$ (b) $4(y + xw - 3)$
(c) $\frac{4(2y - 3w + z)}{3(x + z)}$ (d) $\frac{5(3w - 2xy)}{3z}$

**B** **Follow the instructions carefully in answering questions. Read the symbols used accurately.**

5 Evaluate each expression.
(a) $68 - 2(16 \div 4) + 10 \div 2 - 15$
(b) $24 \div 6 \times 7 - 36 \div 9 \times 3 + 13$
(c) $44 + \frac{44 + 11}{5} - 21 + 2(6 - 4)$
(d) $2[25 - 3 \times 4 \div 6] \div 23 - 7$

6 For each formula, follow the instructions.
(a) $d = vt$; find $d$ when $v = 45$, $t = 9$
(b) $C = 2\pi r$; find $C$ when $\pi \doteq 3.14$, $r = 2.85$
(c) $A = \frac{1}{2}(a + b)h$; find $A$ when $a = 12$, $b = 16$, $h = 10$
(d) $v = u + at$; find $u$ when $v = 36$, $a = 2$, $t = 3$
(e) $S = R\pi d$; find $R$ when $S = 12.56$, $d = 0.50$, use $\pi \doteq 3.14$.
(f) $S = \left(\frac{u + v}{2}\right)t$; find $S$ when $u = 8$, $v = 12$, $t = 4$.

7 In each formula, find the value of the remaining variable.

| formula | values of the variables |
|---|---|
| (a) $P = 2(l + w)$ | $P = 120$, $l = 16$ |
| (b) $P = l^2R$ | $P = 800$, $l = 10$ |
| (c) $y = m(x - a)$ | $y = 8$, $m = \frac{2}{3}$, $x = 3$ |
| (d) $u^2 = v^2 - 30t$ | $u = 8$, $v = 20$ |
| (e) $l = 180(x - 2)$ | $l = 1080$ |

8 The following formula is used for calculating charges for long distance calls.

$T = C + nr$ where $T$ is the total cost in dollars of the call, $C$ is the charge for the first 3 min (in dollars), $n$ is the number of additional minutes, $r$ is the rate per minute for each additional minute.

Calculate each of the following charges, $T$.
(a) $C = 6.08$, $r = 2.30$, $n = 5$
(b) $C = 3.65$, $r = 1.04$, $n = 8$
(c) $C = 5.02$, $r = 1.59$, $n = 16$

9 Plaster Rock is the gateway to northern New Brunswick. To win a free all expenses paid trip for 2 weeks, a contestant is asked to place brackets to make the following true.

$$6 \times 3 + 4 + 7 \times 8 + 3 \times 5 \stackrel{?}{=} 427$$

What is the winner's answer?

10 (a) Copy and complete the pattern.
$2 + 4 = ?$
$2 + 4 + 6 = ?$
$2 + 4 + 6 + 8 = ?$
$2 + 4 + 6 + 8 + 10 = ?$
(b) What pattern for finding the sum do you notice?
(c) Find the sum of the first 10 even numbers.

11 A sum of even numbers is shown as
$2 + 4 + 6 + 8 + 10 + \cdots$
The formula to find the sum, $s$, of $n$ numbers is given by $s = n^2 + n$.
(a) Calculate the sum of the first 3 even numbers using the above formula. Check your answer by adding.
(b) Calculate the sum of the first 10 even numbers using the formula.
(c) Calculate the sum of the first 50 even numbers.

# 1.2 Using Calculators

Often on industrial sites or in laboratories, you will see people using calculators to do on-the-spot calculations. A calculator is a very useful tool in doing mathematics. Each calculator, however, has different features, as well as different looking push buttons for the same feature. For this reason you must refer to the handbook provided with the calculator to learn about any special features.

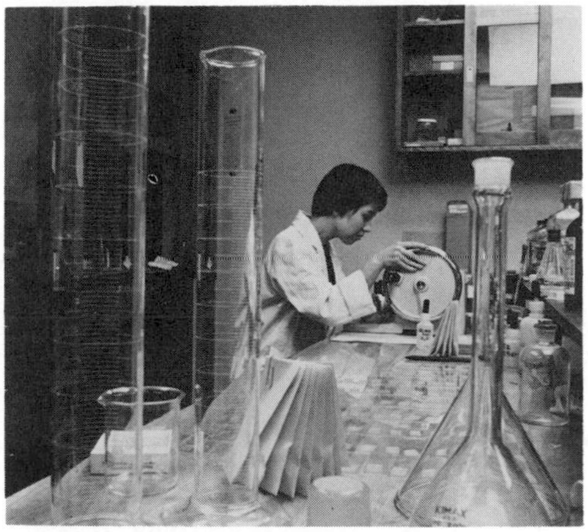

Various tests are made after goods are manufactured to ensure quality and to meet the required specifications.

Whenever you use a calculator
always clear the display.
Push the [C] button first.

In order to use your calculator correctly, you must find the order in which it performs operations. Some calculators automatically follow the rules for the order of operations, but most do not. For example,

to do this calculation
$12 + 7 \times 3$

you follow these steps
[C] 12 [+] 7 [×] 3 [=] ?

**Answer 57**
If the calculator displays 57 as the final answer, then the calculator performs calculations in the order they are entered.

**Answer 33**
If the calculator displays 33 as the final answer, then the calculator performs calculations according to the rules of the order of operations.

**Example**
Calculate $18 + 85 \div 17$.

### Solution

If your calculator does not follow the order of operations, then you need to follow these steps. ⟹

| Press | Display |
|---|---|
| 85 | 85. |
| [÷] | 85. |
| 17 | 17. |
| [+] | 5. |
| 18 | 18. |
| [=] | 23. |

If your calculator follows the order of operations, you need to do these steps. ⟹

| Press | Display |
|---|---|
| 18 | 18. |
| [+] | 18. |
| 85 | 85. |
| [÷] | 85. |
| 17 | 17. |
| [=] | 23. |

On your calculator, you often find features that can assist you in calculations. For example, a useful feature is the reciprocal shown by $\boxed{\frac{1}{x}}$. For example,

To calculate $884 \div (63 - 59)$ $\Longrightarrow$ you can think of the operation as shown:

$$884 \times \frac{1}{63 - 59} \quad \text{or} \quad \frac{1}{63 - 59} \times 884$$

↑ ↑

use the reciprocal key

| Press | Display |
|---|---|
| 63 | 63. |
| $\boxed{-}$ | 63. |
| 59 | 59. |
| $\boxed{=}$ | 4. |
| $\boxed{\frac{1}{x}}$ | 0.25 |
| $\boxed{\times}$ | 0.25 |
| 884 | 884. |
| $\boxed{=}$ | 221. |

## Try These

A calculator does not follow the order of operations. What are the steps to calculate each of the following?

(a) $28 + 36 + 42$
(b) $49 + 36 - 28$
(c) $39 + 18 \times 3$
(d) $96 + 36 \div 3$
(e) $96 \times 21 + 32$
(f) $48 \div 6 + 12$
(g) $96 \times 48 \times 4$
(h) $32 \div 16 \div 4$

Remember: check the manual of your calculator which describes the features.

## Written Exercises

**A** Review the steps for the order of operations. Check whether the calculator follows the order of operations.

1 Evaluate. Follow these instructions.

(a) $\boxed{C}$ 156 $\boxed{+}$ 1209 $\boxed{=}$
(b) $\boxed{C}$ 4243 $\boxed{+}$ 306 $\boxed{+}$ 965 $\boxed{=}$
(c) $\boxed{C}$ 5419 $\boxed{-}$ 1652 $\boxed{=}$
(d) $\boxed{C}$ 8041 $\boxed{-}$ 3652 $\boxed{-}$ 1908 $\boxed{=}$
(e) $\boxed{C}$ 4098 $\boxed{-}$ 2563 $\boxed{+}$ 5491 $\boxed{=}$

2 Follow these instructions. Evaluate.

(a) $\boxed{C}$ 64 $\boxed{\times}$ 152 $\boxed{=}$
(b) $\boxed{C}$ 491 $\boxed{\times}$ 18 $\boxed{\times}$ 845 $\boxed{=}$
(c) $\boxed{C}$ 5472 $\boxed{\div}$ 36 $\boxed{=}$
(d) $\boxed{C}$ 89 $\boxed{\times}$ 643 $\boxed{\div}$ 93 $\boxed{=}$
(e) $\boxed{C}$ 1452 $\boxed{\times}$ 193 $\boxed{\div}$ 648 $\boxed{=}$
(f) $\boxed{C}$ 1728 $\boxed{\div}$ 48 $\boxed{\div}$ 6 $\boxed{=}$

3 Evaluate each of the following.

Remember to push $\boxed{C}$ before any work is done on a calculator.

(a) $18 + 25 \times 3$
(b) $53 + 39 \div 13 - 4$
(c) $84 + 225 \div 15$
(d) $-25 + 964 \div 4$
(e) $55 \times (186 \div 6)$
(f) $15 \times (39 + 74)$
(g) $508 \div 4 - 67$
(h) $29 \times 62 - 742$

4 Simplify using your calculator.

(a) $62 \times 9 + 14$
(b) $(-16) \times (-52) - 26$
(c) $(-28)[(-18) + 69]$
(d) $(-13)(51)(19)$
(e) $(-8.4) + 69.2 - 3.8$
(f) $3.9 + 4.2 \times 11 - 56.7$

**B** Remember: The $\boxed{\frac{1}{x}}$ key can be used to help you do calculations.

5 Calculate. Use a calculator.

(a) $\dfrac{64}{72 - 8}$ (b) $96 \div (40 - 8)$

(c) $220 \div (384 - 296)$ (d) $102 \div (12 - 3 \times 2)$

(e) $735 - (193 - 2 \times 23)$

6 Do these calculations.

(a) $48 \times 8 - 16$ (b) $28 + 6 \times 9$

(c) $48 \times 9 \div 18$ (d) $36 + 48 \div 16 \times 9$

(e) $125 \div 25 \times 50 + 100$

(f) $50 + 36 \times 2 \div 9 + 14$

(g) Find the sum of your answers in (a) through (f).

7 Which answer is greater, A or B?

| | A | B |
|---|---|---|
| (a) | $24 + 62 \times 17$ | $126 + 441 \div 21$ |
| (b) | $128(242 \div 2)$ | $96(18 + 62)$ |
| (c) | $68 \times 4 + 128$ | $128(68 + 4)$ |
| (d) | $75 + 325 \div 25$ | $(75 + 325) \div 25$ |

8 Evaluate. Use a calculator.

(a) $64 + 325 \div 25 - 42$

(b) $93 + (841 - 263) \div 2$

(c) $15 + 63 \times 87 - 209$

(d) $18 + (19 \times 34 - 81) - 65$

(e) $607 - 43 + 17 \times 83$

(f) $88 + (15 \times 13 - 48) - 92$

9 Do the following steps in order. If your calculator has a repeating feature, then A will occur. If it does not, then B will occur.

(a) Calculator A

| Press | Display |
|---|---|
| [C] | 0 |
| 5 | 5. |
| [+] | 5. |
| 8 | 8. |
| [=] | 13. |
| [=] | 21. |
| [=] | 29 |

(b) Calculator B

| Press | Display |
|---|---|
| [C] | 0 |
| 5 | 5. |
| [+] | 5. |
| 8 | 8. |
| [=] | 13. |
| [=] | 13. |
| [=] | 13. |

10 A repeating feature also applies to the operations of subtraction and division. Do the following instructions.

(a) [C] 28 [−] 5 [=] [=] [=]

(b) [C] 32 [÷] 2 [=] [=] [=]

(c) [C] 100 [−] 10 [=] [=] [=] [=] [=]

11 A repeating feature for multiplication also applies to some calculators. On some calculators however, the first number entered into the calculator is the repeated number. On other calculators, the second number is the repeated number. Do these steps to test the repeating feature on your calculator.

(a) [C] 3 × 2 [=] [=] [=]

(b) [C] 2 × 3 [=] [=] [=]

(c) [C] 8 [×] 5 [=] [=] [=] [=]

12 Remember $2^4$ means $2 \times 2 \times 2 \times 2$

You can use a calculator to find $2^4$ by doing these steps

[C] 2 [×] [=] [=] [=]

Calculate each of the following.

(a) $3^3$ (b) $2^5$ (c) $4^3$ (d) $2^6$

(e) $(0.2)^3$ (f) $(0.5)^4$ (g) $10^3$ (h) $10^5$

## Calculator Tip

Throughout the text, *Calculator Tips* will review the various features on your calculator to help you do computation in solving problems. Refer to your manual that describes the following memory features.

[MS] or [STO] means store the display in memory.

[M+] means add the display number to the memory.

[M−] means subtract the display number from memory.

[MR], [RM], [RCL] means recall the number from memory to the display.

[MC] or [CM] means clear the memory.

To calculate $18.6 \div (49.3 - 12.8)$, you can use the following procedure.

[C] 49.3 [−] 12.8 [=] [MS] 18.6 ÷ [MR] [=] ?

# 1.3 Numbers, Charts and Tables

In the study of science, in finding interest on an account, or in finding distance, charts and tables are often used to summarize much information in a compact form. In doing mathematics, you will often use tables or charts to record your own information. To read a chart you need to interpret how the information is recorded. For example, Patricia wants to know how far it is from Moncton to Vancouver by rail. To find the distance, locate the two cities on the chart shown.

Railway Distances between major centres in Canada, in kilometres.

locate the first city (Moncton) — locate the second city (Vancouver)

| | BANFF | CALGARY | CHARLOTTETOWN | CHURCHILL | EDMONTON | FREDERICTON | HALIFAX | KINGSTON | MONCTON | MONTREAL | OTTAWA | PRICE RUPERT | QUEBEC (STE-FOY) | REGINA | SAINT JOHN, N.B. | ST. JOHN'S, Nfld. | SASKATOON | SUDBURY | SYDNEY | THUNDER BAY | TORONTO | VANCOUVER | VICTORIA | WINDSOR |
|---|---|---|---|---|---|---|---|---|---|---|---|---|---|---|---|---|---|---|---|---|---|---|---|---|
| CALGARY | 130 | | | | | | | | | | | | | | | | | | | | | | | |
| CHARLOTTETOWN | 5293 | 5163 | | | | | | | | | | | | | | | | | | | | | | |
| CHURCHILL | 3167 | 3037 | 5520 | | | | | | | | | | | | | | | | | | | | | |
| EDMONTON | 439 | 309 | 5149 | 3054 | | | | | | | | | | | | | | | | | | | | |
| FREDERICTON | 5293 | 5163 | 467 | 3823 | 5180 | | | | | | | | | | | | | | | | | | | |
| HALIFAX | 6396 | 5220 | 524 | 5577 | 5237 | 555 | | | | | | | | | | | | | | | | | | |
| KINGSTON | 3713 | 3583 | 1549 | 3940 | 3600 | 1580 | 1637 | | | | | | | | | | | | | | | | | |
| MONCTON | 5044 | 4914 | 218 | 5271 | 4931 | 249 | 306 | 1331 | | | | | | | | | | | | | | | | |
| MONTREAL | 3998 | 3868 | 1264 | 4225 | 3885 | 1295 | 1352 | 285 | 1046 | | | | | | | | | | | | | | | |
| OTTAWA | 3905 | 3775 | 1451 | 4132 | 3792 | 1482 | 1539 | 190 | 1233 | 187 | | | | | | | | | | | | | | |
| PRICE RUPERT | 1979 | 1849 | 6689 | 4594 | 1540 | 6720 | 6777 | 5140 | 6471 | 5425 | 5332 | | | | | | | | | | | | | |
| QUEBEC (STE-FOY) | 4249 | 4119 | 1005 | 4476 | 4136 | 1036 | 1093 | 536 | 787 | 251 | 438 | 5676 | | | | | | | | | | | | |
| REGINA | 895 | 765 | 4366 | 2271 | 783 | 4397 | 4454 | 2817 | 4148 | 3102 | 3009 | 2323 | 3353 | | | | | | | | | | | |
| SAINT JOHN, N.B. | 5187 | 5057 | 361 | 5414 | 5074 | 106 | 449 | 1474 | 143 | 1189 | 1376 | 6614 | 930 | 4291 | | | | | | | | | | |
| ST. JOHN'S, Nfld. | 7773 | 6799 | 2103 | 7156 | 6816 | 2134 | 1579 | 3216 | 1885 | 2931 | 3118 | 8356 | 2672 | 6033 | 2028 | | | | | | | | | |
| SASKATOON | 959 | 829 | 4629 | 2534 | 520 | 4660 | 4717 | 3080 | 4411 | 3365 | 3272 | 2060 | 3616 | 263 | 4554 | 6296 | | | | | | | | |
| SUDBURY | 3033 | 2903 | 2229 | 3260 | 2920 | 2260 | 2317 | 680 | 2011 | 965 | 712 | 4460 | 776 | 2137 | 2154 | 3996 | 2400 | | | | | | | |
| SYDNEY | 5823 | 5693 | 997 | 6050 | 5710 | 1028 | 473 | 2110 | 779 | 1825 | 2012 | 7250 | 1566 | 4927 | 922 | 1106 | 5190 | 2790 | | | | | | |
| THUNDER BAY | 2144 | 2014 | 3118 | 2371 | 2031 | 3149 | 3206 | 1569 | 2900 | 1854 | 1761 | 3578 | 1665 | 1248 | 3043 | 4785 | 1511 | 889 | 3679 | | | | | |
| TORONTO | 3459 | 3329 | 1803 | 3686 | 3346 | 1834 | 1891 | 254 | 1585 | 539 | 446 | 4886 | 790 | 2563 | 1728 | 3470 | 2826 | 426 | 2364 | 1315 | | | | |
| VANCOUVER | 901 | 1031 | 6163 | 4068 | 1340 | 6194 | 6251 | 4616 | 5945 | 4899 | 4806 | 1506 | 5150 | 1797 | 6088 | 7830 | 2054 | 3934 | 6724 | 3045 | 4360 | | | |
| VICTORIA | 1016 | 1146 | 6278 | 4183 | 1455 | 6309 | 6366 | 4731 | 6060 | 5014 | 4921 | 1621 | 5265 | 1912 | 6203 | 7945 | 2169 | 4049 | 6839 | 3160 | 4475 | 115 | | |
| WINDSOR | 3818 | 3688 | 2162 | 4045 | 3705 | 2193 | 2250 | 613 | 1944 | 898 | 805 | 5245 | 1149 | 2922 | 2087 | 3829 | 3185 | 785 | 2723 | 1674 | 359 | 4719 | 4834 | |
| WINNIPEG | 1470 | 1340 | 3823 | 1697 | 1357 | 3823 | 3880 | 2243 | 3574 | 2528 | 2435 | 2897 | 2779 | 574 | 3717 | 5459 | 837 | 1563 | 4353 | 674 | 1989 | 2371 | 2486 | 2348 |

From the chart, the distance between the cities of Moncton and Vancouver is 5945 km.

Based on the information in the chart, you can solve problems.

### Example

A train travels at an average speed of 65 km/h on a trip from Saskatoon to Halifax. Calculate how long the trip will take, in hours. Express your answer to 1 decimal place.

### Solution

*Step 1*: Find the distance.
From the chart the distance is 4717 km.

*Step 2*: Find the time taken.
To travel 65 km, the train takes 1 h.
To travel 4717 km, the train takes $\frac{4717}{65}$ h
or 72.56 h. Do you have a calculator?

To 1 decimal place, the time taken is 72.6 h.
Always make a final statement.

## Try These

1 From the railroad chart, what is the distance between each pair of cities?

| | | |
|---|---|---|
| (a) | Winnipeg | Saint John, N.B. |
| (b) | Prince Rupert | Sudbury |
| (c) | Sydney | Ottawa |
| (d) | Regina | Windsor |
| (e) | Toronto | Edmonton |
| (f) | Kingston | Saskatoon |
| (g) | Charlottetown | Halifax |

2 Which pair of cities is further apart, A or B?
A Thunder Bay and Regina
B Montreal and Churchill

## Written Exercises

**A** Refer to the railroad distance chart to do questions 1 to 6.

1 Find the distance travelled for each trip.
(a) Calgary to Edmonton to Winnipeg
(b) Moncton to Fredericton to Ottawa
(c) Vancouver to Banff to Calgary

2 For each round trip, how far will you travel?
(a) Winnipeg to Churchill
(b) Toronto to Saskatoon
(c) St. John's, Nfld., to Montreal

3 Which trip is further? By how much?
A Ottawa to Quebec (Ste.-Foy)
B Regina to Saskatoon

4 As part of a See Canada promotion, Jean and Claudette travelled by train on the following route.
Banff, Calgary, Edmonton, Saskatoon, Regina, Winnipeg.
How far did they travel in all?

5 Jennifer and Samuel live in Halifax. They took the train to visit friends in Charlottetown. From there they went to visit relatives in Fredericton and then on to see business associates in Sudbury. What was the total distance of the trip?

6 During the summer vacation, you are going to visit the Maritime cities shown in the chart. You will travel from Moncton to Charlottetown and then to Halifax. Find the total round trip if you live in one of these places.
(a) Sudbury
(b) Regina
(c) Winnipeg
(d) Calgary

Moncton is New Brunswick's second largest city and has many attractions. Near Moncton you can park a car and coast up hill at the tourist site Magnetic Hill, or you can rush down to the Petitcodiac River and wait for the tidal bore.

**B** When you use information given in a chart read the columns and rows carefully.

7 Refer to the railroad distance chart.
(a) Jacob travelled from Sydney to Ottawa. The train averaged 46 km/h for the whole trip. How long was Jacob on the train?
(b) On a trip from Saskatoon to Winnipeg through Regina, the train took 8 h (non stop). How fast was the train travelling?

8 Refer to the railroad distance chart.
(a) Use the information in the chart to create a problem of your own.
(b) Solve your problem in (a).

---

Questions 9 to 12 are based on the following chart. Charts are used to provide information for bus and train timetables. The chart shows the times for buses travelling route 2 and route 3. The headings indicate the time when buses leave various locations, as well as the arrival times.

9 Refer to the bus on route 2.
(a) When does the first bus leave?
(b) What time does it arrive at Parkway Ave. and Hwy. 48?
(c) When does this bus arrive at Hwy. 7 and Hwy. 48?

10 A bus on route 3 leaves Hwy. 7 and Hwy. 48 at 11:20 a.m.
(a) How long is the trip to Southdale Dr. and McCowan Road?
(b) If it takes you 10 min to get to the bus stop at Hwy. 7 and Hwy. 48, how much time will you need to arrive at Grandview Blvd. and Hwy. 7?

11 (a) A bus on route 3 leaves Bullock Dr. and McCowan Road at 10:56, when does it arrive at Hwy. 7 and Hwy. 48?
(b) If you made a round trip in (a), how long would the trip be?

12 Refer to the bus schedule.
(a) Create a problem based on the information in the chart.
(b) Solve your problem in (a).

No Service on Sundays or Holidays

MONDAY-SATURDAY

Service Not Provided on Saturday.

| ROUTE 2 | | | | | ROUTE 3 | | | | | |
|---|---|---|---|---|---|---|---|---|---|---|
| Leaves Hwy. 7 & Hwy. 48 | At Peter St. & 16th Ave. | At Ramona Blvd. & Wootten Way | At Parkway Ave. & Hwy. 48 | Arrives Hwy. 7 & Hwy. 48 | Leaves Hwy. 7 & Hwy. 48 | At Hwy. 7 & Galsworthy Drive | At Bullock Dr. & McCowan Road | At Southdale Dr. & McCowan Road | At Grandview Blvd. & Hwy. 7 | Arrive Hwy. 7 & Hwy. 48 |
| 6:02 a.m. | 6:07 a.m. | 6:12 a.m. | 6:17 a.m. | 6:20 a.m. | 6:20 a.m. | 6:24 a.m. | 6:26 a.m. | 6:28 a.m. | 6:30 a.m. | 6:32 a.m. |
| 6:32 | 6:37 | 6:42 | 6:47 | 6:50 | 6:50 | 6:54 | 6:56 | 6:58 | 7:00 | 7:02 |
| 7:02 | 7:07 | 7:12 | 7:17 | 7:20 | 7:20 | 7:24 | 7:26 | 7:28 | 7:30 | 7:32 |
| 7:32 | 7:37 | 7:42 | 7:47 | 7:50 | 7:50 | 7:54 | 7:56 | 7:58 | 8:00 | 8:02 |
| 8:02 | 8:07 | 8:12 | 8:17 | 8:20 | 8:20 | 8:24 | 8:26 | 8:28 | 8:30 | 8:32 |
| 8:32 | 8:37 | 8:42 | 8:47 | 8:50 | 8:50 | 8:54 | 8:56 | 8:58 | 9:00 | 9:02 |
| 9:02 | 9:07 | 9:12 | 9:17 | 9:20 | 9:20 | 9:24 | 9:26 | 9:28 | 9:30 | 9:32 |
| 9:32 | 9:37 | 9:42 | 9:47 | 9:50 | 9:50 | 9:54 | 9:56 | 9:58 | 10:00 | 10:02 |
| 10:02 | 10:07 | 10:12 | 10:17 | 10:20 | 10:20 | 10:24 | 10:26 | 10:28 | 10:30 | 10:32 |
| 10:32 | 10:37 | 10:42 | 10:47 | 10:50 | 10:50 | 10:54 | 10:56 | 10:58 | 11:00 | 11:02 |
| 11:02 | 11:07 | 11:12 | 11:17 | 11:20 | 11:20 | 11:24 | 11:26 | 11:28 | 11:30 | 11:32 |
| 11:32 | 11:37 | 11:42 | 11:47 | 11:50 | 11:50 | 11:54 | 11:56 | 11:58 | 12:00 p.m. | 12:02 p.m. |
| 12:02 p.m. | 12:07 p.m. | 12:12 p.m. | 12:17 p.m. | 12:20 p.m. | 12:20 p.m. | 12:24 p.m. | 12:26 p.m. | 12:28 p.m. | 12:30 | 12:32 |
| 12:32 | 12:37 | 12:42 | 12:47 | 12:50 | 12:50 | 12:54 | 12:56 | 12:58 | 1:00 | 1:02 |
| 1:02 | 1:07 | 1:12 | 1:17 | 1:20 | 1:20 | 1:24 | 1:26 | 1:28 | 1:30 | 1:32 |
| 1:32 | 1:37 | 1:42 | 1:47 | 1:50 | 1:50 | 1:54 | 1:56 | 1:58 | 2:00 | 2:02 |
| 2:02 | 2:07 | 2:12 | 2:17 | 2:20 | 2:20 | 2:24 | 2:26 | 2:28 | 2:30 | 2:32 |
| 2:32 | 2:37 | 2:42 | 2:47 | 2:50 | 2:50 | 2:54 | 2:56 | 2:58 | 3:00 | 3:02 |
| 3:02 | 3:07 | 3:12 | 3:17 | 3:20 | 3:20 | 3:24 | 3:26 | 3:28 | 3:30 | 3:32 |
| 3:40 | 3:45 | 3:50 | 3:5 | 3:58 | 3:58 | 4:02 | 4:04 | 4:06 | 4:08 | 4:10 |
| 4:10 | 4:15 | 4:20 | 4:25 | 4:28 | 4:28 | 4:32 | 4:34 | 4:36 | 4:38 | 4:40 |
| 4:40 | 4:45 | 4:50 | 4:55 | 4:58 | 4:58 | 5:02 | 5:04 | 5:06 | 5:08 | 5:10 |
| 5:10 | 5:15 | 5:20 | 5:25 | 5:28 | 5:28 | 5:32 | 5:34 | 5:36 | 5:38 | 5:40 |
| 5:40 | 5:45 | 5:50 | 5:55 | 5:58 | 5:58 | 6:02 | 6:04 | 6:06 | 6:08 | 6:10 |
| 6:10 | 6:15 | 6:20 | 6:25 | 6:28 | 6:28 | 6:32 | 6:34 | 6:36 | 6:38 | 6:40 |
| 6:40 | 6:45 | 6:50 | 6:55 | 6:58 | | | | | | |

# 1.4 Skills with Estimation: Reasonable Answers

To solve problems, you often need to do calculations with decimal numbers. When you have completed the work, you should always ask, as a check "Is my answer reasonable?" This skill is also important when using a calculator. To answer this question you have used the skills for rounding numbers.

When you study mathematics look for similarities to help you remember. Compare rounding for tens and tenths.

tens

▶ if the ones digit is 5 or more, round to the next ten

368 rounds to 370

↑ ones digit is 5 or more; ↑ round to the next ten

▶ if the ones digit is less than 5, round to the nearest ten

364 rounds to 360

↑ ones digit is less than 5; ↑ round to the nearest ten

tenths

▶ if the hundredths digit is 5 or more, round to the next tenth.

0.36 rounds to 0.4

↑ hundredths digit is 5 or more; ↑ round to the next tenth

▶ if the hundredths digit is less than 5, round to the nearest tenth.

0.32 rounds to 0.3

↑ hundredths digit is less than 5; ↑ round to the nearest tenth

Once you have listed examples to illustrate rounding, you can use a chart to summarize the skills. A chart will help you identify a pattern. Compare the information shown in the chart.

| tens | hundreds | thousands |
|---|---|---|
| A 368 rounds to 370<br>↑ ones digit is 5 or more; ↑ round to the next ten | A 1384 rounds to 1400<br>↑ tens digit is 5 or more; ↑ round to the next hundred | A 12 935 rounds to 13 000<br>↑ hundreds digit is 5 or more; ↑ round to the next thousand |
| B 364 rounds to 360<br>↑ ones digit is less than 5; ↑ round to the nearest ten | B 1348 rounds to 1300<br>↑ tens digit is less than 5; ↑ round to the nearest hundred | B 12 395 rounds to 12 000<br>↑ hundreds digit is less than 5; ↑ round to the nearest thousand |

| tenths | hundredths | thousandths |
|---|---|---|
| A 0.36 rounds to 0.4<br>↑ (3): hundredths digit is 5 or more<br>↑ (0.4): round to the next tenth | A 0.138 rounds to 0.14<br>↑ (3): thousandths digit is 5 or more<br>↑ (0.14): round to the next hundredth | A 0.1427 rounds to 0.143<br>↑ (2): this digit is 5 or more<br>↑ (0.143): round to the next thousandth |
| B 0.32 rounds to 0.3<br>↑ (3): hundredths digit is less than 5<br>↑ (0.3): round to the nearest tenth | B 0.132 rounds to 0.13<br>↑ (3): thousandths digit is less than 5<br>↑ (0.13): round to the nearest hundredth | B 0.1472 rounds to 0.147<br>↑ (7): this digit is less than 5<br>↑ (0.147): round to the nearest thousandth |

As your last step in learning a skill, you look for a compact way to help you understand and remember a skill. Here is one suggestion to help you remember.

Always look for a general pattern to help you understand and learn mathematics.

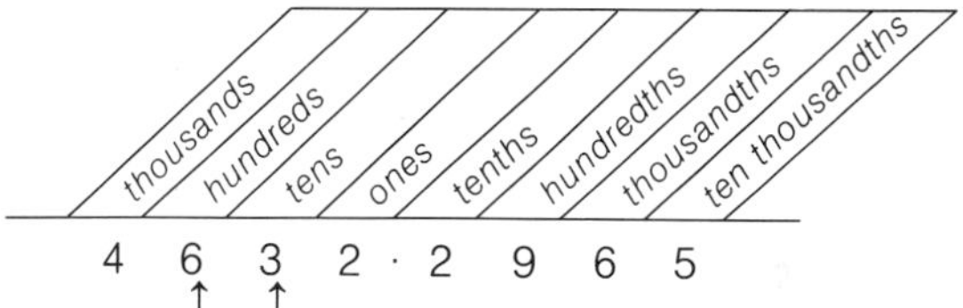

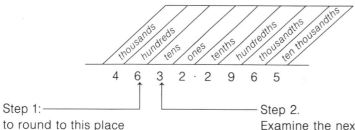

Step 1:
to round to this place
namely, to round
to the nearest hundred

Step 2.
Examine the next digit to the right.
Examine the digit in the tens place:
- ▶ 5 or more, round to the next hundred
- ▶ less than 5, round to the nearest hundred

Once you have learned the skill of rounding, you apply the skill to check whether answers that you obtain in calculations are reasonable. This skill is especially important when finding many answers using a calculator.

## Example

Calculate to the nearest thousandth   $0.089 \times 0.315$

## Solution

Calculation:   $0.089 \times 0.315 = 0.028$ (to the nearest thousandth)

↓

Check: Is my answer reasonable?   $0.09 \times 0.3 \rightarrow 0.027$

✓ answer is reasonable

The following statements in our work have the same meaning
- ▶ round to the nearest tenth
- ▶ round to one decimal place
- ▶ round to the nearest hundredth
- ▶ round to two decimal places.

## Try These

1 Round each number as indicated.

(a) 138 to the nearest ten
(b) 293 to the nearest ten
(c) 1436 to the nearest hundred
(d) 2781 to the nearest hundred
(e) 12 569 to the nearest thousand
(f) 18289 to the nearest thousand

2 Round each number as indicated.

(a) 9.94 to the nearest tenth
(b) 75.63 to 1 decimal place
(c) 8.966 to the nearest hundredth
(d) 0.0499 to 2 decimal places
(e) 0.0017 to 3 decimal places
(f) 42.542 to the nearest hundredth
(g) 7.1844 to the nearest thousandth

## Written Exercises

**A** Review your skills with rounding.
Remember: look for patterns to remember.

1 Round each number as indicated.

(a) 1936.482 to the nearest tenth
(b) 1238.789 to the nearest hundred
(c) 3614.193 to two decimal places
(d) 2319.615 to the nearest hundredth
(e) 4613.395 to one decimal place
(f) 1465.321 to the nearest ten
(g) 13 698.4963 to three decimal places
(h) 24 698.9321 to the nearest thousandth
(i) 48 739.3125 to the nearest thousand

2 For each of the following, 3 estimates are given. Which is the best estimate?

| | A | B | C |
|---|---|---|---|
| (a) $37 \times 28$ | 900 | 1000 | 1200 |
| (b) $1600 + 7500$ | 8000 | 9000 | 9600 |
| (c) $960 \div 34$ | 24 | 31 | 40 |
| (d) $543 - 382$ | 100 | 160 | 195 |
| (e) $3598 \div 196$ | 14 | 18 | 22 |

3 Estimate each value, then calculate.

(a) $51 \times 49$ (b) $96 \div 24$
(c) $62 \times 21$ (d) $138 \div 69$
(e) $197 \times 29$ (f) $833 \div 98$
(g) $204 \div 17$ (h) $19 \times 521$

4 Estimate each of the following. Then calculate.

(a) $74 \times 82$ (b) $848 \times 29$
(c) $1998 \times 91$ (d) $69.8 \times 8.2$
(e) $83 \div 11$ (f) $899 \div 29$
(g) $5004 \div 48$ (h) $59.85 \div 5.7$

5 Calculate. Check whether your answer is reasonable.

(a) $4.7 + 5.3 + 4.9$ (b) $8.7 - 5.1$
(c) $9.5 \times 0.025$ (d) $6.41 \times 15.7$
(e) $22.86 \div 2.4$ (f) $5.17 \div 0.4$
(g) $8.025 - 6.127$
(h) $19.0 + 0.033 + 0.477$

6 Calculate. Round your answers to the accuracy shown.

(a) $87.5 \times 29.4$, to the nearest ten
(b) $257.42 \div 39.35$, to 2 decimal places
(c) $687.88 + 27.091 + 157.604$, to 1 decimal place
(d) $62.043 \times 87.5$, to 2 decimal places

7 Use your calculator to evaluate each of the following to 3 decimal places.

(a) $691.48 \div 61$ (b) $97.87 \times 2.9$
(c) $1.051 \times 4.88$ (d) $0.006791 \div 0.54$
(e) $100 \div 0.18$ (f) $1.6942 \div 1.673$

8 Calculate. Check whether your answer is reasonable.

(a) $\frac{409 \times 196}{98}$ (b) $\frac{19.89 \times 61.4}{62.1}$

(c) $\frac{31.5 + 79.8 + 9.8}{98.9}$ (d) $\frac{74.1 \times 88.7}{61.1 + 19.7}$

**B** For each of the following calculations, round to the accuracy shown.

9 Estimate each cost. Then calculate.
(a) 21 tickets at $8.95 each
(b) 9 calculators at $39.99 each
(c) 4 pizzas at $8.85 each
(d) 92 pencils at 19¢ each

10 For each, 3 estimates are given. Choose the best estimate, A, B, or C.
(a) Samantha bought a blouse for $49.95, a scarf for $18.60, and two pairs of stockings costing $3.95 each. How much did she pay for all the items?

A $70 B $77 C $84

(b) Five tubes of oil paint cost $19.43. What is the cost of twenty tubes?

A $390 B $80 C $100

11 The cost for installing a new roof is $48.75/m². Estimate the cost of roofing each of the following areas. Then calculate to the nearest dollar.
(a) 97 m² (b) 305 m² (c) 593 m²

12 The cost of resurfacing asphalt is $3.69/m². Calculate each of the following.
(a) Resurfacing a driveway that is 118 m².
(b) Resurfacing a tennis court that is 425 m².
(c) Resurfacing a parking lot that is 1250 m².

13 Each calculator requires 8.6 min for assembly. How long would it take to assemble 1200 calculators? Express your answer to the nearest hour.

14 The current value of the coin is $28.35. Jennifer purchased 25 of them as an investment. How much did she pay?

15 Use the prices shown.

| | |
|---|---|
| calculator | $18.96 |
| cassette tape | $4.95 |
| LP record | $14.60 |
| record cleaner | $3.25 |
| batteries | 69¢ |

Estimate the total cost of the following purchases. Then calculate.
(a) 1 calculator, 3 cassette tapes.
(b) 1 record cleaner, 5 LP records, 6 batteries.
(c) 6 cassette tapes, 3 LP records, 1 calculator.

## Career Tip

The *Career Tips* that occur throughout the text suggest information you may want to find out, about various careers of interest to you. Before you choose a career, explore what types of careers are available to you or of interest to you.

A Refer to the career/help wanted sections of the classified ads in the newspaper.
  (a) List the jobs or careers that sound appealing to you.
  (b) Inquire, where possible, about the type of person and skills the employer is looking for to fill the job position.
  (c) Begin a file on careers that are of interest to you.

B Identify from your list in A those that might require the use of calculator or computer skills.

C What type of skills with mathematics do you think might be required by a

| | |
|---|---|
| Lithographer | Print maker |
| Choreographer | Interior Designer |
| Musician | Photo Journalist |
| Jeweller | Furniture Designer? |

## Applications: Foreign Currency

When you travel outside Canada, you need to change your Canadian dollars into the currency used in that country. What amount of local currency you receive for a Canadian dollar depends on the value of the foreign currency. The chart shows the value of various currencies.

**Rates of Exchange**

| Country | Currency | Value of one unit in Canadian dollars |
|---|---|---|
| United States | dollar | 1.376 |
| Britain | pound | 2.001 |
| Japan | yen | 0.007 |
| West Germany | mark | 0.536 |
| Switzerland | franc | 0.653 |
| France | franc | 0.175 |
| China | renminbi | 0.430 |
| Austria | schilling | 0.076 |
| Belgium | franc | 0.026 |
| Hong Kong | dollar | 0.176 |
| Ireland | punt | 1.652 |
| Jamaica | dollar | 0.262 |
| Portugal | escudo | 0.009 |
| Spain | peseta | 0.550 |
| Sweden | krona | 0.653 |

Imagine that you are going to France. How many francs will you get in exchange for $100 Canadian?

$\$0.175 = 1$ franc

$\$1 = \frac{1}{0.175}$ francs

$\$100 = 100 \times \frac{1}{0.175}$ francs

$= 571.43$ francs (to 2 decimal places)

Thus, you would receive 571 francs for 100 Canadian dollars.

---

In the following exercises use the rates of exchange table shown above. Round your answers, as needed to 2 decimal places. All dollars shown are Canadian funds.

16 You have 45 francs left when you leave France. How many Canadian dollars will you receive in exchange?

17 Martha is going to Jamaica for a winter holiday. She plans to take $200 (Canadian) spending money. How many Jamaican dollars can she buy?

18 Jason received a refund of $65.83 from a U.S. mail order house. What is the amount worth in Canadian funds?

19 A compact Japanese car is selling in Winnipeg for $8300.
(a) Express this amount in yen.
(b) Express the price in U.S. dollars

20 When Marianne left for a month's bicycling trip in Europe she took $2000 in Canadian traveller's cheques.
(a) She flew to London. In Britain she spent £278 (pounds). How much was this in Canadian funds?
(b) Then she went to France where she spent 4000 francs, including her train fare to Geneva, Switzerland. Find this amount in Canadian currency.
(c) During her time in Switzerland she exchanged $250 of her traveller's cheques. What amount did she receive in Swiss francs?
(d) From Switzerland, she travelled up the Rhine Valley in West Germany. There she exchanged another $250 worth of her traveller's cheques. How many German marks would she get in exchange?
(e) Marianne flew back home from West Germany. She had 28 marks left which she exchanged back into Canadian currency. How much did she receive for these marks?
(f) How much remained of her original $2000?

# 1.5 Fractions as Decimals: Calculators

As you have seen, a chart can be used to record information.

| Player | Number of hits | Times at bat |
|---|---|---|
| Alfredo | 168 | 465 |
| Andre | 136 | 393 |

In sports, coaches and managers are concerned with players' performances. Many former players in different sports have successfully pursued careers as coaches and managers.

To compare the performance of the players, you can write a fraction.

Alfredo $\frac{168}{465}$ $\qquad \frac{\text{number of hits}}{\text{times at bat}}$ $\qquad$ Andre $\frac{136}{393}$

The batting average is found for each player by writing a decimal number for each fraction expressed to 3 decimal places.

Use a calculator to do the calculation.

$\frac{168}{465} = 0.361$ (to 3 decimal places) $\quad \frac{136}{393} = 0.346$ (to 3 decimal places)

Alfredo has a better batting average. The following 2 examples review your skills for operations with fractions.

**Example 1**
Simplify.

(a) $\frac{1}{2} + 5\frac{3}{4} - 1\frac{5}{12}$ $\qquad$ (b) $\frac{18}{5} \div \frac{9}{35} \times \frac{3}{7}$

**Solution**

(a) $\frac{1}{2} + 5\frac{3}{4} - 1\frac{5}{12}$ Always record the given information.

$= \frac{1}{2} + \frac{23}{4} - \frac{17}{12}$

$= \frac{6}{12} + \frac{69}{12} - \frac{17}{12}$ To add fractions, obtain a common denominator.

$= \frac{58}{12}$ or $4\frac{5}{6}$

(b) $\frac{18}{5} \div \frac{9}{35} \times \frac{3}{7}$ Apply the order of operations to working with fractions.

$= \frac{18}{5} \times \frac{35}{9} \times \frac{3}{7}$

$= \frac{\overset{2}{\cancel{18}}}{\underset{1}{\cancel{5}}} \times \frac{\overset{\overset{1}{\cancel{7}}}{\cancel{35}}}{\underset{1}{\cancel{9}}} \times \frac{3}{\underset{1}{\cancel{7}}}$

$= 6$

### Example 2

Simplify. $1\frac{2}{3} \times 6\frac{2}{3} \div 5\frac{5}{9} - 2\frac{1}{3}$

To avoid error, do each step, one at a time.

### Solution

$$1\frac{2}{3} \times 6\frac{2}{3} \div 5\frac{5}{9} - 2\frac{1}{3} = \frac{5}{3} \times \frac{20}{3} \div \frac{50}{9} - \frac{7}{3}$$

$$= \frac{100}{9} \div \frac{50}{9} - \frac{7}{3}$$

Remember: use the order of operations.

$$= \frac{100}{9} \times \frac{9}{50} - \frac{7}{3}$$

$$= \frac{\overset{2}{\cancel{100}}}{\underset{1}{\cancel{9}}} \times \frac{\overset{1}{\cancel{9}}}{\underset{1}{\cancel{50}}} - \frac{7}{3}$$

$$= 2 - \frac{7}{3}$$

$$= \frac{6}{3} - \frac{7}{3} = -\frac{1}{3}$$

You can use your skills with calculators to perform operations with fractions. To do so, you need to know the mathematical steps for operating with fractions.

Calculate

$$\frac{25}{12} + \frac{7}{20}$$

Think
With a calculator, you do not need to spend time to find the lowest common denominator. Use these steps

Calculator Steps

$\boxed{C}$ 25 $\boxed{\div}$ 12 $\boxed{=}$ $\boxed{MS}$ 7 $\boxed{\div}$ 20 $\boxed{=}$ $\boxed{+}$ $\boxed{MR}$ $\boxed{=}$ Output ?

Can you find other procedures to obtain the same result?

## Try These

1 With calculators, an essential skill is multiplying and dividing by tens. Find each answer.

(a) $10 \times 7.2$ (b) $10 \times 189.4$
(c) $1000 \times 7.83$ (d) $146.7 \div 100$
(e) $19.4 \div 10$ (f) $1.569 \div 1000$
(g) $1000 \times 43.9$ (h) $32.96 \div 10$
(i) $48.13 \div 1000$ (j) $100 \times 2.095$
(k) $3.91 \times 1000$ (l) $0.1325 \div 100$

2 Which number is the greatest?

(a) 9.2, 2.9, 3.1 (b) 1.01, 1.10, 1.001
(c) 3.69, 3.07, 3.689
(d) 0.0495, 0.0459, 0.1049

## Written Exercises

**A** Review your skills for doing operations with fractions.

1 Simplify.

(a) $\frac{1}{2} + \frac{3}{2}$ (b) $\frac{2}{5} + \frac{3}{5} + \frac{4}{5}$

(c) $\frac{3}{7} - \frac{1}{7}$ (d) $\frac{3}{5} \times \frac{5}{3} \times 2$

2 Find the sum.

(a) $1\frac{1}{3} + 4\frac{1}{4}$ (b) $3\frac{2}{3} + 5\frac{1}{6}$

(c) $4\frac{2}{5} + 6\frac{1}{10}$ (d) $\frac{3}{4} + 3\frac{2}{3} + 7\frac{2}{5}$

3 Calculate.

(a) $\frac{5}{8} + \frac{1}{2} - \frac{3}{4}$ (b) $\frac{5}{6} - \frac{3}{4} + \frac{2}{3}$

(c) $3\frac{1}{4} + 4\frac{1}{2} - 2\frac{3}{8}$ (d) $5\frac{1}{3} - 3\frac{1}{6} + 4\frac{1}{2}$

4 Calculate.

(a) $\frac{3}{5} \times 4\frac{3}{5}$ (b) $5\frac{1}{8} \times \frac{4}{3}$

(c) $6\frac{1}{5} \times 3\frac{1}{4}$ (d) $2\frac{3}{4} \times 3\frac{1}{2} \times 5\frac{1}{3}$

5 Calculate.

(a) $32 \div \frac{1}{2}$ (b) $\frac{7}{5} \times \frac{3}{2}$ (c) $24 \div \frac{15}{16}$

(d) $\frac{2}{3} \div \frac{1}{3}$ (e) $3\frac{3}{4} \div \frac{5}{6}$ (f) $15\frac{2}{3} \div 3\frac{2}{3}$

6 (a) Calculate. Which is greater, A or B?

A: $4\left(\frac{1}{2} + \frac{3}{4}\right)$ B: $\left(\frac{3}{5} + \frac{1}{3}\right) \div \frac{1}{2}$

(b) Calculate. Which is smaller, A or B?

A: $3\frac{1}{2} \times \frac{5}{4} \div 1\frac{3}{8}$ B: $\left(8\frac{1}{4} \div 2\frac{1}{2}\right) \div 4$

7 Which number of the pair is greater, A or B?

| | A | B |
|---|---|---|
| (a) | 349.27 | 349.51 |
| (b) | 69.814 | 69.841 |
| (c) | 0.0149 | 0.0296 |
| (d) | 372.5967 | 372.5989 |
| (e) | 0.692 | 0.599 |

8 In each, arrange the numbers in order from the least to the greatest.

(a) 0.3, 3.0, 33.0, 3.30, 3.03, 3.303

(b) 1.49, 0.149, 14.9, 0.0149, 149.9

(c) 0.0016, 0.0160, 0.1601, 0.0061, 0.0611

**B** Remember: Use a calculator to do operations when needed.

9 Use a calculator.

(a) $\frac{1}{2} + \frac{1}{4}$ (b) $\frac{1}{4} + \frac{5}{8}$ (c) $\frac{3}{5} - \frac{1}{4}$

(d) $\frac{1}{4} + \frac{3}{5}$ (e) $\frac{7}{8} - \frac{3}{20}$ (f) $\frac{4}{5} - \frac{7}{20}$

(g) $\frac{3}{5} + \frac{3}{8}$ (h) $\frac{5}{8} + \frac{3}{4}$ (i) $\frac{5}{8} - \frac{3}{10}$

10 Use a calculator. Round your answers to 1 decimal place.

(a) $\frac{3}{4} + \frac{5}{16} + \frac{7}{8}$ (b) $\frac{1}{10} + \frac{3}{8} + \frac{1}{2}$

(c) $\frac{3}{8} + \frac{2}{5} - \frac{2}{3}$ (d) $\frac{1}{4} + \frac{1}{5} - \frac{1}{8}$

(e) $1\frac{1}{4} + 2\frac{1}{8}$ (f) $5\frac{3}{8} - 3\frac{3}{10}$

11 Calculate. Round your answers to 2 decimal places where needed.

(a) $1\frac{3}{8} \times \frac{4}{5} \div \frac{9}{25}$ (b) $2\frac{4}{5} \div \frac{3}{10} + \frac{3}{5}$

(c) $3\frac{4}{5} \times \frac{3}{10} \div \frac{3}{5}$ (d) $3\frac{1}{2} - \frac{3}{5} \times \frac{1}{6}$

(e) $\frac{2}{3} \div \frac{4}{9} \times \frac{1}{2}$ (f) $\frac{2}{3} \times \frac{9}{10} \times 2\frac{3}{4}$

12 Calculate how much gas each driver used on Wednesday and Thursday.

| | Driver | Gas used Wednesday | Gas used Thursday |
|---|---|---|---|
| (a) | Bob | $\frac{1}{2}$ tank | $1\frac{1}{2}$ tank |
| (b) | Jesse | $\frac{2}{3}$ tank | $\frac{3}{4}$ tank |
| (c) | Lorraine | $\frac{3}{5}$ tank | $1\frac{1}{2}$ tanks |
| (d) | Rose Marie | $2\frac{1}{8}$ tanks | $\frac{3}{4}$ tank |
| (e) | Tai | $1\frac{1}{3}$ tanks | $1\frac{3}{4}$ tanks |
| (f) | Carla | $2\frac{3}{8}$ tanks | $3\frac{1}{2}$ tanks |
| (g) | Larry | $3\frac{1}{2}$ tanks | $1\frac{3}{4}$ tanks |

13 Jeremy scored $\frac{1}{3}$ of his total points in the first quarter of the season. In the second quarter he scored $\frac{1}{2}$ times as many points. What fraction of his total points were scored in the second quarter?

14 Linda is refinishing a table. She worked on the task for $3\frac{3}{4}$ h on Friday, $7\frac{1}{3}$ h on Saturday and $5\frac{1}{2}$ h on Sunday. Find the total number of hours spent on the work that weekend.

15 The gas tank is $\frac{3}{4}$ full. Each trip around its route the bus uses $\frac{1}{8}$ of a tank. How many trips can the bus make before the gas tank is empty?

16 A record revolves $33\frac{1}{3}$ times each minute. What time, in seconds is needed for 1 revolution?

17 A science project is assigned. After two days $\frac{4}{9}$ of the class had begun the project. After another day an additional $\frac{2}{5}$ had begun. Find what fraction of the class still had not started the project.

## Computer Tip

In this text, you will find *Computer Tips* to suggest various uses of this technology in doing mathematics. You learn mathematics to develop methods of solving problems in industry, science, business, etc. The computer is a powerful tool for helping people solve problems. Not only does the computer remove some of the drudgery from calculations, but it also provides unique opportunities for exploring mathematics.

To plan the work for a computer you must understand the principles and methods of mathematics. When you prepare instructions for a computer in some computer language you are writing a program. The programmer gives instructions to the computer in a specific computer language such as the one we use in this text: BASIC (Beginners All-Purpose Symbolic Instruction Code)

Two terms that you often hear associated with computers are hardware and software.

- Hardware is the equipment you see.
- Software refers to the programs which are written, or the routines and codes which are used to direct the operation of a computer.

These symbols are used in computer language.

| | | | | | |
|---|---|---|---|---|---|
| + | add | ↑ | exponential | < > | not equal to |
| − | subtract | > | greater than | < | less than |
| * | multiply | > = | greater than or equal to | < = | less than or equal to |
| / | divide | | | | |

Throughout the text, programs will be shown that you can try.

# 1.6 Working with Integers

An important skill throughout the study of mathematics is working with integers.

$I = \{\ldots, -3, -2, -1, 0, +1, +2, +3, \ldots\}$

You have learned various skills with integers. This section provides practice with these skills. Return to these exercises, to sharpen your skills with integers.

These two charts are helpful in remembering the signs when you multiply or divide integers.

Multiplication

| × | positive integer | negative integer |
|---|---|---|
| positive integer | + | − |
| negative integer | − | + |

The sign of the answer when you multiply a positive and a negative integer.

Division

| ÷ | positive integer | negative integer |
|---|---|---|
| positive integer | + | − |
| negative integer | − | + |

The sign of the answer when you divide a negative integer by a negative integer.

## Try These

1 Which integer is greater?
(a) +8 or −9 (b) −12 or +12
(c) −10 or +3 (d) −1 or −4
(e) +3 or −4 (f) −16 or −12

2 Calculate.
(a) 10 + 7 (b) 16 − 3
(c) −9 − 4 (d) −21 + 6

3 What is the product?
(a) (4)(5) (b) (−6)(3)
(c) (−7)(−9) (d) (−3)(−4)(2)

4 What is the quotient?
(a) $\frac{16}{8}$ (b) $\frac{-25}{5}$ (c) $\frac{-63}{-9}$ (d) $\frac{100}{-20}$

## Written Exercises

**A** Remember: read the signs carefully when dealing with integers.

1 Calculate.
(a) 9 + 4 + 1 (b) 12 − 3 − 2
(c) −6 − 2 + 8 (d) −14 + 9 − 3
(e) −33 − 1 + 5 (f) 16 − 21 − 2

2 Simplify.
(a) 24 − (−5)
(b) −16 − 4 − (−8)
(c) −10 + (−5) − (−13)
(d) 25 − (−6) + 8

3 Simplify.

(a) $(-3)(+2)$ (b) $(-3)(-8)$
(c) $(+3)(-3)$ (d) $(+18)(-6)$
(e) $(-9)(-3)$ (f) $(-26)(+2)$

4 Calculate.

(a) $(-12) \div (+3)$ (b) $(-16) \div (-4)$
(c) $(-25) \div (+5)$ (d) $(-96) \div (+12)$
(e) $(+100) \div (-10)$ (f) $(-225) \div (-25)$

5 Calculate. Watch the signs.

(a) $(+3) + (-2)$ (b) $(-3) - (-2)$
(c) $(-3)(+2)$ (d) $(-18) \div (+6)$
(e) $(+2)(-8)$ (f) $(-15) \div (-5)$
(g) $(-15) \div (-15)$ (h) $(+72)(+3)$
(i) $(-4)(-5)$ (j) $(+36) \div (-6)$
(k) $(+30) \div (-6)$ (l) $(+144)(-12)$

6 Simplify.

(a) $-24 - 9 - (-16)$
(b) $(-6)(5)(-3)$
(c) $36 \div 9 \div (-2)$
(d) $(-12)(-4) \div (-16)$
(e) $(-3)(-5)(-3)(-1)$
(f) $-21 - 3 - 5 - (-6)$

7 Simplify.

(a) $-2[4(-3) - 8 + 12]$
(b) $12 + 5[8 \div 4 - (-2)] - 16$
(c) $[16 - 24 \div 8 \times 3 - 1][4 - 3 \times 2]$

**B** Review the steps for the order of operations.

8 Simplify.

(a) $\dfrac{-10 - 41}{-3}$

(b) $\dfrac{(-8) + (-4)}{(-8) - (-4)}$

(c) $\dfrac{-2 + (-32)(-4)}{(-3)(-2)(-7)}$

(d) $\dfrac{(-25) \div (-5) - (-10)}{(-3)(+5)}$

9 Find the missing integer.

(a) $+12 - ? = 3$ (b) $-6 - ? = 2$
(c) $? - (-4) = -10$ (d) $? - (+5) = 16$
(e) $0 - ? = 4$ (f) $-12 - ? = -18$
(g) $-6 \times ? = -42$ (h) $9 \times ? = -108$
(i) $-24 \times ? = 120$ (j) $? \div (-4) = 24$
(k) $45 \div ? = -5$ (l) $? \div (-7) = 3$

10 Calculate the following.

Remember: $-2^3$ means $-(2)(2)(2)$
$(-2)^3$ means $(-2)(-2)(-2)$

(a) $-2^3$ (b) $(-2)^3$ (c) $-4^2$
(d) $(-4)^2$ (e) $-5^2$ (f) $(-5)^2$
(g) $-5^3$ (h) $(-5)^3$ (i) $(-3)^2$

11 Evaluate the expression $2a - 3b + c$ for the following values.

(a) $a = -2, b = 3, c = 0$
(b) $a = 0, b = -4, c = 1$
(c) $a = -3, b = 2, c = -4$
(d) $a = 5, b = 0, c = -2$

12 Use $a = -3$, $b = -1$, $c = 2$. Evaluate each expression.

(a) $a + b + c$ (b) $a - b - c$
(c) $2a - b + c$ (d) $a - 3b - 4c$

13 If $m = 2$, $n = -3$, and $p = -1$, which expression has the greater value?

(a) $m + n - p$ (b) $m - n + 2p$

14 The average of −5, −2, −9, 10, −3, 15 is found by

$$[-5 + (-2) + (-9) + 10 + (-3) + 15] \div 6$$
$$= \frac{-5 - 2 - 9 + 10 - 3 + 15}{6}$$
$$= \frac{6}{6} \text{ or } 1$$

Find the average for each of the following.

(a) −10, −6 (b) 16, −8, −4
(c) −12, 6, −2, 0 (d) −5, −8, 5, −12, 7
(e) −6, −9, 11, 15, 7, −14, 18, −2
(f) 10, 4, −9, −1, 5, −6, −13, −8, −2

15 The temperatures recorded last week in Antigonish, Nova Scotia, are shown.

| | |
|---|---|
| Monday | −3°C |
| Tuesday | −4°C |
| Wednesday | −4°C |
| Thursday | −2°C |
| Friday | 0°C |
| Saturday | 1°C |
| Sunday | 3°C |

What was the average temperature last week?

16 The temperatures for various Canadian cities are given in the chart.

(a) Calculate the increase in temperature (from morning to afternoon) for each of the following places. (i) Victoria (ii) Ottawa (iii) Moncton (iv) Calgary

Wednesday's Temperatures (in degrees Celsius)

| | a.m. | p.m. |
|---|---|---|
| Calgary | −17 | −8 |
| Edmonton | −9 | 6 |
| Halifax | −7 | 1 |
| Fredericton | −11 | 5 |
| Moncton | −14 | 1 |
| Ottawa | 8 | −14 |
| Prince Albert | −21 | 12 |
| Vancouver | 4 | 9 |
| Victoria | 2 | 10 |
| Winnipeg | −19 | −8 |

(b) Which of the cities had the greatest temperature increase?

(c) Which of the cities had the same temperature increase?

## Calculator Tip

Your calculator may have a feature that allows you to work with integers. Look for the key showing [+/−].

A Do each of the following. What is the output in each case?

[C] 4 [+] 6 [=] ?

[C] 4 [+/−] [+] 6 [=] ?

[C] 4 [+] 6 [+/−] [=] ?

[C] 4 [+/−] [+] 6 [+/−] [=] ?

B For each of the procedures in A, what calculation with integers have you done?

## Calculators and Integers

The use of the [+/−] key allows you to perform calculations with integers.

Add 12 and −6

[C] 12 [+] 6 [+/−] [=] ?

Subtract −6 from −8

[C] 8 [+/−] [−] 6 [+/−] [=] ?

Multiply −16.2 by −13.5

[C] 16.2 [+/−] [×] 13.5 [+/−] [=] ?

Divide 18.9 by −6.3

[C] 18.9 [÷] 6.3 [+/−] [=] ?

17 Use a calculator to do each calculation. Then check your answer.

(a) $16 + (-8)$ (b) $-10 + 17$
(c) $-41 - (-5)$ (d) $18 \div (-3)$
(e) $-21 - (-52)$ (f) $(-9)(18)$
(g) $-24 \times (-31)$ (h) $(-125) \div (-25)$

18 Use your calculator to simplify each expression.

(a) $1952 - 347$
(b) $1996 + (-251)$
(c) $-3463 - (-417) - 365$
(d) $7543 - 16\,527 + 4283$
(e) $9051 + (-16\,806) - (-3692)$
(f) $-2457 - (-16\,509) + (-6312)$
(g) $573 - 4126 + (-1634) - (-1569)$

19 Use your calculator to simplify each expression.

(a) $52(-36)$ (b) $-176(176)$
(c) $(-4091)(-4091)$ (d) $9(-6)(-141)$
(e) $8(-5)(-4)(-196)$
(f) $-7(-2)(-6)(-362)(-11)$

20 Simplify. Round to 2 decimal places.

(a) $-825 \div (-15)$ (b) $3964 \div (-34)$
(c) $-14\,350 \div (-60)$ (d) $472\,193 \div (-933)$
(e) $-844\,652 \div 637$ (f) $-963\,508 \div 4094$

21 Use your calculator to perform each of the following operations. Round to 1 decimal place where necessary.

(a) $812 + 153$ (b) $9241 - 2057$
(c) $16\,435 \div (-219)$ (d) $-53\,641 \div 73$
(e) $7523 - 2960$ (f) $0.47 + (-3.69)$
(g) $9.4324 \div (-0.516)$ (h) $-0.00143 \div 0.0056$

# 1.7 Using Percent

On any day, you can glance at a newspaper and find many advertisements using percent. Skills with percent are essential to solve problems in science, in geography, in transportation, in medicine, and so on.

43% means
43 out of every 100

$43\% = \frac{43}{100} = 0.43$

$67\frac{1}{2}\%$ means

$67\frac{1}{2}$ out of every 100

$67\frac{1}{2}\% = \frac{67.5}{100} = 0.675$

**Example 1**
Write each as percent.

(a) $\frac{2}{5}$ (b) $3\frac{1}{2}$ (c) 0.58 (d) 4.25

**Solution**

(a) $\frac{2}{5} \times 100\% = 40\%$

(b) $3\frac{1}{2} \times 100\% = \frac{7}{2} \times 100\%$
$= 350\%$

(c) $0.58 \times 100\% = 58\%$

(d) $4.25 \times 100\% = 425\%$

A basic skill in working with percent is to find the percent of a number.

**Example 2**
(a) Find 35% of 120 tickets.

(b) Find $12\frac{1}{2}\%$ of \$700.

**Solution**

(a) 35% of 120
$= 0.35 \times 120$
$= 42$
Thus 35% of 120 tickets is 42 tickets.

(b) $12\frac{1}{2}\%$ of 700
$= 0.125 \times 700$
$= 87.50$
Thus $12\frac{1}{2}\%$ of \$700 is \$87.50.

Another basic question in working with percent is shown in the following example.

**Example 3**
Of the people interviewed, 380 indicated a preference for public transportation. If this number is 68.5% of the total interviewed, how many people were interviewed?

**Solution**
Use $n$ to represent the number of people interviewed.
68.5% of $n = 380$
$0.685n = 380$

$n = \frac{380}{0.685}$
$= 554.7$ (to 1 decimal place)

Thus 555 people were interviewed.

## Try These

1 What is each percent as a decimal?
(a) 8% (b) 25% (c) 75%
(d) 0.25% (e) 3.6% (f) 99.9%

2 What is each decimal as a percent?
(a) 0.55 (b) 0.09 (c) 1.75
(d) 3 (e) 24 (f) 0.043

3 What is 50% less than each of the following?
(a) \$100 (b) \$1000 (c) \$10 000

4 What is the answer for each?
(a) 10% of 30 (b) 100% of 120
(c) 20% of 100 (d) 50% of 400

## Written Exercises

**A** Where needed, express your answers to 3 decimal place.

1 Write each of the following as a percent.

(a) $\frac{1}{10}$ (b) $\frac{6}{10}$ (c) $\frac{3}{5}$ (d) $\frac{3}{4}$

(e) $\frac{6}{25}$ (f) $\frac{3}{8}$ (g) $\frac{7}{8}$ (h) $\frac{3}{20}$

(i) $\frac{5}{12}$ (j) $\frac{36}{200}$ (k) $1\frac{1}{4}$ (l) $2\frac{1}{2}$

(m) $1\frac{3}{5}$ (n) $3\frac{3}{4}$ (o) $2\frac{3}{5}$

2 Express each percent in fractional form, in lowest terms.
(a) 5% (b) 10% (c) 25% (d) 50%
(e) 60% (f) 28% (g) 75% (h) 44%
(i) 88% (j) 62.5% (k) 87.5% (l) 1.25%
(m) 12.5% (n) 9.2% (o) 100%

3 Find the missing entries in the table.

| | Decimal Number | Percent | Fraction Form |
|---|---|---|---|
| (a) | ? | 50% | ? |
| (b) | 0.125 | ? | ? |
| (c) | ? | ? | $\frac{1}{10}$ |
| (d) | ? | 65.5% | ? |
| (e) | ? | ? | $\frac{7}{4}$ |
| (f) | 0.725 | ? | ? |
| (g) | ? | 120% | ? |

4 Calculate each of the following.
(a) 5% of 600 students (b) 72% of 600 girls
(c) 5% of 250 g (d) 40% of 80 games
(e) 35% of 120 viewers (f) 43% of 200 points
(g) 70% of 190 kg (h) 40% of 120 cm
(i) 23.5% of 400 km (j) $12\frac{1}{2}$% of 300 m
(k) 2% of 14.5 L (l) 8% of \$460

5 Marks for the first term are shown in the table. Express each mark as a percent.

| | Subject | Mark | Total mark for exam | Percent |
|---|---|---|---|---|
| (a) | English | 62 | 80 | ? |
| (b) | Science | 75 | 90 | ? |
| (c) | History | 84 | 95 | ? |
| (d) | Music | 86 | 100 | ? |
| (e) | Mathematics | 91 | 110 | ? |
| (f) | Typing | 63 | 85 | ? |
| (g) | Consumer Education | 70 | 80 | ? |
| (h) | French | 76 | 80 | ? |

6 Some milk has 2% fat. Calculate the amount of fat in 20.8 L of milk.

7 Linda correctly answered 80% of the 20 questions in a quiz.
(a) How many did she answer correctly?
(b) How many did she miss?

8 Air is 78% nitrogen. Calculate the amount of nitrogen in a balloon that has a volume of 5.1 $m^3$.

**B** Skills with percent are used in different subject areas. Be sure you understand the meaning of percent.

9 A box of breakfast cereal, with a mass of 238 g, lists the following nutrients. Determine the mass of each nutrient to the nearest gram.

| | |
|---|---|
| Ash | 1.2% |
| Protein | 12.4% |
| Fat | 3.1% |
| Carbohydrates | 77.8% |
| Crude Fibre | 0.8% |
| Moisture | 4.7% |

10 Many foods have a high percentage of water. Refer to the chart. Calculate the amount of water in each substance to the nearest gram.

| | Item | Mass | Percent that is water |
|---|---|---|---|
| (a) | Tomato | 320 g | 96% |
| (b) | Apple | 160 g | 82% |
| (c) | Pear | 210 g | 90% |
| (d) | Chicken | 950 g | 78% |
| (e) | Man | 65 kg | 70% |

11 At a service station the amount of sales are shown. Complete the missing entries.

| | Amount of sales | Percent of total |
|---|---|---|
| Regular lead-free gas | $240 | ? |
| Super lead-free gas | $190 | ? |
| Regular gas | $350 | ? |
| Super gas | $260 | ? |
| Oil and Transmission fluids | $108 | ? |
| Miscellaneous | $52 | ? |
| Total Sales | $1200 | 100% |

12 From a poll, the following information was obtained about students.

| Information | Number of students | |
|---|---|---|
| | Yes | No |
| Hold part-time jobs | 12 | 18 |
| Have filed income tax returns | 6 | 24 |
| Have life insurance policies | 1 | 29 |
| Drive a car | 10 | 20 |

(a) What fraction of the students hold part-time jobs?

(b) What percent drive a car?

(c) What percentage do not own life insurance policies?

(d) What fraction have not filed an income tax return? What percentage is this?

13 For the Eastern League, the records show the number of complete and incomplete passes.

(a) Find the missing entries in the chart.

*Eastern League*

| Player | Passes | | Percentage of passes completed |
|---|---|---|---|
| | Complete | Incomplete | |
| Jack Jones | 16 | 40 | ? |
| Barry Longnose | 10 | 24 | ? |
| Herman Butts | 25 | 38 | ? |
| Robert Foster | 9 | 22 | ? |
| Jim Moonraker | 6 | 15 | ? |
| Albert Constello | 12 | 20 | ? |
| Igor Rubinoff | 8 | 12 | ? |

(b) Which player had the best record?

(c) Which player had the worst record?

14 A bicycle depreciates (reduces) in value each year at the rate of 8%. A bicycle initially costs $199.80. Calculate its value at the end of the year.

## Calculator Tip

Use your calculator to do the following steps. What calculation have you completed?

| Calculator Procedure | Original Question |
|---|---|
| [C] 58 [%] [×] 625 [=] ? | ? |

## Consumer Tip

Everyday, as a consumer, you are confronted with information. Throughout this text, consumer tips will suggest topics to explore and will help you to find useful information about the topics.

- Examine a container of table cream. What does the symbol 10% on the container actually mean?
- What is meant by 2% milk?
- What is meant by 100% orange juice?

## Applications: Blood Types

Do you know what type of blood you have? Each year thousands of people donate blood so that a supply is readily available for operations and emergencies. When you give blood, you are given a card that tells you your blood type.

| Blood Type | Percent |
|---|---|
| A Positive | 38 |
| O Positive | 37 |
| B Positive | 7 |
| O Negative | 6 |
| A Negative | 6 |
| AB Positive | 4 |
| B Negative | 1.5 |
| AB Negative | 0.5 |

These are different blood types. The percent of the population that have these blood types.

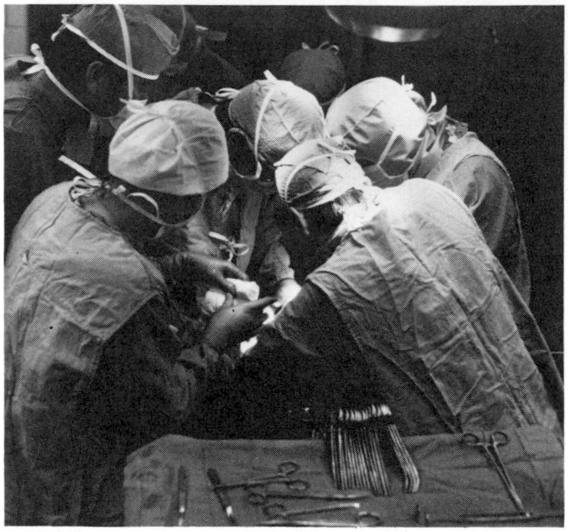

The availability of blood is based on donations by people. Blood cannot be manufactured. When a shortage of blood occurs, operations are cancelled except for emergencies.

15 Use the above chart to find the number of people out of a group of 1500 who have each blood type.
(a) A Positive (b) O Negative
(c) B Negative (d) AB Positive

16 Out of a group of 856 people,
(a) how many more have AB positive than AB negative type blood?
(b) how many more have O Positive blood than A negative blood type?

17 There are 11 885 people living in Dawson Creek, B.C. 535 people have AB negative blood and 4606 have A positive blood. What are the percentages of people having AB negative and A positive blood respectively?

18 6169 people in Bathurst, New Brunswick are found to have O positive blood. Statistics show an average of 37% of the population have type O positive blood. What is the population of Bathurst?

19 (a) 110 of the 7 152 people living in Courtenay, B.C. have B negative blood. What percentage of people have B negative blood in Courtenay?
(b) 46 people have AB negative blood in Chilliwack, B.C. These 46 people constitute 0.5 percent of the population. How many people live in Chilliwack?
(c) If 24 254 people live in Fredericton, N.B. and 364 people have B negative blood, what percentage of people do not have B negative blood?

20 (a) If 12% of the 438 152 people living in Edmonton, Alberta have type B positive blood, how many people is this?
(b) Statistics show that an average of 7% of the population has B positive blood. By how many people is Edmonton over the average?

# 1.8 Organizing Information: Solving Problems

The concepts and skills you learn in mathematics are used to solve problems in mathematics, as well as in other subject areas. Before you solve any problem, whether in mathematics or elsewhere, you must clearly know the answer to these two questions.

*I What information am I asked to find?*
*II What information am I given?*

Deciding where to place a generating station is a complex problem. The answer to each of the questions I and II are dealt with by teams of people, but the same simple questions are dealt with before any solution is attempted.

Once you know the answers to these questions, you then use your skills in mathematics to solve the problem. To solve the problem, you may need to use a skill, or a combination of skills. In order to do the solution, you need to plan your work. Refer to the *Steps for Solving Problems.* Use the suggested steps as a starting point for your own skills to organize your work.

| *Steps for Solving Problems* | |
|---|---|
| *Step A* | Do I understand the problem? |
| | I. What information am I asked to find? |
| | II. What information am I given? |
| *Step B* | Decide on a method. |
| *Step C* | Find the answer. (Do the calculations.) |
| *Step D* | Check my answer in the *original* problem. |
| *Step E* | Write a final statement to answer the question. |

Review the *Steps for Solving Problems* as they are used in the solution of the following example.

**Example**

The price of Mario's new car with extra equipment was \$1658 over the base price of the car. This amounted to 18% of the base price
(a) What was the base price?
(b) Find the total cost of the car.

**Solution**

(a) Let $b$ represent the base price of the car, in dollars.

$$18\% \text{ of } b = 1658$$
$$0.18b = 1658$$
$$b = \frac{1658}{0.18}$$
$$= 9211.11 \text{ (to the nearest cent.)}$$

Thus the base price of the car is \$9211.11.

(b) Total cost = \$9211.11 + \$1658.00
= \$10 869.11

The total cost is \$10 869.11.

## Try These

Review these skills with percent.

1 (a) 1% of a number is 70. What is 20% of the number?
(b) 20% of a number is 520. What is 1% of the number?

2 (a) What is 1% of 3800?
(b) What is 10% of 3800?

3 1% of a number is 82. What is
(a) 10% of the number?
(b) 50% of the number?
(c) 100% of the number?

4 What per cent is
(a) 50 of 100? (b) 50 of 400?
(c) 25 of 75? (d) 19 of 76?

## Written Exercises

**B** For each problem, organize your solution. Refer to the *Steps for Solving Problems.* Where necessary round your answers to 3 decimal places.

1 Marsha bought a used car for \$3150 and paid \$252 tax. What per cent tax was Marsha charged?

2 \$9850 has been contributed to the United Way fund. What is the United Way goal if this amount represents 9% of the goal?

3 During a trip, John went 64 km by bus and 8 km by car. What per cent was
(a) by bus? (b) by car?

4 The label on a cereal box shows the nutrient value per serving. For a serving, what is the mass of
(a) protein? (b) fat? (c) carbohydrates?

| Dry Cereal | |
|---|---|
| 36 g = 1 serving | |
| Fat | 1.12% |
| Protein | 4.76% |
| Carbohydrates | 92.72% |
| Other | 1.40% |

5 A certain test is worth 130 points. How many points are needed to obtain a score of 88%?

6 Petra charged \$169.50 on her credit card last month. She had no previous charges. At the end of the month she must pay at least 5% of this amount. If she pays only this minimum amount, how much does she still have to pay?

7 For a rock concert
56 people came by train
29 people came by bus
17 people came by plane
8298 people came by car
200 people walked
(a) What per cent came by bus?
(b) What per cent came by plane?
(c) What per cent did not walk?
(d) What per cent came by car?

8 Jennifer purchased a small colour T.V. for her bedroom for \$398.99. She sold it after one year to her friend at a loss of 18%. How much did she sell the T.V. for?

9 A cinema has a seating capacity of 1240. If 83% of the seats are occupied, how many people are attending the cinema?

10 In order to sell a trailer, the price was reduced by 15%. Since it did not sell it was reduced a further 25%. If the final sale price was \$1850, find the original selling price.

### Math Tip

It is important to clearly understand the vocabulary of mathematics when solving problems. Make a list of all the new words you have learned in this chapter. Provide a simple example to illustrate each word.

## 1.9 Problem Solving: Interpreting Problems

An essential skill in solving a problem in mathematics and in other areas, is making your problem simpler. To do so, often a summary of the possible types of problems is helpful when interpreting a problem. For example, in working with per cent, there are essentially only three types of problems, as listed below.

| Type | Problem |
|---|---|
| A Finding the per cent of a number. | A Find 20% of 857. |
| B Finding the per cent. | B What per cent of 2460 is 1080? |
| C Finding the number. | C If 35% of a number is 18, find the number. |

Every other problem you meet will be based on one of A, B, C. To solve a problem about per cent, interpret carefully which of the three you are actually solving. In the following example, compare how the solutions are alike, and how they are different.

For each of the following problems, follow these steps.

*Step 1* Read the problem. Identify which type of per cent problem you need to solve.

*Step 2* Know the answers to these two questions.

*I What information am I asked to find?*

*II What information am I given?*

*Step 3* Then solve the problem. Refer to the Steps for Solving Problems to organize your solution.

### Example

(a) What per cent is 54 of 396?

(b) 15% of a number is 48. Find the number.

(c) 19.2% of the 4500 children had cavities. How many children had cavities?

Think: which type of per cent problem is this?

### Solution

(a) $\frac{54}{396} \times 100\%$

$= 0.136 \times 100\%$

$= 13.6\%$

Thus 54 is 13.6% of 396.

(b) Let $x$ represent the number.

$15\%$ of $x = 48$

$\frac{15}{100}x = 48$

$0.15x = 48$

$x = \frac{48}{0.15}$

$= 320$

Thus the number is 320.

Think: which type of per cent problem is this?

(c) 19.2% of 4500

$= 0.192 \times 4500$

$= 864$

Thus 864 children had cavities.

Throughout your work in mathematics, as well as in other subject areas, look for ways to summarize the facts you need to remember and learn.

## Written Exercises

**A** Review skills with per cent. Decide which of the three types you are working with.

1 (a) 1% of a number is 78. What is 10% of the number?
(b) 1% of a number is 124.6. What is 10% of the number?

2 What per cent of
(a) 100 is 20? (b) 100 is 45?
(c) 40.0 is 50? (d) 30.5 is 90?

3 (a) 12 is 25% of what number?
(b) \$16.70 is $1\frac{1}{2}$% of what amount?

4 Increase each of the following by the per cent given.
(a) 24 by 30% (b) 310 by 50%
(c) 100 by $\frac{1}{2}$% (d) 250 by $12\frac{1}{2}$%

5 (a) 20% of what number equals 40?
(b) If 40% of a number is 260, what is the number?
(c) 530 cm are 40% of how many metres?

**B** Express your answer to 1 decimal place, where needed.

6 On Sept. 30, the price of 36 items of food was \$94.63. During October, prices increased 2.9%. What is the cost of the same items on November 1?

7 Of the \$35 Taddy earns each week shovelling snow, she puts \$15 in the bank. Tina earns \$18 a week walking dogs and saves \$10. Who saves the greater per cent of their money each week?

8 To keep fit, Harvey lifts weights 6 times each week, 2 h each time. If he sleeps 8 h each night, for what percentage of his awake hours does he lift weights?

9 A manufacturing firm decreased the production time on an appliance by 3.5%. If the total time used to be 28.6 h how much time is saved?

10 Out of a total of 76 points, Janet scored 29. What per cent did she score?

11 The price of a brand of cereal increased by 12%. If the original price was \$1.69, what is the current selling price?

12 The election results for school president were as follows.

| | | | |
|---|---|---|---|
| Craig | 146 | Mark | 225 |
| Lesley | 301 | Michelle | 283 |

What percentage of the total votes did each candidate receive?

13 The usual tip to pay on a meal is 15%. (TIP means To Improve Performance). If the total paid by a customer was \$21.28, what was the amount of the tip?

14 Jennifer bought a silver coin. It has increased in value by 8%. If the value is now \$396.00, what was the original purchase price?

15 Marie got 32 out of 65 on a test. In reading over her work, Marie found 3 more marks. By how much did her percentage increase?

16 Of the 104 dancers in the dance troup, 12.5% of them have injuries. How many have injuries?

17 38% of the people have already paid for the concert tickets. If this represents 1350 people, how many tickets are there altogether?

18 For a work project, Lisa received a government grant of \$800. If the total cost of the project is \$1850, what per cent did the grant cover?

# Review: Practice and Problems

1 Evaluate.

(a) $40 + 27 \div 3 - 15$

(b) $15 + \dfrac{33 + 37}{35} - 48 \div 6 \times 3$

(c) $19 + 6(50 - 38) + \dfrac{1}{3} \times 12 \div 4$

2 Find the value of each.

(a) $7a - (3b + c)$ when $a = 2$, $b = 4$, and $c = -3$.

(b) $\dfrac{4a + 5b - (8c \div 8)}{4abc}$ when $a = 3$, $b = -2$, and $c = 2$.

3 Find the missing value in each of the following.

(a) $P = 2l + 2w$, $l = 32$, $w = 17$

(b) $C = 2\pi r$, $\pi \doteq 3.14$, $r = 15$

(c) $S = \left(\dfrac{u + V}{2}\right)t$, $V = 32$, $t = 12$, $S = 450$

(d) $u^2 = v^2 - 15t$, $u = 18$, $v = 22$

4 Evaluate. Use a calculator.

(a) $89 + 144 \div 12 - 56$

(b) $259 - 39 + 29 \times 64$

(c) $121 + (16 \times 21 - 94) - 135$

(d) $420 \div [(25 - 4) \times 5] - 30 \div 6$

5 Estimate each of the following. Then calculate.

(a) $67 \times 93$ (b) $567 \times 42$ (c) $2956 \times 88$

(d) $57.4 \times 6.3$ (e) $136 \div 16$ (f) $83.2 \div 6.4$

6 Calculate.

(a) $\dfrac{4}{5} \times 3\dfrac{3}{5}$ (b) $48 \div \dfrac{16}{13}$

(c) $\dfrac{2}{3} + 3\dfrac{3}{4} - 2\dfrac{1}{2}$ (d) $4\dfrac{1}{2} - \dfrac{2}{5} \times \dfrac{5}{3}$

(e) $4\dfrac{1}{2} + 6\dfrac{1}{3} - 3\dfrac{3}{4}$ (f) $4\dfrac{1}{2} \div \dfrac{3}{4} \times 2\dfrac{3}{8}$

7 Use a calculator. Round your answer to 1 decimal place.

(a) $\dfrac{2}{3} + \dfrac{5}{8} + \dfrac{3}{4}$ (b) $6\dfrac{1}{8} - 4\dfrac{7}{10}$

(c) $2\dfrac{1}{4} + \dfrac{3}{5} - \dfrac{2}{3}$ (d) $8\dfrac{1}{2} - 3\dfrac{3}{4} + 5\dfrac{1}{3}$

8 Calculate.

(a) $-16 + 8$ (b) $17 - (-9)$

(c) $-9 + 12 + (-15)$

(d) $-6 \times 8 + 7 \times 2$

(e) $60 - (-14) + 9$

(f) $-9 \times (-12) + 24 \div (-4)$

(g) $-52 - 6 - 7 - (-11) + 27$

(h) $\dfrac{(-20) + (-12)}{(-20) - 12}$

9 Find the average for each of the following.

(a) $-16, -4, -8, -9$

(b) $-6, -11, 12, 15, -7, -21$

(c) $14, -8, -3, 19, -25, -6, -13, -6$

(d) $-18, -12, 4, 21, -9, -16, 0, 32$

10 (a) A hockey rink has seating for 15 984 people. If 93% of the seats are occupied, how many people are present?

(b) The sale price of a 10-speed bicycle is $229.95. If the discount is 30%, calculate the original price.

(c) A swimsuit costs $47.50. Sales Tax is 8%. What is the total cost of the swimsuit?

11 (a) A science test was marked out of 120 marks. How many marks are needed to obtain a score of 86%?

(b) Liz bought a pair of skis for $243.00 and paid $19.44 tax. Find the percent of tax she was charged for the skis.

(c) A clock radio is sold for $67.95 with $\dfrac{1}{3}$ off at the Stereo Mart. At Big Sound the price is $55.50 with 18% off. Which is the better buy?

# A Practice Test

1 (a) Find the value of $3a - (2b + 4c)$ when $a = 2$, $b = -3$, $c = -1$.

(b) Find the missing value in $A = \frac{1}{2}(a + b)h$ where $a = 6$, $b = 8$, $A = 63$.

2 Calculate. Use a calculator.

(a) $\frac{1}{3} + \frac{3}{8} + \frac{3}{4}$ (b) $3\frac{1}{4} - 2\frac{1}{2}$

(c) $2\frac{1}{3} + 1\frac{1}{2} - 2\frac{3}{4}$ (d) $4\frac{1}{2} - \frac{2}{5} \times \frac{1}{3}$

3 Calculate.
(a) $-12 + 6$
(b) $18 \div (-3)$
(c) $-3 + 16 - 3(-12)$
(d) $-3 + 8 - 6 \div (-2)$
(e) $16 - (-4) + (-3)(-4)$
(f) $\dfrac{-30 + 18}{(-2)(6)}$

4 Find the average of
(a) $-2, -6, -3, 8, -2, 12, -13, 12$
(b) $-3, 4, 0, -9, 6, 12, -18, -4$

5 Find each of the following.
(a) What percent of 100 is 30?
(b) 15 is 30% of what number?
(c) 20% of what number is 70?

6 Use your calculator to complete the table by placing the correct operation signs.

| | | | | | | |
|---|---|---|---|---|---|---|
| (a) 396 | ? | 17 | ? | 18 | = | 374 |
| (b) 1803 | ? | 3 | ? | 645 | = | 1246 |
| (c) 14128 | ? | 5725 | ? | 12 | = | 700.25 |
| (d) 781 | ? | 10153 | ? | 13 | = | 1 |

7 By turning down the thermostat just 2°C at night, Jennifer saved 17% of her fuel bill. The saving was $32. Find the cost of heating before turning the thermostat down.

8 (a) 42% of the students in a school are in grades 11 and 12. If this represents 735 students, how many students are enrolled in the school?
(b) During a 2.5 h hockey telecast there were 12 min of commercials. What percent of the time was commercial time?

9 The lower part of the walls of a recreation room is to be panelled. The length of panelling required to panel the four walls is 27.3 m and the height of the panelled portion to be is 1.3 m. The sheets of panelling are 1.3 m wide by 2.6 m long.
(a) How many sheets of panelling will be required to cover the wall?
(b) Find the cost of panelling if you pay $24.95 for a 1.3 m × 2.6 m sheet.

10 The sum of numbers, in sequence, such as 2, 4, 6, 8, 10, 12 can be found by using the formula

$S = \frac{1}{2}n(a + l)$ where $n$ shows how many numbers, $a$ is the first number, $l$ is the last number

Use the formula to find the sum of these numbers.
(a) 10, 12, 14, 16, 18, 20, 22, 24
(b) 36, 33, 30, . . . , 6, 3
(c) $-12, -15, -18, \ldots, -60$

## Career Tip

If you ever want to obtain information on a career contact a company, public office or government office at which the type of work is done. Contact a person who is doing the type of work you would like to do.

- Either this person will give you information to help you
- or they will direct you to a source that can provide the information.

Before you do too much searching, see what information is available in the school guidance office. The few minutes that you spend seeking information may help direct you into a life-long enjoyable career.

# 2 Exponents: Working with Powers

vocabulary of exponents and powers, using calculators, properties of exponents and powers, scientific notation, problem-solving, accuracy in problems, using square roots, fractional exponents, solving problems and applications

## Introduction

In learning mathematics, you need to learn the language. In speaking English you probably know the meaning of more than 5000 words. In mathematics you have far fewer to learn but you must *clearly* understand the meaning of each word. The study of mathematics will help you organize information to solve problems and also will enable you to use formulas to do calculations. You will extend your skills in arithmetic and apply them to learn algebra. Arithmetic and algebra have similar characteristics.

| Arithmetic uses numbers and operations ⇓ to solve problems. | Algebra uses symbols and operations ⇓ to solve problems. |
|---|---|

Using algebra, you can solve problems that you would otherwise not be able to solve by using just arithmetic.

- A computer operator has learned skills with algebra to better understand the workings of a computer.

- A travel agent uses mathematics to calculate not only the profit, but to help in understanding trends in travel.

# 2.1 Working with Powers

The diagram shows a pattern of cell growth.

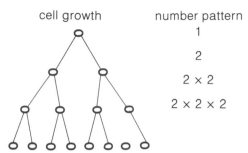

cell growth | number pattern

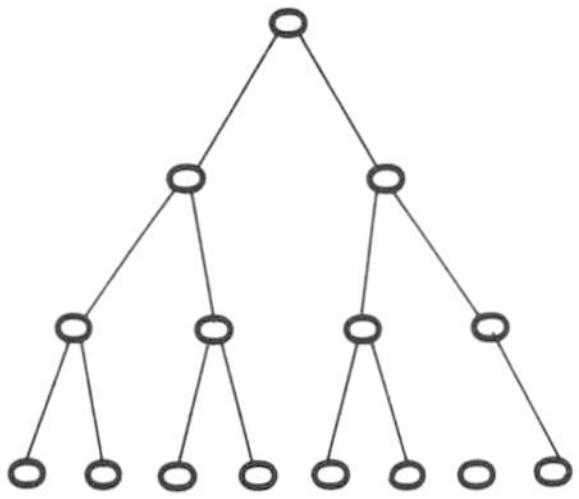

1

2

$2 \times 2$

$2 \times 2 \times 2$

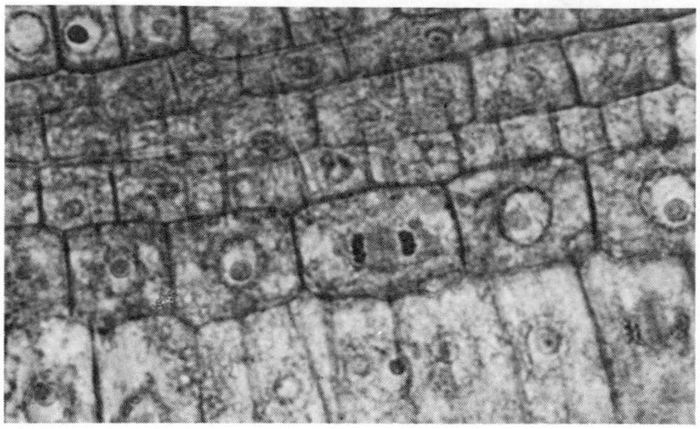

In biology, mitosis is a special type of reproduction in which each cell divides to produce two new cells similar to the original one.

After a cell divides four times there will be $2 \times 2 \times 2 \times 2$ cells. This product can be written in a compact form using a **power**.

$2 \times 2 \times 2 \times 2 = 2^4$ — 2 is the **base**, 4 is the **exponent**.

$2^4$ is read as "two to the exponent four" or "the fourth power of 2"

You can multiply and divide powers with the same base.

$$6^4 \times 6^3$$
$$= \underbrace{6 \times 6 \times 6 \times 6}_{4} \times \underbrace{6 \times 6 \times 6}_{3}$$
Think: $4 + 3 = 7$
$$= 6^7$$

$$6^4 \div 6^3$$
$$= \frac{6 \times \not{6}^1 \times \not{6}^1 \times \not{6}^1}{\not{6}_1 \times \not{6}_1 \times \not{6}_1}$$
$$= 6 \text{ or } 6^1$$

You can use a short cut to write each of the above as a single power.

$6^4 \times 6^3$
$= 6^{4+3}$
$= 6^7$

To multiply like bases add the exponents for the like bases.

$6^4 \div 6^3$
$= 6^{4-3}$
$= 6^1$

To divide like bases subtract the exponents for the like bases.

**Example 1**
Write each as a single power.
(a) $5^8 \times 5^3$

(b) $\left(\frac{1}{2}\right)^7 \div \left(\frac{1}{2}\right)^5$

The base of a power may be a number other than a whole number.

**Solution**
(a) $5^8 \times 5^3 = 5^{8+3}$
$= 5^{11}$

(b) $\left(\frac{1}{2}\right)^7 \div \left(\frac{1}{2}\right)^5 = \left(\frac{1}{2}\right)^{7-5}$
$= \left(\frac{1}{2}\right)^2$

Sometimes you need to find the value of a power. To calculate the values of $2^4$, $(-2)^4$ and $-2^4$, remember that

$$\begin{aligned} 2^4 &= 2 \times 2 \times 2 \times 2 \\ &= 4 \times 2 \times 2 \\ &= 8 \times 2 \\ &= 16 \end{aligned}$$

$$\begin{aligned} (-2)^4 &= (-2) \times (-2) \times (-2) \times (-2) \\ &= 4 \times (-2) \times (-2) \\ &= (-8) \times (-2) \\ &= 16 \end{aligned}$$

$$\begin{aligned} -2^4 &= -(2 \times 2 \times 2 \times 2) \\ &= -(16) \\ &= -16 \end{aligned}$$

To find the value of expressions involving powers and other operations, you need to apply the rules for the order of operations.

**Rules For The Order of Operations**
- Do all calculations in brackets.
- Do calculations involving exponents.
- Multiply and divide, in the order they appear from left to right.
- Add and subtract, in the order they appear from left to right.

### Example 2

Calculate.

(a) $6^2 \div 3^2 \times 2^2 - 4^2$ (b) $(8^2 \div 16 - 5 \times 2) \div 3$

### Solution

(a)
$$\begin{aligned} & 6^2 \div 3^2 \times 2^2 - 4^2 \\ &= \underbrace{36 \div 9} \times 4 - 16 \\ &= 4 \times 4 - 16 \\ &= 16 - 16 \\ &= 0 \end{aligned}$$

First calculate each power.

(b)
$$\begin{aligned} & (8^2 \div 16 - 5 \times 2) \div 3 \\ &= (\underbrace{64 \div 16} - \underbrace{5 \times 2}) \div 3 \\ &= (4 - 10) \div 3 \\ &= (-6) \div 3 \\ &= -2 \end{aligned}$$

Calculate the expression within the brackets.

## Try These

1 What is the base of each power?

(a) $2^6$ (b) $4^3$ (c) $\left(\frac{1}{5}\right)^4$ (d) $(0.16)^5$

2 What is the exponent of each power?

(a) $5^3$ (b) $16^8$ (c) $(1.8)^2$ (d) $\left(2\frac{1}{2}\right)^3$

3 Express each as a single power.

(a) $4 \times 4 \times 4 \times 4 \times 4$ (b) $6.5 \times 6.5 \times 6.5$

4 Find the missing value ▨.

(a) $3^4 = 3 \times 3 \times$ ▨ $\times 3$

(b) $6^{▨} = 6 \times 6 \times 6 \times 6 \times 6$

(c) $10 \times 10 \times 10 \times 10 \times 10 =$ ▨$^5$

(d) $(1.7)^{▨} = 1.7$

5 Express each as a single power.

(a) $2^3 \times 2^2$ (b) $3^3 \times 3^5$

(c) $10^3 \times 10^4$ (d) $5^4 \div 5^2$

(e) $7^5 \div 7^4$ (f) $10^8 \div 10^6$

## Written Exercises

**A** To do mathematics, you need to understand the meaning of words. Review the meaning of base, power, exponent.

1 Write each as a power.
(a) four to the exponent two
(b) two cubed
(c) one to the exponent twenty-five

2 Find the value of each.
(a) six cubed
(b) two to the exponent five
(c) eleven squared

3 Express each as a single power.
(a) $4 \times 4 \times 4 \times 4 \times 4$
(b) $9 \times 9 \times 9$
(c) $52 \times 52 \times 52 \times 52 \times 52 \times 52$

4 Calculate the value of each.
(a) $2^3$ (b) $3^2$ (c) $5^2$
(d) $10^3$ (e) $5^4$ (f) $\left(\frac{1}{3}\right)^3$

**B**

5 Write as a single power.
(a) $8^5 \times 8^3$ (b) $2^6 \times 2^3$
(c) $4^7 \times 4$ (d) $9^3 \times 9^3$
(e) $(3.5)^7 \times (3.5)^4$ (f) $\left(\frac{2}{5}\right)^2 \times \left(\frac{2}{5}\right)^2$
(g) $3^4 \times 3^4 \times 3^2$ (h) $5 \times 5^6 \times 5^2$

6 Write as a single power.
(a) $9^4 \div 9^3$ (b) $5^{10} \div 5^7$
(c) $7^6 \div 7$ (d) $(2.3)^5 \div (2.3)^2$

7 Use $>$, $<$, or $=$ to replace each ◍ to make a true statement. The first one has been done for you.
(a) $3^2$ ◍ $2^3$

$3^2 = 3 \times 3 = 9$  $2^3 = 2 \times 2 \times 2 = 8$

since $9 > 8$, then $3^2 > 2^3$

(b) $5^3$ ◍ $7^2$
(c) $3^4$ ◍ $4^3$
(d) $10^3$ ◍ $11^2$ (e) $8^2$ ◍ $4^3$
(f) $6^3$ ◍ $12^2$ (g) $2^7$ ◍ $7^2$

8 Calculate. Watch the signs.
(a) $4^2 - 2^3$ (b) $6 \times 2^3$
(c) $10^3 \div 5^2$ (d) $(7 + 9) \div 2^3$
(e) $(6^2 - 4) \times 2$ (f) $(9^2 - 81) \times 6$
(g) $10^2 - 6^2 + 8^2$ (h) $4^3 \div 2^4 - 2$
(i) $3^4 + 7 \times 2^3$ (j) $5^2 - 3^2 \div 9 - 1^4$

9 Which has the greater value, A or B?

| | A | B |
|---|---|---|
| (a) | $5^2$ | $6^2 - 4^2$ |
| (b) | $7^2 + 1^2$ | $2 \times 3^3$ |
| (c) | $10^2 + 10$ | $10^3 - 10^2$ |
| (d) | $12^2 \div 4$ | $3^2 \times 4$ |
| (e) | $(2^3 + 4^2) \div 6$ | $8^2 - 2^3 \times 5$ |

10 Which is the correct value of $(0.3)^3$?
A 0.27 B 0.027 C 2.7

11 Calculate.
(a) $(0.1)^2$ (b) $(0.1)^3$ (c) $(0.2)^2$
(d) $(0.5)^3$ (e) $(1.1)^2$ (f) $(0.1)^5$
(g) $(0.03)^2$ (h) $(0.02)^3$ (i) $(0.12)^2$

12 The volume of a cube can be found by cubing the length of one of its sides. The length of one side of a sugar cube is 0.9 cm.
(a) Estimate the volume of one cube.
(b) Estimate the volume of ten cubes.
(c) Calculate the volume of ten of these sugar cubes.

13 If you cut a piece of rope in the middle you have two pieces.
(a) If you put these two halves side by side and cut them in the middle again, how many pieces will you have?
(b) If you put the pieces in (a) side by side and cut them in the middle again, how many pieces will you have?
(c) Repeat the cuts. Write an expression for the number of pieces after n of these cuts.
(d) Check the expression you have written in (c). How many cuts are needed to make 16 pieces?

## Using a Calculator: Exponents

Some calculators have a special key for powers, [$y^x$].
For example, to find the value of $(2.6)^5$ you do these steps.

For a calculator with a [$y^x$] key

| | | | | |
|---|---|---|---|---|
| Press | 2.6 | [$y^x$] | 5 | [=] |
| Display | 2.6 | 2.6 | 5. | 118.81376 |

For a calculator without a power key

| | | | | | | |
|---|---|---|---|---|---|---|
| Press | 2.6 | × | [=] | [=] | [=] | [=] |
| Display | 2.6 | 2.6 | 6.76 | 17.576 | 45.6976 | 118.81376 |

You can also use your calculator in evaluating expressions such as $5 \times 4^3 + 1$.

For a calculator with a [$y^x$] key

| | | | | | | | | | |
|---|---|---|---|---|---|---|---|---|---|
| Press | 5 | [×] | 4 | [$y^x$] | 3 | [=] | [+] | 1 | [=] |
| Display | 5 | 5 | 4 | 4 | 3 | 320 | 320 | 1 | 321 |

The calculator is programmed to use just the preceeding number as the base of the power.

For a calculator without a power key

| | | | | | | | | | | |
|---|---|---|---|---|---|---|---|---|---|---|
| Press | 4 | [×] | [=] | [=] | [×] | 5 | [=] | [+] | 1 | [=] |
| Display | 4. | 4. | 16 | 64 | 64 | 5 | 320 | 320 | 1 | 321 |

To simplify, apply the rules for the order of operations.

---

14 Evaluate each power using a calculator.
(a) $2^7$ (b) $9^6$ (c) $8^5$
(d) $12^4$ (e) $3^9$ (f) $15^4$

15 Estimate the value of each power. Then use a calculator to find the exact value.
(a) $(0.9)^4$ (b) $(1.85)^3$ (c) $(1984)^2$
(d) $(31.5)^3$ (e) $(5.1)^4$ (f) $(1.7)^5$

16 Predict which power has the greatest value. Then check your prediction using a calculator.
(a) $(0.6)^4$, $(0.06)^3$, $(0.06)^2$
(b) $(1.8)^2$, $(1.7)^3$, $(0.9)^4$
(c) $(2.7)^3$, $(7.2)^2$, $(2.2)^4$
(d) $(0.1)^5$, $(1.01)^2$, $(0.001)^2$

17 Evaluate each expression using a calculator.
(a) $8^3 - 10$ (b) $3^6 \times 4 + 62$
(c) $17 + (14)^2$ (d) $(9^4 - 5) \times 8$
(e) $(6^5 + 24) \div 40$ (f) $22 + 7 \times (18^4 - 6)$
(g) $(13 + 39)^3 - 88$ (h) $2.7[8.5 + (4.4)^3]$

18 The power of an electrical system is given by the formula

$$P = \frac{V^2}{R}$$

where $P$ is the power in watts, $V$ is the voltage in volts and $R$ is the resistance in ohms.

Find the power of a stereo speaker if the voltage is 120 V (volts) and the resistance of the system is 480 Ω (ohms).

19 When an object is dropped from a height $H$ (in metres) it falls to the ground because of the force of gravity. After $t$ seconds, the height $h$ of the object above the ground is given by the formula.

$$h = H - 4.9t^2$$

The world's tallest chimney, in Sudbury, is 380 m tall. If you dropped a nickel from the top of the chimney, how high above the ground would it be after 5 seconds?

# 2.2 Properties of Exponents

Often in doing the same steps in mathematics, or in other work, over and over again, you look for a pattern to simplify the steps. For example, your skills for working with powers can be used to develop a pattern for the properties for exponents.

$2^4 \times 2^5 = 2^{4+5} = 2^9$ → suggests the law for multiplying powers with the *same* base → $a^m \times a^n = a^{m+n}$

$6^5 \div 6^2 = 6^{5-2} = 6^3$ → suggests the law for dividing powers with the *same* base → $a^m \div a^n = a^{m-n}$

When more than one exponent is involved, you can again use your earlier skills to develop another property of exponents.

$$(a^2)^3 = a^2 \times a^2 \times a^2 = a^{2+2+2} = a^6$$

$$(a^5)^4 = a^5 \times a^5 \times a^5 \times a^5 = a^{5+5+5+5} = a^{20}$$

These examples suggest the property $(a^m)^n = a^{mn}$

If you use your skills with like factors, you can develop yet other properties of exponents.

$(xy)^4 = (xy)(xy)(xy)(xy) = x^4y^4$ → the example suggests the property → $(ab)^m = a^mb^m$

$\left(\frac{x}{y}\right)^4 = \left(\frac{x}{y}\right)\left(\frac{x}{y}\right)\left(\frac{x}{y}\right)\left(\frac{x}{y}\right) = \frac{x^4}{y^4}$ → which suggests the property → $\left(\frac{a}{b}\right)^m = \frac{a^m}{b^m}$

The properties for exponents are summarized in the table.

**Properties of Exponents**

| | |
|---|---|
| Multiplication | $a^m \times a^n = a^{m+n}$ |
| Division | $a^m \div a^n = a^{m-n}$ |
| Power | $(a^m)^n = a^{mn}$ |
| Power of a product | $(ab)^m = a^mb^m$ |
| Power of a quotient | $\left(\frac{a}{b}\right)^m = \frac{a^m}{b^m}$ |

The properties of exponents are used to simplify and evaluate expressions that involve exponents.

## Example 1

Simplify. (a) $\frac{p^5 \times p^4}{p^3}$ (b) $\frac{(a^2b^3)^2}{b^2}$

## Solution

(a) $\frac{p^5 \times p^4}{p^3} = \frac{p^9}{p^3}$ Use the property of multiplication

$= p^6$ Use the property of division

(b) $\frac{(a^2b^3)^2}{b^2} = \frac{a^4b^6}{b^2}$ Use the property of power of a product

$= a^4b^4$ Use the property of division of powers of base *b*.

### Example 2

Find the value of the expression $\frac{s^7t^5}{(s^3t)^2}$

Use $s = 2$ and $t = -1$.

### Solution

*Step 1* Simplify the expression before substituting for $s$ and $t$.

$$\frac{s^7t^5}{(s^3t)^2} = \frac{s^7t^5}{s^6t^2}$$

$$= st^3$$

*Step 2* Then substitute $s = 2$ and $t = -1$.

$$st^3 = 2 \times (-1)^3$$
$$= 2 \times (-1)$$
$$= -2$$

## Try These

1 What is the missing exponent?
(a) $a^2 \times a^4 = a^?$ (b) $m^5 \times m^5 = m^?$
(c) $p^3 \times p^5 = p^?$ (d) $r^2 \times r = r^?$

2 Express each as a single power.
(a) $m^2 \times m^3$ (b) $p \times p^5$
(c) $k^3 \times k \times k^4$ (d) $n^4 \times n^3 \times n^2$

3 What is the missing exponent?
(a) $\frac{a^7}{a^2} = a^?$ (b) $\frac{m^8}{m^4} = m^?$ (c) $\frac{d^4}{d^?} = d^3$

4 Express each as a single power.
(a) $\frac{t^4}{t^2}$ (b) $\frac{a^5}{a^3}$ (c) $\frac{x^8}{x}$ (d) $\frac{r^{12}}{r^8}$

## Written Exercises

**A** **Review the various properties of exponents.**

1 Write as a single power.
(a) $3^2 \times 3^4$ (b) $m^2 \times m^4$
(c) Which property of exponents did you use?

2 Write each as a single power.
(a) $m^3 \times m^3$ (b) $p^4 \times p^3$ (c) $a \times a^5$
(d) $y \times y$ (e) $n^{10} \times n^4$ (f) $k^2 \times k^3 \times k$

3 Write as a single power for the given base.
(a) $5^6 \div 5^2$ (b) $m^6 \div m^2$
(c) Which property of exponents did you use?

4 Write each as a single power.
(a) $m^6 \div m^4$ (b) $a^3 \div a$ (c) $p^8 \div p^6$
(d) $x^7 \div x^5$ (e) $m^9 \div m$ (f) $b^{15} \div b^{10}$

5 Write with a single exponent.
(a) $(2^3)^2$ (b) $(m^3)^2$
(c) Which property of exponents did you use?

6 Write each with a single exponent.
(a) $(n^2)^5$ (b) $(t^7)^3$ (c) $(d^4)^4$ (d) $(y^3)^4$

7 For each
▶ decide which property of exponents to use,
▶ then simplify.

(a) $\frac{a^9}{a^6}$ (b) $(mn)^3$ (c) $(m^4)(m^5)$

(d) $\left(\frac{x}{y}\right)^6$ (e) $\left(\frac{p}{q}\right)^9$ (f) $(xy)^4$

(g) $(m^3)^5$ (h) $(pq)^5$ (i) $(abc)^7$

(j) $a^9 \div a$ (k) $(a^3b^2)^2$ (l) $\left(\frac{x^3}{y^4}\right)^2$

8 Find the value of each expression for $a = 2$, $b = 4$.
(a) $-ab^2$ (b) $-(ab)^2$ (c) $(-ab)^2$
Why do your answers in (a), (b) and (c) differ?

9 Evaluate each expression for $x = -3$, $y = 2$.
(a) $x^2y$ (b) $(xy)^2$ (c) $xy^2$
Why do your answers in (a), (b) and (c) differ?

**B** Remember: simplify an expression first before substituting for the variable.

10 Find the value of each expression for $a = 2$.
(a) $a^2 \times a$ (b) $a^3 \times a^2$ (c) $a^4 \times a^2 \times a$
(d) $a^8 \div a^5$ (e) $a^3 \div a$ (f) $a \times a^7 \div a^3$

11 Find the value of each expression for $m = 2$, $n = 3$.
(a) $m^2 \times n^2$ (b) $m^3 \times m \times n$
(c) $m \times m^3 \times n$ (d) $m^2 \times n \times n^2$
(e) $m \times m^2 \times n \times n^2$ (f) $m^2 \times m \times n^2 \times n^2$

12 Simplify.
(a) $\frac{a^4b^3}{a^3}$ (b) $\frac{x^6y^5}{x^4}$ (c) $\frac{m^4n^3}{n}$
(d) $\frac{p^4q^4}{p^3q^2}$ (e) $\frac{a^6b^4}{a^4b^3}$ (f) $\frac{k^3t^4m^2}{k^2t^2m}$

13 Simplify.
(a) $\frac{(mn)^4}{m^2n}$ (b) $\left(\frac{p}{q}\right)^3 \times \frac{(pq)^2}{p}$
(c) $(a^2b)^3 \times \left(\frac{a}{b}\right)^2$ (d) $\frac{a^3b^4}{c^2} \times \left(\frac{ac}{b}\right)^3$
(e) $\left(\frac{x^2}{y}\right)^3 \times \left(\frac{x}{y}\right)^2$ (f) $\left(\frac{m^2n^2}{p} \times \frac{m^3n}{p}\right)^2$

14 Find the value of each expression for $p = 3$, $q = -1$.
(a) $(pq^2)^2$ (b) $\frac{p^5q^3}{p^3q^2}$ (c) $pq^2 \times p^2q^2$
(d) $\frac{p^5q^6}{(p^2q^2)^2}$ (e) $\frac{(p^2q^3)^3}{(pq)^4}$ (f) $\frac{(pq)^3 \times (p^3q)^2}{p^7q^4}$

15 The value in dollars of a brass coin that is less than 500 years old can be found by using the formula

$V = \frac{m^4}{n^2}$ where $m$ is the mass in grams and $n$ is the age of the coin in years.

The value $V$ is multiplied by $\frac{n}{m}$ if the coin is more than 500 years old.
(a) Find the value of a coin that is 375 years old and has a mass of 60 g.
(b) Find the value of a coin that is 625 years old and has a mass of 50 g. Use a calculator to check your answer.

16 An advertising agency figures that the number of sales generated by a 30-second T.V. commercial is given by the equation

Sales = $n^2k$ where $n$ is the number of stations showing the commercial and $k$ is the number of times it is shown.

If the commercial is shown during prime time then the above expression, $n^2k$, is cubed.
(a) Write the equation for the sales generated by a prime time commercial.
(b) Find the number of sales generated by a commercial shown at prime time on 10 stations 5 times.

## Career Tip

Regardless of what career you pursue, you will be exposed to computers at some time.
A List types of careers that require the use of a computer.
B List ways in which a computer might be used in business.
C Compile a list of ways that you know in which computers affect or influence your everyday activities.
D Refer to newspapers and magazines. Compile a list of the ways in which computers impact on and influence people that you read about.

## Applications: Safe Load

In constructing houses, the builder must be concerned with the safe load, $S$, in kilograms that a wooden beam or joist can support.

The following formula gives the safe load, $S$, in kilograms

$$S = \frac{1.12wh^2}{L}$$

for a wooden beam where $w$ is the width, $h$ the height of the beam in centimetres and $L$ is the length of the beam in metres.

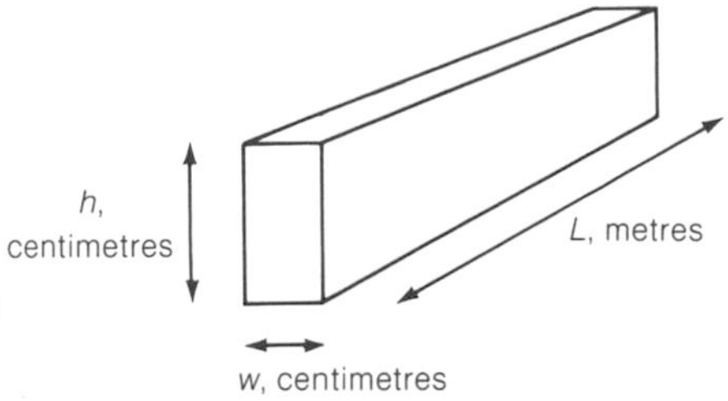


17 Find the safe load for each of the following values.

(a) $w = 6.3$ cm $h = 4.8$ cm $L = 1.1$ m
(b) $w = 9.4$ cm $h = 12.2$ cm $L = 0.6$ m
(c) $w = 8.6$ cm $h = 16.1$ cm $L = 2.3$ m

18 Calculate the safe load for each joist. Each joist is 25 cm high and 5 cm wide. The lengths are as follows.

(a) 1.3 m (b) 2.5 m
(c) 3.0 m (d) 3.6 m
(e) 4.0 m (f) 4.3 m
(g) What do you notice about your answers in (a) to (f)?

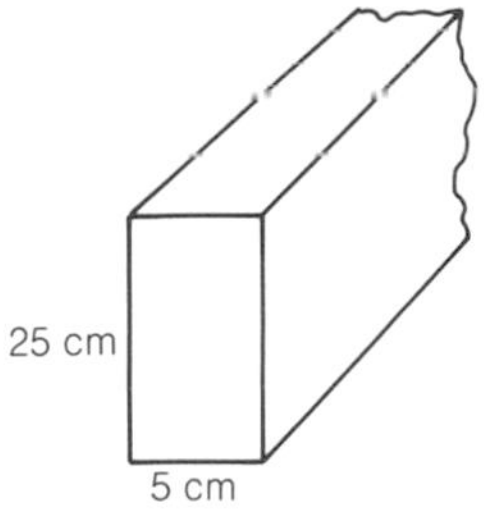


19 Refer to the safe load formula. Express the formula in terms of each of the following variables.

(a) $w$ (b) $h$ (c) $L$

20 Find the safe load for a rafter that measures 12 cm wide, 14.5 cm high, and 1.23 m long.

21 Find the width of a rafter that will support 1016 kg if the rafter is 24.0 m long and 12.6 cm high.

22 (a) Your house has joists with dimensions 25 cm by 5 cm by 4.8 m. What is the safe load of one of the joists in your home?
(b) In (a) you turn the joist on its side. What is the safe load now?

23 A joist measures 5 cm high and 25 cm wide and 3.1 m long. How many persons with average mass 70 kg, can be supported by the joist?

24 The entrance to a home is supported by joists that are 1.83 m long. You want a safe load of 950 kg for each joist. What is the height of the joist if the width is 5 cm?

25 A room has 8 joists supporting the floor. Each joist measures 25 cm high by 5 cm by 3 m. How much will the floor support?

26 Run the following program on a computer.

```
10 PRINT "CALCULATING LOAD"
20 INPUT "WIDTH"; W
30 INPUT "HEIGHT"; H
40 INPUT "LENGTH"; L
50 IF L = 0 THEN 90
60 LOAD = (1.12 * W * H ** 2)/L
70 PRINT "LOAD ="; LOAD
80 GO TO 10
90 END
```

## 2.3 Zero and Negative Exponents

The properties you have used for working with exponents have dealt with the exponents such as 1, 2, 3, 4, . . .

**Properties of Exponents**

| | |
|---|---|
| Multiplication | $a^m \times a^n = a^{m-n}$ |
| Division | $a^m \div a^n = a^{m-n}$ |
| Power | $(a^m)^n = a^{mn}$ |
| Power of a Product | $(ab)^m = a^m b^m$ |
| Power of a Quotient | $\left(\frac{a}{b}\right)^m = \frac{a^m}{b^m}$ |

By finding the answer in a different way and by using the properties of exponents we can give a meaning to a zero exponent and to negative exponents.

Use factors — Compare — Apply properties of exponents

$$\frac{3^5}{3^5} = \frac{\cancel{3}\times\cancel{3}\times\cancel{3}\times\cancel{3}\times\cancel{3}}{\cancel{3}\times\cancel{3}\times\cancel{3}\times\cancel{3}\times\cancel{3}} = 1 \quad \xleftrightarrow{\text{Compare}} \quad \frac{3^5}{3^5} = 3^{5-5} = 3^0$$

$$\frac{p^4}{p^4} = \frac{\cancel{p}\times\cancel{p}\times\cancel{p}\times\cancel{p}}{\cancel{p}\times\cancel{p}\times\cancel{p}\times\cancel{p}} = 1 \quad \xleftrightarrow{\text{Compare}} \quad \frac{p^4}{p^4} = p^{4-4} = p^0$$

The above examples suggest that $3^0 = 1$ and $p^0 = 1$.

For any base $a$, we use $a^0 = 1$, $a \neq 0$

What meaning can be given to a negative exponent?

Use factors — Compare — Apply properties of exponents

$$\frac{3^4}{3^6} = \frac{\cancel{3}\times\cancel{3}\times\cancel{3}\times\cancel{3}}{3\times 3\times\cancel{3}\times\cancel{3}\times\cancel{3}\times\cancel{3}} = \frac{1}{3^2} \quad \xleftrightarrow{\text{Compare}} \quad \frac{3^4}{3^6} = 3^{4-6} = 3^{-2}$$

$$\frac{p^3}{p^6} = \frac{p\times\cancel{p}\times\cancel{p}}{p\times p\times p\times\cancel{p}\times\cancel{p}\times\cancel{p}} = \frac{1}{p^3} \quad \xleftrightarrow{\text{Compare}} \quad \frac{p^3}{p^6} = p^{3-6} = p^{-3}$$

These examples suggest that $3^{-2} = \frac{1}{3^2}$ and $p^{-3} = \frac{1}{p^3}$

For any base $a$, and natural number $n$, we use $a^{-n} = \frac{1}{a^n}$, $a \neq 0$

**Example 1**

Evaluate.

(a) $6^0$ (b) $3^{-2}$ (c) $(2^2)^{-1}$ (d) $4^{-2} \times 5^0$

**Solution**

(a) $6^0 = 1$

(b) $3^{-2} = \frac{1}{3^2}$
$= \frac{1}{9}$

(c) $(2^2)^{-1} = \frac{1}{(2^2)^1}$
$= \frac{1}{2^2}$
$= \frac{1}{4}$

(d) $4^{-2} \times 5^0 = \frac{1}{4^2} \times 1$
$= \frac{1}{16} \times 1$
$= \frac{1}{16}$

You can also apply the laws of exponents to simplify expressions that involve variables.

**Example 2**

Simplify.

(a) $p^{12} \div p^{-3}$

(b) $m^7 \times m^{-3} \times m^{-2}$

**Solution**

(a) $p^{12} \div p^{-3} = p^{12-(-3)}$ Use the division property of exponents
$= p^{15}$

(b) $m^7 \times m^{-3} \times m^{-2} = m^{7+(-3)+(-2)}$
$= m^2$ Use the multiplication property of exponents.

**Example 3**

Find the value of the expression $\frac{m^{-4}(mn^2)^3}{m^2n}$. Use $m = 2$ and $n = -3$.

**Solution**

*Step 1* Use the properties of exponents to simplify the given expression.

$$\frac{m^{-4}(mn^2)^3}{m^2n} = \frac{m^{-4}m^3n^6}{m^2n}$$
$$= \frac{m^{-1}n^6}{m^2n}$$
$$= m^{-1-2}n^{6-1}$$
$$= m^{-3}n^5$$

*Step 2* Substitute $m = 2$, $n = -3$.

$$m^{-3}n^5 = 2^{-3}(-3)^5$$
$$= \frac{1}{2^3} \times (-3)^5$$
$$= \frac{1}{8}(-243)$$
$$= -30.375$$

## Try These

1 What is the value of each?
(a) $3^0$ (b) $10^0$ (c) $7^0$ (d) $n^0$

2 Express each of the following with a positive exponent.
(a) $2^{-1}$ (b) $4^{-2}$ (c) $10^{-5}$ (d) $q^{-3}$

3 Express as a single power.
(a) $r^{-5} \times r^6$ (b) $a^0 \times a^3$ (c) $y^{-2} \times y^{-3}$

4 Simplify. Express as a single power.
(a) $m^{-1} \times m^{-1}$ (b) $w^{-1} \div w^{-2}$
(c) $(x^{-2})^3$ (d) $(t^3)^{-1}$

## Written Exercises

**A** Review the meaning of $a^0$ and $a^{-n}$.

1 Write the value of each.
(a) $9^0$ (b) $1^0$ (c) $(29)^0$
(d) $t^0$ (e) $(18z)^0$ (f) $(-3k)^0$

2 Write each with a positive exponent.
(a) $8^{-1}$ (b) $5^{-2}$ (c) $2^{-4}$
(d) $a^{-3}$ (e) $q^{-5}$ (f) $(2x)^{-1}$

3 Find each value.
(a) $3^{-1}$ (b) $5^{-3}$ (c) $4^0$
(d) $10^{-4}$ (e) $12^{-2}$ (f) $2^{-5}$

4 Find each value.
(a) $2^3$ (b) $2^{-3}$ (c) $(-2)^{-3}$
(d) $-(2)^3$ (e) $-(2^{-3})$ (f) $(-2)^3$

5 Copy and complete each of the following. Find the value of the expression.
(a) $(3^{-1})^2 = 3^{-2}$
$= ?$
(b) $(2^{-2})(2^4) = 2^{-2+4}$
$= ?$
(c) $\dfrac{4^{-2}}{4^{-3}} = 4^?$
$= ?$
(d) $\dfrac{2^{-1}}{2^2} = 2^?$
$= ?$

**B** You need to apply the properties of exponents as well as the meaning of $a^0$ and $a^{-n}$.

6 Simplify.
(a) $4^0$ (b) $3a^0$
(c) $(5m)^0$ (d) $\dfrac{5}{m^0}$
(e) $\dfrac{(4x^0)(5x)^0}{2}$ (f) $\dfrac{(-6a^0)(-2p)^0}{-6}$

7 Express using only positive exponents.
(a) $m^{-3}n^{-4}$ (b) $a^5b^{-2}$ (c) $\dfrac{a^5}{b^{-4}}$
(d) $\dfrac{p^{-3}}{q^{-4}}$ (e) $\dfrac{f}{g^{-2}}$ (f) $\dfrac{k^{-2}}{d^{-2}}$

8 Express as a single power with a positive exponent.
(a) $n^3 \times n^{-5}$ (b) $k^{-2} \times k^{-6}$
(c) $q^{-5} \times q^3 \times q$ (d) $(p^{-4})^8$
(e) $(n^3)^{-2}$ (f) $(z^{-3})^{-2} \times z^5$
(g) $\dfrac{a^{-6}}{a} \times (a^{-2})^{-2}$ (h) $\dfrac{t^7 \times t^{-3}}{t^{-4}}$

9 Evaluate. Watch the signs.
(a) $2^2 + 2^{-2}$ (b) $2^{-1} + 2^{-2}$
(c) $4^{-1} - 4^{-2}$ (d) $10^{-1} \times 10^{-2}$
(e) $2^{-3} \times 5^0$ (f) $(-3)^{-2} \times (-2)^2$
(g) $\dfrac{4^2 \times 4^2}{4^6}$ (h) $3^{-2} \times 2^3$

10 Evaluate each of the following. Did you use a calculator?
(a) $\dfrac{(1.3)^5}{(1.3)^2}$ (b) $\dfrac{(0.6)^2 \times (0.6)^4}{(0.6)^3}$
(c) $\dfrac{(2.5)^0}{(2.5)^3 \times (2.5)^{-3}}$ (d) $\dfrac{(0.15)(0.15)^{-2}}{(0.15)^2}$

11 Simplify.
(a) $\dfrac{m^8 \times m^{-5}}{m^4}$ (b) $\dfrac{a^3 \times a^{-4}}{a^{-2}}$ (c) $\dfrac{t^{-9} \times t^{-10}}{t^{-18}}$
(d) $\dfrac{(a^{-3})^2}{a^4 \times a^{-8}}$ (e) $\dfrac{q^{-5} \times q^5}{(q^2)^{-1}}$ (f) $\dfrac{(d^{-4})^{-2}}{(d^3)^3}$

12 Find the value of each expression. Use $a = 2$ and $b = -1$.
(a) $a^{-3}b$ (b) $(ab)^{-2}$
(c) $2a^{-2}b^{-4}$ (d) $a^{-2} + b^{-2}$
(e) $2a^{-1} - 5b^{-1}$ (f) $a^{-1}b - a^{-2}$
(g) $\dfrac{(a^2)^{-1}b^8}{(b^3)^2}$ (h) $\dfrac{(a^{-2}b^2)^{-1}}{(a^{-3}b^{-2})(ab)}$

**C**

13 Evaluate.
(a) $(3^0 + 2^3)^{-2}$ (b) $(2^{-2} - 3^{-1})^{-1}$
(c) $\dfrac{4^{-2}}{4^{-2} + 4^0}$ (d) $\dfrac{3^{-1}}{3^{-2} - 3^{-1}}$

# 2.4 Applications: Scientific Notation

Astronomers predict that the sun will survive as an energy source for another 7 500 000 years. The earth receives only 0.000 000 0005 of the sun's radiant energy.

In the photo, the solar panels are used to convert the sun's radiant energy into energy to heat the house not only in the daytime but also at night when the outside temperature lowers.

In science very large or very small numbers often occur. Since many zeroes are awkward to read and write, a special method of recording such numbers has been developed. Large or small numbers can be expressed in **scientific notation** by using powers of ten.

| Number in standard decimal form | Number in scientific notation |
|---|---|
| 7 500 000 000 = | $7.5 \times 10^9$ |

$7.5$ — A number between 1 and 10; $10^9$ — the appropriate power of 10

Also $0.000\,000\,000\,5 = 5.0 \times 10^{-10}$

### Example 1

The following are expressed in scientific notation. Write each in standard decimal form.

(a) $6.2 \times 10^{12}$

(b) $3.05 \times 10^{-7}$

### Solution

(a) $6.2 \times 10^{12} = 6\,200\,000\,000\,000$

Use these digits. Place the decimal point 12 places to the right.

(b) $3.05 \times 10^{-7} = 0.000\,000\,305$

Use these digits. Place the decimal point 7 places to the left.

You can multiply or divide with numbers in scientific notation.

### Example 2

Calculate. Express the answer in scientific notation.

$(3.4 \times 10^6) \times (6.5 \times (10^{-9})$

### Solution

$(3.4 \times 10^6) \times (6.5 \times 10^{-9})$

$= 3.4 \times 6.5 \times 10^6 \times 10^{-9}$

$= 22.1 \times 10^{-3}$

$= (2.21 \times 10^1) \times 10^{-3}$

$= 2.21 \times 10^{1+(-3)}$

$= 2.21 \times 10^{-2}$

Sometimes it is necessary to write the numbers in scientific notation first. Try doing the following division using your calculator and you will see why scientific notation is needed.

**Example 3**

Calculate $\dfrac{0.000\,000\,494}{15.2}$

**Solution**

$$\frac{0.000\,000\,494}{15.2} = \frac{4.94 \times 10^{-7}}{1.52 \times 10^{1}}$$
$$= 3.25 \times 10^{-8}$$
$$= 0.000\,000\,032\,5$$

## Try These

1 Each number is to be expressed in scientific notation. What is the missing exponent in each?

(a) $9850 = 9.85 \times 10^{?}$

(b) $65\,000 = 6.5 \times 10^{?}$

(c) $184\,000 = 1.84 \times 10^{?}$

(d) $0.0025 = 2.5 \times 10^{?}$

2 Each number is to be expressed in scientific notation. What is the missing number in each?

(a) $59\,000 =$ ▨ $\times 10^{4}$

(b) $0.000\,072 =$ ▨ $\times 10^{-5}$

(c) $0.529 =$ ▨ $\times 10^{-1}$

(d) $6\,300\,000 =$ ▨ $\times 10^{6}$

## Written Exercises

**A**

1 Find the missing values.

(a) $1900 = 1.9 \times 10^{?}$

(b) $97\,500\,000 = 9.75 \times 10^{?}$

(c) $30\,000 = 3.0 \times 10^{?}$

(d) $0.001\,59 = 1.59 \times 10^{?}$

(e) $0.000\,735 = 7.35 \times 10^{?}$

(f) $0.000\,009\,7 = 9.7 \times 10^{?}$

2 Write each number in scientific notation.

(a) 495 000 (b) 542

(c) 84 100 (d) 16.4

(e) 21 600 000 (f) 0.001 52

(g) 0.000 000 247 (h) 0.006 91

3 Find the missing values.

| | Standard decimal form | Scientific notation |
|---|---|---|
| (a) | 9600 | ? |
| (b) | ? | $4.8 \times 10^{-2}$ |
| (c) | ? | $1.9 \times 10^{-5}$ |
| (d) | 25 400 | ? |
| (e) | 0.000 84 | ? |

4 Each number is expressed in scientific notation. Write each in standard decimal form.

(a) $4.92 \times 10^{4}$ (b) $6.05 \times 10^{-3}$

(c) $5.3 \times 10^{5}$ (d) $9.8 \times 10^{-7}$

(e) $2.67 \times 10^{-2}$ (f) $1.4 \times 10^{8}$

(g) $8.0 \times 10^{-5}$ (h) $3.01 \times 10^{6}$

5 When a product has more than eight digits, scientific calculators automatically display the result in scientific notation. A display of (7.3   08) means $7.3 \times 10^{8}$, or 730 000 000. Find the missing entries in the following table.

| | Calculator display | Scientific notation | Standard decimal form |
|---|---|---|---|
| (a) | 4.98   05 | ? | 498 000 |
| (b) | 8.4   −05 | $8.4 \times 10^{-5}$ | ? |
| (c) | ? | $1.56 \times 10^{8}$ | ? |
| (d) | ? | ? | 0.000 007 2 |
| (e) | 5.814   12 | ? | ? |
| (f) | ? | ? | 1 386 000 000 |

6 Computers also have a special way of writing numbers in scientific notation. The number $9.64 \times 10^5$ appears on the computer screen (or print out) as 9.64E + 05. The number. $8.32 \times 10^{-8}$ appears as 8.32E − 08. Write each of the following numbers in scientific notation as they would appear on a computer screen.

(a) 17 800 (b) 0.000 005 6
(c) 0.000 092 6 (d) 7 964 000 000
(e) 18 200 000 000 (f) 0.000 061 914

**B** Review the properties of exponents. You need to use them to simplify expressions.

7 Express each number in scientific notation.
(a) The area of Canada is about 9 920 000 $km^2$.
(b) The nearest star, Proxima Centauri, is 40 200 000 000 000 km away from Earth.
(c) A helium atom has a diameter of 0.000 000 022 cm.
(d) The earth travels about 9 400 000 000 km in each orbit around the sun.
(e) The mass of a proton is approximately 0.000 000 000 000 000 000 000 016 8 g.
(f) A light-year is 9 460 000 000 000 km. (This is the distance light will travel in one solar year.)

8 Use <, >, or = in place of each ◍ to make true statements.
(a) 18.600 ◍ $1.86 \times 10^5$
(b) $2.07 \times 10^{-4}$ ◍ 0.000 207
(c) $7.2 \times 10^7$ ◍ 7.200 000
(d) 9.24 ◍ $9.24 \times 10^0$
(e) 0.0841 ◍ $8.41 \times 10^2$
(f) 0.000 031 9 ◍ $3.19 \times 10^{-5}$

9 Estimate each product. Then multiply. Express your answers in scientific notation.
(a) $(5.7 \times 10^3) \times (1.4 \times 10^2)$
(b) $(1.34 \times 10^{-4}) \times (2.65 \times 10^8)$
(c) $(9.43 \times 10^{-7}) \times (5.11 \times 10^{-4})$
(d) $(7.4 \times 10^5) \times (8.2 \times 10^{-9})$
(e) $(3.05 \times 10^{-3}) \times (6.72 \times 10^{-1})$
(f) $(6.25 \times 10^4)^2$ ← Remember $(6.25 \times 10^4)^2$ means $(6.25 \times 10^4) \times (6.25 \times 10^4)$
(g) $(7.21 \times 10^{-3})^2$

10 Estimate each answer. Then calculate. Express your answers in scientific notation.

(a) $\dfrac{8.88 \times 10^6}{3.7 \times 10^3}$ (b) $\dfrac{9.03 \times 10^4}{2.15 \times 10^7}$

(c) $\dfrac{4.81 \times 10^{-8}}{7.4 \times 10^{-5}}$ (d) $\dfrac{2.421 \times 10^{-3}}{5.38 \times 10^4}$

11 Express each number in scientific notation and then calculate. Write the answers in standard decimal form.

(a) 1 350 000 000 × 26 000 000
(b) 760 000 000 × 132
(c) 0.000 000 059 × 2400

(d) $\dfrac{0.000\,000\,022\,4}{0.0064}$ (e) $\dfrac{158\,400\,000}{3\,520\,000\,000}$

(f) $\dfrac{13.92}{0.000\,000\,001\,5}$ (g) $\dfrac{804\,100\,000}{0.086}$

12 A catalogue uses product codes consisting of two letters followed by four digits. The number of possible different codes is
$26 \times 26 \times 10 \times 10 \times 10 \times 10$.
Express this number in scientific notation.

13 The diameter of an oxygen molecule is 0.000 000 29 cm. Find the width of 1800 oxygen molecules placed side by side.

14 In each orbit of the earth, the moon travels about $2.408 \times 10^6$ km in 28 days. How far does the moon travel each day?

15 A film of oil on water is 0.000 000 508 cm thick. A quantity of oil is spilled. What area does 381 $cm^3$ of oil cover?

**C**

16 The transmitting frequency $F$, in hertz (Hz), of a television signal is given by
$F = vw^{-1}$
where $v$ is the speed of the signal and $w$ is the wavelength. Find the frequency of a signal travelling at $3.0 \times 10^{10}$ cm/s with a wavelength of $5.0 \times 10^2$ cm.

## Applications: Facts about Humans

There are many interesting facts about the human body. For example, did you know that

- all the capillaries in our bodies placed end to end are longer than the equator of the earth?
- each square centimetre of the skin has 97 sweat glands?
- each eye has more than 2 million light receptors?
- there are over 100 000 hairs on your head?

Facts about the human body require the use of scientific notation.

---

17 Express the measures in the following facts in scientific notation.
(a) the liver has a mass of 1417.5 g
(b) the brain has 1 000 000 000 nerve endings
(c) the small intestine is 609.6 cm long
(d) a flu virus measures 0.000 001 cm in diameter

18 Express the measures in the following facts in standard decimal notation.
(a) there are $1.25 \times 10^5$ hairs on a scalp
(b) hair grows $1.1 \times 10^{-4}$ cm each hour
(c) the kidneys have $1.0 \times 10^6$ tubules for filtering out waste products
(d) the total length of the tubules is $6.436 \times 10^4$ m

19 The human body is made up of about $6.0 \times 10^9$ cells. Each human cell is made up of about $6.3 \times 10^9$ atoms. About how many atoms are in the human body
(a) expressed in scientific notation?
(b) expressed in standard decimal notation?

20 (a) An adult male has about $6.8 \times 10^3$ mL of blood. Each millilitre of blood contains up to $6.2 \times 10^6$ red blood cells. About how many red blood cells does an adult male have? Express your answer in scientific notation.
(b) Adult females have about $3.98 \times 10^3$ mL of blood. Each millilitre contains less red blood cells than the male too: up to $5.4 \times 10^6$ of them. About how many red blood cells does an adult female have?

21 The diameter of a red blood cell is $7.5 \times 10^{-6}$ m. If you could place each red blood cell in a human male side by side, how many kilometres long would the line of cells be?

22 On average an adult has $9.65 \times 10^4$ km of blood capillaries. The circumference of the earth at the equator is about 40 000 km. How many times around the equator would the capillaries reach?

23 On average an adult male has a surface area of $1.8 \times 10^4$ cm$^2$.
(a) Each square centimetre of skin has 9 hairs. Express in standard decimal form the number of hairs over the whole surface area.
(b) Each square centimetre has 97 sweat glands. Express in scientific notation the total number of sweat glands over the whole skin surface.

24 Each eye has $1.25 \times 10^8$ light receptors. These receptors feed signals into the $1.0 \times 10^6$ nerve receptors in the optic nerve, which carries messages to the brain.
(a) How many light receptors feed signals into each nerve receptor?
(b) The light receptors are of two types called rods and cones. The cones are 5% of the total number of receptors. How many cones are there?

# 2.5 Accuracy and Significant Digits

Some answers are exact: the number of people in your classroom. Some answers are approximate because they involve measurement or rounding. The **accuracy** of a measurement is the number of **significant digits** given in the answer. The following examples show how to determine the number of significant digits.

| Measurement | Number of significant digits | Comments |
|---|---|---|
| 3200 m | two | The last two zeroes are placeholders. |
| 5.08 cm | three | 0 is between two other digits so it is significant. |
| 0.0072 km | two | The two zeroes following the decimal point are placeholders. |
| 12.0 L | three | Writing the last zero emphasizes that there are no tenths, so it is significant. |

If something is significant it counts. Sometimes zero is significant, other times it is just a place-holder.

Non-zero digits are always significant. Zero is significant sometimes depending on its position in the number.

For convenience, very large and very small numbers can be written in scientific notation. Any zeroes that are significant must be written with the decimal part.

$$0.000\,000\,580 = 5.80 \times 10^{-7}$$

This number has 3 significant digits.

Keep this last zero because the original number has 3 significant digits.

When you perform operations with approximate numbers, the result can only be as accurate as the least accurate number in the calculation.

**Example 1**

A room measures 8.72 m by 7.05 m. Calculate the area of the room.

**Solution**

Remember: Area = length × width

Use $A = l \times w$

$= 8.72 \times 7.05$

$= 61.476$

The area of the room is 61.5 $m^2$.

Think. Each measure has three significant digits. so round the product to three digits.

**Example 2**

The following expression occurred in a study to measure the depth of an ocean trench.

$$\frac{(9.3 \times 10^{14}) \times (4.7 \times 10^{-4})}{(5.75 \times 10^{5})}$$

Simplify the expression.

**Solution**

$$\frac{(9.3 \times 10^{14}) \times (4.7 \times 10^{-4})}{(5.75 \times 10^{5})}$$

Use a calculator to evaluate the decimal part.

$$= \frac{(9.3 \times 4.70)}{5.75} \times \frac{(10^{14} \times 10^{-4})}{10^{5}}$$

Use the properties of powers, $10^{14+(-4)-5}$

$$= 7.6 \times 10^{5}$$

Round to two significant digits because the least accurate measure in the calculation, 9.3, has two digit accuracy.

## Try These

1 Is the digit zero in each of the following a significant digit?
(a) 5083 km (b) 0.67 m (c) 1.350 kg
(d) 610 L (e) 105 g (f) 62.04 cm

2 How many significant digits does each measurement have?
(a) 18 000 m (b) 1008 kg (c) 0.018 km
(d) 18.0 L (e) 1.08 m (f) 108 000 cm

## Written Exercises

**A** Remember: non-zero digits are always significant.

1 Which of the following measurements have two significant digits?
(a) 279 g (b) 408 m (c) 5.3 cm
(d) 82.0 m (e) 64 000 km (f) 0.000 19 kg
(g) 900.1 cm (h) 7.0 L (i) 0.0403 km

2 Which of the following measurements have three significant digits?
(a) 185 000 m (b) 0.0107 g (c) 9.587 L
(d) 49 005 cm (e) 37.4 kg (f) 0.006 cm
(g) 320 km (h) 4.09 m (i) 0.0750 L

3 Give the number of significant digits in each.
(a) 51 720 mL (b) 0.038 kg
(c) 25.16 m (d) 4.706 km
(e) 12.07 cm (f) 42 000 km
(g) 0.0108 kg (h) 0.000 720 m
(i) 1250.4 cm (j) 75 300 L

4 The following measurements are written in scientific notation. How many significant digits does each have?
(a) $6.4 \times 10^{8}$ km (b) $1.05 \times 10^{-3}$ m
(c) $5.763 \times 10^{4}$ g (d) $3.80 \times 10^{-7}$ cm
(e) $9.106 \times 10^{-1}$ L (f) $8.430\,70 \times 10^{12}$ m

5 Write each measurement in scientific notation.
(a) 81 500 m (b) 508 000 cm
(c) 1 400 000 000 km (d) 0.000 92 kg
(e) 0.008 08 mL (f) 0.000 005 0 m
Which of these has the greatest number of significant digits?

6 Round each measurement to four significant digits.
(a) 514 720 m (b) 0.786 18 g
(c) 1.003 95 L (d) 33 081.0 cm
(e) 0.002 947 kg (f) 610 003 cm

7 In each of the following, which measurement has the least accuracy? How many significant digits does it have?
(a) 50.73 m, 9.07 m, 10.48 m
(b) 380 mL, 285 mL, 79.5 mL
(c) 0.55 kg, 0.08 kg, 0.095 kg
(d) 6.09 km, 9.5 km, 10.3 km

**B** **In Questions 8–12 round your answers to show the appropriate accuracy. Use significant digits in your answer.**

8 A rectangular table measures 1.72 m by 0.96 m. Calculate the area of the table.

9 Each of Beverley's strides is 0.73 m long. How far does she walk in 350 strides?

10 The label on a rolled up piece of carpeting reads | $15\ m^2$ Only $200 |. Clive measured the width of the carpet to be 3.6 m. What is the length?

11 A satellite travels at 28 000 km/h and takes 1.55 h to complete one orbit about the earth. What distance does the satellite travel in each orbit?

12 Light travels at $1.1 \times 10^9$ km/h. Earth is $1.5 \times 10^8$ km from the sun. How long does it take light to travel from the sun to earth?

13 Each of the following expressions occurred in a research project. Do the calculation. Express your answers in scientific notation, rounded to the appropriate degree of accuracy.

**Did you use a calculator?**

(a) $(4.5 \times 10^{12}) \times (7.3 \times 10^6)$
(b) $(8.64 \times 10^{15}) \div (3.1 \times 10^{15})$
(c) $(7.08 \times 10^{-4}) \times (5.96 \times 10^{16})$
(d) $(1.738 \times 10^{-7}) \div (6.54 \times 10^{-11})$
(e) $\dfrac{8.08 \times 10^8) \times (6.3 \times 10^{-7})}{(5.12 \times 10^{-6})}$
(f) $\dfrac{(7.491 \times 10^{-5}) \times (2.38 \times 10^{-3})}{(6.08 \times 10^{-10})}$

## Calculator Tip

You will often find calculators at a job site, whether in construction or business. Calculations to solve problems about structures can be done on a calculator. For example, many bridges have circular arches. To calculate the radius, *r*, for a circular arch of a bridge you can use the formula

$$r = \frac{h}{2} + \frac{2s^2}{h}$$ where *h*, *s* are shown in the diagram.

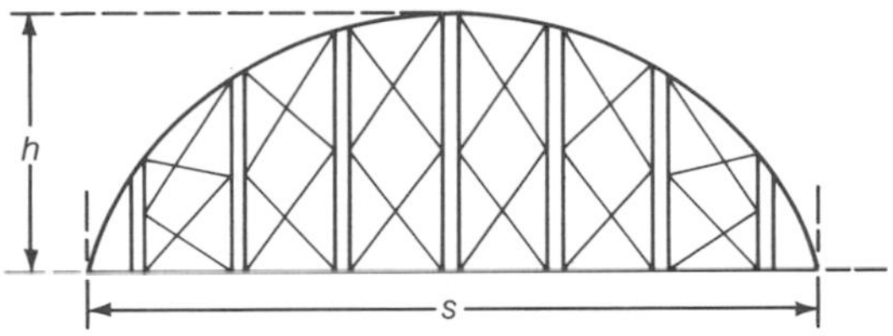


- Calculate the radius, *r*, of a circular arch if the span, *s*, of the bridge is 12.685 m long and the height, *h*, of the arch is 3.872 m.
- Write a computer program to calculate the radius for given inputs of the span of the bridge and the height of the arch.

## Computer Tip

Developing technology to do computation has taken many years. Many people have contributed to the development of computing devices. People such as
- Napier (1550–1617) invented Napier's Bones, a device to do calculations.
- Pascal, in 1642, invented the first calculating machine. This machine had a limited number of operations.
- Leibniz, in 1671, invented a calculating machine that could multiply.

However, the technological development that has occured in the last 40 years far surpasses the achievements in the last 4000 years. A computer can, in a matter of seconds, print a table of values which would have taken hours, if not days, using earlier computing devices.

## Using Scientific Notation on a Calculator

Scientific calculators can work with numbers expressed in scientific notation. To enter the power of 10, you use the [EE] button (or, on some calculators [EEX] or [EXP]).

For example, to calculate $(5.6 \times 10^{8}) \div (2.9 \times 10^{-11})$

| | | | | | | | | |
|---|---|---|---|---|---|---|---|---|
| Press | 5.6 | [EE] | 8 [÷] | 2.9 | [EE] | 11 | [+/−] | [=] |
| Display | (5.6) | (5.6 00) | (5.6 08) | (2.9) | (2.9 00) | (2.9 11) | (2.9 −11) | (1.931 19) |

Changes the exponent 11 to −11. (at [+/−])

output obtained on the display is 1.931 19 (at [=])

So $\dfrac{5.6 \times 10^{8}}{2.9 \times 10^{-11}} = 1.9 \times 10^{19}$

Rounded to 2 significant digits

Check:

$$\frac{5.6 \times 10^{8}}{2.9 \times 10^{-11}} \doteq \frac{6}{3} \times 10^{8-(-11)}$$

$$= 2 \times 10^{19}$$

The answer is reasonable.

---

For Questions 14–18

- ▶ use a scientific calculator.
- ▶ Decide how many significant digits to use to express your answer.
- ▶ Use estimation to check the reasonableness of your answer.

14 Multiply.

(a) $(7.58 \times 10^{12})(6.143 \times 10^{-19})$
(b) $(9.72 \times 10^{16})(3.405 \times 10^{-7})$
(c) $(8.44 \times 10^{23})(7.06 \times 10^{-14})$
(d) $(3.56 \times 10^{8})(5.491 \times 10^{-25})$
(e) $(5.15 \times 10^{-6})(3.274 \times 10^{19})$
(f) $(1.845 \times 10^{-16})(4.474 \times 10^{-7})$

15 Calculate each quotient.

(a) $\dfrac{6.71 \times 10^{14}}{4.38 \times 10^{7}}$ (b) $\dfrac{1.95 \times 10^{16}}{8.67 \times 10^{21}}$

(c) $\dfrac{3.49 \times 10^{-9}}{4.55 \times 10^{-4}}$ (d) $\dfrac{6.17 \times 10^{4}}{1.58 \times 10^{-4}}$

(e) $\dfrac{7.59 \times 10^{8}}{9.06 \times 10^{12}}$ (f) $\dfrac{8.073 \times 10^{-12}}{3.45 \times 10^{17}}$

16 The thickness of some sheet metal is $2.8 \times 10^{-3}$ cm. When the metal is heated it expands by a factor of $6.3 \times 10^{-12}$. By what measure does the thickness of the metal increase?

17 The world's largest nuclear power station is at Pickering, Ontario. At full output this station can generate $2.16 \times 10^{9}$ W. How many 60 W light bulbs is this?

**C**

18 The world's smallest known viruses are a type of tobacco plant virus. These virus are spherical in shape and have a radius of $8.5 \times 10^{-9}$ m. Find the volume of one of these viruses. (Volume of sphere $= \frac{4}{3}\pi r^{3}$, use $\pi \doteq 3.14$)

# 2.6 What if . . . Square Roots?

When you found the square of a number you used exponents to express your answer.

square number = $n^2$

You also used your skills with exponents to find the area of a square.

Area = length × width

$A = s^2$

Often in the study of mathematics, as well as in other work, a question is asked that develops new ideas: "what if . . . ?". For example, what if we know the area of the square, how do we find the measures of the original sides? Refer to the following problem.

The area of a square gymnasium floor is 400 m². Calculate the dimensions of the floor.

To find the measure of each side of the gymnasium you find the square root of 400.

$400 = (20)(20)$

20 is the square root of 400.

Thus the dimensions of the gymnasium are 20 m by 20 m.

The answer for the square root is a positive number since dimensions of figures are positive measures. However, you can write 400 as follows.

$400 = (20)(20)$ 20 is the positive square root of 400

$400 = (-20)(-20)$

−20 is the negative square root of 400

In problems involving measurement, only positive square roots occur. The symbol $\sqrt{\ }$ is used to indicate the positive or principal square root.

$$\sqrt{400} = 20$$

$\sqrt{\ }$ always means the positive square root.

20 is the positive square root of 400

Not all square roots are whole numbers. A chart is used to summarize the square roots of numbers. From the table, to 3 decimal places

$\sqrt{17} = 4.123$ $\sqrt{71} = 8.426$

$\sqrt{38} = 6.164$ $\sqrt{95} = 9.747$

A calculator or computer can be used to find the entries in the chart.

The number — The square root of the number

| | | | | | | | | | |
|---|---|---|---|---|---|---|---|---|---|
| **1** | 1.000 | **26** | 5.099 | **51** | 7.141 | **76** | 8.718 | | |
| **2** | 1.414 | **27** | 5.196 | **52** | 7.211 | **77** | 8.775 | | |
| **3** | 1.732 | **28** | 5.292 | **53** | 7.280 | **78** | 8.832 | | |
| **4** | 2.000 | **29** | 5.385 | **54** | 7.348 | **79** | 8.888 | | |
| **5** | 2.236 | **30** | 5.477 | **55** | 7.416 | **80** | 8.944 | | |
| **6** | 2.449 | **31** | 5.568 | **56** | 7.483 | **81** | 9.000 | | |
| **7** | 2.646 | **32** | 5.657 | **57** | 7.550 | **82** | 9.055 | | |
| **8** | 2.828 | **33** | 5.745 | **58** | 7.616 | **83** | 9.110 | | |
| **9** | 3.000 | **34** | 5.831 | **59** | 7.681 | **84** | 9.165 | | |
| **10** | 3.162 | **35** | 5.916 | **60** | 7.746 | **85** | 9.220 | | |
| **11** | 3.317 | **36** | 6.000 | **61** | 7.810 | **86** | 9.274 | | |
| **12** | 3.464 | **37** | 6.083 | **62** | 7.874 | **87** | 9.327 | | |
| **13** | 3.606 | **38** | 6.164 | **63** | 7.937 | **88** | 9.381 | | |
| **14** | 3.742 | **39** | 6.245 | **64** | 8.000 | **89** | 9.434 | | |
| **15** | 3.873 | **40** | 6.325 | **65** | 8.062 | **90** | 9.487 | | |
| **16** | 4.000 | **41** | 6.403 | **66** | 8.124 | **91** | 9.539 | | |
| **17** | 4.123 | **42** | 6.481 | **67** | 8.185 | **92** | 9.592 | | |
| **18** | 4.243 | **43** | 6.557 | **68** | 8.246 | **93** | 9.644 | | |
| **19** | 4.359 | **44** | 6.633 | **69** | 8.307 | **94** | 9.695 | | |
| **20** | 4.472 | **45** | 6.708 | **70** | 8.367 | **95** | 9.747 | | |
| **21** | 4.583 | **46** | 6.782 | **71** | 8.426 | **96** | 9.798 | | |
| **22** | 4.690 | **47** | 6.856 | **72** | 8.485 | **97** | 9.849 | | |
| **23** | 4.796 | **48** | 6.928 | **73** | 8.544 | **98** | 9.899 | | |
| **24** | 4.899 | **49** | 7.000 | **74** | 8.602 | **99** | 9.950 | | |
| **25** | 5.000 | **50** | 7.071 | **75** | 8.660 | **100** | 10.000 | | |

**Example 1**

A square field has an area of 93 m². What is the measure of each of its sides? Express your answer to 1 decimal place.

**Solution**

Think of a diagram.

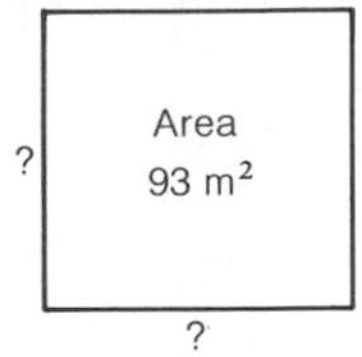


From the table,

$\sqrt{93} = 9.644$

$\doteq 9.6$ (to 1 decimal place)

The measure of each side of the field is 9.6 m, to 1 decimal place.

You can also use your calculator to find the square root of a number. Your calculator may have a key marked $\boxed{\sqrt{\ }}$ or $\boxed{\sqrt{x}}$ for finding the square root of a number.

Find $\sqrt{357}$ using a calculator.

| | | |
|---|---|---|
| Press | 357 | $\boxed{\sqrt{\ }}$ |
| Display | 357 | 18.894 444 |

Thus, $\sqrt{357} \doteq 18.9$ (to 1 decimal place)

The square root symbol $\sqrt{\ }$ often occurs in solving problems such as the following. You need to use your substitution skills.

**Example 2**

In landscaping, the radius $r$ of a circle is found by using the following.

$r = \sqrt{\dfrac{A}{\pi}}$ where $A$ is the area of the circle and $\pi \doteq 3.14$.

A circular pond has an area of 96.0 m². Find the radius to 1 decimal place.

**Solution**

Use $r = \sqrt{\dfrac{A}{\pi}}$  $A = 96.0$, $\pi \doteq 3.14$

$r = \sqrt{\dfrac{96.0}{3.14}}$  Use a calculator or calculate.

$\doteq 30.57$ (to 2 decimal places)

The radius of the pond is 30.6 m.

## Try These

1 What is the positive square root of the number on the right of each equation?
(a) $(5)^2 = 25$  (b) $(8)^2 = 64$
(c) $(3.6)^2 = 12.96$  (d) $(7.8)^2 = 60.84$

2 Use the square root table of values. What is the square root of each number, to 3 decimal places?
(a) 19  (b) 41  (c) 6
(d) 59  (e) 73  (f) 96

3 What is the positive square root of each number?
(a) 16  (b) 25  (c) 49  (d) 64  (e) 81

4 (a) The square root of a number is 7. What is the number?
(b) The square root of a number is −10. What is the number?

## Written Exercises

**A** Refer to the square root table or use a calculator to find the square roots of numbers.

1 What is each value?

(a) $\sqrt{9}$ (b) $\sqrt{25}$ (c) $\sqrt{36}$
(d) $\sqrt{64}$ (e) $\sqrt{81}$ (f) $\sqrt{100}$

2 Find each positive square root. Express your answer to 2 decimal places.

(a) $\sqrt{5}$ (b) $\sqrt{21}$ (c) $\sqrt{44}$
(d) $\sqrt{67}$ (e) $\sqrt{89}$

3 For each of the following.

- ▶ estimate the positive square root,
- ▶ find the square root.

Express your answer to 3 decimal places.

(a) $\sqrt{23}$ (b) $\sqrt{14}$ (c) $\sqrt{53}$ (d) $\sqrt{84}$

4 Estimate the square root of each of the following. Then calculate to 3 decimal places. Use a calculator.

(a) 6.7 (b) 15.7 (c) 80.3
(d) 140 (e) 200 (f) 360

5 From the square root table, $\sqrt{59} \doteq 7.681$.

(a) Without multiplying, what answer would you predict for $(7.681)^2$?
(b) Calculate $(7.681)^2$.
(c) Why do your answers in (a) and (b) differ? By how much?

**B** To solve each problem, organize your solution. Refer to the *Steps for Solving Problems.* Express your answers to 1 decimal place unless indicated otherwise.

6 (a) The area of a square is 144 $cm^2$. What are the measures of the sides?
(b) The area of a square floor is 79.3 $m^2$. Calculate the dimensions of the floor.

7 The area of the stamp is 27.6 $cm^2$. Calculate its dimensions.

8 How much fencing would be needed to enclose each of the following square fields?

(a)

(b)
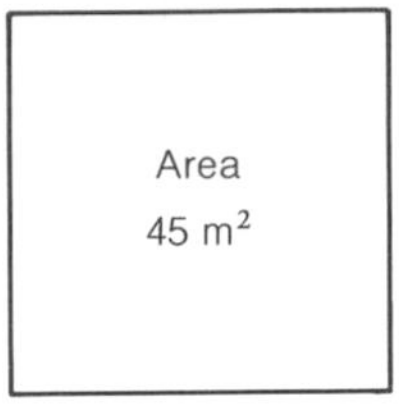


9 The radius, $r$, of a circle is given by

$$r = \sqrt{\frac{A}{\pi}} \quad \text{where } A \text{ is the area; use } \pi \doteq 3.14$$

Find the radius of the circle for each area.

(a) 86.0 $cm^2$ (b) 16.0 $km^2$ (c) 93.2 $mm^2$

10 The length of a diagonal, $d$, in a rectangle with length twice its width, $w$, is given by the formula

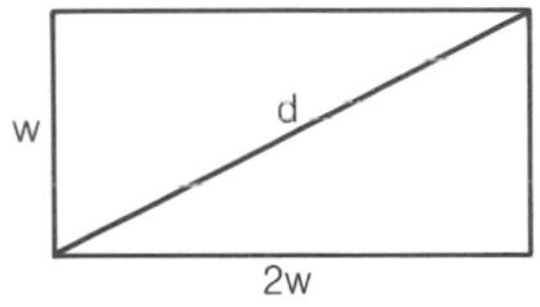


$$d = \sqrt{5}w$$

(a) Find the length of the diagonal if the width is 2.8 m.
(b) Find the width of the rectangle if the length of the diagonal is 4.6 m.

### Calculator Tip

You can use your calculator to explore results.

- Is $\sqrt{2} + \sqrt{3} \stackrel{?}{=} \sqrt{5}$? Use your calculator to test the result. Test other examples such as $\sqrt{3} + \sqrt{5} \stackrel{?}{=} \sqrt{8}$, $\sqrt{2} + \sqrt{5} \stackrel{?}{=} \sqrt{7}$, $\sqrt{6} + \sqrt{3} \stackrel{?}{=} \sqrt{9}$.
- Is $\sqrt{3} + \sqrt{3} = 2\sqrt{3}$? Use your calculator to test the result. Test other examples such as, $\sqrt{2} + \sqrt{2} + \sqrt{2} \stackrel{?}{=} 3\sqrt{2}$, $\sqrt{5} + \sqrt{5} \stackrel{?}{=} 2\sqrt{5}$.

11 The length of time, $t$, in seconds, it takes an object to fall a distance, $d$, in metres, is given by the relationship

$$t = \sqrt{\frac{d}{4.9}}$$

An object fell 60 m. To find the time, use

$$\sqrt{\frac{60}{4.9}} = \sqrt{12.24}$$

(a) Find the value of $\sqrt{12.24}$

(b) How long did it take the object to fall 60 m? Express your answer to 1 decimal place.

12 The approximate distance, $d$, to the horizon, in kilometres, is given by

$d = 3.572\sqrt{h}$ where $h$ is the height, in metres, of the observer

(a) You are at the top of a apartment building by the ocean. If the top is 97.0 m high, how far out to sea can you see?

(b) Find how far away the horizon is if you are in an airplane at 864 m above the ground.

(c) Refer to the photo. The "crow's nest" on this type of ship is at about 30-40 metres. About how far away is land when "Land ahoy" is heard?

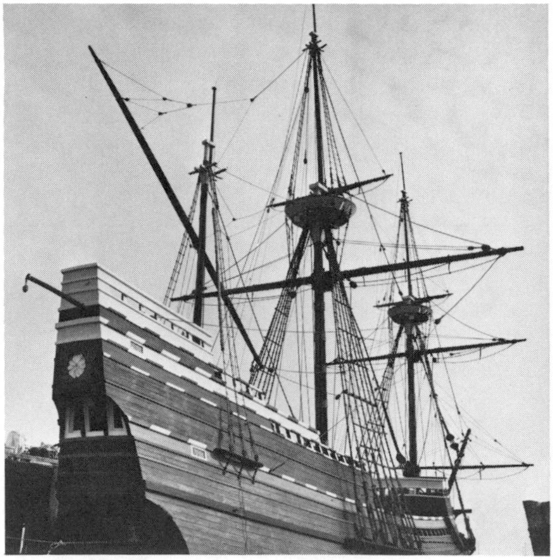

Often at the top of the mast of a tall sailboat is a perch known as the "crow's nest" from which an observer can see any land that might be around. Early explorers always had a person perched at the top and you would hear the famous words, "Land ahoy".

13 The electrical current in a circuit can be calculated using

$I = \sqrt{\frac{P}{R}}$ where $I$ is the electrical current (in amperes), $P$ is the power (in Watts) and $R$ is the resistance (in ohms).

Find the current for each of the following values.

(a) $P = 1250$ (W), $R = 90$ ($\Omega$)

(b) $P = 3100$ (W), $R = 110$ ($\Omega$)

(c) $P = 68.5$ (W), $R = 43$ ($\Omega$)

14 The radius, $r$, of a can may be found by using

$r = \sqrt{\frac{V}{\pi h}}$ where $V$ is the volume, $h$ is the height and $\pi \doteq 3.14$.

Calculate the radius for each can.

(a) $V = 756$ ($cm^3$), $h = 15.3$ (cm)

(b) $V = 1290$ ($m^3$), $h = 16.6$ (m)

(c) $V = 36.9$ ($dm^3$), $h = 14.2$ (dm)

15 Use the relationship between radius, height and volume given in the previous question.

(a) A cylindrical coffee mug stands 9 cm high and has a volume of 385 $cm^3$. What is its radius?

(b) A can of pop holds 284 $cm^3$. It is 10 cm high. What is its radius?

## Calculator Tip

A Test whether any of the following are true.

$(\sqrt{2})(\sqrt{2}) \stackrel{?}{=} 2$

$\sqrt{2}$ is a radical number.

$(\sqrt{3})(\sqrt{3}) \stackrel{?}{=} 3$ $(\sqrt{4})(\sqrt{4}) \stackrel{?}{=} 4$

B Use other examples of your own to test results such as those in A.

C Use your results in A and B. Make a general statement about multiplying a radical number by itself.

# 2.7 Extending Skills: Fractional Exponents

In your previous work with exponents, you used integers. Your skills with exponents can be extended to include fractional exponents. In your previous work you found a meaning for $x^0$ and $x^{-1}$. The meanings for expressions such as those at the right are chosen so that the exponent laws, such as $x^m \times x^n = x^{m+n}$, apply to fractional exponents. For example, compare the following.

$2^{\frac{1}{2}}$ and $10^{\frac{1}{3}}$

**Square Roots**

$$2^{\frac{1}{2}} \times 2^{\frac{1}{2}} = 2^{\frac{1}{2}+\frac{1}{2}} = 2 \qquad \sqrt{2} \times \sqrt{2} = \sqrt{4} = 2$$

Based on this example and others, we choose to interpret $2^{\frac{1}{2}}$ to mean $\sqrt{2}$. $2^{\frac{1}{2}} = \sqrt{2}$ ⟵ radical form

**Cube Root**

10 is the cube root of 1000, since 10 multiplied by itself 3 times is 1000, $(10)^3 = 1000$. We use the radical symbol for cube root, namely $\sqrt[3]{\phantom{x}}$. Thus

$\sqrt[3]{1000} = 10$

means cube root

In a similar way

Exponent Form

$$2^{\frac{1}{3}} \times 2^{\frac{1}{3}} \times 2^{\frac{1}{3}} = 2^{\frac{1}{3}+\frac{1}{3}+\frac{1}{3}} = 2^1$$

Radical Form

$$\sqrt[3]{2} \times \sqrt[3]{2} \times \sqrt[3]{2} = \sqrt[3]{2 \times 2 \times 2} = 2$$

Based on the example, an interpretation of $2^{\frac{1}{3}}$ is the cube root of 2. Thus, we choose $2^{\frac{1}{3}} = \sqrt[3]{2}$

> In general $a^{\frac{1}{n}} = \sqrt[n]{a}$ where $a$ is positive when $n$ is an even number.

Thus, $16^{\frac{1}{4}}$ means the fourth root of 16 or shown in radical form as $\sqrt[4]{16}$.

Think, since $16 = 2 \times 2 \times 2 \times 2$ then 2 is the fourth root of 16.
$16^{\frac{1}{4}} = 2$ or $\sqrt[4]{16} = 2$

$32^{\frac{1}{5}}$ means the fifth root of 32 or shown in radical form as $\sqrt[5]{32}$.

Think, since $32 = 2 \times 2 \times 2 \times 2 \times 2$ Then 2 is the fifth root of 32.
$32^{\frac{1}{5}} = 2$ or $\sqrt[5]{32} = 2$

To interpret the fractional exponent shown by $8^{\frac{2}{3}}$, we can think of

$$8^{\frac{2}{3}} = \left(8^{\frac{1}{3}}\right)^2 = (2)^2 = 4 \qquad \text{think } 8^{\frac{1}{3}} = \sqrt[3]{8}$$

> In general, $a^{\frac{m}{n}} = (\sqrt[n]{a})^m$ where $a$ is positive when $n$ is an even number.

## Example

Evaluate.

(a) $25^{\frac{1}{2}}$ (b) $64^{\frac{1}{3}}$ (c) $16^{-\frac{3}{4}}$

### Solution

(a) $25^{\frac{1}{2}} = \sqrt{25}$
$= 5$

(b) $64^{\frac{1}{3}} = \sqrt[3]{64}$ ← Think $64 = 4 \times 4 \times 4$
$= 4$
Thus 4 is the cube root of 64.

(c) $16^{-\frac{3}{4}} = \left(16^{\frac{1}{4}}\right)^{-3}$
$= (2)^{-3}$
$= \frac{1}{2^3} = \frac{1}{8}$

Think $16^{\frac{1}{4}} = \sqrt[4]{16}$
$16 = 2 \times 2 \times 2 \times 2$
Thus 2 is the fourth root of 16.

You can use your calculator to evaluate expressions with fractional exponents. To evaluate $\sqrt[3]{8.6}$ (to 3 decimal places), use the steps shown. Thus, $\sqrt[3]{8.6} = 2.049$ (to 3 decimal places).

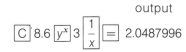

[C] 8.6 [$y^x$] 3 [$\frac{1}{x}$] [=] output 2.0487996

## Written Exercises

**A** 1 Find the value of each of the following.
(a) $9^{\frac{1}{2}}$ (b) $4^{-\frac{1}{2}}$ (c) $27^{\frac{1}{3}}$ (d) $27^{-\frac{1}{3}}$

2 Find the value of each of the following.
(a) $25^{\frac{1}{2}}$ (b) $\sqrt{16}$ (c) $25^{-\frac{1}{2}}$ (d) $(\sqrt{9})^{-1}$
(e) $36^{\frac{1}{2}}$ (f) $16^{\frac{1}{4}}$ (g) $\sqrt[4]{16}$

3 Use a calculator. Find the value of each of the following to 3 decimal places.
(a) $\sqrt[3]{7.2}$ (b) $\sqrt[4]{12.8}$ (c) $(16.3)^{\frac{1}{3}}$
(d) $(23.8)^{\frac{1}{5}}$ (e) $(36.3)^{\frac{1}{4}}$ (f) $(29.63)^{\frac{1}{6}}$

4 Simplify.
(a) $32^{\frac{1}{5}}$ (b) $32^{\frac{2}{5}}$ (c) $32^{\frac{3}{5}}$
(d) $\sqrt[5]{32}$ (e) $(\sqrt[5]{32})^2$ (f) $\sqrt[5]{32^2}$

5 Interpret each of the following in radical form, then evaluate.
(a) $16^{\frac{1}{2}}$ (b) $49^{\frac{1}{2}}$ (c) $144^{\frac{1}{2}}$ (d) $16^{\frac{1}{4}}$
(e) $-27^{\frac{1}{3}}$ (f) $256^{\frac{1}{4}}$ (g) $8^{\frac{2}{3}}$ (h) $64^{\frac{2}{3}}$
(i) $-16^{\frac{3}{2}}$ (j) $-32^{\frac{3}{5}}$ (k) $125^{\frac{2}{3}}$ (l) $-64^{\frac{1}{6}}$

**B** 6 Simplify.
(a) $32^{\frac{1}{5}}$ (b) $16^{\frac{1}{4}}$ (c) $-27^{\frac{1}{3}}$
(d) $-125^{\frac{1}{3}}$ (e) $\sqrt[4]{16}$ (f) $27^{-\frac{2}{3}}$
(g) $-1000^{\frac{1}{3}}$ (h) $-125^{\frac{2}{3}}$ (i) $(\sqrt[3]{8})^2$

7 You can use the reciprocal key on a calculator to evaluate expressions with negative exponents.
To evaluate $8^{-\frac{1}{3}}$ use the steps, [C] 8 [$y^x$] 3 [$\frac{1}{x}$] [+/−] [=] output 0.5
Evaluate each of the following.
(a) $1000^{-\frac{1}{3}}$ (b) $16^{-\frac{1}{4}}$ (c) $32^{-\frac{1}{5}}$ (d) $36^{-\frac{1}{2}}$
(e) $64^{-\frac{1}{6}}$ (f) $125^{-\frac{2}{3}}$ (g) $81^{-\frac{3}{4}}$ (h) $1000^{-\frac{2}{3}}$

8 Simplify.
(a) $36^{\frac{1}{2}} + \sqrt[3]{27} - 16^{\frac{1}{4}} + 81^{\frac{1}{2}}$
(b) $32^{-\frac{1}{5}} - 9^{\frac{1}{2}} - \sqrt[4]{16} + 81^{\frac{1}{4}}$
(c) $-\sqrt{64} + \sqrt[3]{-27} + 16^{-\frac{3}{4}} - 1000^{\frac{1}{3}}$

9 The radius, $r$, of a sphere can be found by using the formula $r = \left(\frac{3V}{4\pi}\right)^{\frac{1}{3}}$ where $V$ is the volume.
Find the radius of each sphere with the given volumes. Express your answer to 2 decimal places.
(a) 500.0 cm³ (b) 150.0 m³ (c) 1000 cm³

10 The cost, $C$, in dollars, of insulating a boiler is given by the formula.
$C = 6pV^{\frac{2}{3}}$ where $V$ is volume of the boiler and $p$ is the cost of insulation.
Find the cost of insulating each boiler.
(a) $V = 1.8$ m³, $p = \$26.82/\text{m}^2$
(b) $V = 6.2$ m³, $p = \$58.96/\text{m}^2$

# Review: Practice and Problems

1 Write as a single power.
(a) $7^3 \times 7^2$ (b) $2^8 \times 2^3$
(c) $5^3 \times 5$ (d) $(6.8)^2 \times (6.8)^4$
(e) $10^6 \div 10^3$ (f) $(3.8)^7 \div (3.8)^5$
(g) $\left(\frac{1}{2}\right)^4 \times \left(\frac{1}{2}\right)^3$ (h) $\left(\frac{1}{2}\right)^4 \div \left(\frac{1}{2}\right)^3$

2 Write as a single power.
(a) $m^5 \div m^3$ (b) $a \times a^7$
(c) $m^3 \times m^4 \times m$ (d) $r^{15} \div r^{11}$
(e) $(3^4)^2$ (f) $(p^4)^3$

3 Find the value of each expression for $p = 3$.
(a) $p^2 \times p$ (b) $p^4 \times p^2$
(c) $p^4 \div p^2$ (d) $p \times p^5 \div p^3$
(e) $p^2 \times p \times p^2$ (f) $p^6 \div p^3 \times p^4$

4 The area of a washer can be found using the formula
$A = \pi(R^2 - r^2)$
where $R$ is the radius of the washer and $r$ is the radius of the hole.

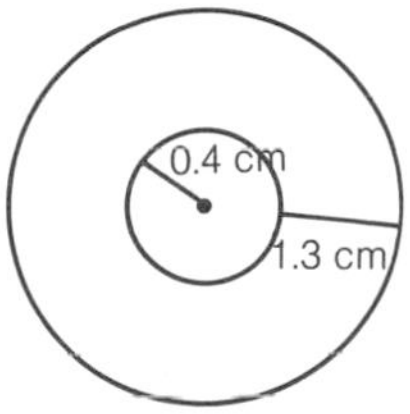


Using $\pi \doteq 3.14$, find the area of the washer surface.

5 Find each value.
(a) $6^0$ (b) $3^{-2}$ (c) $5^{-2}$
(d) $2^4$ (e) $2^{-4}$ (f) $-(3)^2$
(g) $(-2)^4$ (h) $-5^0$ (i) $(6p)^0$

6 Simplify.
(a) $\dfrac{a^6 \times a^{-3}}{a^2}$ (b) $\dfrac{p^{-9} \times p^{-3}}{p^{-10}}$
(c) $\dfrac{(k^{-3})^{-2}}{(k^3)^3}$ (d) $\dfrac{m^{-6} \times m^9}{(m^2)^{-2}}$

7 Write each number in scientific notation.
(a) 695 000 (b) 0.00049
(c) 18.5 (d) 0.025
(e) 364 000 000 (f) 29.4500

8 Write each of the following in standard form.
(a) $6.52 \times 10^3$ (b) $9.04 \times 10^{-4}$
(c) $2.84 \times 10^{-2}$ (d) $5.09 \times 10^7$

9 Express each number in scientific notation.
(a) The mass of a hydrogen atom is 0.000 000 000 000 000 000 000 0017 g.
(b) The distance from the earth to the sun is 150 000 000 km.
(c) The ocean area of the earth is 360 000 000 km$^2$.
(d) There are 5340 mL of blood in a person's body.

10 What is the number of significant digits in each measure?
(a) 68 350 cm (b) 0.925 g
(c) 36.19 mm (d) 0.000 450 m
(e) 68 550 km (f) 7.295 kg

11 Calculate each of the following. Express your answer in scientific notation.
(a) $(6.5 \times 10^{10}) \times (5.9 \times 10^8)$
(b) $(7.35 \times 10^4) \times (4.41 \times 10^{-3})$
(c) $(1.56 \times 10^{-4}) \times (3.92 \times 10^8)$
(d) $(8.44 \times 10^{-6}) \div (21.1 \times 10^3)$
(e) $\dfrac{(9.04 \times 10^9) \times (7.5 \times 10^{-5})}{(4.34 \times 10^{-4})}$

12 Find the square root of each of the following. Use a calculator.
(a) 8.9 (b) 19.3 (c) 64.7
(d) 157 (e) 305.6 (f) 589.1

13 To calculate the diameter, $d$, of a circular design using cobble stone, a landscaper uses the formula,
$d = 1.13\sqrt{A}$ where $A$ is the area of the cobblestones available.
Find the diameter of the circular design for each available amount of cobblestones.
(a) 6.5 m$^2$ (b) 12.6 m$^2$
(c) 16.2 m$^2$ (d) 25.9 m$^2$

# A Practice Test

1 Calculate.
(a) $6^2 - 5^2$ (b) $8^3 \div 2^3$
(c) $10 \times 3^2$ (d) $(8 + 7) \div 5^2$
(e) $4^2 - 3^2 + 7^2$ (f) $4^4 \div 2^4 - 4$
(g) $6^2 - 4^2 \div 4 - 1^3$ (h) $(12^2 - 144) \div 4$

2 (a) Find the value of $\frac{1}{2}$ cubed.
(b) Double $3^2$.
(c) Subtract $5^2$ from $3^3$.
(d) Calculate $(1.2)^2$.

3 Find the value of each expression for $a = 4$, $b = 2$.

(a) $(a^2b)^2$ (b) $\dfrac{a^3b^4}{a^2b^2}$ (c) $ab^3 \times a^2b^2$

4 Use $m = -1$, $n = 3$. Which has the least value A, B, or C?
A $(4m)(-3m^2n)$
B $(-2m)(-7mn^2)$
C $(5mn^2)(-2mn)$

5 Evaluate.
(a) $6^{-2}$ (b) $8^0$ (c) $3^{-1} + 2^{-1}$
(d) $(3 - 1)^{-1}$ (e) $(6^0 - 3^2)^2$
(f) $(4^{-2} + 3^2)^{-2}$ (g) $(2^{-1} - 3^{-2})^{-1}$

(h) $\dfrac{5^0}{4^2 + 3^0}$ (i) $(4^3 - 4^2)2^{-1}$

6 Arrange the values of the following in order from the greatest to the least.
$2^{-3}$, $4^{-2}$, $(150)^0$, $-3^{-2}$, $5^{-1}$

7 Refer to the diagram.

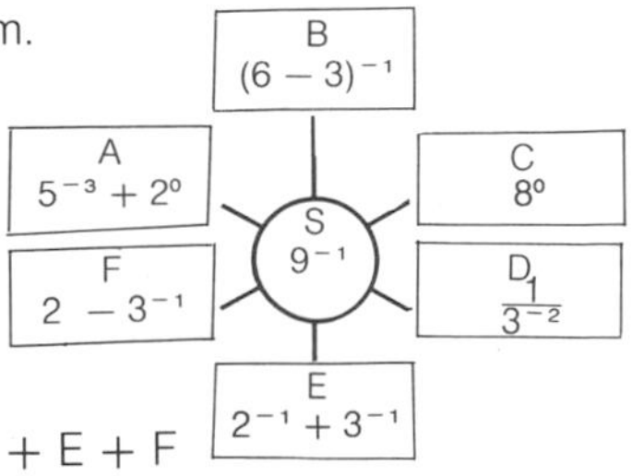

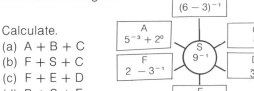

Calculate.
(a) A + B + C
(b) F + S + C
(c) F + E + D
(d) B + S + E
(e) A + B + C + D + E + F

8 Express each number in scientific notation and then calculate. Write your answer in standard form.
(a) 360 500 000 × 259 000
(b) 0.000 000 000 39 × 16 000

(c) $\dfrac{364\,500\,000}{4\,975\,000\,000}$ (d) $\dfrac{29.55}{0.000\,000\,002}$

9 (a) The diameter of an oxygen molecule is 0.000 000 03 cm. Find the length of 1800 molecules placed side by side.
(b) The ocean area of the earth is $3.6 \times 10^8$ km² and the land area of the earth is $1.5 \times 10^8$ km² What is the total area of the earth?
(c) A picosecond means 0.000 000 000 001 second. How many picoseconds are there in an hour? a year?

10 The molecule of a substance is shown. Each segment is 0.000 000 0016 mm long. Find the length of each chain. Express your answer in scientific notation.

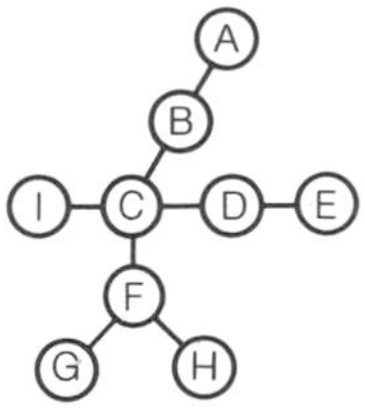


(a) G – F – H (b) C – D – E
(c) A – B – C – D – E (d) G – F – C – D – E

11 Calculate using a calculator. Decide how many significant digits you need to use to express your answer.

(a) $\dfrac{8.46 \times 10^{10}}{2.52 \times 10^6}$ (b) $\dfrac{9.042 \times 10^{-15}}{4.51 \times 10^{19}}$

(c) $(3.492 \times 10^{-12})(6.079 \times 10^{-8})$

12 To a skydiver it is important to know how long it takes for an object to fall to earth from any height (neglecting air resistance). The amount of time, $t$, in seconds, it takes for an object to fall a distance, $d$, in metres, is given by $t = \sqrt{\dfrac{d}{4.9}}$
Calculate how long it takes to fall each of the following distances.
(a) 152.8 m (b) 642.7 m (c) 1395 m

# 3 Skills with Polynomials

language of polynomials, using polynomials, addition and subtraction of polynomials, product of monomials, exponents and monomials, dividing monomials, products of polynomials, squaring binomials, solving problems and applications

## Introduction

The mathematics you study has developed over many years. The advances in mathematics often resulted in an advancement in the study of science. For example, the mathematics used to advance the technology of computing has directly improved our standards of living. Throughout your study of mathematics, you will obtain glimpses into the many applications of mathematics.

The study of mathematics often occurs as a pattern. For example, the skills and concepts you learn are applied to solving problems.

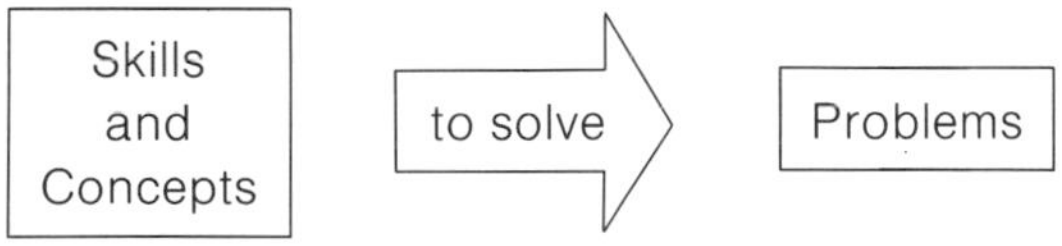


These skills and concepts you learn are then extended to learn new skills and concepts, which in turn provide you with other methods and strategies for solving problems.

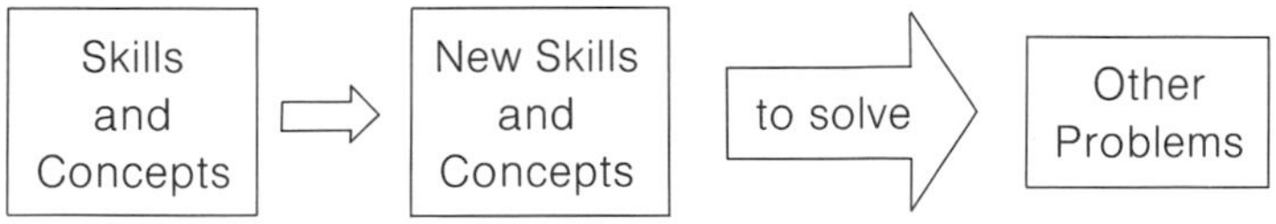


Mathematics is a subject that is the result of many people. Many people have contributed to the growth of mathematics and the subsequent use of mathematics to solve problems. Some of the vocabulary you learn in mathematics and science is based on some persons name, such as, The Cartesian plane (Rene Descartes), Pythogorean property (Phythogoras), Pascal's triangle (Blaise Pascal), Celsius degrees (Anders Celsius). The names shown here are only a few of all the various people who contributed to the study of mathematics.

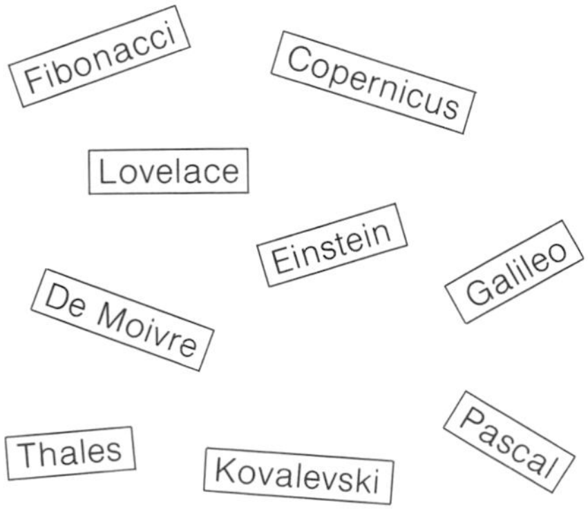

# 3.1 Using Polynomials

You will often see the use of symbols to convey information. For example, in hockey each win receives 2 points.

| wins | points |
|---|---|
| 1 | 2 |
| 2 | $2 \times 2$ |
| 3 | $2 \times 3$ |
| ⋮ | ⋮ |
| $n$ | $2 \times n$ |

The expression $2 \times n$ or $2n$ shows the number of points obtained for $n$ wins.

Symbols are used in many ways at a hockey game. What do A and C mean on the players' sweaters? What symbols are used by the referee to show a penalty?

In arithmetic you used numbers.

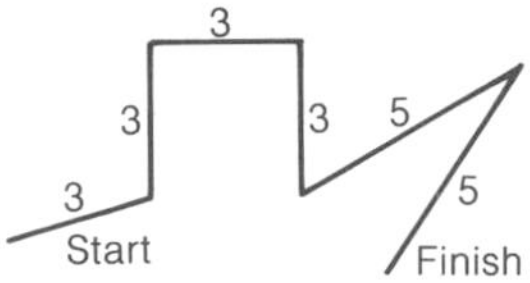


You can write the sum in a compact form.

$$\underbrace{3+3+3+3}_{4 \times 3}+\underbrace{5+5}_{2 \times 5}$$

In algebra, you use variables.

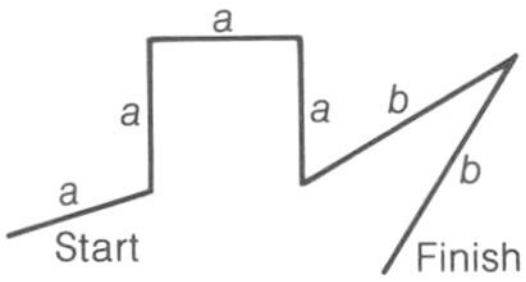


You can write the sum in a compact form.

$$\underbrace{a+a+a+a}_{4a}+\underbrace{b+b}_{2b}$$

The variable expression $4a + 2b$ is an example of a **two-term polynomial**.

$2b$ is a term

$4a$ is a term

**Terms** of a polynomial are separated by addition or subtraction signs. Special words are used to name some polynomials.

| Name | Number of terms | Example |
|---|---|---|
| monomial | 1 | $7y$ |
| binomial | 2 | $3t + 5q$ |
| trinomial | 3 | $6a + 3b - c$ |

$-1$ is the numerical coefficient of the variable $c$

3 is the numerical coefficient of the variable $b$

Polynomials can be simplified by adding or subtracting **like terms**.

$3q + 2q = 5q$

$3q$, $2q$ are like terms

$3m^2 + 5m^2 = 8m^2$

like terms

**Example 1**

Simplify.

(a) $8x - 5x + 3x - x$

(b) $2m - 4m + 3n + 7n + q$

Simplify means to add or subtract the like terms in the expression.

**Solution**

(a) $8x - 5x + 3x - x$

$= 3x + 3x - x$

$= 6x - x$

$= 5x$

$x$ means $1x$

For like terms, add or subtract the numerical coefficients.

(b) $2m - 4m + 3n + 7n + q$

$= -2m + 10n + q$

Think: $7n$ and $q$ are not like terms

When you want to find the value of a polynomial for values of the variable, you can simplify the polynomial first, as shown in the following example.

**Example 2**

Find the value of the polynomial

$2k - 3k + 8k + 3$ for $k = 3$.

**Solution**

*Step 1*: Simplify the polynomial.

$2k - 3k + 8k + 3$

$= -k + 8k + 3$

$= 7k + 3$

*Step 2*: Substitute $k = 3$.

$= 7(3) + 3$

$= 21 + 3$

$= 24$

## Try These

1 Which terms are like terms?

(a) $8p$, $7q$, $2p$, $5$, $-3p$

(b) $mt$, $3mn$, $-mn$, $-7m^2n$

2 Express in a more compact way.

(a) $t + t + t + t + t$

(b) $h + h + h - k - k - k - k$

3 Simplify.

(a) $6d + 3d$ (b) $12h - 3h$

(c) $18w - 7w$ (d) $-5p + 2p$

4 Find the value of the binomial $2m + 1$ for each value of $m$.

(a) $m = 1$ (b) $m = 0$ (c) $m = 5$

## Written Exercises

**A** Remember: to simplify, you add or subtract the like terms in the expression.

1 Write each expression in a more compact way.

(a) $a + a + a + b + b$

(b) $-h - h - h - h - h$

(c) $x + x + x - y - y + z$

2 Which expression in the previous question is

(a) a monomial? (b) a binomial?

(c) a trinomial?

3 Which terms are like terms?

(a) $p$, $3p$, $5q$, $-2p$, $-q$, $-17q$

(b) $6a$, $-5b$, $-3b$, $-14a$, $b$

(c) $4m^2$, $5m$, $-8mn$, $-m^2$, $-mn$, $9m^2n^2$

(d) $16f$, $16$, $-3f$, $4f^2$, $-3$, $-f$

4 Add each pair of terms.

(a) $4x$, $3x$ (b) $10ef$, $4ef$

(c) $14m$, $-2m$ (d) $-4p$, $8p$

(e) $-10a$, $-3a$ (f) $9p$, $-12p$

5 Find the value of the binomial $5 - 2q$ for each value of $q$.
(a) $q = 1$ (b) $q = 0$ (c) $q = -3$

6 Find the value of each polynomial for $d = 3$.
(a) $5d - 7$ (b) $10 - 3d$
(c) $6 + 3d - d^2$

7 The number of points in the standings is given by the expression
$2w + t$ where $w$ is number of wins and $t$ is number of ties.
Find the value of the expression for
(a) $w = 3, t = 1$ (b) $w = 5, t = 0$
(c) $w = 6, t = 3$ (d) $w = 10, t = 12$

**B** **Before you evaluate an expression, simplify the expression. Review the meaning of simplify.**

8 Simplify.
(a) $9d + 3d$ (b) $11t - 8t$
(c) $-5q - 3q$ (d) $-4m + 7m$
(e) $2y - 8y$ (f) $5n + 5n$
(g) $-3d - 6d$ (h) $10h - 13h$
(i) $-7k + 12k$ (j) $-3x^2 + x^2$
(k) $a^2 - 9a^2$ (l) $-5pq - 6pq$

9 Simplify.
(a) $4p - 10p + 6p + 3p$
(b) $5f + 3f - 2f + 5f$
(c) $-a + 3a + 10a - 5d + 9d$
(d) $10x - 3x + 8y - y$
(e) $8n + 3n - 7m - 10m$
(f) $4p - 2p + 1 + 8 - 7q$
Which of your answers above are binomials?

10 Find the value of each expression for $p = 3$, $q = -2$.
(a) $-7p + 12p$ (b) $-3p^2 + p^2$
(c) $-5pq + 3pq$ (d) $q^2 - 5q^2$
(e) $8p + 3q - 2p$ (f) $6q - 3p - 5q$
(g) $8q + 2p - 8q$ (h) $3p - 2q + p - q$

11 For the polynomials, use $p = -2$, $q = 3$. Which have the same values?
(a) $8p - 3p + p - 5q + 2q + 3 - 1$
(b) $-4p + 5p + 5p + 3q - q - q + 7 - 3$
(c) $p + 7p - 2p - q + 2q - 8 + 5 + 7$

12 Find an expression to show the distance around each figure.

(a)
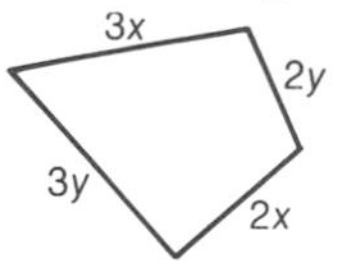


(b)
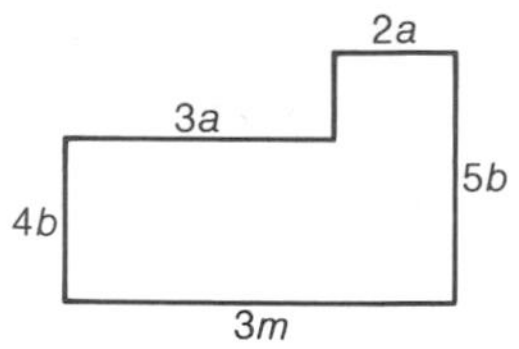


(c)
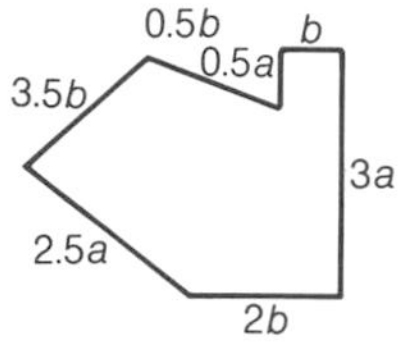


(d)
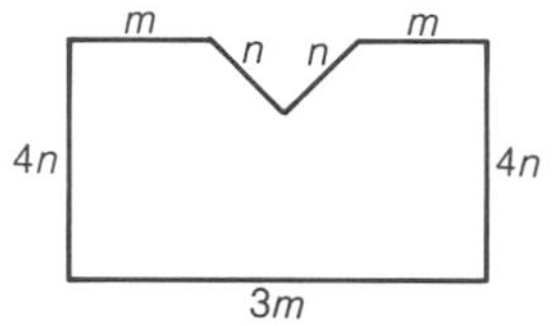


13 Which of the following polynomials have the same value when $m = 2$?
A: $7m - 5m + 8 - 3$ B: $3m - 4m + m - 1$
C: $9 - 2m - 3m$ D: $3 - 8 + 8m - 6m$

14 When $a = -2$ and $b = 5$, which polynomial has the greatest value?
A: $2a - 3a - 5b + 2b - 1$
B: $a + 4a + 3b - 2 - 2$
C: $-3a - a + b + 4b - 3 + 1$

15 When $x = 4.2$ and $y = -1.5$ find which polynomial has the least value.
A: $5x - x + 1 - 2y - 2y$
B: $-3x + 2x - 7y + 10y$
C: $x + 4x - 2x + 5y - y$

16 The amount of fuel, in litres, used in irrigating a field, is given by the expression
$9d + 6v + 3d + 5v$
How much fuel is used when
(a) $d = 6$, $v = 3$? (b) $d = 5$, $v = 8$?
(c) $d = 4.2$, $v = 5.6$? (d) $d = 9.8$, $v = 3.6$?

17 The cost of production, in dollars, is given by the expression
$3.5t + 4.6t - 6.8p + 3.6p$
Find the cost for
(a) $t = 6$, $p = 3$ (b) $t = 8$, $p = 2.5$
(c) $t = 6.5$, $p = 1.5$ (d) $t = 9.8$, $p = 6.3$

# 3.2 Adding and Subtracting Polynomials

In your study of mathematics, you follow these steps often.

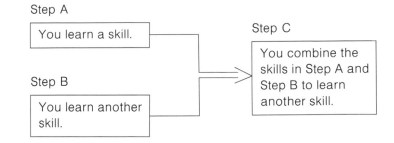

Step A

You learn a skill.

Step B

You learn another skill.

Step C

You combine the skills in Step A and Step B to learn another skill.

For example, in the previous section you learned how to add and subtract like terms. You can use these skills to add two expressions such as two binomials, as in the following example.

**Example 1**

Find the sum of

$3x - 2y$ and $5x - 7y$.

**Solution**

$(3x - 2y) + (5x - 7y)$
$= 3x - 2y + 5x - 7y$
$= 3x + 5x - 2y - 7y$ Collect the like terms.
$= 8x - 9y$

In your earlier work with integers, you learned that "*to subtract an integer, you add its opposite*". Your skills with integers and your skills with like terms are combined to subtract polynomials, as shown in the following example.

**Example 2**

Subtract $3a - 2b$ from $5a - 7b$.

**Solution**

$(5a - 7b) - (3a - 2b)$
$= 5a - 7b - 3a + 2b$ — Think of opposites $-(3a - 2b) = -3a + 2b$
$= 5a - 3a - 7b + 2b$ — Collect like terms
$= 2a - 5b$

When you are asked to find the value of an expression, check whether it can be simplified first.

**Example 3**

Find the value of

$4d - 5e - (3d - e) + 7d$

for $d = 2$ and $e = -1$.

**Solution**

Simplify first

$4d - 5e - (3d - e) + 7d$
$= 4d - 5e - 3d + e + 7d$
$= 4d - 3d + 7d - 5e + e$
$= 8d - 4e$

Then substitute $d = 2$ and $e = -1$.

$8d - 4e = 8(2) - 4(-1)$
$= 16 - (-4)$
$= 16 + 4$
$= 20$

## Try These

1 Simplify.
(a) $4x + y + 3x + 2y$
(b) $m - 3n + 4m - n$
(c) $8e + 3f + 2e - 2f$

2 What is the opposite of each polynomial?
(a) $4a$
(b) $-10m$
(c) $-x^2$
(d) $5p + q$
(e) $-3g - h$
(f) $2y - 3z$

## Written Exercises

**A** Remember: you need to use your skills with integers to add or subtract polynomials. Review your skills.

1 Simplify.
(a) $3a + 4b + 5a$
(b) $2x - 3y + 5x$
(c) $8f + 3f - g$
(d) $10m + 3n - m$
(e) $6p + q - 3q$
(f) $4n - t - 2n$

2 Simplify.
(a) $(5a - 3b) + (4a + 2b)$
(b) $(12m - 3n) + (-m + 7n)$
(c) $(7p - 2q) + (p - 5q)$
(d) $(-3x + 4t) + (5x - 6t)$

3 Simplify. Think: what is your first step?
(a) $4m - (2m + 3n)$
(b) $(4m - 2n) - (n - m)$
(c) $(3n - m) - (m + n)$

4 Simplify.
(a) $(6x - 4y) - (2x + 3y)$
(b) $(-9p + 4q) - (-2p + 3q)$
(c) $(7a - 5) - (8a - 6)$
(d) $(2h + 3k) - (5h + 6k)$

**B** Remember: to find the value of an expression, simplify the expression first.

5 Simplify.
(a) $(4x - 2y) + (2z + x) + (5y - z)$
(b) $(-8a - 2b) + (c + 3a) - (4b + 2c)$
(c) $(4h - 3j) - (k + 2h) + (5j + 3k)$
(d) $(-6m + 4n) - (7 - 9m) - (5n - 10)$
(e) $(5 - 2u) + (w + 2u) - (3w + 7w)$

6 Simplify.
(a) $12r + 5t - (-4r + t)$
(b) $9s - 11u + (3s + 8u)$
(c) $5k + 3j - (2k + j) + (k - 2j)$
(d) $-4f + 3g - 3 + 7f - (2g + 1)$
(e) $3a - 2b + c - (5a - 3b - c)$
(f) $7d^2 - 3d + 6 - (2d^2 + 5d - 3)$
(g) $(6.1m + 3.2n) - (8.2m - 6.3n)$
(h) $(0.5a - 1.5b) + (9.6a - 3.5b)$

7 (a) Simplify the expression.
$10x - 3y + 5z - (7x + 4y - z)$
(b) Find the value of the expression in (a) for $x = 5$, $y = -3$, $z = 4$.

8 Find the value of each expression for $m = 3.5$, $n = 2.8$.
(a) $(6m + 3n) - (8m - 3n)$
(b) $9m - 16n - (20n + 3m)$
(c) $6.1m - 2.6n - (6.8m - 9.6n)$

9 Which of the expressions, A or B has the greater value for $h = 3$ and $k = -2$?
A: $3h - 4k - 4 - (2h + k + 5)$
B: $-2h + k + 3 + 5h - 2k - 1$

10 (a) Find an expression for the perimeter of the quadrilateral.

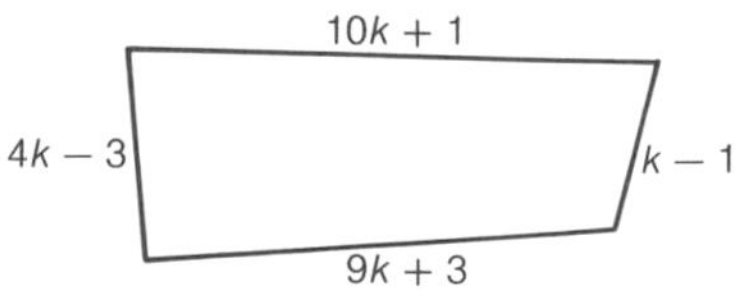


(b) What is the perimeter if $k = 3$ (in metres)?

11 The dimensions of a machine part are shown as variable expressions.

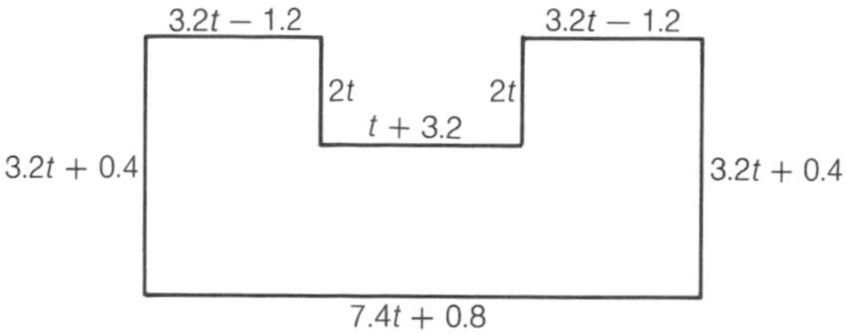


(a) Find an expression for the length of outside edge of the part.
(b) Find the dimensions when $t = 6.2$ (in millimetres).
(c) Find the distance around the outside edges when $t = 4.6$, in millimetres.

12 Clive, Shirley and Megan pooled their savings to start a business. The monies, in dollars, that they each invested were in the amounts $2k + 3$, $3k - 2$, and $5k - 6$.
(a) Find the sum of these amounts.
(b) How much did they invest in the business if $k$ represents $200?
(c) Find your answer in (b) in a different way.

13 To win a trip to Peggy's Cove, find which of the following expressions is closer in value to zero when $x = -3$ and $y = -1$.
(a) $6x - 2y - (-3x - y) - (x - 9y) - 2x$
(b) $5.2x + 3.4y - 2.7x - 4.5y$

Peggy's Cove in Nova Scotia is one of Canada's most popular places for artists and photographers. From here, you can obtain a sweeping view of the ocean and visibly notice the effect of the high and low tides.

## Problem Solving: Reading Carefully

Follow each of these instructions carefully.

14 (a) Subtract $4a - 5b$ from $a - 2b$.
(b) How much less is $-3a + 2b$ than $12a - 6b$?
(c) How much more is $3a - 2b$ than $5a - 6b$?

15 (a) Find the sum of $5x - 3y$, $x - y$ and $2x - 7y$.
(b) Subtract the sum of $a + b$ and $5a - 6b$ from $9a - 2b$.
(c) By how much does the sum of $5m - 2$ and $8m - 3$ exceed the sum of $3m + 2$ and $4m - 1$?

16 (a) Subtract the sum of $6m$ and $-12m + 7n$ from $-5m - 2n$.
(b) Find the value of the binomial in (a) when $m = 3$ and $n = -1$.

17 (a) Find the sum of $3.2x - 5.3y$, $6.1x + 3.6y$ and $-3.2x + 5.2y$.
(b) Subtract the sum of $3.2a - 4.6b$ and $3.5a + 2.6b$ from $4.6a - 3.2b$.

18 Find the value of the sum of $3.2a - 6.5b$ and $4.6a - 2.8b$ when $a = 1.6$ and $b = -0.32$.

19 When $a = 6.3$ and $b = -0.36$, which has the greater value P or Q?
P $4.6a + 3.2b$ added to $-3.6a - 2.1b$
Q $6.8a + 3.0b$ subtracted from $3.2a - 4.6b$

### Consumer Tip

Whenever you make a long distance telephone call, you can save a lot of money if you plan when you make the calls. You can obtain a discount depending on when you make the call.

A Refer to a telephone directory. Locate information on discounts for making calls. How much money can you save if you call from your place to Halifax, on Sunday morning, rather than at 3 o'clock on a Friday afternoon?

B What other discounts are offered for making telephone calls?

# 3.3 Product of Monomials

The price of oranges varies greatly according to the time of year. The price of one orange is given by the variable expression $4k$ cents, where $k$ is given a value depending on the time of year.

Fresh citrus fruit is brought to various parts of Canada by large trucks that travel constantly to the north from the south, while we sleep. The average Canadian eats or drinks the equivalent of 840 oranges a year.

The cost of 5 oranges is given by

$5 \times 4k$ or $20k$ cents.

The cost of $n$ of the oranges is given by

$n \times 4k$ or $4nk$ cents.

Remember: $4nk$ is a monomial expression.

To find the cost of $3n$ oranges, you need to find the product of monomials.

$$3n \times 4k = 12nk$$

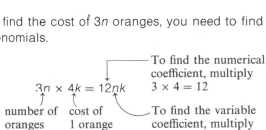

- $3n$: number of oranges
- $4k$: cost of 1 orange
- To find the numerical coefficient, multiply $3 \times 4 = 12$
- To find the variable coefficient, multiply the variables. $n \times k = nk$

In the above example, $3n$ and $4k$ are each monomials. To multiply monomials

*Step 1*: multiply the numerical coefficients

*Step 2*: multiply the variable coefficients

### Example 1

For each product.

(a) $(6m)(5n)$ (b) $(-4p)(3q)$ (c) $(-a)(-4b)$

### Solution

(a) $(6m)(5n)$
$= 30mn$

(b) $(-4p)(3q)$
$= -12pq$ ← $(-4)(3) = -12$

(c) $(-a)(-4b)$
$= 4ab$ ← $(-1)(-4) = 4$

You can use these skills to obtain variable expressions to solve problems.

### Example 2

The dimensions, in metres, of a floating dock are given as variable expressions.

(a) Find an expression for the area.

(b) For which values does the dock have the greater surface area?

I: $p = 2.5,\ q = 1.6$ II: $p = 1.8,\ q = 1.5$

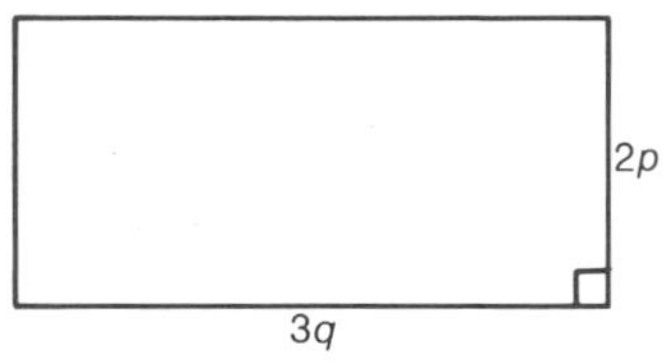


### Solution

(a) Area = length × width

$A = (2p)(3q)$

$= 6pq$

(b) For I, $p = 2.5,\ q = 1.6$ For II, $p = 1.8,\ q = 1.5$

$6pq = 6(2.5)(1.6)$
$= 24\ (\text{m}^2)$

$6pq = 6(1.8)(1.5)$
$= 16.2\ (\text{m}^2)$

Thus the dock has greater surface area when $p = 2.5,\ q = 1.6$.

## Try These

1 What is the missing numerical coefficient?
 (a) $(5y)(3z) = ?yz$
 (b) $(-2a)(4b) = ?ab$
 (c) $(-t)(-7w) = ?tw$
 (d) $(3k)(-6m) = ?km$

2 What is the missing variable coefficient?
 (a) $(4p)(3q) = 12?$
 (b) $(-7k)(2m) = -14?$
 (c) $(3b)(-5z) = -15?$
 (d) $(-6r)(5s) = -30?$

## Written Exercises

**A** Remember: to multiply monomials, find the numerical coefficient. Then find the variable coefficient.

1 A motorcycle has a mass of $b$ kg. Find the mass of the following number of these motorcycles.
 (a) 4 (b) $x$ (c) $5x$

2 Track suits cost $\$4k$ each. How much do each of the following cost?
 (a) 2 track suits (b) $n$ track suits
 (c) $3n$ track suits

3 The price of $n$ oranges is given by the expression $4nk$.
 (a) In winter $k = 9.6$. Find the cost, in cents, when $n = 3$.
 (b) In summer $k = 7.2$. Find the cost, in cents, when $n = 12$.

4 The price of $n$ grapefruit is given by the expression $6nd$.
 (a) In winter $d = 10.2$. Find the cost, in cents, when $n = 7$.
 (b) In summer, $d = 5.5$. Find the cost, in cents, when $n = 12$.

5 Stephanie used concrete tiles measuring $m$ units by $n$ units to cover the floor of a shed.

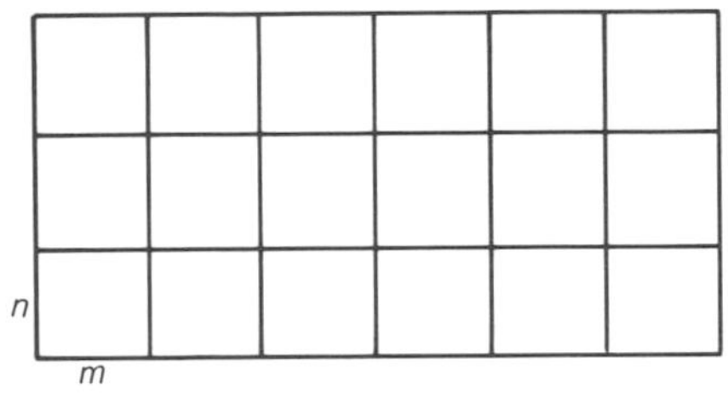


(a) Write an expression for the area of each tile.
(b) Use the diagram to find the number of tiles that Stephanie used.
(c) Use the result from (a) and (b) to find an expression for the area of the shed.
(d) Find the area when $n = 1.5$, $m = 1.5$.

6 Refer to the diagram in the previous question.
(a) Write an expression for the width of the shed in terms of $n$.
(b) Write an expression for the length of the shed in terms of $m$.
(c) Use your results from (a) and (b) to find an expression for the area of the shed floor.
(d) Find the area when $n = 1.5$, $m = 1.5$. How does this answer compare to your answer in the previous question?

**B** Remember: to multiply monomials, you must know your skills for multiplying integers. Review these skills.

7 Find each product.
(a) $(5p)(7q)$ (b) $(8x)(-4y)$
(c) $(-3m)(-2n)$ (d) $(-9t)(5w)$
(e) $(8b)(5d)$ (f) $(-h)(-10k)$
(g) $(6f)(-3g)$ (h) $(-5y)(-5z)$
(i) $(-2r)(-9s)$ (j) $(12k)(-t)$

8 Find each product.
(a) $(4m)(-6n)$ (b) $(-3m)(8n)$
(c) $(-12m)(2n)$ (d) $(-6m)(-4n)$
(e) $(-8m)(-3n)$ (f) $(2m)(12n)$
What do you notice about the answers?

9 Find each product.
(a) $5d(-3e)$ ⟵ This means the same as $(5d)(-3e)$.
(b) $-9p(3q)$ (c) $8x(5y)$
(d) $-12r(-2t)$ (e) $-k(7m)$
(f) $10m(-p)$ (g) $-7tz(-8q)$

10 Simplify each product. The first one is done for you.
(a) $(3a)(2b)(-2c)$

$$(3a)(2b)(-2c)$$
$$= 6ab(-2c)$$
$$= -12abc$$

(b) $(-x)(-2y)(3z)$ (c) $6e(-4f)(-3g)$
(d) $(-2p)(3q)(-r)$ (e) $(-m)(-2r)(-3p)$
(f) $3t(-2r)(-w)$ (g) $(-5k)(2t)(-m)(3n)$

11 Find each product.
(a) $(4a)(3.5b)$ (b) $(5c)(-6.2d)$
(c) $(-3x)(-4.7y)$ (d) $(-4.2u)(-2.1v)(-3.5w)$

Which product has the greatest numerical coefficient?

---

In Questions 12–14 the measures are in metres.

12 Use the diagram shown. Write an expression for the measure of
(a) the base.
(b) the height.
(c) the area.

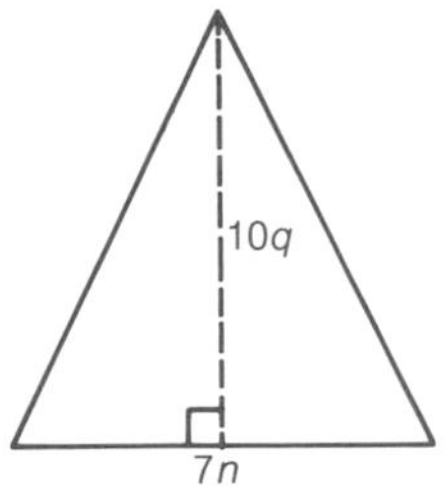


Remember: for a triangle

$$\text{Area} = \frac{1}{2} \times \text{base} \times \text{height}$$

13 Which triangle has the greater area?

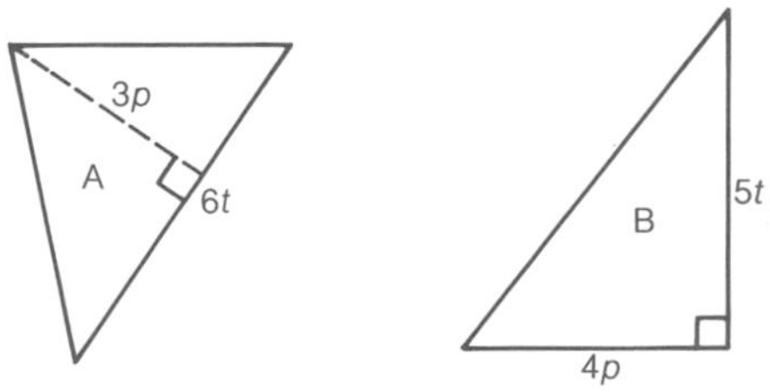

14 Which rectangle has the greater area?

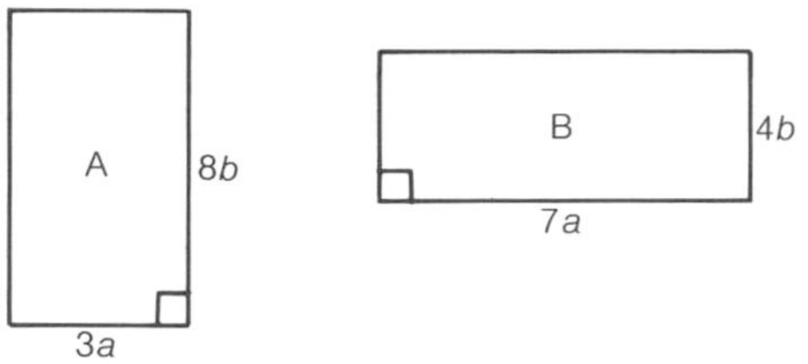


Questions 15 to 17 are based on the following information. An architect may use variable expressions to represent lengths on a computer screen. Different values of the variable are then used to find the best design.

15 The opening of an air conditioning duct is shown by the figure.

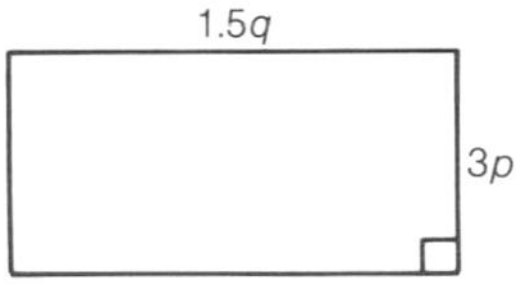


(a) Find a variable expression for the area of the opening.

(b) Find the area, in square metres, for
(i) $p = 1.8$, $q = 2$ (ii) $p = 2.2$, $q = 1.2$

16 A triangular support is shown on the screen.

(a) Find the variable expression for the area of the support.

(b) Find the area, in square metres, for
(i) $q = 4.2$, $n = 2$
(ii) $q = 2$, $n = 2.2$

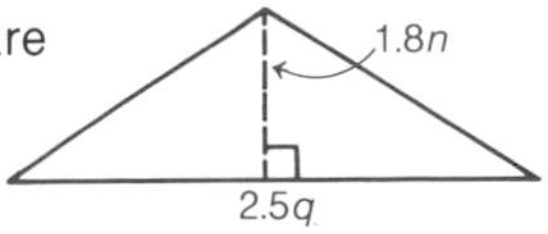


17 The architect calls up a picture of a window frame to the screen.

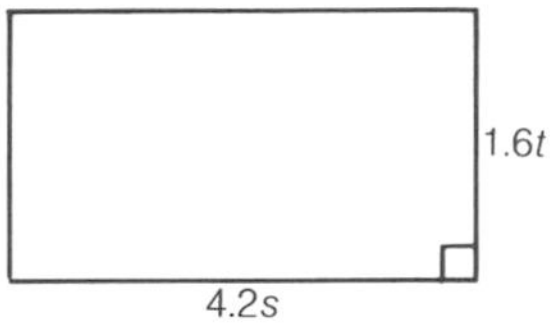


(a) Find a variable expression for the area of the window.

(b) Find the area, in square metres for
(i) $s = 2.7$, $t = 3$ (ii) $s = 2.5$, $t = 2.4$

## Calculator Tip

If you enter a number incorrectly, on many calculators you can correct it without having to redo any previous steps. On some calculators, the clear button has a two-step action. The first time you press it ([C/CE]), it clears just the last number entered. You can then enter the next number again and continue with the calculation. Other calculators have two separate clearing buttons. The [CE] button clears the last entry only. The [C] or [CA] is used to clear all previous entries.

## Career Tip

Often the questions you ask yourself about obtaining a part-time or summer job will be similar to those you might ask about full-time employment.

- ✓ Do I want to earn a lot of money?
- ✓ Do I want to do physical work?
- ✓ Do I want to meet people?
- ✓ Do I want to be on the go, busy?
- ✓ Do I want to work alone?
- ✓ Do I want to work with adults? With children? With retired people?
- ✓ Do I want the work to be at night or in the daytime?
- ✓ Do I want to take work home with me at night?
- ✓ Do I want "fringe" benefits such as travel in my job, etc?

A Choose a job listed in the "Help Wanted" newspaper ads.

B Write a letter to apply for the job.

# 3.4 Using Exponents: Multiplying Monomials

Often you can combine two skills that you already know to develop a new skill.

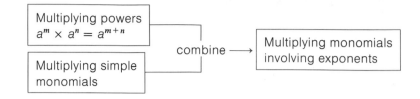

Multiplying powers $a^m \times a^n = a^{m+n}$

Multiplying simple monomials

combine → Multiplying monomials involving exponents

**Example 1**

Find each product.

(a) $(3a^4)(2a^5)$ (b) $(-4m^2n)(-2m^3n^2)$

**Solution**

(a) $(3a^4)(2a^5) = 6a^9$

Think: find the numerical coefficient. $3 \times 2 = 6$

Think: find the variable coefficient. $a^4 \times a^5 = a^9$

(b) $(-4m^2n)(-2m^3n^2) = 8m^5n^3$

$(-4)(-2) = 8$

$(m^2n)(m^3n^2) = m^5n^3$

Sometimes these skills are needed to solve problems in the business world. To simplify the substitution of values, the product of monomials is first obtained.

**Example 2**

A musician's profit, in dollars, from a record is given by the expression $5k^2w^5$ where $k$ and $w$ are production and marketing factors. The recording company determines that a video will increase profits by a factor of $2kw$.

(a) Find an expression for the artist's profit if the recording company makes the video.

(b) Find the profit in (a) when $k = 10$ and $w = 2$.

**Solution**

(a) Profits with video $= (5k^2w^5)(2kw)$

$= 10k^3w^6$

(b) Use $k = 10$, $w = 2$.

Profit $= 10k^3w^6$

$= 10(10^3)(2^6)$

$= (10^4)(64)$

$= 640\,000$

The profit is \$640 000.

## Try These

1 What is the missing part?

(a) $(-3g^2)(4g^3) = ?g^5$

(b) $(6w^4)(5w^2) = ?w^6$

(c) $(-k^6)(-7k) = ?k^7$

2 What is the missing part?

(a) $(3x^3)(-2x) = -6?$

(b) $(-4a^2)(-a^2) = 4?$

(c) $(5d^2)(-3d^4) = -15?$

## Written Exercises

**A** Remember: to multiply monomials, you need to use the properties of exponents. Review the properties of exponents.

1 Multiply.
(a) $(e^4)(e^5)$ (b) $(a^7)(a^3)$
(c) $(m^3)(m)$ (d) $t^6 \times t^6$
(e) $(mn^2)(m^2n)$ (f) $(xy^3)(x^2y^2)$
(g) $(a^3b)(ab^2)$ (h) $(p^3q^2)(qp^2)$

2 To find each product, what is your first step? Find the products.
(a) $(-2x)(5x^2)$ (b) $8f^2)(-3f)$
(c) $(-10p^2)(-3p^3)$ (d) $(-m^2)(-2n)$

3 Find the missing parts.
(a) $(3m^2)(-2m) = ?m^?$
(b) $(-4w^3)(-5w^2) = 20?$
(c) $(-6y)(4y^4) = ?y^?$
(d) $(8p^4)(7p^6) = 56p^?$
(e) $(-2m^2n)(-4mn^3) = 8m^?n^?$
(f) $(4pq^3)(-3p^2q) = ?p^?q^?$
(g) $(-5r^2s^2)(2rs) = -10?$

4 (a) Find the value of each expression for $m = 2$.

| A | B |
|---|---|
| $(-2m^2)(-3m^3)$ | $6m^5$ |

What do you notice about the answers?
(b) Repeat the steps in (a) for $m = -1$. What do you notice?
(c) Try values of your own for $m$ in (a). What do you notice each time?

5 (a) Find the value of each expression for $p = -1$.

| A | B |
|---|---|
| $(-3p)(-2p^3)(-p^2)$ | $-6p^6$ |

What do you notice about your answers?
(b) Repeat the steps in (a) for $p = 3$. What do you notice?
(c) Try values of your own for $p$ in (a). What do you notice each time?

**B** Remember: use your skills with integers and exponents to multiply monomials.

6 Find each product.
(a) $(2d^3)(-5d^2)$ (b) $(4x^3)(8x)$
(c) $(-3y^2)(-3y^4)$ (d) $(-5m^4)(-m^3)$
(e) $(4t)(-7t^2)$ (f) $(-k^2)(-k^5)$
(g) $(6d^2)(3d^2)$ (h) $(5w^4)(-7w)$

7 Find each product. Remember that the product $(-5a)(4a^2)$ may be written as $-5a(4a^2)$.
(a) $4m^3(-3m^2)$ (b) $8t(-3t^4)$
(c) $-k^2(5k^2)$ (d) $3p^3(5p)$
(e) $-2n^4(-7n)$ (f) $5r^2(-r^5)$
(g) $8a^5(2a^3)$ (h) $-4y^3(-4y^3)$

8 (a) Find an expression for the area of the triangle.
(b) What is the area for $m = 2$?

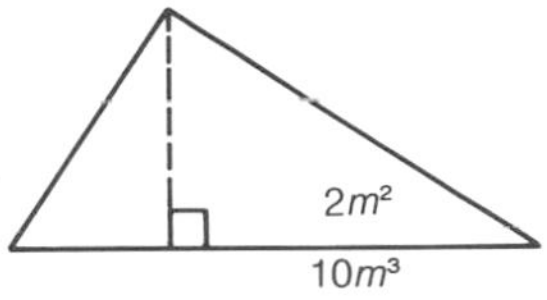


9 Use $a = 3$. Which triangle has the greater area, A or B?

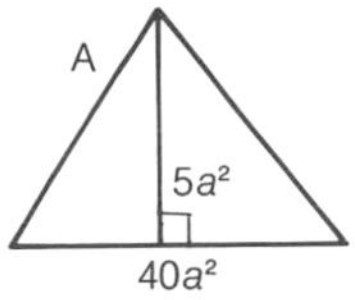


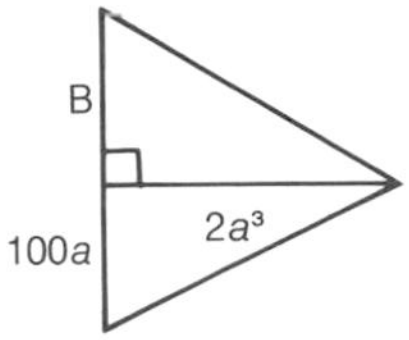


10 Find each product.
(a) $(-2a^2b)(ab^3)$ (b) $(4m^2n)(-5mn^2)$
(c) $3k^3r^2(-k^5r^4)$ (d) $(-6p^3q^4)(-3p^2q^5)$
(e) $(4np^2)(-3n^2p^2)$ (f) $(-7u^3v^2)(-7u^3v^2)$
(g) $(-5s^4t^2)(2st^3)$ (h) $(9cd^4)(-c^2d)$

11 Find each product.
(a) $(2p)(-3p^2)(-4p^3)$ (b) $-m^2(3m)(-4m^2)$
(c) $r^2(-r^3)(2r)$ (d) $3f^2(-2f)(-5f^3)$
(e) $(-4y^3)(-3y)(-6y^4)$ (f) $-2h(-2h^3)(-2h^3)$
(g) $(a^2b)(-3ab)(ab^2)$ (h) $4m(-6mn^2)(n^2m)$
(i) $(-x^2y)(4xy)(-5y^2)$ (j) $(-3a^2b)(a^2b^2)(2b^3)$

12 Simplify. You can use the property of exponents: $(a^m)^n = a^{mn}$. The first one is done for you.

(a) $(-2p^3q^2)^2$ $\qquad (-2p^3q^2)^2 = (-2)^2p^6q^4 = 4p^6q^4$ (3 × 2)

(b) $(2a^2b^2)^3$ (c) $(-3xy^2)^3$ (d) $(-mn^5)^4$

(e) $(6p^3q^4)^2$ (f) $(-4h^3k^4)^3$ (g) $(2d^2t)^5$

13 (a) Use $m = 2$, $n = -1$. Evaluate each of the following.

A: $(2mn^3)^3$ B: $(-3mn)^2$ C: $(-m^2n^2)^2$

(b) Which has the least value, A, B, or C?

14 (a) Simplify each product.

A: $(-3a^2b^3)^2(4ab^2)$

B: $(-2ab^2)(6ab^3)(3ab^4)$

(b) Which expression in (a) has the greater value when $a = 2$ and $b = -1$?

15 In the fall, the volume of water in a river is given by the expression $3k^3$, where $k$ is a constant related to the amount of rainfall. In spring, the volume is multiplied by a factor of $3k^2$. Write a single term expression for the volume in spring.

16 The end wall of the apartment building has the measures, in metres, shown.

(a) Find an expression for the area of the end wall.

(b) Find the area if $p = 2$ and $q = 3$.

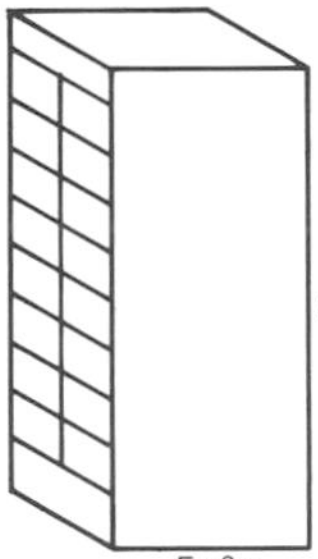


17 The profit from a benefit, in dollars, is given by the expression

$2.5np^2$ where $n$ is the advertising factor and $p$ is the weather factor.

The profit is increased by a factor of $3np$ when a favourite star makes an appearance at the benefit.

(a) Find the expression for the profit when a star appears at the benefit.

(b) Find the profit, to the nearest dollar, when $n = 15$ and $p = 1.3$, if the celebrity appears.

18 The number of people listening to a radio commercial in the daytime is given by the expression

$\frac{1}{2}tL^2$ where $t$ is the time-of-day factor and $L$ is the length of the commercial.

If the commercial occurs in the evening, the number of people is increased by a factor of $20tL$.

(a) Find an expression for the number of people listening in the evening.

(b) How many people listened to a commercial in the evening if $t = 3.2$ and $L = 4.0$? Round your answer to the nearest hundred.

## C

19 The diagram shows the proportions of a piece of stretchable plastic food wrapping. Due to the construction of the material the width can be stretched by a factor of $2k$ before it rips and the length by a factor of $3k^2$. Find an expression for the maximum area of the piece shown.

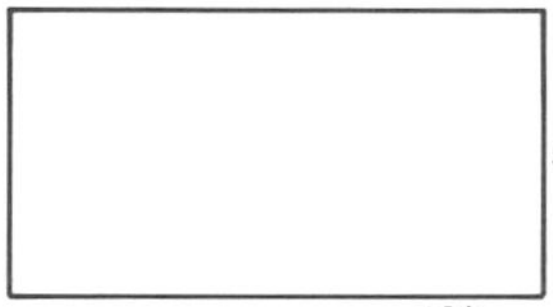


### Consumer Tip

Make a list of your assets and liabilities. Would you be a "good" or "poor" credit risk?

### Math Tip

It is important to clearly understand the vocabulary of mathematics when solving problems. You cannot use mathematics to solve problems if you don't know the vocabulary.

- Make a list of all the words you review and learn in this chapter.
- Provide a simple example to illustrate the meaning of each word.

# 3.5 Dividing Monomials

The methods and the patterns you learn in your study of mathematics occur again and again. For example, to explore the properties of exponents when you multiplied powers, you used the meaning of exponents, namely

$a^5 = a \times a \times a \times a \times a$

To divide monomials that involve powers, we can use a similar method.

Arithmetic

$$\frac{3^5}{3^2} = \frac{3 \times 3 \times 3 \times 3 \times 3}{3 \times 3}$$
$$= \frac{\overset{1}{\cancel{3}} \times \overset{1}{\cancel{3}} \times 3 \times 3 \times 3}{\underset{1}{\cancel{3}} \times \underset{1}{\cancel{3}}}$$
$$= 3 \times 3 \times 3$$
$$= 3^3$$
$$\frac{3^5}{3^2} = 3^3 \leftarrow \text{Think } 5 - 2 - 3$$

Algebra

$$\frac{a^5}{a^2} = \frac{a \times a \times a \times a \times a}{a \times a}$$
$$= \frac{\overset{1}{\cancel{a}} \times \overset{1}{\cancel{a}} \times a \times a \times a}{\underset{1}{\cancel{a}} \times \underset{1}{\cancel{a}}}$$
$$= a \times a \times a$$
$$= a^3$$
$$\frac{a^5}{a^2} = a^3 \leftarrow \text{Think } 5 \quad 2 = 3$$

The above examples suggest the following result.

*To divide powers with like bases, subtract the exponents.*

$$\frac{a^m}{a^n} = a^{m-n} \qquad a \neq 0, m > n$$

Just as in the multiplication of monomials, in order to divide monomials you need to obtain

- the numerical coefficient
- the variable coefficient.

These steps are shown in the next example.

## Example 1

Simplify each of the following.

(a) $2^{10} \div 2^6$

(b) $-15p^3 \div 5p$

(c) $\dfrac{-64a^2b^3c^4}{-8ab^2c^2}$

## Solution

(a) $2^{10} \div 2^6 = 2^{10-6}$
$= 2^4$

(b) $-\dfrac{15p^3}{5p} = -3p^2$

Think: find the numerical coefficient $-\dfrac{15}{5} = -3$

Think: find the variable coefficient $\dfrac{p^3}{p} = p^{3-1} = p^2$

(c) $\dfrac{-64a^2b^3c^4}{-8ab^2c^2} = 8abc^2$

What are the steps?

What are the steps?

Before you substitute to evaluate an expression, you need to simplify the expression as shown in the following example.

**Example 2**

Find the value of the expression.

$$\frac{-160m^2n^3}{+80mn^2}$$

Use $m = -4$, $n = -3$.

**Solution**

Simplify the expression. Divide the monomials.

$$\frac{-160m^2n^3}{+80mn^2} = -2mn$$

Substitute $m = -4$, $n = -3$

$$\begin{aligned} -2mn &= -2(-4)(-3) \\ &= -24 \end{aligned}$$

## Try These

1 You need to know how to divide integers before you can divide monomials. What is each answer?

(a) $\frac{-25}{5}$ (b) $\frac{16}{-8}$ (c) $\frac{-52}{13}$

(d) $\frac{-125}{-25}$ (e) $\frac{225}{-15}$ (f) $\frac{-900}{30}$

2 What is each answer?

(a) $\frac{15m}{3}$ (b) $\frac{-21a}{7}$ (c) $\frac{-49p}{-7}$

(d) $\frac{-30f}{-15}$ (e) $\frac{-48q}{8}$ (f) $\frac{-24f}{-8}$

## Written Exercises

**A** To divide monomials, you need to divide integers. Review your skills for dividing integers.

1 Divide.

(a) $g^4 \div g^2$ (b) $m^7 \div m^3$

(c) $m^3 \div m$ (d) $t^8 \div t^4$

(e) $m^3n^2 \div mn$ (f) $x^3y \div xy$

(g) $p^4q^3 \div p^2q^2$ (h) $a^3b^5 \div a^2b^3$

2 Simplify.

(a) $\frac{6mn}{m}$ (b) $\frac{25pq}{5p}$ (c) $\frac{-30ab}{-6b}$

(d) $\frac{-45mn}{-9n}$ (e) $\frac{80xy}{-8x}$ (f) $\frac{-150pq}{-150q}$

3 Find each quotient.

(a) $\frac{18mn}{9m}$ (b) $\frac{24pq}{-6q}$ (c) $\frac{35ab}{-7ab}$

(d) $\frac{-50ef}{-25e}$ (e) $\frac{-21ab^2}{-7b}$ (f) $\frac{-40xy}{-10y}$

4 (a) Find the value of each expression for $m = 2$.

A: $\frac{-8m^3}{4m}$ B: $-2m^2$

(b) Repeat the steps in (a) for $m = -3$. What do you notice?

(c) Try your own values of $m$, and substitute. What do you notice each time?

5 To find each answer, what is your first step? Find the answer.

(a) $(30p^3) \div (-5p^2)$

(b) $(24m^4) \div (-8m^2)$

(c) $(58b^4) \div (-29b)$

(d) $(-36x^5y^4) \div (-18x^3y^2)$

**B** To substitute values in expressions, remember to simplify first. Use a calculator in your work.

6 Simplify.

(a) $\frac{16mn}{-8m}$ (b) $\frac{-24abc}{-6ab}$ (c) $\frac{32pq^2}{-8p}$

(d) $\frac{-50pq^2}{-10q}$ (e) $\frac{-81p^2q}{-9pq}$ (f) $\frac{-120a^2b^2}{-12ab}$

(g) $\frac{-20a^2b^3}{-10ab^2}$ (h) $\frac{19p^4q^3}{19p^2q}$ (i) $\frac{25m^3n^2}{-5mn}$

7 Find the value of each expression. Use $p = -2$.

(a) $\frac{8p}{4}$ (b) $\frac{-12p}{-4}$ (c) $\frac{-20p}{-10}$

(d) $\frac{-36p^2}{+6}$ (e) $\frac{-45p^2}{-9p}$ (f) $\frac{-50p^3}{-10p}$

8 Use $x = -3$, $y = -1$. Find the value of each of the following.

(a) $\frac{30x^2y}{-6x}$ (b) $\frac{-44xy^3}{-22y}$ (c) $\frac{-65x^4y^3}{+13x^3y}$

9 Which expression has the greater value for $a = -4$, $b = 2$?

(a) $\frac{49ab^2}{-7b}$ (b) $\frac{-63a^2b^3}{-9ab}$

10 An expression is used to calculate the profit.

Find the value of the expression $\frac{36h^2p^5}{12hp^4}$ for each pair of values.

(a) $h = 8$ $p = 1.2$ (b) $h = 10$ $p = 1.4$
(c) $h = 9.6$ $p = 1.5$ (d) $h = 1.85$ $p = 2.60$
(e) For which pair of values is the profit the greatest?

11 The area for each figure is shown in square units. Find the missing measure.

(a)

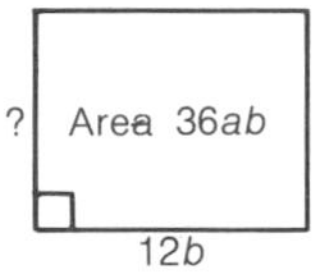


(b)

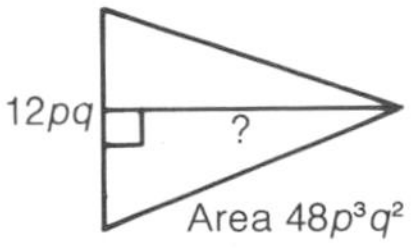


12 (a) A rectangular swimming pool has area $85mn$ square units. The width is $5n$ units. What is the length?
(b) A square patio has an area $36p^2q^4$ square units. Find the length of each side.
(c) A sail in the shape of a triangle has an area of $50m^4n$ square units. The base of the sail is $5mn$ units. What is the height of the sail?

13 (a) The cost of an excursion was $100a^3b$ dollars. If each person paid $2ab$ dollars, how many persons went?
(b) The price paid for $8mt^2$ machine parts was $56m^2t^3$ dollars. What was the price of each machine part?
(c) The charge for renting a truck was $216n^4q^3$ dollars. The truck was driven $9n^3q^3$ kilometres. What was the charge per kilometre?

14 (a) Susan drove her mini bike a distance, in kilometres represented by the expression $45p^2q^3$. Her speed, in kilometres per hour, was given by the expression $9pq$. Find the time she rode the mini bike.
(b) Miroslav skated a distance of $156d^2r^4$ metres in $12dr^3$ seconds. Find an expression for his speed, in metres per second.

15 Simplify.

(a) $\frac{(8p)(6pq)}{-12p}$ (b) $\frac{(-4r)(-7ru)}{28u}$

(c) $\frac{(-10x)(-15xy)}{-5x^2y}$ (d) $\frac{(-2pq)(-11p^2q^2)}{-22pq^2}$

(e) $\frac{(12m^2n)(-34mn^2)}{-17m^2n}$ (f) $\frac{(-xy)(-9x^2y^3)}{-3xy^2}$

16 Find each quotient.

(a) $\frac{(5x)(-6xy)}{15x^2}$ (b) $\frac{(3mn^2)(-8m^2n^3)}{-12m^2n^4}$

(c) $\frac{(5pq)(6p)(-4q^2)}{15p^2q}$ (d) $\frac{(-8ab)(-13a^2b^3)}{(-26a^2b)(-ab)}$

# 3.6 Finding Products: Polynomials

In arithmetic, you learn skills to simplify expressions by using the properties of numbers. These skills in arithmetic are helpful in developing skills to simplify expressions in algebra.

The words and methods used in arithmetic extend to algebra. Look for the similarities to help you learn skills in algebra. Compare these skills in arithmetic and algebra.

| In arithmetic | | In algebra | |
|---|---|---|---|
| $3(5 + 8)$ | $2(8 - 3)$ | $3(x + 2)$ | $2(m - 2)$ |
| $= 15 + 24$ | $= 16 - 6$ | $= 3x + 6$ | $= 2m - 6$ |
| $= 39$ | $= 10$ | | |

The examples illustrate the distributive property that is used to simplify expressions in algebra such as shown in the following example.

### Example

Simplify.

(a) $3(x - 5) + 2(x + 8)$ (b) $2y(y - 3) - 3y(y + 3)$

### Solution

Record the original expression as the first step of your solution.

(a)
$$3(x - 5) + 2(x + 8)$$
$$= 3x - 15 + 2x + 16$$
$$= 5x + 1$$

(b)
$$2y(y - 3) - 3y(y + 2)$$
$$= 2y^2 - 6y - 3y^2 - 6y$$
$$= -y^2 - 12y$$

As with earlier skills in algebra, when you are asked to evaluate an expression, simplify it first as shown in the next example.

### Example 2

Find the value of the expression

$3m(m - n) - 3m(2m - 3n)$

for $m = -3$, $n = 2$.

### Solution

Simplify the expression.

$$3m(m - n) - 3m(2m - 3n)$$
$$= 3m^2 - 3mn - 6m^2 + 9mn$$
$$= -3m^2 + 6mn$$

Substitute the values $m = -3$, $n = 2$.

$$-3m^2 + 6mn = -3(-3)^2 + 6(-3)(2)$$
$$= -27 - 36$$
$$= -63$$

Often in solving scientific problems, some complex expressions occur. Before evaluating expressions, you again simplify the expressions and then substitute. Refer to the following example.

### Example 3

(a) Simplify $2k[8k - 3(2k + 8)] + 48k$

(b) Find the value of the expression in (a) for $k = 2$, $k = 2.5$, $k = 2.75$.

### Solution

Remember: record the original expression

(a) $2k[8k - 3(2k + 8)] + 48k$

Simplify the inside bracket

$= 2k[8k - 6k - 24] + 48k$

$= 2k[2k - 24] + 48k$

$= 4k^2 - 48k + 48k$

$= 4k^2$

A simplified expression can be used more readily to calculate different values.

(b)

| $k = 2$ | $k = 2.5$ | $k = 2.75$ |
|---|---|---|
| $4k^2 = 4(2)^2$ | $4k^2 = 4(2.5)^2$ | $4k^2 = 4(2.75)^2$ |
| $= 16$ | $= 25$ | $= 30.25$ |

### Try These

1 Expand.

(a) $3(x + y)$ (b) $2(a - b)$

(c) $5(2x + y)$ (d) $6(3m - 2n)$

(e) $4(m^2 + 2n - 1)$ (f) $-5(3x^2 - 2x + 1)$

2 Expand.

(a) $3x(x + 2)$ (b) $2y(3y - 3)$

(c) $-4a(a - 3)$ (d) $6b(2b - 3)$

(e) $-3a(a^2 + a + 1)$ (f) $-2y(2y^2 - y + 3)$

## Written Exercises

**A** Remember: to multiply a polynomial by a monomial, multiply each term by the monomial.

1 Expand. Use the distributive property.

(a) $3(x - 3)$ (b) $-2(y + 6)$

(c) $8(2a - 3b)$ (d) $-6(p + 4q)$

(e) $-3(5p + 7q)$ (f) $-2(-3a - 2b)$

(g) $3(2a - 3b + 4c)$

(h) $-5(-5q + 3r - 2s)$

2 Write each expression without parentheses.

(a) $-2a(a - b)$ (b) $-2p(a + b)$

(c) $t(2p - q)$ (d) $3m(2p - 4q)$

(e) $5a(b - c)$ (f) $2m(-3n + p)$

3 Expand.

(a) $4a(a + 2)$ (b) $2p(p - 6)$

(c) $-3m(2m - 2)$ (d) $-4n(-3n + 4)$

(e) $(3p - 2)p$ (f) $(6 - 3q)q$

(g) $(2y - 3)(-2y)$ (h) $(8 - 6n)(-2k)$

4 Find the value of each of the following for $a = 3$.
(a) $3a(a - 4)$ (b) $-2a(-3a + 2)$
(c) $-5a(-a - 1)$ (d) $4a(-3a - 5)$

5 (a) Multiply $(8x^2 - 4x + 4)$ by $2x$.
(b) Multiply $(-2a^2 + 5a - 4)$ by $-3a$.
(c) Multiply $(-4p^2 - 3p + 6)$ by $-4p^2$

**B**

6 Simplify.
(a) $7m + 3(m - 2)$ (b) $8a - 2(a - 8)$
(c) $4(2p - 3) - 5p$ (d) $-8(-3x - 3) - 12$

7 Find the value of each expression for $m = 3$.
(a) $2(3m - 2) - 5m$
(b) $9 + 3(m - 5) + 2m$
(c) $-5(-m - 2) - 2m$
(d) $-12m - 4(-m - 2)$

8 Simplify each of the following.
(a) $5m + 6 - 3(m - 2)$
(b) $7a - 6 + 2(a - 3)$
(c) $-3(4 - a) - a + 9$
(d) $-5(8 - 3x) - (x - 9)$
(e) $6(x - 5) + (2x + 3)(2)$
(f) $-5(4 - m) - 4(m - 4)$
(g) $0 - 8a - 3(a - 3) + 5$
(h) $12 - 3f - (6 - 2f) - 2f$

9 (a) Do not simplify. Evaluate $3(2x - y) - 2(x - 3y)$ for $x = 2$, $y = 3$.
(b) Now simplify the expression in (a). Then evaluate the expression in (a) for $x = 2$ and $y = 3$.
(c) Which solution requires more computations (a) or (b)?

10 Evaluate each expression for $p = -2$ and $q = -3$.
(a) $3(2p - q) - 4(p + q)$
(b) $-5(3p + q) - 3(-q - 2p)$
(c) $-2p(p - q) - 4q(p + q)$

11 Simplify.
(a) $3(2a - 2b) - 3(a + 2b) - 4(a - 3b)$
(b) $5(x + 3y) + 2(4x - 7y) - 3(2x - y)$
(c) $3m(m - 1) - 2m(m + 6) - m(m - 1)$
(d) $2k(3 - k) + 3k(1 + k) - 4k(2 - 3k)$

12 Use $a = -2$. Find the value of each expression.
(a) $2(a^2 - 3a + 1) - 4(2a^2 + 5a - 6)$
(b) $3(a^2 + 5a - 3) + 5(a^2 - 4a - 1)$
(c) $a(a^2 - 3a + 7) - a(a^2 + 2a - 4)$

13 Simplify.
(a) $3k^2 - 2k[k - 3(k - 2)]$
(b) $3p[p - 3 - 6(p - 2)] - 3p$
(c) $8[3(p + 2) - 2(p + 3)] + 5p$
(d) $t^2 + 3[t(2t + 1) - 4t(t - 5)]$
(e) $2m[m(m - 1) - 3m(2m + 5)] + 4m^3$

14 (a) Simplify $3(m - 2) - 9[m - 3(m - 8)]$.
(b) Evaluate the expression (a) for $m = -3$.

15 Evaluate each expression for $t = -3$.
(a) $2(2t - 1) - t[t - 1 - 3(t - 2)]$
(b) $4t(t + 2) + 5[6t - t(t + 3)]$
(c) $3t - t(t + 1) - 2t[t + 2 - 5(t + 3)]$

16 An expression is used to give the profit, in dollars, for a landscaping firm:
$12.5(8k - 2) + 1.8(3k + 1)$
where $k$ is determined by the overhead costs.
Find the profit for each $k$ factor.
(a) $k = 8$ (b) $k = 7.6$ (c) $k = 9.8$

17 The temperature, in degrees Celsius, inside an unheated greenhouse is given by the expression
$4(1.4 - 0.3t) + 0.5(3.8 + 4t)$
where $t$ is the temperature of the air outside.
Find the temperature inside the greenhouse for each value of $t$.
(a) $t = 15$ (b) $t = 8.5$ (c) $t = -3$

18 House painters use the following expression to calculate their charge, in dollars, for painting a room.
$5.8[6.5(a + 1.2) + a(0.1a - 4)]$
where $a$ is the area to be painted, in square metres.
Find the charge for each value of $a$.
(a) $a = 12$ (b) $a = 20$ (c) $a = 17.5$

# 3.7 Squaring Binomials

Many of the skills you learn in mathematics have taken years and years to organize. In fact, what you will learn in mathematics this year, and the applications based on the skills, took an average person in ancient times a life time to learn.

For monomials, you can write squares:
$(2m)^2 = (2m)(2m)$

For binomials, you can write squares:
$(y + 3)^2 = (y + 3)(y + 3)$

**Remember: The operation of multiplication is understood here.**

To find the product of binomials, you again use the distributive property. Remember

$y(y + 3) = y^2 + 3y \qquad (y + 3)y = y^2 + 3y$

When you use the distributive property, look for a pattern.

$$\begin{aligned}(\ ?\ )(y + 3) &= (\ ?\ )y + (\ ?\ )3\\ (y + 3)(y + 3) &= (y + 3)y + (y + 3)3\\ &= y^2 + 3y + 3y + 9\\ &= y^2 + 6y + 9\end{aligned}$$

Once you obtain the square of a binomial, look for a pattern. What pattern do you see for these examples?

$(y + 3)^2 = y^2 + 6y + 9 \qquad (y - 2)^2 = y^2 - 4y + 4$
$(y + 6)^2 = y^2 + 12y + 36 \qquad (y - 6)^2 = y^2 - 12y + 36$

A pattern can be used to find the product.

$(y + 3)^2 = (y + 3)(y + 3) = y^2 + 6y + 9$

(pattern: $y^2$, $9$, $3y$, $3y$)

**Example**
Expand (a) $(x - 5)^2$ (b) $(2x - 1)^2$

**Solution**

(a) Think: $x^2$, $25$, $-5x$, $-5x$

$(x - 5)^2 = (x - 5)(x - 5)$
$= x^2 - 10x + 25$

(b) Think: $4x^2$, $1$, $-2x$, $-2x$

$(2x - 1)^2 = (2x - 1)(2x - 1)$
$= 4x^2 - 4x + 1$

In studying mathematics, you often find another method of finding an answer. For example, the square of a binomial is shown by a diagram.

Area of the square is shown by
$(y + 3)(y + 3)$
$= (y + 3)^2$

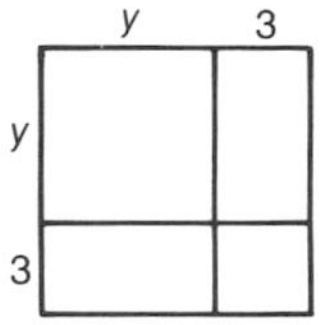

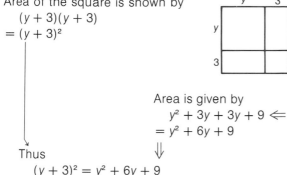

You can show the area by
$\Rightarrow$ finding the area of the parts.
$\Downarrow$

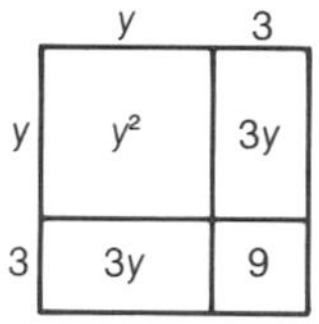


Area is given by
$y^2 + 3y + 3y + 9 \Leftarrow$
$= y^2 + 6y + 9$
$\Downarrow$

Thus
$(y + 3)^2 = y^2 + 6y + 9$

## Try These

1 What are the missing parts?
(a) $(y + 4)^2 = ?(y + 4) + 4(y + 4)$
(b) $(m + 3)^2 = ?(m + 3) + ?(m + 3)$
(c) $(x - 3)^2 = x(?) + ?(x - 3)$
(d) $(p - 2)^2 = ?(p - 2) + ?(p - 2)$

2 In each diagram, what is the area of each part?
(a)

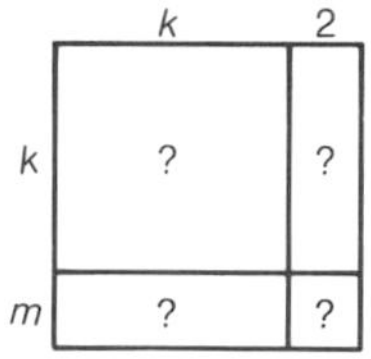


(b)

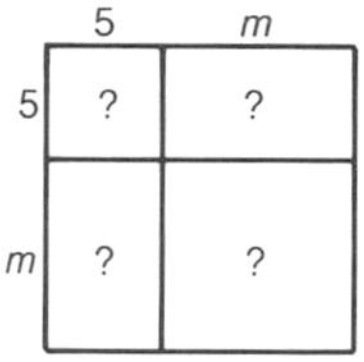


3 What are the missing parts?
(a)

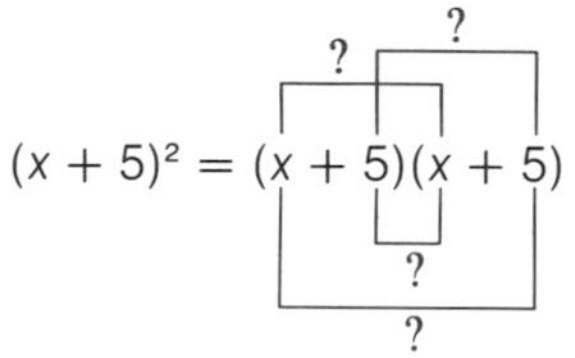


(b)

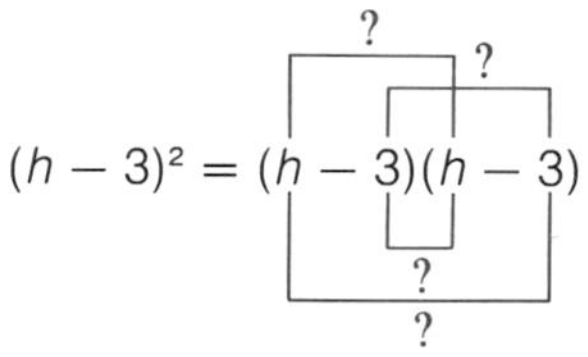


## Written Exercises

**A** Remember: use the distributive property to help you understand how to obtain the product of binomials.

1 Complete each of the following.
(a) $(x + 6)^2 = ?(x + 6) + 6(x + 6)$
(b) $(a + 3)^2 = ?(a + 3) + ?(a + 3)$
(c) $(m - 5)^2 = m(?) - 5(m - 5)$
(d) $(9 - x)^2 = ?(9 - x) - x(?)$

2 A diagram is used to illustrate each binomial square. Find the missing parts for each region.
(a)

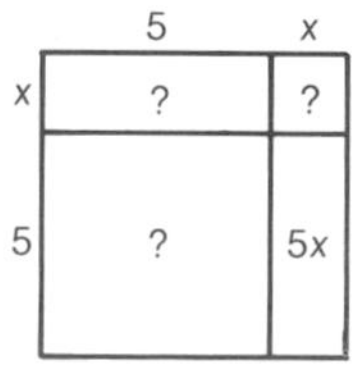


(b)

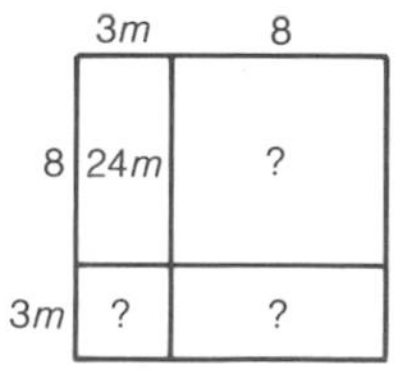

3 Simplify each of the following. Use a diagram to help you.
(a) $(x + 3)^2$ (b) $(2x + 1)^2$
(c) $(x + 3y)^2$ (d) $(2m + 3n)^2$

4 Expand and simplify.
(a) $(x + 2)^2$ (b) $(y + 5)^2$
(c) $(x - 4)^2$ (d) $(k - 8)^2$
(e) $(3m + 1)^2$ (f) $(2a - 1)^2$

**B** To find the squares of binomials, do them mentally.

Expand $(y + 3)^2$ ⇒ Think and write $y^2 + 6y + 9$

5 Find the square of each binomial. Do them mentally.
(a) $(h + 6)^2$ (b) $(y - 2)^2$
(c) $(y - 8)^2$ (d) $(h + 3)^2$
(e) $(2h + 1)^2$ (f) $(2k - 1)^2$
(g) $(3 + p)^2$ (h) $(3 - p)^2$
(i) $(2p + 3)^2$ (j) $(3a - 2)^2$

6 Expand.
(a) $(p + 2)(p + 2)$ (b) $(a - 8)(a - 8)$
(c) $(3q - 2)^2$ (d) $(4m - 3)^2$
(e) $(2p - q)^2$ (f) $(2p - 2q)^2$
(g) $(2a^2 - 3)^2$ (h) $(3p^2 - 5)^2$

7 Simplify each of the following. The first one has been done for you.
(a) $3(y + 2)^2$

$$3(y + 2)^2 = 3(y^2 + 4y + 4) = 3y^2 + 12y + 12$$

(b) $2(m + 2)^2$ (c) $3(p - 2)^2$
(d) $-2(y + 1)^2$ (e) $-3(k - 3)^2$
(f) $3(2t - 1)^2$ (g) $-2(3y + 2)^2$

8 To find each product you need to use your skills with exponents. Find each product.
(a) $3m(m + 1)^2$ (b) $2p(3 + p)^2$
(c) $-4y(y - 4)^2$ (d) $5a(a - 3)^2$
(e) $4c(3 + c)^2$ (f) $-m^2(5 - m)^2$
(g) $p^2(6 + p)^2$ (h) $-4t^2(2t - 2)^2$
(i) $6r(2 + 3r)^2$ (j) $p^3(3 - 2p)^2$

9 (a) Simplify $2(a - 1)^2$.
(b) Simplify $(2a - 1)^2$.
(c) Why do the answers in (a) and (b) differ?

## Math Tip

The method of finding products can be applied to computing mentally. To find the product $25^2$ mentally, we can use the skills in this chapter.

Think mentally.

$$25^2 = (20 + 5)^2 = 20^2 + 2(20)(5) + 5^2 = 400 + 200 + 25 = 625$$

$$58^2 = (60 - 2)^2 = 60^2 + 2(60)(-2) + (-2)^2 = 3600 - 240 + 4 = 3364$$

A Calculate each of the following. How many can you do mentally?
(a) $11^2$ (b) $22^2$ (c) $23^2$
(d) $45^2$ (e) $53^2$ (f) $29^2$
(g) $49^2$ (h) $61^2$ (i) $99^2$

B Calculate each of the following. How many can you do mentally?
(a) $101^2$ (b) $102^2$ (c) $105^2$
(d) $109^2$ (e) $199^2$ (f) $998^2$

## Math Tip

Often in mathematics, a word may be used to suggest a procedure. This memory device may help you remember to pattern a rule for finding the square of a binomial.

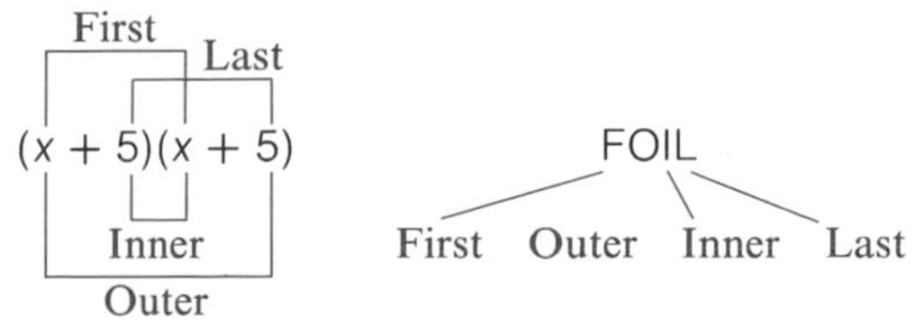

# 3.8 Extending Skills: Multiplying Binomials

In learning mathematics, you acquire a skill, practice it, and then apply it. The steps in learning mathematics are like a chain.

At each step you learn a skill. There are no links missing in the chain.

⇓

You can apply the skills you have learned.

A link is missing in this chain. ⟶ You cannot proceed to the next step.

⇓

You cannot apply the skills successfully.

To find the products of binomials, you can again use your skills with the distributive property to find products.

$$\begin{aligned}(m+2)(m+5) &= m(m+5)+2(m+5)\\ &= m^2+5m+2m+10\\ &= m^2+7m+10\end{aligned}$$

Once you obtain a number of products, you can look for a pattern.

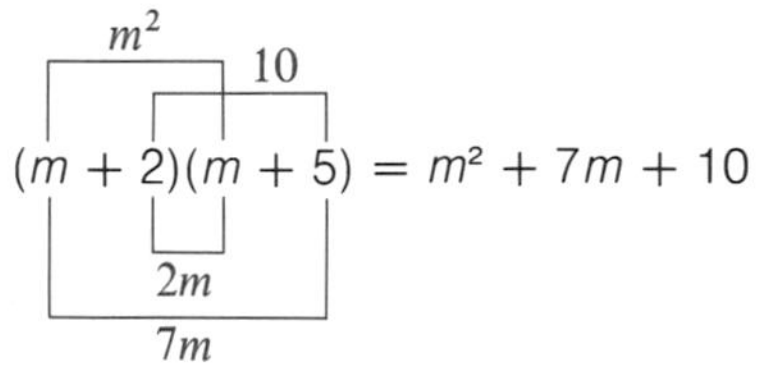


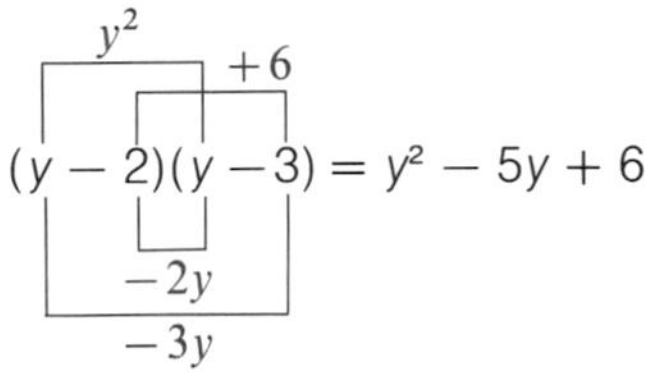


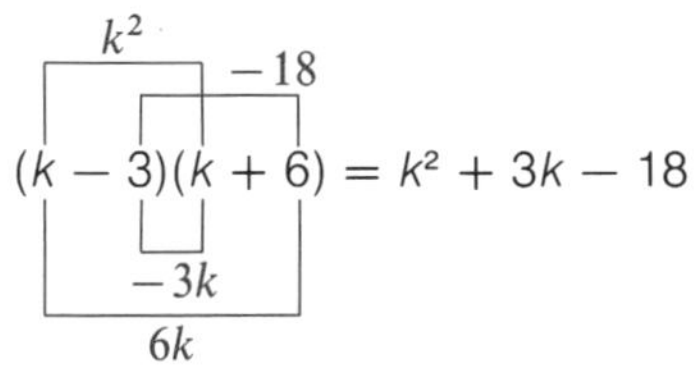


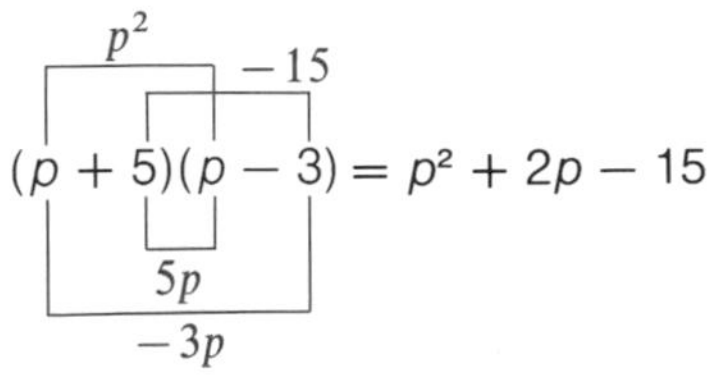


From the examples, you can use the pattern to help you find products mentally and apply them to simplify expressions as shown in the following example. As well, you can apply the square of a binomial.

## Example

(a) Simplify $(x - 3)(x + 2) - (x - 5)^2$

(b) Find the value of the expression for $x = 2$, $x = -3$, $x = 1.5$.

## Solution

(a) $(x - 3)(x + 2) - (x - 5)^2$

$= x^2 - x - 6 - (x^2 - 10x + 25)$ ← find the products mentally

$= x^2 - x - 6 - x^2 + 10x - 25$

$= 9x - 31$

(b) for $x = 2$

$9x - 31 = 9(2) - 31$

$= 18 - 31$

$= -13$

for $x = -3$

$9x - 31 = 9(-3) - 31$

$= -27 - 31$

$= -58$

for $x = 1.5$

$9x - 31 = 9(1.5) - 31$

$= -17.5$

## Try These

1 What are the missing parts?

(a) $(y + 3)(y + 6) = y(y + 6) + ?(y + 6)$

(b) $(y - 3)(y + 6) = ?(y + 6) - 3(y + 6)$

(c) $(y + 3)(y - 6) = y(y - ?) + 3(y - 6)$

(d) $(y - 3)(y - 6) = y(y - 6) - 3(?)$

2 For each diagram, what is the area of each part?

(a)

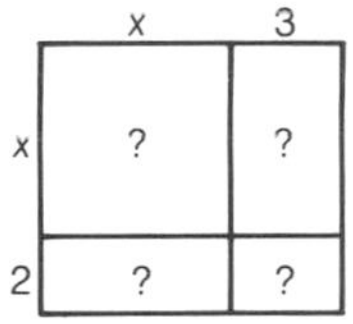


(b)

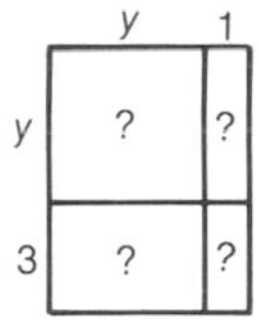


3 What are the missing parts?

(a)

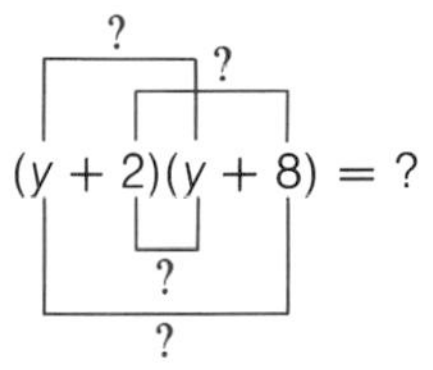


(b)

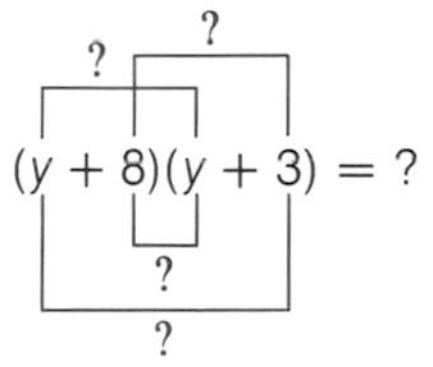


## Written Exercises

**A** To multiply binomials, you must know your skills with integers.

1 Complete each of the following.

(a) $(y + 2)(y - 6) = y(?) + 2(y - 6)$

(b) $(k - 3)(k + 8) = ?(k + 8) - 3(?)$

(c) $(p - 3)(p - 8) = p(?) - 3(?)$

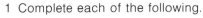

2 For each product of a binomial, a diagram is shown. Use the diagram to help you find each product.

(a) $(x + 3)(x + 5) = ?$ (b) $(x + 6)(x + 6) = ?$

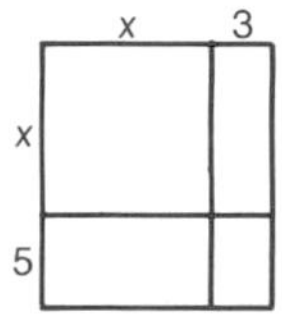


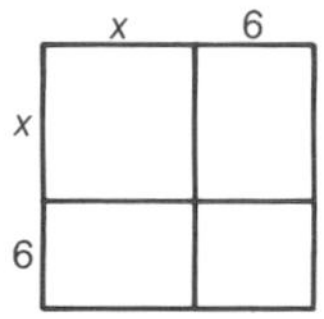

3 Use a diagram to help you find each of the following products.

(a) $(x + 1)(x + 8)$ (b) $(m + 4)(m + 2)$
(c) $(n + 3)(n + 5)$ (d) $(k + 7)(k + 10)$

4 Find the missing term in each of the following.

(a) $(a + 2)(a + 2) = a^2$ ? $+ 2a + 4$
(b) $(m + 3)(m + 1) = m^2 + m$ ? $+ 3$
(c) $(x + 5)(x - 2) = x^2 - 2x$ ? $- 10$
(d) $(k - 2)(k - 1) = k^2$ ? $-2k + 2$
(e) $(p - 3)(2p + 3) =$ ? $+ 3p - 6p - 9$

5 Find each product.

(a) $a(a + 2) + 3(a + 2)$
(b) $p(p - 3) + 5(p - 3)$
(c) $q(q + 1) - 2(q + 1)$
(d) $3a(2a - 3) - 7(2a - 3)$

6 Multiply.

(a) $(a + 2)(a + 5)$ (b) $(m + 1)(m + 4)$
(c) $(y + 6)(y - 4)$ (d) $(y - 4)(y + 1)$
(e) $(f - 3)(f + 2)$ (f) $(y + 8)(y - 8)$

## B

7 Expand and simplify.

(a) $(x + 4)(x + 5)$ (b) $(m + 9)(m - 1)$
(c) $(a + 8)(a - 4)$ (d) $(w - 3)(w + 5)$
(e) $(a - 7)(a + 8)$ (f) $(p + 6)(p - 2)$

8 Find each product.

(a) $(m - 2)(m + 2)$ (b) $(p + 7)(p - 7)$
(c) $(a + b)(a - b)$ (d) $(m + n)(m - n)$

What do you notice about your answers in the above?

9 To find each product, use the same method mentally.

(a) $(3x + 1)(3x + 2)$ Think

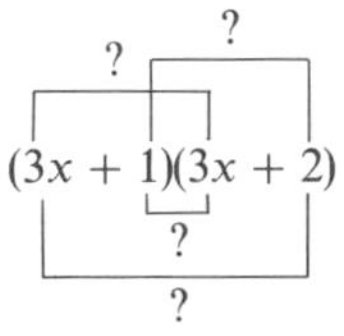


(b) $(2p - 6)(3p + 3)$ (c) $(3b - 2)(2b + 3)$
(d) $(3m + 2)(2m + 1)$ (e) $(2s - 7)(5s + 3)$
(f) $(2s - 3)(4s + 5)$ (g) $(3h - 1)(2h - 3)$

10 Find each product.

(a) $3(m - 3)(m + 4)$ (b) $-2(5 - y)(4 - y)$
(c) $5(2m - 5)(m - 4)$ (d) $-3(2x + 1)(3x + 1)$
(e) $-2y(6 + y)(3 - y)$ (f) $3y(5 - 3y)(1 - y)$

11 Simplify.

(a) $(x - 4)(x + 2) - 2(x - 4)(x + 5)$
(b) $3(2 - y)(3 + y) - 2(y - 1)(y + 2)$
(c) $(a - 2)(2a + 1) + 2(2a + 3)(2a - 1)$
(d) $3(m + 4)(m - 2) - 2(m - 4)(m + 1)$

12 Simplify.

(a) $(x + 5)^2 + 2(x - 2)(x + 3)$
(b) $(y - 2)(y + 5) + 3(y - 3)^2$
(c) $(y - 6)(y - 3) - 3(y - 5)^2$
(d) $(2 + m)(3 - m) + 3(m - 5)^2$
(e) $(3p + 2)(3p + 5) - 2(p - 3)^2$

13 (a) Find the value of the expression for $x = -3$.
$(2x - 3)(x + 5) - 3(x - 2)(x + 1)$
(b) Find the value of the expression for $k = 5$.
$2(k + 6)(k - 3) - 3(k - 2)^2$

14 Find the value of each expression for the value shown,

(a) $(t - 3)(t + 6) - (3t - 2)^2$; $t = 1.5$
(b) $(3k - 1)(3k + 5) - 3(2k - 1)^2$; $k = 2.8$
(c) $2(s - 3)(2s + 1) - 3(s + 5)(s - 2)$; $s = -3.6$

15 The owner of a bicycle shop finds that his daily profit, in dollars, is given by the expression
$(2b + 3)(b - 1) - (b + 1)^2$
where $b$ is the number of bicycles sold.
Find the profit for each value of $b$.

(a) $b = 12$ (b) $b = 20$ (c) $b = 2$
(d) What does your answer in part (c) mean?

16 The value of an antique clock, in dollars, is given by the expression
$2a + 3(a + 3)(a - 1)$
where $a$ is the age of the clock in years.
Find the value of the clock for each value of $a$.

(a) $a = 100$ (b) $a = 200$ (c) $a = 160$

17 The distance, in millimetres, that a glacier moves in a day is given by the expression
$2(c - 6)^2 - (2c + 3)(c - 15)$
where $c$ is the temperature in degrees Celsius.
Find the distance for each value of $c$.

(a) $c = 10$ (b) $c = 0$ (c) $c = -10$

## Applications: Areas and Algebra

18 (a) Find an expression for the area of the rectangle in simplest terms.

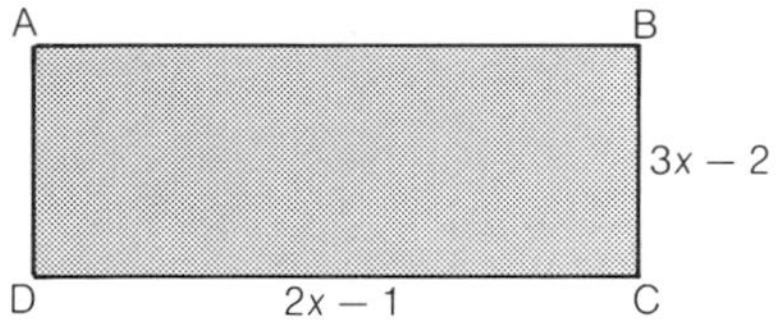


(b) Find the area when $x = 3$.

19 (a) Find the area of each rectangle.

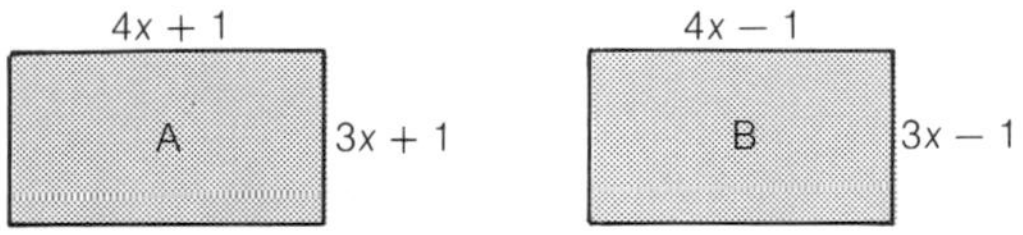


(b) By how much does the area of A exceed that of B?

20 (a) Find the area of a rectangle whose sides, in metres, measure $2x - 3$ by $4x - 2$.

(b) Find the perimeter of the rectangle in (a).

(c) Find the area of a square whose sides, in metres, are $2y - 5$.

21 (a) Find an expression for the area of rectangle ABCD.

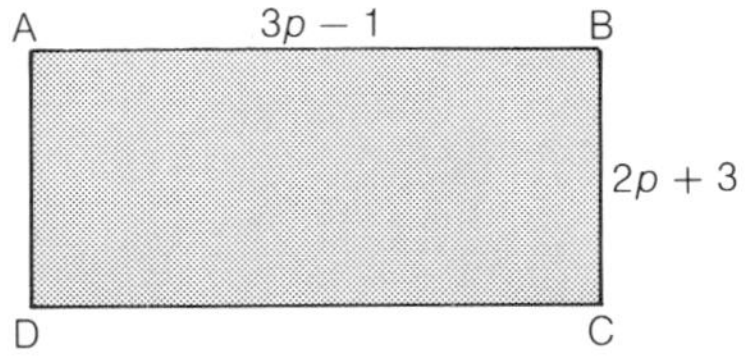


(b) Find an expression for the area of rectangle EFGH.

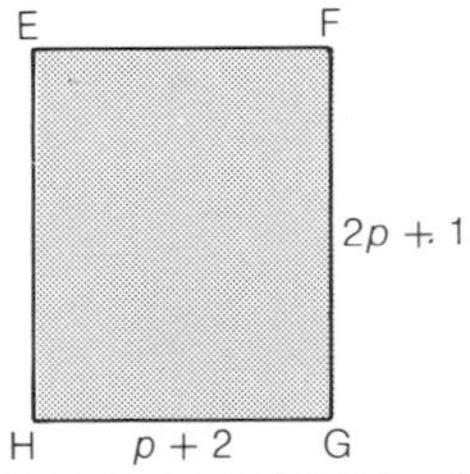


(c) How can the areas in (a) and (b) be used to find an expression for the area of the following floor plan.

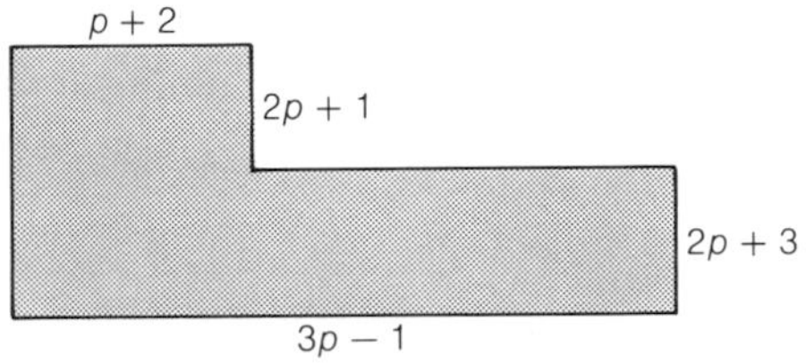


22 (a) Find an expression for the area of the following figure.

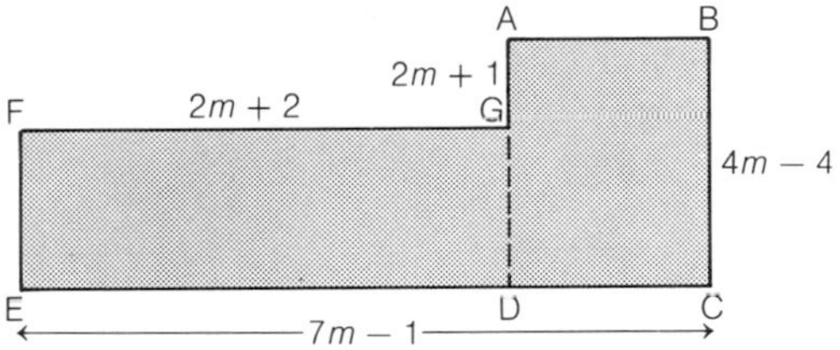


(b) Calculate the area for $m = 2$.

(c) What is a value of $m$ that cannot be substituted into the expression in (a)?

23 Find an expression in simplest terms of the area in each figure.

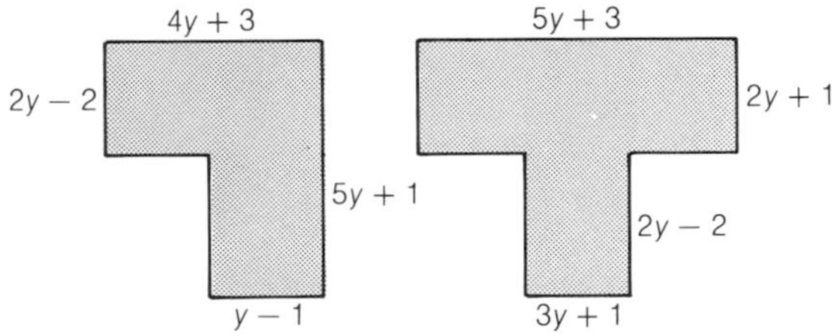


24 (a) Find an expression, in simplest terms, for the area of the shaded region.

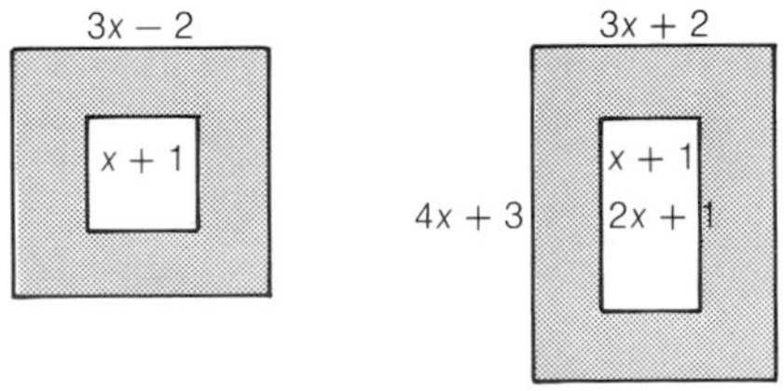


(b) Find each shaded area for $x = 2$.

## Review: Practice and Problems

1 Simplify.
(a) $16m + 3n - (-5m + 2n)$
(b) $4a - 2b + 2c - (6a - 3b - 7c)$
(c) $(2.5p - 1.5q) + (3.6p + 4.8q - p)$

2 (a) Find an expression for the perimeter of this figure.

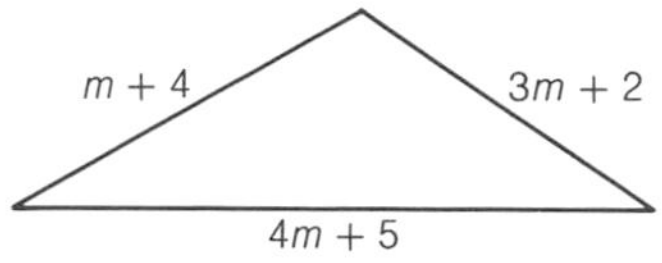


(b) Find the value of the perimeter if $m = 2$.

3 Shirts cost $5p each. How much do each of the following cost?
(a) 3 shirts (b) $q$ shirts
(c) $3q$ shirts (d) $5qr$ shirts

4 Simplify.
(a) $(3m^2)(4m^3)$ (b) $(5x^3)(-5x)$
(c) $(-5y^4)(-3y)^3$ (d) $(-6r^2)(-4r^5)$

5 A rectangular garden has an area of $68mn$ square units. The width is $17n$ units. Find the length of the garden.

6 Simplify.

(a) $\frac{12pq}{p}$ (b) $\frac{-36mn}{-12n}$ (c) $\frac{-68m^2n}{17m}$

7 The profit, $P$, in dollars, for a Chicken Villa is given by the equation
$P = 4(16m - 18) + 3(5m - 2)$
Find the profit, $P$, for
(a) $m = 1$ (b) $m = 12$ (c) $m = 100$

8 Simplify.
(a) $(x + 4)^2$ (b) $(2a - 1)^2$ (c) $(4p + 2)^2$
(d) $(2a - 3b)^2$ (e) $2(m + 1)^2$ (f) $-3(a - 4)^2$

9 (a) Evaluate each expression for $a = -2$ and $b = -5$.
A $3(2a - b) - 4(a + 3b)$
B $-6(3a + 2b) + 2(-5a - b)$
(b) Which has the greater value, A or B?

## A Practice Test

1 Simplify.
(a) $7m - 4n + 5m - 6n$
(b) $9m + 2n - 12n + 3n$
(c) $3a - 2b + 6c - (a - b + c)$
(d) $3(a - 2b) + 4(a + 3b)$

2 Which of the following expressions is closer in value to 5 when $a = -4$ and $b = 3$?
(a) $5a - 3b - 7a - (3a - 9b) - (a + 6b)$
(b) $(8a - 2b) - (-3a + b) - 2a - 7b$

3 (a) Find an expression for the area and for the perimeter of the rectangle.

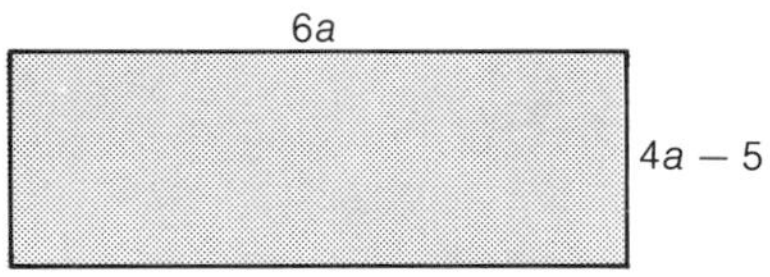


(b) Find the area for $a = 3$.
(c) Find the perimeter for $a = 5$.

4 (a) Simplify each product.
A $(-4p^2q^2)^2(3pq^3)$
B $(5pq^4)(-p^2q)(pq)$
(b) Which expression in (a) has the greater value when $p = 3$ and $q = -2$?

5 The area of a rectangle is $12mn^3$ square units.
(a) If the length is $6mn^2$ units, find an expression for the width.
(b) If $m = 3$ and $n = 2$, find the
(i) width (ii) length

6 Find each product.
(a) $-3(2x + 3)(3x - 4)$ (b) $2x(x + 5)(x - 7)$
(c) $-2p(6 - 2p)(1 - p)$ (d) $-4m^2(3 - 2m)(5 + 3m)$
(e) $-8(4 - 2p)^2$ (f) $(a - 4)^2 - 3(3 + a)^2$

7 (a) Simplify first, then evaluate the values for $a = 5$, $b = 3$.
$2(a - b)(a + 3b) - 4(a + b)(2a - 3b)$
(b) Which has the greater value for $m = -4$, $n = 3$.
A $(m - n)^2 - (m + n)^2$
B $(m + 2n)^2 - 2(m - n)^2$

# 4 Methods of Factoring: Applications

finding common factors, developing methods, factoring trinomials, problem-solving, using patterns, difference of squares, organizing skills, using clues, simplifying expressions, multiplying and dividing expressions, solving problems and applications

## Introduction

It has been often said mathematics is a study of symbols. Symbols are not new to you since you need to use them constantly. What do the following symbols mean? Where might you find these symbols?

In mathematics you also use symbols to replace words or provide information. For this reason you must clearly understand the significance of each symbol and how it is used. Completing a problem successfully may depend on you remembering the meaning of a specific symbol.

As you learn new skills and concepts you increase your vocabulary which enables you to make further progress in mathematics. New words lead to the use of new symbols. Many symbols in mathematics are used in everyday situations. For example, the stroke is used to mean "not".

No Smoking

$\neq$

Not Equal

In your study of mathematics and its symbols you will acquire a variety of strategies and methods of doing mathematics, and of solving problems. You will often encounter the following process in the study of mathematics. Be aware of this process!

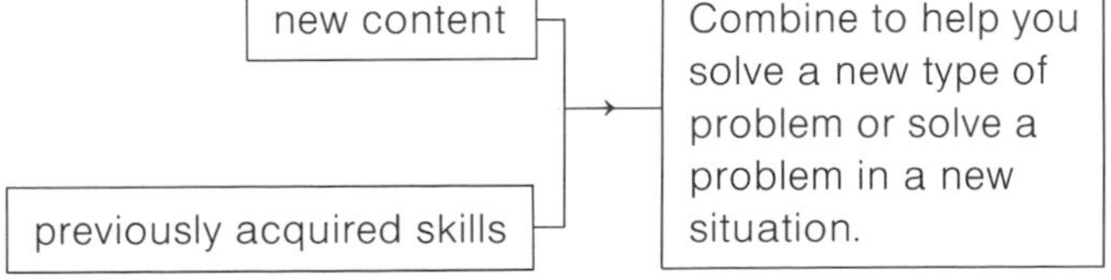

# 4.1 Using Common Factors

Often amazing number tricks performed by people are based on mathematics. For example, to calculate this expression mentally, at first glance, seems difficult.

$36 \times 70 + 36 \times 30$

The expression can be rewritten to simplify the calculation as follows.

$$\begin{aligned} 36 \times 70 + 36 \times 30 &= 36(70 + 30) \\ &= 36(100) \\ &= 3600 \end{aligned}$$

To do the calculation, the original expression was rewritten as a product. To factor means to write as a product. Skills with factoring are used in doing calculations as well as simplifying expressions in algebra.

Expanding and factoring are related.

To expand: write as a sum or difference ⟹

$3(m + n) = 3m + 3n$

(3 and $(m + n)$ are factors; $3m$ and $3n$ are terms)

To factor: write as a product ⟸

$3(m + n) = 3m + 3n$

3 is said to be a common factor of each term ($3m$ and $3n$ are terms)

When you are asked to factor an expression, you find the greatest common factor.

5 is a common factor of $5a^2b + 5ab^2$.

$5ab$ is the greatest common factor of $5a^2b + 5ab^2$.

$5a^2b + 5ab^2 = 5ab(a + b)$ ← $5ab$: greatest common factor

### Example 1

Factor each expression.

(a) $4m + 4n$ (b) $10xy^2 - 5x^2y$ (c) $3c^2 + 12c^4$

### Solution

Remember: look for the greatest common factor.

(a) $4m + 4n$
$= 4(m + n)$

(b) $10xy^2 - 5x^2y$
$= 5xy(2y - x)$

Always check whether the expression can be factored again.

(c) $3c^2 + 12c^4$
$= 3c^2(1 + 4c^2)$

$3c^2$ is the greatest common factor

Finding a common factor is useful in reducing the number of calculations needed to evaluate an expression.

### Example 2

Calculate $\frac{1}{2}ah + \frac{1}{2}bh$ where $a = 2.25$, $b = 3.82$ and $h = 4.00$.

### Solution

$\frac{1}{2}ah + \frac{1}{2}bh$ — Always record the original expression.

$= \frac{1}{2}h(a + b)$

$= \frac{1}{2}(4.00)(2.25 + 3.82)$ — In this factored form, you can do the calculation directly with a calculator.

$= 12.14$ — [C] 2.25 [+] 3.82 [×] 4.00 [÷] 2 [=] 12.14

## Try These

1 Expand.
(a) $3(m + n)$ (b) $5(p - q)$
(c) $2x(x + y)$ (d) $-3f(f + g)$
(e) $-3y(y - 3)$ (f) $2x^2(1 - x)$

2 What is the missing factor?
(a) $5a - 10 = ( \ ? \ )(a - 2)$
(b) $6a - 12b = 6( \ ? \ )$
(c) $4ab - 12ac = 4a( \ ? \ )$
(d) $2x^2 - 4x = 2x( \ ? \ )$

## Written Exercises

**A** Remember: look for the greatest common factor.

1 (a) Find the missing factor.
$3a + 21 = ( \ ? \ )(a + 7)$
(b) Check your answer by multiplying.

2 (a) Find the missing factor.
$10x - 30y = ( \ ? \ )(x - 3y)$
(b) Check your answer by multiplying.

3 Find the missing factor in each.
(a) $ab - ac = a( \ ? \ )$
(b) $15mp + 5mn = 5m( \ ? \ )$
(c) $21x^2y - 30xy^2 = ( \ ? \ )(7x - 10y)$
(d) $-18m^3 + 6m^2 = ( \ ? \ )(-3m + 1)$

4 Factor. Check your answer.
(a) $3b + ab$ (b) $mn + np$
(c) $8a + 4b$ (d) $7d - 14e^2$
(e) $ab + 6a$ (f) $bc - 3bd$
(g) $p^2 + pr$ (h) $15x^3 - 10x$

5 Factor.
(a) $10ab - 15bc$ (b) $7p^2 - 14p$
(c) $3m^4 - 12m^3$ (d) $-12pq - 48p$
(e) $8r^3 - 24r^2$ (f) $9f^2 - 27$

6 (a) Find the value of $3a^2b - 2ab^2$ for $a = 4$ and $b = 6$.
(b) Find the value of $ab(3a - 2b)$ for $a = 4$ and $b = 6$.
(c) Which has fewer calculations (a) or (b)?

**B** Remember: check your factors by multiplying.

7 Evaluate each of the following for $x = -2$, $y = 2$.
(a) $6xy - 48x$ (b) $6x^3 - 8x^2y$
(c) $4x^3 - 8x^2$ (d) $6x^2y - 12x^3y^2$
(e) $12x^2 + 24x^2y$ (f) $3xy - 12y^2$
(g) $6x^3y + 12xy^2$ (h) $24x^3y - 18x^2y^2$

8 (a) Factor the expression $6ab - 12ac$.
(b) Find the value of the expression in (a). Use $a = 5.2$, $b = 3.4$ and $c = 2.1$.

9 Factor each expression. Then evaluate the expression.
(a) $5m^2n - 15mn^2$ $m = 4, n = 2$
(b) $-3p^2q^2 - 9pq$ $p = 2, q = 3$
(c) $12a^3b + 24a^2b^2$ $a = 5, b = 4$

10 (a) What factor is common to each term?
$m^3 - 2m^2 + 5m$
(b) Write the expression in (a) in factored form.

11 Find the missing factors.
(a) $a^4 - 3a^3 + 5a^2 = a^2(\ ?\ )$
(b) $10pq - 5p^2q + 20p = 5p(\ ?\ )$
(c) $16a^2b^2c - 48abc - 32a$
$= (\ ?\ )(ab^2c - 3bc - 2)$
(d) $-4p^2q^2 + 8p^2q - 12pq$
$= (\ ?\ )(-pq + 2p - 3)$

12 Factor each of the following.
(a) $m^2 + 12mn - m$ (b) $4p^2 - 16p - 12$
(c) $25a^2 + 75ab + 50b^2$
(d) $8m^2n - 4mn^2 - 12n$

13 The total value of an investment is given by the expression
$P + 0.14P$
(a) Factor the expression.
(b) Use the factored form in (a). Calculate the value for $P = \$369.85$.

14 The total cost of the tickets is given by the expression
$8.65n + 4.75n$
Calculate the cost for $n = 126$.

15 The perimeter of a rectangle is given by
$2l + 2w$ where
$l$, length
$w$, width

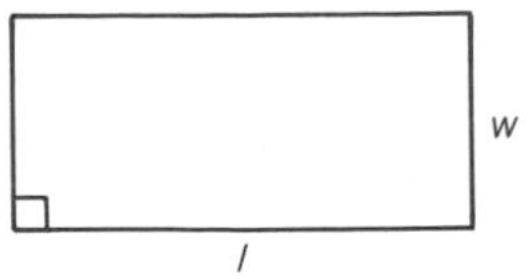


(a) Write an expression for the perimeter in factored form.
(b) Find the value of the perimeter for $l = 9.25$ and $w = 5.63$. Use a calculator.
(c) Find the perimeter for each of the following.
(i) $l = 152$, $w = 93$
(ii) $l = 64.7$, $w = 39.4$
(iii) $l = 139.6$, $w = 94.9$

16 To find the sum shown by
$1 + 2 + 3 + 4 + \cdots + n$ ← There are $n$ numbers.
You can use the expression
$$\frac{n^2 + n}{2}.$$
(a) Write the expression in a factored form.
(b) Find the sum of
$1 + 2 + 3 + 4 + \cdots + 50$
(c) Find the sum of
$1 + 2 + 3 + 4 + \cdots + 100$

17 Calculate each of the following. (Look for a common factor).
(a) $39 \times 58 + 39 \times 42$
(b) $56 \times 1.75 + 56 \times 8.25$
(c) $84.5 \times 39 + 84.5 \times 61$
(d) $143.7 \times 3.4 + 143.7 \times 6.6$
(e) $0.9 \times 617 + 0.9 \times 383$

## Computer Tip

Write a BASIC computer program to calculate,
$1 + 2 + 3 + 4 + \cdots + n$ for any number $n$.
Hint: refer to the formula given in question 16.

## Calculator Tip

Lost the instruction book? Borrowing a strange calculator? Test how the machine operates by using easy calculations that you can find the answer to mentally.

# 4.2 Developing Methods: Factoring

Often methods you use in mathematics are also the same methods you use to solve problems in other subjects. For example, to develop a method to factor an expression such as $4a^2 + 12a + 9$, you use the steps shown.

Step A

> Examine the results for various examples for which you know the answer.

Step B

> Use the results from Step A to develop a method to factor an expression such as $4a^2 + 12a + 9$.

In your previous work, you learned how to find these products. (Step A)

| Square | Factored Form | Expanded Form |
|---|---|---|
| $(a + 1)^2$ | $(a + 1)(a + 1)$ | $a^2 + 2a + 1$ |
| $(a - 1)^2$ | $(a - 1)(a - 1)$ | $a^2 - 2a + 1$ |
| $(2a + 3)^2$ | $(2a + 3)(2a + 3)$ | $4a^2 + 12a + 9$ |

An expression such as $a^2 + 2a + 1$ is called a **trinomial square** since $a^2 + 2a + 1 = (a + 1)^2$

The trinomial can be written as a square.

To find the factors of the trinomial, you examine the terms and work backwards.

Examine the example. (Step A)

$4a^2$ 9

$$4a^2 + 12a + 9 = (2a + 3)(2a + 3)$$

$6a$

$6a$

Develop a method. (Step B)

Think: Step 1

$4a^2 + 12a + 9 = (2a \quad )(2a \quad )$

Think: Step 2

$4a^2 + 12a + 9 = (2a \quad 3)(2a \quad 3)$

Think: Step 3

$4a^2 + 12a + 9 = (2a + 3)(2a + 3) = (2a + 3)^2$

**Example 1**

Factor. $25h^2 - 10h + 1$

**Solution**

think

$25h^2 - 10h + 1 = (5h - 1)(5h - 1) = (5h - 1)^2$

think

Check: $(5h - 1)(5h - 1) = 25h^2 - 10h + 1$

checks ✓

When you factor, always check whether there is a common factor.

**Example 2**

Factor $8a^2 + 8ab + 2b^2$.

**Solution**

$8a^2 + 8ab + 2b^2$ ← 2 is a common factor of each term

$= 2(4a^2 + 4ab + b^2)$

$= 2(2a + b)(2a + b)$

## Try These

1 Each is a trinomial square. What is the missing term?

(a) $a^2 + 4a + ?$ (b) $a^2 - 6a + ?$
(c) $a^2 + 2ab + ?$ (d) $a^2 - 2ab + ?$
(e) $a^2 + 4ab + ?$ (f) $a^2 - 4ab + ?$

2 Express each square as a trinomial.

(a) $(x - 3)^2$ (b) $(y + 4)^2$
(c) $(k + 6)^2$ (d) $(2x - 3)^2$
(e) $(3y - x)^2$ (f) $(2a + 3b)^2$
(g) $(5a + 2b)^2$ (h) $(3x - 2y)^2$

## Written Exercises

**A** Remember the form of a trinomial square.

$(a + b)^2 = a^2 + 2ab + b^2$
$(a - b)^2 = a^2 - 2ab + b^2$

1 What are the missing terms?

(a) $(a + b)^2 = ? + 2ab + b^2$
(b) $(a - b)^2 = a^2 - 2ab + ?$
(c) $(a + 6)^2 = a^2 \; ? + 36$
(d) $(a - 6)^2 = ? - 12a + 36$
(e) $(2a + b)^2 = 4a^2 \; ? + b^2$
(f) $(2a - b)^2 = 4a^2 \; ? + b^2$

2 What are the missing terms?

(a) $a^2 + 4a + 4 = (a + ?)^2$
(b) $y^2 - 6y + 9 = (y - ?)^2$
(c) $4x^2 - 4x + 1 = (2x - ?)^2$
(d) $9k^2 + 6k + 1 = (3k + ?)^2$
(e) $4p^2 - 12p + 9 = (2p - ?)^2$
(f) $9t^2 + 12t + 4 = (3t + ?)^2$

3 Find the value of ▨ for each to be a trinomial square.

(a) $x^2 - 4x +$ ▨ (b) $y^2 +$ ▨$y + 16$
(c) ▨ $- 4y + y^2$ (d) $9 +$ ▨$k + k^2$
(e) $x^2 + 4xy +$ ▨$y^2$ (f) ▨$a^2 - 6ab + 9b^2$
(g) $4p^2 +$ ▨$pq + q^2$ (h) $s^2 - 6st +$ ▨$t^2$

**B** Remember: Before you factor, always check for a common factor.

4 Express each trinomial as a square.

(a) $m^2 - 10m + 25$ (b) $a^2 + 4a + 4$
(c) $x^2 - 6x + 9$ (d) $x^2 - 6xy + 9y^2$
(e) $4a^2 + 4ab + b^2$ (f) $9 - 24y + 16y^2$
(g) $9a^2 - 12ab + 4b^2$ (h) $x^2 - 12xy + 36y^2$
(i) $81 - 36y + 4y^2$ (j) $25p^2 + 20pq + 4q^2$

5 Factor. Did you check for common factors first?

(a) $m^2 + 10m + 25$ (b) $3y^2 - 18y + 27$
(c) $a^2 + 6ab + 9b^2$ (d) $9ax^2 + 12ax + 4a$
(e) $4x^3 + 4x^2 + x$ (f) $4y^2 - 4xy + x^2$
(g) $9a^2 - 24a + 16$ (h) $y^3 - 6y^2 + 9y$
(i) $9m^2n - 12mn^2 + 4n^3$
(j) $25a^2 - 10a + 1$

6 Use $x = 3$, and $y = 5$.

(a) Find the value of $x^2 + 2xy + y^2$.
(b) Find the value of $(x + y)^2$.
(c) Which answer (a) or (b) was more easily obtained?

7 Use $m = 3.5$, and $n = 4.2$.

(a) Find the value of $4m^2 - 4mn + n^2$.
(b) Find the value of $(2m - n)^2$.
(c) Which answer (a) or (b) was more easily obtained?

8 Use the values shown. Evaluate $m^2 + 6mn + 9n^2$.

(a) $m = 3, n = 2$ (b) $m = 4, n = -3$
(c) $m = 1.5, n = 0.8$ (d) $m = 4.3, n = -2.3$

9 Use the values shown. Evaluate $9a^2 - 12ab + 4b^2$.

(a) $a = 3, b = -2$ (b) $a = 1.5, b = -0.5$
(c) $a = 3.6, b = 2.9$ (d) $a = 1.25, b = 1.16$

10 Evaluate each expression. Use the values of the variables shown.

(a) $a^2 + 4ab + 4b^2$ $a = 3, b = -2$
(b) $x^2 - 6xy + 9y^2$ $x = 3.2, y = 1.6$

# 4.3 Factoring Trinomials

To solve problems, an important method is to use the known to develop a strategy for solving the unknown. For example,

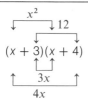

| Known | Unknown |
|---|---|
| You know how to find the product of binomials. | You want to develop a method to find the factors of any trinomial. |

$x^2$ 12

$(x+3)(x+4)$

$3x$

$4x$

Ask: how is each term obtained in the trinomial?

$x^2 + 7x + 12$

$(x)(x)$ $3x$ $(3)(4)$

$+4x$

$7x$

To factor a trinomial, you ask two important questions.

What two numbers have this sum? What two numbers have this product?

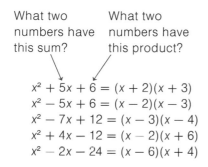

$$x^2 + 5x + 6 = (x + 2)(x + 3)$$
$$x^2 - 5x + 6 = (x - 2)(x - 3)$$
$$x^2 - 7x + 12 = (x - 3)(x - 4)$$
$$x^2 + 4x - 12 = (x - 2)(x + 6)$$
$$x^2 - 2x - 24 = (x - 6)(x + 4)$$

The answers to the two questions help you write the factors.

| Sum | Product | Numbers |
|---|---|---|
| +5 | +6 | +2, +3 |
| −5 | +6 | −2, −3 |
| −7 | +12 | −3, −4 |
| +4 | −12 | −2, +6 |
| −2 | −24 | −6, +4 |

### Example 1

Factor each of the following.

(a) $x^2 + x - 6$ (b) $t^2 - 7t - 30$

### Solution

(a) $x^2 + x - 6 = (x + 3)(x - 2)$

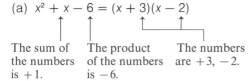

The sum of the numbers is +1. The product of the numbers is −6. The numbers are +3, −2.

(b) $t^2 - 7t - 30 = (t - 10)(t + 3)$

The sum of the numbers is −7. The product of the numbers is −30. The numbers are −10 and +3.

The same questions are asked when there is more than 1 variable, as shown in the following example.

### Example 2

Factor each of the following.

(a) $a^2 + 6ab + 9b^2$ (b) $x^2 - xy - 30y^2$

### Solution

(a) $a^2 + 6ab + 9b^2 = (a + 3b)(a + 3b)$ $\quad b^2 = b \times b$

The sum of the numbers is +6. The product is +9. The numbers are +3 and +3.

(b) $x^2 - xy - 30y^2 = (x - 6y)(x + 5y)$

The sum of the numbers is −1. The product is −30. The numbers are −6 and +5.

## Try These

1 What is the missing factor?
 (a) $a^2 - 3a + 2 = (a - 2)(\ ?\ )$
 (b) $p^2 - 8p + 12 = (\ ?\ )(p - 2)$
 (c) $x^2 - 7x + 12 = (x - 4)(\ ?\ )$
 (d) $m^2 - 14m + 49 = (x - 7)(\ ?\ )$

2 What is the missing term?
 (a) $a^2\ ? - 10 = (a - 5)(a + 2)$
 (b) $m^2 - m\ ? = (m - 2)(m + 1)$
 (c) $t^2\ ? - 24 = (t - 6)(t + 4)$
 (d) $? + 3x - 4 = (x + 4)(x - 1)$
 (e) $k^2 + 4k\ ? = (k + 7)(k - 3)$

## Written Exercises

**A** Remember: to factor trinomials, you ask two important questions as shown in the first question.

1 Write two numbers whose
 (a) product is +15 and sum is −8.
 (b) product is −32 and sum is −4.
 (c) product is −18 and sum is −3.
 (d) product is −96 and sum is −4.
 (e) product is −60 and sum is +4.

2 What two numbers have each sum and product?

| | Sum | Product |
|---|---|---|
| (a) | +7 | +12 |
| (b) | −5 | +6 |
| (c) | −9 | +20 |
| (d) | −3 | −18 |
| (e) | +3 | −40 |
| (f) | −9 | +18 |
| (g) | −2 | −35 |

3 (a) What two numbers have a product of 20 and a sum of −9?
 (b) Use your answer in (a) to write the factor of $m^2 - 9m + 20 = (m\ \ ?)(m\ \ ?)$.

4 (a) What two numbers have a product of −14 and a sum of −5?
 (b) Use your answer in (a) to write the factors of $y^2 - 5y - 14 = (y\ \ ?)(y\ \ ?)$.

5 (a) What two numbers have a product of −30 and a sum of +1?
 (b) Use your answer in (a) to write the factors of $x^2 + x - 30 = (x\ \ ?)(x\ \ ?)$.

6 Find the missing factors.
 (a) $x^2 - 11x + 30 = (x - 5)(\ ?\ )$
 (b) $x^2 - 5x + 4 = (x - 1)(\ ?\ )$
 (c) $a^2 + 6a + 5 = (\ ?\ )(a + 1)$
 (d) $p^2 + 4p - 5 = (p + 5)(\ ?\ )$
 (e) $y^2 - 2y - 8 = (\ ?\ )(y - 4)$

**B** Remember: to check your factors, find the product.

7 Factor each trinomial.
(a) $f^2 - 3f - 10$ (b) $d^2 + d - 6$
(c) $p^2 - p - 2$ (d) $r^2 + 4r + 4$
(e) $y^2 + 10y + 9$ (f) $t^2 - 2t - 24$
(g) $t^2 + 2t - 48$ (h) $x^2 - 11x + 18$
(i) $t^2 - 9t + 20$ (j) $h^2 + 8h + 12$
(k) $c^2 + 14c + 33$ (l) $m^2 - 11m + 30$

8 Write as the product of two factors.
(a) $25 - 10p + p^2$ (b) $18 - 9f + f^2$
(c) $9 - 10d + d^2$ (d) $96 - 20t + t^2$

9 Factor.
(a) $a^2 - 13ab + 40b^2$ (b) $f^2 - 11fg + 28g^2$
(c) $x^2 - 12xy - 85y^2$ (d) $p^2 - 5pq - 50q^2$
(e) $d^2 - 3de + 2e^2$ (f) $a^2 - 10ab + 25b^2$
(g) $m^2 - 6mn - 27n^2$ (h) $d^2 - de - 12e^2$

10 Factor. Check for a common factor first.
(a) $3m^2 + 9m + 6$ (b) $2x^2 + 2x - 4$
(c) $2a^2 + 8a + 8$ (d) $3y^2 + 24y + 48$
(e) $5a^2 + 10a + 5$ (f) $2y^2 - 18y + 40$
(g) $4x^2 + 16x - 20$ (h) $x^3 - 2x^2 - 48x$

11 Factor.
(a) $x^2 + 15x - 54$ (b) $x^2 - 9x + 20$
(c) $m^2 - 13m + 42$ (d) $m^2 + 14m - 51$
(e) $p^2 + 29p + 54$ (f) $f^2 - 9fg - 90g^2$
(g) $y^2 - 3yz - 10z^2$ (h) $25 - 10p + p^2$
(i) $18 - 9a + a^2$ (j) $4f^2 - 4f + 1$
(k) $d^2 - 7d + 12$ (l) $4b^2 + 44b - 104$
(m) $2n^2 + 22n + 36$ (n) $20 - 12g + g^2$

12 Use $x = 4$ and $y = -2$.
(a) Find the value of $x^2 + 2xy - 48y^2$
(b) Find the value of $(x - 6y)(x + 8y)$
(c) Which answer (a) or (b) was more readily obtained?

13 Use $p = 4.8$ and $q = 3.2$.
(a) Find the value of $p^2 + 16pq + 48q^2$.
(b) Find the value of $(p + 4q)(p + 12q)$.
(c) Which answer (a) or (b) was more readily obtained?

14 Use the values shown.
Evaluate $m^2 - 10mn + 9n^2$.
(a) $m = 4, n = -3$ (b) $m = 8, n = -6$
(c) $m = 4.6, n = -3.1$ (d) $m = 1.25, n = 1.10$

15 Evaluate each expression. Use the values of the variables shown.
(a) $m^2 + 6mn + 8n^2$ $m = 6, n = -3$
(b) $a^2 - ab - 2b^2$ $a = 16, b = 12$
(c) $p^2 - pq - 20q^2$ $p = 4.6, q = -1.9$

16 The area and dimensions of various rectangles are shown in the chart. Find the missing dimensions.

| | Area | Length | Width |
|---|---|---|---|
| (a) | $b^2 - 15b + 56$ | $(b - 8)$ | ? |
| (b) | $x^2 + 8x + 12$ | $(x + 6)$ | ? |
| (c) | $y^2 - 3y - 10$ | ? | $(y - 5)$ |
| (d) | $x^2 - 18x + 45$ | ? | $(x - 3)$ |

17 (a) A rectangular field has an area represented by the expression $x^2 + 10x - 24$. If the length is represented by the expression $x + 12$, find an expression for the width.
(b) A square field has an area represented by $a^2 + 8a + 16$. Find an expression for its length of side.

18 Distance is given by speed × time.
Find the missing expressions in the table.

| | Distance | Speed | Time |
|---|---|---|---|
| (a) | $y^2 + 6y + 8$ | $(y + 4)$ | ? |
| (b) | $h^2 - 8h + 12$ | ? | $(h - 2)$ |
| (c) | $m^2 + 10m - 11$ | $(m - 1)$ | ? |
| (d) | $t^2 - 2t - 48$ | ? | $(t - 8)$ |

19 The product of $I$ and $R$ is used to find a value for $V$. (Namely $V = I \times R$) Find the missing expressions in the chart.

| | $V$ | $I$ | $R$ |
|---|---|---|---|
| (a) | $a^2 + 20a + 100$ | $(a + 10)$ | ? |
| (b) | $m^2 + 15m + 54$ | ? | $(m + 6)$ |
| (c) | $p^2 + 16p + 64$ | $(p + 8)$ | ? |
| (d) | $f^2 - 13f + 36$ | ? | $(f - 9)$ |

# 4.4 Problem Solving Strategy: Using Patterns

Often in using factoring skills you need to recognize when to use a particular skill. In multiplying these binomials, you obtained a pattern.

Compare the form of the binomials. → A **difference of squares** is obtained.

$$(x+2)(x-2) = x^2 - 4$$
$$(x+y)(x-y) = x^2 - y^2$$
$$(x+2y)(x-2y) = x^2 - 4y^2$$
$$(2m+3)(2m-3) = 4m^2 - 9$$

different signs

To find the factors of a difference of squares you can use the known results to develop a method.

Difference of squares → $x^2 - 4 = (x)^2 - (2)^2 = (x+2)(x-2)$ ← Factors of a difference of squares

compare

$x^2 - 4y^2 = (x)^2 - (2y)^2 = (x+2y)(x-2y)$

compare

To find the factors of $p^2 - 16q^2$, you can use the pattern

$$p^2 - 16q^2 = (p)^2 - (4q)^2 = (p+4q)(p-4q)$$

Step 1: write the terms as squares. Step 2: write the factors.

To factor a difference of squares think about the following form.

$$a^2 - b^2 = (a+b)(a-b)$$

Each term is a square. The signs are different.

The terms in each factor are the same except for the operation sign.

### Example 1

Factor. (a) $9m^2 - 1$ (b) $25p^2 - 16q^2$

### Solution

Think: recognize the form of a difference of squares.

(a) $9m^2 - 1$
$= (3m)^2 - (1)^2$
$= (3m+1)(3m-1)$

(b) $25p^2 - 16q^2$
$= (5p)^2 - (4q)^2$
$= (5p+4q)(5p-4q)$

After you factor an expression, check whether the expressions are factored completely. In the next example, you can factor again.

**Example 2**

Factor completely $x^4 - 81$.

**Solution**

$x^4 - 81$ ⟵ Think $x^4 - 81 = (x^2)^2 - (9)^2$
Then write the factors

$= (x^2 + 9)(x^2 - 9)$ ⟵ Check the factors: $x^2 - 9$ can be factored again.

$= (x^2 + 9)(x + 3)(x - 3)$

## Try These

1 What are the products?
(a) $(m + 2)(m - 2)$
(b) $(p + 3)(p - 3)$
(c) $(n - 10)(n + 10)$
(d) $(1 - a)(1 + a)$

2 What are the products?
(a) $(a - 2b)(a + 2b)$
(b) $(2m + 3)(2m - 3)$
(c) $(p - 2q)(p + 2q)$

3 What are the missing factors?
(a) $a^2 - 9 = (a - 3)(\ ?\ )$
(b) $p^2 - 25 = (\ ?\ )(p + 5)$
(c) $m^2 - 49 = (m + 7)(\ ?\ )$
(d) $1 - n^2 = (\ ?\ )(1 - n)$

## Written Exercises

**A** Remember: First write each term of a difference of squares in the form
$a^2 - b^2 = (a)^2 - (b)^2$.

1 An important skill is to recognize squares. Which of the following are squares?
(a) $9k^2$ (b) $25x^2$ (c) $16m^2$ (d) $48x^2$
(e) $4t^2$ (f) $36m^4$ (g) $18m^2$ (h) $100k$
(i) $x^2y^2$ (j) $4ab$ (k) $49R^2$ (l) $26n$

2 To write factors for a difference of squares, you need to write terms as squares. Find the missing parts.
(a) $x^2 - 25 = (x)^2 - (?)^2$
(b) $m^2 - 4n^2 = (m)^2 - (?)^2$
(c) $a^2 - 9b^2 = (a)^2 - (?)^2$
(d) $9m^2 - n^2 = (?)^2 - (n)^2$
(e) $p^2 - 16 = (p)^2 - (?)^2$
(f) $a^2 - 25b^2 = (a)^2 - (?)^2$

3 Find the missing parts.
(a) $49 - 36p^2 = (?)^2 - (?)^2$
(b) $4m^2 - 81n^2 = (?)^2 - (?)^2$
(c) $16x^2 - 36y^2 = (?)^2 - (?)^2$

4 (a) Find the missing parts.
$x^2 - 16y^2 = (?)^2 - (?)^2$
(b) Write the factors of the expression in (a).

5 (a) Find the missing parts.
$4a^2 - 25b^2 = (?)^2 - (?)^2$
(b) Write the factors of the expression in (a).

6 Find the missing factors.
(a) $x^2 - 16m^2 = (x - 4m)(\ ?\ )$
(b) $25y^2 - x^2 = (\ ?\ )(5y + x)$
(c) $a^2 - 9b^2 = (a - 3b)(\ ?\ )$
(d) $16k^2 - 1 = (\ ?\ )(4k + 1)$
(e) $4k^2 - 9m^2 = (2k - 3m)(\ ?\ )$
(f) $9x^2 - 49y^2 = (\ ?\ )(3x + 7y)$

**B** Remember: Before you factor, check for a common factor.

7 Factor each of the following.
(a) $x^2 - 64$ (b) $y^2 - 36$
(c) $a^2 - 100b^2$ (d) $x^2 - 1$
(e) $9k^2 - 16m^2$ (f) $1 - 25n^2$
(g) $9n^2 - 36x^2$ (h) $81 - y^2$
(i) $49m^2 - 100h^2$ (j) $16x^2 - 25y^2$

8 Factor: Remember, check for a common factor first.
(a) $2a^2 - 2b^2$ (b) $3m^2 - 12n^2$
(c) $2p^2 - 2$ (d) $3n^2 - 48$
(e) $2x^2 - 128$ (f) $98 - 2f^2$
(g) $3 - 75d^2$ (h) $50q^2 - 2$
(i) $108 - 3y^2$ (j) $72 - 98c^2$

9 Factor each of the following. (Check whether the expressions are factored completely.)
(a) $x^4 - 1$ (b) $p^4 - 16$
(c) $f^4 - 49$ (d) $81 - n^4$

10 (a) Find the missing parts.

$$-m^2 + 64 = 64 - m^2$$
$$= (?)^2 - (?)^2$$

(b) Use the steps in (a). Factor each of the following
(i) $-p^2 + 16$ (ii) $-d^2 + 49$

11 Factor each of the following.
(a) $a^2b^2 - 36$ (b) $p^2q^2 - 64$
(c) $100 - x^2y^2$ (d) $c^2d^2 - e^2$
(e) $49a^2b^2 - 1$ (f) $1 - 4m^2n^2$

12 Factor each of the following. There are two expressions that cannot be factored. Be careful.
(a) $a^2 - d^2$ (b) $9k^2 - 1$
(c) $4p^2 - 9q^2$ (d) $p^2 - 9m^2$
(e) $16p^2 - 25y^2$ (f) $3m^2 - 48$
(g) $10a^4 - 4b^4$ (h) $x^2 + 9$
(i) $-4a^2 + 1$ (j) $108 - 3x^2$
(k) $x^3 - 16x$ (l) $-9y^2 + 25$
(m) $x^4 - 1$ (n) $2m^2 - 72$
(o) $81 - y^4$ (p) $25t^2 + 4m^2$
(q) $a^2v^2 - h^2$ (r) $100 - a^2b^2$
(s) $x^2 - \frac{1}{9}$ (t) $\frac{x^2}{4} - 25$

**C**

13 Find the factors.
(a) $(a + b)^2 - c^2$ (b) $(x - y)^2 - k^2$
(c) $(x + y)^2 - p^2$ (d) $(x - 3y)^2 - y^2$
(e) $(2x - y)^2 - (x - 2y)^2$
(f) $(p + 3q)^2 - 49(p - 3q)^2$

## Math Tip

You can use your factoring skills to again multiply mentally, but you need practice. For example, how quickly can you compute $101^2 - 99^2$?
Here's a way using the difference of squares to calculate the expression and impress people with how fast you are!

Write the expression as a difference of a product of factors, mentally.
↓

$$101^2 - 99^2 = (101 - 99)(101 + 99)$$
$$= 2(200) \leftarrow \text{Now do the arithmetic mentally.}$$
$$= 400$$

Calculate each of the following. How many can you do mentally?

A (a) $19^2 - 9^2$ (b) $35^2 - 25^2$
(c) $75^2 - 25^2$ (d) $96^2 - 4^2$
(e) $105^2 - 95^2$ (f) $201^2 - 199^2$

B Complete each of the following. How many can you complete mentally?
(a) $21 \times 19 = (20 + ?)(20 - ?) = ?$
(b) $39 \times 41 = (40 - ?)(40 + ?) = ?$
(c) $104 \times 96 = (100 + ?)(100 - ?) = ?$

## Computer Tip

What is the output of the following program?

```
10 INPUT N
20 PRINT "FIND LARGEST FACTOR OF"; N
30 LET F = INT (N/2)
40 FOR D = F TO 2 STEP -1
50 IF N/D = INT (N/D) THEN 90
60 NEXT D
70 PRINT N; "IS PRIME"
80 GO TO 100
90 PRINT "THE LARGEST FACTOR IS"; D
100 END
```

## Applications: Factoring and Calculators

Whenever you have many calculations to do, often it is wise to plan your work so that you minimize the number of calculations you need to do. For example, a formula to calculate the amount, $V$, of material in the pipe is given by the following

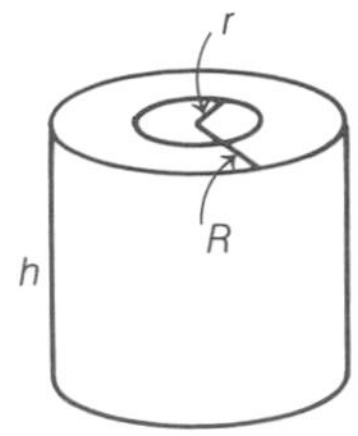


$V = \pi R^2h - \pi r^2h$
where $R$ is the outside radius, $r$ is the inside radius and $h$ is the height.

Have you ever wondered where all the water goes in the middle of a city after a thunderstorm? Underneath a city is a complex system of large concrete pipes that are designed to withstand the great pressure of large volumes of water that occur after a heavy rainstorm.

The expression written in factored form reduces the number of steps to be performed and thus saves time.

$$\begin{aligned} V &= \pi R^2h - \pi r^2h \\ &= \pi h(R^2 - r^2) \\ &= \pi h(R - r)(R + r) \end{aligned}$$

To use a calculator, follow this procedure where $R$, $r$, and $h$ are the measures you input.

[C] $R$ [+] $r$ [=] [MS] $R$ [−] $r$ [=] [×] $h$ [×] [$\pi$] [×] [MR] = Output ?

---

14 Use the previous formula. Calculate the amount of material in each pipe.

| | Outside Radius | Inside Radius | Length |
|---|---|---|---|
| (a) | 0.86 m | 0.79 m | 6.50 m |
| (b) | 1.23 m | 1.08 m | 3.20 m |
| (c) | 1.65 m | 1.48 m | 2.45 m |

15 A concrete pipe has an outside diameter of 1.18 m, an inside diameter of 1.05 m and is 3.25 m long.
(a) Calculate the amount of material used to construct the pipe.
(b) How much water, when filled, will this piece of pipe hold?

16 A pipe has an outside diameter 2.43 m.
(a) Calculate the amount of material used to construct a pipe with inside diameter 2.25 m if the pipe is 3.50 m in length.
(b) How much less material is needed if outside radius of the pipe is reduced by 2 cm?

17 The shaded area A is given by the formula
$A = \pi R^2 - \pi r^2$
Complete the chart.

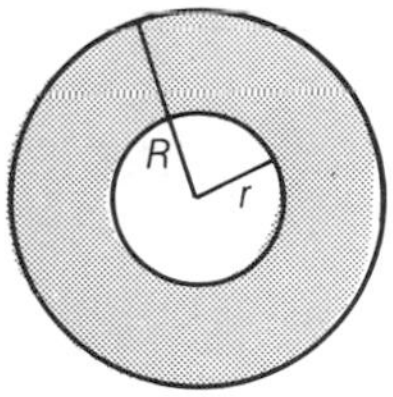


| | $R$ | $r$ | $A$ |
|---|---|---|---|
| (a) | 1.7 cm | 1.4 cm | ? |
| (b) | 2.3 cm | 1.2 cm | ? |
| (c) | 3.65 cm | 2.80 cm | ? |

18 Refer to the formula in the previous question. A circular flowerbed, as shown, has a diameter of 8.6 m and has a cobblestone centre with radius 1.8 m.

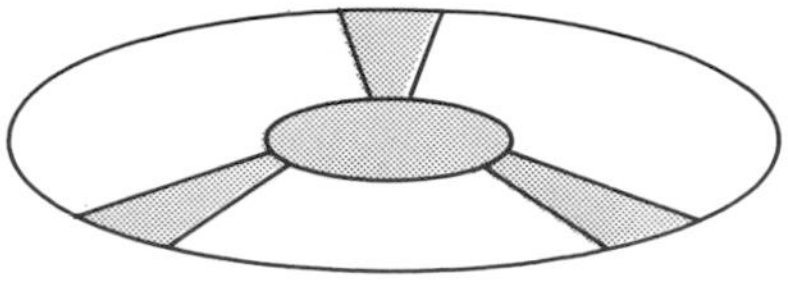

Calculate the area used for planting if the walks account for 5.6 m².

# 4.5 Organizing Skills: Using Clues

When you are solving a problem, or applying a skill, it is important that you choose the correct skill. In factoring expressions you should look for the needed clues.

| Trinomial | Difference of squares | Common factor |
|---|---|---|
| $\underbrace{x^2 + 13x + 36}_{\text{3 terms}}$ | difference<br>$x^2 - 9y^2$<br>squares | $2x^2 - 2y^2$<br>Each term has common factor |

In factoring expressions, remember these important steps.

1 Check for a common factor.
2 Check whether you are factoring a binomial or a trinomial.
3 Ask yourself: Can I rearrange the terms to obtain an expression that I can factor?
4 Once you have finished, check whether the expression can be factored again.

## Try These

For each expression, what are the clues that suggest the factors?

(a) $m^2 + 2m - 8$ (b) $4y^2 - x^2$ (c) $3x + 6y$ (d) $x^2 - xy^2$
(e) $25m^2 - 1$ (f) $-4 + 16k^2$ (g) $y^2 - 3y + 2$ (h) $p^2 - 3pq - 18q^2$

## Written Exercises

**B** Make a list of the various types of factoring you have used. You will need to apply them in the following.

Factor each of the following. Then check by expanding.

1 $3x + 12$ 2 $m^2 - 5m$
3 $a^2b + ab^2$ 4 $p^3q - p^2q^2$
5 $5m^2 - 40m - 100$ 6 $5p^2 + 5p + 15$
7 $ab^2 - ba$ 8 $rq^2 - 16r$
9 $4m^2 - 36n^2$ 10 $4m^2 - 16$
11 $3p^2 - 75$ 12 $3y^2 - 24y + 36$
13 $a^3 - 91a$ 14 $a^3 - 25a$
15 $5a^2 - 5$ 16 $k^2 - 5k - 24$
17 $9x^2 - 36$ 18 $2x^2 + 20x + 50$

Factor each of the following. There are two expressions that cannot be factored. Be careful.

19 $2a^2 - 8$ 20 $m^2 + 2m - 8$
21 $2p^2 - 12p + 18$ 22 $3a^2 - 27b^2$
23 $x^2 + 7x + 12$ 24 $n^2 - 7n + 10$
25 $x^2 - 2x - 24$ 26 $48 - 3x^2$
27 $4n^2 - 4n - 80$ 28 $2n^2 - 50$
29 $-a^2 - 2ab - b^2$ 30 $25x^4 - 16y^4$
31 $25m^2 - 16n^2$ 32 $8x^2 - 24y^2$
33 $9x^2 + 25y^2$ 34 $abc + abd$
35 $y^2 - 2y - 3$ 36 $m^4 + 5m^2 - 36$
37 $16x^2 - 8x + 1$ 38 $y^2 - 10y - 24$
39 $2y^3 + 8y^2$ 40 $x - xy^2$
41 $-(1 - x^4)$ 42 $x^2 + 4y^2$
43 $m^2 + 4mn + 4n^2$ 44 $a^3 - 4ab^2$

# 4.6 Applying Skills: Using Factoring

In your work in mathematics, expressions will occur that need to be simplified. You have already learned that in finding the value of an expression, it is useful to simplify the expression first. Sometimes you need to apply your skills with factoring to simplify expressions.

### Example 1

Simplify. (a) $\dfrac{6xy + 2x}{2x}$ (b) $\dfrac{x^2 - 4xy + 3y}{x^2 - y^2}$

### Solution

(a) $\dfrac{6xy + 2x}{2x}$ ⟵ Check the expression for factors.

$= \dfrac{2x(3y + x)}{2x}$

$= \dfrac{\overset{1}{\cancel{2x}}(3y + x)}{\cancel{2x}}$

$= 3y + x$ ⟵ You have now written the expression in lowest terms.

(b) $\dfrac{x^2 - 4xy + 3y^2}{x^2 - y^2}$ ⟵ Check whether the expressions can be factored. Then write the factors.

$= \dfrac{(x - y)(x - 3y)}{(x - y)(x + y)}$

$= \dfrac{\overset{1}{\cancel{(x - y)}}(x - 3y)}{\underset{1}{\cancel{(x - y)}}(x + y)}$

$= \dfrac{x - 3y}{x + y}$

You can reduce many calculations by simplifying expressions first.

A Evaluate for $x = 3$, $y = -2$

$\dfrac{x^2 - 4xy + 3y^2}{x^2 - y^2}$ This expression has been simplified. ⟹

B Evaluate for $x = 3$, $y = -2$

$\dfrac{x - 3y}{x + y}$

You would obtain the same answer, but with different amounts of work. When you work with expressions such as $\dfrac{3x}{x + y}$ $\dfrac{x^2 - y^2}{x^2 - 2xy + y^2}$ you must be careful that you do not choose values of the variables that give a denominator equal to zero. Remember: you cannot divide by zero.

## Try These

1 What are the factors?

(a) $3x + 3y$ (b) $4k + 4m$

(c) $2ax + 2ay$ (d) $x^3 - x^2$

2 What are the factors?

(a) $x^2 - y^2$ (b) $4a^2 - 1$

(c) $16y^2 - 9$ (d) $4x^2 - 25y^2$

## Written Exercises

**A** Throughout our work, the denominators of the expressions are not equal to zero. Look for clues to help you decide which factoring patterns to use.

1 Simplify.

(a) $\frac{ab}{ax - ay}$ (b) $\frac{cx + cy}{cd}$ (c) $\frac{a(x + y)}{b(x + y)}$

(d) $\frac{24}{15(x + y)}$ (e) $\frac{m(x - y)^2}{n(x - y)}$ (f) $\frac{30a}{25(x - a)}$

2 Simplify.

(a) $\frac{p^2 - 7p + 6}{p - 6}$ (b) $\frac{d^2 - 9d + 20}{d - 5}$

(c) $\frac{x^2 + 6x + 5}{x + 1}$ (d) $\frac{x^2 - 2x - 48}{x + 6}$

3 Simplify.

(a) $\frac{36x}{15(x + 2)}$ (b) $\frac{15(m + n)}{6(2m + n)}$

(c) $\frac{3x^2 - xy}{xy + 3x^2}$ (d) $\frac{3x - 6y}{9x + 12y}$

4 (a) Find the value of $\frac{x^2 - 9}{x + 3}$ for $x = 6$.
(b) Find the value of $x - 3$ for $x = 6$.
(c) Why are the answers in (a) and (b) the same?

5 (a) Find the value of $(100 - y^2) \div (10 - y)$ for $y = 3$.
(b) Find the value of $10 + y$ for $y = 3$.
(c) When are the answers in (a) and (b) the same?

**B**

6 Simplify.

(a) $\frac{x^2 + x - 6}{x^2 - 3x - 18}$ (b) $\frac{x^2 - 9}{x + 3}$

(c) $\frac{10 - y}{100 - y^2}$ (d) $\frac{x^2 + 2x - 3}{x^2 - 4x + 3}$

(e) $\frac{x^2 - y^2}{x^2 - 2xy + y^2}$ (f) $\frac{3a + 3b}{a^2 + 2ab + b^2}$

7 Find the value of each expression for $a = -3$, $b = 2$.

(a) $\frac{a^2b - ab^2}{a^2b^2 + ab^2}$ (b) $\frac{ab + b^2}{a^2 - b^2}$

8 The side of a square is given by the expression

$$\frac{a^2 + 10ab + 25b^2}{a + 5b}$$

Find the dimension for each pair of values.
(a) $a = 12$, $b = 4$ (b) $a = 8$, $b = 6$
(c) $a = 2.6$, $b = 1.4$ (d) $a = 2.15$, $b = 1.75$

9 The time taken for a competition is given by the expression $(x^2 - y^2) \div (x - y)$.
Find the time for each pair of values.
(a) $x = 6$, $y = 3$ (b) $x = 11.5$, $y = 9.5$
(c) $x = 8.32$, $y = 1.46$ (d) $x = 3.08$, $y = 9.61$

10 In producing a machine part, the cost per unit, in dollars, is given by the expression $(4x^2 - 9y^2) \div (4x + 6y)$. Calculate the cost for each pair of values.
(a) $x = 6.5$, $y = 3.5$ (b) $x = 9.6$, $y = 2.3$
(c) $x = 7.65$, $y = 4.32$ (d) $x = 12.8$, $y = 6.2$

11 The resistance in an electrical circuit is given by the expression
$(m^2 - im - 6i^2) \div (m^2 - 9i^2)$
Calculate a value for the expression for each pair of values. Round your answer to 1 decimal place.
(a) $m = 6.8$, $i = 3.2$ (b) $m = 14.3$, $i = 12.1$

**C**

12 For each of the following
- ▶ simplify the expression
- ▶ decide which values of the variable cannot be used to evaluate the expression.

(a) $\frac{2x^2 + 6x + 4}{4x^2 - 12x - 16}$ (b) $\frac{-x^2 + x + 6}{x^2 - 10x + 21}$

(c) $\frac{a^3 - ab^2}{a^2 - 2ab + b^2}$ (d) $\frac{x^2 - 3x - 4}{2x^2 + 10x + 8}$

# 4.7 Multiplying Expressions

The skills you have learned in arithmetic extend to skills in algebra.

- ▶ When you multiply expressions, you simplify first.
- ▶ When you have completed the calculations, you check your answer and express it in lowest terms.

These same steps apply to working with expression in algebra.

### Example

Find the product of the expressions

$$\frac{3x^2 - 6x}{x^2 - 4} \quad \text{and} \quad \frac{x^2 + x - 2}{6x^2}.$$

### Solution

$$\frac{3x^2 - 6x}{x^2 - 4} \times \frac{x^2 + x - 2}{6x^2} = \frac{3x(x-2)}{(x-2)(x+2)} \times \frac{(x+2)(x-1)}{6x^2}$$

Be sure to record the original expressions as the first step of your solution.

$$= \frac{3x\cancel{(x-2)}^{1}}{\cancel{(x-2)}_{1}(x+2)} \times \frac{(x+2)(x-1)}{6x^2}$$

Think. Simplify numerators and denominators

$$= \frac{\cancel{3x}^{1}}{\cancel{(x+2)}_{1}} \times \frac{\cancel{(x+2)}^{1}(x-1)}{\cancel{6x^2}_{2x}}$$

Think: now simplify the product

$$= \frac{x-1}{2x}$$

Think: Check your final answer. Is it expressed in lowest terms?

As in your earlier work, when you are asked to evaluate an expression, be sure it is written in the lowest terms possible. This habit will save you many extra steps in doing calculations.

### Try These

Each expression has been factored. What is the product?

1 $\frac{2x^2}{x+y} \times \frac{x+y}{x}$

2 $\frac{3y}{a+b} \times \frac{b+a}{3+y}$

3 $\frac{(x-5)}{(x+2)} \times \frac{x+2}{x-5}$

4 $\frac{x-3}{9y^2} \times \frac{3y}{x-3}$

5 $(x-5) \times \frac{x+5}{4(x-5)}$

6 $n(a+b) \times \frac{1}{m(a+b)}$

## Written Exercises

**A** Remember: look for clues to help you decide which factoring problems to use.

1 Simplify.

(a) $\frac{36}{y^2 + 2y} \times \frac{y + 2}{9}$

(b) $\frac{x^2y}{2x - 2} \times \frac{2}{xy^2}$

(c) $\frac{n - 1}{3n} \times \frac{n}{n^2 - 1}$

(d) $\frac{x + 1}{x^2 - 1} \times \frac{x - 1}{x}$

2 (a) Which factoring patterns do you see in the following expression? Factor all expressions.

$$\frac{m^2 + 5m}{m^2 - 16} \times \frac{m^2 - 4m}{m^2 - 25}$$

(b) Express your answer in (a) in lowest terms.

3 (a) Which factoring pattern do you see in the following expression? Factor all expressions.

$$\frac{a^2 - 7a + 10}{6 - 3a} \times \frac{9a + 45}{a^2 - 25}$$

(b) Express your answer in (a) in lowest terms.

4 (a) Decide: What is your first step to simplify the following?

$$\frac{x^2 - 4y^2}{x^2 - y^2} \times \frac{3x^2y^2}{x + 2y}$$

(b) Simplify the expression in (a).

5 (a) Decide: What is your first step in simplifying the following?

$$\frac{x^2 + x - 2}{x^3 - 4x^2} \times \frac{2x^2 - 14x + 12}{x + 2}$$

(b) Simplify the expression in (a).

**B** Remember: check your final answer. Is it expressed in lowest terms?

6 Simplify.

(a) $\frac{x^2 - 25}{x^2 - 64} \times \frac{x^2 - 8x}{x - 5}$

(b) $\frac{9}{4p^2 - 16} \times \frac{2p - 4}{27}$

(c) $\frac{5b^2}{a^2 - ab} \times \frac{b^2 - a^2}{10ab}$

(d) $\frac{3a^2 - 48b^2}{2a^2 - 8b^2} \times \frac{3a + 6b}{3a + 12b}$

(e) $\frac{3x^2 - 6x}{x^2 - 4} \times \frac{x^2 + x - 2}{6x^2}$

(f) $\frac{7n^2 - 14}{2n + 3} \times \frac{4n^2 - 9}{14n - 21}$

7 (a) Use $x = 3$. Find the value of

$$\frac{x^2 - 6x + 5}{x - 1} \times \frac{x - 1}{x - 5}$$

(b) Use $p = -2$. Find the value of

$$\frac{p^2 - 6p}{p - 6} \times \frac{p + 3}{p}$$

(c) Use $a = 6.8$. Find the value of

$$\frac{a^2 - 30 - a}{a^2 - 24 - 2a} \times \frac{a^2 - 16}{a + 5}$$

8 (a) Use $t = 4.5$. Calculate the value of each expression, A and B.

A: $\frac{t^2 - 4}{t^2} \times \frac{t^2 - 3t}{t^2 - 5t + 6}$

B: $\frac{(t - 1)^3}{(t - 2)^3} \times \frac{t^2 - 4t + 4}{t^2 - 2t + 1}$

(b) Which expression has the greater value?

9 (a) Use $a = 3$. Calculate the value of the expressions A and B.

A: $\dfrac{a^2 - 3a - 10}{(a-2)^2} \times \dfrac{a-2}{a-5}$

B: $\dfrac{24a^2}{3(a^2 - 4a + 4)} \times \dfrac{3a-6}{2a}$

(b) Which value is the lesser, A or B?

10 The following expression shows the profit for an ice skating rink.

$$\frac{a^3c + a^2c^2}{a^2c - ac^2} \times \frac{3a^3c - 3ac^3}{a^3 + 2a^2c + ac^2}$$

Calculate the value for each pair of values $a$ and $c$.
(a) $a = 20$, $c = 15$
(b) $a = 9.6$, $c = 3.2$
(c) $c = 16.8$, $a = 23.4$
(d) $a = 63.1$, $c = 39.6$

11 If $a = -4$, find the value of each of the following.

(a) $\dfrac{a^2 - 121}{a^2 - 4} \times \dfrac{a+2}{a+11}$

(b) $\dfrac{a^2 - 4a + 4}{3a - 6} \times \dfrac{5a + 10}{a^2 - 4}$

(c) $\dfrac{14a^2 - 7a}{12a^3 + 24a^2} \times \dfrac{a^2 + 2a}{2a - 1}$

12 (a) What is your first step to simplify the following expression?

$$\frac{a^2-9}{a^2+7a+12} \times \frac{a+2}{4a^2-9} \times \frac{2a^2+11a+12}{a-3}$$

(b) Write the expression in (a) in lowest terms.

13 Simplify.

Be sure to organize the steps of your solution.

(a) $\dfrac{a^2 - 18a + 80}{a^2 - 5a - 50} \times \dfrac{a^2 - 6a - 7}{a^2 - 15a + 56} \times \dfrac{a+5}{a+1}$

(b) $\dfrac{y^2 + 7yz + 10z^2}{y^2 + 6yz + 5z^2} \times \dfrac{y+z}{y^2 + 4yz + 4z^2} \times \dfrac{y+2z}{1}$

(c) $\dfrac{2x - 3y}{x^2 + 4xy + 4y^2} \times \dfrac{4x^2 - 4y^2}{4x^2 - 9y^2} \times \dfrac{5x^2 + 10xy}{3xy - 3y^2}$

## Career Tip

In many careers you are given projects or tasks for which you need to study and to analyze what you are given, in order to arrive at an answer. Skills in mathematics help you to analyze.

A For example, study each design.
- What construction lines are missing?
- What lines are hidden?
- How are the lengths related?
- How are the angles related?

Now construct a copy of each design.

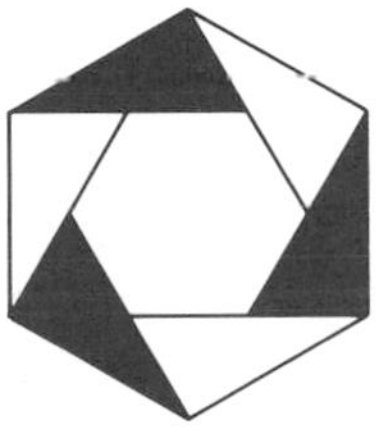

B How might the above skill be useful in the following careers?

| | |
|---|---|
| Animator | Fashion Designer |
| Tailor | Cartographer |
| Architect | Choreographer |
| Sound Editor | Air Traffic Controller |
| Surveyor | Sheet Metal Worker |

## Math Tip

It is important to clearly understand the vocabulary of mathematics when solving problems.
- Make a list of all the new words you have met in this chapter.
- Provide a simple example to illustrate each word.

# 4.8 Using Factoring Skills: Dividing

The skills you have learned with factoring are also applied when you divide expressions as shown in the following example.

### Example

Simplify $\dfrac{x^2 - 9}{x^2 + 3x} \div \dfrac{x^2 - 11x + 24}{x + 3}$

### Solution

$$\frac{x^2 - 9}{x^2 + 3x} \div \frac{x^2 - 11x + 24}{x + 3}$$

Remember: record the original expression first.

$$= \frac{x^2 - 9}{x^2 + 3x} \times \frac{x + 3}{x^2 - 11x + 24}$$

To divide, you follow the same steps as with simpler expressions and in doing computation.

$$= \frac{(x - 3)(x + 3)}{x(x + 3)} \times \frac{x + 3}{(x - 3)(x - 8)}$$

Apply your factoring skills. Look for the clues to help you factor.

$$= \frac{x + 3}{x(x - 8)}$$

Express your final answer in lowest terms.

Remember when simplifying expressions
- ▶ check for common factors first
- ▶ look for clues to factor
- ▶ check your final answer. Is it expressed in lowest terms?

## Try These

For each expression
- ▶ What is the first step?
- ▶ What is your final answer?

1 $\dfrac{3(x + 2)}{5} \div \dfrac{2(x + 2)}{15}$

2 $\dfrac{(x + y)}{2} \div \dfrac{(x + y)}{8}$

3 $\dfrac{(a + 3)^2}{b} \div \dfrac{5(a + 3)}{4b^2}$

4 $\dfrac{(m + n)^2}{7} \div \dfrac{4(m + n)}{14}$

5 $\dfrac{(m + 5n)}{1} \div \dfrac{(m + 5n)^2}{4}$

## Written Exercises

**A** Remember: To divide by an expression, you need to invert and multiply by the expression.

1 Simplify each of the following.

(a) $\dfrac{2(x+y)^2}{x} \div \dfrac{x+y}{x}$

(b) $\dfrac{6(x-y)}{8} \div \dfrac{12(x-y)^2}{32}$

(c) $\dfrac{3(x+y)}{x-y} \div \dfrac{x+y}{x-y}$

(d) $\dfrac{8(x+1)(x+2)}{3(x+3)} \div \dfrac{x+2}{(x+3)}$

2 (a) To simplify the expression, what is your first step? $\dfrac{x^2-9}{x+2} \div \dfrac{x^2+6x+9}{2x+4}$

(b) Simplify the expression in (a).

3 (a) You are asked to simplify the following. What patterns for factoring do you see?

$\dfrac{m^2-2m-15}{m^2-9} \div \dfrac{2m-10}{m+3}$

(b) Simplify the expression in (a).

4 (a) To simplify the expression, what is your first step? $\dfrac{k^2-6k+9}{k-3} \div \dfrac{k-6}{k+3}$

(b) Find the value of the expression in (a) for $k = 9$.

**B**

5 Simplify each of the following.

(a) $\dfrac{y^2-3y}{y^2-9} \div \dfrac{y}{3+y}$ (b) $\dfrac{5x+3}{3x+2} \div \dfrac{10x^2+6x}{6x^2+4x}$

(c) $\dfrac{5a}{a^2+7a+12} \div \dfrac{10a^2}{a^2+4a}$

(d) $\dfrac{r^2+8r+16}{r+4} \div \dfrac{r^2-16}{r-4}$

6 (a) For $x = 2$, find the value of the expression.

$\dfrac{x^2+2x+1}{3x} \div (x+1)$

(b) For $x = 3$, find the value of the expression.

$\dfrac{x^2-49}{7x-49} \div \dfrac{x^2+13x+42}{x^3+6x^2}$

(c) For $x = 2.5$, find the value of

$\dfrac{x^2-16}{6x^3} \div \dfrac{x^2-5x+4}{12x^3-12x^2}$

7 To evaluate the expression, what is your first step?

$\dfrac{x-y}{x+y} \div \dfrac{5x^2-5y^2}{3x+3y}$

Find the value of the expression for pairs of values as shown.

(a) $x = 3$, $y = -1$ (b) $x = -4$, $y = 2$
(c) $x = 1.6$, $y = 3.2$ (d) $x = 2.5$, $y = 1.5$

8 Evaluate the following expression for values of $a$ and $b$ as shown.

$\dfrac{5a^2-5ab}{ab+b^2} \div \dfrac{5a^2-5b^2}{b}$

(a) $a = 3$, $b = 2$ (b) $a = -4$, $b = -1$
(c) $a = -3$, $b = 5$ (d) $a = 1.5$, $b = 2.5$

9 (a) Use $x = 3$, $y = -2$. Find the value of each expression A and B.

A: $\dfrac{4x^2-4xy-3y^2}{3x^2y} \div \dfrac{4x^2-3xy}{6x^3}$

B: $\dfrac{x^2+7xy+12y^2}{x-2y} \div \dfrac{x^2-9y^2}{x^2-5xy+6y^2}$

(b) Which has the greater value, A or B?

# Review: Practice and Problems

1 Factor. Check your answer.

(a) $5m + 9m$ (b) $pq + qr$
(c) $6e - 12f^2$ (d) $15m^3 - 10m$
(e) $4p^4 - 16p^3$ (f) $8r^2 - 24$

2 (a) Factor $5mn - 10mq$.
(b) Find the value of the expression in (a). Use $m = 9.3$, $n = 6.8$, and $q = 7.2$.
(c) Find the value of $6p^3q^2 - 12p^2q^2$ for $p = 4$ and $q = -5$.

3 (a) Find the value of $16m^2 - 8mn + n^2$ when $m = 2.5$ and $n = 4.1$.
(b) Find the value of $(4m - n)^2$.
(c) Which answer, (a) or (b) was more easily obtained?

4 (a) What two numbers have a product of $-21$ and a sum of $-4$?
(b) Use your answer in (a) to write the factors of $x^2 - 4x - 21 = (x \quad ?)(x \quad ?)$.

5 Factor.

(a) $x^2 - 1$ (b) $25a^2 - 4$
(c) $36x - 49x^3$ (d) $49m^2 - 81$
(e) $16x - 81x^3$ (f) $9a^2 - 16$
(g) $36p^2 - 64q^2$ (h) $100r^2 - 81q^2$
(i) $x^4 - 1$ (j) $m^4 - 25$
(k) $100 - p^4$ (l) $-r^2 + 81$

6 Factor each of the following.

(a) $4m^3 + m^2$ (b) $x^2 - 9y^2$
(c) $16a^4 - 1$ (d) $a^2b^2 - 1$
(e) $(m - n)^2 - 25$ (f) $y^2 - 13y + 36$
(g) $x^4 - 64$ (h) $a^2 + 4a - 21$
(i) $2p^2 - 2p - 12$ (j) $3m^5 + 15m^3 + 12m$

7 Which of the following cannot be factored?

(a) $x^2 + 13x + 36$ (b) $4m^2 - 36n^2$
(c) $4x^2 + 3y^2$ (d) $x^4 + 15x^2 + 36$

8 The area $A$ of a rectangular field is found by the formula $A = l \times w$. Find the missing expressions in the chart.

| | $A$ | $l$ | $w$ |
|---|---|---|---|
| (a) | $r^2 + 2r + 1$ | $r + 1$ | ? |
| (b) | ? | $x + 7$ | $x + 2$ |
| (c) | $4m^2 + 4mn + n^2$ | ? | $(2m + n)$ |
| (d) | ? | $(2x + 3y)$ | $(3x + 2y)$ |

9 For $m = 12$, which has the greater value A or B?

A $\dfrac{5m - 15}{5m + 15}$ B $\dfrac{m^2 - 25}{m^2 + m - 20}$

10 Simplify.

(a) $\dfrac{p^2 - 1}{p - 1}$ (b) $\dfrac{6r^2 - 54}{4r^2 - 36}$

(c) $\dfrac{a^2 - 10a + 21}{a^2 + 3a - 18}$ (d) $\dfrac{5f + 5}{f^2 + 7f + 6}$

11 Simplify.

(a) $\dfrac{m - 5}{6} \times \dfrac{4}{m - 5}$ (b) $\dfrac{4t + 4}{12} \times \dfrac{4}{3t + 3}$

(c) $\dfrac{16}{4x - 4} \times \dfrac{6x - 6}{4}$ (d) $\dfrac{m^2}{m^2 - 4} \times \dfrac{m^2 - 5m + 6}{m^2 - 3m}$

12 In calculating the profit, which expression, A or B gives the greater value when $n = 3$?

A $\dfrac{4n^2}{3n^2 - 12n + 12} \times \dfrac{3n - 6}{2n}$

B $\dfrac{n^2 - 4n}{n - 4} \times \dfrac{n + 2}{n}$

13 Simplify.

(a) $\dfrac{m^2}{n + 2} \div \dfrac{m}{n + 2}$ (b) $\dfrac{y^2 - 16}{y^2 - 64} \div \dfrac{y + 4}{y - 8}$

(c) $\dfrac{x^2 - x}{5x - 5} \div \dfrac{x^2y - x^2}{15y - 15}$

(d) $\dfrac{p^2 + 3p + 2}{(p + 1)^2} \div \dfrac{p^2 + 4p + 3}{p^2 + 5p + 6}$

# A Practice Test

1 (a) What is the first step to factor $14p^3q^2 - 28pq^2$?
(b) Factor the expression in (a).

2 Factor each of the following.
(a) $6m^2 + 9$ (b) $8pq + 12mn$
(c) $27r^2 - 21t$ (e) $15pq^2 + 20p^2$
(f) $3f^2 + 3fg$ (g) $27a^2b - 9a$

3 Determine the missing term for each of the following. Each is a perfect square.
(a) $x^2 + ? + 4$ (b) $x^2 + ? + 36$
(c) $4a^2 + ? + 25$ (d) $9p^2 - ? + 16$
(e) $a^2 + 6at + ?$ (f) $r^2 - 12rt + ?$
(g) $4p^2 + 16pt + ?$ (h) $9a^2 - 6at + ?$

4 (a) What two numbers have a product of $-16$ and a sum of $-6$?
(b) Use your answers in (a) to write the factors of $p^2 - 6p - 16 = (p \quad ?)(p \quad ?)$.

5 Factor.
(a) $x^2 + 12x + 36$ (b) $a^2 - 12a + 36$
(c) $64m^2 - 48m + 9$ (d) $b^2 - 6bc + 9c^2$
(e) What property do (a) to (d) have in common?

6 Factor fully.
(a) $x^2 - 144$ (b) $2r^2 - 18$
(c) $ab^2 - 9a$ (d) $7m^2 - 63$
(e) $27 - 3p^2$ (f) $25m^2 - 16$
(g) What property do the above have in common?

7 Factor.
(a) $16x^2 - 1$ (b) $2p^2 + 22p + 60$
(c) $m^2 + 16mn + 64n^2$ (d) $72 - 2f^2$
(e) $12m^2 + 15m + 3$ (f) $m^2 - 16$
(g) $2x^2 - 2x - 16$ (h) $x^2 - 6x - 16$
(i) $f^3 - 2f^2 - 35f$ (j) $9a^2 + 24a + 16$

8 (a) Find the value of $\dfrac{m^2 - 121}{m - 11}$ for $m = 15$.
(b) Find the value of $m + 11$ for $m = 15$.
(c) Why are the answers in (a) and (b) the same?

9 (a) Evaluate for $a = -3$, $b = 4$.

$$\text{A} \quad \frac{a^2 - 3a - 28}{a - 7} \qquad \text{B} \quad \frac{4ab + b^2}{16a^2 - b^2}$$

(b) Which has the greater value, A or B?

10 The expense ratio E involved in manufacturing two different ball point pens is given by A and B.

$$\text{A} \quad \frac{n^2 - 4n + 4}{n^2 - 4} \qquad \text{B} \quad \frac{n^2 + 8n + 16}{n^2 - 16}$$

For $n = 1250$, which has the greater value?

11 (a) What is your first step in simplifying the expression?

$$\frac{a^2 - 49}{3a^2 - 20a - 7} \times \frac{3a^2 + a}{a^2 + 11a + 28}$$

Simplify the expression in (a).
(b) Find the value of $S$ given by the following expression for $p = 6$.

$$S = \frac{p^2 - 4p + 3}{p^2 - 5p + 6} \times \frac{p^3 - 3p^2 + 2p}{p^2 - 2p + 1}$$

12 The time factor, $T$, for salmon to reach their spawning grounds is given by the expression

$$T = \frac{d^2 - 6d - 7}{(d + 1)^2} \times \frac{d^2 + 2d + 1}{d^2 - 49}$$

Find $T$ for $d = 13$.

13 Simplify.

(a) $\dfrac{3a + 30}{2a} \times \dfrac{4a}{4a + 40}$

(b) $\dfrac{1}{a^2 + a - 12} \times \dfrac{a + 4}{(a - 3)}$

(c) $\dfrac{a^2 + 2ab + b^2}{3a} \div \dfrac{a^2 - b^2}{2}$

(d) $\dfrac{p^2 - 36}{p^2 - 12p + 36} \div \dfrac{p^2 + 6p + 5}{p^2 - 1}$

# Update: A Cumulative Review

1 Many foods have a high percentage of water. Calculate the amount of water in each substance to the nearest gram.
(a) Lobster 2300 g 83%
(b) Pineapple 2000 g 90%

2 (a) Find the product of $6p^2 - 4p + 1$ and $-5p$.
(b) What is the product of $12a^2 - 3a - 5$ and $3a^2$?
(c) Find the value of the product in (b) if $a = 2$.

3 Copy and complete the table.

| | Decimal number | Per cent | Fraction form |
|---|---|---|---|
| (a) | 0.325 | ? | ? |
| (b) | ? | 75% | ? |
| (c) | ? | ? | $\frac{1}{8}$ |
| (d) | 0.666 | ? | ? |
| (e) | ? | 150% | ? |

4 Salmonella is a bacteria that causes food poisoning. The bacteria are reproduced by a splitting process called mitosis. Under certain conditions, each salmonella will divide to form two new salmonella every 20 minutes. If there are 500 salmonella at the start, find the number of salmonella after
(a) 60 minutes.
(b) 140 minutes.
(c) 200 minutes.

5 Evaluate each expression for $m = 4$, $n = -3$.
(a) $-5m + 3n$
(b) $-2m^2 - 3q^2$
(c) $-2mn + 5mn^2$
(d) $6m - 3n - 2mn$

6 Simplify each of the following.
(a) $5a - 5b - (3a - 2b) + 6a$
(b) $-(a^2 + 3) + a^2 + 9 - (a^2 - 2a)$
(c) $m + 6 - (m - 3) - (2m + 1)$
(d) $p^2 - 4p + 2p^2 - (2p - p^2) - 6p$
(e) $9m - 2n - (8m + n) + (3m - n)$
(f) $-(6a - 2b) + (a - 3b) - (7a - 2b)$

7 Find each quotient.
(a) $\dfrac{(9p^2)(-24pq^2)}{(-12pq)(-3p)}$
(b) $\dfrac{(-10mn)(-2m^2n^3)}{(-4m)(-5n^3)}$

8 The value of each dollar invested is given by the formula
$A = (1.12)^n$, where $n$ = number of years, A = amount or value of investment
(a) Calculate the value of one dollar after 5 years.
(b) If you invested $900, calculate the amount of your investment after 8 years.

9 Find an expression for the area of each figure.
(a) (b)

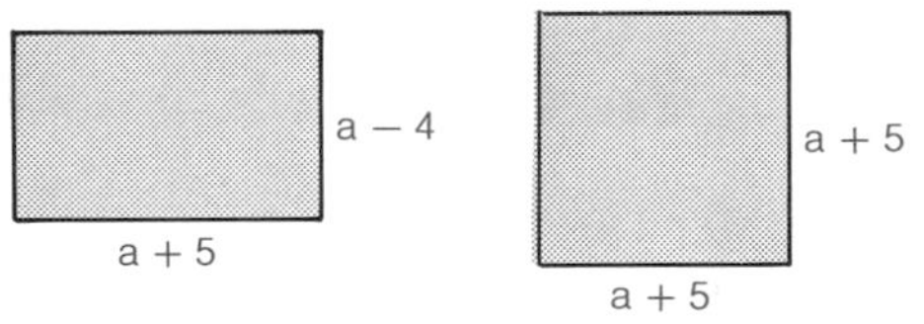


(c) Which has the greater area? Give reasons for your answer.

10 Factor completely.
(a) $8x + 8$
(b) $7x - 14$
(c) $x^2 - 7x + 10$
(d) $x^2 - 10x + 25$
(e) $x^3 + 2x^2 - 3x$
(f) $3x^4 - 48$
(g) $9m^2 - 16$
(h) $3a^2 - 75$
(i) $p^2 - 2p - 15$
(j) $2r^2 - 50$

11 Simplify.
(a) $\dfrac{12 + 6m}{15 - 3m} \times \dfrac{15mn - 3m^2n}{2m^2 + 4m}$
(b) $\dfrac{a + 3}{a - 3} \div \dfrac{a + 3}{a^2 - 8a + 15}$
(c) $\dfrac{r^2 + 3r^3}{4 - r^2} \times \dfrac{2r + r^2}{r^3 + 2r^2 - 3r}$

# 5 Working with Equations

properties of equations, solving equations, applying skills to problems, using and solving formulas, solving quadratic equations and problems, graphing solutions for inequations, solving problems and applications

## Introduction

To precisely build bridges, roads, structures, you apply the properties of equations. To solve the many technical problems involved in a construction project you need to apply skills with equations.

- When the historic first powered flight occurred on December 17, 1903, Orville Wright was at the controls and his brother, Wilbur, ran alongside the aircraft. To obtain the successful flight, skills with equations were employed to do calculations needed to properly assemble parts with the correct proportions.

- In the photograph, to design a complex transportation system and to make the curves fit, skills with equations were used in conjunction with computers. Although the equations are more complex than those we will deal with, the principles you will use are the same.

To solve the complex problems involved in the above photographs, you first need to understand skills applied to simpler equations. In studying mathematics, you extend your skills as follows.

*Step A* You learn skills, then you practise them.
*Step B* You extend the skills in Step A to learn new skills.
*Step C* You now look for a pattern to help you find patterns for the skills you learned in Step B.
*Step D* You practise the skill in Step C to gain accuracy and speed and apply them when solving problems.

Throughout this chapter and the ones that follow, look for similar patterns in learning skills in mathematics: for the steps A, B, C, and D.

# 5.1 Properties of Equations: Solving Equations

The need to solve equations occurs in many, if not all, construction projects.

- ▶ designing buildings and bridges
- ▶ manufacturing vehicles and motorcycles
- ▶ digging the foundation for a sports complex

The skills with solving equations, whether simple or advanced, are based on an understanding of the properties of equations.

The precise ratio used to mix cement, sand and stone must be carefully controlled. The ratio used for a sidewalk curb differs from that used for the foundation of a skyscraper.

You begin with $k = 8$

A | You can add the same value to both sides of an equation

$$k = 8$$
$$k + 4 = 8 + 4$$
$$k + 4 = 12$$

B | You can subtract the same value from both sides of an equation

$$k = 8$$
$$k - 4 = 8 - 4$$
$$k - 4 = 4$$

C | You can multiply both sides of an equation by the same value

$$k = 8$$
$$2(k) = 2(8)$$
$$2k = 16$$

D | You can divide both sides of an equation by the same value

$$k = 8$$
$$\frac{k}{4} = \frac{8}{4}$$
$$\frac{k}{4} = 2$$

To solve an equation means to find a value for the variable. The key to solving equations is to remember to keep the balance of the equation. What operation you perform on one side of the equation, you must also do to the other side. To solve the equation you may use the properties above.

Solving Equations

| | |
|---|---|
| A | Add the same quantity on both sides |
| B | Subtract the same quantity from both sides |
| C | Multiply both sides by the same quantity |
| D | Divide both sides by the same quantity |

To solve an equation, you need to plan what steps need to be applied to obtain a value for the variable, as shown in the following example.

**Example 1**
Solve and check.
$4x - 5 = 2x + 29$

**Solution**

$$
\begin{aligned}
4x - 5 &= 2x + 29 \\
4x - 5 + 5 &= 2x + 29 + 5 \\
4x &= 2x + 34 \\
4x - 2x &= 2x - 2x + 34 \\
2x &= 34 \\
\frac{2x}{2} &= \frac{34}{2} \\
x &= 17
\end{aligned}
$$

Think: Add 5 to both sides to isolate the term $4x$.

Think: Subtract $2x$ from each side to collect all terms containing $x$.

Think: Divide by 2 to obtain a value for $x$.

L.S. $= 4x - 5$
$= 4(17) - 5$
$= 68 - 5$
$= 63$

R.S. $= 2x + 29$
$= 2(17) + 29$
$= 63$

Thus, $x = 17$

In the study of mathematics, there are often different ways to express the same meaning, such the following.

| | |
|---|---|
| $x = 17$ | The solution is $x = 17$. |
| The root is 17. | The solution set is $\{17\}$. |

Skills you have learned earlier with polynomials are applied to solve the equation in the following example.

**Example 2**
Find the root of the equation
$2(2x - 5) - (x - 6) = 8 - x$
Verify your answer.

Remember: Verify in the original equation.

**Solution**

$$
\begin{aligned}
2(2x - 5) - (x - 6) &= 8 - x \\
4x - 10 - x + 6 &= 8 - x \\
3x - 4 &= 8 - x \\
3x - 4 + 4 &= 8 + 4 - x \\
3x &= 12 - x \\
3x + x &= 12 - x + x \\
4x &= 12 \\
\frac{4x}{4} &= \frac{12}{4} \\
x &= 3
\end{aligned}
$$

You may eventually do these steps mentally

Verify:
L.S. $= 2(2x - 5) - (x - 6)$
$= 2(6 - 5) - (3 - 6)$
$= 2(1) - (-3)$
$= 2 + 3$
$= 5$
R.S. $= 8 - x$
$= 8 - 3 = 5$

The root is 3.

## Try These

1 Which equations have 2 as their root?
(a) $3 = 5n$ (b) $7 - a = 5$
(c) $\frac{t}{2} = 1$ (d) $q + 3 = 3q$

2 Solve each equation.
(a) $x + 1 = 3$ (b) $k - 2 = 6$
(c) $2 = h - 3$ (d) $m + 4 = 1$

3 Find the root of each equation.
(a) $4n = 8 + 3n$ (b) $d + 5 = 2d$
(c) $3k = 2k - 4$ (d) $4t - 3 = 5t$

## Written Exercises

**A** Review the meaning of root, solution, solution set, and verify.

1 Match each equation with its corresponding solution set.

| Equation | Solution Set |
|---|---|
| (a) $x + 5 = 12$ | A $\{6\}$ |
| (b) $p - 4 = 9$ | B $\{-4\}$ |
| (c) $a + 1 = 7$ | C $\{7\}$ |
| (d) $m - 6 = -10$ | D $\{13\}$ |

2 Solve.
(a) $x + 5 = 8$ (b) $p - 3 = 21$
(c) $4 = k + 2$ (d) $7 = 10 + h$
(e) $6 - t = 0$ (f) $6r = 10 + 5r$
(g) $q - 1 = 2q$ (h) $-8 = 2 - 3n$

3 Find the root of each equation.
(a) $4a = 12$ (b) $-2d = 10$
(c) $15 = 3q$ (d) $-8 = -2k$
(e) $\frac{1}{2}m = 3$ (f) $\frac{n}{3} = 5$
(g) $-2 = \frac{t}{4}$ (h) $-\frac{1}{5}h = 2$

4 Three values are given for each equation. Which is the root?

| | A | B | C |
|---|---|---|---|
| (a) $a + 12 = 3$ | $-10$ | 4 | $-9$ |
| (b) $2m - 3 = 15$ | $-5$ | 9 | 6 |
| (c) $10 + 4x = 30$ | 8 | $-4$ | 5 |
| (d) $-4 - 2x = -24$ | 10 | $-6$ | 5 |

5 Solve and check.
(a) $3d + 4 = 16$ (b) $5m - 4 = 21$
(c) $18 - y = 20$ (d) $36 = 4a + 12$
(e) $3t - 6 = 15$ (f) $4p + 13 = -31$
(g) $60 = 12p - 12$ (h) $2x - 5 = -15$

6 (a) To solve the equation, what is your first step?
$$8 - (5 - x) = -3$$
(b) Solve the equation. Check your answer.

7 (a) To solve the equation, what is your first step?
$$3(m - 6) = 2m - 6$$
(b) Solve the equation. Check your answer.

**B** Remember: To solve equations, you use the properties of equations. Review these properties. Check your answers.

8 Find the root of each equation. Verify your answer.
(a) $5a = 9 + 3a$ (b) $4t - 16 = 6t$
(c) $8y - 35 = 3y$ (d) $5p = p - 32$
(e) $3k + 12 = 5k$ (f) $27 - 3t = 6t$

9 Which of these equations have the same root?
(a) $2m + 9 = 27$ (b) $18 - 4k = -k$
(c) $16 + 3q = 25$ (d) $17 = \frac{1}{3}y + 14$
(e) $5 - 2n = -13$ (f) $4d - 36 = d$

10 Solve and verify.

(a) $\frac{m}{4} + 1 = 3$
(b) $\frac{a}{5} - 2 = 1$
(c) $\frac{1}{4}x - 2 = 4$
(d) $5 = \frac{p}{2} + 1$
(e) $\frac{1}{4}k - 3 = -6$
(f) $\frac{d}{5} - 2 = -10$
(g) $\frac{3}{4}k + 8 = 36$
(h) $3 - \frac{5}{4}m = -17$

11 Solve and check.
(a) $5t + 9 = 3t - 21$
(b) $3m + 18 = 58 - m$
(c) $60 + 6a = 12 - 2a$
(d) $6p + 3 = 2p + 11$
(e) $5 - 2r = 3r + 25$
(f) $10 - 5x = 3x + 14$
(g) $k + 10 = \frac{1}{2}k + 8$
(h) $9 + 1.3m = 7 - 0.7m$

12 For each equation
▶ first simplify any expressions
▶ then find the root.
(a) $3(p + 4) = 6$
(b) $4(2t - 3) = 5t$
(c) $10 - (3 - 2x) = 9$
(d) $3(5 + 3a) - 8 = 88$
(e) $2(3x - 2) = 5x + 7$
(f) $5q - (2q + 8) = 16$

13 Solve and verify. Check your answers with a calculator.
(a) $2(x - 1) + 4.3 = 11.3$
(b) $3m - 2 = 4(m - 1) - 2.6$
(c) $2.1k - 6.8 = 3(2 - k) + 7.6$

14 Solve each equation.
(a) $10 - 3(2f - 1) = 1$
(b) $-5(3 - 2y) - 8y = 25$
(c) $5(m + 4) = 3(m - 2)$
(d) $4(a - 5) - (2a + 3) + 13 = 0$

15 The most goals scored in a season in the NHL was achieved by Wayne Gretzky during the 1981–2 season. Find the root of the equation to find the number of goals scored.
$3(m - 6) + 225 = 5m + 23$

16 Baseball is attributed to Colonel Abner Doubleday. He was the first person to lay out the regular baseball diamond and to formulate the rules of play. To find the year in which this happened, solve the following equation.
$2(x - 1450) + 4(x + 810) = 2(x + 3848)$

17 The longest covered bridge in the world is that at Hartland, New Brunswick. To find its length in metres, find the root of the equation.
$3(x - 90.7) - 2(x + 24.3) = 2x - 611.5$

## Computer Tip

You can use a computer to find the roots of an equation.
Run the following program. What equation has been solved?

```
 10 FOR X = 2 TO 13
 20 LET S1 = 2.1 * X + 6.8
 30 LET S2 = 3 * (2 – X) + 31.4
 40 PRINT S1, S2
 50 IF S1 = S2 THEN 90
 60 PRINT X; "IS NOT A ROOT"
 70 NEXT X
 80 GO TO 100
 90 PRINT X; "IS A ROOT"
100 END
```

Modify the program to solve an equation of your own.

## Career Tip

Technicians often need to translate technical and scientific ideas into products and services. They provide a vital link between scientists and engineers and the production workers. They perform tests, solve problems and write up their results to assist scientists and engineers.

- Explore the various types of fields in which technicians work.
- What common essential skills do they need to have?

# 5.2 Combining Skills: Solving Equations

In doing mathematics, you will use these steps over and over again.

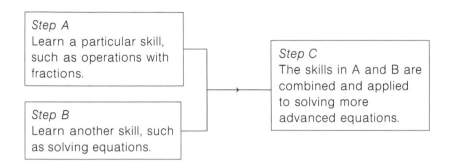

*Step A*
Learn a particular skill, such as operations with fractions.

*Step B*
Learn another skill, such as solving equations.

→

*Step C*
The skills in A and B are combined and applied to solving more advanced equations.

For example, to solve equations that involve fractions you apply steps A and B. The equation is first simplified by using your skills with fractions. Then the equation is solved using your previous skills. Each of the following equations are solved involving a different strategy.

### Example

Solve and check.

(a) $\frac{x}{3} + 8 = \frac{x}{2} + 2$ (b) $x - \frac{3}{5}(x + 5) = \frac{3}{4}(x + 10)$

### Solution

(a)

$$\frac{x}{3} + 8 = \frac{x}{2} + 2$$

$$\frac{2x}{6} + \frac{48}{6} = \frac{3x}{6} + \frac{12}{6}$$ ← Find a common denominator for each term. Then multiply each term by 6.

$$\begin{aligned} 2x + 48 &= 3x + 12 \\ 2x - 2x + 48 &= 3x - 2x + 12 \\ 48 &= x + 12 \\ 48 - 12 &= x + 12 - 12 \\ 36 &= x \text{ or } x = 36 \end{aligned}$$

Check: L.S. $= \frac{36}{3} + 8$ R.S. $= \frac{36}{2} + 2$

$= 12 + 8$ $= 18 + 2$

$= 20$ $= 20$

Checks ✓

(b)

$$x - \frac{3}{5}(x + 5) = \frac{3}{4}(x + 10)$$

$$20\left[x - \frac{3}{5}(x + 5)\right] = 20\left[\frac{3}{4}(x + 10)\right]$$

$$\begin{aligned} 20x - 12(x + 5) &= 15(x + 10) \\ 20x - 12x - 60 &= 15x + 150 \\ 8x - 60 &= 15x + 150 \\ 8x - 15x - 60 &= 15x - 15x + 150 \\ -7x - 60 &= 150 \\ -7x - 60 + 60 &= 150 + 60 \\ -7x &= 210 \\ \frac{-7x}{-7} &= \frac{210}{-7} \\ x &= -30 \end{aligned}$$

Remember: be sure to check your answer in the original equations.

In solving the previous two equations, essentially the same strategy is used: namely simplify the equation by eliminating the fractions. Throughout the exercise, plan ahead the steps that you are going to use to solve the equation.

## Try These

1 To eliminate the fractions in each equation, what is your first step?

(a) $\frac{3m}{2} = 4 + \frac{m}{3}$ (b) $\frac{1}{2} + x = \frac{3}{5}x$

(c) $\frac{5}{8}(x + 2) = \frac{1}{6}(x - 1)$

(d) $6x - 5 = \frac{3}{4} + \frac{x}{5}$

2 For each equation, two numbers are shown. Which number is the root?

(a) $\frac{x + 1}{2} + \frac{x - 3}{3} = 2$ 1, 3

(b) $\frac{x}{3} + 1 = \frac{x}{2} - 1$ 0, 12

(c) $\frac{y}{2} = \frac{1}{5}(y + 15)$ 10, −10

## Written Exercises

**A** Remember that $\frac{3m}{2}$ and $\frac{3}{2}m$ are two different forms of the same expression.

1 Each equation in the right column has been simplified from one of the equations in the left column. Match the equations that are related.

(a) $\frac{2}{3}y + 1 = 3y$

(b) $\frac{3}{5}y + 2 = 10$

(c) $\frac{1}{2}y + 1 = \frac{2}{3}y$

(d) $y + \frac{2}{5} = \frac{1}{2}y$

(e) $\frac{5}{6}y + \frac{1}{3} = 2$

A $3y + 10 = 50$
B $3y + 6 = 4y$
C $5y + 4 = y$
D $5y + 2 = 12$
E $2y + 3 = 9y$
F $10y + 4 = 5y$

2 Solve and check.

(a) $\frac{2}{3}k + 5 = 1$ (b) $3 - \frac{4y}{5} = -1$

(c) $15 - \frac{3}{4}x = 3$ (d) $\frac{2}{3}a - 5 = \frac{3}{4}a$

(e) $\frac{y}{2} + 6 = \frac{1}{3}y$ (f) $\frac{m}{5} + 3 = \frac{m}{8}$

3 Find the root of each equation.

(a) $\frac{1}{2}x - 3 = \frac{1}{3}x + \frac{1}{3}$ (b) $\frac{x}{3} + \frac{2x}{5} = \frac{17}{5} + \frac{4}{15}$

(c) $\frac{3}{4}t + 2 = \frac{1}{2}t + 12$ (d) $\frac{2x}{3} + 3 = \frac{x}{6} - 1$

4 (a) To solve the equation, Ken found the common denominator as shown.

$$\frac{q + 2}{3} + \frac{q - 1}{6} = 4$$

$$\frac{2(q + 2)}{6} + \frac{q - 1}{6} = 4$$

Complete the solution to find the value of $q$.

(b) Check your answer in (a).

5 (a) To solve the following equation Kate multiplied each side of the equation by the least common multiple of 2 and 3, namely 6.

$$\frac{m+1}{2} + \frac{m-3}{3} = 2$$

$$6\left(\frac{m+1}{2} + \frac{m-3}{3}\right) = 6(2)$$

Complete the solution to find the value of $m$.

(b) Verify your answer.

**B** Remember: $\frac{a+2}{2}$ and $\frac{1}{2}(a+2)$ are different forms of the same expression.

6 Solve each equation. Verify your answer.

(a) $\frac{a+2}{2} = \frac{a-5}{3}$ (b) $\frac{x}{4} = \frac{1}{5}(x-3)$

7 Solve.

(a) $\frac{2m+4}{4} - \frac{m+4}{3} = 3$

(b) $\frac{n+1}{3} + 5 = \frac{1}{2}n$

(c) $\frac{5y+20}{10} + \frac{y-8}{2} = 3$

(d) $\frac{2a+2}{7} + \frac{3a-6}{3} = a$

8 Find the root of each equation.

(a) $\frac{6+3p}{2} - \frac{p-4}{5} - \frac{p}{3} = p - 2$

(b) $\frac{3}{4}(a-5) - a = \frac{2}{3}(a+4)$

(c) $\frac{m}{4} + \frac{1}{6}(m-2) = \frac{1}{3}(m-2)$

(d) $\frac{2x-1}{3} - \frac{x}{4} = \frac{1}{2}$

Remember $\frac{2}{3}(a+4)$ and $\frac{2(a+4)}{3}$ are equal.

9 Find the solution set for each equation.

(a) $\frac{1}{6}(x-3) - 2x = \frac{3}{2}(1-x)$

(b) $\frac{3}{4}(2k+5) - \frac{5}{8}(3k-1) = 1$

(c) $\frac{1}{3}(x-2) + \frac{2}{5}(x+3) = \frac{1}{2}(x-5)$

10 To solve equations, you need to decide which method to use.

(a) $\frac{3}{4}x = \frac{x}{3} + \frac{5}{6}$ (b) $5(2x-3) - 8x = 25$

(c) $\frac{-1-3m}{4} - \frac{2+m}{6} = \frac{1}{3}$

(d) $\frac{1}{2}(4-2n) + 2n = \frac{2}{3}(n-4) + 5$

(e) $16 - (5-2k) + 3k = 4(2+k)$

11 In ice hockey Phil Esposito holds the record for the greatest number of games in which he scored 3 goals or more. To find his record solve the equation,

$$\frac{1}{6}(7g - 32) = 16 + \frac{1}{2}g$$

12 The tallest bank building in the world is the Bank of Montreal's First Bank Tower in Toronto. The number of floors in the building is the root of the equation,

$$2n + \frac{2}{3}(n-9) = 210 - \frac{1}{3}n$$

Find the number of floors.

13 Solve the equation below to find the fastest speed, in kilometres per hour, ever travelled on water. The speed was attained by K. Warby in 1978 in the boat Spirit of Australia.

$$\frac{x-4}{4} - \frac{2x+8}{3} + x = \frac{262}{3}$$

## Solving Problems: Making Decisions

Once you learn a skill, you apply the skill to solve a problem. Refer to the steps for solving problems to help you organize your work to solve this problem.

The concert sold 872 tickets. Adult tickets were \$5.50 and student tickets were \$2.50. The total receipts were \$3992. How many of each type were sold?

To solve the problem you need to organize your work, but be sure you understand what the problem asks you to do.

*Steps for Solving Problems*

*Step A* Do I understand the problem?
I. What information am I asked to find?
II. What information am I given?

*Step B* Decide on a method. (Introduce a variable. Write an equation).

*Step C* Do the work (solve the equation).

*Step D* Check the answer in the original problem. (Does your answer satisfy the information in the problem).

*Step E* Write a final statement to answer the question.

*Step 1* Introduce a variable.

Let the number of adult tickets be represented by $n$. Then there are $872 - n$ student tickets.

*Step 2* Write the equation.

$5.50n + 2.50(872 - n) = 3992$

---

14 (a) Solve the equation in Step 2 above.
(b) Check whether the answer is reasonable in the original problem.
(c) Make a final statement. How many of each type of tickets were sold?

15 Solve each problem.
(a) When 25 is subtracted from five times a certain number, the result is 120. What is the number?
(b) A 4.5 m board is cut into two pieces, one twice as long as the other. How long are the pieces?

16 (a) Jean and Martha earned \$43.50. Jean is to receive twice as much as Martha. How much should each receive?
(b) The larger of two numbers is 16 more than 3 times the smaller number. Their sum is 184. Find the numbers.

17 Margo has \$4 less than six times as much money as Kevin. Laura has as much money as Margo and Kevin together. If all three people have a total of \$132, find the amount of money that Laura has.

18 Larry budgets a portion of his \$260 weekly salary for rent. Half of his remaining income exceeds the amount budgeted for rent by \$35. How much money does Larry budget for rent each week?

19 For a fund raising project the student athletic council decided to sell a small and large pennant at \$1.35 and \$2.50 each. They collected \$284.60 for the 135 pennants sold. How many of each type of pennant were sold?

### Math Tip

*Remember*: to solve a word problem that uses an equation, think of the following.

- Use a variable to represent what you are to find. Use variables that suggest information to you such as $t$ for time, $h$ for height, $b$ for base, and so on.
- Use a chart, table, etc to help you organize the given information.
- Write an equation. Plan ahead before you begin to solve the equation. Use the skills for solving equations in this section.
- Check your answer in the original problem.
- Always write a final statement that translates your mathematical answer into English.

# 5.3 Working with Formulas: Extending Skills

Once you learn a skill in mathematics it is applied to new situations. For example, the skills you have learned for solving equations are very useful when working with formulas. For example, the pressure exerted on the floor by the heel of a shoe is given by the formula.

$$P = \frac{100m}{w^2}$$

where $P$ is the pressure measured in kiloPascals (kP), $m$ is the mass of the person in kilograms, and $w$ is the width of the heel in centimetres. You can use this formula to find the mass, $m$, when $P$ and $w$ are known.

For example if the pressure exerted by a person with heels that are 2 cm wide is 1300 kP, then you can find the person's mass.

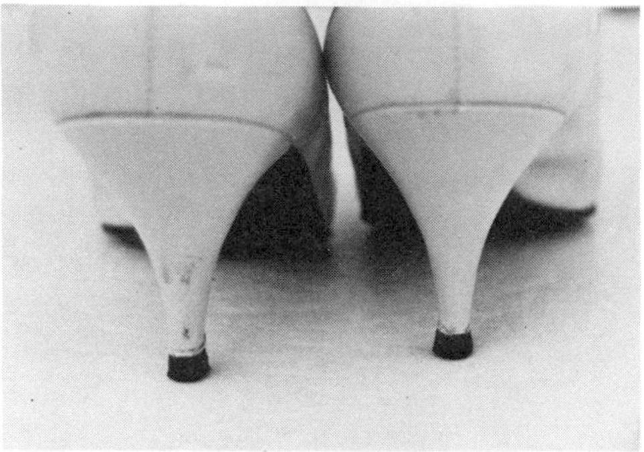

Dance floors have to be strong if they are not to be dented by tiny heels. Steel, for example, will resist 300 000 kP of pressure.

*Method A*

One method is to substitute the known values into the formula, and solve for the remaining variable.

$$P = \frac{100m}{w^2} \qquad P = 1300 \quad w = 2$$

$$1300 = \frac{100m}{2^2} \qquad \text{Substitute.}$$

$$1300 = \frac{100m}{4} \qquad \text{Solve the equation for } m.$$

$$1300 = 25m$$

$$\frac{1300}{25} = \frac{25m}{25}$$

$$52 = m$$

The mass of the person is 52 kg.

*Method B*

Another method is to first solve the formula for the variable $m$. This method is useful when you are to repeat similar calculations such as finding the entries for a table.

$$P = \frac{100m}{w^2}$$

First solve the formula for $m$. Namely, express $m$ in terms of the remaining variables.

$$w^2(P) = w^2\left(\frac{100m}{w^2}\right)$$

$$w^2P = 100m$$

$$\frac{w^2P}{100} = \frac{100m}{100}$$

$$\frac{w^2P}{100} = m \quad \text{or} \quad m = \frac{w^2P}{100}$$

Substitute $P = 1300$, $w = 2$

$$m = \frac{w^2P}{100}$$

$$= \frac{2^2 \times (1300)}{100}$$

$$= 52$$

Method B is useful to complete a table of values where you repeat the same calculations a number of times.
The steps followed in this method are sometimes referred to as *changing the subject of the formula*.

| $m$ | $w$ | $P$ |
|---|---|---|
| ? | 2 | 1250 |
| ? | 3 | 1000 |
| ? | 4 | 2000 |

**Example 1**

Solve the formula for the variable indicated.

(a) $v = u + at$, for $t$ (b) $A = \frac{1}{2}(a + b)h$, for $b$

**Solution**

(a)
$$v = u + at$$
$$v - u = u - u + at$$
$$v - u = at$$

Think: To isolate the term with $t$, subtract $u$ from each side of the equation.

$$\frac{v-u}{a} = \frac{at}{a}$$

Think: To isolate the variable, $t$ divide both sides by $a$.

$$\frac{v-u}{a} = t \text{ or } t = \frac{v-u}{a}$$

(b)
$$A = \frac{1}{2}(a + b)h$$
$$2A = 2 \times \frac{1}{2}(a + b)h$$

First eliminate the fraction, by multiplying both sides by 2.

$$2A = (a + b)h$$
$$2A = ah + bh$$

To solve for $b$, you need to expand the bracket.

$$2A - ah = ah - ah + bh$$
$$2A - ah = bh$$

Isolate the term containing $b$. Subtract $ah$ from both sides.

$$\frac{2A - ah}{h} = \frac{bh}{h}$$
$$\frac{2A - ah}{h} = b \text{ or } b = \frac{2A - ah}{h}$$

## Try These

1 Use the formula $P = 4s$. Find $P$ when
(a) $s = 5$ (b) $s = 12$ (c) $s = \frac{1}{2}$

2 Use the formula $P = 4s$. Find $s$ when
(a) $P = 24$ (b) $P = 32$ (c) $P = 100$

3 Use the formula $A = lw$. Find $A$ when
(a) $l = 2, w = 3$ (b) $l = 5, w = 6$

4 Use the formula $A = lw$. Find $l$ when
(a) $A = 24, w = 3$ (b) $A = 40, l = 10$

## Written Exercises

### A

1 The formula for the area of a triangle is $A = \frac{1}{2}bh$ where $b$ is the base and $h$ the height. Use the values shown and substitute into this formula. Solving for the remaining variable.
(a) $b = 8, h = 5$ (b) $A = 10, b = 4$
(c) $A = 18, h = 9$ (d) $A = 1.5, b = 3.0$

2 Solve the formula $A = \frac{1}{2}bh$ for $b$. Use the values for the remaining variables to find the value of $b$.
(a) $A = 12, h = 4$ (b) $A = 20, h = 5$

3 Solve the formula $A = \frac{1}{2}bh$ for $h$. Find $h$ in each triangle.
(a) $A = 36$, $b = 9$ (b) $A = 4$, $b = 4$

4 The formula for the cost of renting a video machine is
$C = 15 + 4d$
where $C$ is the cost in dollars and $d$ is the number of days rented.
(a) If the cost was \$51, for how many days was the machine rented?
(b) Rearrange the equation so you have a formula for finding $d$.

**B** **Once you obtain a value for the variable, check your answer. Substitute into the original formula to verify your work.**

5 Find the missing value in each of the following.
(a) $V = lwh$; $V = 8000$, $w = 20$, $l = 40$
(b) $I = prt$; $p = 1500$, $r = 0.1$, $t = 3$
(c) $L = t(a - b)$; $a = 20$, $b = 7$, $t = 25$
(d) $I = \frac{E}{R + r}$; $E = 240$, $R = 110$, $r = 10$
(e) $v = u + at$; $v = 50$, $u = 25$, $t = 5$
(f) $V = \frac{1}{3}\pi r^2 h$; $V = 628$, $r = 10$, $h = 6$

6 Find the missing value for each of the following.
(a) $A = \frac{1}{2}(a + b)h$; $a = 32$, $b = 18$, $h = 9$
(b) $L = \frac{a - t}{4t}$; $a = 180$, $t = 20$
(c) $P = I^2R$; $P = 800$, $I = 20$
(d) $v^2 = u^2 + 12t$; $u = 16$, $v = 20$
(e) $a = S(1 + r^2)$; $S = 100$, $r = 5$
(f) $M = \frac{xy - 5}{n}$; $M = 1500$, $x = 5$, $y = 901$

7 Find the value indicated.
(a) $E$ when $I = 6$ and $R = 18$. Use $E = IR$.
(b) $L$ when $P = 146$ and $W = 17$. Use $P = 2L + 2W$.
(c) $u$ when $V = 114$, $g = 9$ and $t = 4$. Use $V = u + gt$.
(d) $A$ when $r = 8$, $h = 21$ and $\pi = 3.14$. Use $A = 2\pi rh$.
(e) $L$ when $a = 4$, $n = 35$, $d = 3$. Use $L = a + (n - 1)d$.
(f) $S$ when $u = 50$, $g = 10$, $t = 3$. Use $S = ut + \frac{1}{2}gt^2$.

8 Find the missing value for each of the following.
(a) $S = \left(\frac{u + v}{2}\right)t$; $v = 16$, $t = 40$, $S = 600$
(b) $y = m(x - a)$; $y = 9$, $m = \frac{1}{4}$, $a = 12$
(c) $v = u + at$; $v = -30$, $u = 10$, $t = 4$
(d) $S = 180(n - 2)$; $S = 1440$

9 (a) Solve the formula for $m$.
$y = mx + b$
(b) Use your formula in (a) to complete the table.

| m | x | y | b |
|---|---|---|---|
| ? | 2 | 10 | 4 |
| ? | −3 | 4 | −2 |
| ? | 3 | 0 | −3 |

10 (a) Solve the formula for $s$.
$t = 3(p + s)$
(b) Use your formula in (a) to complete the chart.

| t | p | s |
|---|---|---|
| 32.4 | 6.5 | ? |
| 39.3 | 9.6 | ? |
| 37.2 | 4.8 | ? |
| 22.8 | 9.3 | ? |

Did you use a calculator?

11 Use the formula to complete the entries in the table.
$$A = \left(\frac{a + b}{2}\right)t$$

| | A | a | b | t |
|---|---|---|---|---|
| (a) | 18 | 8 | ? | 3 |
| (b) | 12 | 6 | ? | 1.5 |
| (c) | 11.2 | 4.8 | ? | 2 |

12 Solve each formula for the variable indicated.
(a) $v^2 = u^2 + 30t$, for $t$
(b) $s = 180(n - 2)$, for $n$
(c) $v^2 = 2gt$, for $g$

13 Solve each equation to give a formula for the variable indicated.
(a) $2x + 3y = 15$, for $y$
(b) $I = prt$, for $t$
(c) $T = \frac{x - y}{z}$, for $z$
(d) $H = \frac{2}{5}(T - 10)$, for $T$
(e) $S = \left(\frac{u + v}{2}\right)t$, for $u$
(f) $E = mc^2$, for $c$

14 Distance ($d$), speed ($s$) and time ($t$) are related by thc formula $d - st$.
(a) What distance does a train travelling at a steady speed of 90 km/h travel in 3 h?
(b) What is the speed of a helicopter that travels 860 km in 4 h?
(c) How long does it take a cyclist travelling at an average speed of 18 km/h to go 45 km?

15 The stopping distance, $d$, of a car on dry concrete is given by the formula
$$d = 0.005v^2$$
where $d$ is the distance in metres and $v$ is the speed of the car in kilometres per hour.
(a) How many metres does the car take to stop when it is travelling at 100 km/h?
(b) If the skid marks left by a car measured 24.5 m at what speed was it travelling?

16 The distance that a bicycle travels with each revolution of the pedals is given by the formula
$$d = \pi b \frac{n}{N}$$
where $d$ is the distance in centimetres, $\pi = 3.14$, $b$ is the diameter of the bicycle's wheels in centimetres, $n$ is the number of teeth on the chain-wheel and $N$ is the number of teeth on the rear sprocket.

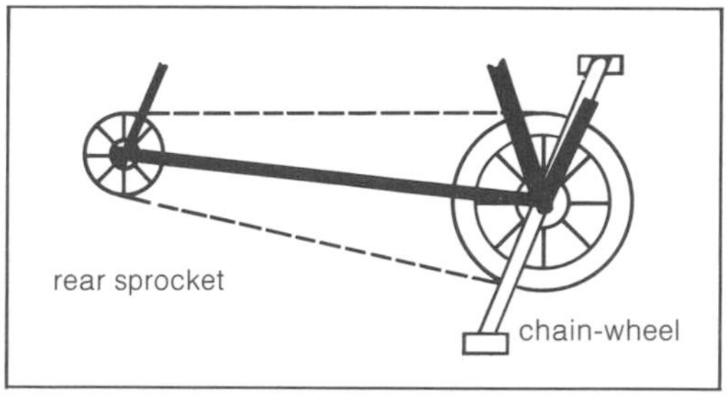


(a) How far will a bicycle with 72 cm wheels travel for each revolution of the pedals if the chain-wheel has 60 teeth and the rear sprocket has 24 teeth?
(b) If a bicycle with 65 cm wheels travels 408.2 cm with one turn of the pedals and it has 25 teeth on the rear sprocket, how many teeth does it have on the chain-wheel?

## C

17 The combined resistance $R$, measured in ohms ($\Omega$), of the parallel circuit shown is given by
$$\frac{1}{R} = \frac{1}{R_1} + \frac{1}{R_2}$$

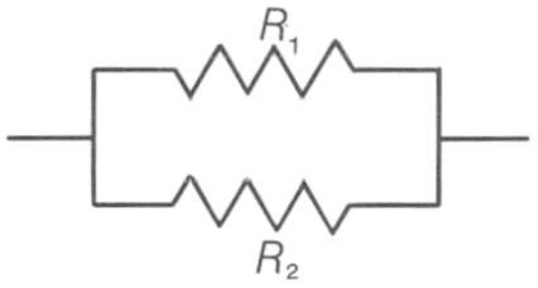


(a) Find $R$ when $R_1$ is 3 $\Omega$ and $R_2$ is 2 $\Omega$.
(b) If the combined resistance is 8 $\Omega$ when $R_1$ is 12 $\Omega$, what is the resistance of $R_2$?

### Calculator Tip

Often in using a calculator you have more than one procedure you can follow. To calculate $d = 0.083v^2$ for $v = 48.6$, compare the two procedures:
- When would procedure A be used? B be used?
- When would you not use procedure A?

Procedure A [C] 48.6 [×] 48.6 [×] 0.083 [=] output ?

Procedure B [C] 48.6 [$y^x$] 2 [=] [×] 0.083 [=] output ?

# 5.4 Solving Quadratic Equations

The height of a drop of water in the fountain is described by the formula
$h = 5 + 4t - t^2$
where $h$ is the height in metres and $t$ is the time in seconds. You can find how long a drop of water is in the air by substituting $h = 0$ and solving the resulting equation. $0 = 5 + 4t - t^2$ or more commonly written as $5 + 4t - t^2 = 0$. This is a **quadratic equation**.

You can solve it using your factoring skills.

$5 + 4t - t^2$
$(5 - t)(1 + t)$

Now you can use the property of numbers to obtain the solution. If $ab = 0$ then either $a = 0$ or $b = 0$. An equation in factored form is expressed as follows

(a factor) × (another factor) = 0

For this product to equal zero, one or other of the factors must equal zero. This principle is applied to solve quadratic equations.

$2(5 - t)(1 + t) = 0$
either $5 - t = 0$ or $1 + t = 0$

then $\quad t = 5$ or $t = -1$ — The value $-1$ is not possible since time is positive.

The drop of water is in the air for 5 s.

## Example

Find the roots and verify.
(a) $x^2 + 9x = 0$ (b) $x^2 + 2x - 24 = 0$

## Solution

(a) $x^2 + 9x = 0$ — $x$ is a common factor
$x(x + 9) = 0$
So either $x = 0$ or $x + 9 = 0$
$x = -9$

Check:

When $x = 0$,
L.S. $= x^2 + 9x$
$= 0^2 + 9(0)$
$= 0$
= R.S. Checks ✓

When $x = -9$
L.S. $= x^2 + 9x$
$= (-9)^2 + 9(-9)$
$= 81 + (-81)$
$= 0$
= R.S. Checks ✓

The roots are 0 and $-9$.

(b) $x^2 + 2x - 24 = 0$
$(x + 6)(x - 4) = 0$
So either $x + 6 = 0$ or $x - 4 = 0$
then $x = -6$ or $x = 4$

Check:

When $x = -6$
L.S. $= x^2 + 2x - 24$
$= (-6)^2 + 2(-6) - 24$
$= 36 + (-12) - 24$
$= 0$
= R.S.

When $x = 4$
L.S. $= x^2 + 2x - 24$
$= 4^2 + 2(4) - 24$
$= 16 + 8 - 24$
$= 0$
= R.S.

The roots are $-6$ and 4.

## Try These

1 What are the roots of each factored quadratic?
(a) $n(n-4)=0$
(b) $(m+2)(m+2)=0$
(c) $5(k+1)(k-1)=0$
(d) $4t(t-7)=0$
(e) $(2d-1)(d-3)=0$
(f) $(a+4)(3a-2)=0$

2 Solve for $x$.
(a) $(x+1)(x+2)=0$
(b) $(x+3)(x+5)=0$
(c) $(x-2)(x+1)=0$
(d) $(x-6)(x+5)=0$
(e) $(x-2)(x+2)=0$
(f) $(x-3)(x+8)=0$

## Written Exercises

**A** Remember: Use the principle to solve quadratic equations. If $ab=0$ then either $a=0$ or $b=0$.

1 Solve by factoring. Check your results.
(a) $x^2+3x+2=0$ (b) $x^2-6x-7=0$
(c) $x^2-x-2=0$ (d) $x^2-6x+5=0$
(e) $x^2-5x+6=0$ (f) $x^2+2x-3=0$

2 Solve and verify.

Remember to check for any common factors first.

(a) $m^2-25=0$ (b) $y^2+6y=0$
(c) $3x^2-3x-6=0$ (d) $n^2+8n-33=0$
(e) $4p^2-28p=0$ (f) $2f^2-6f-20=0$

3 Factor. Then find the roots.
(a) $x^2+9x+8=0$ (b) $a^2-3a+2=0$
(c) $p^2-36=0$ (d) $m^2-2m-8=0$
(e) $r^2-r-6=0$ (f) $y^2-2y-15=0$
(g) $x^2-4x-21=0$ (h) $x^2-x-42=0$

4 (a) Solve and check.
$x^2+6x+9=0$
(b) How many roots did you find in (a)?
(c) How are these roots related?

5 (a) Solve and check.
$x^2-9=0$
(b) How many roots did you find in (a)?
(c) How are the roots related?

**B** Once you factor the equation, check your factors. Remember to look for common factors first.

6 Find the roots. Verify your answers.
(a) $x^2+2x+1=0$
(b) $a^2-4a-12=0$
(c) $d^2+3d-10=0$
(d) $m^2-8m+12=0$
(e) $t^2-8t+16=0$
(f) $6q^2-3q=0$
(g) $a^2+8a+15=0$
(h) $2x^2+10x+8=0$

7 Solve and check.
(a) $3w^2-12w-36=0$
(b) $4y^2+28y-72=0$
(c) $2p^2+10p+8=0$
(d) $3x^2-12x-63=0$
(e) $5k^2-10k-40=0$
(f) $3a^2-6a+3=0$
(g) $3h^2-12=0$
(h) $4m^2-8m+4=0$

8 A jewelry company finds that the best size of cardboard on which to market its earrings is given by the roots of the equation
$x^2-14x+48=0$
where $x$ is the length of a side measured in centimetres. Find the dimensions of the cardboard.

9 The jewelry company finds that the maximum profit they can obtain from the earrings occurs when the selling price is given by the equation

$$0 = p^2 - 4p - 12$$

where $p$ is the price in dollars. Find the best selling price.

Did you know that the most precious gems are not diamonds, or even sapphires, but rather the elusive ruby. At present rubies command the highest price for precious gems. The rarest gem is called painite, named after its discoverer A.C. Pain. However you can probably guess which gem is the hardest.

10 (a) To solve the following equation, what is your first step?

$$x^2 - 11x = 12$$

(b) Solve the equation in (a). Verify your answer.

11 Solve each quadratic equation. Check your answer.

(a) $y^2 + 5y = 14$ (b) $f^2 = 18 + 7f$
(c) $q^2 + 20 = 9q$ (d) $n^2 + 2n = 24$
(e) $t^2 = t + 12$ (f) $r^2 = 10r$
(g) $3p^2 - 12p = 36$ (h) $x^2 - 4 = 2 - 5x$

12 Write each equation in a suitable form. Then find its roots.

(a) $m^2 + m - 3 = 12 - m$
(b) $2x^2 + 3x - 5 = x^2 + 3x + 20$
(c) $3(n^2 + 1) - 2n = 2(n^2 + n)$
(d) $(h + 5)(h - 1) = 19 - h$

13 The height of a soccer ball is given by the equation

$$h = 35t - 5t^2$$

where $h$ is the height in metres and $t$ is the time in seconds, the ball is in the air.

(a) Find $t$ when $h = 0$.
(b) For how many seconds was the ball in the air?
(c) After how many seconds is the ball at a height of 30 m?
(d) How do you explain the two answers in part (c)?

14 To solve each equation, you need to decide which skills to use.

▶ Examine each equation carefully.
▶ Then solve (check your answers).

(a) $3x + 5 - x = 13 - 6x$
(b) $2a^2 - 2a + 6 = a^2 + 3a$
(c) $t^2 + 4t - 1 = t^2 + 3t - 4$
(d) $5y + 3 = 4 + 5y - y^2$
(e) $3a^2 - 5a - 3 = a^2 + 3a - 3$
(f) $2m^2 - 7m = m - 4 - 2m^2$

## Computer Tip

You can use a computer to find the roots of a quadratic equation. You need to know the formula. The roots of the quadratic equation $ax^2 + bx + c = 0$ are given by the formula

$$x = \frac{-b + \sqrt{b^2 - 4ac}}{2a} \qquad x = \frac{-b - \sqrt{b^2 - 4ac}}{2a}$$

Choose a quadratic equation. Input the values for $a$, $b$, and $c$ when you run the following program.

```
10 INPUT A, B, C
20 LET D = B ↑ 2 − 4 * A * C
30 IF D < 0 THEN 80
40 LET ROOT 1 = (−B + SQR(D))/(2 * A)
50 LET ROOT 2 = (−B − SQR(D))/(2 * A)
60 PRINT "THE ROOTS ARE"; ROOT 1, ROOT 2
70 GO TO 90
80 PRINT "THE ROOTS ARE NOT REAL"
90 END
```

Try the program for quadratic equations in this section. Remember, you must first use your skills in mathematics to write the equation in the form $ax^2 + bx + c = 0$.

## Applications: Facts from Equations

Once you learn a skill, whether mathematics related or career related, you often will follow this procedure: Step A and Step B.

*Step A* → *Step B*

Learn a skill → Apply the skill to solve a problem

The skills you have learned for solving quadratic equations are applied to solve problems.

An arborist has been trained to understand the science of tree care, as well as to undertake preventative programs to maintain healthy trees. The many diverse skills are applied to solve many problems involving trees.

---

15 The dimensions, in metres, of a swimming pool are given by the roots of the quadratic equation $y^2 - 18y + 72 = 0$. Solve the equation to find the dimensions of the pool.

16 The minimum distance of Halley's comet from the sun is given by the root of the quadratic equation (expressed in millions of kilometres).

$$x^2 - 86x - 267 = 0$$

Find the distance.

17 The root of the quadratic equation

$$2x^2 - 54x - 648 = 0$$

gives the calculated height of the highest ocean wave. Solve the equation to find the height in metres.

18 During the 1984 summer Olympics in Los Angeles, California, Canada won a number of gold and silver medals. Solve the quadratic equation to find the number of each. (There were more silver medals won than gold medals). $3x^2 - 84x + 540 = 0$

19 Canadian Prime Minister, Lester B. Pearson, was awarded the Nobel Peace Prize for organizing the United Nations intervention of the Suez Canal Crisis. The year in which the award was made is a root of

$$x^2 - 1950x - 13\,699 = 0$$

20 The width for the most efficient tunnel for people to walk through is given by a root of the equation,

$$-0.03x^2 + 0.66x \quad 0.63 = 0$$

Find the width in metres.

21 The St. Lawrence Seaway opened on April 25th, but do you know in what year? The root of the quadratic equation gives the year in which water transportation was stretched almost halfway across Canada.

$$x^2 - 1957x - 3918 = 0$$

### Consumer Tip

As a consumer, you look for ways to cut costs. For example, if you lower your thermostat one degree in winter, you can save a considerable amount of money without any discomfort. By opening a window at night to let in fresh air, you increase your heating bill.

A List ways in which energy can be wasted in a home. List any suggestions to save energy and thus money.

B List some ways in which energy can be wasted in a school. List any suggestions to save energy, and thus money.

C List some ways in which energy can be wasted in driving a car. List any suggestions to save energy and thus money.

# 5.5 Solving Inequations

In learning mathematics, look for what is alike and what is different to help you remember. For example, to solve equations you used these properties.

- ▶ You can add equal values to each side of an equation.
- ▶ You can subtract equal values from each side of an equation.
- ▶ You can multiply both sides of an equation by equal values.
- ▶ You can divide both sides of an equation by equal values.

In a similar way, you can use the skills you have learned to solve equations to help you solve inequations.
But remember, look for how the properties are different.

| Statement | Example | |
|---|---|---|
| ▶ You can add or subtract equal values to both sides of an inequation. | $m > 3$<br>$m + 2 > 5$ | (Add 2 on both sides. |
| ▶ You can multiply or divide both sides of an inequation by the same positive value. | $m > 3$<br>$2m > 6$ | (Multiply by 2 on both sides. |

However, what happens if you multiply or divide both sides of an inequation by negative values? To check this, try an example.

$4 > 3$. Now multiply both sides by $-2$
Is $-2 \times 4 > -2 \times 3$ true?
The statement is not true. In fact $-2 \times 4 < -2 \times 3$ since $-8 < -6$.

The example illustrates an important property of inequations.

| | | |
|---|---|---|
| ▶ If you multiply or divide both sides of an inequation by a negative equal value then the inequality is reversed. | $m > 3$<br>$-2m < -6$ ← | Multiply both sides by $-2$, reverse the inequality |

These properties of inequations are applied to obtain the solutions to an inequation.

## Example

Solve each inequation. Graph the solution set.

(a) $2x + 3 \geqq 7,\ x \in I$ ← *I* is the set of integers

(b) $2(3 - n) > 8,\ n \in R$ ← *n* belongs to the set of real numbers

## Solution

(a)

$$2x + 3 \geqq 7$$
$$2x + 3 - 3 \geqq 7 - 3$$
$$2x \geqq 4$$
$$\frac{2x}{2} \geqq \frac{4}{2}$$
$$x \geqq 2$$

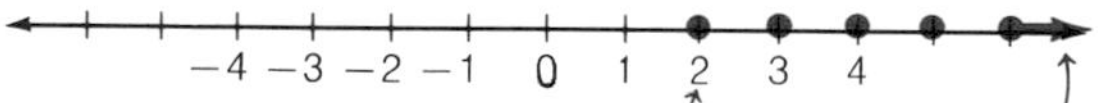

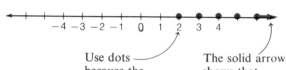

Use dots because the solutions are the integers 2, 3, 4 . . .

The solid arrow shows that thc solutions continue.

(b)

$$2(3 - x) > 8$$
$$6 - 2x > 8$$
$$6 - 6 - 2x > 8 - 6$$
$$-2x > 2$$
$$\frac{-2x}{-2} < \frac{2}{-2}$$
$$x < -1$$

← The inequality is reversed because we are dividing by −2.

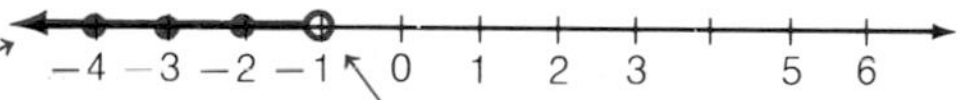


A solid arrow shows all the real numbers less than −1.

An open circle is used to show that −1 is not included in the solution set.

## Try These

1 Decide whether each statement is true or false.
(a) $6 \geqq 4$ (b) $3 > 8$ (c) $5 \leqq -2$
(d) $-10 > 15$ (e) $-4 \geqq -6$ (f) $12 < -18$

2 What is the solution set? $n \in I$.
(a) $n \geqq 3$ (b) $n > 5$ (c) $n < 2$
(d) $n \leqq -2$ (e) $n > -1$ (f) $n \leqq 0$

3 Match each inequation with the graph of its solution set.

(a) $x < 1,\ x \in I$ A 

(b) $x \leqq 1,\ x \in R$ B 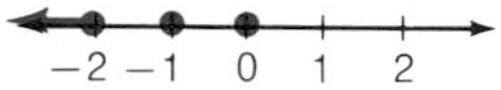


(c) $x > -1,\ x \in R$ C 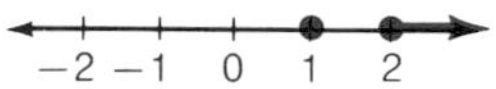


(d) $x \geqq 1,\ x \in I$ D 

## Written Exercises

**A** Unless indicated otherwise, the variables represent real numbers.

1 Solve each inequation.
(a) $a + 5 \geqq 12$ (b) $k - 3 < 2$
(c) $x + 3 < 8$ (d) $t - 4 \leqq 0$
(e) $-4 + q > -5$ (f) $2a < 5 + a$

2 Solve each inequation.
(a) $5t > 20$ (b) $-3y \leqq 18$
(c) $4y < -12$ (d) $\frac{1}{3}k > -2$
(e) $-p > 6$ (f) $\frac{-x}{2} \geqq 3$

3 Write the inequation shown by each graph. In each the variable, $n$, represents real numbers.

(a)

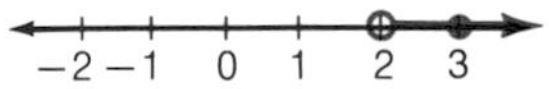

(b)

(c)

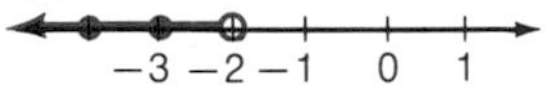

(d)

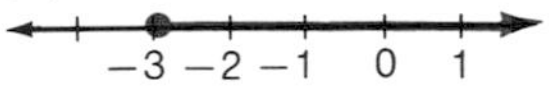

4 In the following graphs the variable, $k$, represents integers. Write two possible inequations that can describe each. The first one is done for you.

(a)

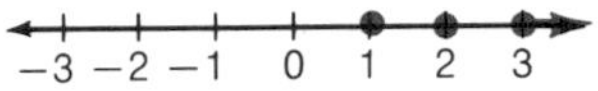

$k \geqq 1$ or $k > 0$

(b)

(c)

(d)

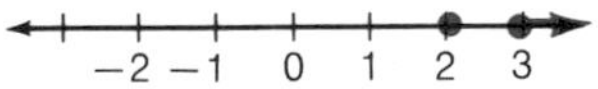

(e)

**B** Review the properties of inequations. Use these to find the solution sets.

5 Draw a graph of the solution set for

(a) $2x + 3 \leqq 15 - 2x,\ x \in R$

(b) Draw a graph of the solution set for $2x + 3 \leqq 15 - 2x,\ x \in I$

(c) How are the answers in (a) and (b) alike? How are they different?

6 Solve each inequation.

(a) $p + 5 \leqq 2(p - 5)$

(b) $-4 + x \geqq -5 + 3x$

(c) $30 < 3(y - 4)$

(d) $a \geqq 3(8 - a)$

(e) $8y - 14 > 3(y - 3)$

(f) $\frac{1}{2}(m - 4) < 10$

(g) $3(n + 4) \geqq 2(n - 7)$

(h) $2(x - 3) + 4 > 8$

7 Solve each of the following.

(a) $3x + 5 \leqq 2x - 6,\ x \in R$

(b) $2x - 4 \geqq 3x + 2,\ x \in I$

(c) $5a - 2a + a > -6,\ a \in I$

(d) $2(p - 3) + 4 > 14 - p,\ p \in R$

8 Solve each of the following.

(a) $2(x + 3) < x$

(b) $2m > 3(m - 4)$

(c) $4(a - 1) \leqq -12$

(d) $-3(2m - 2) \geqq -54$

(e) $-7 - 3m \leqq 14 + 2(m - 1)$

(f) $3(p - 2) + 6 < 24 - p$

(g) $5(3x + 5) \geqq 4(4x - 1) + 6$

(h) $3(a + 2) + 4a \leqq 6(a - 3) + 15$

**C**

9 Solve and graph the solution set, $x \in R$.

(a) $\frac{8x + 5}{3} < 15$  (b) $\frac{1}{2}x + \frac{3}{4}x \leqq 5$

(c) $x + \frac{3}{4}(x - 4) \geqq \frac{2}{3}(x + 2)$

(d) $\frac{5x + 1}{6} \leqq \frac{4x + 3}{5} - \frac{1}{2}$

## Consumer Tip

Is a free chequing account really "free"? Phone three different banks and obtain information about their "free" chequing accounts. Is a minimum balance needed? Do you get your cheques back? Do you get a statement each month? Are there any service charges whatsoever? (You will explore this topic further in Chapters 7 to 9. Read on!)

## Calculator Tip

Review what these keys do on a calculator. Refer to a manual whenever you need to.

| | | | | | | |
|---|---|---|---|---|---|---|
| $\sqrt{x}$ | $\frac{1}{x}$ | +/− | % | $x^2$ | $y^x$ | MS |
| MR | M+ | M− | $\pi$ | C | AC | $\sqrt[x]{x}$ |

# 5.6 Problem Solving: Combining Skills

Often you can combine different skills that you have learned to develop a method to solve a new type of problem.

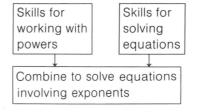

When solving equations involving exponents, you need to use this property of exponents.

| Skills for working with powers | Skills for solving equations |
|---|---|

↓ Combine to solve equations involving exponents

Property

> If two powers are equal and their bases are the same then their exponents must be equal.

Example
If $2^x = 2^5$
then $x = 5$

To solve some equations, you must first express the powers with the same base. To do this you need to recognize which property of exponents to use.

**Example**
Solve.
$3^{3m} = 9^{m+5}$

**Solution**

$3^{3m} = 9^{m+5}$

$3^{3m} = (3^2)^{m+5}$ ← Write base 9 as 3.

$3^{3m} = 3^{2m+10}$ ← Use the property of powers of a power.

$3m = 2m + 10$ ← Both powers have base 3, so exponents are equal.

$3m - 2m = 2m - 2m + 10$

$m = 10$

## Written Exercises

**B**

1 Solve. Check your answers.
(a) $3^{x+2} = 3^4$ (b) $2^5 = 2^{2k-1}$
(c) $7^{3n+1} = 7^{n+4}$ (d) $5^{3q+1} = \frac{1}{5^2}$

2 Which of these equations have the same root?
(a) $4^{2m} = 4^{m-7}$ (b) $5^{3r-2} = 5^{4r-7}$
(c) $2^{2x-3} = 2^{2+x}$ (d) $7^{3y-3} = 7^{y+7}$

3 Solve. Remember ask yourself what the first step is to solve the equation.
(a) $2^{3t-1} = 4$ (b) $9^{3f} = 3^{5f-12}$
(c) $121 = 11^{4-3z}$ (d) $25^k = 125^{4-k}$

4 Solve.
(a) $5^4 = \frac{1}{5^{2k}}$ (b) $9^t = 27^{2+t}$
(c) $8 = \frac{1}{2^p}$ (d) $1 = 7^{k+2}$

5 Solve. Check your answer.
(a) $2^{2x} = 2^{x+20}$ (b) $3^{3x+4} = 3^{2x-15}$
(c) $2^x = 32$ (d) $3^x = \frac{1}{3}$
(e) $2^x = \frac{1}{4}$ (f) $4^x = 2^8$
(g) $7^{2x-8} = 1$ (h) $3^{3m-1} = 9^{m+5}$
(i) $5^{x-2} = 25^{x+3}$ (j) $3^x = \frac{1}{27}$
(k) $5^{2x} = \frac{1}{25}$ (l) $10^x = 0.01$

6 Solve.
(a) $9^x = 27^{x-1}$ (b) $125^{x-1} = 25^x$
(c) $8^{x+2} = 16^{x-1}$ (d) $100^{2x} = 1000^{x-1}$

## Review: Practice and Problems

1 Solve. Check your answers.
(a) $5m - 16 = 2(m + 4)$
(b) $\frac{2}{5}m + 2 = 1$
(c) $6(x - 2) = 12x - (x - 3)$
(d) $\frac{8 + 3a}{3} - \frac{a - 5}{2} = a - 1$

2 Find the missing value.
(a) $U = V - at$; $a = 8$, $V = 60$, $U = 35$
(b) $R = \frac{P}{I^2}$; $P = 1200$, $I = 30$
(c) $A = \frac{xy + 8}{z}$; $A = 2400$, $x = 10$, $y = 856$

3 Solve.
(a) $x^2 + 5x + 6 = 0$
(b) $x^2 - 7x + 12 = 0$
(c) $x^2 - x - 12 = 0$
(d) $p^2 - 1 = 0$

4 Solve.
(a) $3x + 4 = 10$
(b) $m + 8 = 3(m - 4)$

5 The distance (in kilometres) via railway between Ottawa and Winnipeg is given by the root of the following equation.

$$\frac{1}{2}(x + 5) - 3(x + 2) = -3x + 1214$$

Solve the equation to find the distance.

6 A stone is shot upwards and its height, $h$, in metres after time, $t$, in seconds is given by

$$h = 72\,t - 8t^2$$

(a) After how many seconds is the stone at the height of 112 m?
(b) Why are there two answers in (a)?

### Math Tip

To solve problems you must understand the meaning of each mathematical word. Make a list of all the new words you read in this chapter. Use an example to illustrate the meaning of each word.

## A Practice Test

1 Solve and verify.
(a) $4x - 10 = 6x + 58$
(b) $5(y - 7) + 9 = 2(3y + 5)$

2 Solve.
(a) $\frac{3a - 1}{5} = \frac{4a + 6}{6}$
(b) $\frac{x - 4}{4} + 5 = \frac{2x - 7}{3}$

3 Solve. Graph the solution set, $x \in R$.
(a) $\frac{2x - 6}{4} < 4$
(b) $3(2t + 5) \geqq -4(5 - t) - 3t$

4 Use the formula $S = \frac{n}{2}[2a + (n - 1)d]$
Find $d$ when $S = 1079$, $n = 26$, $a = 4$.

5 The power output $P$ of a motor is given by the formula,

voltage (volts)
resistance (ohms)

$$P = VI - I^2R$$

power (Watts)
current (amperes)

where $V$ represents the voltage, $R$ the resistance and $I$ the current. Find the power, $P$, of an electric motor if $V = 120$ (volts), $I = 12$ (amperes) and $R = 4$ (ohms).

6 The earth's circumference, $C$, in kilometres, is given by the root of the equation

$$3(C - 1) + 8052 = 168\,817 - C$$

Solve the equation. What is the earth's circumference?

7 The number of diagonals that can be drawn in a polygon of $n$ sides is given by

$$\frac{n(n - 3)}{2}$$

If a polygon has 20 diagonals, how many sides does it have?

# 6 Measurement: Formulas, Skills and Applications

skills with perimeter, circumference of a circle, formulas for areas, surface area of prisms and pyramids, problem-solving, cylinders, cone, spheres, principles of volume, formulas for volume, solving problems and applications

## Introduction

There are many occasions when you need to measure or as a consumer make a decision based on measurement. There are many careers in which you will need measuring skills. In each of the photographs, measurement played an important role. What skills in measurement do you think were used?

# 6.1 Working with Perimeter

When you find the distance around a figure you are finding its perimeter. Problems about perimeter occur in many situations.

- the landscaper wants to know how many bushes are needed to plant around the yard.
- the farmer needs to know how much fencing is needed.
- the race driver must know the distance around the track.

The Pentagon is the largest office building in the world. It is named after its regular five-sided shape. Each of its outside walls is 302 m long.

If the figure is a regular polygon, you can use a short cut to find its perimeter. For example, the Pentagon has five equal sides.

$$\text{Perimeter} = 5 \times 302 \text{ m} = 1510 \text{ m}$$

(Five equal sides, each 302 m long.)

The perimeter of the Pentagon is 1510 m.

If the polygon is not regular, then you find its perimeter by finding the distance around, as shown in the following example.

### Example 1

Calculate the perimeter of each polygon.

(a)

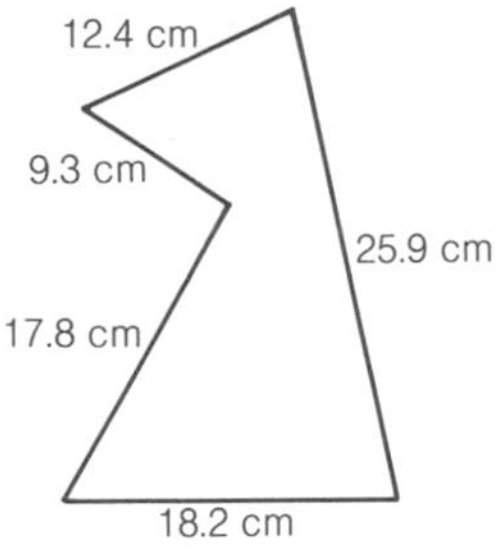


(b)

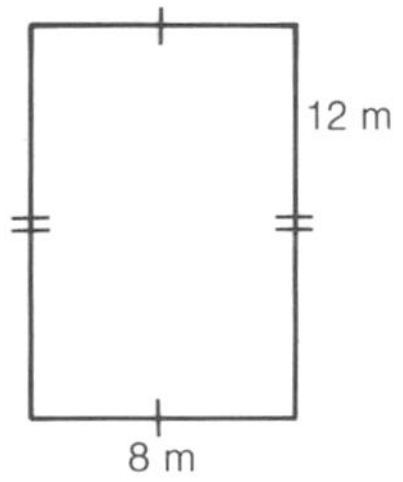


### Solution

(a) $P = 12.4 + 25.9 + 18.2 + 17.8 + 9.3$
$= 83.6$

The perimeter is 83.6 cm.

(b) $P = 2(l + w)$
$P = 2(8 + 12)$
$= 2(20)$
$= 40$

The perimeter is 40 m.

Think:
Since the figure is a rectangle use a short cut.

Skills with perimeter are often needed to solve problems.

### Example 2

Weatherstripping costs $0.89/m. Find the cost of putting weatherstripping around the basement door shown.

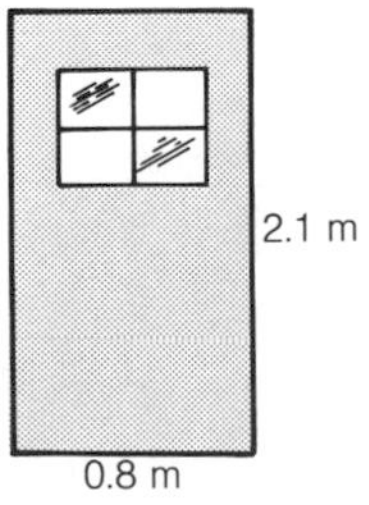


### Solution

*Step 1*: $P = 2(l + w)$
$P = 2(2.1 + 0.8)$
$= 2(2.9)$
$= 5.8$

Think:
Find the perimeter of the door.

*Step 2*: $\text{Cost} = 5.8 \times \$0.89$
$= \$5.162$

Think:
Calculate the cost.

The weatherstripping costs $5.16.

## Try These

1 What is the perimeter of each polygon?

(a)

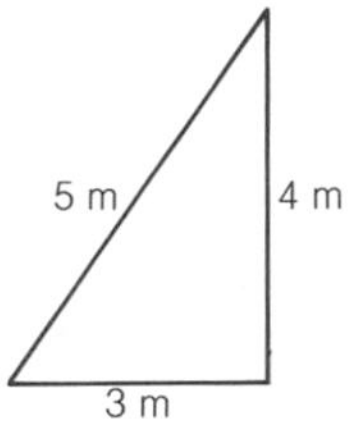


(b)

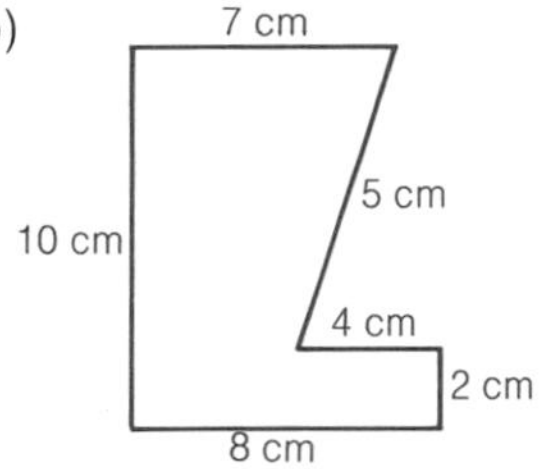


2 Find the perimeter of each regular polygon.

(a)

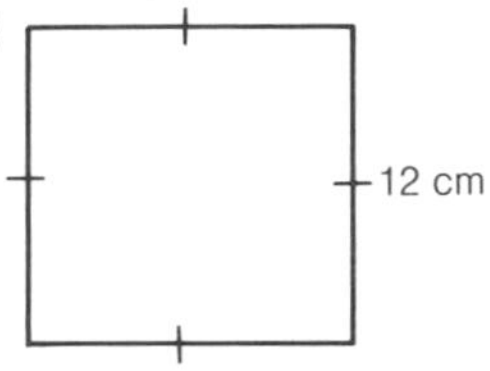


(b)

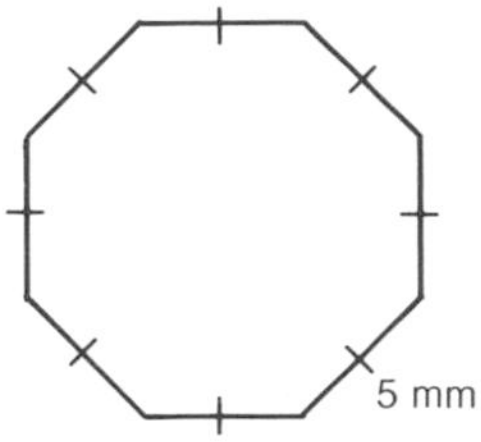


## Written Exercises

**A Remember: look for patterns or short cuts to help you find perimeters. Use a calculator to check your work.**

1 Estimate the perimeter of each figure. Then calculate.

(a)

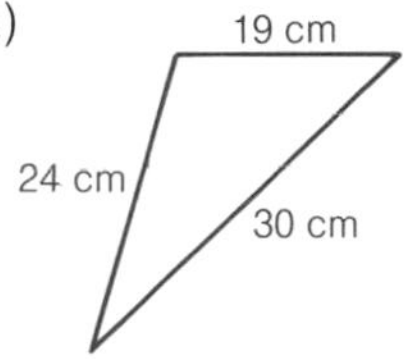


(b)

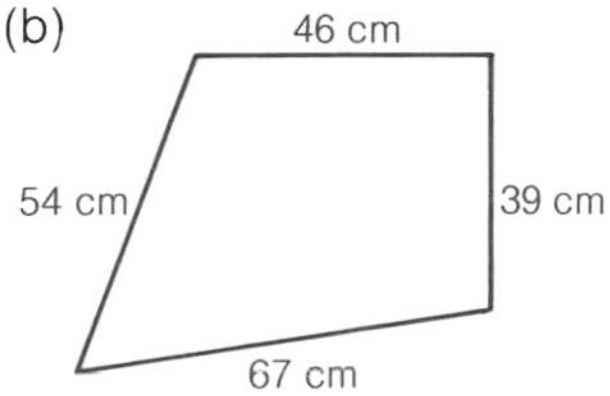


(c)

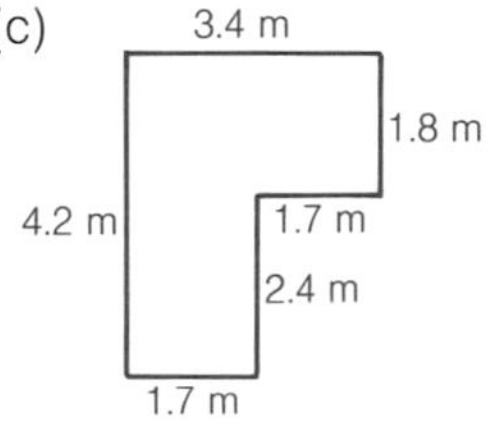


(d)

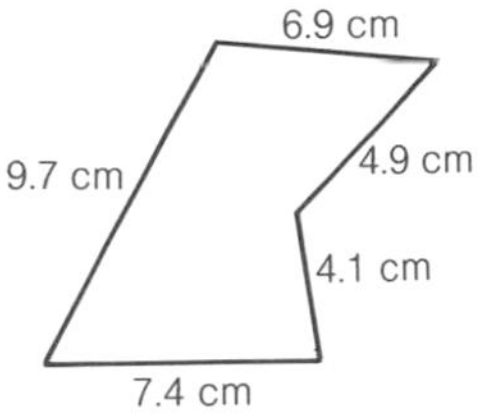


2 Predict which figure has the greatest perimeter. Which has the least? Calculate to check your predictions.

(a)

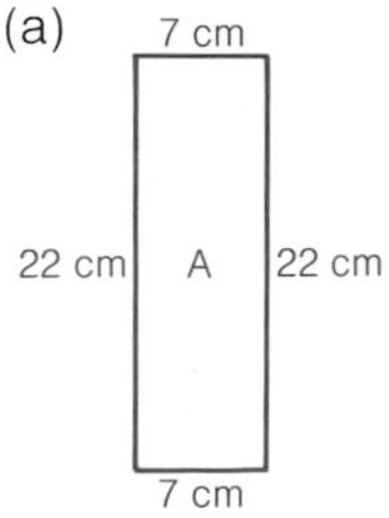


(b)

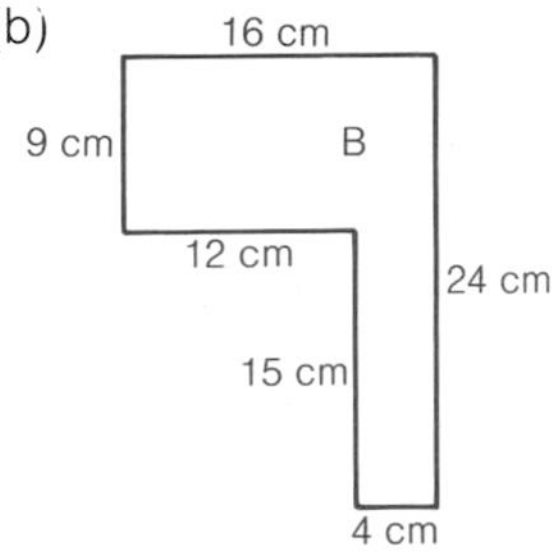


(c)

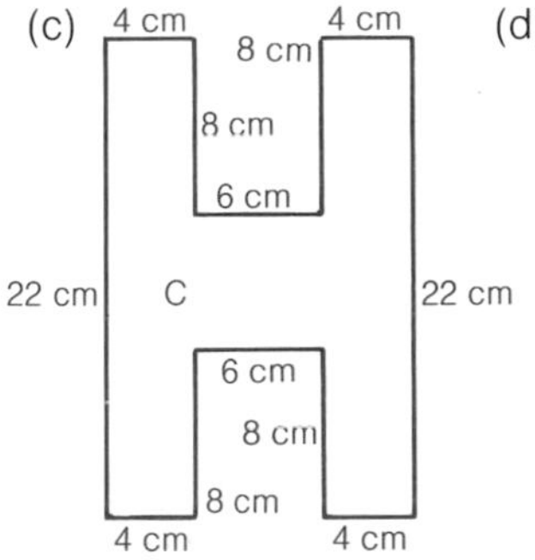


(d)

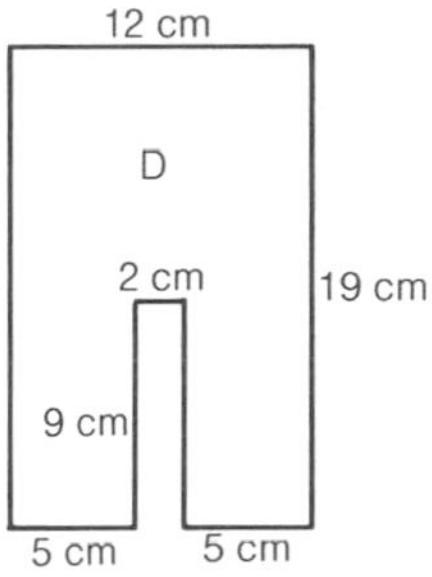


3 Use a short cut to find the perimeter of each figure.

(a)

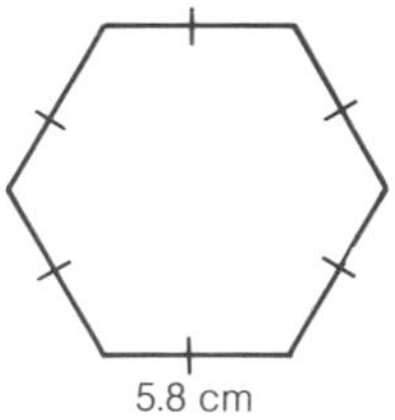


(b)

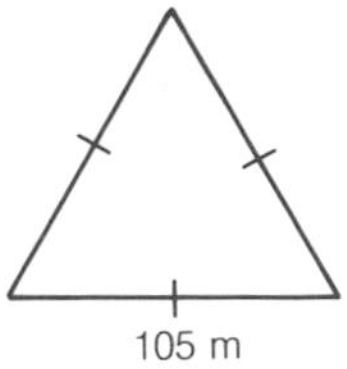


(c)

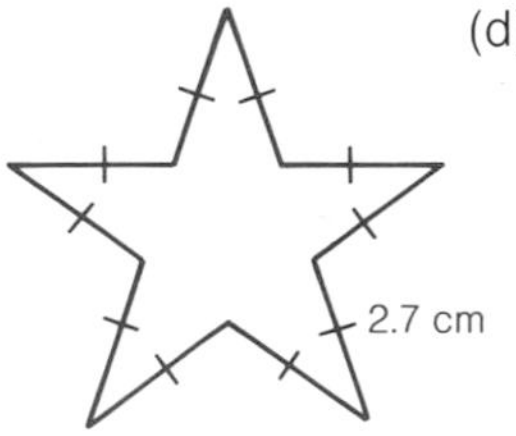


(d)

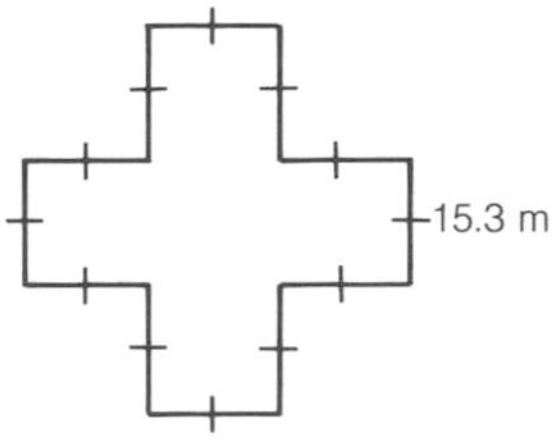

4 Write a formula for the perimeter $P$ of each polygon. Use the symbols shown on each polygon.

(a)

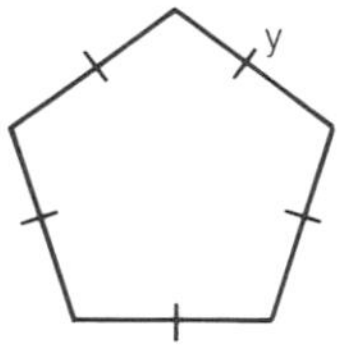


(b)

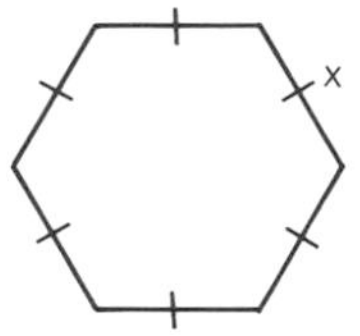


(c)

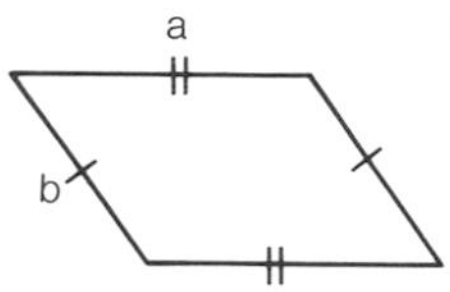


(d)

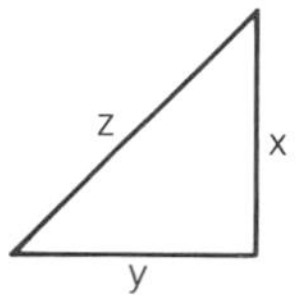


(e)

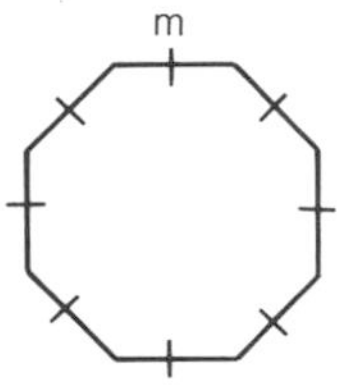


(f)

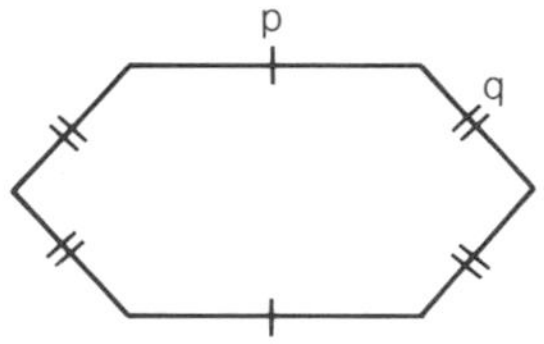


**B** **To solve problems, you need to organize your work. Refer to the *Steps of Solving Problems.***

5 The perimeter of each figure is shown. Find the measure of the missing side.

(a)

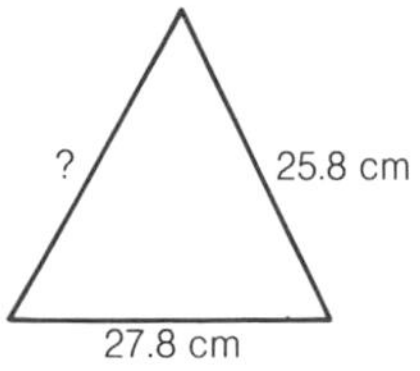


Perimeter = 84.8 cm

(b)

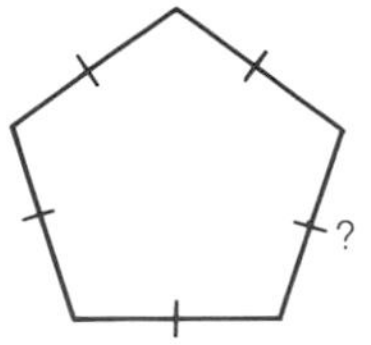


Perimeter = 36.5 cm

(c)

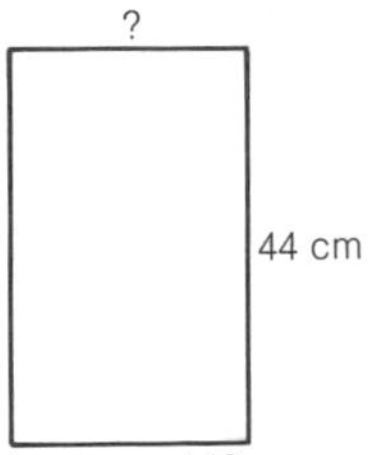


Perimeter = 140 cm

(d)

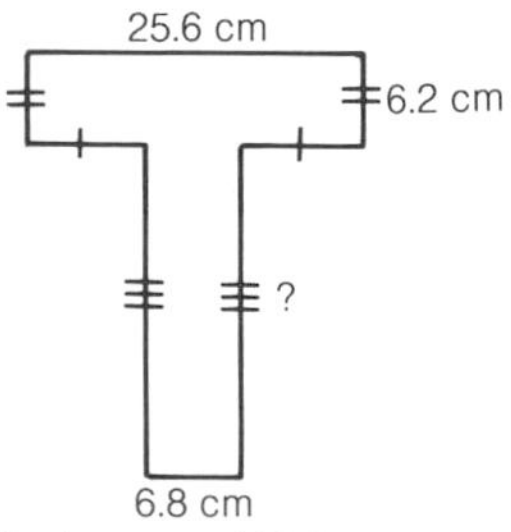


Perimeter = 102.8 cm

6 For each figure

- Find the length of the missing side
- Then calculate the perimeter.

(a)

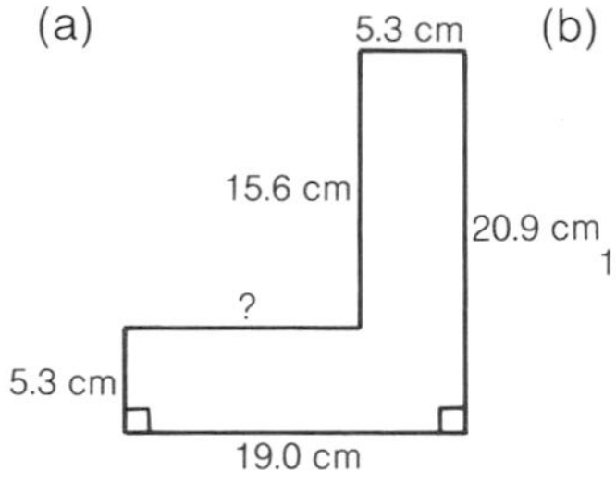


(b)

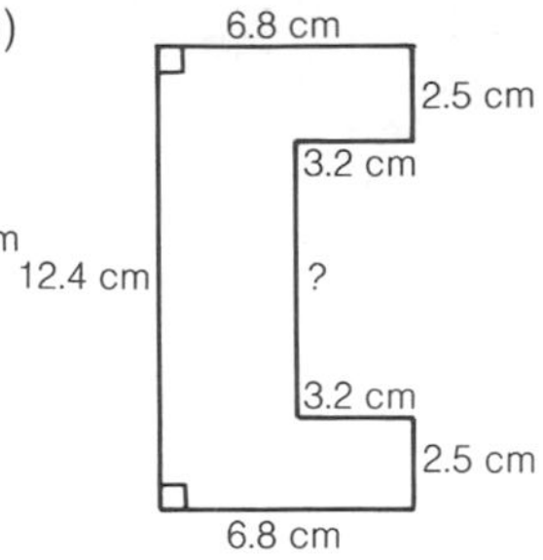


(c)

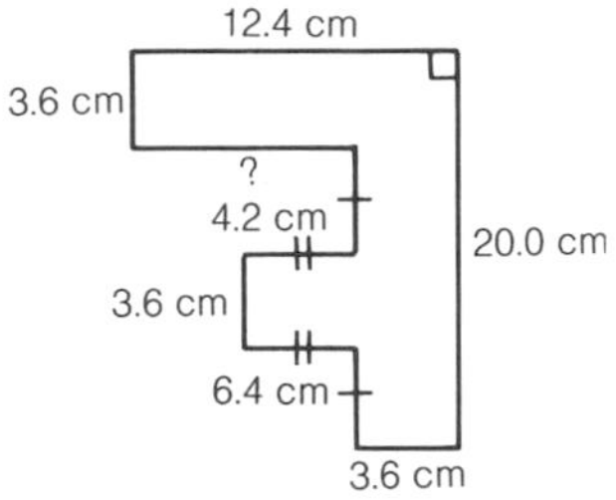


7 A room is shown in the diagram.

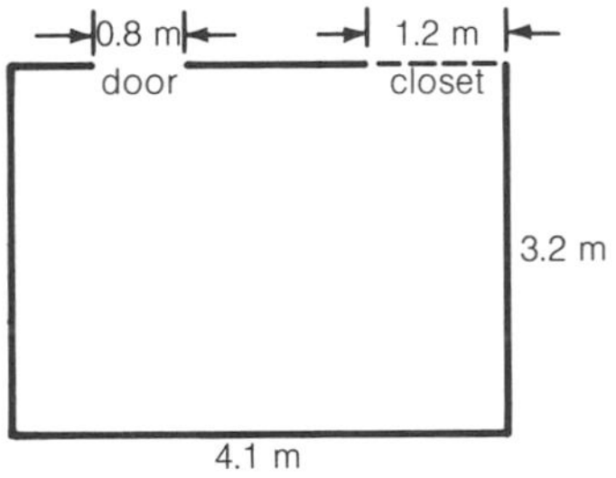


(a) What is the perimeter of the room?
(b) How much baseboard moulding is required for the room? (Remember you do not include the door or closet).

8 A flowerbed is in the shape of a regular hexagon.

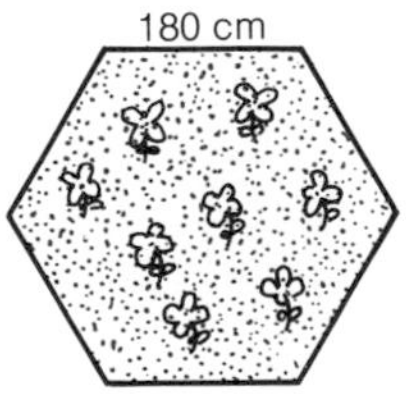


(a) What is the perimeter of the flowerbed?
(b) How many bricks are needed to make a border for the flowerbed if the length of each brick is 22.5 cm?

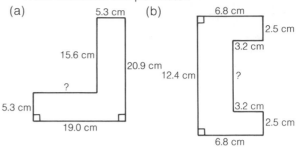

9 The Canadian Coast Guard patrols an area shown by the diagram.

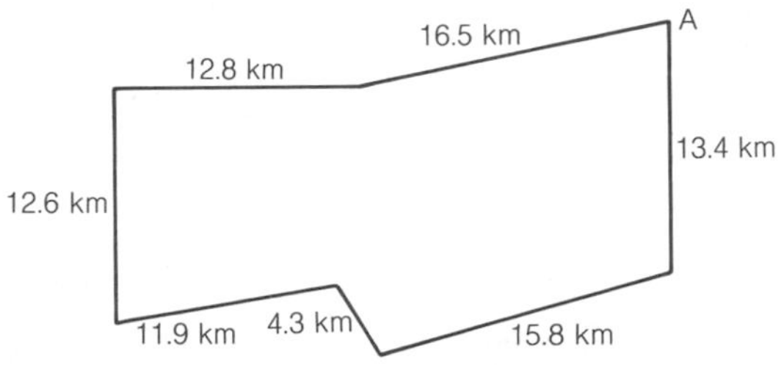


(a) Calculate the distance travelled.
(b) Five stops are made during each patrol. If the stops are equally spaced, how far apart are the stops?

10 A rectangular Japanese garden measures 32.6 m by 57.5 m.
(a) Calculate the perimeter of the garden.
(b) Calculate the cost of placing a chain link fence around the garden if fencing costs $3.94/m.

11 Carrie wants to put a fence around her 12 m by 6 m pool, leaving a walk 2 m inside between the pool and fence.

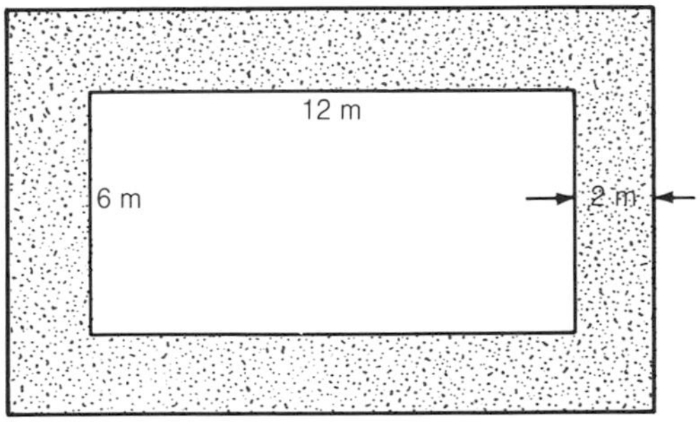


(a) How much fencing should Carrie buy?
(b) If she chooses fencing that costs $6.70/m, how much does the material cost her?
(c) How many fence posts will be required if the distance between each post is 2 m?

12 The diagram shows the courtyard at Winston's Plaza.

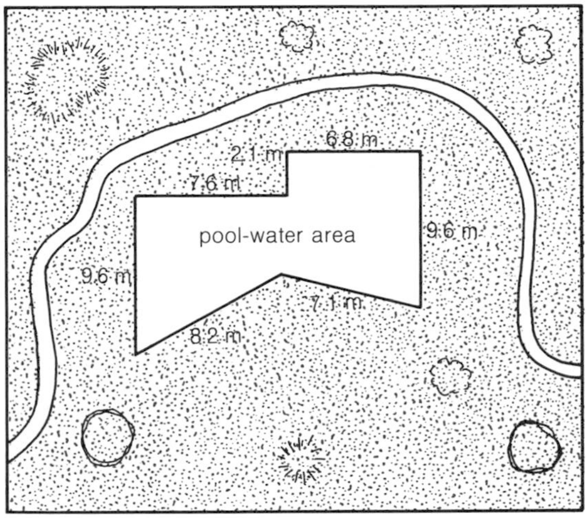


(a) Calculate the perimeter of the pool-water area.
(b) A hedge is planted along the perimeter in (a). Calculate the cost if a plant is placed every 0.3 m. Each plant costs $3.10.

13 Refer to the diagram in the previous question.
(a) Create a problem of your own based on the information in the diagram.
(b) Write a solution for your problem in (a).

## Calculator Tip

To use a calculator efficiently, you must plan ahead. For example, to evaluate the expression $lw + \frac{1}{2}\pi r^2$ for $l = 6.8$, $w = 4.3$, $r = 3.4$, you need to use the memory keys.

[MS] memory store [MR] memory recall

Check your calculator. The keys may be labelled in a different way. Follow these steps. Can you think of a more efficient procedure?

[C] 6.8 [×] 4.3 [=] [MS] 3.4 [×] 3.4
[×] [π] [÷] 2 [=] [+] [MR] [=] ?

Remember:
- Since each calculator may have different features, refer to the manual given with the calculator.

# 6.2 Circumference of a Circle

The largest "dome stadium" in Roman times was the Pantheon, built in Rome in 112 AD. It has a diameter of 43.4 m.

The Pantheon has a diameter of 43.4 m. The largest modern dome stadium, the Louisiana Superdome has a diameter of 207.3 m.

The perimeter, or *circumference* $C$ of a circle is related to its diameter, $d$.

$$\text{circumference} = \pi \times \text{diameter}$$
$$C = \pi d$$

where $\pi$ is approximately 3.14

We can use this relation to find the circumference of the Pantheon.

Use $C = \pi \times d$     $d = 43.4$ (in metres)

$C \doteq 3.14 \times 43.4$

$= 136.276$

The circumference of the Pantheon is about 136 m. ← Round to 3 significant digits since the least accurate measure in the product has 3 significant digits

The relation $C = \pi d$ and the equivalent relation $C = 2\pi r$, where $r$ is the radius, are both very important in solving problems involving circular objects.

## Example

The tire in the photo has a radius of 74 cm.

(a) Find the circumference of the tire.

(b) How many turns would the wheel make over a distance of 4 km?

## Solution

(a) Use $C = 2\pi r$     $r = 74$ (in centimetres)

$C \doteq 2 \times 3.14 \times 74$

$= 464.72$

The circumference is 460 cm (expressed to 2 significant digits).

(b) $1 \text{ km} = 1000 \text{ m}$

$= 100\,000 \text{ cm}$

$4 \text{ km} = 400\,000 \text{ cm}$

Think:
$1 \text{ m} = 100 \text{ cm}$
$1000 \text{ m} = 1000 \times 100 \text{ cm}$
$= 100\,000 \text{ cm}$

In one turn the wheel travels 460 cm.
In 4 km, the number of turns is given by $400\,000 \div 460$ turns or 870 turns.
Thus the wheel will turn about 870 times over a distance of 4 km.

## Try These

1 What is the circumference of each circle?

(a)

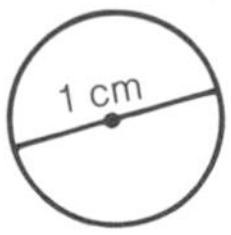


(b)

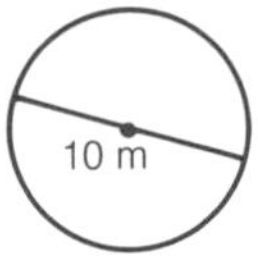


(c)

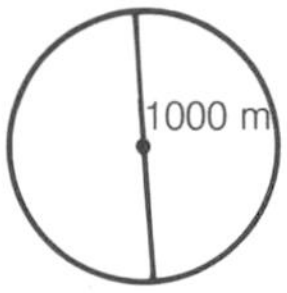


2 Find the circumference of each circle.

(a)

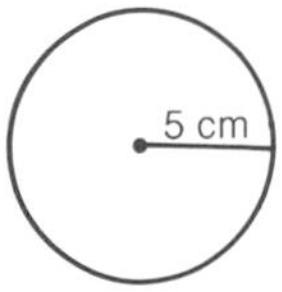


(b)

(c)

## Written Exercises

**A** **Use $\pi \doteq 3.14$. Round your answers to the appropriate degree of accuracy (see Section 2.5).**

1 Calculate the circumference of each circle.

(a)

(b)

(c)

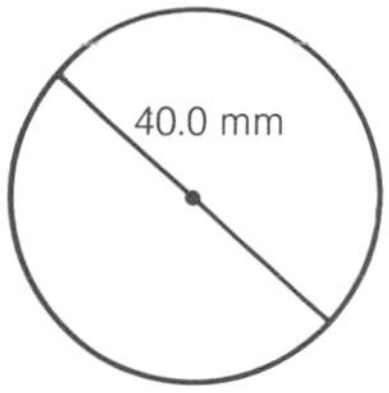


(d)

2 Calculate each circumference.

(a)

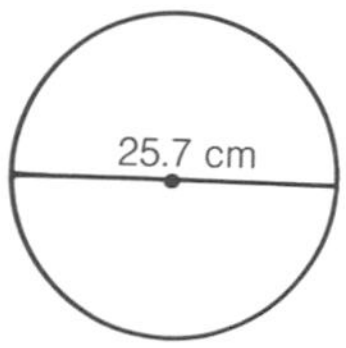


(b)

(c)

(d)

3 Find the missing parts in the table.

| | Radius ($r$) | Diameter ($d$) | Circumference ($C$) |
|---|---|---|---|
| (a) | 24 mm | ? | ? |
| (b) | ? | 36.4 m | ? |
| (c) | ? | ? | 78.5 cm |
| (d) | ? | ? | 95.6 km |

4 (a) The diameter of a hockey puck is 7.62 cm. What is its circumference?
(b) The diameter of a long-playing record is 30.5 cm. What is the circumference of the record?
(c) The warmup circle in baseball has a diameter of approximately 1.50 m. What is the circumference?
(d) The aircraft travelled in a circle on its rescue mission. The diameter of the circle was 16.8 km. Calculate the distance travelled.

**B** **To solve problems about circles, you must know the meaning of the symbols in $C = \pi d$ and $C = 2\pi r$.**

5 The distance around a circular swimming pool is 37.7 m. What is the diameter of the pool?

6 A round tablecloth has a radius of 1.40 m.
(a) Calculate the length of fringe needed for the edge.
(b) Find the cost of the fringe if it costs $2.98/m.

7 The radius of the earth is about 6400 km. A satellite is located 320 km above the earth's surface. Find the distance travelled by the satellite after 5 orbits.

8 A bicycle rim has a diameter of 68.0 cm. When the tire is fully inflated it adds 4.0 cm to the diameter.
(a) Find the circumference of the rim.
(b) Find the circumference of the inflated tire.

9 (a) The diameter of a motorcycle tire is 64.8 cm. How many turns will the tire make in travelling 10 km?
(b) The diameter of a racing tire is 72.6 cm. How many turns will the tire make in travelling the same distance as in (a)?
(c) An underinflated tire is 69.3 cm. How many more turns will it make for the same distance?

The greatest speed obtained on land was by Stan Barrett who reached 1190 km/h. The greatest speed at which a human has travelled occurred in space at a speed of 39 900 km/h in the command Module of Apollo X.

10 The tire of a jet has a diameter of 2.20 m.
(a) Calculate the circumference of the tire.
(b) The runway is 716.0 m long. Calculate the number of turns the tire will make during take-off if it uses half of the runway.

11 A two pointed knitting needle is 47.1 cm long. The needle is bent around in the shape of a circle. What is the radius of the circle formed?

12 A circular running track is shown. Paul runs on the outside of the track and Melinda on the inside.

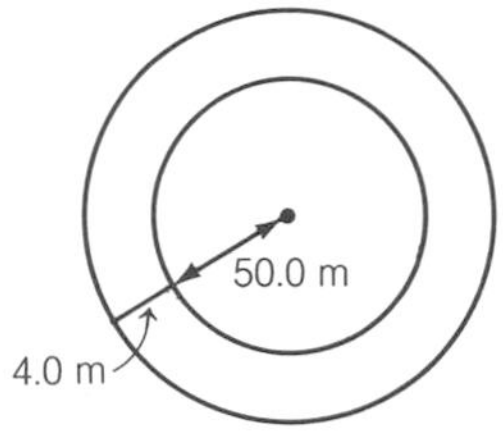


(a) How far does Paul run in one lap?
(b) How far does Melinda run in one lap?
(c) If the two runners start at the same place, how much further will Paul have run than Melinda after 6 laps? 30 laps?

13 Calculate the perimeter of each figure.

(a)

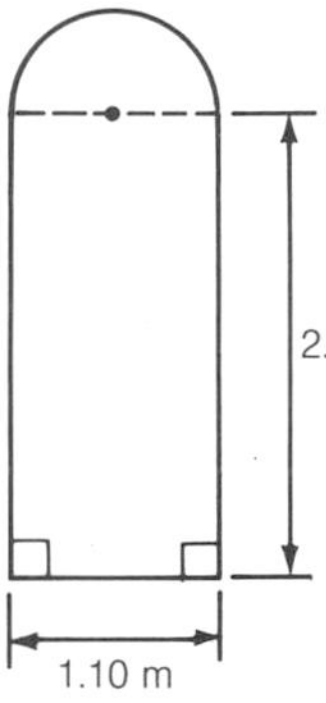


(b)

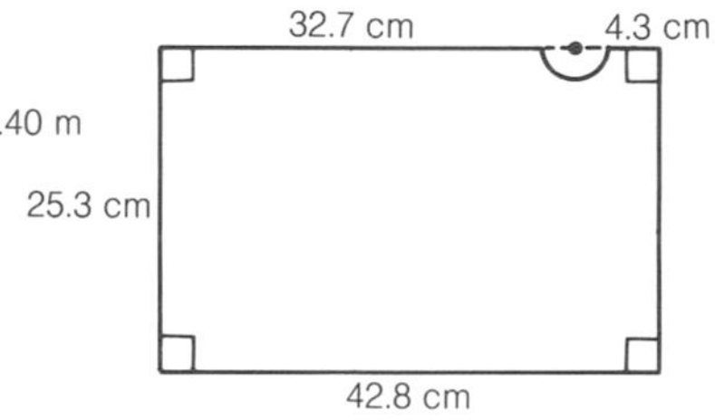


(c)

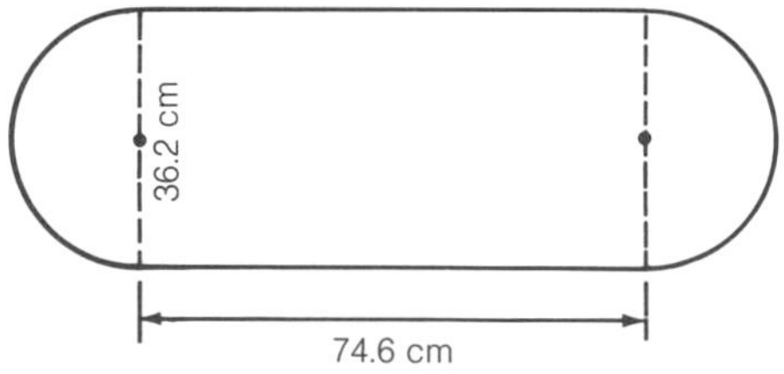


## C

14 A sheet of metal measures 50 cm by 85 cm. The sheet is to be bent to form a chimney. What are the two possible diameters of the chimney?

## Applications: Circles in Sports

Circles play an important role in many sports including basketball. The hoop is a circle with diameter of 46.0 cm. The center circle has inner radius 0.61 m and outer radius 1.83 m. The free throw area is a semi-circle with radius 1.83 m.

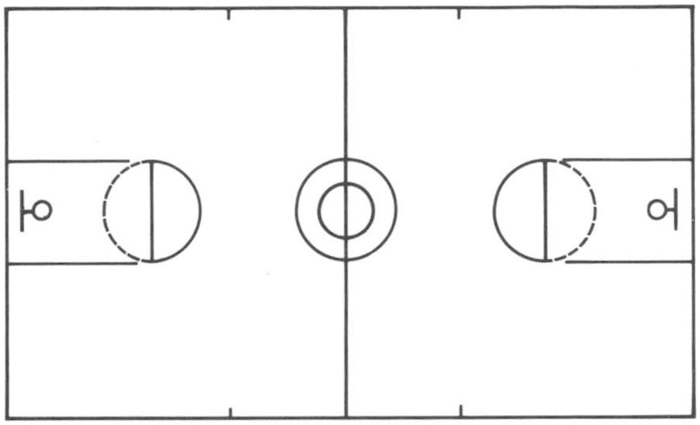

15 For the basketball court in the diagram calculate:
(a) the circumference of the hoop
(b) the perimeter of the free-throw area

16 The running track at Pearson High School has the dimensions shown. Calculate the distance run in twenty laps of the track.

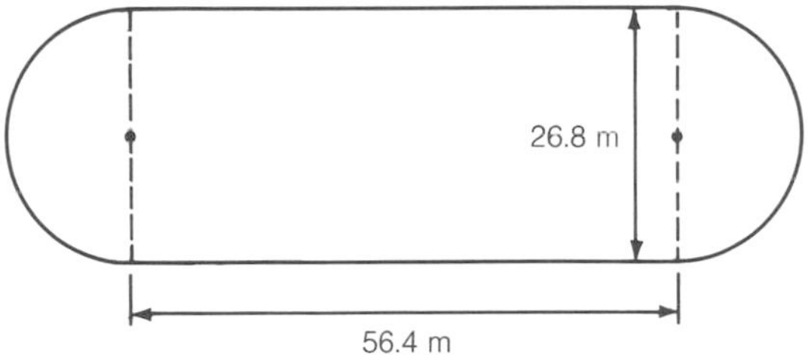


17 Marty is lining a soccer field. In the centre of the field there is a circle with radius 10.8 m. Find the circumference of this circle.

18 Eileen is training for the 5000 m race. The track she uses is circular with a radius of 50.0 m. How many times does she need to go around this track?

19 The straight sections of a 400 m track are 110 m long. Find the radius of the semi-circular sections at either end of this track.

20 A wrestling mat is about 7.3 m by 7.3 m. A red line is drawn around the edges. In the middle of the mat is a red circle having a diameter of 3.0 m. How many metres of red lining are needed for around the mat and the circle?

21 Sheila is making an archery target. The target has 5 circles, each with the same centre. The inner circle has a radius of 12.2 cm. The radius of each of the other four rings is 6.3 cm greater than that of the circle inside it. Find the circumference of each circle.

It is only in recent times that archery has been accepted in the Olympic games. In the World Championship competition, 36 arrows are shot at 90 m, 36 at 70 m, 36 at 50 m and 36 at 30 m.

# 6.3 Formulas for Areas

Many layers of material are cut at one time in the commercial production of clothing. The pieces for clothing are designed to obtain the least amount of waste during cutting.

Area is important in each of these situations.

- ▶ To insulate a house, you need to know how much insulation is to be used.
- ▶ To sod a lawn, you need to know how much surface you will cover.
- ▶ To make a dress, you need to know how much material you need.
- ▶ To seed a field with corn, you need to know the area of the field.

For each of the above, you need to know the area of a region. The area of a region is the number of square units that are needed to cover the region. Formulas provide a method of calculating the area of particular shapes. The figures below are covered by centimetre squares.

Rectangle

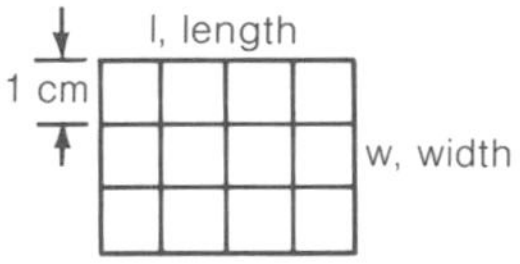


$A = l \times w$

$A = 4 \times 3$

$= 12$

The area of the rectangle is 12 $cm^2$.

Use square units for area.

Square

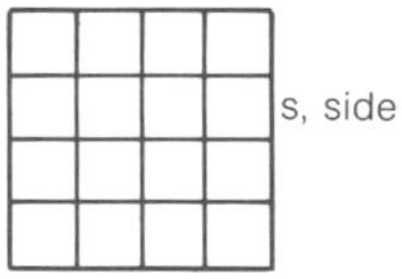


$A = s^2$

$A = 4^2$

$= 16$

The area of the square is 16 $cm^2$.

Parallelogram

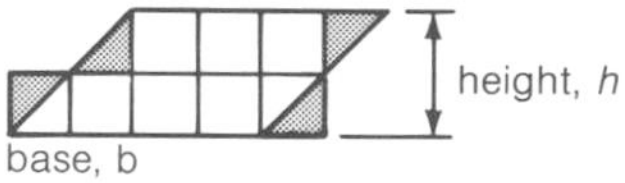


$A = b \times h$

$A = 4 \times 2$

$= 8$

The area of the parallelogram is 8 $cm^2$.

Triangle

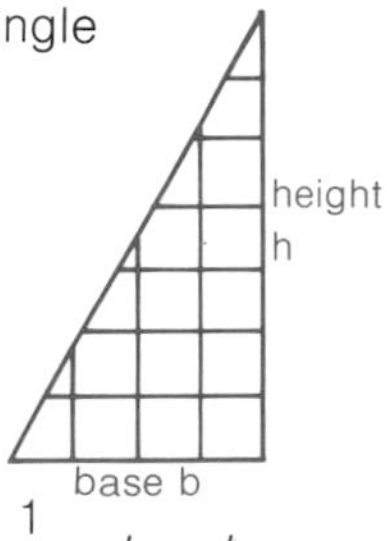


$A = \frac{1}{2} \times b \times h$

$A = \frac{1}{2} \times 4 \times 7$

$= 14$

The area of the triangle is 14 $cm^2$.

Trapezoid

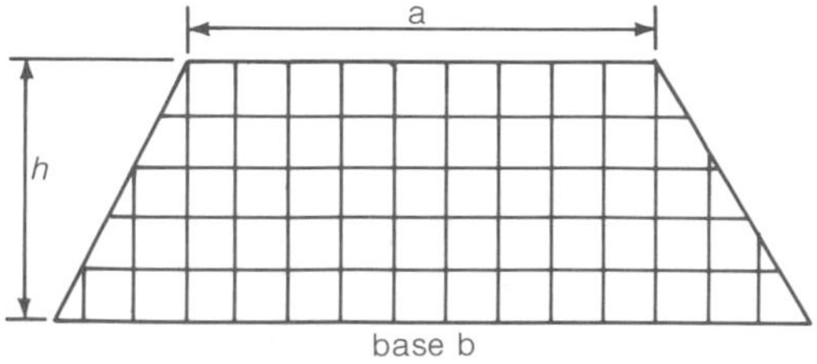


A trapezoid has one pair of parallel sides, shown by *a*, *b*.

$A = \frac{1}{2}h(a + b)$

$A = \frac{1}{2} \times 5 \times (9 + 15)$

$= \frac{1}{2} \times 5 \times 24$

$= 60$

The area of the trapezoid is 60 $cm^2$.

The formulas for area can be combined with your earlier skills to solve problems.

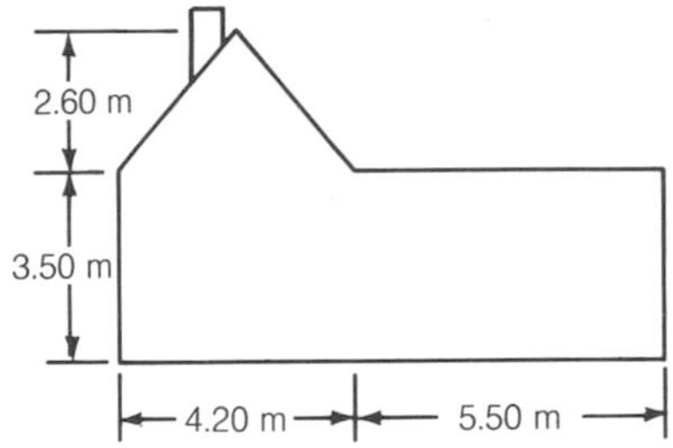


## Example

The north side of a house has the dimensions shown.

(a) Calculate the area of this side of the house.

(b) The cost of aluminum siding is $38.63/m² installed. Calculate the cost of installing aluminum siding on the side of the house shown.

## Solution

Think: Split the shape into regions for which you know a formula for the area.

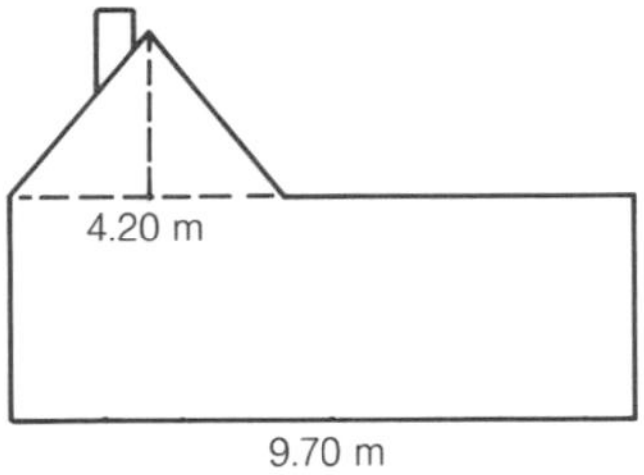


(a) Area = area of triangle + area of rectangle

$$A = \frac{1}{2} \times b \times h + l \times w$$

$$A = \frac{1}{2} \times 4.20 \times 2.60 + 9.70 \times 3.50$$ ←

Think: Use a calculator to do these calculations.

[C] 9.7 [×] 3.5 [=] [MS] 4.2 [×] 2.6 [×] 0.5 [=]
Output
[+] [MR] [=] ?

$$= 5.46 + 33.95$$
$$= 39.41$$

The area of the side of the house is 39.4 m².

(b) Cost of aluminum = 39.4 × \$38.63
= \$15 22.02

The cost of installing the aluminum siding is \$1522.02.

Remember to check your work by estimating. 40 × 40 = 1600; the answer is reasonable.

## Try These

1 Which formula would you use to calculate the area of each?

(a)

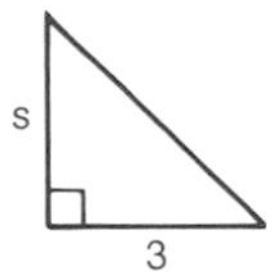


(b)

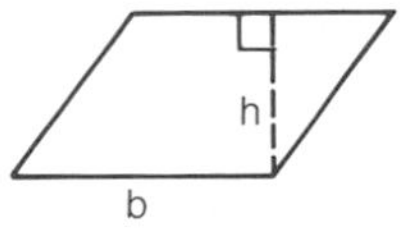


(c)

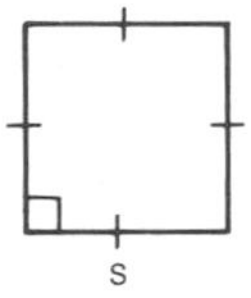


(d)

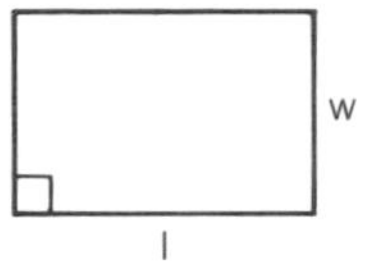


(e)

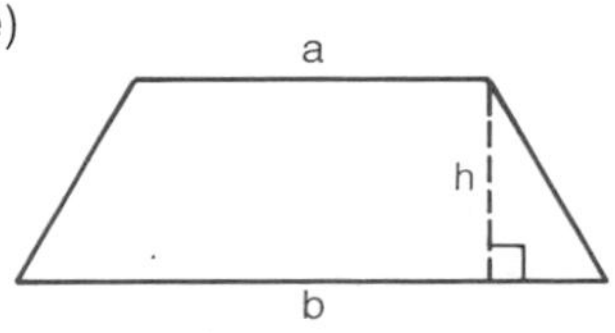


2 Find the area of each shape.

(a)

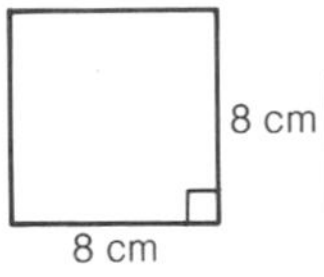


(b)

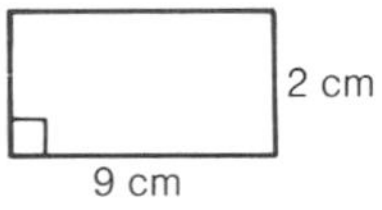


(c)

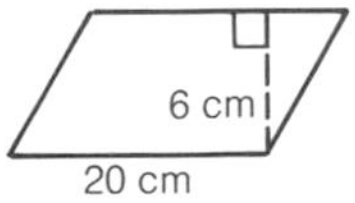


(d)

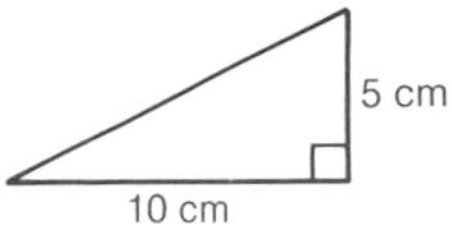


(e)

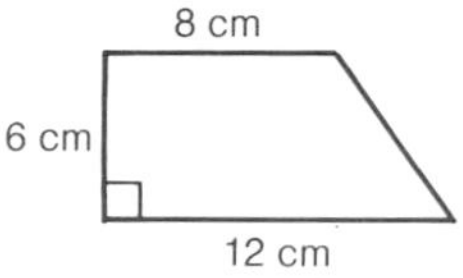

## Written Exercises

**A Review the various formulas that you have learned to calculate the areas of shapes.**

1 Calculate the area of each rectangle.

(a)

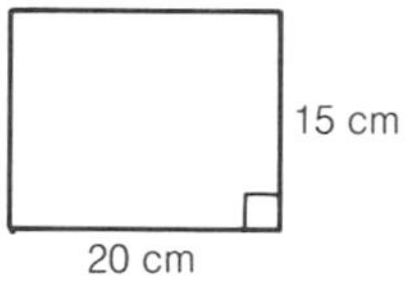


(b)

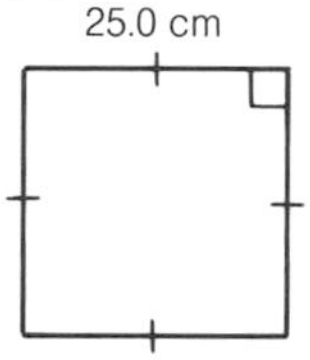


(c)

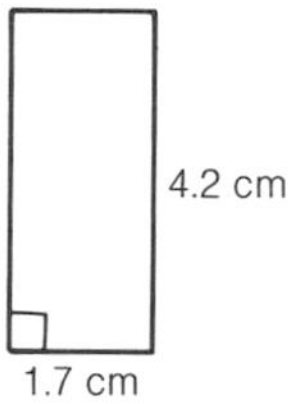


2 Calculate the area of each parallelogram.

(a)

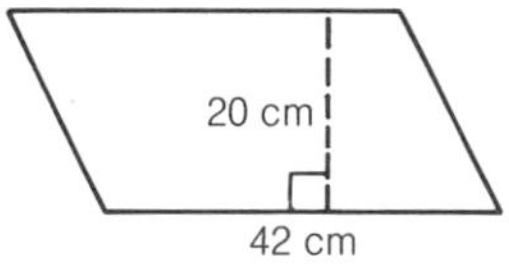


(b)

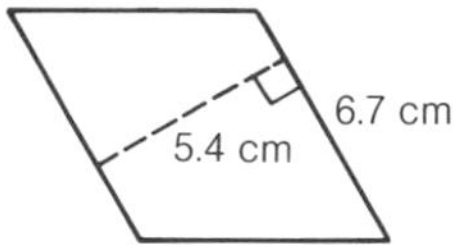


(c)

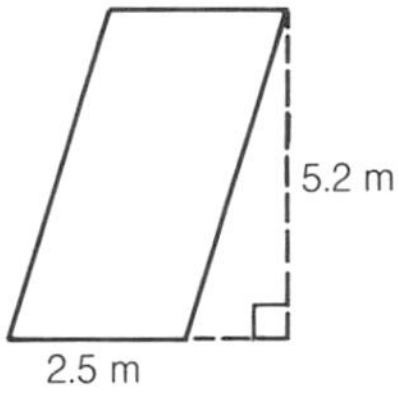


3 Calculate the area of each triangle.

(a)

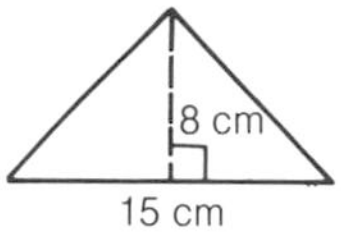


(b)

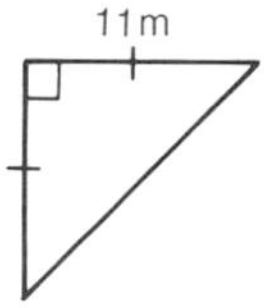


(c)

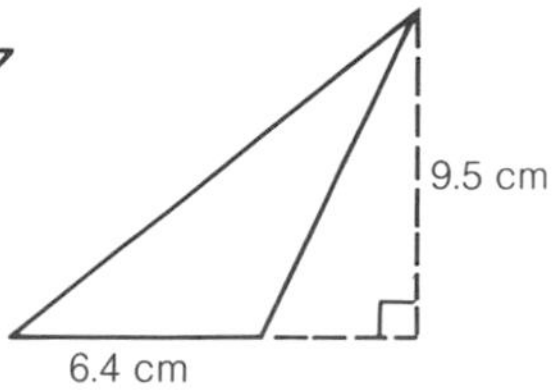


4 Calculate the area of each trapezoid.

(a)

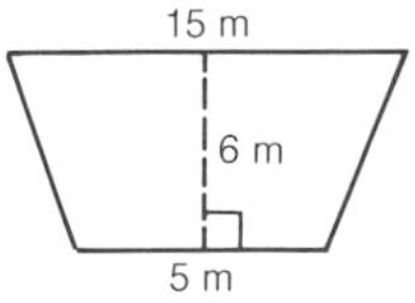


(b)

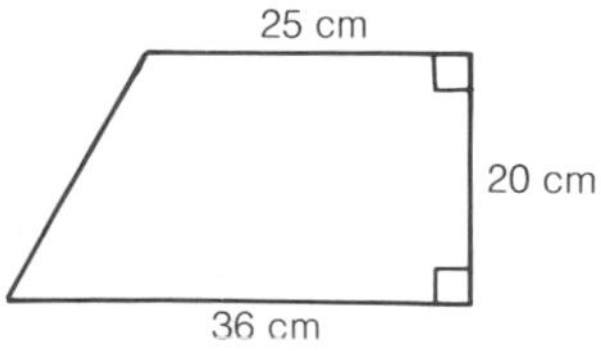


5 Find the area of each of the following.

(a) a square whose sides each measure 1.4 cm

(b) a rectangle with length 23 cm and width 10 cm

(c) a triangle with base 8.6 cm and height 5.5 cm

(d) a parallelogram with base 18.0 cm and height 12.0 cm

(e) a trapezoid in which the parallel sides measure 2.3 cm and 5.7 cm, and the height measures 3.5 cm.

**B Remember: make a final statement when writing your solutions.**

6 ▶ Predict which figure you think has the greatest area.

▶ Calculate to check your prediction.

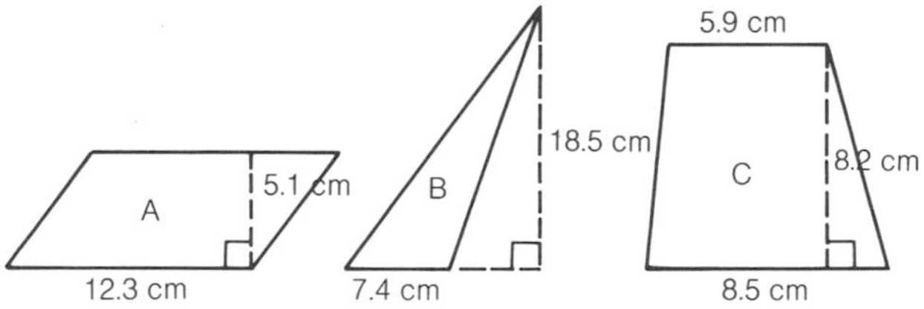


7 Estimate and then calculate the area of each.

(a)

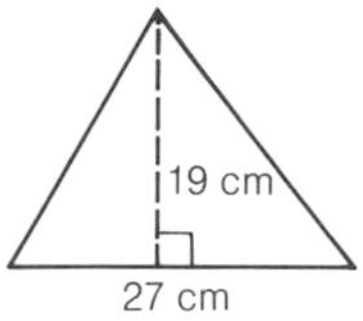


(b)

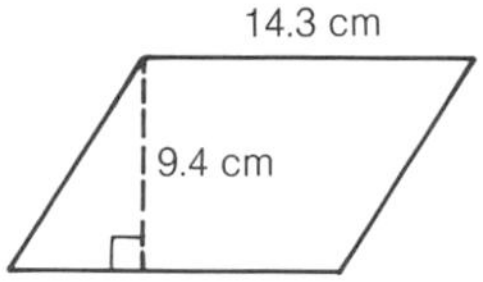


(c)

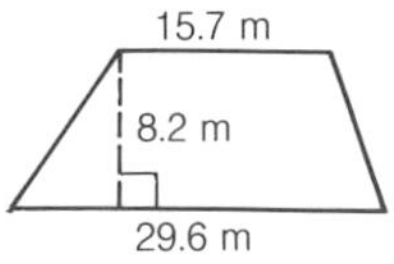


(d)

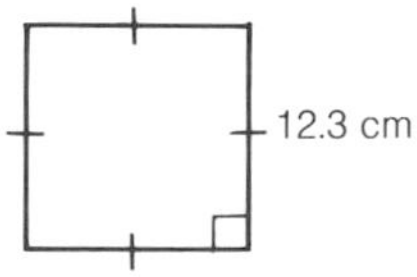


(e)

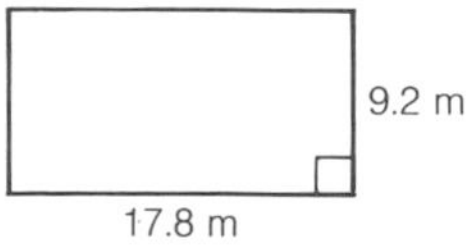

8 Calculate the area of each stamp.
(a) (b)

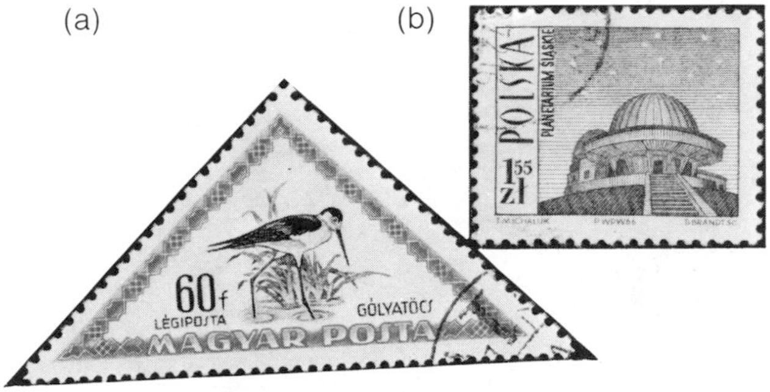


9 (a) A square has an area of 900 cm². Find its perimeter.
(b) A rectangle has an area of 320 cm². If the length is 12 cm, what is its perimeter?
(c) A triangle has an area of 95 cm². If the base is 10 cm, find the height.

10 The side of an escalator is in the shape of a trapezoid. Calculate the area.

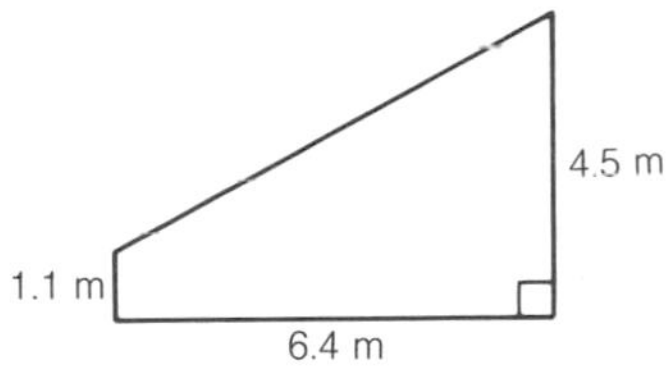


11 The grassed area of a property is shown.

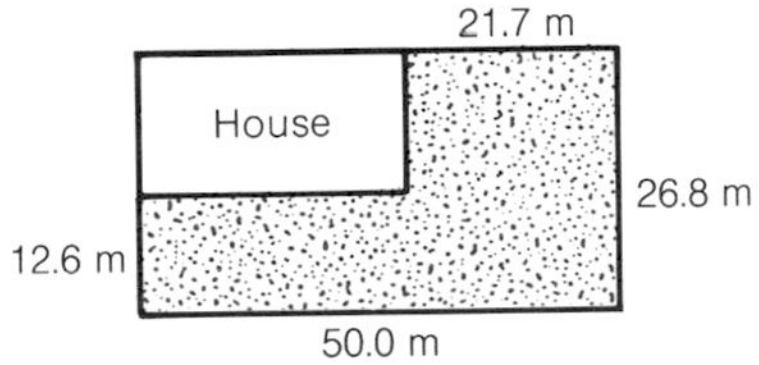


(a) Find the dimension of the missing sides of the grassed area.
(b) Calculate the shaded area.
(c) Sod costs $1.69/m². Calculate the cost to cover the shaded area.

12 (a) Find how many square centimetres of material are required to make the apron shown.
(b) How many square metres is this?

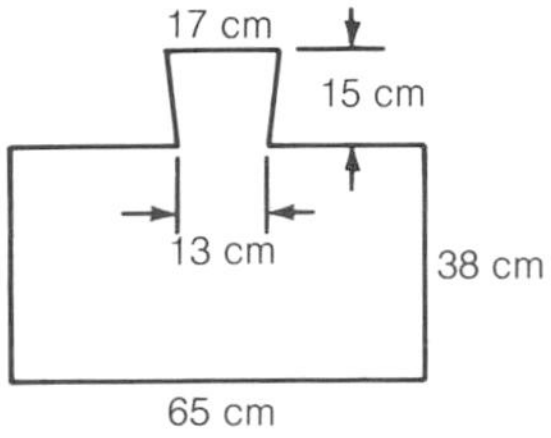


13 (a) The side wall of a swimming pool is shaped as shown in the diagram. Its measurements are shown. Find the area of the side shown.

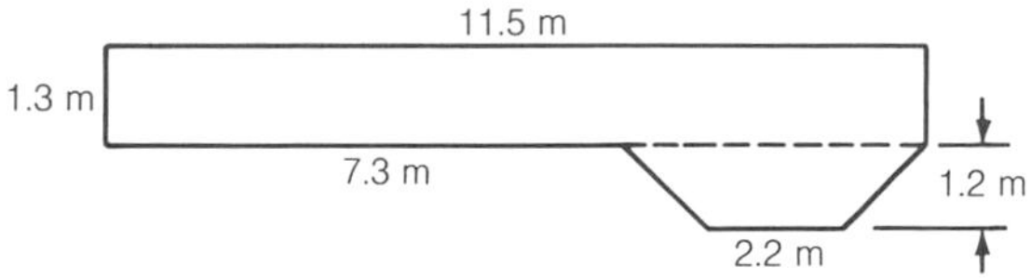


(b) The pool is 5.0 m wide. Find the total area of the four walls.
(c) The side walls are to be painted with pool paint that covers 3.0 m²/L. The paint costs $5.29/L, what is the cost for painting the four walls?

14 Find the area of the shaded region in each diagram
(a) (b)

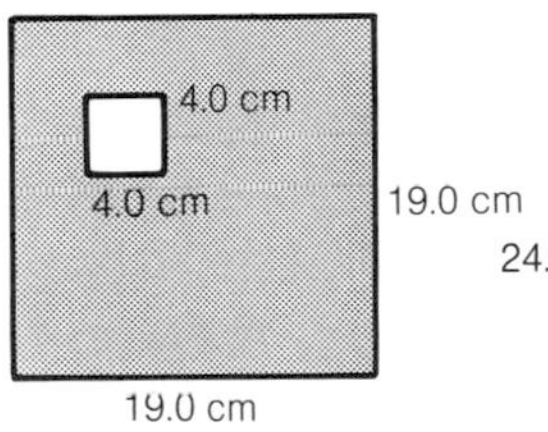


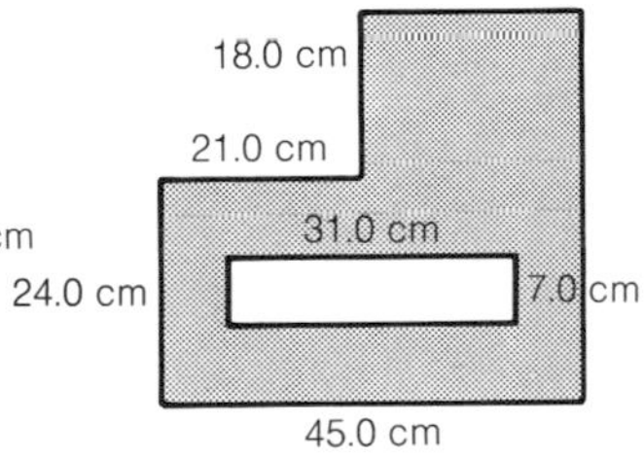


(c)

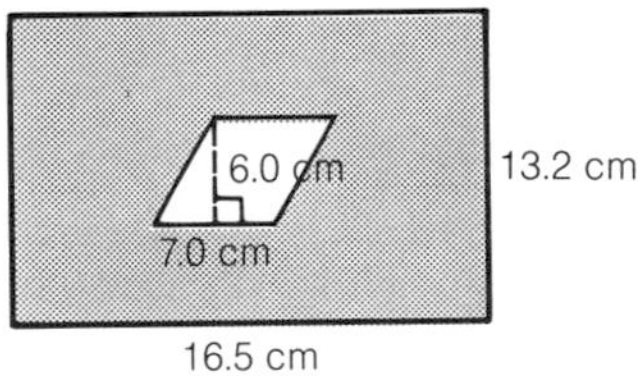


15 A machine part is shown. Find its area.

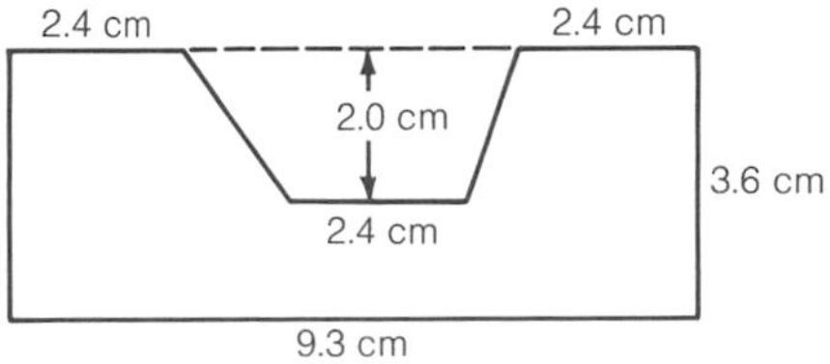

# 6.4 Applications with Circles

Mathematics is involved every time you play a record and listen to it.

- ▶ The manufacturer needs to prepare a cover to hold the record. How much material is used?
- ▶ The size of the hole must be precise. The grooved edge must be exact.
- ▶ Different sizes of records are used to play at different speeds. How is the exact size determined?

Do you know what the top-selling single ever recorded was? If you don't know, then guess what the second most popular recorded single was. Look for the answer later in this section.

The area of a circle is found by using the formula:

$A = \pi r^2$ where $r$ is the radius.

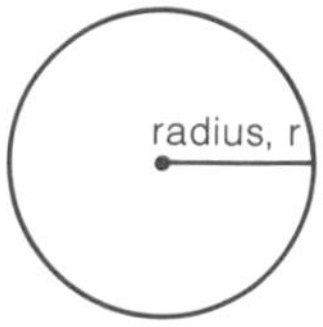


### Example

A single-play record has a diameter of 17.5 cm. The label has a diameter of 9.2 cm. Calculate the grooved area of the record.

### Solution

Area of record:

$A = \pi r^2$

$A \doteq 3.14 \times (8.75)^2$

$\doteq 240$

Area of label:

$A = \pi r^2$

$A \doteq 3.14 \times (4.6)^2$

$\doteq 66$

Calculate the grooved area.

$240 - 66 = 174$

The grooved area of the record is about 174 cm².

## Try These

1 To calculate the area of each circle, what value of $r$ is needed?

(a) (b) (c)

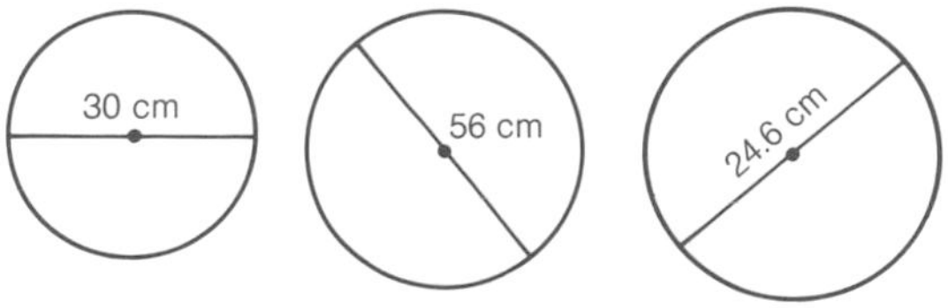


2 Match each circle with the calculation that you would use to find its area.

(a) $A \doteq 3.14 \times 8^2$

(b) $A \doteq 3.14 \times 40^2$

(c) $A \doteq 3.14 \times 20^2$

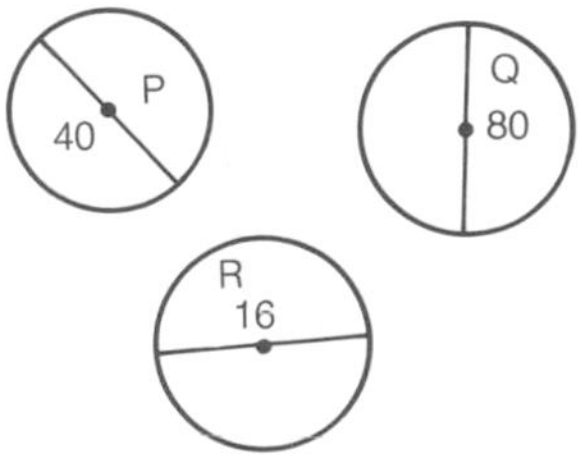

## Written Exercises

**A** **Review the meaning of the variables in the formulas $d = 2r$, $A = \pi r^2$.**

1 Calculate the area of each circle.

(a) (b) (c)

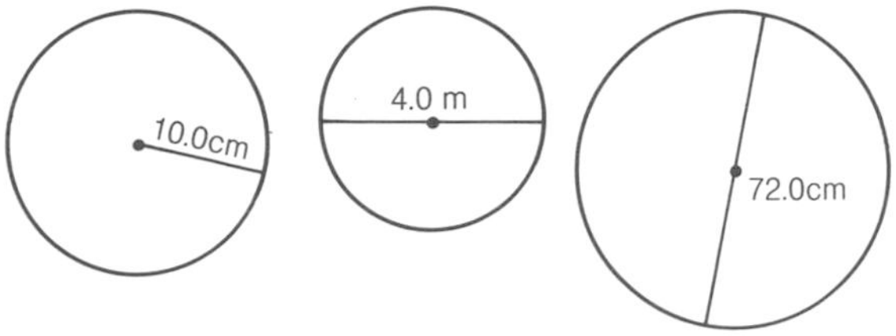


2 A round table has a diameter of 2.20 m. What is the area of the table?

3 A frying pan has a diameter of 25.0 cm. What is the area of the frying surface?

4 A dime has a diameter of 17.5 mm. What is its area?

5 Find the missing values in the chart

| | Radius | Diameter | Area |
|---|---|---|---|
| (a) | ? | 10.0 m | ? |
| (b) | 15.0 cm | ? | ? |
| (c) | ? | ? | 12.0 cm$^2$ |
| (d) | ? | ? | 150 m$^2$ |

**B** **Remember: to solve problems you must know the answers to these two questions:**

*I* *What information does the problem ask me to find?*

*II* *What information am I given?*

6 Deep Bay, part of Reindeer Lake in Saskatchewan, is a water filled meteorite crater and is almost a perfect circle. It has a radius of 16.0 km. Find the area of Deep Bay.

7 In the discus throwing event, the part within which the athlete must stand to throw the discus is one quarter of a circle with radius 2.50 m. Calculate the area in which the athlete stands.

8 The Friendly Islands of Tonga are known to issue such unique stamps as the banana stamp and the valentine stamp. The stamp shown has a diameter of 3.2 cm.

(a) Calculate its area.

(b) If 1007 stamps are cut from a sheet measuring 100 cm by 100 cm, what area of paper is discarded?

9 The "house" or target in curling consists of the area within four concentric circles. The radius of the innermost circle, the "button", is 0.45 m. The width of each ring around the button is also 0.45 m. Find the area of the house.

Curling has been a popular Scottish sport during the last three centuries, but now can be found in most parts of the world. The stone, which is a block of granite polished smooth, is given a rotary motion which more or less makes it go in a curve and hence the name of the game as *curling*.

10 A flat metal washer has an inner diameter of 2.8 cm and an outer diameter of 5.2 cm. Find the area of the washer.

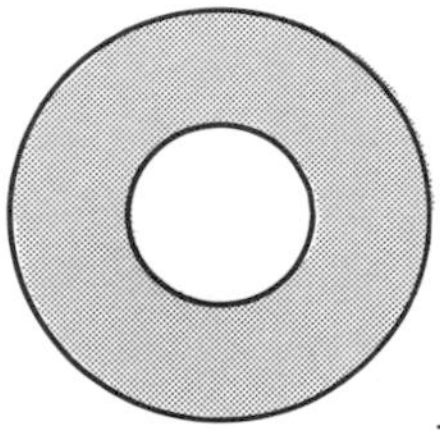

11 Sandra has 40.0 m of fencing with which to enclose an area of the back yard for her dog.
(a) If she encloses a square what area of the yard would her dog have?
(b) If she made a circle instead what area would be enclosed?
(c) Compare your answer in (a) and (b), which shape has greater area for the same amount of fencing?

12 The diagram shows the dimensions of the glass face of a clock. What is the area of this glass face?

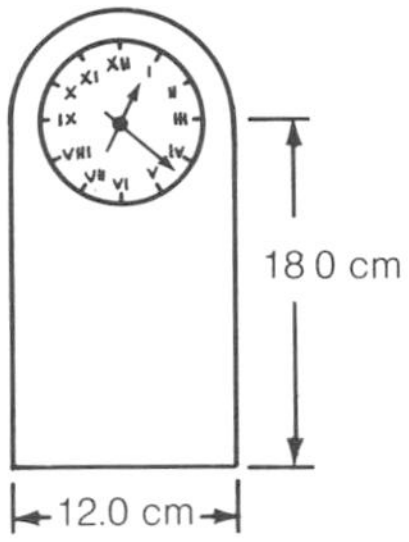


13 Calculate the area of the shaded part of each.

(a)

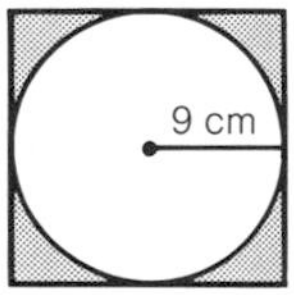


(b)

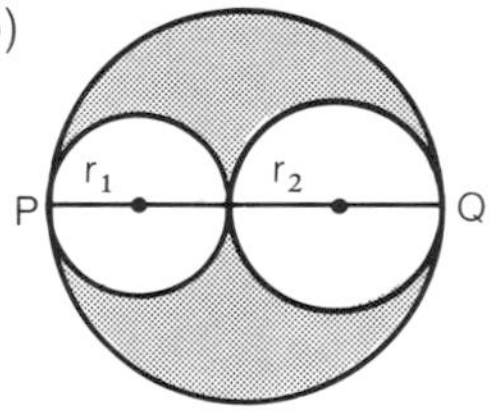


PQ = 62.0 cm, $r_1 = 14.3$ cm
$r_2 = 16.7$ cm

(c)

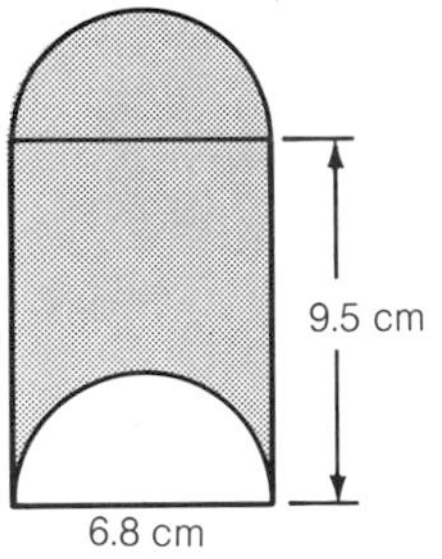


(d)

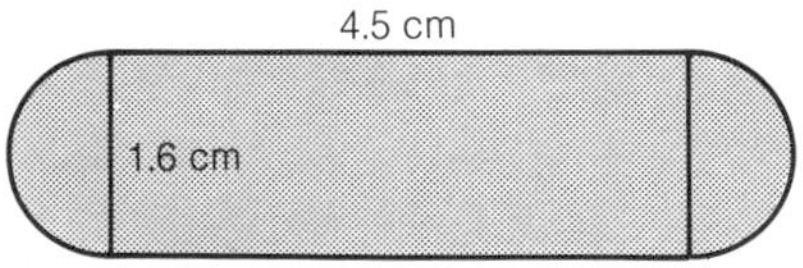

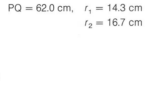

The answer to the caption to the photo is:
The most popular single was Bing Crosby's White Christmas. Second to this was Gene Autry's Rudolph the Red-Nosed Reindeer.
Current popular songs have a long way to go.

14 Find the area of each of the following machine parts.

(a)

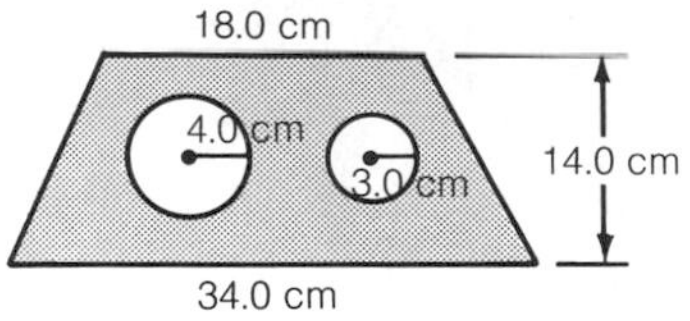


(b)

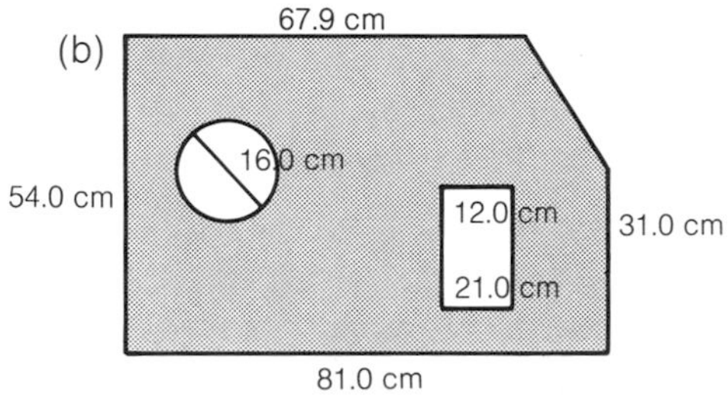


(c)

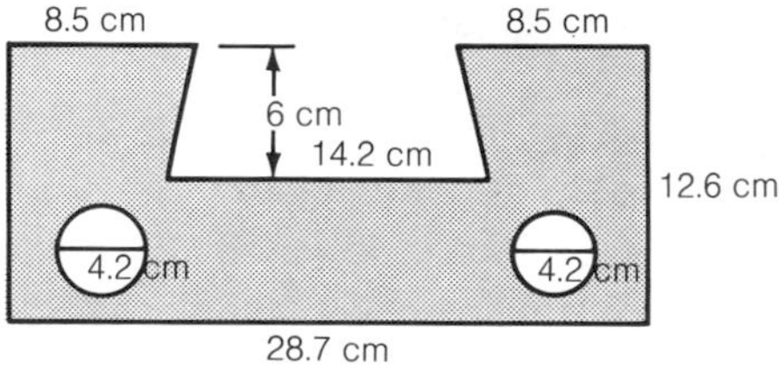


## Computer Tip

- Refer to the computer program. What is it designed to do? Run the program.

```
10 PRINT "DIAMETER"
20 FOR D = 2 to 20
30 LET R = D/2
40 PRINT D, 3.14159 * R * R
50 NEXT D
60 END
```

- Run the following program on a computer. Predict the output for the program.

```
10 READ S
15 IF S = 0.0 THEN 100
20 LET A = S * S
30 LET P = 4 * S
40 PRINT "SIDE MEASURES"; S; "CM"
50 PRINT "AREA = "; A; "SQ CM"
60 PRINT "PERIMETER = "; P; "CM"
70 PRINT
80 GO TO 10
90 DATA 12.35, 41.2, 84.6, 98.7, 0.0
100 END
```

# 6.5 Surface Area: Prisms and Pyramids

Manufacturers consider marketing and cost factors when deciding on the shape and size of packaging for their products. They are also concerned with the amount of material needed to make a package. The net is a pattern that shows how the box in example 1 is constructed. To calculate the surface area, you can record the measurements on a net.

## Example 1

Find the surface area of the crackers box shown.

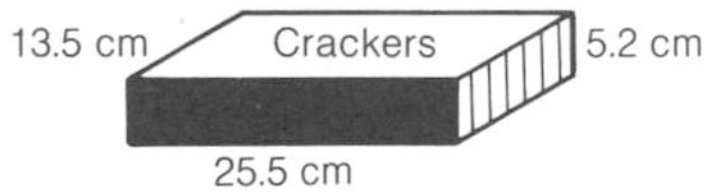


## Solution

Sketch the net. Record the measures.

There are 2A, 2B and 2C rectangles.

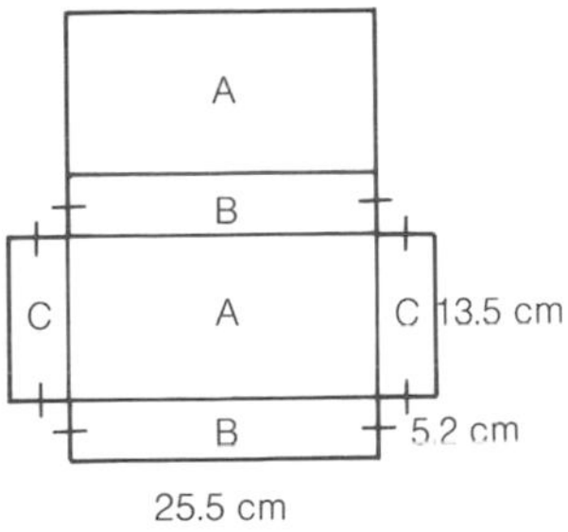


Do the calculations.

$$\begin{aligned} \text{Surface area} &= 2(\text{area A} + \text{area B} + \text{area C}) \\ &= 2(13.5 \times 25.5 + 5.2 \times 25.5 + 5.2 \times 13.5) \\ &= 2(344.25 + 132.6 + 70.2) \\ &= 2(547.05) \\ &= 1094.1 \end{aligned}$$

The surface area of the crackers box is about 1100 cm$^2$.

Round the answer to 2 significant digits since the measure in the calculation with the least number of significant digits is 5.2 cm.

To plan your calculations, draw a net and record the measurements to help you organize your solution, as shown in the following example.

## Example 2

Find the surface area of the triangular prism.

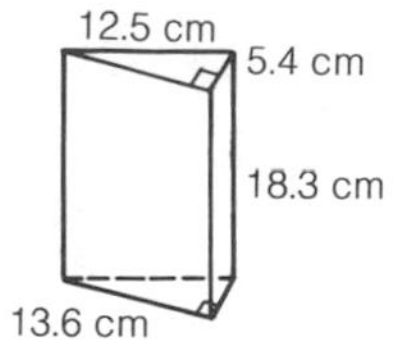


## Solution

Sketch the net.
Record the measures.

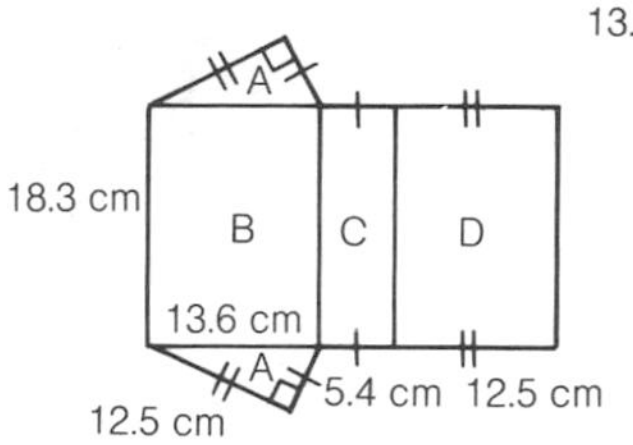


Surface area = 2 × area A + area B + area C + area D

$$= 2 \times \frac{1}{2} \times 12.5 \times 5.4 + 18.3 \times 13.6 + 18.3 \times 5.4 + 18.3 \times 12.5$$

$$= 67.5 + 248.88 + 98.82 + 228.75$$
$$= 643.95$$

Think: Use a calculator. What are the most efficient steps you can use to do the calculation?

The surface area of the triangular prism is 640 $cm^2$, to 2 significant digits.

## Try These

1 Match each prism or pyramid with its net.

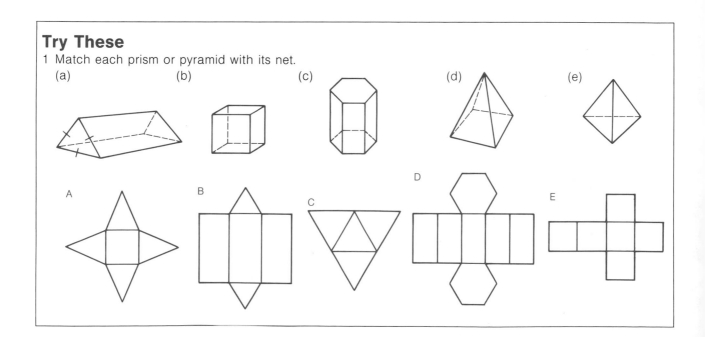

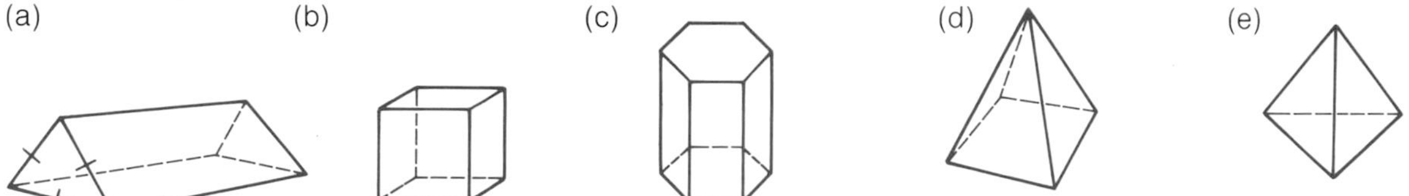


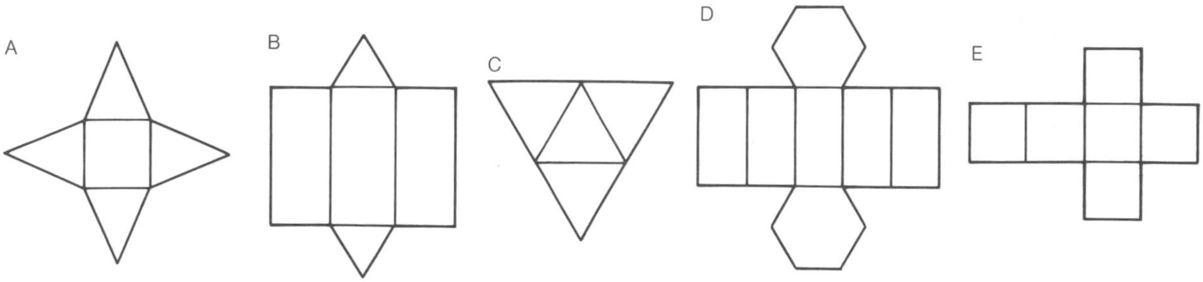

## Written Exercises

**A** **A net is helpful when you are planning the calculations.**

1 A rectangular prism is shown.

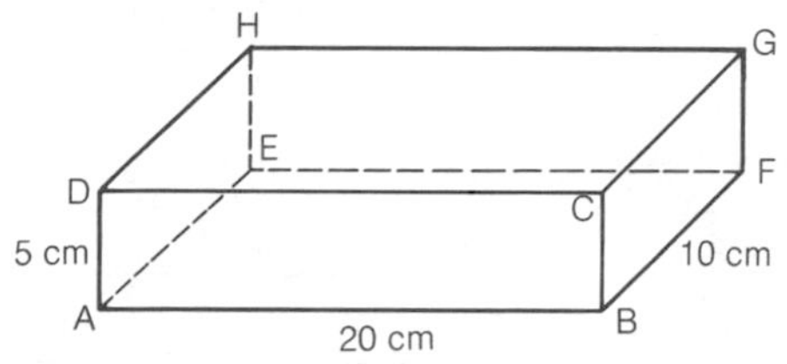


(a) What is the area of the face ABCD?
(b) Which face has the same area as in (a)?
(c) What is the area of the face DCGH?
(d) Which face has the same area as in (c)?
(e) What is the area of the face BFGC?
(f) Which face has the same area as in (e)?
(g) What is the surface area of the rectangular prism?

2 A square-based pyramid is shown.

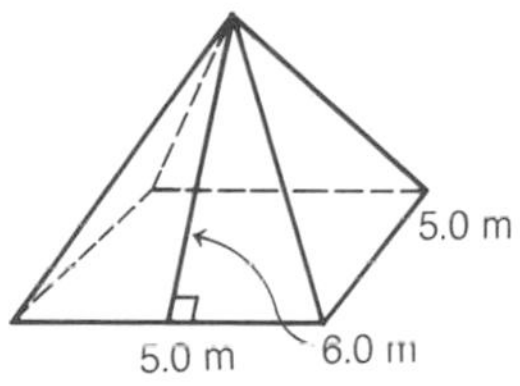


(a) Sketch a net for the pyramid.
(b) Record the measures on the net.
(c) What is the area of the base?
(d) What is the area of one of the triangular faces?
(e) Find the surface area of the square-based pyramid.

3 (a) Draw the net of the box shown.

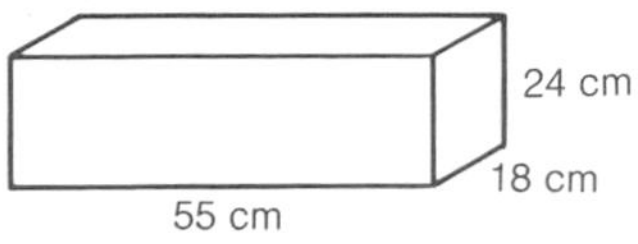


(b) Calculate the surface area.

**B** **Check your units before you make a final statement to a problem.**

4 Calculate the surface area of each rectangular prism.

(a)

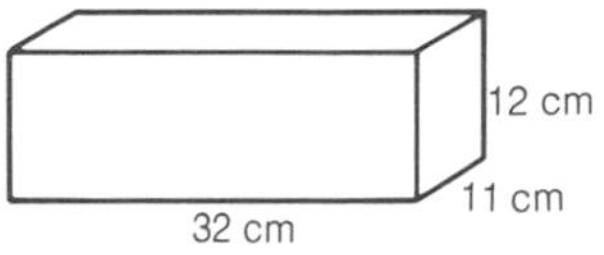


(b)

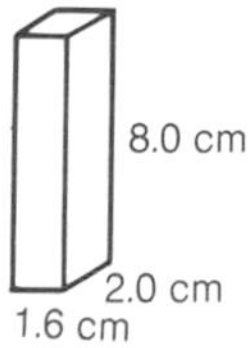


(c)

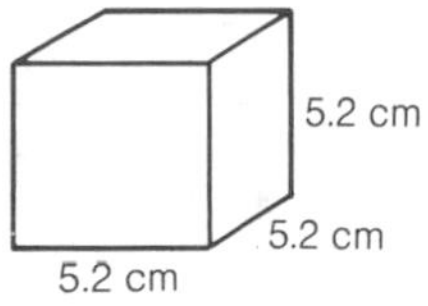


(d)

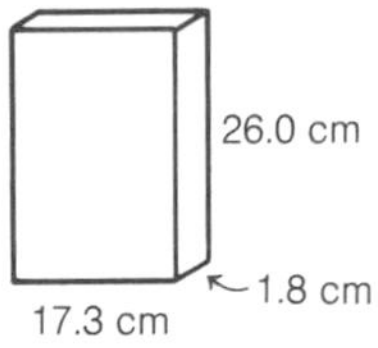


5 For each solid
- sketch a net
- calculate the surface area

(a)

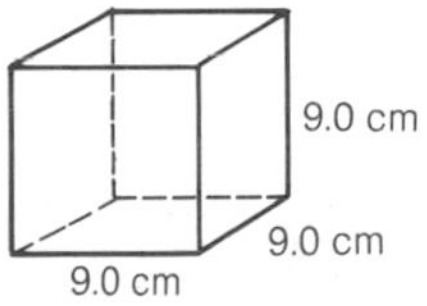


(b)

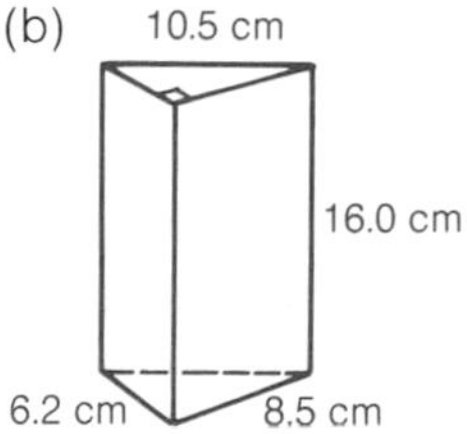


(c)

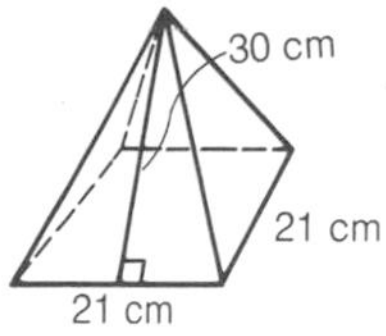


6 Calculate the surface of each.

(a)

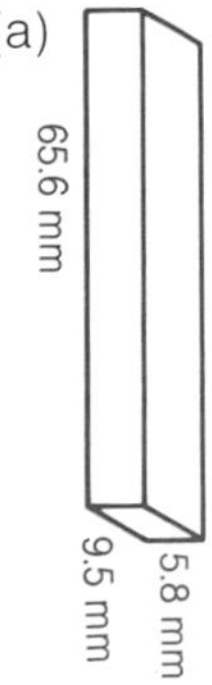


(b)

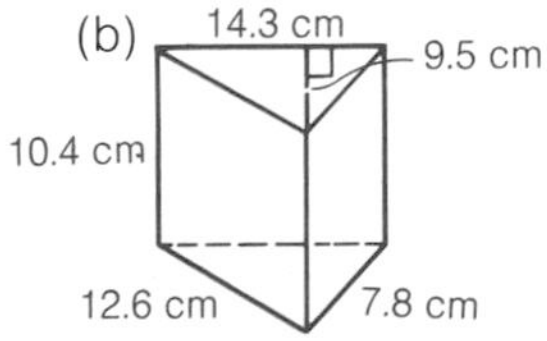


(c)

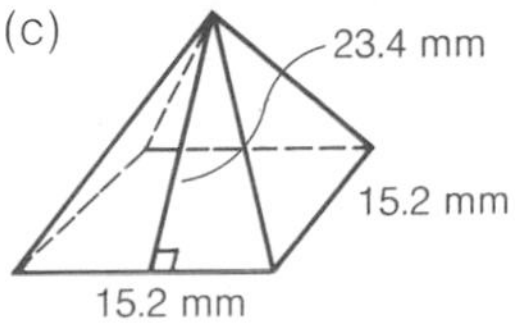

7 Refer to the triangular prism.
(a) What is the shape of the top and bottom faces?
(b) Find the area of the top and bottom faces.
(c) Find the area of each side.
(d) Find the surface area of the prism.

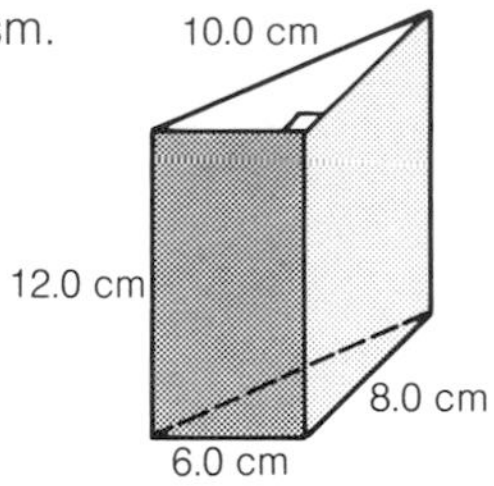


8 A portable wooden ramp is built in the shape of a triangular prism as shown.
(a) Sketch a net for the ramp.
(b) Calculate the surface area of the ramp.

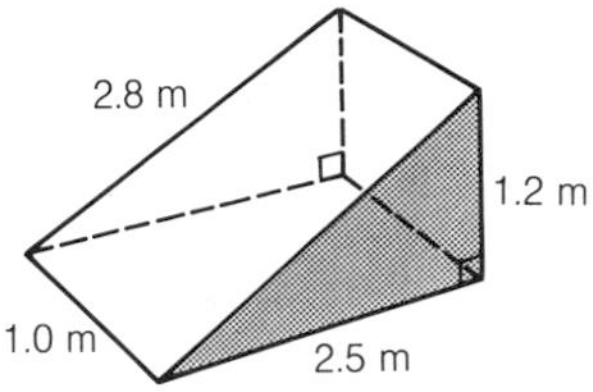


9 Which trunk has the greater surface area?

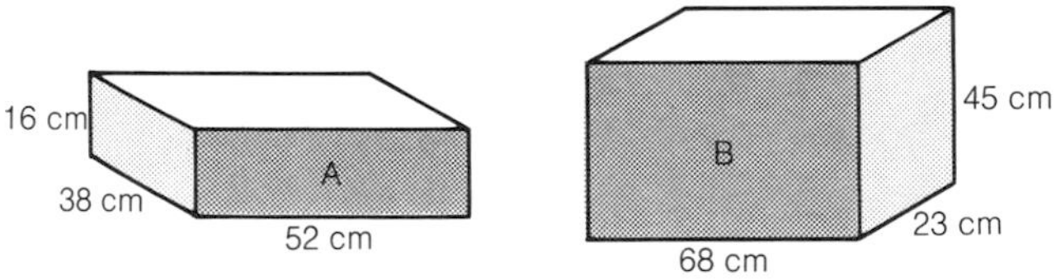


10 A cheese box is in the shape of a triangular prism. Calculate its surface area.

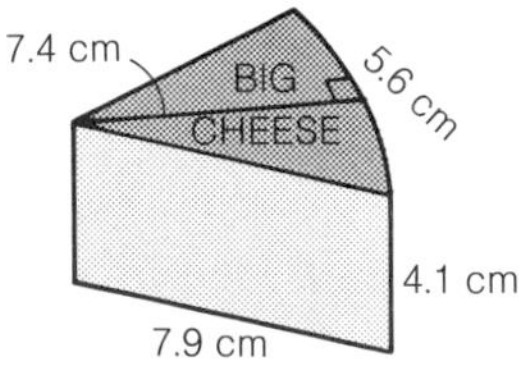


11 An aquarium is shown.
(a) Calculate the amount of glass needed to construct the aquarium.
(b) Find the cost of the glass at 16 ¢/cm².

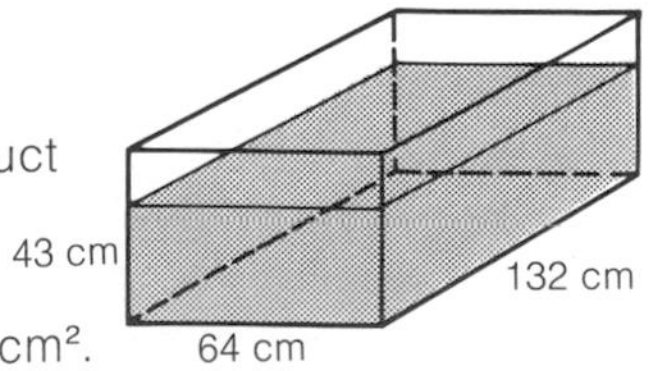


12 A popular garden shed is shown.

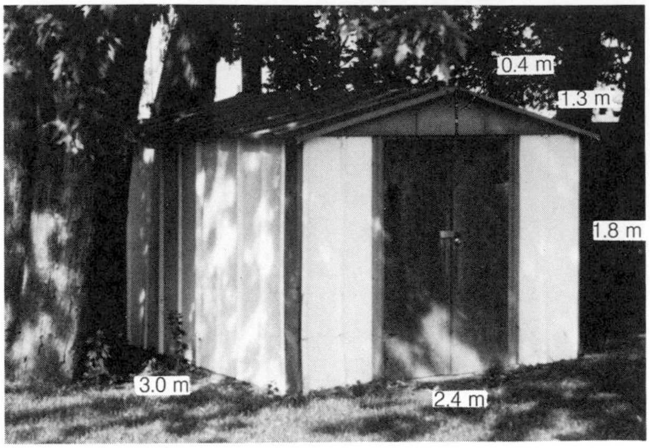


(a) Calculate the amount of material needed to make the shed. Include 10% extra to provide materials for any overlap.
(b) Find the cost of the sheet metal to make the shed $6.75/m². (Sales tax is not included.)

13 A gift box is in the shape of a regular pentagonal prism as shown.

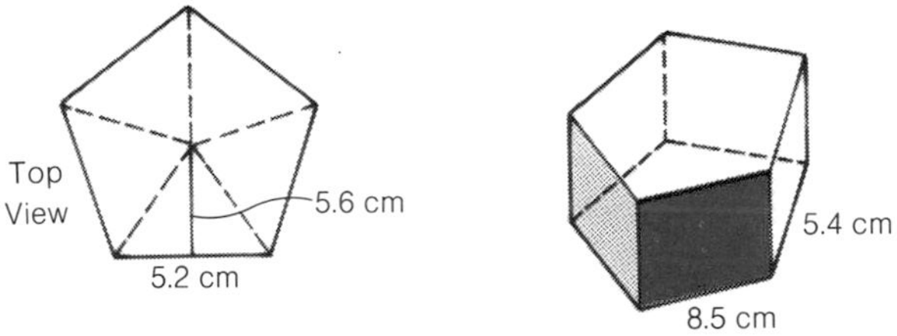


(a) Sketch a net for the box. Record the measures on the sketch.
(b) What is the area of each rectangular side face?
(c) What is the area of the top of the box?
(d) Find the surface area of the box.
(e) If you wrap the box, and include 8% extra paper, how much paper will you need?

## C

14 A square cake pan measures 28 cm on each side and is 8 cm deep. The pan is to be coated on the inside with a non-stick material. If the amount of non-stick material available covers 120 m², how many pans can be coated?

# 6.6 Formulas: Surface Area

In your study of mathematics, the strategies you learn are applied often in new topics. For example, in finding surface area, you sketched a net and recorded the measures to help you plan the calculations. This strategy is again applied to finding the surface areas of shapes which are circular, such as cylinders.

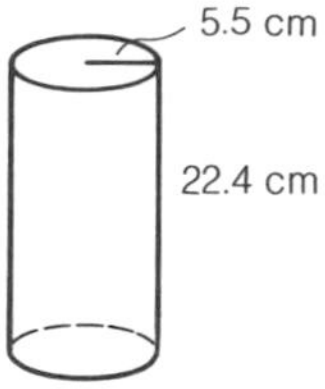


For example, if you sketch a net for the cylinder shown it will have a circular top and base. The curved surface is shown as a rectangle.

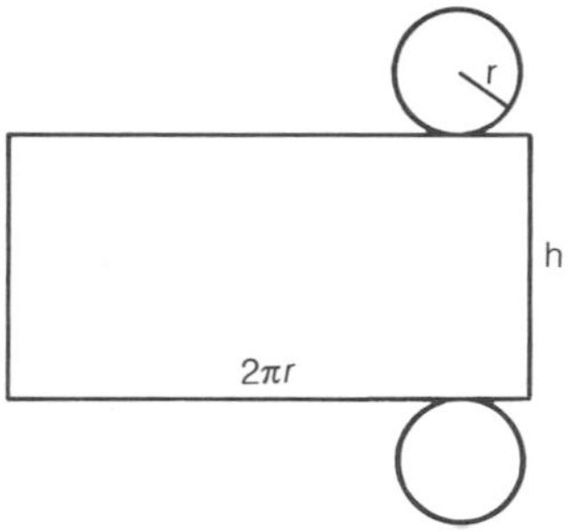


Surface area = 2 × area circle + area rectangle

You can make a formula to show the surface area, $A$.

$$A = 2 \times \pi r^2 + 2\pi r \times h$$

**The length of the rectangle is the circumference of the circle.**

$$A = 2\pi r^2 + 2\pi rh$$

Calculate the area for the cylinder shown, use $\pi \doteq 3.14$.

$$\begin{aligned} A &\doteq 2 \times 3.14 \times 5.5^2 + 2 \times 3.14 \times 5.5 \times 22.4 \\ &= 189.97 + 773.696 \\ &= 963.666 \end{aligned}$$

The answer is rounded to 2 significant digits since the least accurate measurement in this problem is 5.5 cm.

The surface area of the cylinder is about 960 cm².

Formulas have been developed for surface area, $A$, of other shapes, such as the cone and sphere.

cone

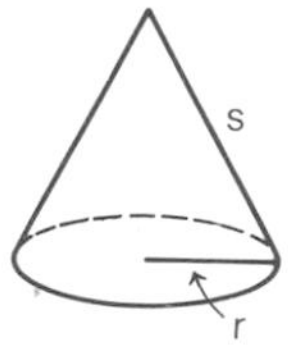


$s$ is the slant height

$r$, is the radius of the cone

$$A = \underbrace{\pi r^2}_{\text{area of base circle}} + \underbrace{\pi rs}_{\text{area of curved surface}}$$

($A$: surface area)

sphere

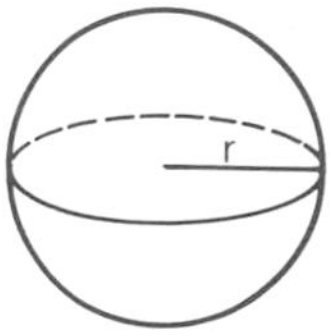


$$A = 4\pi r^2$$

($A$: surface area; $r$ is the radius of the sphere.)

The formulas can be used to solve problems.

### Example

An emergency road hazard marker is cone shaped. The curved surface of these cones is spray-painted bright orange. How many of the cones can be painted with 1 L of the paint if each litre covers 5500 $cm^2$?

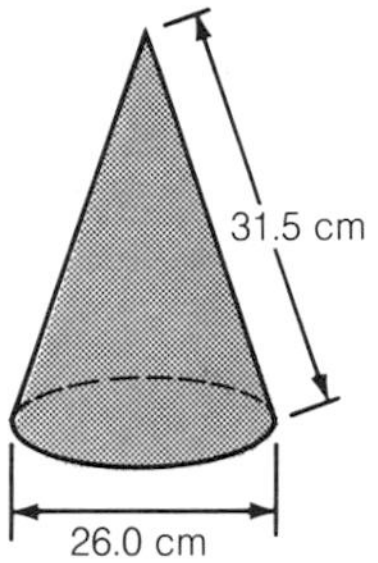


### Solution

*Step 1*: $A = \pi rs$

$A \doteq 3.14 \times 13.0 \times 31.5$

$= 1285.83$

Think: Calculate area of curved surface of cone.

The area of the curved surface of one cone is about 1290 $cm^2$.

Think: Find how many cones can be painted.

*Step 2*: 1 L of paint covers 5500 $cm^2$.

Each cone has 1290 $cm^2$.

Thus 1 L of paint will cover $\frac{5500}{1290}$ cones.

$\frac{5500}{1290} = 4.26$

Just over 4 cones

Each litre will paint 4 cones.

Make a final statement

## Try These

1 Which formula would you use to calculate the shaded area of each shape?

| | |
|---|---|
| $A = \pi r^2$ | $A = 4\pi r^2$ |
| $A = \pi r^2 + \pi rs$ | $A = \pi rs$ |
| $A = 2\pi r^2 + 2\pi rh$ | $A = 2\pi rh$ |

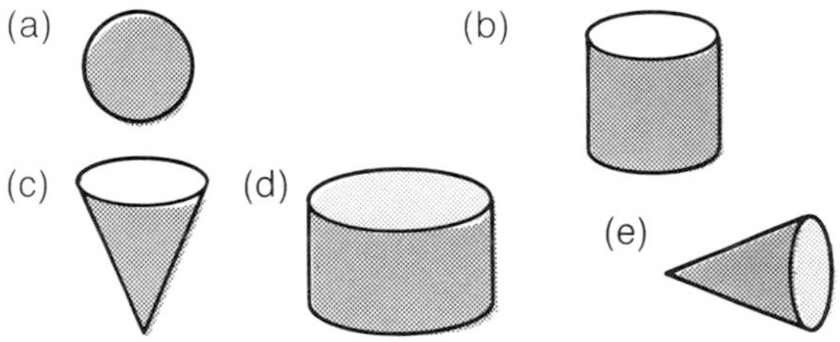


## Written Exercises

**A** **To solve problems, you must be able to decide which formula to use to find area. Review the formulas and the meaning of the variables.**

1 Which would you use to find the surface area of the can?

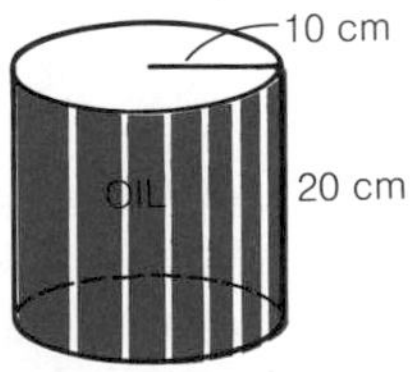


A: $A = 2 \times \pi \times 10^2 + \pi \times 10 \times 10$

B: $A = 2 \times \pi \times 10^2 + 2 \times \pi \times 10 \times 20$

C: $A = 2 \times \pi \times 20^2 + \pi \times 20 \times 20$

2 (a) Find the area of each end of the can.

(b) What are the dimensions of the curved surface?

(c) Find the surface area.

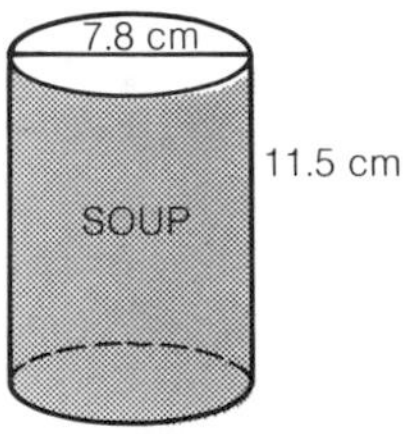


Think: Use a calculator to find the surface area efficiently.

3 Find the surface area of each cylinder

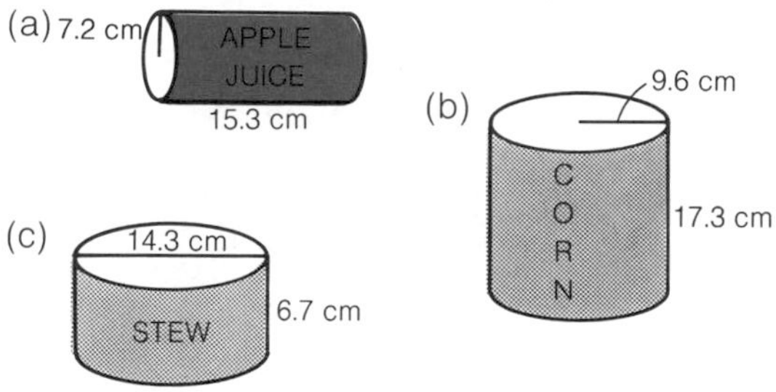


4 The cone has a radius of 25.1 cm and a slant height, *s*, of 42.5 cm.
(a) Find the area of the base.
(b) Find the area of the curved surface.
(c) What is the surface area?

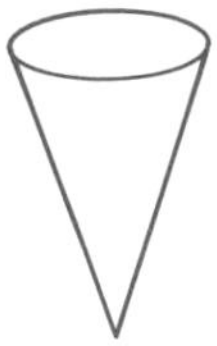

5 Find the surface area of each cone.
(a) (b) (c)

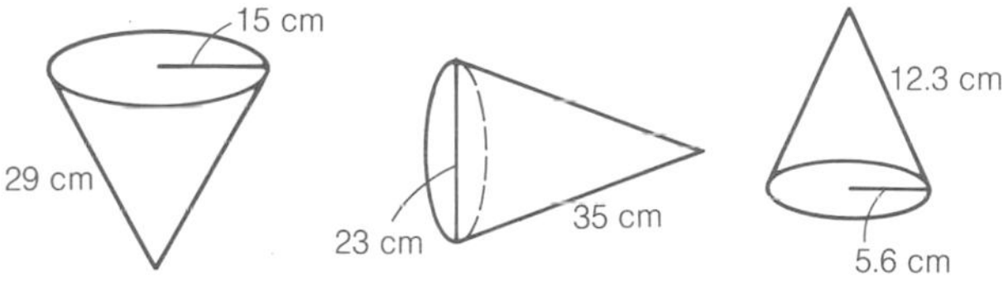


6 Find the surface of each sphere.
(a) (b) (c)

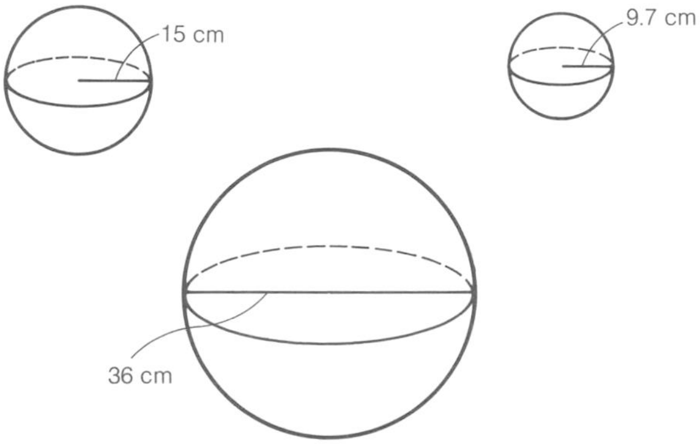


**B** **Round your answers to the accuracy shown by the measures in each problem.**

7 A baseball has diameter 7.4 cm. How much leather is required to cover the ball?

8\. A spherical tank shown in the photograph has a diameter of 7.8 m. Calculate the surface area of the tank.

A spherical shape is the most efficient use of material to make a tank. If you increase the radius by 1 m, you increase the volume by 44%.

9 A water heater with the dimensions shown is to be painted.
(a) Calculate the surface area of the top and sides of the water heater.

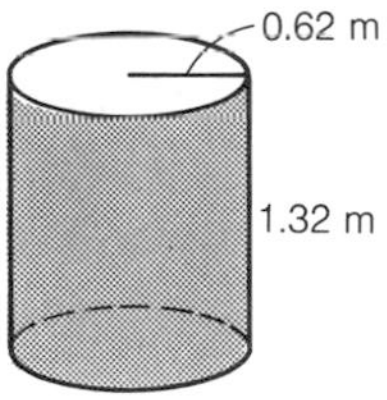


(b) If one can of paint covers 0.8 m² how many cans of paint are needed to paint the water heater?

10 (a) Predict which you think has more surface area, shape A or shape B.
Shape A a cone with radius 18 cm and slant height 18 m
Shape B a sphere with radius 18 cm
(b) Check your prediction. Do the calculations.

11 The woofer in a stereo speaker is cone shaped as shown. It has a diameter of 27.0 cm and a slant height of 15.0 cm. Find the curved surface area of the woofer.

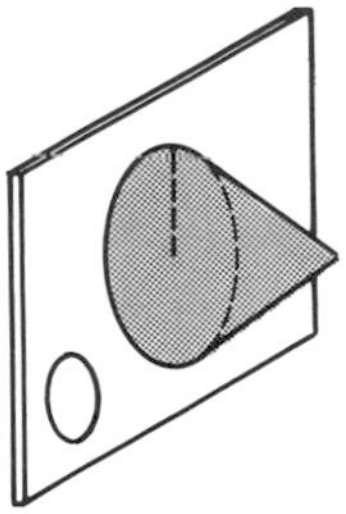

12 Coins are encased in a plastic wrapper.

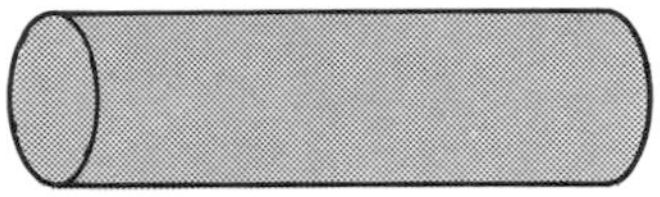

A roll of dimes contains 50 coins. Each dime has a diameter of 17.5 mm and a thickness of 1.0 mm.

(a) Find the surface area of the plastic wrapper for a roll of dimes.

(b) Express your results in (a) in square centimetres.

13 A large gasoline tanker is to be painted with two coats of rustproof paint. The diameter of the tank is 2.4 m and its length is 10.5 m. The back end of the tank is hemi-spherical.

(a) Calculate the surface area of the tank.

(b) How many litres of paint are needed if 1 L covers 5.8 m$^2$?

14 A cake-icing utensil is in the shape of an open cylinder with a cone on one end. What area of metal is needed to make each utensil?

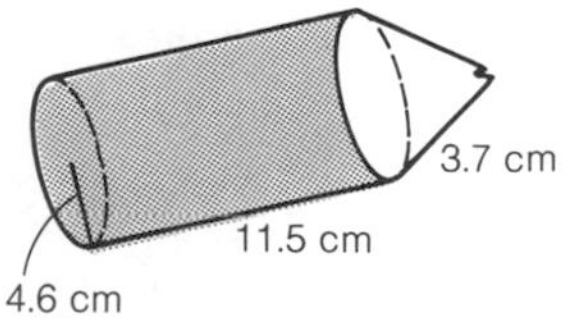


15 The propane storage tank shown has a diameter of 1.2 m. The length of the cylindrical part is 3.5 m. Each end is hemispherical in shape. What is the surface area of the tank?

**C**

16 A square nut is shown in the diagram. As a prize for the best engineering design, the nut is coated with a layer of gold plate.

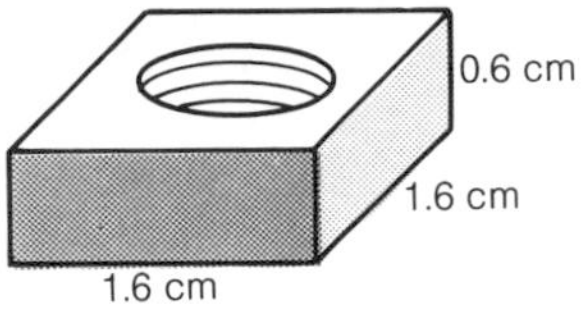


(a) Find the surface area of the nut. The hole has a diameter of 1.1 cm.

(b) Calculate the amount of gold used if the gold is 0.015 mm thick.

## Consumer Tip

When you buy a gold necklace, or ring, the purity is measured by karats.

- What is meant by 10k, 14k gold?
- Which is more expensive, 18k or 14k gold?
- A retailer has told you that the symbol 18k was accidently left off the gold necklace, but the necklace is a terrific buy, what should you do?

## Math Tip

It is important to clearly understand the vocabulary of mathematics when solving problems. Make a list of all the new words you have met in this chapter. Provide a simple example to illustrate each word.

# 6.7 Principles of Volume

The volume $V$ of a rectangular prism is the number of cubic units needed to fill the solid. For the solid shown, there are 3 layers each measuring 6 cm by 2 cm.

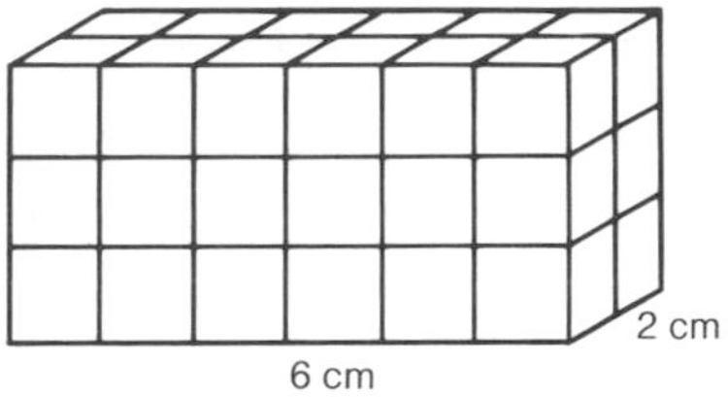


length, $l$ width, $w$ height, $h$

$V = 6 \times 2 \times 3$

$= 36$

The volume is 36 $cm^3$. Use cubic units for volume.

In studying mathematics, you can often interpret formulas in different, more useful ways. For example, the formula for volume can be thought of in two ways when doing calculations.

Volume = length × width × height $\quad V = l \times w \times h$

or

Volume = area of base × height $\quad V = B \times h$ ← This form is useful whenever the base of the solid is not rectangular, as shown in the following example.

### Example

Cheeses shipped from Europe come in large containers and then are cut into triangular wedges. Find the volume of the wedge in cubic centimetres.

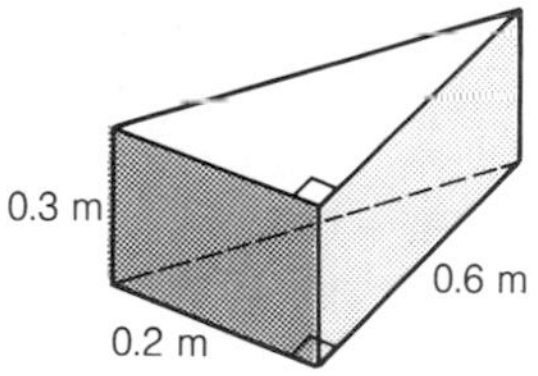


### Solution

Think: Record measures as centimetres

0.3 m = 30 cm 0.2 m = 20 cm 0.6 m = 60 cm

$$V = \left(\frac{1}{2} \times 20 \times 60\right) \times 30$$

← Base is triangular

$= 18\,000$

The volume of the wedge of cheese is 18 000 $cm^3$.

The largest cheese made was a 15 700 kg piece of cheddar, nick-named the "Big Cheese"

## Try These

1 What is the volume of each box?

(a)

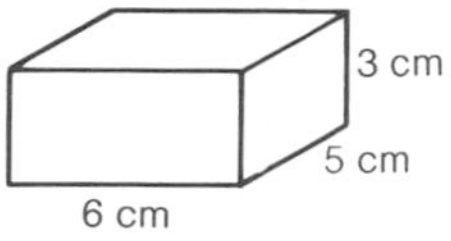


(b)

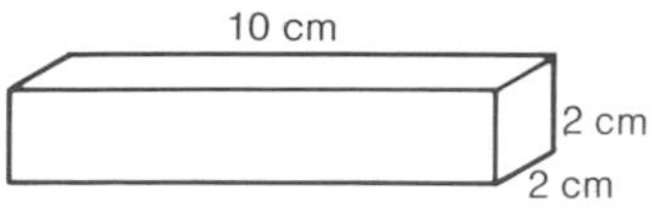


2 For each triangular prism

- ▶ Find the area of the base
- ▶ then find the volume.

(a)

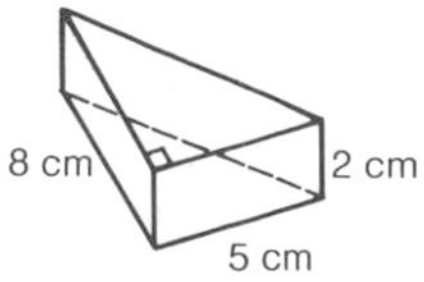


(b)

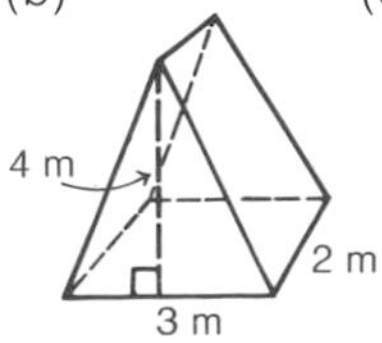


(c)

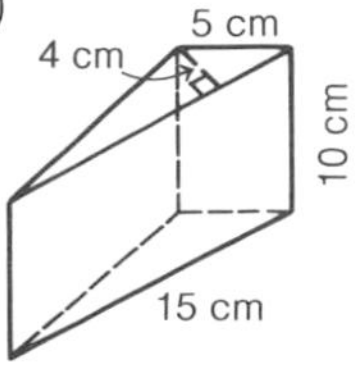

## Written Exercises

**A** **Use the formulas $V = l \times w \times h$, $V = B \times h$. Review the meaning of each variable.**

1 Calculate the volume of each rectangular prism.

(a)

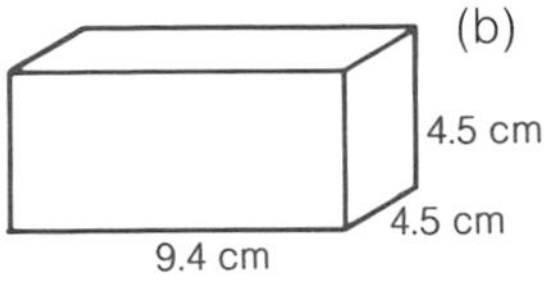


(b)

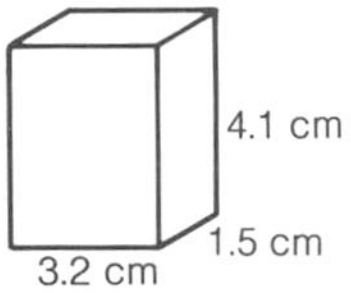


(c)

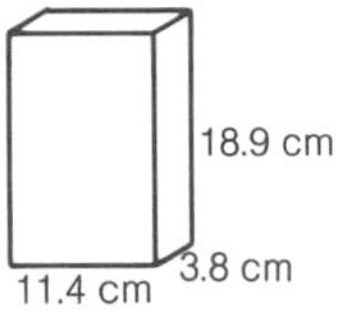


(d)

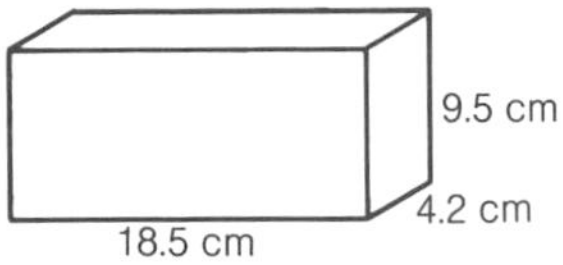


2 What is the volume of each rectangular prism with the following dimensions?

| | Length | Width | Height |
|---|---|---|---|
| (a) | 4 cm | 5 cm | 3 cm |
| (b) | 15 mm | 4 mm | 10 mm |
| (c) | 10 cm | 20 cm | 4 cm |
| (d) | 12 mm | 20 mm | 15 mm |

3 Calculate the volume of each solid.

| | Area of base | Height |
|---|---|---|
| (a) | 20 $m^2$ | 3 m |
| (b) | 8 $cm^2$ | 5 cm |
| (c) | 6.5 $mm^2$ | 8.0 mm |
| (d) | 1.4 $km^2$ | 0.5 km |

4 Find the volume of each triangular prism.

(a)

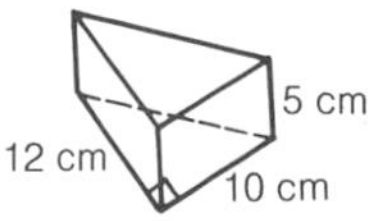


(b)

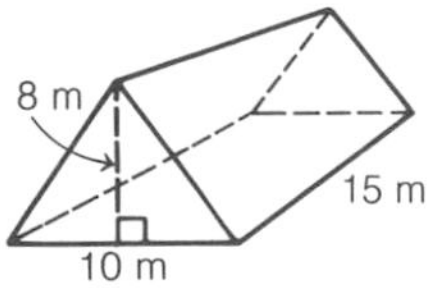


(c)

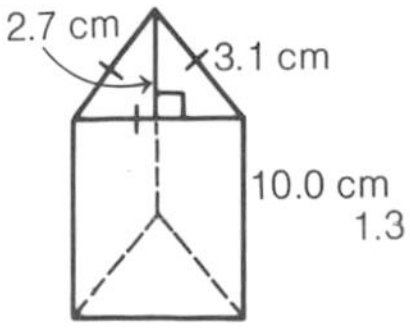


(d)

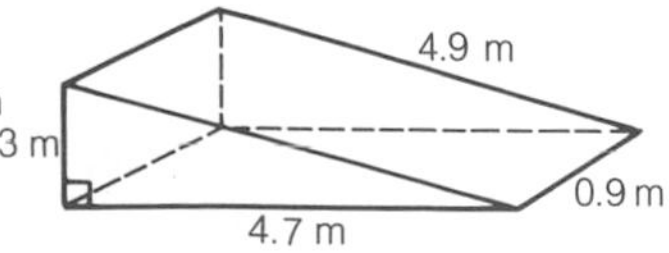


**B** **Be sure to make a final statement in answering each problem.**

5 In each pair, estimate which has the greater volume. Then check by calculating.

(a)

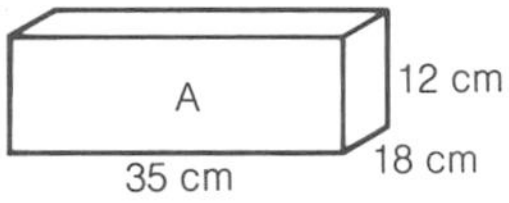


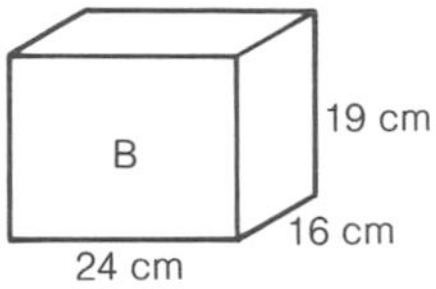


(b)

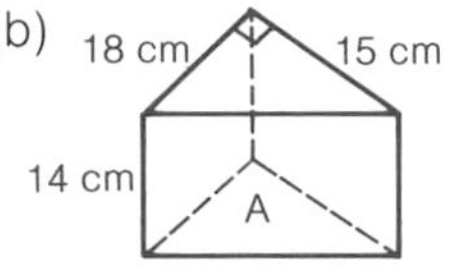


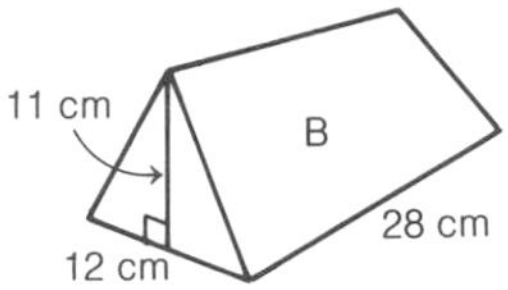


6 Find the missing values.

| | Area of base | Height | Volume |
|---|---|---|---|
| (a) | 25 $cm^2$ | 4 cm | ? |
| (b) | ? | 12 m | 180 $m^3$ |
| (c) | 8.5 $cm^2$ | ? | 28 $cm^3$ |
| (d) | ? | 1.42 m | 4.97 $m^3$ |

7 A classroom measures 10 m long, 9 m wide and 4 m high. To be comfortable, each person in the classroom needs 8 $m^3$ of air. Find how many students should be allowed in the classroom if it is to be comfortable.

8 A driveway is 27.0 m long and 4.0 m wide. Blacktop will be spread on top of the driveway with a thickness of 6 cm. How many cubic metres of blacktop are needed?

9 An aquarium is 54.6 cm long, 22.3 cm wide, and 18.4 cm deep.

(a) Calculate how many litres of water the tank will hold when full. **Remember: 1 L = 1000 $cm^3$**

(b) The tank is filled so that the water is 5.2 cm from the top. How much water is in the tank? Give your answer to the nearest tenth.

10 On a construction site, earth is being excavated to a depth of 12 m from a rectangular area measuring 85 m by 54 m. The earth is being removed in dump trucks which are capable of carrying 42 $m^3$ of earth.

(a) Find the volume of the earth that will be excavated.
(b) How many truck loads will be required to remove the earth?

11 A freezer is 1.80 m long, 0.92 m deep and 1.35 m high (outside dimensions).
(a) Find the amount of space occupied by the freezer.
(b) Find the volume of the inside of the freezer if the thickness of each side is 6 cm.

12 A rectangular container is 30.0 cm wide, 56.0 cm long and contains water to a depth of 18.0 cm. A stone is placed in the water and the water rises 2.9 cm. What is the volume of the stone?

13 To calculate the volume of the solid, C, you may think of 2 rectangular solids, A and B.

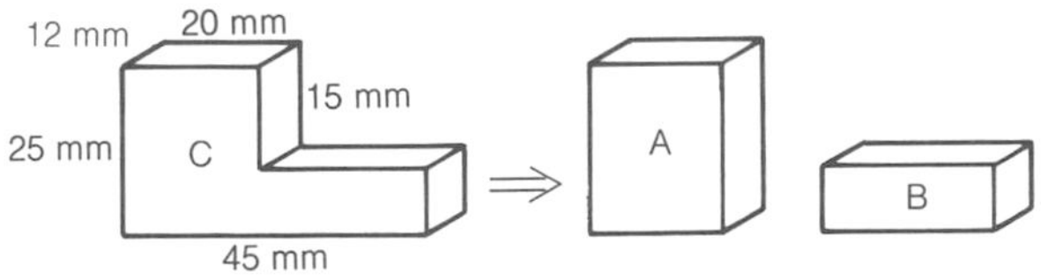


(a) Calculate the volume of rectangular solid A.
(b) Calculate the volume of rectangular solid B.
(c) What is the volume of the solid C?

14 Calculate the volume of each solid.

(a)

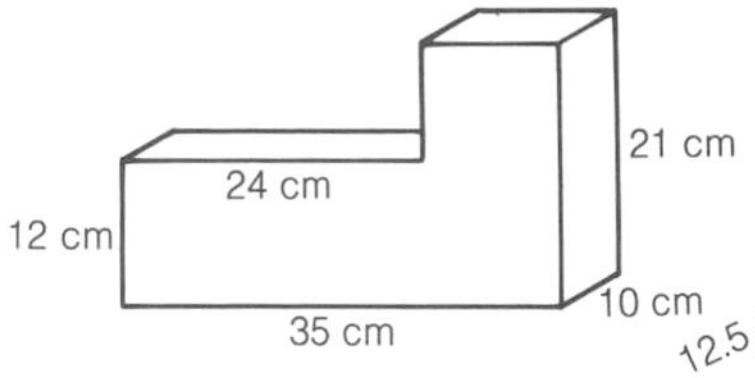


(b)

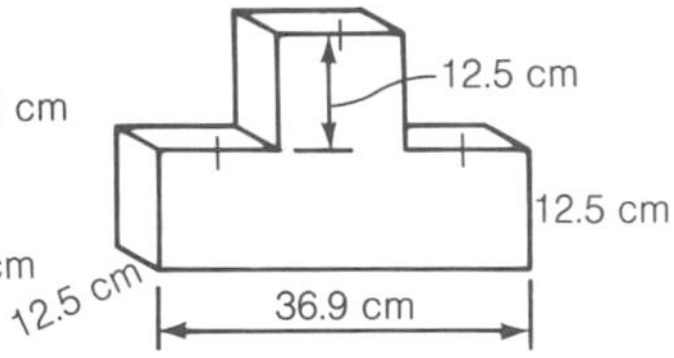


(c)

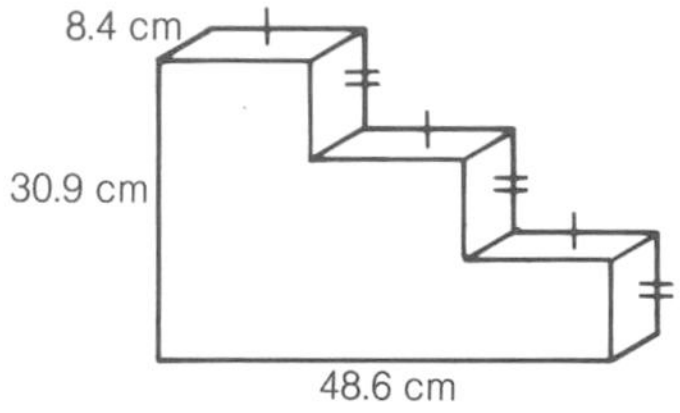


(d)

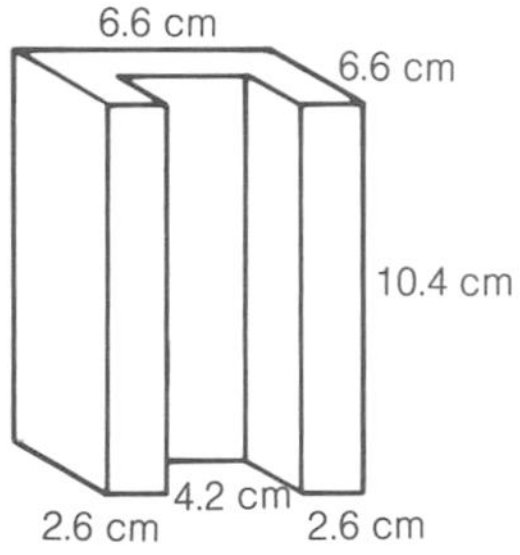


15 The dimensions of a cottage are shown. Find the volume of the cottage.

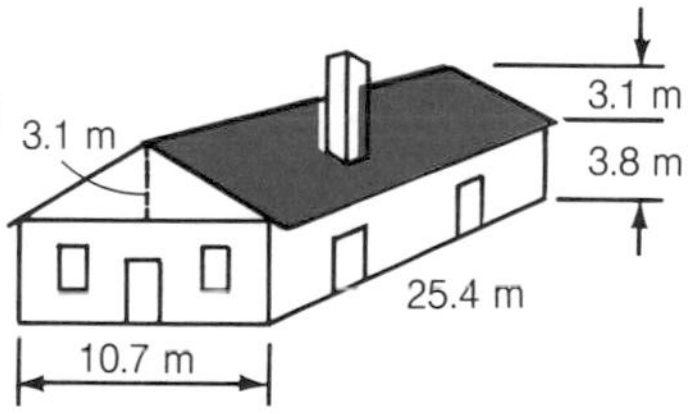


## C

16 A chocolate manufacturer decides to change the boxes from a hexagonal base shown to a square base shape. The square-based box is to have the same height and contain the same volume as the hexagonal-based box. Calculate the length of each side of the square base.

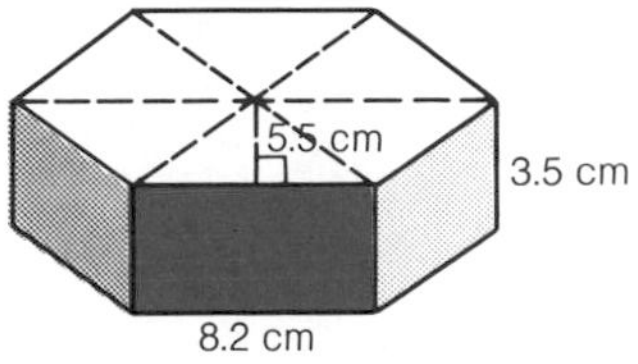

# 6.8 Formulas for Volume

The general formula (volume = area of base × height), is the basis for developing special formulas for finding volume.

### Cylinder

$V = \pi r^2 \times h$

↑ area of base ↑ height

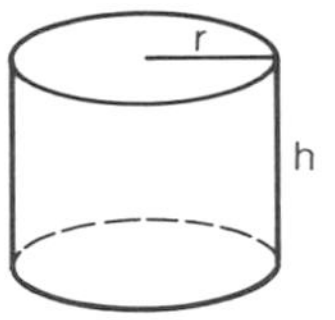


### Square-based pyramid

$V = \frac{1}{3} \times \text{area of base} \times \text{height}$

$V = \frac{1}{3}s^2h$

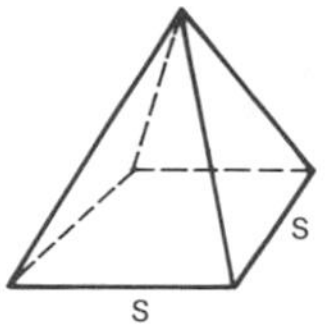


We also need to calculate the volume of these shapes.

### Cone

$V = \frac{1}{3}\pi r^2 h$

Compare this formula with that for a **cylinder.**

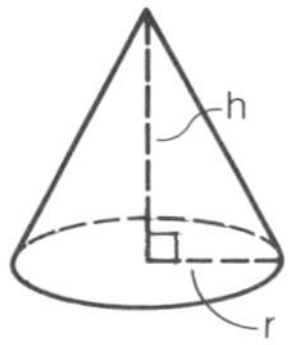


### Sphere

$V = \frac{4}{3}\pi r^3$

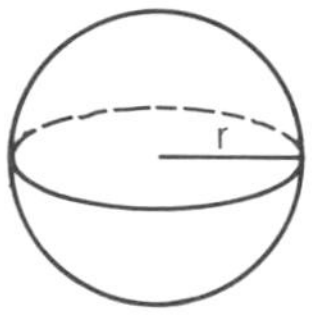


In studying mathematics, you often use familiar steps to solve problems.

To solve some problems you need to combine these formulas with other skills you have learned.

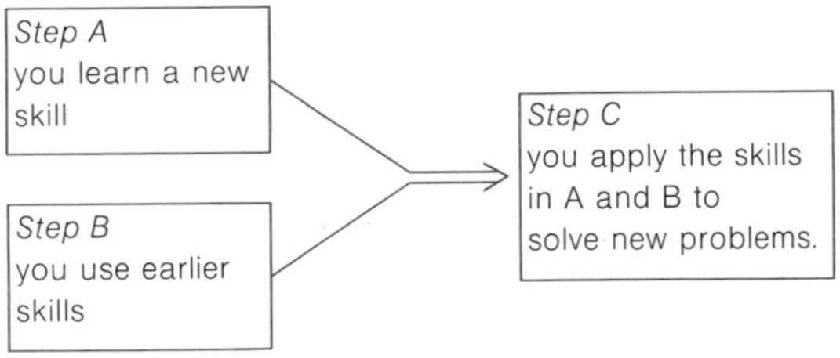


## Example

(a) Find the volume of the funnel.

(b) How many litres will it hold?

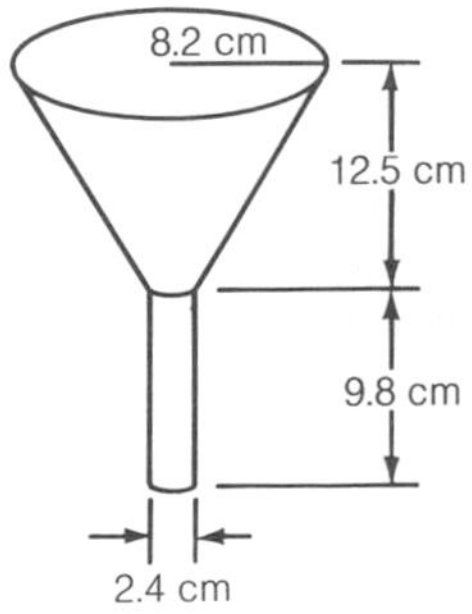


Remember:
$1 \text{ cm}^3 = 1 \text{ mL}$

## Solution

(a) The funnel has two parts, a cone-shaped part and a cylindrical part.
For the cone part:

$$V = \frac{1}{3}\pi r^2 h$$

$$V \doteq \frac{1}{3} \times 3.14 \times 8.2^2 \times 12.5$$

$$= \frac{1}{3} \times 3.14 \times 67.24 \times 12.5$$

$$\doteq 880$$

Use a calculator. Follow these steps to do the calculation.

C 1.2 $x^2$ × 9.8 × π = Output ?

Use the π key.

For the cylinder part:

$V = \pi r^2 h$

$V \doteq 3.14 \times 1.2^2 \times 9.8$

$\doteq 44$

Volume of funnel $= 880 + 44$

$= 924$

The volume of the funnel is about 924 $cm^3$.

(b) Use 1 $cm^3$ = 1 mL

924 $cm^3$ = 924 mL

= 0.924 L

The funnel can hold 0.924 L.

## Try These

1 Which formula would you use to calculate the volume of each shape?

(a)

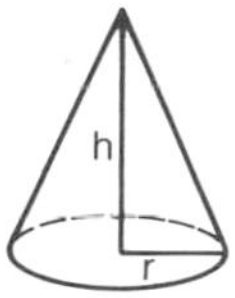


(b)

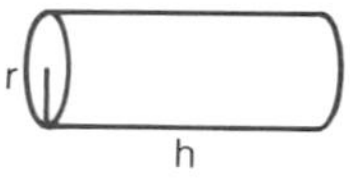


(c)

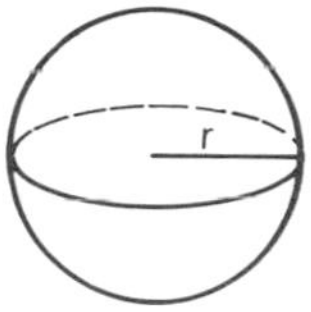


(d)

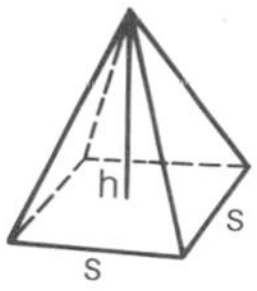


(e)

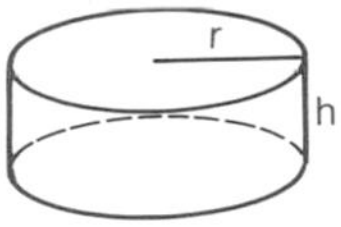


(f)

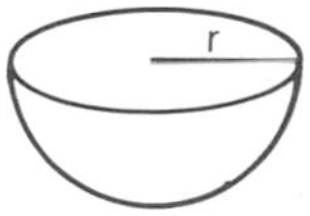


2 For which shape is each of the following formula used to calculate the volume?

(a) $V = \frac{1}{3}\pi r^2 h$ (b) $V = \frac{4}{3}\pi r^3$

(c) $V = \pi r^2 h$ (d) $V = \frac{1}{3}s^2 h$

3 For each shape, what values of $r$ and $h$ are used to calculate the volume?

(a)

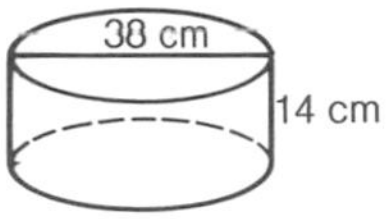


(b)

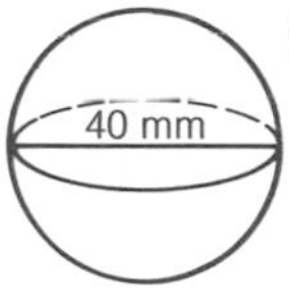


(c)

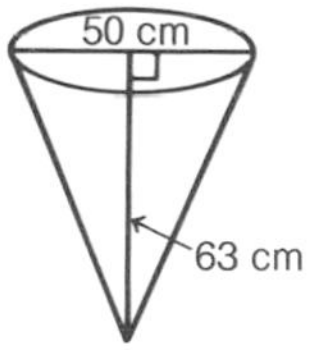


## Written Exercises

**A** **Review the various formulas for finding volume.**

1 Find the volume of each cylinder.

(a)

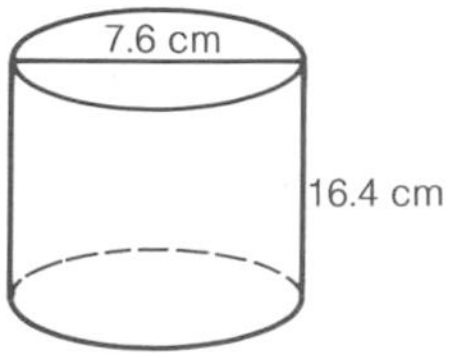


(b)

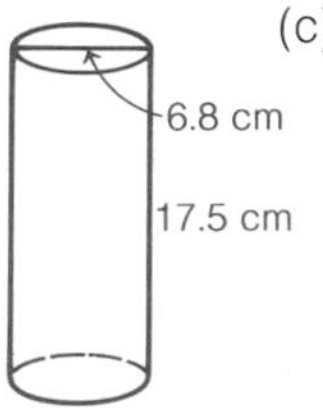


(c)

2 (a) Record the formula used to calculate the volume of a cone.

(b) Calculate the volume of the cone shown.

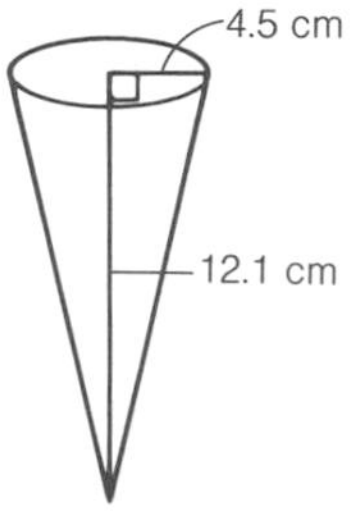

3 (a) Record the formula used to calculate the volume of a square-based pyramid.
(b) Calculate the volume of the pyramid shown.

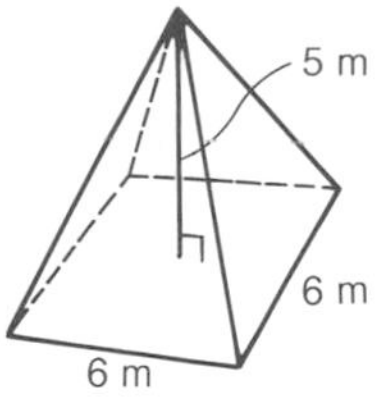


4 Find the volume of each pyramid or cone.

(a)

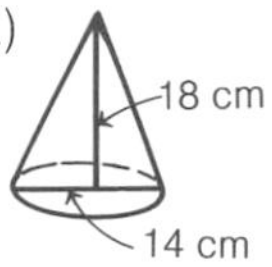


(b)

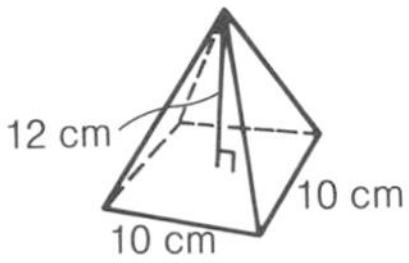


(c)

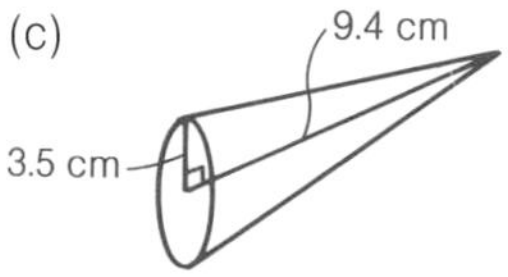


(d)

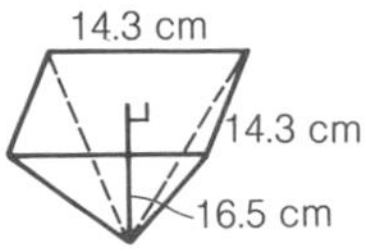


5 (a) Record the formula for the volume of a sphere.
(b) Find the volume of the sphere shown.

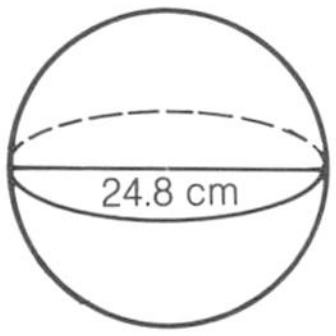


6 Find the volume of a sphere with each radius.
(a) 14 cm (b) 34 cm (c) 9.5 cm

7 Find the volume of a sphere with each diameter.
(a) 26 cm (b) 14.6 cm (c) 25.8 cm

**B** **Record the measures for each shape before you substitute into the formula and do the calculations.**

8 Find the volume of a soccer ball that has a diameter of 30 cm.

9 A jar of nail polish has the dimensions shown. How many millilitres can it hold? (Express your answer to the nearest millilitre.)

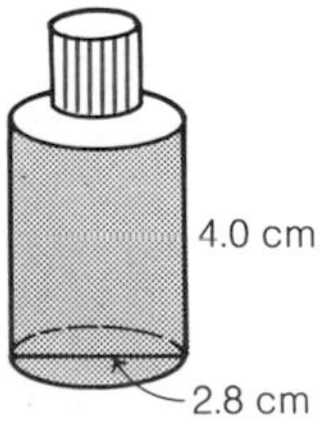


10 A fish pond is the shape of an inverted cone. The diameter of the pond is 12.4 m and its maximum depth is 0.6 m. How many litres of water are in the pond?

11 A diamond is cut into the shape of a square pyramid. Find the volume of the diamond.

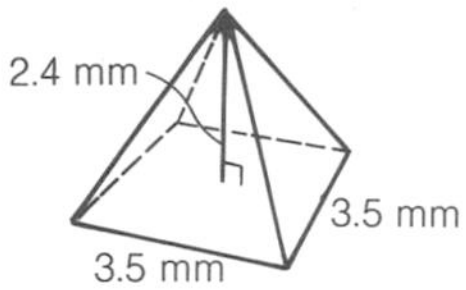


12 A steel ball-bearing has a diameter of 2.0 cm. Calculate the mass of 30 bearings if steel has a mass of 32 g/cm³.

13 Panty hose can be purchased in a small carton shaped as shown. Find the volume of the carton.

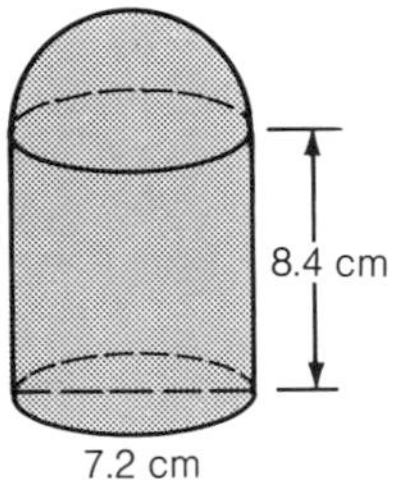


14 A boiler is cylindrical with hemi-spherical ends, as shown. Calculate the volume of the boiler.

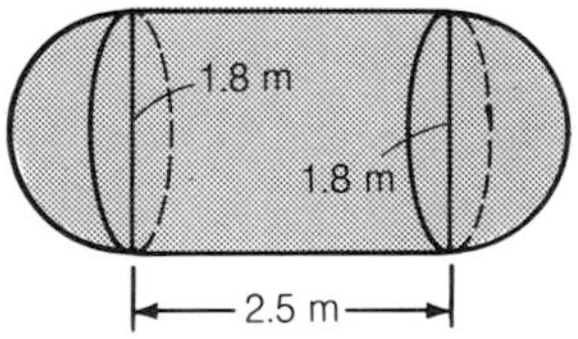


15 Inside a silo, grain is stored in a container which has a large cylinder welded to a cone. Calculate the volume of grain this silo can hold.

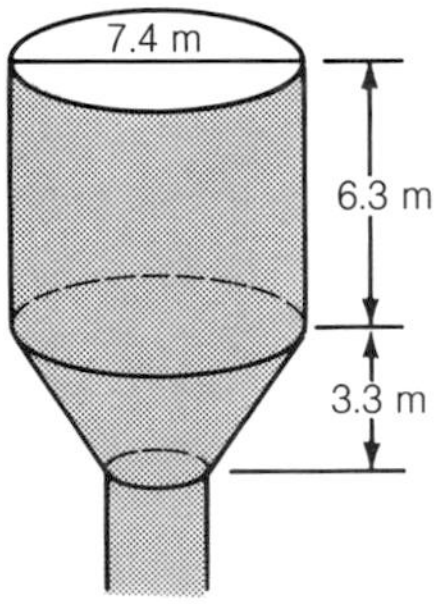


16 A concrete storm pipe has an outer diameter of 3.8 m and an inner diameter of 3.6 m. Find the volume of concrete in 100 m of this pipe.

**C**

17 A copper smelter produces copper wire that is cylindrical and has a diameter of 2 mm. What length of wire can be made from a rectangular block measuring 8.0 cm by 15.0 cm by 3.0 cm?

# Review: Practice and Problems

1 Calculate the perimeter of each figure.

(a)

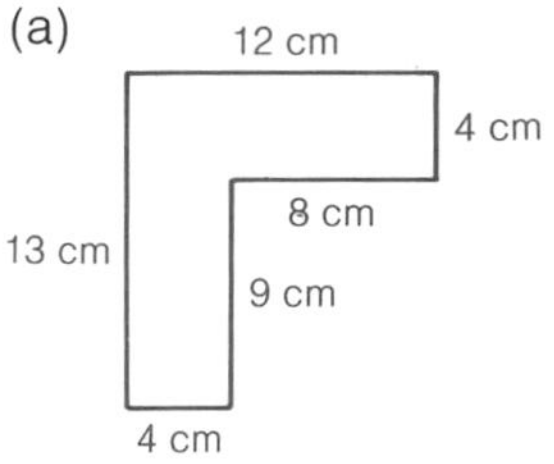


(b)

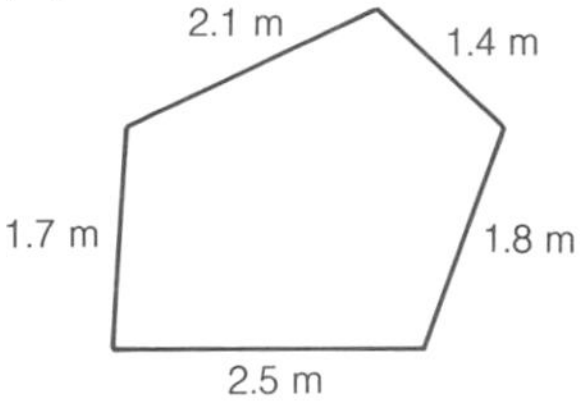


2 Refer to the picture.

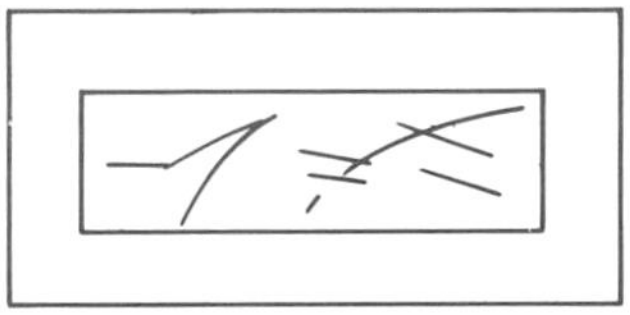

The picture measures 32 cm by 46 cm and has a 4.7 cm border.

(a) Find the perimeter of the picture.

(b) Find the outside perimeter of the frame.

3 A patio umbrella has a radius of 1.5 m. Calculate the length of the fringe needed for the edge. Express your answer to 1 decimal place.

4 (a) Calculate the area of each stamp.

(b) How many of each stamp would you need to cover the two outside surfaces of this text?

5 A circle has a circumference of 54.6 cm. Find the area of the circle.

6 Calculate the surface area for each figure.

(a)

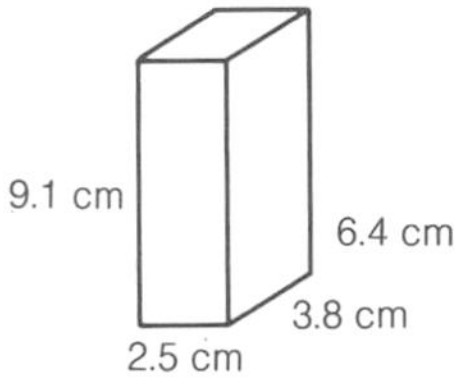


(b)

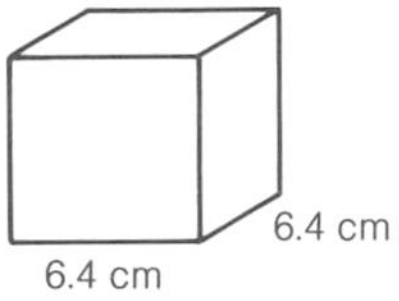


(c)

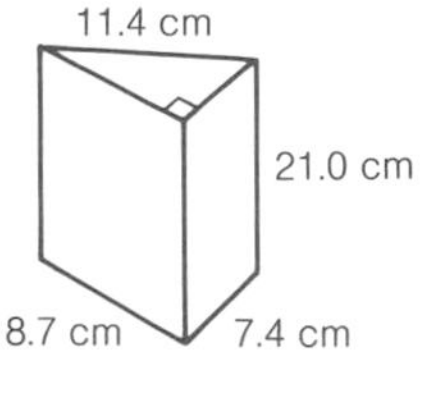


7 Find the area of

(a) the base

(b) one side face

(c) 4 side faces

(d) Find the surface area of the pyramid.

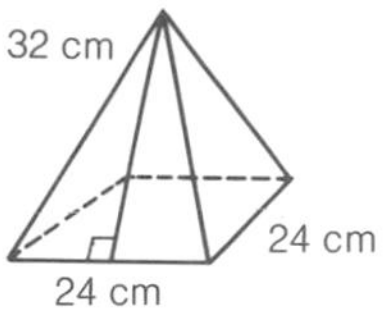


8 Find the surface area of a box with no top that is 48 cm long, 22 cm wide and 15 cm high.

9 Find the volume of each of the following.

(a)

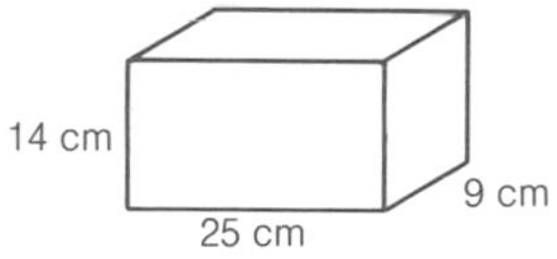


(b)

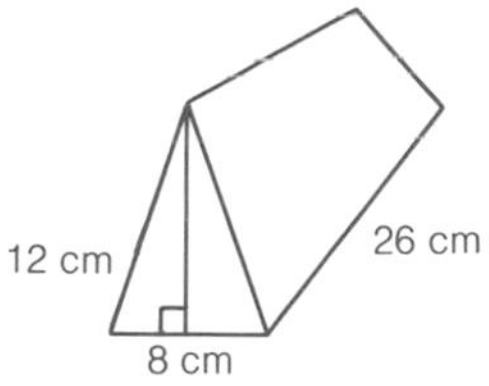


10 Find the volume and surface area of each figure.

(a)

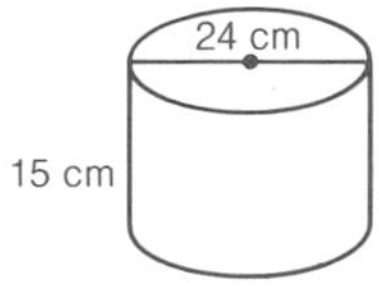


(b)

(c)

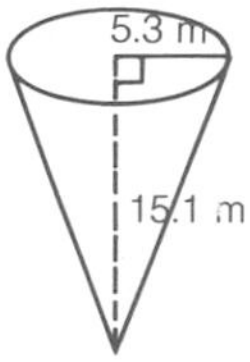


11 (a) Find the volume of a pyramid 15.6 m high with a rectangular base measuring 7.6 m by 3.8 m.

(b) Find the volume of a cone 3.8 m in diameter and 6.7 m high.

# A Practice Test

1 (a) Calculate the perimeter of the figure.

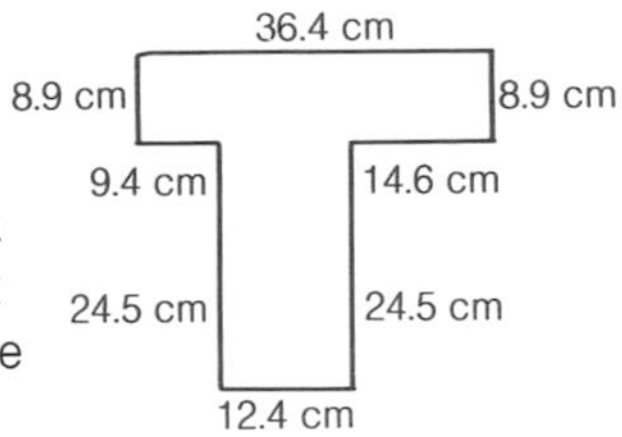


(b) The perimeter of a square parking lot is 196.4 m. Find the length of the one side of the parking lot.

2 Calculate the area of each figure.

(a)

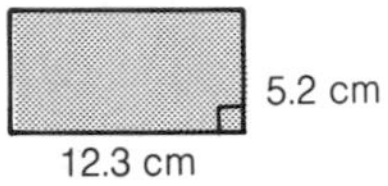


(b)

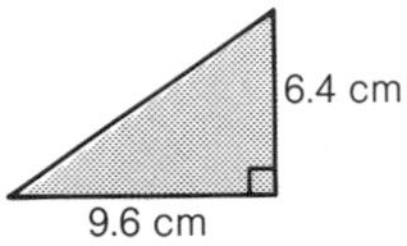


(c)

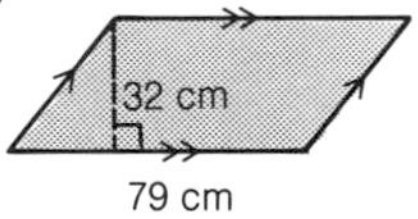


(d)

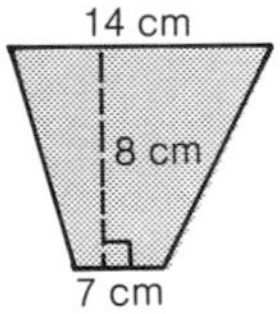


3 Find the area and circumference of each circle,
(a) with radius 6.8 m.
(b) with diameter 10.4 cm.

4 A circular track is shown. Sophia runs on the outside path and Carmella on the inside path.

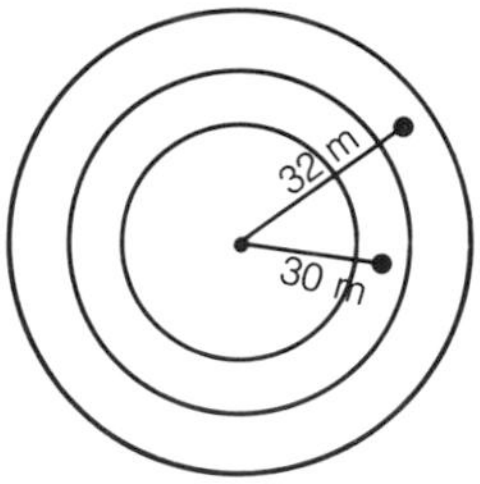


(a) Find the distance run by each runner in one lap.
(b) Who runs further? By how much?

5 Find the area of the shaded part.

(a)

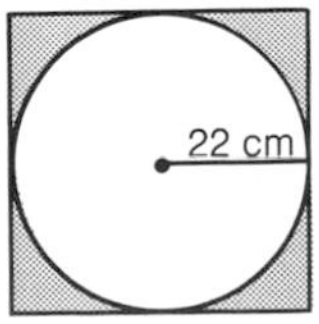


(b)

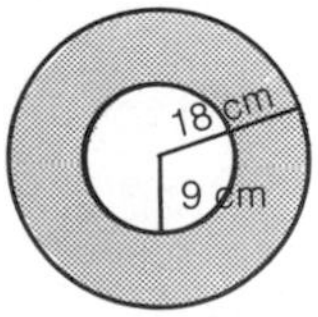


6 (a) A square has an area of 169 cm². Find the perimeter.
(b) A rectangle has a perimeter of 144 cm. If the length is 54 cm, find the area.

7 Find the surface area of each shape.

(a)

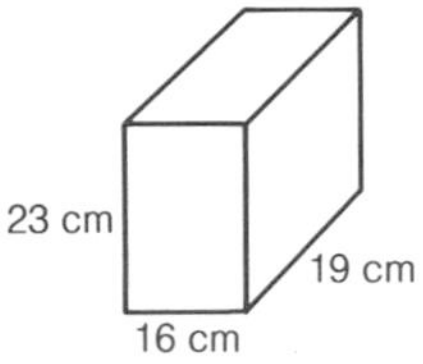


(b)

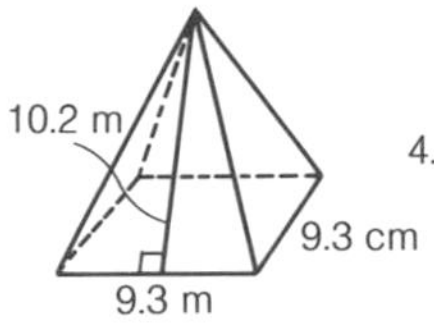


(c)

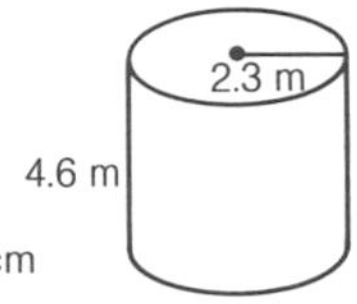


8 Find the volume of each shape.

(a)

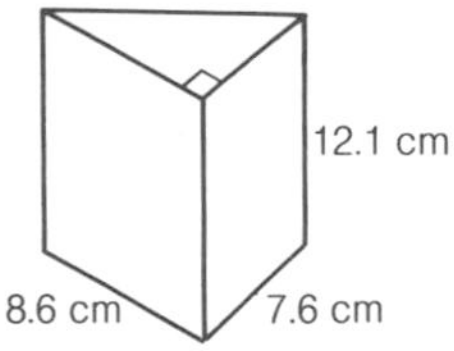


(b)

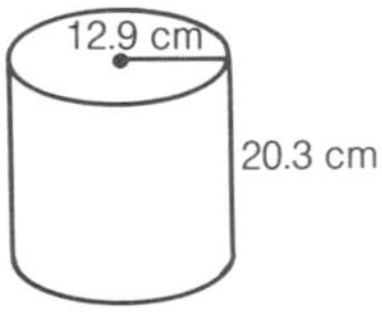


9 (a) A storage hut is in the shape of a square based pyramid. Plywood is used to construct the sides. Calculate the surface area of the sides.

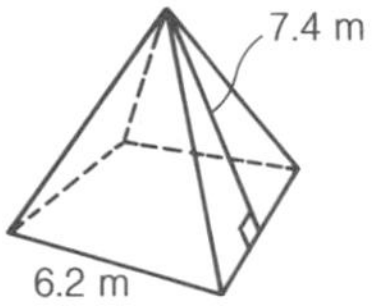


(b) The cost of finishing the hut is $12.80/m². Find the total cost of the finishing for the hut in (a).

10 A driveway is 27 m long and 4 m wide. Black top will be spread on top of the driveway with a thickness of 6 cm. Find the volume of blacktop needed if the driveway is rectangular.

# 7 Consumer Skills and Personal Finance

simple and compound interest, using formulas and calculators, paying sales tax, purchasing a car, finding hidden costs, problem solving, buying an annuity, financial planning, using present value, solving problems and applications

## Introduction

Many of the skills and strategies you learn in mathematics, play an important role in your making decisions as a consumer, or in planning your financial future. In this and the next two chapters you will explore many of these skills so that you can be not only a wise consumer but also be wise in planning your finances.

- Skills learned in one discipline often apply to solving problems in another. For example, many of the skills and strategies employed in good accounting principles, or bookkeeping practise, are mathematical in nature.

- There are few careers that do not employ a sound knowledge of the nature and principles of mathematics. Even though the actual skill you have learned may not be actively used, the process you followed to learn the skill can be applied to solve any problem.

Some of the questions you will explore in this and the subsequent chapters need to be answered regardless of the career you choose to follow.

- How can I obtain the best rate of return on my money?
- What does owning a car really cost? What are the hidden costs?
- How can I invest a certain amount of money now and make it grow wisely?
- How can I wisely obtain the maximum deductions towards my income tax?
- What are my obligations if I earn money? What are different methods by which I can save and earn money?
- Do I really want to use plastic credit?
- Should I invest in bonds or in the stock market? What are the risks?

# 7.1 Finding Simple Interest

In your study of consumer skills, the principles of interest occur throughout as you lend money, borrow money or save money. You see various financial institutions advertising their services: banks, trust companies, credit unions. You can deposit your money in an account to earn interest or you may need to borrow money in which case you will pay the bank the loan amount plus interest. The amount of money that you deposit or borrow is called the **principal**. The **rate of interest** varies with Canada's economy. When interest is paid each time period on the original principal only, it is called **simple** interest.

CANADA TRUST

OPEN
TO SERVE YOU BETTER

8 a.m. til 8 p.m.
Sat. 8 a.m.–5 p.m.

VISIT US SOON

The following formula is used to compute simple interest.

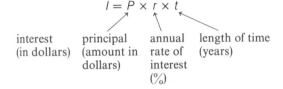

$$I = P \times r \times t$$

| $I$ | $P$ | $r$ | $t$ |
|---|---|---|---|
| interest (in dollars) | principal (amount in dollars) | annual rate of interest (%) | length of time (years) |

### Example 1

Clive borrowed $3000 at 12% for 2 years. Find the interest that he will be charged.

### Solution

*Step 1*: List the given information.
$P = 3000, \quad r = 0.12, \quad t = 2$
($12\% = 0.12$)

*Step 2*: Use the formula
$$\begin{aligned} I &= P \times r \times t \\ &= 3000 \times 0.12 \times 2 \\ &= 720 \end{aligned}$$

*Step 3*: Write a concluding statement.
Clive will be charged $720 interest.

To solve problems involving interest, you must be clear about what the problem asks you to do. What pieces of information are you given? Are you asked to find the rate, or the time, or the principal?

You can use your skills with rearranging formulas to obtain the following equivalent forms.

$$I = Prt \qquad P = \frac{I}{rt} \qquad r = \frac{I}{Pt} \qquad t = \frac{I}{Pr}$$

To decide which form of the formula to use in solving a problem, ask yourself the following questions.

I *What information does the problem ask me to find?*

II *What information do I know?*

**Example 2**
Neena put \$500 into a savings account that pays simple interest. She withdrew the money 6 months later to go on a holiday. The bank gave her \$517.50. What was the rate of interest?

**Solution**

$P = 500$, $t = 0.5$, $I = 17.50 \longleftarrow \$517.50 - \$500.00$

(6 months $= \frac{1}{2}$ year or 0.5 year)

Use $r = \dfrac{I}{Pt}$

$= \dfrac{17.50}{500 \times 0.5}$

$= 0.07$

Check your work with a calculator

The rate of interest was 7%.

## Try These

1 Express each percent as a decimal.
(a) 17% (b) 9% (c) 11.5%
(d) 12.75% (e) $15\frac{1}{2}$% (f) 14.35%

2 In each calculation for interest, $I$, what is the value of
▶ the principal? ▶ the rate? ▶ the time?
(a) $I = 200 \times 0.08 \times 2$ (b) $I = 750 \times 0.1 \times 0.25$

3 In each situation what value will you use for $P$, for $r$, and for $t$ in the calculation of simple interest?
(a) \$250 is deposited for 2 years in an account that pays 6% interest.
(b) \$4000 is borrowed at 11% for 3 years.
(c) \$375 is owed for 9 months to a credit company that charges 12.5%.

## Written Exercises

**A** All interest rates are given as the annual rate of simple interest unless stated otherwise. Round answers as necessary to the nearest cent.

1 Calculate the interest earned in 1 year on each deposit.
(a) \$700 at 11% (b) \$1250 at 9%

2 Calculate the interest charged on each loan for 1 year.

| | Principal | Rate of Interest |
|---|---|---|
| (a) | \$200 | 9% |
| (b) | \$1000 | $10\frac{1}{2}$% |
| (c) | \$600 | 11.25% |
| (d) | \$125 | $10\frac{3}{4}$% |

3 Calculate the amount you would need to pay back to the bank at end of 1 year.

| | Principal | Rate of Interest |
|---|---|---|
| (a) | \$400 | 11% |
| (b) | \$680 | 10% |
| (c) | \$1200 | $10\frac{1}{2}$% |
| (d) | \$850 | $12\frac{1}{4}$% |

4 How much would each of the following deposits have increased to by the end of the time shown?

| | Principal | Rate | Time |
|---|---|---|---|
| (a) | \$240 | 5% | 1 year |
| (b) | \$75 | 8% | 3 years |
| (c) | \$310 | $3\frac{1}{2}$% | 2 years |
| (d) | \$562 | $4\frac{3}{4}$% | 6 months |

5 Find the interest for each of the following.
  (a) a principal of $1250 in a trust account for 2 years at $9\frac{1}{2}$%
  (b) a debt of $629 is owed on an account for 4 months at $15\frac{1}{2}$%
  (c) an inheritance of $1500 is left in a term deposit for 5 years at $12\frac{3}{4}$%
  (d) a bill of $218.50 has interest charged at 18% for 45 days.

6 Find the amount needed to pay off each of the following loans.
  (a) Mark borrowed $3800 at $14\frac{1}{2}$% for 3 years.
  (b) Rebecca borrowed $750 from her brother. The loan was paid 18 months later with 12% interest.
  (c) Leonardo borrowed $1450 from a credit union. He signed a contract promising to pay the loan with $10\frac{1}{2}$% interest in 150 days.

**B** Round your answers to the nearest cent.

7 Who pays the greater amount of interest on a loan?
  A Maria borrowed $925 for a year at $13\frac{1}{2}$%/a.
  B Mario borrowed $806 for a year at $14\frac{1}{4}$%/a.

8 Eaton's Canada advertises a credit charge of 1.75% per month. Harvey's balance on his account is $630.42.
  (a) Find the interest that Harvey has to pay at the end of the month.
  (b) How much simple interest would be paid after a year?

9 At the end of the summer. Mike deposited his savings of $1530 at a trust company in an account paying simple interest at 8%. He withdrew the money $1\frac{1}{2}$ years later to go on a trip to Europe. How much did he withdraw?

10 Alex borrowed $3200 from her uncle to buy a car. She agreed to repay the loan on her 21st birthday, in $3\frac{1}{2}$ years time, with interest calculated at $10\frac{1}{4}$%. How much does she owe on the agreed repayment day?

11 In each of the following problems decide
  ▶ what the problem asks you to do—find rate, interest or principal?
  ▶ Then solve the problem.
  (a) A deposit of $120 earned $14.40 interest in 2 years. What was the rate of interest?
  (b) The interest charged on a $500 loan at $10\frac{1}{2}$% was $26.25. How long was the loan outstanding?
  (c) In a checking account, money earns interest at $3\frac{1}{2}$%. Ben earned $70 interest in $2\frac{1}{2}$ years. How much did he deposit in the account?
  (d) $18 interest was charged when a loan of $800 was repaid 3 months later. What was the rate of interest?

12 When Arlene was born her grandparents deposited an amount in a trust fund that paid $10\frac{1}{4}$% simple interest. The amount in the fund was to be paid on Arlene's eighteenth birthday. If she received $2767.50, how much was deposited?

13 Clayton borrowed $2000 to buy a dirt bike. When he repaid the loan 2 years later, he was charged $510 interest. What rate of simple interest was used?

14 A credit card company charges $1\frac{1}{2}$% per month on any unpaid balance. If a balance of $562.63 is to be paid off after 45 days, how much interest will be added?

15 Ryan has $156.80 in his savings account, which pays interest at the rate of $7\frac{1}{2}$%. How long will he have to let his deposit stay in this account for it to double?

**C**

16 Erin borrowed $1000 from a friend. She repaid the $1000 and a total interest charge $113.48 in 12 monthly payments of $92.79 each.
  (a) Find the annual interest rate for this loan. Give your answer to the nearest tenth.
  (b) What percent of $1000 is the interest charge of $113.48 for this loan?
  (c) What can you conclude about your answers in (a) and (b)?

# 7.2 Making Money Grow: Compound Interest

In today's financial world, most financial institutions use compound interest to calculate the interest payable. With compound interest the amount at the end of each time period becomes the principal for the next time period. With compound interest, you are paid interest on the interest as shown in the following calculations.

Banking in Canada provides better services than in any other country. For example, in Canada there is a bank or branch for every 3000 Canadians, but in the United States there is only one for every 9000 persons.

Suppose you deposit \$400 into an account that pays interest at the rate of 9% per year compounded annually. The amount, A, in the account will grow each year as follows.

First year

Amount = Principal + Interest

$A = P + Prt$

$A = 400 + 400 \times 0.09 \times 1$ (400 is a common factor)

$= 400(1 + 0.09)$

$= 400(1.09)$

$= 436.00$

The amount is \$436.00.

Second Year:

Amount = Principal + Interest

$A = P + Prt$

$A = 436 + 436 \times 0.09 \times 1$

$= 436(1 + 0.09)$

$= 436(1.09)$

$= 475.24$

The amount is \$475.24.

Compare this with the amount you would have obtained if simple interest was used.

$I = Prt$

$= 400 \times 0.09 \times 2$

$= 72.00$

The interest is \$72.00.

So by the end of 2 years, the balance using either method of calculating interest is:

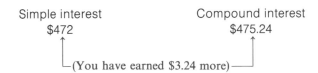

| Simple interest | Compound interest |
|---|---|
| \$472 | \$475.24 |

(You have earned \$3.24 more)

**Example**

Sasha borrowed \$750 from a bank that charges interest at the rate of 12%/a compounded semi-annually. What amount is needed to pay off the loan at the end of one year?

**Solution**

First 6-month period:

$$\begin{aligned} A_1 &= P + I \\ &= P + Prt \\ &= 750 + 750 \times 0.06 \times 1 \\ &= 750(1 + 0.06) \\ &= 750(1.06) \end{aligned}$$

12%/a or 6% semi-annually

Second 6-month period:

$$\begin{aligned} A_2 &= P + I \\ &= \underbrace{750(1.06)} + \underbrace{750(1.06)} \times 0.06 \times 1 \\ &= 750(1.06)[1 + 0.06] \\ &= 750(1.06)(1.06) \\ &= 750(1.06)^2 \\ &= 842.7 \end{aligned}$$

This is the principal used in the calculation

Use a calculator to check your work.

The amount needed to pay off the loan at the end of one year is \$842.70.

## Try These

1 The yearly rate of interest for a loan is 12%. Express this rate as a
 (a) semi-annual rate (b) quarterly rate
 (c) monthly rate

2 Find the following amounts:
 (a) $A = 100(1.08)$ (b) $A = 100(1.12)$
 (c) $A = 1000(1.175)$ (d) $A = 1000(1.15)$

Throughout your work, use a calculator to find compound amounts.

3 An expression is shown to find the amount for each problem. Match the expression with the problem.
 A: $500(1.05)^2$ B: $500(1.1)^2$ C: $500(1.025)^3$
 (a) \$500 is deposited for 2 years in an account paying 10%/a compounded annually.
 (b) On a loan for 9 months of \$500, interest is charged at 10%/a compounded quarterly.
 (c) On an outstanding balance of \$500, interest is charged at 10%/a compounded semi-annually.

## Written Exercises

**A** Express your answers to the nearest cent as necessary.

1 Calculate the interest earned on
 (a) \$300 at 11%/a for 1 year compounded annually.
 (b) \$80 at 6%/a for 1 year compounded semi-annually.
 (c) \$2500 at 12%/a for 9 months compounded quarterly.

2 Simon deposited \$200 into a savings account that pays interest at the rate of 8%/a compounded semi-annually.
 (a) What is the semi-annual interest rate?
 (b) Write an expression for the amount in his account at the end of 6 months.
 (c) Write an expression for the amount at the end of 1 year.
 (d) Calculate the amount at the end of 1 year.

3 Julie put $1500 into a term deposit that pays interest of 9%/a compounded annually. What is her deposit worth at the end of 2 years?

4 Brian took out a loan of $1000. He agreed to pay back the loan in 2 years time with interest at 12%/a compounded semi-annually. How much does he have to repay?

5 Interest at 10%/a is paid on a deposit of $500. Calculate the amount after 2 years using
  (a) simple interest
  (b) interest compounded annually
  (c) By how much do the amounts in (a) and (b) differ?

6 Cathy deposited her savings of $800 with a trust company that pays interest at 8%/a. Calculate the amount after 1 year using
  (a) simple interest
  (b) interest compounded quarterly
  (c) How much more interest does she earn using compound interest?

**B** Round your answers to the nearest cent.

7 Martin has $3500 to deposit. Calculate the amount after one year if the money is invested at 10%/a compounded
  (a) annually (b) semi-annually
  (c) quarterly

8 Dina borrows $2000 to set up her own apartment. The bank that gave her the personal loan charges interest at 12.5%/a.
  (a) Find how much she has to pay to clear the debt after 2 years if the interest is compounded annually.
  (b) In another institution, she could borrow the money at the same terms but compounded semi-annually. How much will she save?

9 Find the compound amount according to each of the following terms.
  (a) a deposit of $450 at $8\frac{1}{2}$% compounded annually for 3 years
  (b) a loan of $15 000 at $8\frac{1}{2}$% compounded semi-annually for 2 years
  (c) an investment of $6600 at 12% compounded quarterly for one year

10 If you have $1000 to invest for 3 years, which has the better return?
  (a) bonds paying $11\frac{3}{4}$%/a simple interest
  (b) a savings account paying 11%/a compounded annually

11 A principal of $5000 is deposited in each of two banks.
  Bank A: Pays compound interest at 10%/a calculated semi-annually
  Bank B: Pays compound interest at 9%/a calculated every 4 months
  Which is the better investment after
  (a) 1 year? (b) 2 years?

12 Karin and Daniel each received $500 from an inheritance. Karin put her money in a term deposit that pays $10\frac{1}{2}$%/a simple interest. Daniel deposited his money in a savings account that pays 10%/a compounded semi-annually. Which is the better investment after
  (a) 1 year? (b) 2 years?

13 Miles opened a savings account with a credit union. He deposited $400. The interest is compounded semi-annually at 7%/a. One year later he deposited $500 more.
  (a) Find the balance of his account at the end of the first year.
  (b) What is his principal at the beginning of the second year?
  (c) Calculate his balance at the end of the second year.

14 Lisa borrowed $700 from a chartered bank at 12%/a compounded quarterly. She paid back $400 at the end of the first quarter. Find the amount she still owed at the end of the second quarter.

**C**

15 Noelle borrowed $6000 from her bank at 11%/a compounded semi-annually. She then invested the money in a business venture that paid her 12%/a compounded quarterly. How much money will she make at the end of one year.

# 7.3 Using Formulas: Compound Interest

An important skill that mathematics helps you to learn is the ability to recognize a pattern. In studying mathematics, look for patterns in specific examples, so that the patterns can be used to develop general rules or formulas. You may have begun to notice a pattern in your work with compound interest.

Make your money
work for you!
Earn interest
compounded daily
at 3%/a

Examine the calculations in the following example.

> Sandy placed \$100 in a term deposit that pays interest at 10%/a compounded semi-annually. Find the value of her investment at the end of 2 years.

Use a chart to organize the calculations.

| Time period | Principal | Calculation ($P + Prt$) | Amount |
|---|---|---|---|
| First | \$100 | 100 + 100(0.05) | \$105 |
| Second | \$105 | 105 + 105(0.05) | \$110.25 |
| Third | \$110.25 | 110.25 + 110.25(0.05) | \$115.76 |
| Fourth | \$115.76 | 115.76 + 115.76(0.05) | \$121.55 |

Sandy's investment is worth \$121.55 at the end of 2 years, or after the fourth time period.

You can see that the calculations in the chart form a pattern.

After 1st period, Amount = 100(1.05)
After 2nd period, Amount = 100(1.05)(1.05) or $100(1.05)^2$
After 3rd period, Amount = $100(1.05)^2(1.05)$ or $100(1.05)^3$
After 4th period, Amount = $100(1.05)^3(1.05)$ or $100(1.05)^4$

> Use a calculator to do the calculation. Find out how the [$y^x$] key works. To calculate $100(1.05)^4$ do these steps.
>
> [C] 1.05 [$y^x$] 4 [=] [×] 100 [=] Output ?

These calculations suggest that compound interest can be calculated by a formula.

$A = P(1 + i)^n$ where $A$ = amount in dollars
$P$ = principal in dollars
$i$ = interest rate per period (as a decimal)
$n$ = number of interest periods

To assist in making calculations using the compound interest formula, computer generated values of $(1 + i)^n$ are given in table form for various values of $i$ and $n$. Complete tables are on pages 461 to 463.

Some calculators have features that give you the compound interest values in the table.

**Compound Interest**
Amount of $1(1 + i)^n$

| $n$ | 3.5% | 4% | 4.5% | 5% | 5.5% | 6% | 6.5% | 7% | 7.5% | 8% |
|---|---|---|---|---|---|---|---|---|---|---|
| 1 | 1.035 000 | 1.040 000 | 1.045 000 | 1.050 000 | 1.055 000 | 1.060 000 | 1.065 000 | 1.070 000 | 1.075 000 | 1.080 000 |
| 2 | 1.071 225 | 1.081 600 | 1.092 025 | 1.102 500 | 1.113 025 | 1.123 600 | 1.134 225 | 1.144 900 | 1.155 625 | 1.166 400 |
| 3 | 1.108 718 | 1.124 864 | 1.141 166 | 1.157 625 | 1.174 241 | 1.191 016 | 1.207 950 | 1.225 043 | 1.242 297 | 1.259 712 |
| 4 | 1.147 523 | 1.169 859 | 1.192 519 | 1.215 506 | 1.238 825 | 1.262 477 | 1.286 466 | 1.310 796 | 1.335 469 | 1.360 489 |
| 5 | 1.187 686 | 1.216 653 | 1.246 182 | 1.276 282 | 1.306 960 | 1.338 226 | 1.370 087 | 1.402 552 | 1.435 629 | 1.469 328 |
| 6 | 1.229 255 | 1.265 319 | 1.302 260 | 1.340 096 | 1.378 843 | 1.418 519 | 1.459 142 | 1.500 730 | 1.543 302 | 1.586 874 |
| 7 | 1.272 279 | 1.315 932 | 1.360 862 | 1.407 100 | 1.454 679 | 1.503 630 | 1.553 987 | 1.605 781 | 1.659 049 | 1.713 824 |
| 8 | 1.316 809 | 1.368 569 | 1.422 101 | 1.477 455 | 1.534 687 | 1.593 848 | 1.654 996 | 1.718 186 | 1.783 478 | 1.850 930 |
| 9 | 1.362 897 | 1.423 312 | 1.486 095 | 1.551 328 | 1.619 094 | 1.689 479 | 1.762 570 | 1.838 459 | 1.917 239 | 1.999 005 |
| 10 | 1.410 599 | 1.480 244 | 1.552 969 | 1.628 895 | 1.708 144 | 1.790 848 | 1.877 137 | 1.967 151 | 2.061 032 | 2.158 925 |
| 11 | 1.459 970 | 1.539 454 | 1.622 853 | 1.710 339 | 1.802 092 | 1.898 299 | 1.999 151 | 2.104 852 | 2.215 609 | 2.331 639 |
| 12 | 1.511 069 | 1.601 032 | 1.695 881 | 1.795 856 | 1.901 207 | 2.012 196 | 2.129 096 | 2.252 192 | 2.381 780 | 2.518 170 |
| 13 | 1.563 956 | 1.665 074 | 1.772 196 | 1.885 649 | 2.005 774 | 2.132 928 | 2.267 487 | 2.409 845 | 2.560 413 | 2.719 624 |
| 14 | 1.618 695 | 1.731 676 | 1.851 945 | 1.979 932 | 2.116 091 | 2.260 904 | 2.414 874 | 2.578 534 | 2.752 444 | 2.937 194 |
| 15 | 1.675 349 | 1.800 944 | 1.935 282 | 2.078 928 | 2.232 476 | 2.396 558 | 2.571 841 | 2.759 032 | 2.958 877 | 3.172 169 |

To use the table, follow these steps

$100(1.05)^4$ ⟵ Refer to the table to locate the 5% column.
$= 100(1.215\,506)$
$= 121.5506$ Use the value for $n = 4$.

Thus the amount of \$100 after 4 time periods at 5% is \$121.55

Refer to the calculations on the previous page. The amounts are the same.

## Try These

1 The formula for calculating the amount with compound interest is
$A = P(1 + i)^n$
What do each of the symbols represent?
(a) $A$ (b) $P$ (c) $i$ (d) $n$

2 Use the compound interest table to find the value of each.
(a) $(1.07)^5$ (b) $(1.055)^7$ (c) $(1.075)^{12}$

3 Use the formula $A = P(1 + i)^n$ to find an expression for the amount $A$ in each of the following
(a) \$500 for 2 years at 7% compounded annually
(b) \$75 for 4 years at 8% compounded semi-annually
(c) \$850 for 9 years at 15% compounded semi-annually

## Written Exercises

**A** To find the amounts, you need to find values for $(1 + i)^n$ for different values of $i$, $n$. Refer to the table of compound interest or use a calculator.

1 Each of the following expressions occurs in finding the answer to a compound interest problem. Calculate.
(a) $A = 100(1.12)^7$ (b) $A = 300(1.09)^6$
(c) $A = 1000(1.11)^8$ (d) $A = 2000(1.125)^5$
(e) $A = 3000(1.14)^{10}$ (f) $A = 5000(1.155)^{12}$

2 Each expression is the result of using the compound interest formula. For each, what is the principal, the rate of interest and the time?
(a) $80(1.06)^{10}$, semi-annually
(b) $250(1.02)^{20}$, quarterly
(c) $175(1.11)^{3}$, annually
(d) 58.26(1.015), monthly
(e) 656.50(1.0225), quarterly

3 Find the amount at the end of each time.

| | Principal | Rate | Time |
|---|---|---|---|
| (a) | \$600 | 8%/a, semi-annually | 3 years |
| (b) | \$175 | 10%/a, quarterly | 2 years |
| (c) | \$580 | 12%/a, monthly | 8 months |
| (d) | \$1125 | $7\frac{1}{2}$%/a, annually | 15 years |

4 Find the amount of each of the following using the terms shown.
(a) an investment of \$800 at 11%/a compounded semi-annually for $3\frac{1}{2}$ years
(b) A deposit of \$346 with interest compounded quarterly at 10%/a for 4 years
(c) a loan of \$2500 with interest compounded semi-annually at 14%/a for 5 years
(d) a savings account has \$85.20 left for 15 months at 9%/a compounded monthly

**B** Express your answer to the nearest cent. Be sure to make a final statement in answering the problems.

5 (a) Calculate the amount of compound interest paid on \$4100 at the end of 2 years for each rate.
A 12%/a compounded annually
B 12%/a compounded semi-annually
C 12%/a compounded quarterly
D 12%/a compounded monthly
(b) Which is the best rate? How much more money is paid in interest at the best rate than at the least rate?

6 Fiona deposited \$1450 in an account on the first of January. If interest is paid at the rate of 12%/a compounded monthly, what amount will there be in the account on Dec. 1 of the same year?

7 Vidal borrowed \$4800 at the rate of 11%/a compounded quarterly. He paid back \$1200 at the end of 6 months. How much did he still owe at the end of the year?

8 A deposit of \$1200 will amount to \$1656.75 in 2 years. Find the interest rate to the nearest percent if interest is calculated annually.

9 Paula has \$3500 to invest for 5 years. Predict which of the following options will give her the best return. Then calculate to check your prediction.
A In a savings account at 10%/a compounded quarterly
B In a term deposit that pays $10\frac{1}{4}$%/a compounded annually
C In a special savings account that pays 9%/a compounded monthly

10 Steve wants to borrow \$4000 to buy a car. The car dealership offers to finance the loan at 13% compounded semi-annually. Steve's bank will give him a personal loan at 12% compounded quarterly. If he repays the loan 2 years later, which is the better loan to take?

11 On May 1, Dianne deposited \$650 into a new savings/checking account that pays monthly interest at the rate of 6%/a. Two months later she deposited \$520. Calculate how much is in her account at the end of 4 months.

12 Ivan invested \$2500 in a savings bond. After 3 years he cashed in the bond and received \$3271.61.
(a) What was the interest rate if it was calculated semi-annually?
(b) Find the rate if it was actually compounded monthly.

## Calculator Tip

Review the various features on your calculator that you have used. Are there any features that you have as yet not used? Try to find out what they do.

# 7.4 Paying Sales Tax

The principles of percent occur throughout your study of consumer problems. Provincial sales tax is a tax on the purchase price of an article. Thus, the total cost of the item is the purchase price plus the sales tax.

The chart shows the rate of tax charged in each province.

| Province | Sales Tax Charged |
|---|---|
| Manitoba | 6% |
| Saskatchewan | 5% |
| Ontario<br>British Columbia | 7% |
| Alberta | 0% |
| Nova Scotia, Prince Edward Island | 10% |
| Québec | 9% |
| Newfoundland | 12% |
| New Brunswick | 11% |

### Example

In Nova Scotia, a sweater is on sale for $37.89.
(a) Find the sales tax on the item.
(b) Find the total cost.

### Solution

(a) Sales Tax = Rate of tax × Cost of item
= 0.1 × $37.89
= $3.79
The sales tax is $3.79 (to the nearest cent)

(b) Total cost = Price + Sales Tax
= $37.89 + $3.79
= $40.92
The total cost is $41.68.

## Try These

1 What is the rate of sales tax in each of the following provinces?
(a) Alberta (b) New Brunswick
(c) Ontario (d) Newfoundland
(e) Manitoba (f) Quebec

2 Express each percent as a decimal.
(a) 8% (b) 5% (c) 12%
(d) 9% (e) $9\frac{1}{2}$% (f) 8.25%

3 For each purchase, in which province will you pay more?

| | Item | Price | Provinces |
|---|---|---|---|
| (a) | skates | $85.00 | Ontario or Quebec |
| (b) | jeans | $39.95 | B.C. or Nova Scotia |
| (c) | radio | $159.00 | Manitoba or P.E.I. |

## Written Exercises

**A** Round answers where necessary to the nearest cent.

1 Calculate each of the following.
(a) 10% of $129.50 (b) 8% of $27.99
(c) 6% of $356.00 (d) 7% of $950.00

2 Calculate the sales tax in Manitoba on each item.
(a) Canoe $249.98
(b) Turntable $475.59
(c) VCR $395.95

3 Calculate the sales tax in Nova Scotia for each item.
(a) shirt $24.95
(b) ski jacket $79.99
(c) motor home $14 980.50
(d) car $9752.86

4 Find the sales tax you will pay in each province.

| | Item | Price | Province |
|---|---|---|---|
| (a) | Belt | $12.50 | New Brunswick |
| (b) | Bicycle | $299.00 | Ontario |
| (c) | Watch | $18.29 | Saskatchewan |
| (d) | Coat | $195.00 | Alberta |
| (e) | Television | $498.00 | Nova Scotia |
| (f) | Record | $10.39 | British Columbia |

5 Calculate the total cost of each item.

Think: total cost = price + sales tax

(a) in Manitoba, a pair of shoes is priced at $49.95
(b) a T-shirt on sale for $8.25 in Ontario
(c) a sports bag that retails for $16.29 in New Brunswick
(d) in Newfoundland a snowmobile listed at $2058.00

6 Which sales tax amount is correct, A or B? Estimate your answer and then calculate to check.

| | Price | Province | A | B |
|---|---|---|---|---|
| (a) | computer monitor $489.95 | Ontario | $29.75 | $34.30 |
| (b) | motor bike $1295.59 | Nova Scotia | $129.56 | $120.17 |
| (c) | jacket $85.60 | B.C. | $8.56 | $5.99 |
| (d) | dishwasher $599.75 | Saskatchewan | $29.99 | $24.75 |
| (e) | swimsuit $39.98 | Newfoundland | $3.99 | $4.80 |

**B**

7 Morley bought a set of luggage priced at $119.50 in New Brunswick.
(a) Estimate the total cost with sales tax.
(b) Calculate the total cost.

8 A cross-country ski package is selling for $239.95 in Brandon, Manitoba.
(a) Estimate the cost with sales tax
(b) Calculate the total cost

9 Shirley chooses a suit that is on sale in Montreal for $158.29. Estimate and then calculate the cost of the suit including provincial sales tax.

10 A store in Vancouver has its raincoats on sale for $79.50. What would the total cost of two of these costs be with tax? Check whether your answer is reasonable.

11 (a) Calculate the total cost of a typewriter priced at $269.95 in Nova Scotia.
(b) How much more will you pay in New Brunswick for the same purchase?

12 Samouli bought the following items while vacationing in B.C.

| | |
|---|---|
| Shoes | $49.95 |
| Jacket | $107.50 |
| Binoculars | $98.99 |
| Dress | $70.00 |
| Camera | $85.98 |

Calculate the total cost of her purchases.

13 Roger and Brenda did their weekly grocery shopping and spent $86.93, including a tax amount of $2.73.
(a) If the tax rate was 7%, what amount of money was taxed?
(b) What amount of money was not taxed?

14 While vacationing, Fiona bought several souvenirs.

| | | | |
|---|---|---|---|
| coasters | $6.95 | glasses | $19.52 |
| towels | $32.50 | swim suit | $17.50 |
| sea shells | $9.90 | lobster trap | $39.95 |

If Fiona paid $141.48 in all, from which province did she buy the souvenirs?

**C**

15 Alex has saved up $500 to buy a stereo set in Winnipeg. What is the most that the stereo can be priced at so that he has enough money?

# 7.5 Buying a Car

When you need a car you must make many decisions:

▶ Should you buy a new car or a used car?
A new car might be a "lemon". Various parts may shortly need replacing on a used car.

▶ Should you lease or rent a car, rather than buying?
If you only need the car for a short period of time, leasing or renting a new car may be more convenient.

### Example 1

Stella bought a new car. The initial price was \$12 200. She made a down payment of \$5000 and the car dealership financed the balance at 14% over 4 years. The sales tax is 7%.

(a) Find the total price that she will pay.
(b) What are her monthly payments?

### Solution

(a)

| | |
|---|---|
| Price of car | \$12 200 |
| Sales tax (7%) | 854 |
| Total cost | \$13 054 |
| Down payment | 5 000 |
| Amount to be financed | \$8 054 |

$P = 8054, \quad r = 0.14, \quad t = 4$

$I = Prt$
$= 8054 \times 0.14 \times 4$
$= 4510.24$

Total amount owing = \$8054 + \$4510.24
= \$12 564.24

Total cost of car = Down payment + financed cost
= \$5000 + 12 564.24
= \$17 564.24 ← Remember this is over 4 years

Stella pays \$17 564.24 altogether.

(b) $\text{Monthly payment} = \dfrac{\text{Total amount owing}}{\text{Number of payments}}$ ← 4 years or 48 payments

$= \dfrac{\$12\,564.24}{48}$

$= \$261.755$

Stella's monthly payment is \$261.76 (rounded to the nearest cent).

---

SOME GUIDELINES FOR CAR BUYERS

**Initial Cost**
The initial cost is the cash price of the car. The actual cost is influenced by such items as options, taxes, insurance coverage, registration fees, freight fees and the cost of financing a car loan.

**Interest Charges**
If you cannot pay for the car in cash, then you have to finance the car and thus pay interest charges on the balance owing. If you had not bought the car, but had your money in a savings account, then it would have earned interest for you.

**Optional Equipment**
Decide on the options you want to purchase. Ask yourself: Does the cost justify the actual need I have for the option? Do I really need power windows?

**Warranty**
This is the written guarantee given to you by the car dealership. A warranty may cover all parts and labour for one year or 25 000 km, whichever comes first (for new cars). A used-car warranty will vary considerably from dealer to dealer. Read each contract carefully to understand your warranty.

**Trade-in Value**
This is the amount offered on your old car toward the purchase of another car (new or used).

**Repair and Upkeep**
In order to keep your car running economically and safely, you will need to pay regularly for maintenance, as well as for repairs including the cost of parts and labour.

When you buy a car, it is important to compare methods of financing the initial cost. A personal loan from your bank may cost you less than the car dealership's rates.

**Example 2**
Winston bought a used van for $3950, plus 8% sales tax. He had saved $2500 towards the cost. For the balance he took out a personal loan at his bank. He agreed to repay the loan in 1 year's time with interest at 10%/a compounded quarterly. Find the total cost of the van.

**Solution**

| | |
|---|---|
| Price of van | 3950 ← in dollars |
| Sales tax (8%) | 316 |
| Total Price | 4266 |
| Savings | 2500 |
| Bank Loan | 1766 |

Amount owing on loan $= \$1766(1.025)^4$
$= \$1949.333$

Total cost = cash amount + loan amount
= $2500 + $1949.33
= $4449.33

The total cost of the van is $4449.33.

## Try These

1 If you buy a car, you need to know the meaning of these terms. What is meant by each of the following?
(a) cash price
(b) sales tax
(c) insurance
(d) financing
(e) optional equipment
(f) licence cost
(g) warranty
(h) trade-in value

2 Find the sales tax at 5% on each of these car prices.
(a) $8000 (b) $9000 (c) $20 000

3 The price of a used car is $4000. The sales tax rate is 12%. What is the total cost of the car?

## Written Exercises

**A** Round answers as necessary to the nearest cent. Refer as needed to the sales tax chart for provinces.

1 Find the sales tax payable on each car purchase.
(a) a new pickup truck for $11 599 in Manitoba
(b) a used family car for $7500 in Quebec
(c) a new sports car for $15 800 in British Columbia
(d) a station wagon for $13 520 in New Brunswick

2 Find the cost of each car.

| | Price of Car | Options | Province |
|---|---|---|---|
| (a) | $6200 | $43, $96.50 | Manitoba |
| (b) | $8350 | $69, $425 | British Columbia |
| (c) | $11 930 | $85, $360, $425 | Newfoundland |
| (d) | $14 590 | $96, $85.70, $396 | Nova Scotia |

3 Refer to the price list of options.

Find the cost of each car.

| | |
|---|---|
| tinted windows | $190 |
| plush upholstry | $210 |
| rear window defroster | $249 |
| power steering (p.s.) | $410 |
| power locks | $185 |
| stereo radio | $560 |
| power brakes (p.b.) | $290 |
| elegant dash system | $225 |

(a) in Manitoba, price of car $8650, options: tinted windows, power lock.
(b) in Ontario, price of car $9350, options: power brakes, elegant dash system.
(c) in Alberta, price of car $12 630, options: plush upholstry, rear window defroster, p.s., p.b..

4 Find the total price including sales tax of the following new car purchases with the options listed.
(a) Marvin bought a standard two-door hatchback in Ottawa for $9200. He ordered a rear window defroster for $275 and a stereo radio system for $695.
(b) Betty bought a new sedan in Regina for $13 499. She requested power steering at an extra $425 and power brakes at $315.

**B** After you complete your work, check whether your answers are reasonable.

5 1981 Toyota Celica. Radial Tires, AM/FM Stereo, 57 000 km, Rust proofed. New brakes. $4000 or best offer.

Kelly went and inspected this used car and liked it. She agreed to buy it for $3500.
(a) What per cent of the asking price did Kelly pay?
(b) Kelly lives in British Columbia. What does the car cost her including sales tax?

6 1984 K-car. Must sell, owner leaving country. 38 000 km. Power steering and brakes. Excellent condition inside and out. Asking $6500.

Chad was interested in this car. The owner let him have it checked out by a garage. The check cost him $42. He bought the car for $6200. Calculate how much the purchase cost him altogether with the Nova Scotia sales tax.

7 Pauline bought a new car for $8548, including tax. She paid 40% down and agreed to pay the balance in 30 monthly payments of $229.79.
(a) Find the total price that she paid for the car.
(b) How much extra did the financing cost her?

8 At a used car lot in Manitoba Nancy likes a car advertised for $4850. She bargained with the salesperson and got the price reduced 15%.

(a) What was the reduced selling price?
(b) How much does she pay for the car with sales tax?

9 Three different car dealers in Scarborough, Ontario, are selling the same year and model of used car at the prices shown.

| Dealer A | Dealer B | Dealer C |
|---|---|---|
| $5250 | $5100 | $5399 |

(a) Including sales tax, what is the price of the most expensive of these cars?
(b) What is the price of the least expensive one with tax?

10 Four different car showrooms in Vancouver have the same model of new car for sale.

| Dealer | A | B | C | D |
|---|---|---|---|---|
| Price | $9875 | $10 050 | $9789 | $9950 |

(a) How much money can you save by shopping around?
(b) How much would you save by buying from Showroom A rather than Showroom D?
(c) Find the average cost at these four locations, including tax.

11 Jason bought a new car for \$7950, plus 7% sales tax. Shipping and storage and options cost him an extra \$850. He paid \$5000 down and financed the balance in 12 monthly payments of \$440.
   (a) How much did he actually pay for the car altogether?
   (b) How much extra did the financing cost him?

12 Marcia bought a car costing \$9820 in Charlottetown.
   (a) Find the cost of the car by each of the following methods.
      A cash
      B \$4000 down and the balance financed by the car dealership at \$209.15/month for 36 months.
      C \$3000 down and the remainder borrowed from her bank at \$169.20/month for 4 years.
   (b) What is the most amount of money she can save?

13 Tien bought a sports car in Halifax for \$14 299. He made a down payment of \$6000 and financed the rest. The car dealership offered him financing for 48 months at 12%/a. His bank will loan him the balance for 36 months at 11%/a. How much does he save by taking the bank loan?

14 Peter chose a new Buick, priced at \$12 399.00 for the basic model. He ordered the following options.

| | | | |
|---|---|---|---|
| Air conditioning | \$952 | Rust proofing | \$420 |
| Power steering | \$349 | Pulse wipers | \$58 |
| Power brakes | \$310 | Rear defroster | \$168 |
| Stereo | \$520 | | |

   (a) Find the total price with 9% sales tax.
   (b) He made a down payment of \$7500 and financed the balance at 12.5%/a for 48 months. Find his monthly payments.
   (c) How much does he actually pay for the car?

## Consumer Tip

- Federal Sales Tax is applied to manufactured goods or goods imported into Canada. A Federal Tax of 12% with some goods at a lower rate and others exempt, is usually charged for goods manufactured in Canada. The tax is calculated on the manufacturer's selling prices. There is no Federal Sales Tax on some goods, such as educational goods, religious goods, and so on. The Federal government provides a list of goods that are exempt.
- Excise Taxes are applied on luxury items, such as tobacco, jewelry, clocks, and watches, etc. An Excise Tax may be a fixed amount or a percentage of the manufacturer's selling price. There are many items that are subject to both Federal Sales Tax and Excise Tax.

A The excise tax is 10% on jewelry. A shipment of jewelry imported from Europe by a retailer, had a value of \$128 525.45 Canadian.
   (a) Find the excise tax.
   (b) Find the federal tax, at 12%.

B A shipment of cigars is imported by a retailer and its value is \$3847.59 Canadian.
   (a) Find the federal sales tax at 12%.
   (b) Find the excise tax at a rate of 17.5%.

C The excise tax is 15% on radios, record players, and VCR's. A department store chain imported \$67 521.94 worth of televisions from Japan.
   (a) Calculate the excise tax.
   (b) Calculate the federal sales tax at 12%.
   (c) Based on (a) and (b), what is the total cost of the goods?

## Career Tip

Customs officers use skills with percent to calculate duties payable on certain goods that are imported into Canada. They also need to have a clear understanding of the rates of duty that are charged on such goods.

# 7.6 Hidden Costs: Car Ownership

The costs of actually running a car are of two types. The fixed costs include the insurance and licence fee. The variable costs depend on how much you drive the car. These costs include gas, oil, repairs, regular maintenance, and so on.

**Don't Speed**
From a recent survey of what it costs to insure a car, it was found that speeding tickets can in many instances increase the cost of your insurance by over 100%. A spokesperson was quoted as saying "if you receive one ticket your insurance costs will not be affected but after that you can expect

## Example

Sarah drives a used Volvo. She keeps a record of the annual costs of running the car as shown below.

| | |
|---|---|
| Licence and Insurance | $535 |
| Oil and gas | $3126.72 |
| Repairs | $746.89 |
| Miscellaneous | $150.00 |

(a) What was the total of the fixed costs for running the car?
(b) What was the total of the variable costs?
(c) Find the average cost per month for running the car.

## Solution

(a) Fixed costs = licence + insurance
= $535
The fixed costs for running Sarah's car were $535.

(b) Variable costs:

| | |
|---|---|
| Oil and gas | $3126.72 |
| Repairs | $746.89 |
| Miscellaneous | $150.00 |
| | $4023.61 |

The variable costs for running the car were $4023.61.

(c) Total running costs = $535 + $4023.61
= $4558.61

$$\text{Average monthly cost} = \frac{\$4558.61}{12}$$
$$= \$379.88$$

The average cost per month of running the car was $379.88.

The greatest fixed cost is the insurance coverage. This cost varies depending on many factors:

- model of car
- year of car
- age and sex of driver
- number of years driving experience
- driving record
- type of usage of the car, personal or business
- location, where you live, where you work
- type of insurance required (see below)

Car insurance is needed to protect you in the event of an accident. An accident can be very costly. If you have no insurance, and the accident is your fault, you may lose your life savings to pay the damages. Insurance can cover both the driver and the vehicle, and other people. In Canada, by law you must have at least third-party liability insurance. Refer to the next chart.

**Insurance Coverage**

For the driver

- **Collision insurance**
  pays for damages to the driver's car.
- **Medical insurance**
  pays for medical expenses of people in the car, you and others.
- **Comprehensive insurance**
  pays for damages that occur other ways such as theft, vandalism, fire.

For Others (Third-party liability)

- **Public liability insurance**
  pays for medical expenses of any others hurt by the accident.
- **Property damage insurance**
  pays for any expenses claimed for property damage due to the accident.

## Try These

1 Which of the following are variable costs?

| | | |
|---|---|---|
| (a) | wheel alignment | $73.00 |
| (b) | insurance | $365.00 |
| (c) | hot wax treatment | $15.00 |
| (d) | rust-proofing | $250.00 |
| (e) | tune-up | $81.79 |

2 Explain the meaning of each of the following insurance terms.
  (a) public liability of $500 000
  (b) medical insurance, up to $1 000 000
  (c) comprehensive insurance, no limit
  (d) collision insurance, $10 000 maximum with $200 deductible

## Written Exercises

**A** Review the meaning of fixed and variable costs for purchasing a car.

Questions 1 to 5 are based on the following information.

Ellen bought a sub-compact car. She kept a record of her expenses for the first year.

| | |
|---|---|
| insurance and licence | $572.16 |
| gas and oil | $2056.42 |
| transmission repair | $696.00 |
| seat covers | $75.89 |
| car washes | $215.00 |
| miscellaneous | $48.00 |
| maintenance (air filter, gas filter, etc . . .) | $39.80 |

1 Find the total of the variable costs.

2 How much did it cost Ellen to run the car for the year?

3 (a) Calculate her monthly cost to have a car.
  (b) Calculate her weekly cost.

4 Did Ellen buy a new or used car? Give reasons for your answer.

5 Before she bought the car, Ellen spent $38.50 each month on public transportation. Which means of transportation cost her less? How much less?

---

Questions 6 to 9 are based on the following information.
Tony drives an old station wagon. His running costs for 6 months are shown.

| Item | Cost |
|---|---|
| new battery | $89.27 |
| front shocks | $119.10 |
| insurance and licence (6 months) | $816.00 |
| gas and oil | $1582.34 |
| brake job | $97.28 |

6 Find his total cost for running the car.

7 What was the average cost per month?

8 Tony doesn't have any collision insurance on the vehicle. Why do you think this is so?

9 Estimate Tony's age. Provide reasons to justify your answer.

**B** **Round answers, when necessary, to the nearest cent. Check your calculations.**

10 Carla bought a moped for $1950. She paid $520 for the licence and insurance. During the first year she spent $628.17 on gas and $210.14 on maintenance.
(a) Find her total expenditure on the moped in the first year.
(b) If she drove 12 750 km in the year, find the cost per kilometre.

11 During the second year that he owned his car, Darryl drove 21 820 km. His car uses 0.11 L of gas per kilometre. That year the average cost of gas was 50¢/L. His other running costs for the year were

| Item | Costs |
|---|---|
| Regular Servicing | $158.72 |
| Radial tires | $675.85 |
| Insurance and licence | $386.00 |
| New radiator | $156.12 |

(a) Calculate how much he spent on gasoline that year.
(b) Find his total annual cost for the car.
(c) What was the running cost per 100 km?

12 Marcie bought a used car for $2000 plus 5% sales tax. For the licence and insurance she paid a total of $473.75. She drove about 10 000 km during the first year that she had the car. Her car uses 16 L of gas for every 100 km. Gas costs her an average of $0.52/L. She took the car in for 5-point service twice, at $48.75. A new starter-motor cost her $76.25, installed.
(a) Calculate how much she spent in total on the car.
(b) A stone flew up and broke her windshield, which cost $275 to replace. Marcie recorded the licence number of the other vehicle. Who is going to pay the bill of $275? Give reasons for your answer.

13 When Josh started a new job he needed a reliable car. He bought a new mid-size model for $13 500 plus 7% sales tax. He paid $4000 down and the car dealership financed the balance at 9%/a compounded semi-annually for 36 months. Josh's running costs for the first six months were:

| | |
|---|---|
| insurance and licence | $315.00 |
| gas and oil | $2172.47 |
| servicing | $146.00 |
| stereo | $576.29 |

(a) Calculate the amount of the loan that Josh takes from the car dealership.
(b) What is the compound amount of this loan for the full period?
(c) Calculate Josh's monthly payments on the loan.
(d) Calculate the total amount that Josh spends on the car over the first six months.

14 The chart shows a sample of insurance rates for a particular model of car and sample age groups.

| Ford Tempo | No driving experience | | | | 3 years experience or driver's education | | | |
|---|---|---|---|---|---|---|---|---|
| | Male Age | | Female Age | | Male Age | | Female Age | |
| Type of Insurance | <19 | 19–25 | <19 | 19–25 | <19 | 19–25 | <19 | 19–25 |
| Collision | 970 | 724 | 379 | 315 | 672 | 507 | 560 | 412 |
| Medical | 19 | 17 | 19 | 17 | 19 | 19 | 19 | 17 |
| Comprehensive | 126 | 126 | 126 | 126 | 126 | 126 | 126 | 126 |
| Public Liability | 681 | 543 | 420 | 336 | 492 | 389 | 401 | 327 |

Find the annual insurance premium for the following people.
(a) Mike, 20 years old with 3 years driving experience, wants collision, medical and public liability.
(b) Shirley, 23 years old with no driving experience, wants all four types of insurance shown.
(c) Karl, 18 years old and with driver's education, wants medical and public liability.

## Applications: Cost of Depreciation

Another factor that can affect your decision on whether to buy a particular car is depreciation. Most cars lose value quickly. As soon as you drive your new car it loses up to 20% of the price you paid for it! The rate at which cars depreciate does vary according to the type of car. The chart shows the average depreciation of a medium-priced North American car.

| Time | Depreciation (Percent of previous year's value) |
|---|---|
| First year | 30% |
| Second year | 15% |
| Third year | 15% |
| Fourth year | 10% |
| Fifth year | 8% |

For example, if you buy a new car for $14 000, its value over 2 years will decrease as shown.

| | | |
|---|---|---|
| New value | $14 000 | |
| 1st year depreciation | $4 200 | ← 30% of $14 000 = $4200 |
| 2nd year value | $9 800 | |
| 2nd year depreciation | $1 470 | ← 15% of $9800 = $1470 |
| 3rd year value | $8 330 | |

The value of the car at the start of the third year is $8330.

---

15 Linda paid $11 246 for a new Malibu. Calculate the value of the car after each period of time
(a) 1 year (b) 2 years (c) 4 years

16 Armand bought a new Fiero for $17 500. Calculate the approximate value of the car 3 years later.

17 Sasha paid $8075 for a new K-car 4 years ago. Now she is trading it in on the latest model.
(a) Use the depreciation values to calculate approximately how much the car is worth.
(b) The new model costs $10 649 plus 8% sales tax. She has $4500 saved towards the cost. She negotiates with the car dealership, and they agree to credit her with the trade-in value in (a). Find the balance owing after her trade-in.
(c) Find the amount owing if she takes out a bank loan for the balance for 2 years with interest at 9%/a compounded semi-annually.

18 Paul bought a new Ford Tempo paying $8752 cash including tax and licence plates. Paul was 22 years old at the time.
(a) Calculate how much the car depreciated during the first year.
(b) Paul estimates that his variable costs averaged 42¢/km. He drove 9682 km during the first year. Calculate the variable running costs for the year.
(c) Calculate the total cost, including depreciation of owning and running the car for the year.
(d) Find the cost for full insurance coverage if Paul has no driving experience, and didn't take the driver's education course at his school. (refer to question 14)

### Consumer Tip

Contact a local insurance agent and find out how much it would cost you to insure a car of your choice.

# 7.7 Buying an Annuity

When you plan to make a major purchase such as a new car, you may decide to save up the money first. You can budget to save a certain amount each year. You would deposit the money into an account to earn interest. For example, Lou decided to save \$1000 each year for 3 years. She deposited the money into a savings account that pays interest at 8%/a compounded annually. You can use a time-line diagram to show the information.

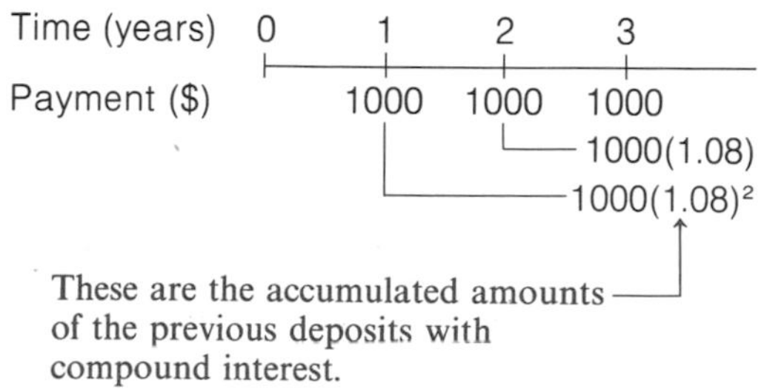


The total amount accumulated by the end of the third year is given by

$$\begin{aligned} A &= 1000(1.08)^2 + 1000(1.08) + 1000 \\ &= 1000(1.1664) + 1080 + 1000 \\ &= 1166.4 + 1080 + 1000 \\ &= 3246.4 \end{aligned}$$

The amount accumulated is \$3246.40

A savings plan such as the above is often called an **annuity**. In an annuity, fixed amounts of money are invested or paid out (at regular intervals) over a specified period of time. Certain vocabulary is used to work with annuities.

**Term** is the time interval from the beginning of the first to the end of the last interval.
**Periodic payment** is the amount of money paid at each interval.
**Payment interval** is the time occurring between each payment.

## Example

After a sports injury, the team's insurance company pays Keith \$2000 at the beginning of each month for 4 months. (He invested the money in an account paying 12%/a compounded monthly.) What is the accumulated value of the money at the end of the fourth month?

## Solution

*Step 1*: Record the information on a time-line diagram.

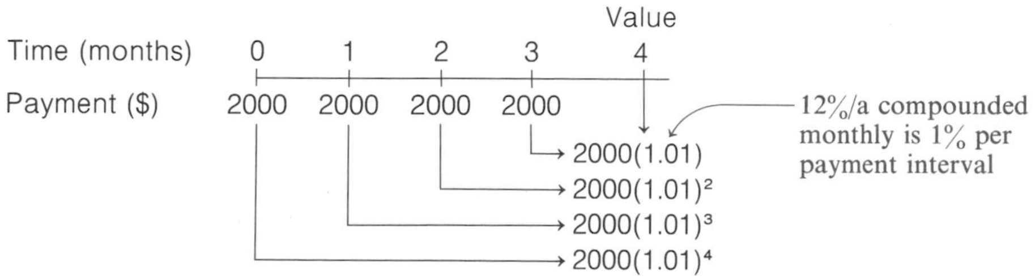

*Step 2*: Calculate the accumulated amount.

$$A = 2000(1.01) + 2000(1.01)^2 + 2000(1.01)^3 + 2000(1.01)^4$$
$$= 2020 + 2040.20 + 2060.602 + 2081.208$$
$$= 8202.01$$

The accumulated value of the money is \$8202.01.

## Try These

1 Each of the following terms is used to work with annuities. What is meant by each of the following?
(a) periodic payment
(b) term
(c) accumulated amount
(d) payment interval
(e) periodic rate of interest

2 A time-line diagram is drawn to show the details for an annuity. For the annuity what is
(a) the periodic payment?
(b) the terms?
(c) the periodic rate of interest?
(d) the annual rate of interest?

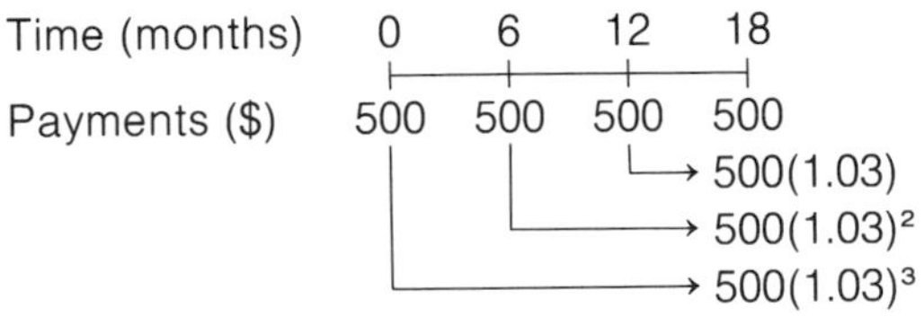


## Written Exercises

**A** Refer to the compound interest tables on pages 461 to 463 or use a calculator. Round answers to the nearest cent as necessary.

1 To do the calculations involving annuities you need to use the compound interest tables. Find the value of each of the following.

(a) $(1.04)^3$ (b) $(1.025)^5$ (c) $(1.09)^2$
(d) $(1.12)^4$ (e) $(1.015)^3$ (f) $(1.005)^4$

2 The time-line shows an annuity.

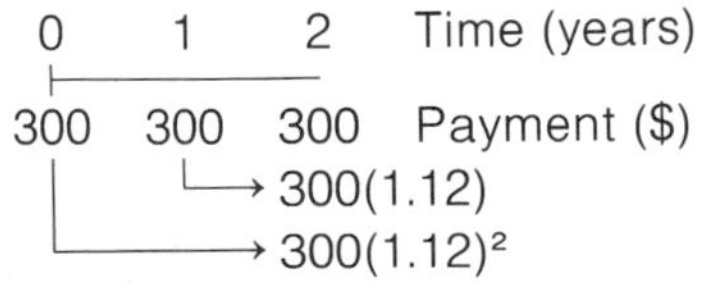


(a) What is the term of the annuity?
(b) What is the rate of interest?
(c) What is the payment interval?
(d) What is the value of the first payment by the end of the term shown?
(e) What is the value of the second payment by the end of the term?
(f) What is value of the third payment by the end of the term?
(g) Find the total accumulated amount.

3 Gayle deposited \$1500 at the end of each year for 3 years into a savings account that pays 9.5%/a interest compounded annually. Gayle drew a time-line to help her visualize the growth of her money.

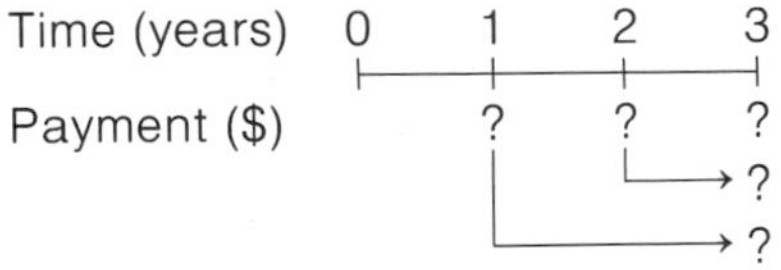


(a) Copy and complete the time-line diagram.
(b) Calculate the accumulated amount at the end of the 3 years.

4 Rob won an award that gives him $1000 immediately and $1000 at the end of every three months for 12 months. He deposited the money into an account that pays interest at 10%/a compounded quarterly. Rob drew a time-line to help him find how much the award amounts to.

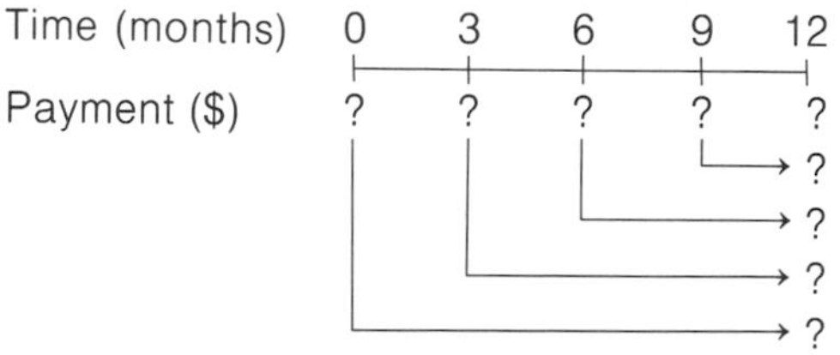


(a) Copy and complete the time-line diagram.
(b) Calculate the accumulated amount of the award, at the end of 12 months.

**B** To solve each problem first show the information in a time-line diagram.

5 For the first three months that she was working Cindy was able to save $250 each month. She deposited the money into a savings account paying interest at 9%/a compounded monthly. Find the accumulated amount at the end of the third month.

6 A fitness club set aside $8000 at the beginning of each year for 5 years to provide funds for a new swimming pool. They invested the money in a trust fund paying $11\frac{1}{4}$%/a compounded annually. Find the accumulated amount by the end of the fifth year.

7 Gerard receives a disability pension of $1000 at the beginning of every month. He decides to save the money for 4 months so that he can buy a microcomputer. He puts the money into a special savings account that pays 12%/a compounded monthly. Find the amount accumulated by the end of the fourth month.

8 Fay bought one of the bonds advertised at the beginning of the year for 3 years. Find the accumulated value of her bonds by the end of the third year.

| $500 Bonds earn $11\frac{3}{4}$% compounded annually |
|---|

9 Mathew is saving to buy a boat. He bought two $1000 GIC's (Guaranteed Investment Certificates) and two more six months later. Find the accumulated value of his investment by the end of the year.

| Make money with GIC's! *G*uarenteed *I*nvestment *C*ertificates now paying $12\frac{1}{2}$%/a compounded semi-annually. (Minimum $1000). |
|---|

10 (a) Predict who will have accumulated more money by the end of the fourth year.
A Bonnie makes a deposit of $1800 at the end of each year into an account paying $11\frac{1}{2}$% compounded annually.
B John deposits $750 now and every 6 months following into an account paying 11%/a compounded semi-annually.
(b) Calculate to check your prediction in (a).

**C**

11 Mohammed won a lottery. He has to choose between two methods of receiving the prize money. Which method is better?
A He can take a lump sum of $10 000 now. He knows that he could invest this in a 5 year investment certificate paying 10.5%/a compounded semi-annually.
B The lottery organization will give him $1000 at the end of each month for one year. Mohammed would deposit each payment into a special savings account paying 12%/a compounded monthly. At the end of the year he would transfer the accumulated amount into a term deposit for 4 years at 10%/a compounded semi-annually.

# 7.8 Finding Present Value

If you are planning for a special expense that is to occur some time in the future, you may want to find out how much you need to invest now so that it will amount to the goal you set for yourself. This type of calculation is referred to as finding the present value of an amount.

**Example**

Peter plans to buy a motorcycle when he finishes high school. How much does he need to invest now, so that he will have $2500 in 2 years time? He plans to invest the money in a term deposit that pays interest at 13%/a compounded semi-annually.

**Solution**

In the compound interest formula, use

$A = 2500, \quad i = 6.5\%, \quad n = 4$

$$A = P(1 + i)^n$$

$$2500 = P(1.065)^4$$

$$\frac{2500}{(1.065)^4} = P \qquad P = \frac{2500}{1.286\,466}$$

$$= 1943.308$$

Peter needs to invest $1943.31 now, so that he will have $2500 in 2 years time.

Stated in a different way, in present value problems, you are finding what principal needs to be invested so that it will grow with compound interest to a desired amount.

Rearranging the formula for compound amounts, you get the following formula for present value, *PV*.

$$PV = \frac{A}{(1 + i)^n}$$

where $A$ is the required compound amount,
$i$ is the rate of interest per period,
$n$ is the number of periods.

> Follow these steps on a calculator to do the calculation
>
> $\frac{2500}{(1.065)^4}$
>
> [C] 1.065 [$y^x$] 4 [=] [MS] 2500 [÷] [MR] [=]
>
> Output ?
>
> Can you do the steps more efficiently?

## Try These

1 The formula used for calculating the present value of an amount is given by

$$PV = \frac{A}{(1 + i)^n}$$

What do each of the symbols mean?

(a) *PV* (b) *A* (c) *i* (d) *n*

2 Hilda wants to invest an amount now so that in 3 years time she will have $2000 available for a trip to Tokyo. She uses a bank that pays interest at 10%/a compounded quarterly. What value would you use for each variable to solve the problem?

(a) *A* (b) *i* (c) *n*

## Written Exercises

**A** Round your answers to the nearest cent as necessary.

1 An expression is shown to find the present value for each problem. Match the expression with the problem.

(a) An amount is invested now at 4%/a compounded annually to give \$1000 in 3 years.

(b) Money is invested now at 12%/a compounded quarterly to give \$1000 in 2 years.

(c) A lump sum is invested now at 8%/a compounded semi-annually to give \$1000 in 3 years.

A $\dfrac{1000}{(1.04)^6}$

B $\dfrac{1000}{(1.03)^8}$

C $\dfrac{1000}{(1.04)^3}$

2 Find the present value in each of the following.

(a) $PV = \dfrac{3000}{(1.12)^4}$ (b) $PV = \dfrac{4500}{(1.10)^7}$

(c) $PV = \dfrac{6000}{(1.085)^6}$ (d) $PV = \dfrac{5265}{(1.125)^5}$

3 What amount of money should be invested now to obtain \$800 at each future time?

| | Time (years) | Rate of Interest |
|---|---|---|
| (a) | 3 | 8% compounded annually |
| (b) | 2 | 10% compounded semi-annually |
| (c) | 5 | 12% compounded quarterly |
| (d) | 8 | 9% compounded annually |
| (e) | 2 | 12% compounded monthly |

4 Find the present value of each of the following.
(a) an amount of \$1800 in 3 years time, interest at $8\frac{1}{2}$%/a compounded annually
(b) the amount of \$4500 in 5 years time, interest at 12%/a compounded quarterly
(c) a sum of \$6000 in 2 years time, interest at 12%/a compounded monthly

5 Determine the present value of each amount.

| | Amount | Time | Rate | Compounding Period |
|---|---|---|---|---|
| (a) | \$950 | 3 years | 8% | quarterly |
| (b) | \$1670 | 4 years | 10% | semi-annually |
| (c) | \$2480 | 2 years | 13% | annually |
| (d) | \$5740 | 6 years | 12% | monthly |
| (e) | \$8466 | 10 years | 9% | annually |
| (f) | \$8466 | 10 years | 12% | quarterly |

6 Find what principal invested at 9%/a semi-annually will amount to \$5500 in each time.
(a) 6 months (b) 2 years
(c) 5 years (d) 10 years

**B**

7 How much must Kevin invest today at 8%/a compounded quarterly to have \$9000 in his account 12 years from now?

8 Frimiko purchased a life insurance policy that pays her \$42 000 in 20 years time. If money is worth 14%/a compounded semi-annually, what is the present value of the policy?

9 David estimates that he will need \$9500 to take a computer course in 4 years. How much money should he invest today at 11%/a compounded semi-annually in order to take the course?

10 At the birth of a daughter, the parents want to invest enough money to have \$10 000 in an account when she is 19 years old. If the money earns 12%/a compounded monthly, find how much they should invest.

11 Pat wants to invest part of her summer earnings so that in 4 years time she will have \$3000 available to buy furniture. She can invest her money at 9% compounded semi-annually. How much should she deposit now?

## Applications: Present Value of an Annuity

In your study of mathematics, you will often use these steps to solve problems

| *Step A* | → | *Step B* | → | *Step C* |
|---|---|---|---|---|
| You learn a skill: such as annuities | | You learn other skills such as present value | | You combine these skills to solve a new problem |

You can now combine your skills with present value and annuities to calculate the amount that needs to be invested now to give a regular amount at repeated intervals. For example, to find how much should be invested now to provide $1000 at the end of each year for 3 years, the money is invested at 9%/a compounded annually. Use a time-line diagram.

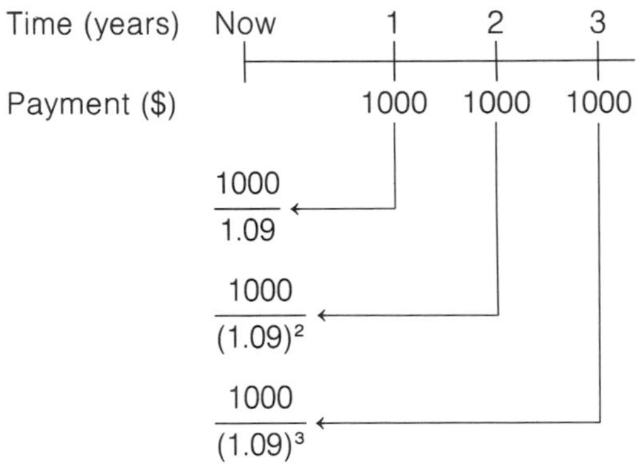


Find the present value of each payment

$$\text{Present value} = \frac{1000}{1.09} + \frac{1000}{(1.09)^2} + \frac{1000}{(1.09)^3}$$
$$= 917.43 + 841.68 + 772.18$$
$$= 2531.29$$

So $2531.29 should be invested now to provide the annuity.

---

12 Don wants to calculate how much he should invest now so that he can withdraw $500 at the end of each year for 2 years. He plans to invest in a savings account paying 11%/a compounded annually.

(a) Show the information on a time-line diagram.

(b) Calculate the present value of the first withdrawal.

(c) Calculate the present value of the second withdrawal.

(d) How much does he need to invest now to provide the required funds?

13 Mona wants to invest some money now, to provide $400 at the end of each of the next three months while she is taking a course. Her bank pays interest at 12%/a compounded monthly. Calculate how much she needs to deposit.

14 Bill sponsors a foster child in Columbia. He sends the child $250 every three months. Find how much he needs to invest at the beginning of the year to provide his four payments. He can invest at 10%/a compounded quarterly.

# Review: Practice and Problems

1 Find the interest earned for each of the following.

| | $P$ | $r$ | $t$ (years) |
|---|---|---|---|
| (a) | \$1450 | 12% | 2.5 |
| (b) | \$2500 | 9.5% | 4 |
| (c) | \$6108.59 | 13.5% | 5 |

2 Find the value of $A$.
(a) $A = 100(1.09)^6$ (b) $A = 750(1.065)^5$
(c) $A = 1000(1.13)^7$ (d) $A = 2200(1.105)^4$

3 Calculate the interest earned on
(a) \$650 at 9% for 2 years compounded annually.
(b) \$1550 at 8.5% for 4 years compounded semi-annually.
(c) \$3200 at 11.2% for 3 years compounded quarterly.

4 Calculate the sales tax in British Columbia on each item.
(a) Colour T.V. \$598.95
(b) Motorbike \$1995.50
(c) Car \$12 875.85

5 Find the cost of each car.
(a) Bought in Ontario at a cost of \$8795.00, plus sales tax.
(b) Purchased in Nova Scotia for \$11 506.83, plus sales tax.
(c) Purchased in British Columbia for \$14 095.19, plus sales tax.

6 Find each value, $PV$.
(a) $PV = \frac{6000}{(1.10)^5}$ (b) $PV = \frac{1780}{(1.12)^6}$
(c) $PV = \frac{8790}{(1.09)^7}$ (d) $PV = \frac{14\,900}{(1.125)^4}$

7 Eileen has \$1490 and wants to deposit the money in a bank. Calculate the amount after one year if the money is invested at 8% compounded
(a) annually (b) semi-annually (c) quarterly

8 Samuel borrowed \$2400 at the rate of 10% compounded quarterly. He paid back \$800 at the end of 6 months. Find the amount he still owed at the end of the year.

9 It costs 43¢/km to operate Lori's car.
(a) What will it cost her to drive the car 3792 km?
(b) If she drives 650 km each month, find the cost of driving the car for a year.

10 Rob bought a used car for \$3550 plus 8% tax and drove it for 24 500 km in the first year. Find the amount he spent during the first year for the following (include the cost of the car, plus tax).
Insurance \$468.90
Oil Changes (5 at \$19.95)
Gas (9 km/L at 49¢/L)
Repairs \$569.70
Tires \$294.17
Miscellaneous \$120.00

11 Jennifer bought the following items at a department store in New Brunswick.

| | | | |
|---|---|---|---|
| Blouse | \$49.50 | Perfume | \$56.00 |
| Skirt | \$86.00 | Makeup | \$19.95 |
| Purse | \$32.95 | Shoes | \$68.00 |

(a) Calculate the total sales tax.
(b) Calculate Jennifer's total bill.

12 Jackie set aside \$650 at the beginning of each year for 10 years to provide funds for a new tractor. She invested the money in a trust fund paying $12\frac{1}{2}$%/a compounded annually. Find the amount she would have by the end of the tenth year.

## Consumer Tip

Whenever you are to sign your signature to a contract, be sure you know what you are committing yourself to. Also be sure to read the fine print. Find some examples of fine print. Is the information given in the fine print essential information?

# A Practice Test

1 Calculate each amount.

(a) $A = 1250(1.09)^3$ (b) $PV = \frac{1650}{(1.08)^4}$

2 Find the sales tax on each purchase.
(a) $169.75 in New Brunswick
(b) $39.85 in Ontario.
(c) $429.36 in Alberta
(d) $12 696.36 in Nova Scotia.

3 Penelope wants to purchase a pair of downhill skis costing $219.50. She has $192.84 in her bank account. Find how much more money she would need if she buys the skis in
(a) Manitoba (b) British Columbia
(c) Ontario (d) Nova Scotia

4 Calculate the interest earned on
(a) $525 invested at 9%/a for one year compounded semi-annually.
(b) $12 500 invested at 8.5%/a for 4 years compounded annually.

5 Pete borrowed $200 from a Trust Company at an interest rate of 14%/a compounded semi-annually. He paid back $200 at the end of 6 months. Find how much he still owes at the end of the year.

6 Miriam bought savings bonds totalling $1200. She cashed her bonds after 5 years and received a total of $1947.82. What was the annual rate of simple interest that she earned?

7 Monika bought a sub-compact car for $8485.00. She selected the following options.

| | | | |
|---|---|---|---|
| Interior trim | $84 | Rear defroster | $129 |
| Sports mirror | $26 | Console | $217 |
| Tinted glass | $108 | AM/FM radio | $228 |
| Power steering | $239 | Air conditioning | $653 |

(a) Find the tax charged for the car if she lived on Prince Edward Island.
(b) Find the total cost of the car.

8 Lee drove his compact car 29 960 km one year. He used 0.12 L of gas per kilometre. Gasoline cost an average of 48.5¢/L that year. He also spent the following amounts on repairs and servicing.

| | |
|---|---|
| Oil Changes | $64.19 |
| New Carburettor | $169.47 |
| Battery | $59.65 |
| Insurance & License | $496.25 |
| Tires | $168.15 |
| Other Expenses | $369.85 |

(a) Calculate how much he spent on gasoline.
(b) What was the total cost for operating the car per month?
(c) Find the cost of operating the car per 100 km.

9 Frederika bought a used car in Alberta for $1864.00. She made a down payment of $500 and financed the rest. A credit union gave her financing for 36 months at 13%/a. A trust company offers the loan for 24 months at 12.5%. Which is a better deal?

10 (a) Clancy wants to invest some money so that in three years he will have $4500 to purchase a car. The best rate he can obtain is 10% compounded semi-annually. How much should he deposit now in order to buy the car in 3 years?
(b) In solving the problem in (a), what assumption did you make?

## Computer Tip

- Run this program. What type of interest is calculated?

```
10 REM INTEREST PROGRAM
20 LET P = 200
30 LET R = 0.145
40 LET T = 1.5
50 LET I = P * R * T
60 PRINT I
70 END
```

- Review the formula to calculate compound interest in Section 7.3. Write a computer program to calculate compound interest.

# 8 Making Money: Paying Income Taxes

individuals making money, working with commission, income calculations paying income tax, learning the vocabulary of income tax, filing income tax, calculator skills, problem solving, making money in business, sales discounts, solving problems, applications

## Introduction

In solving any problem, the two most important questions you can ask are shown by I and II. You must clearly understand the answers to these questions before you can use what you know to find the answer to what you don't know.

I What information am I asked to find?
II What information am I given or do I know?

In earlier chapters, you were encouraged to organize your work to solve problems. In business, it is not enough that you know the answer, but you must communicate your results to other people, in a clear and understandable fashion. For this reason, the *Steps for Solving Problems* provides you with a framework within which you can plan and organize your solution. In the chart below the shaded areas are completed by different information depending on the problem you are solving.

Remember that the *Steps for Solving Problems* provide you with a suggestion for organizing your thoughts and steps to solve a problem. Always think of ways to improve the procedure. A procedure allows you to keep track of your goal and the steps which you must complete to arrive at that goal.

The more mathematics you do and the more problems you solve, the more likely you are to begin to apply your skills of organizing the solution to a problem. You must develop organizational skills for writing solutions, whether they be your own or whether they are modified from suggestions such as the *Steps for Solving Problems*.

**Steps for Solving Problems**

*Step A:* *Understand the problem.*
- What are you asked to find?
- What are you given?

*Step B:* *Decide on a method.*

*Step C:* *Find the answer.* Do the work.

*Step D:* *Check your answer.*
- Is it reasonable?
- Are your calculations correct?

*Step E:* *Write a final statement.*

# 8.1 Earning Money: the Individual

You have probably earned money in the past by delivering newspapers, babysitting or some other form of part time job. As you earn money now, the mathematics involved in determining your income becomes more involved. The income you earn may be paid to you in different ways, some of which are described as shown.

**A Hourly Wage**
An employer pays you so much per hour for the total number of hours worked in the week. The money you make during the week is called your weekly wage.

**B Piecework Wage**
An employer pays you depending on the number of products you make or sell. The more you make or sell, the more money you earn.

**C Commission**
An employer pays you a certain percentage of your total sales. Sometimes people receive a salary plus commission.

**D Annual Salary**
Your annual salary is usually paid in equal monthly, semi-monthly, bi-weekly, or weekly amounts.

**E Fees**
Most professional people such as doctors, lawyers, dentists, accountants have incomes that are based on fees that they receive for their services.

Involved with receiving income at an hourly rate you need to understand various terms and calculations related to your earnings. These are described as follows.

**Calculating Gross Income or Wages**
Gross income or gross earnings is the amount of money earned before deductions. To calculate gross income you use the formula shown below.

Gross Income = Number of hours worked × hourly rate

**Overtime**
Usually the employer and employee have an agreement as to the number of regular hours the employee is expected to work. For example, an employee might work 40 regular hours in one week. All hours in excess of 40 h are called overtime hours. Overtime hours are usually paid as time-and-a-half.

| Regular rate of pay | Overtime rate of pay | |
|---|---|---|
| \$6.00 | \$9.00 | ← one and a half times the regular pay $1.5 \times \$6.00 = \$9.00$ |

**Working on Saturday, Sunday or a holiday**
Part of the agreement between the employer and the employee describes the regular days the employee is expected to work, usually Monday to Friday. Then, if you work on days other than the regular days, the employer may, as part of the agreement, pay double time.

| Regular rate of pay | Double time rate |
|---|---|
| \$6.00 | \$12.00 |

**Shift Premiums**
Part of the agreement between the employer and employee may describe the types of shifts you are expected to work. As a bonus, often shift premiums are paid to employees who work late afternoons (4:00 p.m.–12:00 p.m.) or the night shift (12:00 a.m.–8:00 a.m.). The hourly rate might be increased by a

certain amount such as 40¢ for the afternoon shift and 75¢ for the evening shift.

| Regular rate | Afternoon shift rate | Night shift |
|---|---|---|
| \$6.00 | \$6.40 | \$6.75 |

**Bonuses**

Some employers give bonuses in order to encourage greater productivity. For example Jacoba works for a computer firm where she installs micro chips. Her base pay is \$8.72/h, plus a bonus of \$1.69 for every computer assembled in excess of 37 in any 8 hour shift. One day she assembled 52 computers in 8 hours.

Regular rate of pay: Bonus:
8 × \$8.72 = \$69.76 15 × \$1.69 = \$25.35
Total gross pay: \$69.76 + \$25.35 = \$95.11

**Payroll periods**

A payroll period indicates the number of times that the employee receives a pay cheque.

| | |
|---|---|
| Weekly | every week for 52 periods a year |
| Bi-weekly | every two weeks for 26 periods a year |
| Semi-monthly | twice a month for 24 periods a year |
| Monthly | every month for 12 periods a year |

## Example

Laura works at a department store. She is paid a regular hourly rate of \$5.50/h for a 40-h week, Monday to Friday. She is paid double time for each hour she works on a holiday and she is paid time and a half for all other overtime. During one week in April, Laura worked 52.5 h, including 8 h on a provincial holiday. Find her gross pay for that week. Round your answers to the nearest cent.

## Solution

*Step 1* For a 40-h week, Laura earned
40 × \$5.50 = \$220.00 (\$5.50 ← regular rate of pay)

*Step 2* For the 8 h worked on the holiday, she earned
8 × \$11.00 = \$88.00 (\$11.00 ← double time rate of pay)

*Step 3* She worked an additional 4.5 h of overtime.
4.5 × \$8.25 = \$37.13 (\$8.25 ← time and a half rate of pay)

*Step 4* Calculate the gross pay.
Gross pay = \$220.00 + \$88.00 + \$37.13
= \$345.13

Thus, during that week, Laura earned \$345.13.

In calculating your gross income at your place of employment, you must know what the agreement is between the employer and the employees as to the regular rate of pay, overtime rate of pay, expected days of work, and so on. In this way you can calculate the amount of money you expect to earn and these will agree with what the employer actually pays you.

## Try These

1 Find the weekly gross earnings for 10 h of work at each rate of pay.
(a) $4.50/h (b) $5.17/h (c) $6.06/h

2 Overtime is paid at the rate of time-and-a-half. Find the overtime rate to pay for each of the following regular hourly rates.
(a) $9.00 (b) $8.40 (c) $11.50

3 If a shift premium of 75¢ per hour is paid find the hourly rate for each of the following regular rates.
(a) $4.60/h (b) $8.75/h (c) $11.30/h

## Written Exercises

**A** **Use your calculator to aid you in doing these questions.**

1 Find the gross pay for each of the following regular hourly rates.
(a) $4.50/h for 24 h (b) $5.15/h for 18 h
(c) $6.05/h for 20 h (d) $8.19/h for 30 h

2 Find the gross income for each of the following number of hours worked. All hours over 40 are paid time-and-a-half. The regular pay rate is $8.30/h.
(a) 20 h (b) 32 h (c) 40 h
(d) 44 h (e) 50 h (f) 52.5 h

3 Find the gross pay, to the nearest cent, for each of the following number of hours worked.

| | Regular hours worked | Overtime hours worked | Regular hourly rate |
|---|---|---|---|
| (a) | 34 | 12 | $6.25 |
| (b) | 28 | 6 | $7.30 |
| (c) | 38.5 | 8 | $9.80 |
| (d) | 40 | 5 | $7.65 |
| (e) | 33 | 4 | $5.10 |
| (f) | 40 | 3.5 | $6.40 |

4 Calculate the gross pay for each of the following people if they each are paid double time for all hours worked overtime. Hours over 40 are overtime.

| | Name | Total hours worked | Regular hourly rate |
|---|---|---|---|
| (a) | Linda | 40 | $6.80 |
| (b) | George | 44 | $5.90 |
| (c) | Vito | 48.5 | $7.62 |
| (d) | Sheila | 52.75 | $9.36 |

**B** **Round your answers to the nearest cent where necessary.**

5 Lori works as a typist for a cable company. She is paid $6.30/h for a 37.5 h week with overtime at time-and-a-half. Calculate her gross pay for a week in which she works 49.5 h.

6 Ronaldo is a waiter and earns $8.36/h for a forty hour week. During one week his tips amounted to $317.82. He gives 10% of his tips to the cashier. Calculate Ronaldo's gross pay for this week.

7 Calculate the basic gross annual earnings for each of the following workers. All of the rates given are for a regular 40-h week.

| | Type of job | Rate of pay |
|---|---|---|
| (a) | truck driver | $1872 monthly |
| (b) | store manager | $1256.20 semi-monthly |
| (c) | driving instructor | $237.50 weekly |
| (d) | legal secretary | $11.55/h |
| (e) | sales clerk | $228.71 weekly |
| (f) | painter | $740 bi-weekly |
| (g) | nurse | $724.10 bi-weekly |
| (h) | cashier | $8.65/h |

8 Mishko receives time-and-a-half for all work over 8 hours in a day, time-and-a-half for all Saturday work and double time for work on holidays and Sundays. During a recent week, Mishko worked the following hours.

| | | | | | |
|---|---|---|---|---|---|
| Monday | 9 | Tuesday | 8 | Sunday | $3\frac{1}{2}$ |
| Wednesday | 7 | Thursday | 10 | | |
| Friday | $8\frac{1}{2}$ | Saturday | 5 | | |

If his regular hourly rate is $12.60, what were his gross earnings for the week?

9 A time card is shown for an employee. The employer-employee agreement indicates that hours worked over 40 per week during Monday to Friday receive time-and-a-half. A one hour lunch is allowed each day without pay. On weekends, time-and-a-half is paid. Calculate Marsha's gross earnings.

Name: Marsha S.
Job Title: Cashier
Week Ending: Aug. 23 Emp. No. 341002

| DAY | IN | OUT | HOURS WORKED |
|---|---|---|---|
| Mon. | 09:00 | 18:00 | ? |
| Tues. | 08:30 | 18:30 | ? |
| Wed. | 08:00 | 19:00 | ? |
| Thurs. | 09:00 | 16:00 | ? |
| Fri. | 08:30 | 17:30 | ? |
| Sat. | 09:00 | 18:00 | ? |
| Sun. | — | — | — |

| | | | |
|---|---|---|---|
| Regular Hours ? | Regular Rate $7.23 | Regular Earnings ? | |
| Overtime Hours ? | Overtime Rate ? | Overtime Earnings ? | Gross Pay ? |

## Consumer Tip

The money you receive when you start working will not be enough in order to make a major purchase, such as a car or a house. Thus, you may need to apply for credit. Before anyone can obtain a loan, the lender will do a thorough check on the person's credit rating. Usually a person's credit rating is determined by five very important characteristics.

- Character
- Capacity
- Conditions
- Collateral
- Common Sense

A To apply for credit, you may need to provide the following information.

- ✓ How may years have you lived at your present address?
- ✓ What is your previous address?
- ✓ Do you own your house, or do you rent?
- ✓ How many dependents do you have?
- ✓ What is your gross monthly income?
- ✓ What is your spouse's gross monthly income?
- ✓ Who is your present and previous employer?
- ✓ Where do you bank? What is your account number?
- ✓ To whom do you owe any money? What is your social insurance number?

Why do you think the above information is requested for a credit application?

B Obtain a copy of a charge card application. What other information is requested from you in addition to the information listed in A?

C You are the manager of a credit approval department.

(a) List some conditions for which you would be able to approve a credit application with *no hesitation*?

(b) List some conditions for which you would be able to approve a credit application with *some hesitation.*

(c) List some conditions for which you would *reject* an application for credit.

# 8.2 Principles of Commission

Often in a store, a sales clerk may be paid a commission on each sale that is made. A commission is a payment made by the store to its sales people and provides an incentive for making sales. Often the commission is based on a percentage of the sales. In many stores, a salesperson is paid a salary plus a commission as shown in the following example.

### Example 1

Jeff sells memberships and receives $225 per week plus 5.5% commission on his sales each day. Calculate his wages after a 5 day week.

| Day | 1 | 2 | 3 | 4 | 5 |
|---|---|---|---|---|---|
| Sales | $680 | $450 | $925 | $1200 | $1375 |

### Solution

Total value of sales = $4630

Commission = 5.5% of $4630
= 0.055 × $4630
= $254.65

Wages = Regular pay + Commission
= $225 + $254.65
= $479.65

Jeff's wages for the 5 day week were $479.65.

You can use your skills with equations to solve problems involving commission.

### Example 2

Refer to Jeff's salary and commission terms in the previous question.

During another week, Jeff received wages in the amount of $427.95. What were his sales that week?

### Solution

Let $S represent the amount of sales. Jeff's wages are given by the equation:

$$225 + 0.055S = 427.95$$
$$0.055S = 202.95$$
$$S = 3690$$

Thus Jeff's sales were $3690 that week.

Check:

| | | |
|---|---|---|
| Commission | 0.055 × $3690 | = 202.95 |
| | Salary | = 225.00 |
| | Checks ✓ | $427.95 |

## Try These

1 A commission of 10% is paid on each of the following sales. Calculate the amount of commission.
(a) $690 (b) $825 (c) $1283
(d) $9683.56 (e) $36 000 (f) $125 000

2 The amount of commission paid on various sales is shown. The rate of commission is 10%. Calculate the amount of sales.
(a) $12 (b) $16.90 (c) $128
(d) $136.50 (e) $1200 (f) $2865

## Written Exercises

**A** Round your answers to the nearest cent.

1 Find the missing amounts.

| | Rate of commission | Amount of Sales | Amount of commission |
|---|---|---|---|
| (a) | 3% | $396.50 | ? |
| (b) | 4.5% | $608.10 | ? |
| (c) | $2\frac{1}{4}$% | $965.40 | ? |
| (d) | 8.75% | $1260.00 | ? |

2 Find the missing amounts.

| | Rate of commission | Amount of sales | Commission earned |
|---|---|---|---|
| (a) | 5% | $789.50 | ? |
| (b) | 8.25% | ? | $103.09 |
| (c) | ? | $5918.44 | $568.17 |
| (d) | ? | $3489.00 | $340.18 |
| (e) | 16% | ? | $939.75 |

3 A real estate agent earns 2.5% on the sale of a house. Find the amount of commission received if a house sold for $139 700.00.

4 Carroll is an agent for a mail-order panti-hose company. She earns 20% commission on her orders. Find how much she earns on orders totalling $165.48.

5 A house sold for $95 800. If the amount of commission paid was $2874, calculate the rate of commission.

**B** Be sure to make a final statement in answering the problems.

6 In the restaurant where Mark is a waiter, 15% gratuity (tip) is added automatically to each person's bill. One week the checks from Mark's tables added up to $715.29. How much should he receive in gratuities?

7 Brent has summer employment in a furniture store. In any week he receives 10% commission on the amount by which his sales exceed $1000. How much commission does he earn for a week in which his sales totalled $1762?

8 Stella has a part-time job at a fashion boutique. She earns commission on her sales. The rate of commission is 5% on sales up to $1000 in a week and 8% on sales over $1000. How much commission does she earn from a week in which her sales were $1392.50?

9 Jackson earns $325 per week plus 8% on sales above $3000. If he earned $685 one week, how much were his sales?

10 Brenda helps her mother sell cosmetics privately. They receive 20% commission on regular items and 25% on monthly special items. One December they sold $728.00 worth of the Christmas special items, plus $54.00 in regular items. How much commission did they earn?

11 Stuart works part-time in a shoe store. He is paid $4.85/h plus 3% commission on all the shoes he sells.

(a) Find his gross pay for a week during which he worked 18 h and had sales totalling $1152.00.

(b) The next week, the store had a 30% off sale. Stuart again worked 18 h and had sales of $1200.00. What was his gross pay?

12 Melissa sells appliances and receives the following commission on her sales in each week.

- 7% on the first $1200
- 10.5% on the next $2400
- 18% on sales above $3600

Find the total commission earned for weeks in which she had the following sales.

(a) $1075 (b) $759.18
(c) $1786.90 (d) $2808.63
(e) $4854.59 (f) $7475.86
(g) $8903.09 (h) $12 564.52

# 8.3 Calculations for Income

Related to your gross earnings, there are additional terms and calculations that determine how much money you actually receive and can use to spend. The following four terms are basic to understanding the meaning of finding your net income.

- **Gross Earnings** is the total amount of money you receive in earnings including, where applicable, overtime, commissions and taxable benefits.
- **Deductions:** on your income statement various monies are deducted, such as contributions to Canada Pension Plan and Unemployment Insurance, which are described below, as well as personal deductions for medical plans, insurance plans, pension plans. There are also other deductions such as income tax. We will deal with income tax deductions in detail in later sections.
- **Taxable Income** is the income on which your employer calculates the income tax you must contribute to the government.
- **Net Income** is the amount of money you receive (or take home) after all deductions have been taken away from your gross earnings.

**Canada Pension Plan Contribution (C.P.P.)**
If you are a person under 18, working less than 20 hours per week, you do not have Canada Pension Plan contributions deducted. All others must pay C.P.P. contributions. Canada Pension deductions will be returned to you, when you retire, in the form of a pension, based on very complex calculations, determined by the government of Canada.

**Unemployment Insurance Contributions (U.I.)**
If you are a person under 18, working less than 20 hours per week, you do not have U.I.C. deducted. All others must pay unemployment insurance. The regulations and rules covering U.I. are made available to persons working, and describe the terms and conditions under which you can receive monies when you are no longer employed.

Tables and charts are used by employers to aid them in calculating deductions from your gross earnings. For example, the following are parts of the table used to calculate the C.P.P. and U.I. deductions for a weekly pay period. A full table is provided on page 464. The amounts shown in the table vary from year to year.

**CANADA PENSION PLAN CONTRIBUTIONS**
WEEKLY PAY PERIOD

| Remuneration *Rémunération* From-*de* To-*à* | C.P.P. *R.P.C.* | Remuneration *Rémunération* From-*de* To-*à* | C.P.P. *R.P.C.* |
|---|---|---|---|
| 208.96 – 209.50 | 2.97 | 213.96 – 214.50 | 3.06 |
| 209.51 – 210.06 | 2.98 | 214.51 – 215.06 | 3.07 |
| 210.07 – 210.61 | 2.99 | 215.07 – 215.61 | 3.08 |
| 210.62 – 211.17 | 3.00 | 215.62 – 216.17 | 3.09 |
| 211.18 – 211.72 | 3.01 | 216.18 – 216.72 | 3.10 |
| 211.73 – 212.28 | 3.02 | 216.73 – 217.28 | 3.11 |
| 212.29 – 212.84 | 3.03 | 217.29 – 217.84 | 3.12 |
| 212.85 – 213.39 | 3.04 | 217.85 – 218.39 | 3.13 |
| 213.40 – 213.95 | 3.05 | 218.40 – 218.95 | 3.14 |

**UNEMPLOYMENT INSURANCE PREMIUMS**
WEEKLY PAY PERIOD

| Remuneration *Rémunération* From-*de* To-*à* | U.I. Premium *Prime d'a.-c.* | Remuneration *Rémunération* From-*de* To-*à* | U.I. Premium *Prime d'a.-c.* |
|---|---|---|---|
| 210.86 – 211.27 | 4.96 | 214.69 – 215.10 | 5.05 |
| 211.28 – 211.70 | 4.97 | 215.11 – 215.53 | 5.06 |
| 211.71 – 212.12 | 4.98 | 215.54 – 215.95 | 5.07 |
| 212.13 – 212.55 | 4.99 | 215.96 – 216.38 | 5.08 |
| 212.56 – 212.97 | 5.00 | 216.39 – 216.80 | 5.09 |
| 212.98 – 213.40 | 5.01 | 216.81 – 217.23 | 5.10 |
| 213.41 – 213.82 | 5.02 | 217.24 – 217.65 | 5.11 |
| 213.83 – 214.25 | 5.03 | 217.66 – 218.08 | 5.12 |
| 214.26 – 214.68 | 5.04 | 218.09 – 218.51 | 5.13 |

**Income Tax Deductions**
In a similar way, a table is also provided by the government for income tax deductions. Part of a table is shown below for various weekly pays—the digits, 1, 2, . . . . 13 indicate the *net claim code* described below, under personal exemptions. A full table is given on page 466. The amounts shown in the table vary from year to year.

**WEEKLY TAX DEDUCTIONS**
**Basis — 52 Pay Periods per Year**

| WEEKLY PAY Use appropriate bracket — PAIE PAR SEMAINE Utilisez le palier approprié | IF THE EMPLOYEE'S "NET CLAIM CODE" ON FORM TD1 IS — SI LE CODE DE DEMANDE NETTE DE L'EMPLOYÉ SELON LA FORMULE TD1 EST DE | | | | | | | | | | | | |
|---|---|---|---|---|---|---|---|---|---|---|---|---|---|
| | **1** | **2** | **3** | **4** | **5** | **6** | **7** | **8** | **9** | **10** | **11** | **12** | **13** |
| | DEDUCT FROM EACH PAY—*RETENEZ SUR CHAQUE PAIE* | | | | | | | | | | | | |
| 197.00 – 198.99 | 20.65 | 18.70 | 15.35 | 12.15 | 8.65 | 5.85 | 4.15 | 1.60 | | | | | |
| 199.00 – 200.99 | 21.20 | 19.25 | 15.85 | 12.65 | 9.15 | 6.30 | 4.65 | 2.05 | | | | | |
| 201.00 – 202.99 | 21.70 | 19.75 | 16.40 | 13.15 | 9.70 | 6.80 | 5.10 | 2.55 | | | | | |
| 203.00 – 204.99 | 22.25 | 20.30 | 16.90 | 13.65 | 10.20 | 7.30 | 5.60 | 3.00 | | | | | |
| 205.00 – 206.99 | 22.80 | 20.85 | 17.40 | 14.15 | 10.70 | 7.85 | 6.05 | 3.50 | | | | | |
| 207.00 – 208.99 | 23.30 | 21.35 | 17.90 | 14.65 | 11.20 | 8.35 | 6.55 | 3.95 | | | | | |
| 209.00 – 210.99 | 23.85 | 21.90 | 18.40 | 15.15 | 11.70 | 8.85 | 7.05 | 4.40 | | | | | |
| 211.00 – 212.99 | 24.40 | 22.45 | 18.90 | 15.65 | 12.20 | 9.35 | 7.55 | 4.90 | 1.30 | | | | |
| 213.00 – 214.99 | 24.90 | 22.95 | 19.45 | 16.15 | 12.70 | 9.85 | 8.05 | 5.35 | 1.80 | | | | |
| 215.00 – 216.99 | 25.45 | 23.50 | 19.95 | 16.65 | 13.20 | 10.35 | 8.55 | 5.85 | 2.30 | | | | |

On the above form, certain terms occur such as the following.

**Net Claim Code**
When you start a new job, you are required to complete a Tax Exemption Return (TD1) form. From the information you fill out in this form concerning your marital status, number of dependents, you will find out how much of your gross earnings you can claim to be exempt from paying C.P.P., U.I., and income taxes. This amount is referred to as your personal exemption. Your personal exemption is used in the table to find your *net claim code*. For example, if your personal exemptions are $9845, then your net claim code is 10 as shown. Each category for the net claim code has a specific meaning as described in the handbooks provided by employers. For example:

Net claim code 1: This is the amount deducted if you have no dependents,
Net claim code 2: This is the amount deducted if you have 1 child,

and so on.

| **Table of Net Claim Codes** | |
|---|---|
| Net Claim Exceeding – Not exceeding | Net Claim Code |
| For use re: Tables 11 and 12 | 0 |
| $4 139 – 4 190 | 1 |
| 4 190 – 4 850 | 2 |
| 4 850 – 5 570 | 3 |
| 5 570 – 6 190 | 4 |
| 6 190 – 7 000 | 5 |
| 7 000 – 7 370 | 6 |
| 7 370 – 7 740 | 7 |
| $ 7 740 – 8 500 | 8 |
| 8 500 – 9 300 | 9 |
| 9 300 – 10 170 | 10 |
| 10 170 – 11 020 | 11 |
| 11 020 – 11 840 | 12 |
| 11 840 – 12 470 | 13 |
| 12 470 and up | X |
| No tax withholding required | E |

$9 845 lies between $9 300 and $10 170

An employer has very straightforward rules and regulations to follow to calculate your net pay, namely the amount shown on your pay cheque. To do so, a main part of the task is to identify the correct amounts shown in the tables. Usually when you receive your pay cheque, details are provided to explain the deductions that have been made. These details vary from company to company but the principles employed are essentially the same.

| STATEMENT OF EARNINGS AND DEDUCTIONS | | | | | | |
|---|---|---|---|---|---|---|
| Earnings | Hours | Amount | Deductions | | | |
| Regular | 37 | 240.50 | U.I. | 8.40 | Fed. Tax | 65.70 |
| Overtime | 12 | 117.00 | C.P.P. | 5.64 | Co. Pen. | 12.62 |
| Total Earnings | | 357.50 | Total Deductions | | | 92.36 |
| | | | | | Net Pay | 265.14 |
| Name: Jo Santos | | | | | | |
| Date: 08-10-85 | | | | | | |

## Example

Maureen started a job as a stock clerk at \$4.90/h. Her personal exemptions are \$4365. Find Maureen's gross earnings and her net earnings for a 40 h week with 3 h overtime at time-and-a-half. Use any C.P.P., U.I., and Income tax deductions.

## Solution

*Step 1*: Calculate Maureen's gross earnings.

| Regular Earnings | Overtime Earnings | Gross Earnings |
|---|---|---|
| 40 × \$4.90 | 3 × \$7.35 | \$196.00 |
| = \$196.00 | = \$22.05 | + 22.05 |
| | | \$218.05 |

*Step 2*: Calculate taxable income. Use the tables.

C.P.P. is \$3.13 U.I. is \$5.12

Taxable income = \$218.05 − (\$3.13 + \$5.12)
= \$218.05 − (\$8.25)
= \$209.80

*Step 3*: Calculate the income tax deduction. Her personal exemptions are \$4365.00. From the table, her net claim code is 2.

| Taxable income | Net claim code | Income tax deduction |
|---|---|---|
| \$209.80 | 2 | \$21.90 |

*Step 4*: Calculate Maureen's net income.

Net Income = Gross earnings − Deductions
= \$218.05 − \$3.13 − \$5.12 − \$21.90
= \$187.90 (\$3.13 C.P.P., \$5.12 U.I., \$21.90 income tax)

Thus Maureen's gross earnings were \$218.05. Her net income was \$187.90.

**Remember: make a final statement to answer the original question.**

## Try These

1 Refer to the table showing C.P.P. and U.I. deductions. Determine the deductions.

| | Weekly wages | Deductions C.P.P. | U.I. |
|---|---|---|---|
| (a) | $216.75 | ? | ? |
| (b) | $214.32 | ? | ? |
| (c) | $213.92 | ? | ? |
| (d) | $217.14 | ? | ? |
| (e) | $215.33 | ? | ? |
| (f) | $217.52 | ? | ? |

2 Refer to the chart showing income tax deductions. Determine the amount of income tax to be deducted for each weekly wage.

| | Weekly wages | Net claim code | Income tax deducted |
|---|---|---|---|
| (a) | $197.45 | 1 | ? |
| (b) | $216.35 | 2 | ? |
| (c) | $207.63 | 5 | ? |
| (d) | $213.24 | 9 | ? |
| (e) | $219.31 | 7 | ? |
| (f) | $200.00 | 3 | ? |

## Written Exercises

**A** Refer to the tables for U.I., C.P.P. and income tax as shown on pages 464 to 466.

1 Use the tables to find the weekly deductions for C.P.P. and U.I. for each of the following incomes.
(a) $223.00 (b) $296.52 (c) $319.58
(d) $336.08 (e) $307.19 (f) $287.63

2 Find the amount of income tax deducted in each of the following.

| | Taxable income | Net claim code |
|---|---|---|
| (a) | $269.72 | 3 |
| (b) | $307.54 | 2 |
| (c) | $209.16 | 1 |
| (d) | $263.15 | 5 |
| (e) | $319.78 | 6 |

3 For each of the following, find
- ▶ deductions for C.P.P., U.I.
- ▶ taxable income
- ▶ income tax deduction
- ▶ take-home pay.

| | Gross earnings | Net claim code |
|---|---|---|
| (a) | $217.24 | 2 |
| (b) | $315.08 | 1 |
| (c) | $273.49 | 3 |
| (d) | $242.00 | 1 |
| (e) | $302.71 | 4 |

4 Morgan works as a telephone installer. Find her net pay using the following information.

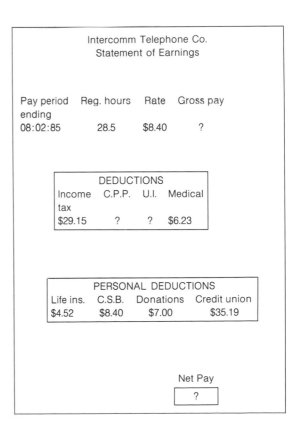

Intercomm Telephone Co.
Statement of Earnings

| Pay period ending | Reg. hours | Rate | Gross pay |
|---|---|---|---|
| 08:02:85 | 28.5 | $8.40 | ? |

DEDUCTIONS

| Income tax | C.P.P. | U.I. | Medical |
|---|---|---|---|
| $29.15 | ? | ? | $6.23 |

PERSONAL DEDUCTIONS

| Life ins. | C.S.B. | Donations | Credit union |
|---|---|---|---|
| $4.52 | $8.40 | $7.00 | $35.19 |

Net Pay: ?

5 His net claim code is 1. Find the net pay for the following employee.

AUDIO-SOUND CORPORATION
EMPLOYEE EARNING RECORD

| Period ending | Hours worked | Hourly rate | Gross pay |
|---|---|---|---|
| June 1, 1985 | 35 | $9.25 | ? |

| Cheque No. |
|---|
| 136045-8 |

DEDUCTIONS

| U.I. | C.P.P. | Income tax | Life ins. | Ext. health | Vac. pay | Union dues | Total deductions |
|---|---|---|---|---|---|---|---|
| ? | ? | ? | $7.15 | $3.12 | — | $6.53 | ? |

| Net Pay |
|---|
| ? |

**B** Use your calculator to aid you in your calculations.

Questions 6 to 9 are based on the following information. The table below shows various employees and their earnings.

| Person | Weekly earnings | Net claim code |
|---|---|---|
| Sean | 38 h at $5.75/h | 3 |
| Betty | $324.95 per week | 2 |
| Abdul | 40 h regular time at $7.12/h plus 4.5 h at time-and-a-half | 1 |
| George | $296.05 per week | 3 |
| Paula | 35 h regular time at $4.55/h plus 6.75 h double time | 5 |
| Joe | $251.90 per week | 4 |

6 Calculate the gross earnings for each of the following people for the week.
(a) Sean (b) Paula (c) Abdul

7 Calculate the U.I., C.P.P. and Income tax deductions for each person.
(a) Betty (b) Abdul (c) George

8 If there are no other deductions, calculate the net income for each employee.
(a) Paula (b) George (c) Sean

9 Use the information in the chart.
(a) Create a problem of your own based on the information.
(b) Solve the problem in (a).

10 Mary Lou works as a dietician and is paid $7.15/h for a 40 h week. She has net claim code 5. The total of her other deductions amount to $107.52. Find her net pay for one week.

11 Suzo sells medical instruments and is paid $269.75/week plus a commission of 1.5% of the value of his sales. During one week, Suzo sold $3976.74 worth of instruments. As well as C.P.P. and U.I., Suzo has $18.04 deducted each pay cheque for a savings plan. Calculate Suzo's net pay for the week. He has net claim code 2.

12 Marilyn works as a waitress. She earns $162.40/week and keeps 75% of the tips she receives. She has net claim code 3 and pays $9.46/week for her dental plan, plus deductions for C.P.P., U.I. and income tax. Calculate Marilyn's net pay for one week if her tips during this week amounted to $168.10.

## Computer Tip

- Run the following BASIC program.

```
10 REM THIS PROGRAM COMPUTES GROSS PAY
20 LET R = 8.35
30 LET H = 35
40 LET P = R * H
50 PRINT "HOURLY RATE", "HOURS WORKED",
   "GROSS PAY"
60 PRINT R, H, P
70 END
```

- Revise the computer program so that you can input any hourly rate or number of hours worked.

# 8.4 Paying Income Taxes

When you earn income, the Federal government is paid a part of it, in the form of income tax, which is a tax on income. The main source of funds to provide the many government services is the income tax you pay. These taxes are spent on behalf of Canadians in the form of health and welfare, defence, economic development as well as on transportation, education, culture and recreation. Income tax is paid both by individuals and by businesses.

**APRIL 30 LOOMS AGAIN**
Each year around April 30, you see people hurrying to submit their income tax return. April 30 is the due date. This is the last day on which you can file your income tax return and not receive any penalties. Every person who is a resident of Canada must file an income tax return if money in the form of taxes is owed to the government.

When income tax was first introduced at the time of the first world war, it was intended to be a temporary measure. Since then income tax has been retained as the monies collected are needed to provide many benefits to Canadians (transportation, pension plans, social benefits and so on) as well as other important services (such as defence, public works, post office).

The income tax we pay is a progressive tax since the higher your income, the higher the rate at which you pay income tax. Every country has different rules and regulations by which individuals and corporations calculate the income taxes owed. In some countries, you do not pay any income taxes, but you may not want to live there.

You are informed about 3 months later that your income tax return is assessed and approved. All you need to do then is wait for the next April 30.

The steps and principles for calculating income tax and completing tax returns remain essentially the same year after year. We will examine these steps and principles in this and subsequent sections.

The steps for paying income tax are regulated by law.

A Each employer must deduct and send income tax payments on your behalf to Revenue Canada. Income tax is deducted from your wages based on your tax category and the amount of wages you earn. Such a system of payments reduces your burden of paying all of the income tax owed at one time. If you are self-employed you need to submit quarterly installment payments of income tax based on your calculations.

B The employer informs you of the amount of your total earnings as well as your income tax deductions during the year on a T4 slip shown as follows. The information is also sent to Revenue Canada.

If you work for more than one employer during the year, each employer sends you a T4 slip. The T4 slip also shows any other deductions made on your behalf such as

- Canada Pension Plan: This plan is compulsory for employees aged 18 to 70. Based on your "category," deductions are made and paid into the Canada Pension Plan fund or if you live in Quebec, to the Quebec Pension Plan.
- Unemployment Insurance: This deduction is paid into the government fund so that certain benefits can be paid out to eligible employees that are out of work.
- Various other deductions are shown on a T4 slip such as employment commissions, registered pension plan contributions, charitable donations, union dues, and so on, depending on each employee's particular situation.

From year to year, the specific instructions and details on completing an income tax return, and the calculation of income taxes may differ. For this reason, be sure to refer to a current income tax return to compare the suggestions that follow in this section and subsequent sections.

C On or before April 30 of each year, you complete the income

Revenue Canada Taxation | Revenu Canada Impôt | T4-YEAR Supplementary - *Supplémentaire* | **STATEMENT OF REMUNERATION PAID** ***ÉTAT DE LA RÉMUNÉRATION PAYÉE***

| (C) EMPLOYMENT INCOME BEFORE DEDUCTIONS | (D) EMPLOYEE'S PENSION CONTRIBUTION CANADA PLAN | QUEBEC PLAN | (E) U.I. PREMIUM | (F) REGISTERED PENSION PLAN CONTRIBUTION | (G) INCOME TAX DEDUCTED | (H) U.I. INSURABLE EARNINGS | (I) C.P.P. PENSIONABLE EARNINGS | (J) EXEMPT C.P.P./Q.P.P. | U.I. |
|---|---|---|---|---|---|---|---|---|---|
| 15 308 27 | 379 73 | | 356 14 | | 560 28 | 14 572 30 | | | |
| *REVENUS D'EMPLOI AVANT RETENUES* | *DU CANADA* | *DU QUÉBEC* *COTISATION DE PENSION (EMPLOYÉ)* | *PRIME D'A.-C.* | *COTISATIONS RÉGIME ENREGISTRÉ DE PENSIONS* | *IMPÔT SUR LE REVENU RETENU* | *GAINS ASSURABLES A.-C.* | *GAINS OUVRANT DROIT À PENSIONS-R.P.C.* | RPC/RRQ | *A.-C.* *EXONÉRATION* |

| BOX (C) AMOUNT INCLUDES ANY AMOUNTS IN BOXES (K), (L), (M), (N), (O) AND (P) *LE MONTANT DE LA CASE (C) COMPREND TOUS LES MONTANTS FIGURANT AUX CASES (K), (L), (M), (N), (O) AND (P)* | TAXABLE ALLOWANCES AND BENEFITS ▶ *AVANTAGES IMPOSABLES* | (K) BOARD AND LODGING *NOURRITURE ET LOGEMENT* | (L) RENT FREE AND LOW RENT HOUSING *LOGEMENT GRATUIT OU ÀCOÛT MODIQUE* | (M) PERSONAL USE OF EMPLOYER'S AUTO *USAGE PERSONNEL DE L'AUTO DE L'EMPLOYEUR* | (N) INTEREST FREE AND LOW INTEREST LOANS *PRÊTS SANS INTÉRÊT OU À FAIBLE INTÉRÊT* | (O) OTHER TAXABLE ALLOW AND BENEFITS *AUTRES AVANTAGES IMPOSABLES* |
|---|---|---|---|---|---|---|

| (P) EMPLOYMENT COMMISSIONS | (Q) PENSION PLAN REGISTRATION NUMBER | (R) PAYMENTS TO DPSP | (S) CHARITABLE DONATIONS | (T) UNION DUES | (A) PROVINCE OF EMPLOYMENT | (B) SOCIAL INSURANCE NUMBER | (U) EMPLOYEE NO. |
|---|---|---|---|---|---|---|---|
| | | | | | Ont. | 123 654 789 | 12 |
| *COMMISSIONS D'EMPLOI* | *Nº D'ENREGISTREMENT RÉGIME DE PENSIONS* | *PAIEMENTS ÀUN RPDB* | *DONS DE CHARITÉ* | *COTISATIONS SYNDICALES* | *PROVINCE D'EMPLOI* | *Nº D'ASSURANCE SOCIALE* | *Nº DE L'EMPLOYÉ* |

EMPLOYEE: SURNAME FIRST (in capital letters). USUAL FIRST NAME AND INITIALS AND FULL ADDRESS
*EMPLOYÉ: NOM DE FAMILLE D'ABORD (en capitales). PRÉNOM USUEL ET ADRESSE COMPLÈTE*

Daniel Chang
513 Main Street
Townsville, Ontario
X1Q 2K3

NAME AND ADDRESS OF EMPLOYER OR PAYOR
*NOM ET ADRESSE DE L'EMPLOYEUR OU DU PAYEUR*

Shopper's Mart
West Mall
Townsville, Ont.
X5Y 4Z3

● **Attach to your Income Tax Return**
**SEE INFORMATION ON REVERSE**

tax return and provide the information needed under these general headings.

Calculation of Total Income
- Income from employment
- Pension income
- Income from other sources
- Self-employed income

Calculation of Taxable Income
- Allowable deductions
- Personal exemptions (deductions)
- Other deductions

Once your taxable income is determined based on the information you volunteer, the tax return provides the steps needed to calculate each of the following income taxes that you owe.

I Federal tax payable II Provincial tax payable

Remember:
Always check (verify) the deductions reported on your T4 slip against the deductions made throughout the year on your pay stubs.

D Based on your calculations, you will know whether

I You have paid too much income tax, in which case you apply for a refund.

II You have not paid enough income tax in which case you need to submit the tax owed payable to the Receiver General of Canada.

When the employer deducts income tax on your behalf, the information that you have submitted is used as a basis to determine the calculations. Each of these situations can affect the amount of income tax that you owe:

- you may receive income from another source, a part-time job
- you may receive income in the form of interest for money deposited in a bank
- you may marry or have a child.

The income tax return offers you the opportunity to provide updated information about yourself in the previous year.

| (1) | | (2) | (3) |
|---|---|---|---|
| *Taxable Income: over* | *not over* | *Federal Tax* | *Ontario Tax Payable* |
| **$ 6400**– | 6410 | $ 846 | $ 453.80 |
| 6410– | 6420 | 847 | 454.70 |
| 6420– | 6430 | 849 | 455.60 |
| 6430– | 6440 | 851 | 456.40 |
| 6440– | 6450 | 853 | 457.30 |
| 6450– | 6460 | 855 | 458.20 |
| 6460– | 6470 | 856 | 459.00 |
| 6470– | 6480 | 858 | 459.90 |
| 6480– | 6490 | 860 | 460.80 |
| 6490– | 6500 | 862 | 461.60 |
| **$ 6500**– | 6510 | $ 864 | $ 462.50 |
| 6510– | 6520 | 865 | 463.30 |
| 6520– | 6530 | 867 | 464.20 |
| 6530– | 6540 | 869 | 465.10 |
| 6540– | 6550 | 871 | 465.90 |
| 6550– | 6560 | 873 | 466.80 |
| 6560– | 6570 | 874 | 467.70 |
| 6570– | 6580 | 876 | 468.50 |
| 6580– | 6590 | 878 | 469.40 |
| 6590– | 6600 | 880 | 470.30 |
| **$ 6600**– | 6610 | $ 882 | $ 471.10 |
| [illegible]610– | 6620 | 883 | 472.00 |
| [illegible] | [illegible] | 885 | 472.80 |
| [illegible] | [illegible] | [illegible]87 | 473.70 |

To calculate the amount of tax you owe, tables are provided. A portion of the tables is shown. For example, for a taxable income of $6485.90 the table show the following taxes are owed:

| | |
|---|---|
| Federal tax | $860.00 |
| Provincial tax | $460.80 |
| Total income tax | $1320.80 |

On the last page of this section, a full page of tables is provided.

**Example**

Jeremy works in a bank. He calculates his taxable income to be $12 605.28. His T4 slips indicate that throughout the year he has paid $3465.80 in income taxes. Will he get a refund or need to make a further payment? How much will it be?

**Solution**

From the tax table, for a taxable income of $12 605.28,

| | |
|---|---|
| Federal tax payable | $2010.00 |
| Provincial tax payable | 1012.60 |
| Total taxes due | $3022.60 |
| Amount deducted T4 slips | $3465.80 |
| Total taxes due | $3022.60 |
| Refund claimed | $ 443.20 |

Thus Jeremy will receive a refund of $443.20.

## Written Exercises

**A** For the following questions, refer to the income tax tables provided at the end of these exercises.

1 Each of these terms appear on a current T4. What is meant by each of the following?
(a) employment income before deductions, Box (C)
(b) employee's pension contribution: Canada Plan, Box (D)
(c) U.I. premium, Box (E)
(d) Registered pension contribution, Box (F)
(e) income tax deducted, Box (G)
(f) Employment commissions, Box (P)
(g) charitable donations, Box (S)
(h) union dues, Box (T)
(i) social insurance number, Box (B)
(j) province of employment, Box (A)
(k) Employee No., Box (U)

2 For each taxable income, calculate the total income taxes payable.
(a) $7236.35 (b) $7648.50 (c) $2268.96
(d) $1078.50 (e) $8162.20 (f) $7576.23

3 Jennifer received her T4 slip from her employer which showed $1836.65 had been deducted in income tax.

(a) After she completed her income tax return, her taxable income was $8212.65. How much is payable in income taxes?

(b) Will she receive a refund of income taxes, or will she need to make an additional payment? How much would it be?

**B** Round your answers to the nearest cent, where needed.

4 (a) This year after Jerome completed his income tax return, he will receive a refund of $236.80. What are some possible reasons that Jerome will receive the income tax refund?

(b) Heather will need to pay an additional $365.80 in income tax based on her calculations. What are some possible reasons that Heather will need to make the additional payment in income taxes?

5 Find the missing amounts in the chart.

| | Taxable income | Federal tax payable | Provincial tax payable | Total tax payable |
|---|---|---|---|---|
| (a) | $7328.65 | ? | ? | ? |
| (b) | ? | $146 | ? | ? |
| (c) | ? | ? | $628.70 | ? |
| (d) | ? | $1960 | ? | ? |

6 The total income taxes you owe is shown. What is your taxable income?

(a) $273.20 (b) $1760.10 (c) $255.00
(d) $1517.70 (e) $2948.90 (f) $1827.00

7 During the year Jerome changed jobs. He received two different T4 slips at the end of the year.

| T4 | Company A | Company B |
|---|---|---|
| Total earnings before deductions | $8635.00 | $4925.00 |
| Income tax deducted | $1720.33 | $981.17 |

After his income tax calculations, Jerome determined his taxable income to be $8368.93. Decide whether Jerome will receive a refund or need to make an additional payment. How much will it be?

8 The Canada or Quebec Pension Plan contributions are deducted from each pay. A maximum amount that you pay is stated on your income tax return as follows.

| | |
|---|---|
| Canada or Quebec Pension Plan contributions<br>Contributions through employment from Box (D)<br>on all T4 slips (maximum $379.80) | **202** |

For each of the following, determine whether a refund is to be obtained. Calculate the amount, if any, of the refund.

Amount of Canada, Quebec Pension Plan paid on each T4

| | Employee | T4 #1 | T4 #2 | T4 #3 |
|---|---|---|---|---|
| (a) | Larry | $136.90 | $286.40 | — |
| (b) | Barbara | $338.40 | $123.60 | — |
| (c) | Michael | $123.25 | $76.92 | $203.60 |
| (d) | Franko | $126.35 | $379.80 | $69.20 |

9 The unemployment insurance premium is deducted from each pay. A maximum amount that you need to pay is stated on your income tax return as follows.

| | |
|---|---|
| Unemployment Insurance premiums from Box (E)<br>on all T4 slips (maximum $562.12) | **204** |

For each of the following, determine whether a refund is to be obtained. Calculate the amount, if any, of the refund.

Amount of U.I. paid in each T4

| | Employee | T4 #1 | T4 #2 | T4 #3 |
|---|---|---|---|---|
| (a) | Shirley | $165.80 | $465.20 | — |
| (b) | Les | $386.80 | $96.76 | $263.50 |
| (c) | Steven | $186.90 | $195.20 | $296.75 |
| (d) | Sandra | $123.25 | $562.08 | $69.20 |
| (e) | Joanne | $478.65 | $169.80 | — |

## Career Tip

To do their jobs, income tax consultants must clearly understand the meanings of terms on an income tax return. Complete the questions on the Vocabulary of Income Tax found on page 218. Read Section 8.6 to list what skills are needed to file an income tax return.

The parts of tables shown below are a sample of the actual tables provided in an income tax return for calculating the federal and provincial taxes payable by the individual.

## FEDERAL AND PROVINCIAL TAX TABLE

| (1) Taxable Income: over | not over | (2) Federal Tax | (3) Provincial Tax Payable |
|---|---|---|---|
| **$ 1000**– | 1010 | $ 0 | $ .00 |
| 1010– | | 0 | .00 |
| 1020– | 1030 | 0 | .00 |
| 1030– | 1040 | 0 | .00 |
| 1040– | 1050 | 0 | .00 |
| 1050– | 1060 | 0 | .00 |
| 1060– | 1070 | 0 | .00 |
| 1070– | 1080 | 0 | .00 |
| 1080– | 1090 | 0 | .00 |
| 1090– | 1100 | 0 | .00 |
| **$ 1100**– | 1110 | $ 0 | $ .00 |
| 1110– | 1120 | 0 | .00 |
| 1120– | 1130 | 0 | .00 |
| 1130– | 1140 | 0 | .00 |
| 1140– | 1150 | 0 | .00 |
| 1150– | 1160 | 0 | .00 |
| 1160– | 1170 | 0 | .00 |
| 1170– | 1180 | 0 | .00 |
| 1180– | 1190 | 0 | .00 |
| 1190– | 1200 | 0 | .00 |
| **$ 1200**– | | | |

| (1) Taxable Income: over | not over | (2) Federal Tax | (3) Provincial Tax Payable |
|---|---|---|---|
| **$ 1400**– | 1410 | $ 0 | $ .00 |
| 1410– | 1420 | 0 | .00 |
| 1420– | 1430 | 0 | .00 |
| 1430– | 1440 | 0 | 1.20 |
| 1440– | 1450 | 2 | 7.00 |
| 1450– | 1460 | 4 | 12.70 |
| 1460– | 1470 | 5 | 18.50 |
| 1470– | 1480 | 7 | 24.30 |
| 1480– | 1490 | 8 | 30.00 |
| 1490– | 1500 | 10 | 35.80 |
| **$ 1500**– | 1510 | $ 12 | $ 41.60 |
| 1510– | 1520 | 13 | 47.30 |
| 1520– | 1530 | 15 | 53.10 |
| 1530– | 1540 | 16 | 55.90 |
| 1540– | 1550 | 18 | 56.60 |
| 1550– | 1560 | 20 | 57.40 |
| 1560– | 1570 | 21 | |
| 1570– | 1580 | 23 | |
| 1580– | 1590 | 24 | |
| 1590– | 1600 | | |
| **$ 1600**– | | | |

| (1) Taxable Income: over | not over | (2) Federal Tax | (3) Provincial Tax Payable |
|---|---|---|---|
| **$ 2200**– | 2210 | $ 124 | $ 107.30 |
| 2210– | 2220 | 125 | 108.10 |
| 2220– | 2230 | 127 | 108.90 |
| 2230– | 2240 | 128 | 109.60 |
| 2240– | 2250 | 130 | 110.40 |
| 2250– | 2260 | 132 | 111.20 |
| 2260– | 2270 | 133 | 111.90 |
| 2270– | 2280 | 135 | 112.70 |
| 2280– | 2290 | 136 | 113.50 |
| 2290– | 2300 | 138 | 114.20 |
| **$ 2300**– | 2310 | $ 140 | $ 115.00 |
| 2310– | 2320 | 141 | 115.80 |
| 2320– | 2330 | 143 | 116.50 |
| 2330– | 2340 | 144 | 117.30 |
| 2340– | 2350 | 146 | 118.10 |
| 2350– | 2360 | 148 | 118.80 |
| 2360– | 2370 | 149 | 119.60 |
| 2370– | 2380 | 151 | 120.40 |
| 2380– | 2390 | 152 | 121.20 |
| 2390– | 2400 | 154 | 121.90 |
| **$ 2400**– | 2410 | $ 156 | $ 122.70 |
| 2410– | 2420 | 157 | 123.50 |
| 2420– | 2430 | 159 | 124.20 |
| 2430– | 2440 | 160 | |
| 2440– | 2450 | | |
| 2450– | 2460 | | |

| (1) Taxable Income: over | not over | (2) Federal Tax | (3) Provincial Tax Payable |
|---|---|---|---|
| **$ 7200**– | 7210 | $ 990 | $ 523.00 |
| 7210– | 7220 | 991 | 523.80 |
| 7220– | 7230 | 993 | 524.70 |
| 7230– | 7240 | 995 | 525.60 |
| 7240– | 7250 | 997 | 526.40 |
| 7250– | 7260 | 999 | 527.30 |
| 7260– | 7270 | 1000 | 528.10 |
| 7270– | 7280 | 1002 | 529.10 |
| 7280– | 7290 | 1004 | 529.90 |
| 7290– | 7200 | 1006 | 530.70 |
| **$ 7300**– | 7310 | $1008 | $ 531.60 |
| 7310– | 7320 | 1009 | 532.50 |
| 7320– | 7330 | 1011 | 533.30 |
| 7330– | 7340 | 1013 | 534.20 |
| 7340– | 7350 | 1015 | 535.10 |
| 7350– | 7360 | 1017 | 535.90 |
| 7360– | 7370 | 1018 | 536.80 |
| 7370– | 7380 | 1020 | 537.60 |
| 7380– | 7390 | 1022 | 538.50 |
| 7390– | 7400 | 1024 | 539.40 |
| **$ 7400**– | 7410 | $1026 | $ 540.20 |
| 7410– | 7420 | 1027 | 541.10 |
| 7420– | 7430 | 1029 | 542.00 |
| 7430– | 7440 | 1031 | 542.80 |
| 7440– | 7450 | 1033 | 543.70 |
| 7450– | 7460 | 1035 | 544.60 |
| 7460– | 7470 | 1036 | 545.40 |
| 7470– | 7480 | 1038 | 546.30 |
| 7480– | 7490 | 1040 | 547.20 |
| 7490– | 7500 | 1042 | 548.00 |
| **$ 7500**– | 7510 | $1044 | $ 548.90 |
| 7510– | 7520 | 1045 | 549.70 |
| 7520– | 7530 | 1047 | 550.60 |
| 7530– | 7540 | 1049 | 551.50 |
| 7540– | 7550 | 1051 | 552.30 |
| 7550– | 7560 | 1053 | 553.20 |
| 7560– | 7570 | 1054 | 554.10 |
| 7570– | 7580 | 1056 | 554.90 |
| 7580– | 7590 | 1058 | 555.80 |
| 7590– | 7600 | 1060 | 556.70 |
| **$ 7600**– | 7610 | $1062 | $ 557.50 |
| 7610– | | 1063 | 558.40 |
| 7620– | 7630 | 1065 | 559.20 |
| 7630– | 7640 | 1067 | 560.10 |
| 7640– | 7650 | 1069 | 561.00 |
| 7650– | 7660 | 1071 | 561.80 |
| 7660– | 7670 | 1072 | 562.70 |
| 7670– | 7680 | 1074 | 563.60 |
| 7680– | 7690 | 1076 | 564.40 |
| 7690– | 7700 | 1078 | 565.30 |

| (1) Taxable Income: over | not over | (2) Federal Tax | (3) Provincial Tax Payable |
|---|---|---|---|
| **$ 8100**– | 8110 | $1155 | $ 602.20 |
| 8110– | 8120 | 1157 | 603.10 |
| 8120– | 8130 | 1158 | 604.10 |
| 8130– | 8140 | 1160 | 605.00 |
| 8140– | 8150 | 1162 | 605.90 |
| 8150– | 8160 | 1164 | 606.80 |
| 8160– | 8170 | 1166 | 607.70 |
| 8170– | 8180 | 1168 | 608.60 |
| 8180– | 8190 | 1170 | 609.50 |
| 8190– | 8200 | 1172 | 610.40 |
| **$ 8200**– | 8210 | $1174 | $ 611.40 |
| 8210– | 8220 | 1176 | 612.30 |
| 8220– | 8230 | 1177 | 613.20 |
| 8230– | 8240 | 1179 | 614.10 |
| 8240– | 8250 | 1181 | 615.00 |
| 8250– | 8260 | 1183 | 615.90 |
| 8260– | 8270 | 1185 | 616.80 |
| 8270– | 8280 | 1187 | 617.70 |
| 8280– | 8290 | 1189 | 618.60 |
| 8290– | 8300 | 1191 | 619.60 |
| **$ 8300**– | 8310 | $1193 | $ 620.50 |
| 8310– | 8320 | 1195 | 621.40 |
| 8320– | 8330 | 1196 | 622.30 |
| 8330– | 8340 | 1198 | 623.20 |
| 8340– | 8350 | 1200 | 624.10 |
| 8350– | 8360 | 1202 | 625.00 |
| 8360– | 8370 | 1204 | 625.90 |
| 8370– | 8380 | 1206 | 626.90 |
| 8380– | 8390 | 1208 | 627.80 |
| 8390– | 8400 | 1210 | 628.70 |

| (1) Taxable Income: over | not over | (2) Federal Tax | (3) Provincial Tax Payable |
|---|---|---|---|
| 10990– | 11000 | | |
| **$11000**– | 11010 | $1706 | $ 866.70 |
| 11010– | 11020 | 1708 | 867.60 |
| 11020– | 11030 | 1709 | 868.50 |
| 11030– | 11040 | 1711 | 869.40 |
| 11040– | 11050 | 1713 | 870.40 |
| 11050– | 11060 | 1715 | 871.30 |
| 11060– | 11070 | 1717 | 872.20 |
| 11070– | 11080 | 1719 | 873.10 |
| 11080– | 11090 | 1721 | 874.00 |
| 11090– | 11100 | 1723 | 874.90 |
| **$11100**– | 11110 | $1725 | $ 875.80 |
| 11110– | 11120 | 1727 | 876.70 |
| 11120– | 11130 | 1728 | 877.70 |
| 11130– | 11140 | 1730 | 878.60 |
| 11140– | 11150 | 1732 | 879.50 |
| 11150– | 11160 | 1734 | 880.40 |
| 11160– | 11170 | 1736 | 881.30 |
| 11170– | 11180 | 1738 | 882.20 |
| 11180– | 11190 | 1740 | 883.10 |
| 11190– | 11200 | 1742 | 884.00 |

| (1) Taxable Income: over | not over | (2) Federal Tax | (3) Provincial Tax Payable |
|---|---|---|---|
| **$12300**– | 12310 | $1953 | $ 985.30 |
| 12310– | 12320 | 1955 | 986.20 |
| 12320– | 12330 | 1956 | 987.10 |
| 12330– | 12340 | 1958 | 988.00 |
| 12340– | 12350 | 1960 | 988.90 |
| 12350– | 12360 | 1962 | 989.80 |
| 12360– | 12370 | 1964 | 990.70 |
| 12370– | 12380 | 1966 | 991.70 |
| 12380– | 12390 | 1968 | 992.60 |
| 12390– | 12400 | 1970 | 993.50 |
| **$12400**– | 12410 | $1972 | $ 994.40 |
| 12410– | 12420 | 1974 | 995.30 |
| 12420– | 12430 | 1975 | 996.20 |
| 12430– | 12440 | 1977 | 997.10 |
| 12440– | 12450 | 1979 | 998.00 |
| 12450– | 12460 | 1981 | 999.00 |
| 12460– | 12470 | 1983 | 999.90 |
| 12470– | 12480 | 1985 | 1000.80 |
| 12480– | 12490 | 1987 | 1001.70 |
| 12490– | 12500 | 1989 | 1002.60 |
| **$12500**– | 12510 | $1991 | $1003.50 |
| 12510– | 12520 | 1993 | 1004.40 |
| 12520– | 12520 | 1994 | 1005.30 |
| 12530– | 12540 | 1996 | 1006.20 |
| 12540– | 12550 | 1998 | 1007.20 |
| 12550– | 12560 | 2000 | 1008.10 |
| 12560– | 12570 | 2002 | 1009.00 |
| 12570– | 12580 | 2004 | 1009.90 |
| 12580– | 12590 | 2006 | 1010.80 |
| 12590– | 12600 | 2008 | 1011.70 |
| **$12600**– | 12610 | $2010 | $1012.60 |
| 12610– | 12620 | 2012 | 1013.50 |
| 12620– | 12630 | 2013 | 1014.50 |
| 12630– | 12640 | 2015 | 1015.40 |
| 12640– | 12650 | 2017 | 1016.30 |
| 12650– | 12660 | 2019 | 1017.20 |
| 12660– | 12670 | 2021 | 1018.10 |
| 12670– | 12680 | 2023 | 1019.00 |
| 12680– | 12690 | 2025 | 1019.90 |
| 12690– | 12700 | 2027 | 1020.80 |
| **$12700**– | 12710 | $2029 | $1021.80 |
| 12710– | 12720 | 2031 | 1022.70 |
| 12720– | 12730 | 2032 | 1023.60 |
| 12730– | 12740 | 2034 | 1024.50 |
| 12740– | 12750 | 2036 | 1025.40 |
| 12750– | 12760 | 2038 | 1026.30 |
| 12760– | 12770 | 2040 | 1027.20 |
| 12770– | 12780 | 2042 | 1028.10 |
| 12780– | 12790 | 2044 | 1029.00 |
| 12790– | 12800 | 2046 | 1030.00 |
| **$12800**– | 12810 | $2048 | $1030.90 |
| 12810– | 12820 | 2050 | 1031.80 |
| | 12830 | 2051 | 1032.70 |
| | | 2053 | 1033.60 |

| (1) Taxable Income: over | not over | (2) Federal Tax | (3) Provincial Tax Payable |
|---|---|---|---|
| **$13500**– | 13510 | $2187 | $1097.80 |
| 13510– | 13520 | 2189 | 1098.70 |
| 13520– | 13530 | 2191 | 1099.70 |
| 13530– | 13540 | 2193 | 1100.60 |
| 13540– | 13550 | 2195 | 1101.60 |
| 13550– | 13560 | 2197 | 1102.60 |
| 13560– | 13570 | 2199 | 1103.50 |
| 13570– | 13580 | 2201 | 1104.50 |
| 13580– | 13590 | 2203 | 1105.40 |
| 13590– | 13600 | 2205 | 1106.40 |
| **$13600**– | 13610 | $2207 | $1107.40 |
| 13610– | 13620 | 2209 | 1108.30 |
| 13620– | 13630 | 2211 | 1109.30 |
| 13630– | 13640 | 2213 | 1110.20 |
| 13640– | 13650 | 2215 | 1111.20 |
| 13650– | 13660 | 2217 | 1112.20 |
| 13660– | 13670 | 2219 | 1113.10 |
| 13670– | 13680 | 2221 | 1114.10 |
| 13680– | 13690 | 2223 | 1115.00 |
| 13690– | 13700 | 2225 | 1116.00 |
| **$13700**– | 13710 | $2227 | $1117.00 |
| 13710– | 13720 | 2229 | 1117.90 |
| 13720– | 13730 | 2231 | 1118.90 |
| 13730– | 13740 | 2233 | 1119.80 |
| 13740– | 13750 | 2235 | 1120.80 |
| 13750– | 13760 | 2237 | 1121.80 |
| 13760– | 13770 | 2239 | 1122.70 |
| 13770– | 13780 | 2241 | 1123.70 |
| 13780– | 13790 | 2243 | 1124.60 |
| 13790– | 13800 | 2245 | 1125.60 |

| (1) Taxable Income: over | not over | (2) Federal Tax | (3) Provincial Tax Payable |
|---|---|---|---|
| **$17900**– | 17910 | $3067 | $1520.20 |
| 17910– | 17920 | 3069 | 1521.10 |
| 17920– | 17930 | 3071 | 1522.10 |
| 17930– | 17940 | 3073 | 1523.00 |
| 17940– | 17950 | 3075 | 1524.00 |
| 17950– | 17960 | 3077 | 1525.00 |
| 17960– | 17970 | 3079 | 1525.90 |
| 17970– | 17980 | 3081 | 1526.90 |
| 17980– | 17990 | 3083 | 1527.80 |
| 17990– | 18000 | 3085 | 1528.80 |
| **$18000**– | 18010 | $3087 | $1529.80 |
| 18010– | 18020 | 3089 | 1530.70 |
| 18020– | 18030 | 3091 | 1531.70 |
| 18030– | 18040 | 3093 | 1532.60 |
| 18040– | 18050 | 3095 | 1533.60 |
| 18050– | 18060 | 3097 | 1534.60 |
| 18060– | 18070 | 3099 | 1535.50 |
| 18070– | 18080 | 3101 | 1536.50 |
| 18080– | 18090 | 3103 | 1537.40 |
| 18090– | 18100 | 3105 | 1538.40 |
| **$18100**– | 18110 | $3107 | $1539.40 |
| 18110– | 18120 | 3109 | 1540.30 |
| 18120– | 18130 | 3111 | 1541.30 |
| 18130– | 18140 | 3113 | 1542.30 |
| 18140– | 18150 | 3115 | 1543.40 |
| 18150– | 18160 | 3118 | 1544.50 |
| 18160– | 18170 | 3120 | 1545.60 |
| 18170– | 18180 | 3122 | 1546.70 |
| 18180– | 18190 | 3125 | 1547.80 |
| | | | 1548.90 |

| (1) Taxable Income: over | not over | (2) Federal Tax | (3) Provincial Tax Payable |
|---|---|---|---|
| 21540– | 21550 | | |
| 21550– | 21560 | 3900 | |
| 21560– | 21570 | 3902 | 1921.00 |
| 21570– | 21580 | 3904 | 1922.10 |
| 21580– | 21590 | 3907 | 1923.20 |
| 21590– | 21600 | 3909 | 1924.30 |
| **$21600**– | 21610 | $3911 | $1925.40 |
| 21610– | 21620 | 3914 | 1926.50 |
| 21620– | 21630 | 3916 | 1927.60 |
| 21630– | 21640 | 3918 | 1928.70 |
| 21640– | 21650 | 3920 | 1929.80 |
| 21650– | 21660 | 3923 | 1930.90 |
| 21660– | 21670 | 3925 | 1932.00 |
| 21670– | 21680 | 3927 | 1933.10 |
| 21680– | 21690 | 3930 | 1934.20 |
| 21690– | 21700 | 3932 | 1935.30 |

## Vocabulary of Income Tax

To complete an income tax return, you must clearly understand the meanings of the words that occur on a tax return. Understanding the vocabulary helps you ensure that you will claim the full deductions you are entitled to. Each year, use the current information provided in the General Tax Guide to complete your income tax. Each year read over the list of income tax changes provided in the Tax Guide before you begin the task of completing your income tax return.

To complete income tax returns for other people, you need to take special courses. There are over 10 000 people whose full time occupation is in the area of Income Tax. If you understand how to complete income tax returns, your friends and relatives may ask you to help them to do theirs!

To answer the following, refer to a current copy of the General Tax guide provided by Revenue Canada. Each of the following terms occur on an income tax return.

> In completing your income tax return, certain questions may arise. To obtain a clear interpretation, you can call the Revenue Canada District Taxation office in your area. Their addresses, as well as important telephone numbers are listed in the General Tax Guide.
> Remember: Don't guess at any meaning. Be sure you clearly understand the terms related to you on the income tax return before you do the calculations.

---

10 What is meant by each of the following terms?
- (a) employment income
- (b) commissions
- (c) employment expense deduction
- (d) pension income
- (e) old age security pension
- (f) Canada or Quebec pension plan benefits
- (g) taxable family allowance benefits
- (h) unemployment insurance benefits
- (i) taxable amount of dividends
- (j) interest income
- (k) investment income
- (l) rental income
- (m) taxable capital gains
- (n) income from self-employment

11 Refer to the General Tax Guide. What is meant by each of the following terms that occur in calculating deductions from total income?
- (a) Canada Pension Plan contribution
- (b) Quebec Pension Plan contribution
- (c) Unemployment Insurance premium
- (d) Registered Pension Plan contribution
- (e) Registered Retirement Savings Plan
- (f) Annual Union or Professional dues
- (g) Tuition fees
- (h) Child care expenses

12 To claim your personal exemptions you need to understand additional terms. What is meant by the following?
- (a) Income of spouse or dependents
- (b) Non-resident dependents
- (c) Age exemption
- (d) Interest and dividend deduction
- (e) Pension income deduction
- (f) Charitable donations
- (g) Capital gains exemption

13 Revenue Canada issues various pamphlets to assist you in doing your tax return. They are available from the District Taxation Office. Obtain and read the following.
- (a) pamphlet No. 17 Farmer's Income Tax Guide
- (b) pamphlet No. 6 Moving Expenses
- (c) Form No. T1-19, Claim for moving expenses
- (d) Form No. TL2, Claim for Board and Lodging expenses
- (e) Refer to the list on the General Income Tax Guide. Are there any others that may be of interest or use to you?

# 8.5 Calculations with Income Tax

The principles of completing an income tax return are not complex. The chart below shows the steps you need to complete by April 30 of each year.

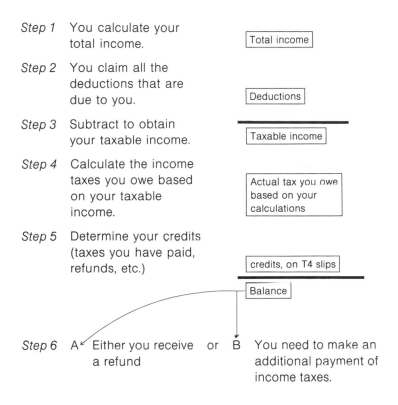

| | | |
|---|---|---|
| *Step 1* | You calculate your total income. | Total income |
| *Step 2* | You claim all the deductions that are due to you. | Deductions |
| *Step 3* | Subtract to obtain your taxable income. | Taxable income |
| *Step 4* | Calculate the income taxes you owe based on your taxable income. | Actual tax you owe based on your calculations |
| *Step 5* | Determine your credits (taxes you have paid, refunds, etc.) | credits, on T4 slips |
| | | Balance |

*Step 6* A Either you receive a refund or B You need to make an additional payment of income taxes.

In completing an income tax return, you need to follow similar procedures as you do when you solve a problem, draw a diagram, write a test and so on. These are:

A You must follow the instructions precisely—you must understand what the instructions ask you to do.

B You must understand the meanings of the various terms that occur on your income tax return so that you will receive full credit for any deductions that you are entitled to. If ever you need further information, you can obtain it by writing or calling the District Taxation Offices across Canada. If in doubt, ask questions.

An income tax return is designed to cover all situations that a taxpayer may need to complete. For this reason, when you complete a tax return, there may be many blanks left because the part is not applicable to you.

Throughout this section and the next one, it would be very useful for you to compare the examples that follow with the actual pages of an income tax return. You can obtain a tax return at a district taxation office or, at tax time, at post offices.

## Example 1

Jeremy works at a bakery and his T4 slip shows he received income of $13 680.50. As a part-time gasoline attendant he received $3940.36, shown on another T4 slip. He also received a T5 slip which reported that he earned $365.20 in interest on his bank balance. Complete a tax return to show his total income.

**Solution** Page 1 of the Income Tax Return

# Calculation of Total Income

| Section | Item | | Line | | Amount |
|---|---|---|---|---|---|
| Income from Employment | Employment Income Before Deductions from Box (C) on all T4 slips (attach copy 2 of T4 slips) | | 101 | | 17 620.86 |
| | Commissions from Box (P) on all T4 slips, included in above total | 102 | | | |
| | Other employment income including training allowances, tips and gratuities, etc. (please specify) | | 104 | | |
| | Total employment earnings (add lines 101 and 104) | | 105 | | 17 620.86 |
| | Subtract: Employment expense deduction–If line 105 above is $2 500.00 or more, claim $500.00. If less, claim 20% of line 105. | 108 | | 500.00 | |
| | Other allowable expenses (please specify) | 109 | | | |
| | Total employment expenses (add lines 108 and 109) | 110 | | 500.00 | 500.00 |
| | Net employment earnings (subtract line 110 from line 105) | | 111 | | 17 120.86 |
| Pension Income | Old Age Security Pension (attach copy of T4A(OAS) slip) | | 113 | | |
| | Canada or Quebec Pension Plan benefits (attach copy 2 of T4A(P) slip) | | 114 | | |
| | Other pensions or superannuation (attach copy 3 of T4A slips) | | 115 | | |
| Income from Other Sources | Taxable Family Allowance payments (attach copy of TFA1 slip) | | 118 | | |
| | Unemployment Insurance benefits (attach copy 2 of T4U slip) | | 119 | | |
| | Taxable amount of dividends from taxable Canadian corporations (attach completed Schedule 4) | | 120 | | |
| | Interest and other investment income (attach completed Schedule 4) | | 121 | | 365.20 |
| | Rental income (Schedule 7) | Gross 160 | Net 126 | | |
| | Taxable capital gains (Allowable capital losses)–complete and attach Schedule 3 | | 127 | | |
| | Other income (please specify) | | 130 | | |
| Self-Employed Income | Business income | Gross 162 | Net 135 | | |
| | Professional income | Gross 164 | Net 137 | | |
| | Commission income | Gross 166 | Net 139 | | |
| | Farming income | Gross 168 | Net 141 | | |
| | Fishing income | Gross 170 | Net 143 | | |
| **Total Income** | (add lines 111 to 143 inclusive–please enter this amount on line 200 on page 2) | | 150 | | 17 486.06 ⇨ 17 486.06 |

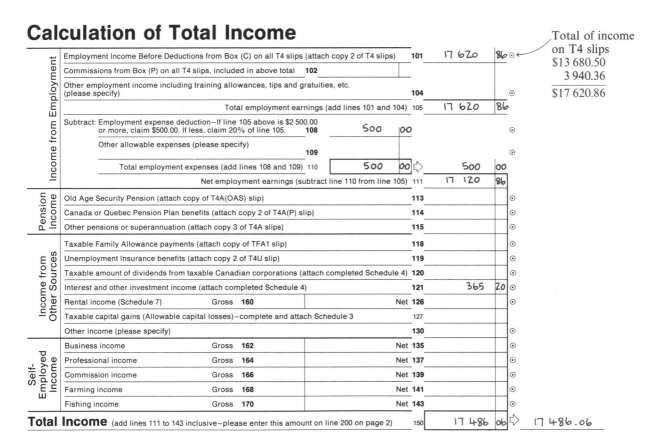

Total of income on T4 slips
$13 680.50
3 940.36
$17 620.86

Once you calculate your total income, you need to determine your deductions. In the tax return, deductions occur in these categories.

- Deductions from Total Income: includes pension plan contributions, union dues, child care expenses, etc. Each category is explained fully for the taxpayer in the Federal Tax Guide that accompanies each tax return.
- Claim for Personal Exemptions: includes your basic personal exemption, exemptions for dependents (children, and other dependents) and so on.
- Other Deductions: includes interest deductions, pension income deductions, education deductions, charitable donations, and so on.

## Example 2

During the year, Jeremy (from Example 1) paid $254.18 CPP and $197.69 U.I. He does not belong to a pension plan so he purchased a registered retirement savings plan (RRSP) for $1600.00. During the year he supported a wife who earned $1620. His children were born in 1975 and 1981. His union dues were $120 and he had $268.00 in charitable donations. Complete page 2 of his tax return.

## Solution

# Calculation of Taxable Income

Total Income (from line 150 on page 1) 200 17 486 | 06

**Deductions from Total Income**

| Item | Line | Amount | | |
|---|---|---|---|---|
| Canada or Quebec Pension Plan contributions | | | | |
| Contributions through employment from Box (D) on all T4 slips (maximum $379.80) | 202 | 254 18 | | |
| Contribution payable on self-employed earnings (from page 3) | 203 | | | |
| Unemployment Insurance premiums from Box (E) on all T4 slips (maximum $562.12) | 204 | 197 69 | | |
| Registered pension plan contributions (if over $3 500.00, See Guide "Line 207") | 207 | | | |
| Registered retirement savings plan premiums (attach receipts) | 208 | 1 600 00 | | |
| | | | | |
| Annual union, professional or like dues (attach receipts) | 212 | 120 00 | | |
| Tuition fees-claimable by student only (attach receipts) | 213 | | | |
| Child care expenses (complete and attach Schedule 5) | 214 | | | |
| Allowable business investment losses | 217 | | | |
| Indexed Security Investment Plan-allowable capital losses (attach copy of form T5 ISIP) | 218 | | | |
| Other deductions (please specify) | 222 | | | |
| Add lines 202 to 222 inclusive | 223 | 2 171 87 | ⇨ | 2 171 87 |
| **Net Income** (subtract line 223 from line 200) | 224 | | | 15 314 19 |
| Add: Accumulated Forward Averaging Amount Withdrawal (from form T581) | 225 | | | |
| | 228 | | | 15 314 19 |

**Claim for Personal Exemptions**

| Item | Claim | Line | Amount |
|---|---|---|---|
| **Basic Personal Exemption** | **Claim $4 140.00** | | 4 140 00 |
| **Age Exemption**–If you were born in 1920 or earlier (If you did not receive the Old Age Security Pension, attach a letter giving reasons.) | **Claim $2 590.00** | | |
| **Married Exemption**–If applicable, please check ✓ box 1. or 2. **Married on or before December 31, and supported spouse** 1. whose net income in that year, while married, was not over $510.00 1.☐ | **Claim $3 630.00** | | |
| 2. whose net income in that year, while married, was over $510.00 but not over $4 140.00 | | 230 | 2 520 00 |
| (If your marital status changed 2.☑ | 4140 00 | | |
| please give date of change) Subtract: spouse's net income while married | 1 620 00 | | |
| Claim | 2 520 00 | | |

**Exemption for Dependent Children**–Provide details below and claim according to child's age and net income. **See Guide "Line 231" if child's net income exceeds limit.**
**Children born in 1968 or later**–Claim **$710.00** for each child whose net income was not over $2 720.00
**Children born in 1967 or earlier**–Claim **$1 420.00** for each child whose net income was not over $2 720.00 and who, if born in 1963 or earlier, was in full-time attendance at a school or university or was infirm.

| *Name of child (attach list if space insufficient)* | *Relationship to you* | *Date of birth of child Day* | *Month* | *Year* | *If born in 1963 or earlier state whether infirm or school attended* | *Net income in year $* | *Claim* |
|---|---|---|---|---|---|---|---|
| Josie | Daughter | 3 | 12 | 75 | | – | 710 00 |
| Chris | Son | 10 | 5 | 81 | | – | 710 00 |
| | | | | | | | |

| Item | Line | Amount | | |
|---|---|---|---|---|
| Total claim for dependent children | 231 | 1 420 00 ⇨ | 1 420 00 | |
| **Additional Personal Exemptions** from Schedule 6 attached | 233 | | | |
| **Total Personal Exemptions** (add above items) | 235 | 8 080 00 | ⇨ | 8 080 00 |
| Subtract line 235 from line 228 | 236 | | | 7 234 19 |

*Continues on next page*

The first $1000 of interest can be used as a deduction.

Other deductions from Net Income

| | | | |
|---|---|---|---|
| **Interest and dividend income deduction** (attach completed Schedule 4) | 238 | 365 20 | |
| **Pension income deduction** | 240 | - | |
| **Medical expenses**–(attach receipts and complete Schedule 9) 241 | | | |
| Subtract: 3% of "Net Income" (line 224 above) | | | |
| Allowable portion of medial expenses | 242 | | |
| **Charitable donations** (attach receipts) | 243 | 268 00 | |
| **Gifts to Canada or a province** (attach receipts) | 245 | | |
| **Deduction** for blind persons or persons confined to a bed or wheelchair Claim relates to: Self ☐ or dependent other than spouse (specify) | 246 | | |
| **Education deduction** (attach completed form T2202 or T2202A) | 247 | | |
| **Employee stock option deduction** (from T4 slip) | 249 | | |
| **Unemployment Insurance benefit repayment payable** from page 3 | 250 | | |
| **Deductions transferred from spouse** (attach completed Schedule 2) | 251 | | |
| **Non-capital losses of other years** | 252 | | |
| **Capital losses of other years** | 253 | | |
| **Captial gains exemption** | 254 | | |
| Add lines 238, 240 and lines 242 to 254 inclusive | 255 | 633 20 | 633 20 |
| Subtract line 255 from line 236 | 256 | | 6600 99 |
| **Subtract: Forward Averaging Elective Income Deduction from form T540** | 257 | | |
| **Taxable Income** (enter this amount on page 4) | 260 | | 6600 99 |

Once Jeremy has calculated his taxable income, he can determine exactly whether he will receive a refund or need to make a further payment of income taxes. To do so, he has completed the summary of tax and credits (page 4 of the income tax return). See the following page.

## Tip for Taxpayers

In order that you receive the proper credit for your return, you need to complete the Identification section on page 1 of your Income Tax return shown below.

### Identification

Note: 1. For your records, please enter the formation preprinted on your mailing copy or the corrections made to that information.
2. Detailed information can be found in the Guide under corresponding line number.

Social Insurance Number ☐☐☐ ☐☐☐ ☐☐☐

Spouse's Social Insurance Number ☐☐☐ ☐☐☐ ☐☐☐

Name ____________

Address ____________

**Complete the following**

On December 31, Year, you were: Married 1 ☐ Widow(er) 2 ☐ Divorced 3 ☐ Separated 4 ☐ Single 5 ☐

Name of Spouse ____________

Address of Spouse: same as mine ☐ or ____________

# 4 Summary of Tax and Credits

There are two methods of tax calculation (see Guide).

| | | | |
|---|---|---|---|
| **Taxable Income** from line 260 on page 2 | 400 | 6600 99 | |
| **Calculation of Federal Tax Payable:** | | | |
| **Federal Tax from Tax Table** | 402 | 882 00 | |
| Subtract: Unused portion of Spouse's Federal Tax Reduction | **403** | 100 00 • | |
| | 405 | 782 00 | |
| Federal Tax Payable - from line 405 above or from line 406 on Schedule 1 | 406 | | 782 00 |
| Subtract: **Federal Political Contribution Tax Credit** Total Contributions **409** | | ⊙ | |
| from calculation on page 3 Allowable Tax Credit | 410 | | |
| **Share-Purchase Tax Credit** from form T2111 | **411** | • | |
| **Investment Tax Credit** from form T2038(IND.) | **412** | • | |
| **Employment Tax Credit Claimed** from form T2208 | 413 | | |
| Total of above credits | 416 | - - | - - |
| Federal Tax Payable Before Federal Forward Averaging Tax and Federal Surtax Payable | 417 | | |
| Add: **Federal Forward Averaging Tax on Elective Income** from form T540 | 418 | | |
| **Federal Surtax Payable** from line 419 on Schedule 1 (See Guide "Line 419") | 419 | | |
| **Net Federal Tax Payable** | 420 | | 782 00 |
| Add: **Ontario Tax Payable** from Tax Table in Guide or from line 423 on Schedule 1 | 423 | 471 10 | |
| Add: Ontario Forward Averaging Tax on Elective Income from form T540 | 426 | | |
| **Net Ontario Tax Payable** | 427 | 471 10 | 471 10 |
| Canada Pension Plan Contribution Payable on Self-Employed Earnings from page 3 | 432 | | |
| Unemployment Insurance Benefit Repayment Payable from page 3 | 433 | | |
| **Total Payable** | 435 | | 1253 10 • |

From the T4 slips →

379.28
1216.80

1596.08

Each province provides tax credits. The tax-payer completes a form.

| | | | |
|---|---|---|---|
| **Total tax deducted per information slips** | **440** | 1596 08 • ⊙ | |
| **Provincial Tax Credits** | **448** | 227 98 • | |
| **Child Tax Credit** (attach completed Schedule 10) | **450** | • | |
| Canada Pension Plan Overpayment | **453** | • | |
| Unemployment Insurance Overpayment | **454** | • | |
| Amounts paid by instalments | **455** | • | |
| Forward Averaging Tax Credit (from form T581) | **458** | • | |
| Refund of Investment Tax Credit (from form T2038-IND.) | **459** | • | |
| **Total Credits** | 463 | 1824 06 | 1824 06 |

Subtract line 463 from line 435 and enter the difference in applicable space below. -570 96

*A difference of less than $1.00 is neither charged nor refunded.*

**Refund 464** 570 96 •

**IMPORTANT:** The inside front cover of your guide tells you when to expect your refund.

**Balance Due 465** •
(See Guide "Line 465")

Refund transferred to spouse
**468** •
(See Guide "Line 468")

**Amount Enclosed** •
Please attach cheque or money order **payable to the Receiver General. Do not mail cash.**
Payment is due not later than April 30.

The computer at Revenue Canada will automatically calculate and refund any overpayment.

**467**

Name and address of any individual or firm, other than the taxpayer, who has prepared this return for compensation.

Name

Address

Telephone

I hereby certify that the information given in this return and in any documents attached is true, correct and complete in every respect and fully discloses my income from all sources.

Please sign here

Telephone Date

It is a serious offence to make a false return.

Form authorized and prescribed by order of the Minister of National Revenue for purposes of Part I and Part I.1 of the Income Tax Act, Part I of the Canada Pension Plan and Part VIII of the Unemployment Insurance Act, 1971.

Privacy Act Personal Information Bank number RC-T-P20

## Try These

Refer to the pages of the income tax return.

1 What is the maximum Canada or Quebec pension plan contribution?

2 What is the maximum unemployment insurance premium you need to pay?

3 How much is each of the following?
(a) basic personal exemption
(b) married exemption
(c) exemption for a 3 year-old daughter
(d) exemption for an 18 year-old son

4 Your total employment earnings are more than $2500. How much is your employment expense deduction?

## Written Exercises

**A** To file an income tax return properly, you need to follow instructions carefully, and record information correctly.

1 Refer to page 1 of the income tax return (See example 1). What is meant by each of the following terms?
(a) employment income before deductions, line 101
(b) employment expense deduction, line 108
(c) taxable family allowance payment, line 118
(d) interest and other investment income, line 121
(e) rental income, line 126
(f) total income, line 150

2 Refer to page 2 of the tax return (see example 2 solution). What is meant by each of the following terms?
(a) deductions
(b) net income
(c) basic personal exemption
(d) taxable income
(e) Canada Pension Plan
(f) Unemployment Insurance
(g) union dues
(h) interest and dividend income deduction
(i) medical expenses
(j) charitable donations

3 (a) How much is the Basic Personal Exemption?
(b) You are married, and your spouse does not have any income. How much are you allowed for a Married Exemption?
(c) Your son is 4 years old. How much are you allowed to claim on your income tax as personal exemption on behalf of this dependent child?
(d) Your daughter is 17 years of age and is attending school. How much can you claim as a personal exemption?

4 Calculate the employment expense deduction (line 108) for each of the following amounts of Total employment earnings (line 105).
(a) $1863.50 (b) $1209.36
(c) $6543.20 (d) $12 653.62

5 The total deductions for CPP (Canada Pension Plan) on your T4 slips is $438.50.
(a) What is the maximum amount you need to pay?
(b) How much of a refund is due?

6 You are married and your spouse earned $1850.75. How much are you allowed as a Married Exemption on your tax return?

7 Your net income is $12 650.80. You have $675.90 in medical expenses. What is the allowable portion of medical expenses that you can claim on your income tax? (Refer to line 241 on page 2 of the income tax return)

8 You are allowed to claim an interest deduction to a maximum of $1000.00. During the year your savings accounts earned interest in the amounts of $680.75, $463.96 and $325.65. How much of the interest will you pay income tax on?

9 On your T4 slips, unemployment insurance deductions were made in the amounts of $369.70 and $321.65.
(a) What is the maximum unemployment insurance premium you need to pay?
(b) How much of a refund will you receive?

**B** **Round your amounts to the nearest cent, where needed.**

10 Calculate the net income for each person.
(a) Yvonne

| | |
|---|---|
| Total income (line 150) | $8696.50 |
| CPP deduction | $123.85 |
| UI premium | $96.32 |

(b) Gregory

| | |
|---|---|
| Total income (line 150) | $7965.32 |
| CPP deduction | $119.83 |
| UI premium | $144.19 |
| Union dues | $110.00 |

11 Calculate the taxable income for each person.
(a) Roger
net income $23 650.25, married, wife has no income, daughter 10 years old, total of $365.83 medical expenses
(b) Margo
net income $16 974.32, not married, claimed $365.20 interest, total of $685.32 medical expenses
(c) Tabitha
net income $14 695.20, married, spouse made $985.00, no children, $270 charitable donations, $820.00 medical expenses

12 Irene received $9680.50 in employment income before deductions Box (C), as well as $668.30 in commissions Box (P). She also earned $430.23 in interest on her savings.
(a) Calculate her employment expense deduction.
(b) Calculate her total income (line 150).

13 Lloyd earned $12 685.33 according to Box (C) of his T4 slip. He also received $375.24 in taxable family allowance payments. His bank account earned $469.25 in interest. The net rental income he receives is $985.20.
(a) Calculate his employment expense deduction.
(b) Calculate his total income (line 150).

14 On line 200 of Toni's income tax return, the total income is shown as $9648.50. Toni is single, and paid $173.67 in Canada Pension Plan as well as $135.08 in unemployment insurance premiums. She purchased a RRSP (Registered Retirement Savings Plan) for $460.80. Her union dues were $36.80. She had $465.35 in medical expenses.
(a) Calculate Toni's net income.
(b) What is the allowable portion of medical expenses she can claim on her income tax?
(c) Calculate her taxable income.

15 The total income shown on Scott's return is $18 925.80 of which $960.80 was interest. His wife earned $968.25 at her part-time job. They have two children aged 4 and 6 years. He paid $1875 into the company pension fund, as well as $338.40 CPP and $259.86 UI. Calculate
(a) the total of his personal exemptions.
(b) the taxable income on his income tax return.

16 Nora's taxable income is $11 108.96. The amounts of income tax deducted on her T4 slips are $1485.78 and $1396.20. She also receives a provincial credit of $221.65; and overpaid CPP in the amount of $162.37. Refer to page 4 of a tax return and calculate whether Nora will receive a refund or will owe tax. Determine how much.

# 8.6 Filing Income Tax

The first time you need to complete an income tax return it appears as a difficult and time consuming job. Any task you embark on the first time will require additional time to familiarize yourself with the new never-before-done steps. Each year you should refer to the General Tax Guide provided by Revenue Canada and use it to follow each step in completing your income tax return. Revenue Canada is constantly making the task on April 30 less difficult by improving instructions to you as well as providing useful details in the General Tax Guide.

For example, a part of the contents page is shown. Before you complete your tax return, read the parts that apply to you so that you will take all of your entitled deductions. Certain parts of the General Tax Guide are shown.

## CONTENTS



In the exercises, you are going to file an income tax return. Each of the following persons dealt with are fictitious. Certain information about each of them is provided with respect to income, exemptions, and deductions. Use the income tax pages 1 to 4 in the previous section to determine whether each person is to receive a refund or to pay more tax to Revenue Canada. You will also need to refer to the portion of the tax tables in section 8.4 to calculate the federal and provincial income taxes that are due.

## Written Exercises

**B**
- Round your answers to the nearest cent
- Use pages 1 to 4 of the income tax return, see section 8.5
- Use the tax tables in section 8.4 to calculate income taxes payable.

1 Calculate the income taxes payable by Susan Dora, single, on earnings of $17 075.25.
- $1265 interest on Canada Savings Bonds
- Rental income $1650
- CPP deductions $338.40
- UI premium $237.64
- Registered pension plan $780.86
- Charitable donations $365.00

2 Calculate the income tax payable by John Pearson on earnings of $23 964.25.
- Married, wife earned $1263.50
- Two children ages 6 and 10 years
- $636.50 interest on bank account
- Taxable family allowance payments $890.40
- UI premium $498.04
- CPP deduction maximum paid
- $1200 Registered Retirement Savings Plan
- $496.00 medical expenses
- $250 charitable donations

3 Calculate the income taxes payable by Claude Sappora who earned $19 630.75 in Box (C) on the T4 slip,
- Married, wife earned $2320.50
- $625 bank interest, $1200 bond interest
- Taxable family allowance payments $445.20
- CPP deduction maximum paid
- UI premium maximum paid
- Received $680 in commission payments
- daughter, 14 years of age, earned $1206.00
- purchased Registered Retirement Savings plan for $1850.00
- $685.20 medical expenses
- $320.00 charitable donations

4 Julian Promisso earned $31153.40 reported in Box (C) of his T4 slip. As well, the T4 slip indicated
- income tax deducted $6583.60
- CPP $338.40 and UI $401.15
- union dues $158.50

He is married, and has 2 children ages 12 and 19. His wife earned $1850.00 and his 19 year-old earned $2300.00. The total medical expenses were $825.50, and charitable donations accumulated to $325.00. Julian received commission (Box P) in the amount of $2320. He paid $1200.00 into the company pension plan and purchased a registered retirement savings plan for $1500.00. When Julian Promisso files his tax return will he receive a refund or will he owe tax? How much will it be?

5 Jennifer Robins' total earnings as reported on her T4 slips Box (C) was $17 500. She reported other income as tips in the amount of $2800.00. She is single but supports a family member and claimed the Additional Personal Exemption (line 233) in the amount of $3470.00. She received $353.50 in interest on her bank accounts and $500.00 in interest on a Term Deposit. Her T4 slips indicate she paid CPP amounts of $186.20, $96.35 and $128.80. She also paid Unemployment Insurance deductions in the amounts of $144.79, $74.73 and $100.42. Her medical expenses in all were $562.93 and her charitable donations $310.00. She also paid $2942.76 in income tax and claimed $186.20 as a provincial tax credit. When Jennifer Robins files her income tax return, will she receive a refund or will she owe tax? How much will it be?

Remember, that each year changes are made in the rules and regulations for completing an income tax return. However, the method to complete the income tax return essentially remains the same. Refer to the General Tax Guide each year to obtain the latest information.

# 8.7 Earning Money in Business

If you go into business yourself, you do so to make a profit. To run a business you need to know the meaning of the vocabulary and the terms involved. The amount of profit you make from your business depends on many factors, one of which is the pricing of goods. For example, suppose you sell jeans. The selling price of the jeans must include

A the cost of buying the jeans
B the operating expenses (or overhead) of the business
C the profit you require

A, B, and C are connected by a formula that is very important to a person in business.

Selling Price = Cost of buying (A; or Cost price) + Expenses (B) + Profit (C)

There is no point to running a business if the selling price is only equal to the cost of buying (A) and your operating expenses (B). You might as well do something else for a living.

**Example 1**
Jean City buys jeans for \$16.32 each. Operating expenses of the business are 30% of cost of the jeans. The company requires a profit of 42% of the cost. Find the selling price of the jeans.

**Solution**

*Step 1* Record the information.

Cost price = \$16.32
Operating Expenses = 30% of \$16.32
= \$4.90
Profit = 42% of \$16.32
= \$6.85

*Step 2* Use the formula.

Selling Price = Cost Price + Expenses + Profit
= \$16.32 + \$4.90 + \$6.85
= \$28.07

The jeans are sold at \$28.07.

In the previous example you used

Selling Price = \$28.07 Cost Price = \$16.32

The difference between the selling price and the cost price is \$28.07 − \$16.32 or \$11.75 and is called the **markup** or **margin**. It is also referred to as the **gross profit**.

Markup = Operating Expenses + Profit

Also, Selling Price = Cost Price + Markup

or Markup = Selling Price − Cost Price

The actual markup in the previous formula can be used in different ways to obtain two other terms:

A as a percentage of the Cost Price

$$\textbf{Rate of markup} = \frac{\text{markup}}{\text{cost price}} \times 100\%$$

B as a percentage of the Selling Price

$$\textbf{Rate of margin} = \frac{\text{markup}}{\text{selling price}} \times 100\%$$

### Example 2

A watch costs \$53.10 wholesale and sells in a jewellery store for \$99.99. Find

(a) the markup

(b) the rate of markup

Express your answer to 1 decimal place.

### Solution

(a) Markup = Selling Price − Cost Price
= \$99.99 − \$53.10
= \$46.89

The markup is \$46.89.

(b) $$\text{Rate of markup} = \frac{\text{Markup}}{\text{Cost Price}} \times 100\%$$
$$= \frac{46.89}{53.10} \times 100\%$$
$$= 0.8830 \times 100\%$$
$$= 88.3\% \text{ (to 1 decimal place)}$$

The rate of markup is 88.3%.

## Try These

1 The formula for the selling price of an item is given by S.P. = C + E + P
What does each of the following letters represent?
(a) C (b) E (c) P

2 The formula for markup is given by
M = E + P
What does each of the following letters represent?
(a) E (b) P (c) M

## Written Exercises

**A** Review the various formula involving selling price, operating expenses, profit, cost price and markup.

1 Calculate the selling price of each item.

| | Cost price | Expenses | Profit |
|---|---|---|---|
| (a) | \$68.00 | 20% | 10% |
| (b) | \$91.50 | 30% | 15% |
| (c) | \$143.75 | 25% | 16% |
| (d) | \$346.50 | 30% | 23% |

← as percentage of cost price

2 For the items in the chart, the markup is 30% of the cost price. Calculate the selling price of each item.

| | Item | Cost price |
|---|---|---|
| (a) | T-shirt | \$4.50 |
| (b) | running shoes | \$17.00 |
| (c) | shirt | \$21.95 |
| (d) | book | \$14.40 |
| (e) | coffee mug | \$1.38 |
| (f) | record album | \$6.59 |
| (g) | bag of chips | \$0.23 |

3 Find the selling price for each item.
  (a) cost price of a calculator is $29.50, with markup of 42%
  (b) cost price of colour T.V. is $480.95 and the markup is 35%
  (c) cost price of a car is $5599.95, with a markup of 33%

4 What is the selling price of an article costing $86.50 if the markup is
  (a) 35% of the cost price?
  (b) 48% of the selling price?

5 What is the cost of an article selling for $48.75 if the markup is
  (a) 25% of the selling price?
  (b) 36% of the cost price?

**B** **You can only solve problems in business if you know the exact meanings of the words. Review the meaning of all words dealt with in this section.**

6 An item's cost price is $37.00. The selling price is $58.95. If the overhead is 20% of the cost price, calculate the rate of markup.

7 A merchant purchases a toaster for the cost price of $39.00, and sells it for $75.00. The overhead is calculated as 25% of the selling price. Calculate the rate of margin.

8 Portable T.V. sets are selling for $398 and have been marked up $84.50 above cost. What is
  (a) the cost price?
  (b) the rate of markup?
  (c) the rate of margin?

9 Technology Inc. buys two types of calculators for sale. Model A costs $17.60 and sells for $29.95. Model B costs $24.15 and sells for $39.95. The overhead expenses are 29% of cost. For each model determine
  (a) the markup
  (b) the operating expenses
  (c) the profit.

10 The rate of markup on a motorcycle selling for $2995.95 is 32%.
  (a) Find the cost price of the motorcycle.
  (b) Find the rate of margin.

11 Canadian Tire sells bicycles for $129.95. The rate of margin is 48%.
  (a) What is the cost price of these bicycles?
  (b) What is the rate of markup?

12 Sandra owns a flower shop. She buys a flower arrangement from a distributor at $21.50 less 28%. Her overhead is 36% of cost and profit is 25% of cost. How much should she sell the arrangement for?

## Calculator Tip

To use your calculator effectively, you need to organize the steps of your work carefully. In business, there are many procedures that are invented to make the business steps flow properly. Use the flow chart below to help you organize your work to do calculations in solving a problem.

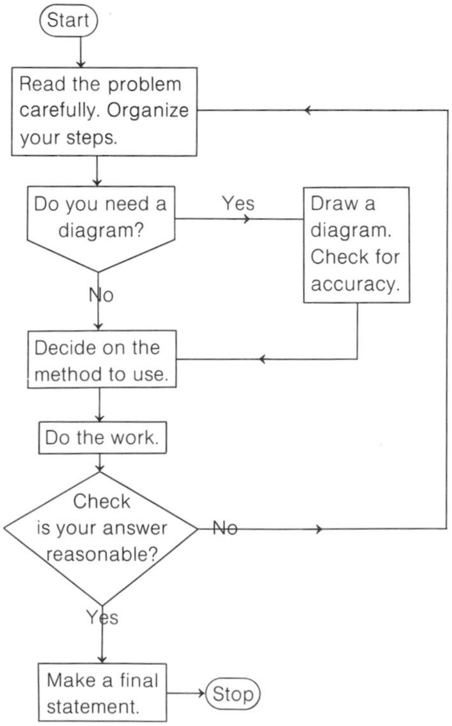

# 8.8 Using Sales Discounts

Often the retailer's selling price is referred to as the **list price** or the **catalogue price**. This is the regular price of the goods that are stocked in the store. The list price is often the price suggested by the wholesaler or manufacturer at which the retailer might sell the goods. This price is called the suggested list price and often occurs in newspaper advertisements. However, to remain competitive, retailers will reduce prices to attract the consumer to their particular stores. As a retailer, you may also eventually need to make further reductions on merchandise that isn't selling or when a new season in clothes is approaching and you wish to make room for the new stock. In order to attract more customers, you may use sales discounts or price markdowns. The reduction in price is called the **sales discount** or **markdown**.
The resulting price is called the sale or net price, and is given by

Sale or net price = Regular Selling Price − Markdown

Often you will see the markdown advertised as a percent reduction or as a fraction.
50% or $\frac{1}{2}$ off
The percent of reduction from the regular selling price is called the **rate of sales discount** or **rate of discount**.

### Example 1

Refer to the ad. Calculate the discount, and the sale or net price of the television.

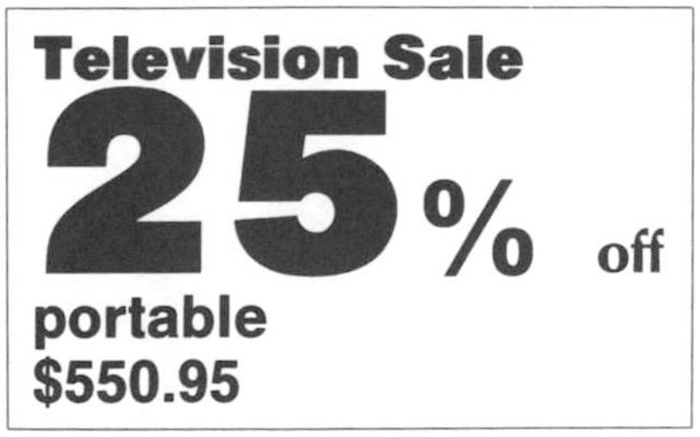


### Solution

Sale price = Regular Selling Price − Markdown (Remember: means sales discount)

Markdown = 25% of 550.95
= 0.25 × 550.95
= 137.74

Regular selling price = \$550.95
Sales Discount = \$137.74
Sale price = \$413.21

Thus the discount is \$137.74.
The net price is \$413.21.

Often during a sale, merchandise is marked down. As a further incentive the store may offer 10% off on all your purchases. When more than one discount is given, the first discount occurs on the regular selling price, and the other discounts on the sale price as shown in the next example.

**Example 2**

(a) Find the net price of an article which is priced at \$150, less 20% discount. A further 10% discount is offered on Mondays.
(b) Find the total discount.

**Solution**

(a) *Step 1* Find the first discount.

$$20\% \text{ of } \$150 = 0.20 \times \$150 = \$30$$

$$\text{Sale or net price} = \$150 - \$30 = \$120$$

*Step 2* Find the second discount.

$$10\% \text{ of } \$120 = 0.10 \times \$120 = \$12$$

$$\text{Net price} = \$120 - \$12 = \$108$$

Thus the net or sale price is \$108.00.

(b) The total discount is given by \$30 + \$12 or \$42.00.

If you know the regular selling price and you know the sale price, you can calculate the rate of sales discount or markdown.

**Example 3**

Francine works in a hardware store. She sold a lawn mower regularly priced at \$295.95 for \$229.00.
(a) What is the amount of markdown?
(b) What is the rate of markdown? Express your answer to 1 decimal place.

**Solution**

(a)
$$\text{Amount of markdown} = \text{List price} - \text{Sale price} = \$295.95 - \$229.00 = \$66.95$$

The amount of markdown is \$66.95

(b)
$$\text{Rate of markdown} = \frac{\text{amount of markdown}}{\text{selling price}} \times 100\% = \frac{\$66.95}{\$295.95} \times 100\% = 22.62\%$$

The rate of markdown is 22.6%, to 1 decimal place.

When a retailer purchases goods from the wholesaler, or manufacturer, a discount is offered so that the retailer can then sell the goods at a profit. Such a discount is called a trade discount. The same method is used to calculate a trade discount.

Trade discount = Suggested list price − price paid by retailer

## Try These

What is meant by each of these terms?

| | | |
|---|---|---|
| (a) sale price | (b) catalogue price | (c) selling price |
| (d) list price | (e) markdown | (f) trade discount |
| (g) rate of markdown | (h) sales discount | (i) net price |

## Written Exercises

**A** Express your answers to the nearest cent.

1 Calculate the amount of discount for each.
(a) $36 less 20%  (b) $6.50 less 15%
(c) $780 less 25%  (d) $1269.95 less 30%

2 Calculate the net price for each.
(a) $589 less 20%  (b) $2.98 less 15%
(c) $845.50 less 30%  (d) $445 less 17%

3 Calculate the amount of trade discount for each of the following.
(a) $500, 50% off  (b) $850, 25% off
(c) $659.50, 33.5% off  (d) $496.35, 65% off

4 A trade discount is shown for each price. At what price will the retailer buy the goods?
(a) $800, 45% off  (b) $650, 29% off
(c) $695, 39.5% off  (d) $863.40, 45.8% off

5 Refer to the ad.
(a) Calculate the amount of discount.
(b) Calculate the sale price.

| Applicance Sale<br>30% off<br><br>Dishwasher $650 |
|---|

6 For each of the following goods, calculate:
- the amount of the discount
- the sale price.

| Item | Selling price | Discount |
|---|---|---|
| (a) shirt | $49.50 | 30% |
| (b) dress | $119.80 | 25% |
| (c) refrigerator | $896.75 | 15% |
| (d) automobile | $9680.50 | 9.5% |

**B** Express percentages to 1 decimal place.
Express amounts of money to the nearest cent.

7 A track suit regularly sells for $89.95 and is marked down 35% during a clearance sale. Find the sale price of the track suit.

8 A stereo system sells regularly at $238.75.
(a) Calculate the sale price if the store offers a $\frac{1}{3}$ discount.
(b) How much will the consumer pay if 7% sales tax is also paid on the purchase?

9 A wholesaler's list price is $325.00 on a kitchen set. If a trade discount of 39% is given to the retailer. Calculate the price the retailer will pay.

10 An exercise set usually sells for $329.80. During a sale, the price is marked down to $285.75. Calculate the rate of discount.

11 Discounts of 25%, and 5.5% are offered on the following regular selling prices. Calculate each final sale price.
(a) $69.50  (b) $28.75
(c) $369.99  (d) $12 365.00

12 For each item, the list price is shown. Calculate the trade discount price.

| | | | |
|---|---|---|---|
| (a) | Calculator | $49.80 | 35%, 15% |
| (b) | Weights | $169.50 | 75%, 6.5% |
| (c) | Shipment of clothing | $10 680.50 | $46\frac{1}{2}$%, $3\frac{1}{2}$% |

13 A jumpsuit that sells regularly for $79.95 is marked down in the price by $\frac{1}{3}$ off. During the week, the store offers a further discount of 10%.
(a) Find the sale price.
(b) Find the total amount of discount.

14 A compact car sells at $9865.75. To encourage sales, the retailer drops the price by 6.5%. At the end of the season a further discount of $3\frac{1}{2}$% is given.
(a) What is the selling price at the end of the season?
(b) Calculate the total amount of the discount.

15 The list price for a hair spray is $27.50 per dozen with a trade discount of 32%. Find the price per can that the retailer pays.

**C**

16 Discounts of 15% and 10% are given on a computer listed at $1450.75.
(a) Find the sale price.
(b) Calculate the single rate of discount that discounts of 15% and 10% are equivalent to.

# Review: Practice and Problems

1 Karen's contract outlines that she is paid $6/h and is to work 40 h each week. She is paid time and a half for the next 4.5 h and double time for any hours above that.

(a) Find her earnings for a week if she worked 43 hours.

(b) What are her earnings if she worked 47.5 h for the next week?

2 Sean is paid 4.5% commission on the first $4500 of monthly sales and 6% on monthly sales over $4500. If his monthly sales were $8680.95, find the amount of commission he earned.

3 For each of the following gross earnings, calculate the total of the C.P.P. and U.I. deductions.

(a) $218.56 (b) $329.68
(c) $263.76 (d) $272.98
(e) $318.09 (f) $229.68

4 Lee works as a technician in a pharmacy and is paid $10.95/h for a 40 h week. Find his net pay for one week if his total deductions amount to $123.57.

5 Find the total taxes payable for each of the following taxable incomes.

(a) $8125.53 (b) $13 771.06
(c) $2352.98 (d) $1063.74
(e) $1543.97 (f) $7494.30

6 Moira is single and lives with her parents. Her T4 slip shows earnings before deductions of $19 256.40. Her C.P.P. contributions is $189.60 and U.I. of $203.50. She donated $250 to charity. Find her taxable income.

7 Leslie received income of $7764.80 with a C.P.P. deduction of $136.59 and U.I. premium of $98.27. He paid union dues of $120 and pension plan of $525.70.

(a) Calculate his net income.

(b) How much income tax will he pay?

8 Leanna had total earnings of $19 506.52. Leanna is single with no dependents. Find the income tax she owes after these deductions.

| | |
|---|---|
| C.P.P. contribution | $294.52 |
| U.I. Premium | $204.19 |
| Registered Pension Plan | $684.91 |
| Tuition Fees | $245.50 |
| Interest from Canada Savings Bonds | $1341.12 |

9 Calculate the income tax owed by Andrew who earned $27 562.71 and had the following deductions.

| | |
|---|---|
| C.P.P. Deduction | $306.52 |
| U.I. Premium | $231.14 |
| Medical Expenses | $905.92 |
| Charitable Donations | $450.00 |
| Taxable Family Allowances | $539.25 |
| Two daughters age 6 & 10 | |
| Married, wife earned | $1253.17 |

10 Find the amount of trade discount for each of the following.

(a) $820, 42% off

(b) $195, 20% off

(c) $1245.75, 33.5% off

(d) $2887.60, 45% off

11 Find the selling price of each of the following.

(a) Cost price of a VCR is $469.95 with markup of 39%.

(b) Cost price of a refrigerated truck is $32 695.50 with a markup of 16%.

12 Refer to the ad.

(a) Calculate the sale price.

Tape recorders
20% off

Regular Price $95.96

(b) Two weeks later a further discount is offered of 5%. Calculate the sale price.

(c) What is the total amount of discount for the tape recorder?

# A Practice Test

1 What is meant by each of the terms?
 (a) married exemption
 (b) basic personal exemption
 (c) employment income
 (d) pension income
 (e) investment income
 (f) unemployment insurance premium
 (g) annual union dues
 (h) medical expenses deduction

2 Mariene delivers newspapers. Out of each 25¢ that she collects for a newspaper, she receives $2\frac{1}{2}$¢.
 (a) What is her percentage commission?
 (b) Mariene delivers Monday to Friday to 65 homes. How much does she earn per week?

3 The following persons have different pay periods.
Andy is paid $466 semi-monthly.
Bev is paid $68 per day and works 4 days each week.
Carl is paid $995.43 per month.
Dan is paid a bi-weekly salary of $556.72
All are paid for a 52-week year.
 (a) Find the yearly salary of each.
 (b) What is the equivalent weekly salary for each person?
 (c) For each person, calculate the deduction for C.P.P. and U.I.

4 A. B. Electrical Supply Inc. uses the following method to determine a salesperson's commission. For a weekly basis the rate is $3\frac{1}{2}$% for the first $1500, 7% for the next $4000, and 9% for sales above $5500. A salesperson sold $9455 during one week. Find the commission earned.

5 Sally works in a restaurant and earns $275.80/week. She keeps 80% of her tips. She pays $88.93 per week for C.P.P., U.I, and Income Tax. Find her net pay for the week if her tips during the week were $154.35.

6 Daniel works for an insurance company and has a taxable income of $13 768.52. According to his T4 slip he has paid $3793.12 in income taxes. Find whether Daniel will receive a refund or will have to pay more income tax.

7 Audrey has a taxable income of $18 079.44. She had an overpayment on her C.P.P. of $131.17 and her T4 slip indicated that she had paid $3109.57 in income taxes.
 (a) Will Audrey receive a refund or owe tax?
 (b) How much of a refund would Audrey have received if she had paid $5092.56 in income taxes?

8 Kathy earned $17 504.31 as a bookkeeper last year. She is single and has a Registered Retirement Savings Plan for $2850. Medical expenses amounted to $952.18 and charitable donations were $465.00. She received $929 in interest. Her net claim code was 6.
 (a) Calculate her C.P.P. deduction and U.I. premium.
 (b) What is her taxable income?
 (c) How much income tax must Kathy pay the Government?

9 (a) A tape recorder is purchased for $79.95 and sold for $95.50. Find the markup as a percent of (i) the cost price (ii) the selling price
 (b) Socks are priced at 2 pairs for $3.96 in a special sale. If they cost $16.50 per dozen pair, what is the percent markup on the selling price?

10 A van sells for $14 600.50. During a sale, the dealer drops the price by 7.5%. The van does not sell after two months so it is dropped again by $4\frac{1}{2}$%.
 (a) Find the amount of the discount.
 (b) Find the selling price.
 (c) How much money would a buyer save?
 (d) If the dealer had given the buyer a 12% discount, would the selling price have been the same as in (b)? Why or why not?

# Update: A Cumulative Review

1 Round each number as indicated.
(a) A slice of salami is 0.603 mm thick (to two decimal places).
(b) A pole is 4.579 m long (to the nearest tenth of a metre).
(c) The distance travelled by bicycle was 9.48 km (to the nearest kilometre).

2 Find how long it would take for $1250 to double if the interest rate is $9\frac{1}{2}$%/a compounded annually.

3 The world's largest omelette was cooked on June 27, 1981 at Southcentre Mall in Calgary. They used a pan measuring 3.04 m by 1.00 m and a lot of eggs. Find the number of eggs in the record breaking omelette by solving the equation. $3(x + 2) - \frac{x}{2} = \frac{1}{3}x + 43\,592.9$

4 Simplify.

(a) $\frac{25a^5b^6}{5a^4b^4}$ (b) $(-4m^5n^3)(-3mn^4)$ (c) $\frac{-21a^4b^3}{3a^4b}$

(d) $(3a)^2$ (e) $(-4pq^2)^2$ (f) $\frac{(-2x^2y^3)^3}{2x^3y^2}$

5 Find the area of a rectangle whose sides, in centimetres, are $4p - 5$ and $3p + 6$.

6 (a) Find the volume of a pyramid 16.2 m high, with a rectangular base measuring 6.7 m by 2.8 m.
(b) A marble has a diameter of 1.0 cm. Calculate the mass of 30 marbles made of glass if glass has a mass of 1.2 g/cm³.

7 The roots of the quadratic equation gives the year in which the Olympics were held in Helsinki. Solve the equation to find the year.
$x^2 - 1948x - 7808 = 0$

8 Simplify. (a) $\frac{a + 4}{a - 1} \div \frac{5a + 20}{a - 2}$

(b) $\frac{x^2 - 9}{x^2 + 7x + 12} \times \frac{x + 2}{4x^2 - 9} \times \frac{(2x + 3)(x + 4)}{x - 3}$

9 A piece of paper is 0.06 mm thick, and is cut in half, and each piece is stacked. The height of the stack, after each cut, is given by
$h = 0.06 \times 2^n$ where $n$ is the number of cuts.
Find the height of the stack after
(a) 6 cuts (b) 10 cuts

10 A keyboard sold for $795.99 and had a 37% markup.
(a) Find amount of the markup.
(b) Find the rate of margin based on the selling price.

11 Evaluate the following for $x = 4$.

$$\frac{x^2 + 2x - 15}{x^2 + 4x - 5} \times \frac{x^2 + x}{x^2 - x - 6}$$

12 Barbara sells real estate and her terms of employment are as follows:
- a commission of 2.5% is paid on the first $100 000 of the selling price of each house,
- a commission of 3.25% is paid on the amount over $100 000.

Find her total earnings for the following twelve month period.

| Month | Prices of homes sold |
|---|---|
| September | $83 400 |
| October | $97 700 |
| November | $86 125 |
| December | $98 750, $110 150 |
| January | $126 340 |
| February | none |
| March | $84 912, $112 705 |
| April | $144 795 |
| May | none |
| June | none |
| July | $135 660, $96 970, $114 500 |
| August | none |

13 Barry plans to start his own business in 3 years time. He will need $10 000 for equipment, and start up costs. How much should he invest now at 10%/a compounded quarterly to have the amount he needs?

# 9 Keeping Your Money

skills with money management, banking services, rates of interest, term deposits, using money wisely, problem-solving, plastic credit, installment buying, true interest rate, buying bonds, investing in bonds and stocks, solving problems and applications

## Introduction

The skills you learn in mathematics provide a useful basis for managing money, as well as spending money wisely. To solve a problem about money, you use similar skills. For example, to solve a problem in mathematics, you may require a combination of skills you have learned. As you learn different strategies and skills to solve problems, you improve your ability to solve a problem you have never met before. However, basic to solving any problem whether about money or mathematics you must clearly answer these two questions,

A: What information am I asked to find?
B: What information am I given in the problem?

In this chapter, you will learn about some aspects of the mathematics involved with money based on applying skills and concepts of mathematics to make wise decisions. Skills with mathematics allow you to understand ways to save hard earned money, as well as obtain the maximum benefit of your earned dollars. By doing so you can take that holiday to some exotic place, or buy something you always wanted to have.

If you save \$8 a week for $2\frac{1}{2}$ years, invested at the best possible rate of interest, you can save a lot of money to buy those luxuries. Read on!

# 9.1 Banking Services: Savings Institutions

You may receive money from different sources, such as a gift, but the main source of money you receive will be income for working. Keeping large amounts of money at home is not wise, and you decide to deposit the money into a savings institution, not only to earn interest, but also for safe keeping.

There are three main types of saving and lending institutions that are available as described at the right: chartered banks, trust companies, and credit unions.

All institutions provide essentially the same services such as chequing and savings accounts, term deposits, loans, mortgages, traveller's cheques, bonds, safety deposit boxes, and so forth. Before you decide to open an account you need to decide what your needs are and compare the services of each type of institution. Refer to the information given at the end of this section *Making Decisions: Savings Institutions.*

To manage your money, you follow these principles.

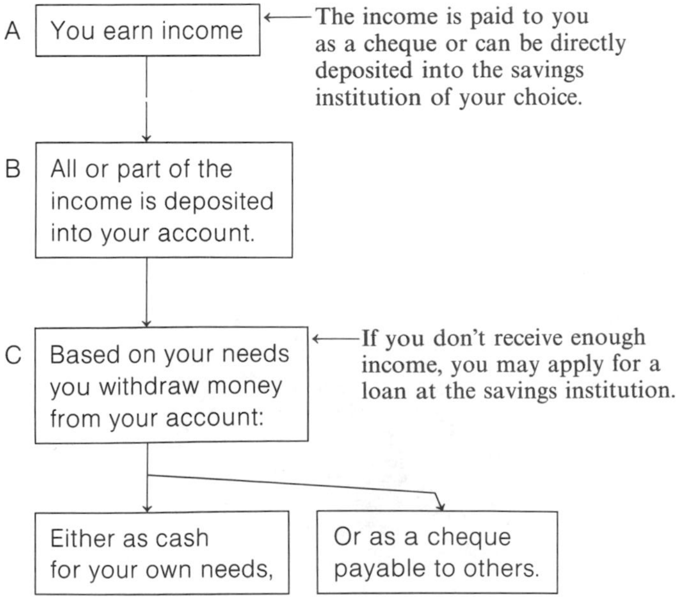
A
You earn income
The income is paid to you as a cheque or can be directly deposited into the savings institution of your choice.
B
All or part of the income is deposited into your account.
C
Based on your needs you withdraw money from your account:
If you don't receive enough income, you may apply for a loan at the savings institution.
Either as cash for your own needs,
Or as a cheque payable to others.

**Chartered Banks**
The chartered banks are privately owned and there is, on average, one branch for every 3000 Canadians. In 1868 there were only 123 branches and this has steadily risen to about 6000 branches today. They are called chartered banks because they operate under a charter granted by the Canadian Parliament. The Bank Act, passed by Parliament outlines what banks can and cannot do. There are also Provincial Banks, at which you can do your banking, that are operated by the Provincial governments. On the other hand, the Bank of Canada is a government owned central bank, established in 1934. It issues all the paper money, deals with the chartered banks, manages the public debt, and is the vehicle by which Canada's monetary policy is administered. Each branch of the chartered banks provide a full range of banking facilities and you can often conduct your banking at any of the branches of the chartered bank you deal with. Make a list of the names of the chartered banks that you could deposit your money with.

**Trust Companies**
There are a variety of trust companies that are also eager that you deposit your savings with them. However, most of the funds in a trust company are obtained by offering special deposits and investment certificates. They offer competitive interest rates and are especially active in mortgage loans. Trust companies also provide special services, such as stock transfer services, buying and selling real estate, as well as administering estate and pension funds. Trust companies are licensed by either the federal or the provincial governments. Make a list of the various trust companies that you can do business with.

**Credit Unions**
Credit Unions differ from other financial institutions in that they are owned by the members. As a member you have the right to vote on policy decisions at the annual meeting. Each member has one vote. Credit Union services are similar to those of any bank. However, savings are accepted and loans are made only to members rather than to the general public. Find out how to become a member of a credit union in your area.

Each banking institution offers a variety of savings accounts. When you decide to open an account, you also have to choose an account which will best suit your needs while earning the most interest for you. The main types of savings accounts which occur in the different financial institutions are as follows.

**A: Personal Chequing Account (PCA) or True Chequing Account**

Rather than carry large amounts of cash to pay your bills, you can use cheques. On this type of account you can deposit, withdraw, or write cheques but the bank pays you little or no interest (depending on the balance of your account). Sometimes you are allowed a certain number of free cheques (depending on your minimum monthly balance or some other arrangement provided by the institution). There is often a charge for administering the account. All of your cancelled cheques are processed and can be returned to you along with a monthly statement. Your cancelled cheques can then be kept as receipts, as proof of payment of your bills.

**B: True Savings Accounts**

The financial institutions offer accounts for people who write few, if any, cheques. A True Savings Account allows you to make deposits or withdrawals in person, but does not allow you to write cheques. However, true savings accounts offer you a greater rate of interest. These accounts are often advertised under different names as Blue Chip, TS Accounts, etc. You must inquire when opening an account as to its specific features.

**C: Savings/Chequing Accounts**

To provide flexibility in choosing an account for your needs, you can choose an account that combines the features of a savings and chequing account. With this type of account, you can manage not only your savings but the payments of any bills by using cheques. However, the rate of interest is lower than on a True Savings Account. Again, the various institutions use different names to describe this type of account.

To manage your financial affairs and show the record of the transactions in your account, each financial institution provides you with either a passbook or a statement.

When you deposit your money, an important consideration is to compare the rates of interest. The calculation of the amount of interest may vary depending on the type of account. For example,

- **Blue Chip Account:** Interest is calculated on the minimum monthly balance. The interest is credited to the account quarterly.
- **C/S Account:** Interest is calculated daily on the closing balance. Interest is credited to the account at the end of each month.

## Example

Jennifer has an account that pays interest at the rate of 8.5% on the minimum monthly balance. Interest is credited at the end of the month. A monthly passbook statement is shown for her account. Calculate the opening balance for the next month.

| DA | RE | WD | DEP | BAL | |
|---|---|---|---|---|---|
| JAN 31 | INT | 1.96 | | 696.18 | |
| FEB 03 | DEP | | 46.50 | ? | 742.68 |
| FEB 03 | CHQ | 17.23 | | ? | 725.45 |
| FEB 10 | CHQ | 16.96 | | ? | 708.49 |
| FEB 12 | DEP | | 22.55 | ? | 731.04 |
| FEB 16 | CHQ | 23.35 | | ? | 707.69 |
| FEB 20 | WD | 46.86 | | ? | 660.83 |
| FEB 23 | WD | 92.72 | | ? | 568.11 |
| FEB 27 | DEP | | 86.53 | ? | 654.64 |
| FEB 28 | INT | | ? | ? | |

## Solution

*Step 1*: Calculate the missing balance for each date (DA).

*Step 2*: Calculate the interest. Use $I = prt$.

minimum monthly balance → 568.11; rate of interest → 0.085; time 28 days → $\frac{28}{365}$

$$I = 568.11 \times 0.085 \times \frac{28}{365}$$

$$= 3.7043885$$ ← Use your calculator

The interest is \$3.70 (rounded to the nearest cent). The opening balance for the next month is given by \$654.64 + \$3.70 or \$658.34.

## Try These

A monthly statement is shown for Syrena's account. Answer the following questions.

1 What information is given by each of the labels?
   (a) Branch (b) Account (c) Description
   (d) Debit (e) Credit (f) Balance

2 (a) What is the amount of each cheque?
   ▶ Cheque 138 ▶ Cheque 141
   ▶ Cheque 146
   (d) Given reasons why the cheque numbers do not occur in order.
   (c) Why do you think cheque numbers 140, 142, 143 and 145 are missing?

3 (a) How much is the service charge? Why is the charge made? Why do you think the charge is made?
   (b) What will the opening balance on the next statement be?
   (c) Why do you think the interest calculation occurs in the middle of the statement?
   (d) What type of account do you think this is?

| Combination Account | | | | |
|---|---|---|---|---|
| Branch 369 | Account 369-42131 | | | Statement March 14 |
| **Date** | **Description** | **Debit** | **Credit** | **Balance** |
| Feb 15 | Balance Forward | | | 963.28 |
| Feb 18 | Cheque 146 | 69.36 | | 893.92 |
| Feb 21 | Cheque 138 | 23.48 | | 870.44 |
| Feb 22 | Deposit | | 136.50 | 1006.94 |
| Feb 25 | Deposit | | 75.32 | 1082.26 |
| Feb 28 | Interest | | 6.78 | 1089.04 |
| Mar 3 | Deposit | 29.63 | | 1059.41 |
| Mar 9 | Cheque 139 | 28.96 | | 1030.45 |
| Mar 10 | Cheque 144 | 55.60 | | 974.85 |
| Mar 14 | Cheque 141 | 43.21 | | 931.64 |
| Mar 14 | Service Charge | 2.25 | | 929.39 |

## Written Exercises

**A** Round your answers to the nearest cent.

1 What is meant by each of the following?
(a) Chartered Bank
(b) Credit Union
(c) Trust Company
(d) True Chequing Account
(e) True Savings Account
(f) Savings/Chequing Account

2 Interest is calculated on the minimum monthly balance. Some institutions will pay a greater rate of interest for a greater balance. Calculate the interest earned on the following.

| | Minimum monthly balance | Rate of interest |
|---|---|---|
| (a) | 362.96 | 5% |
| (b) | 123.85 | 3.5% |
| (c) | 1263.25 | 6.5% |
| (d) | 8961.12 | 8.5% |

3 Refer to the passbook statement. On this account interest is calculated on the minimum monthly balance at $6\frac{1}{2}\%$ per annum.

| DATE | | WITHDRAWAL | DEPOSIT | BALANCE |
|---|---|---|---|---|
| JUNE 30 | DEP | | 124.80 | 986.17 |
| JUNE 30 | INT | | 8.25 | ? |
| JULY 06 | WD | 86.15 | | ? |
| JULY 19 | DEP | | 70.15 | ? |
| JULY 23 | WD | 36.17 | | ? |
| JULY 31 | INT | | ? | ? |
| AUG 05 | WD | 48.37 | | ? |
| AUG 17 | DEP | | 56.10 | ? |
| AUG 31 | INT | | ? | ? |

(a) What is the opening balance on July 1?
(b) Calculate the interest payable on July 31.
(c) What is the opening balance on Sept. 1?

4 Interest for some accounts is paid daily. The closing balance is used each day to calculate the amount of interest. Find the missing entries in the chart. Calculate the interest for each day at $8\frac{1}{4}\%$ per annum.

| | Date | Closing Balance | Interest |
|---|---|---|---|
| (a) | Feb 6 | 690.00 | ? |
| (b) | Mar 12 | 363.25 | ? |
| (c) | Apr 18 | 1296.83 | ? |
| (d) | May 10 | 10 965.35 | ? |

5 Daily interest is calculated at $5\frac{1}{2}\%$ on the closing balance each day for John's account and credited at the end of the month. Calculate the interest earned for the days shown.

(a)

| DATE | ITEM | WITHDRAWAL | DEPOSIT | BALANCE |
|---|---|---|---|---|
| Oct 6 | DEP | | 36.92 | 426.83 |
| Oct 7 | WD | 18.96 | | ? |
| Oct 8 | WD | 196.28 | | ? |
| Oct 9 | DEP | | 123.45 | ? |

(b)

| | | | | |
|---|---|---|---|---|
| Jan 12 | WD | 43.25 | | 823.22 |
| Jan 13 | DEP | | 25.00 | ? |
| Jan 14 | WD | 16.25 | | ? |
| | WD | 28.96 | | ? |
| | WD | 36.21 | | ? |
| Jan 15 | DEP | | 60.00 | ? |

6 A chequing/savings account pays
- no interest on balance less than $300
- 3.5% on balance $300 to $1000
- 6% on balance $1000 to $5000
- 7.5% on balance greater than $5000

Calculate the interest earned for 30 days on each balance.
(a) $686.93 (b) $293.25 (c) $4362.92
(d) $12 696.25 (e) $928.65 (f) $1965.34

**B** Remember: Check your work. Use a calculator to do your calculations.

7 Howard has a savings account in a trust company. During the six month period from June 30 to Dec 31, his account had a minimum balance of $2356.62. Find the interest that Howard receives if the trust company pays 8.75%/a on the minimum balance.

8 Jacksons flower shop has a chequing/savings account. The opening balance for September is $1436.95. Calculate the balance of the account after the following deposits are made.

| CASH | CHEQUES | CREDIT CARD PAYMENTS |
|---|---|---|
| 24 $20 bills | $28.52 | $8.96 |
| 35 $10 bills | $63.14 | $13.50 |
| 51 $5 bills | $17.52 | $36.82 |
| 29 $1 bills | $36.94 | $25.60 |
| 17 $2 bills | $12.80 | $31.19 |
| 41 quarters | $93.17 | $9.70 |
| 83 dimes | $18.96 | |
| 64 nickels | | |

9 Lanny's balance on November 1 in his Credit Union account was $517.09. The following cheques were processed in his account during November.

| Shell | The Bay | Loan | Loblaws | Visa | Sports |
|---|---|---|---|---|---|
| Nov 3 | Nov 8 | Nov 10 | Nov 15 | Nov 28 | Nov 29 |
| $63.15 | $59.95 | $82.50 | $34.16 | $36.75 | $49.15 |

The Credit Union also deducted $2.25 for the service charge for handling the cheques. He deposited $625 from his pay on November 18. Find the balance in his account on November 30.

10 Ginger pays her bills by cheque. In November she wrote the following cheques: Master Charge $78.52; Visa $124.00; Petro Canada $41.04; Eaton's $36.79; Telephone $19.58; Rent $469.85. The opening balance in her account for November was $128.65, and her employment cheques for this month totalling $963.25 were deposited.
(a) What is the balance of her account?
(b) The interest on her account is calculated at $6\frac{1}{4}$% on the minimum monthly balance. Calculate the interest earned this month.

Questions 11 to 13 are based on the following page of Meryl's bank account passbook.

| DATE | DES | WD | DEP | BAL |
|---|---|---|---|---|
| Sept 30 | INT | | 4.28 | 869.36 |
| Oct 06 | DEP | | 28.96 | ? |
| Oct 17 | CHQ 23 | 39.84 | | ? |
| Oct 25 | DEP | | 163.50 | ? |
| Oct 31 | INT | | ? | ? |
| Nov 05 | CHQ 26 | 75.81 | | ? |
| Nov 13 | CHQ 25 | 36.19 | | ? |
| Nov 20 | CHQ 24 | 7.52 | | ? |
| Nov 25 | DEP | | 45.63 | ? |
| Nov 30 | INT | | ? | ? |

11 Interest is calculated at 6%/a on the minimum monthly balance and credited at the end of the month. Calculate the interest payable on
(a) October 31 (b) November 30

12 (a) What is the opening balance for December?
(b) If no deposits or withdrawals are made, what interest is payable on December 31?

13 Meryl had made a deposit of $86.90 on October 21, but the bank credited the deposit to the wrong account (always keep track of your deposits and withdrawals). Correct her bank statement.
(a) What is the interest payable on October 31?
(b) Calculate the opening balance for December 1.

## Career Tip

Have you ever stood in a line waiting for service in a bank? Virtually every activity in a bank depends on mathematics in one form or another.

- The teller who takes in money, as well as pays it out, is one of the most important members of a bank's staff. Most important of all, the teller meets the public most frequently.
- List the skills that you think tellers need in order to perform their duties.
- Next time you are in a bank, note the various activities that are going on. Which activities require skills in mathematics?

## Making Decisions: Savings Institutions

To receive the best return on your money, you must explore the various interest rates and terms offered by different savings institutions. These institutions pay you interest for the use of your money. They then lend it to other people at a higher rate of interest. The interest rates offered to have you deposit your money with a particular institution is often competitive, since one institution may need more funds to satisfy the loan demands of their customers. Thus, it is worthwhile to compare the features of each financial institution so that you are getting the best return on your money.

Paper money was first introduced into Canada in 1686 when a severe shortage of coins occurred. Only the Bank of Canada is permitted to issue paper money and every working day about $4 000 000 of worn out paper money is burned.

---

14 (a) What is meant by a passbook account. What are the charges for this type of account?
(b) What is meant by a statement account? What are the charges for this type of account?

15 What is meant by each of the following? Use an example to illustrate your answer.
(a) Interest is calculated on the minimum monthly balance and posted every quarter.
(b) Interest is calculated daily and posted monthly.
(c) Interest is calculated on the minimum semi-annual balance.
(d) Interest is not paid on an account with a balance less than $100.
(e) Free cheques are provided for each $100 of the minimum monthly balance.
(f) Super Saver interest is credited for balances that exceed $5000.

16 Contact a bank. Obtain information about the following.
(a) What type of bank accounts do they offer?
(b) How are the accounts in (a) alike? How are they different?
(c) List the various charges for the types of accounts in (a).
(d) What are the interest rates offered for term deposits?
(e) What are the regular hours for banking?

17 Using the previous question, obtain the same information for the following institutions.
(a) credit union (b) trust company

18 Based on the information you have obtained, how do banks, trust companies and credit unions differ?

19 Obtain information on how your deposits are protected when you place them into the following institutions.
(a) chartered bank (b) provincial bank
(c) credit union (d) trust company

20 Refer to the yellow pages of a telephone book. What are some of the financial institutions shown for each of these types?
(a) chartered banks (b) trust companies
(c) credit unions (d) provincial banks

21 Use your list in the previous question.
(a) Find what services they provide.
(b) What are the current rates of interest?
(c) What are the current charges on various accounts?

22 You have $5000 that you received as an inheritance. Based on the information you have explored,
(a) What type of accounts should you open?
(b) Should you invest part of your money in a term deposit? Why or why not?

# 9.2 A Better Rate of Interest: Term Deposit

You will often see advertisements to invest your money for longer periods of time. Financial institutions offer you a better rate of interest if you deposit your money for a longer length of time. Such investments are called Term Deposits or Investment Certificates. Once you deposit the money, you cannot withdraw it until the time period has been completed. In this way the financial institution knows it can count on having the use of your money for a fixed time and can offer you a better rate of interest. However, you lose the flexibility of a bank account because you cannot withdraw money except at the end of the term of your term deposit. If you do withdraw before the end of the term, you pay a penalty.

| Term Deposit Rates | |
|---|---|
| Term | Rate of Interest |
| 30–89 days | 8% |
| 90–119 days | 8.25% |
| 120–179 days | 8.5% |
| 180–269 days | 8.5% |
| 270–364 days | 8.5% |
| 1 year | 9% |
| 2 years | 10.25% |
| 3–5 years | 10.75% |

### Example

Carol received $4500 from a trust and she decided to place the money in a term deposit for 100 days, until she could decide how to invest it. Calculate the interest earned.

### Solution

Remember: Record the given information. Use $I = prt$.

Principal = $4500 Rate of Interest = 8.25% Time = 100 days
= 0.0825

$I = prt$

$= 4500 \times 0.0825 \times \frac{100}{365}$ ← The money is deposited for 100 days of the year.

$= 101.71233$ ← 8 digits are given on the calculator display.

The interest earned by the term deposit is $101.71.

## Try These

Refer to the chart of Term Deposit Rates.

1 Each amount is placed in a term deposit for 1 year. Calculate the amount of interest paid for each deposit.
(a) $100 (b) $1000 (c) $10 000

2 What rate of interest is paid for each of the following?
(a) $250 deposited for 50 days.
(b) $1000 deposited for 120 days.
(c) $5000 deposited for 136 days.
(d) $4500 deposited for 3 years.

3 For each interest calculation
▶ What is the rate of interest?
▶ For how many days is the term deposit?

(a) $I = 750 \times 0.0725 \times \frac{67}{365}$

(b) $I = 1600 \times 0.085 \times \frac{145}{365}$

(c) $I = 4500 \times 0.0975 \times \frac{306}{365}$

## Written Exercises

**A** 1 Express each percent as a decimal.

(a) $7\frac{1}{4}\%$ (b) $8\frac{1}{2}\%$ (c) $8\frac{3}{4}\%$
(d) 9.5% (e) 10.25% (f) 11.85%

2 Calculate the interest earned on each term deposit for 100 days, at the rate shown.

(a) \$800 at $8\frac{1}{2}\%$ (b) \$1450 at 7.5%
(c) \$325 at $9\frac{1}{4}\%$ (d) \$3690 at 11.8%

3 Each calculation is used to find the interest payable on a term deposit. For each calculation, identify (i) the rate of interest, (ii) the number of days. Then do the calculation to find the interest paid.

(a) $I = 365 \times 0.10 \times \frac{159}{365}$

(b) $I = 962 \times 0.085 \times \frac{200}{365}$

4 Find the amount of interest paid on each of the following term deposits for 270 days.

| | Principal | Rate of interest |
|---|---|---|
| (a) | \$950 | $7\frac{1}{4}\%$ |
| (b) | \$1675 | $8\frac{1}{2}\%$ |
| (c) | \$3500 | $9\frac{3}{4}\%$ |
| (d) | \$6000 | $10\frac{1}{4}\%$ |

5 Find the interest for each term deposit.

| | Amount of term deposit | Rate of interest | Term of deposit |
|---|---|---|---|
| (a) | \$1350 | $7\frac{1}{2}\%$ | 165 days |
| (b) | \$2400 | $8\frac{1}{4}\%$ | 98 days |
| (c) | \$4675 | 9.5% | 30 days |
| (d) | \$5450 | 10.75% | 79 days |
| (e) | \$7900 | $9\frac{1}{4}\%$ | 310 days |

6 The rate of interest paid by a Trust Company for an investment certificate is $9\frac{3}{4}\%$ per annum. The interest is paid at the end of each year to the owner of the certificate. Calculate the interest earned by each certificate.

(a) \$650 for 1 year (b) \$1275 for 2 years
(c) \$725.80 for 3 years

**B** 7 Melinda made a term deposit of \$525 at the Credit Union for 250 days. The term deposit paid interest at $9\frac{3}{4}\%$. How much did she receive in interest?

8 Megan purchased an \$1850 investment certificate from her bank for 5 years at $10\frac{3}{4}\%$ interest. Find the total interest she will receive.

9 Tobey obtained an investment certificate for \$850 that pays $8\frac{3}{4}\%$ per annum.

(a) Calculate the interest paid for a 90 day term.
(b) How much money will she have in 90 days to reinvest?

10 Calculate the interest you will earn by depositing \$4500 for a 5 year term at 10% per annum. The day after you made your deposit the rates dropped by $\frac{1}{4}\%$. How much interest would you lose by using the lower rate?

11 (a) Tony sold a rare coin for \$970. Which is the better investment?

▶ deposit the money in a savings account paying $7\frac{3}{4}\%$ for 240 days?
▶ Obtain a term deposit that pays $8\frac{1}{2}\%$ for 8 months?

(b) What are the advantages of a term deposit over a savings account? What are the disadvantages?

12 Find the amount deposited in an investment certificate which earns \$143 interest after 216 days at $9\frac{3}{4}\%$.

13 What is the interest rate if your term deposit of \$2850 for 3 years pays \$923.65 in interest? Express the interest rate to 1 decimal place.

**C** 14 Scott invested \$960 for 60 days into a term deposit that pays $8\frac{1}{4}\%$. When the term deposit matured he invested the amount in another term deposit for 120 days and received \$28.00 at the end of the term deposit. At what rate of interest was the second term deposit invested?

# 9.3 Using Money Wisely

Once you receive your income, you invest part of it in order to earn even more income. The rest of your income you spend on your needs and pay bills, but you attempt always to make your money stretch. An important step to managing your money is to budget properly and increase your savings.

Income − Expenses = Savings

> Besides obtaining the best interest rate on your savings, there are many other ways by which you can make your money stretch.
> - buy when items are on sale
> - share the cost of a major purchase with a friend or neighbour, such as a snowblower or lawnmover.
> - stock up on quantities of goods when they go on sale, such as toothpaste, deodorant, pens, and so on
> - pay bills on the date they are due and not before
> - rent rather than buy costly items that you probably use a few times, such as a post-hole digger, or cement mixer
>
> Look in the exercise for other ways that help you stretch your money.

### Example

Calvin received \$329.62 from his weekly paycheck. He budgeted 65% to be spent on housing, food, entertainment, and miscellaneous. He placed the remainder in a term deposit at $9\frac{1}{4}$% for one year.

(a) Calculate the interest he earned.

(b) How much interest would he earn if he deposited the money at $10\frac{3}{4}$% for 5 years?

### Solution

(a) *Step 1*: Calculate the savings.

| | |
|---|---|
| Income | \$329.62 |
| Expense | \$214.25 |
| Savings | \$115.37 |

65% of \$329.62 = \$214.25

*Step 2*: Calculate interest. Use $I = Prt$.

Principal \$115.37, rate $9\frac{1}{4}$%, time 1 year

$I = 115.37 \times 0.0925 \times 1$

$= 10.671725$

The interest earned is \$10.67 for 1 year.

(b) Use $I = Prt$.

Principal \$115.37, rate $10\frac{3}{4}$%, time 5 years

$I = \underbrace{115.37 \times 0.1075}_{\text{interest for 1 year}} \times 5$ ← interest for 5 years

$= 62.011375$

The interest earned is \$62.01 for 5 years.

## Try These

1 If you budget to save 10% of your earnings, how much is saved for each income?
(a) \$500.00 (b) \$328.65 (c) \$463.95

2 The penalty for each account is 1% when payment is received after the due date. Calculate the amount of the penalty.
(a) \$365.36 (b) \$169.80 (c) \$1275.63

## Written Exercises

**A** Express your answer to the nearest cent. Express per cents to 1 decimal place.

1 Calculate.

(a) 15% of $165
(b) 62% of $465
(c) 12% of $362.75
(d) $12\frac{1}{2}$% of $65.75
(e) $1\frac{1}{2}$% of $496.25
(f) $9\frac{1}{4}$% of $1293.50

2 Find the missing entries.

| | Income | Savings | Expenses |
|---|---|---|---|
| (a) | $325 | 68.96 | ? |
| (b) | $486.50 | ? | $362.98 |
| (c) | ? | $249.30 | $539.95 |

3 Calculate the percent saved from each income.

| | Income | Expenses |
|---|---|---|
| (a) | $250 | $213.80 |
| (b) | $375 | $283.75 |
| (c) | $426.86 | $315.60 |

4 The penalty for not paying the balance of an account is $1\frac{1}{2}$% per month, with a $2.50 minimum penalty charge. Calculate the penalty on a late payment for each account.

(a) $362.75
(b) $275.00
(c) $196.35
(d) $3.85
(e) $925.63
(f) $10.86

5 Find the missing entries in the table.

| | Income | Percent budgeted for expenses | Amount of expenses |
|---|---|---|---|
| (a) | $360.00 | 55% | ? |
| (b) | $275.86 | 65% | ? |
| (c) | $462.75 | ? | $268.40 |
| (d) | $623.65 | ? | $137.76 |

6 Monica's part-time income last year was $496.28. She spent $325.85. What per cent of her income did she spend?

7 In the previous year Yvonne's weekly budget for transportation averaged $22.96. This year it averaged out to $28.95. By what per cent did her budget for transportation increase?

**B** Remember: List the various ways you can save money when you complete the exercises.

8 On weekends Lloyd works in a bicycle store earning $62.75. The table shows his weekly budget and the amount actually spent for the following week.

| Item | Amount budgeted | Amount spent |
|---|---|---|
| Lunches | $14.25 | $16.75 |
| Clothes | $17.50 | $19.00 |
| Entertainment | $11.00 | $9.75 |
| Transportation | $3.00 | $5.50 |
| Reading material | $2.00 | $4.60 |

(a) For which items did Lloyd spend
  (i) less than he had budgeted?
  (ii) more than he had budgeted?
(b) Calculate the per cent that he saved that week.
(c) Based on your results in (b), estimate how much Lloyd will save if he earns a total of $3372.20 during the year.

9 Ben, Carmina, and Henri are neighbours. They decide to buy a snowblower which sells regularly for $899.99. During March it is on sale at 25% off.

(a) Find the total price paid for the snowblower. Include sales tax at 8%.
(b) How much does each person save by sharing rather than buying their own snowblower?

Arthur Sicard of Quebec invented the snowblower. He first had the idea as a young man working on a farm but did not manage to build a working machine until after he retired. He used his snowblower for the first time in Montreal in 1925.

10 Dolores works part-time at the Pizza Villa earning $4.75/h for 18 hours. After deductions, her take home pay is 88% of her earnings.

(a) What is her take home pay?

(b) She spends 17% of her take home pay on transportation. What per cent of her earnings before deductions is this?

(c) To buy a stereo, she plans to save 25% of her take home pay. If the total cost of the stereo is $368.96, for how many weeks does she need to save?

11 Tickets for a concert cost $22.50 each, plus $1.50 handling charge on each ticket. On the day of the performance any unsold tickets are sold at the theatre for half of the regular price.

(a) Craig purchased 3 tickets at the theatre on the day of the concert. How much did he save?

(b) List any advantages or disadvantages of using the method in (a).

12 Faye wants to buy a video player. The prices for the same model are as follows.

A: Video Junction $857.95

B: Super Store $949.50, sale on now 10% off

C: East End Discount $849.00, orders only and takes up to 8 weeks to deliver.

(a) Which store has the best price?

(b) From which store should Faye buy the video player? Give reasons for your answer.

13 Budget T.V. Rental advertises Model 68C at $29.95 a month, plus sales tax. Sandra purchased the same T.V. for $698.00. The rate of sales tax is 7%.

(a) Which do you think is the better deal; renting or buying? Give reasons for your answer.

(b) After how many monthly rent payments will the total paid equal the cost of buying the T.V.?

14 Onions can be bought in a 10-kg sack for $5.99. The same onions are also sold at 89¢/kg.

(a) Find how much is saved per kilogram by buying the 10-kg sack.

(b) Suggest reasons why you might not want to buy onions by the large sack.

15 When a charge card is used to make purchases, you must pay the balance of your statement by the due date or pay a penalty.

(a) Camilla's balance due is $239.65. The penalty on overdue payments is $1\frac{1}{2}$% per month. Calculate the penalty if Camilla sends her payment the day after the due date.

(b) Money is worth 8% per annum means that you can invest your money at a rate of interest of 8%. Calculate the interest lost if Camilla pays her bill 25 days before the due date in (a).

## Consumer Tip

To use money wisely, you really need to shop around. To live alone or as a family, you need to plan a budget and look for ways to get the most from your earnings. Do each of the following.

A You are going to cook most of your own meals. To do so, you need to plan an answer for each of the following.

(a) Make a list of the cooking utensils you will need.

(b) Make a list of the groceries you need for a week.

(c) What other supplies do you need in order to do your own cooking?

(d) Find the total cost of the items you have listed in (a) to (c).

B You plan to live on your own and have decided you want to live in a 2 bedroom apartment. Refer to the classified ads to answer the following questions.

(a) What is the price range of rent for a 2-bedroom apartment in your area?

(b) Does the rent include utilities?

(c) Do you have to pay any type of a deposit when you rent the apartment?

(d) Do you have to sign any legal document to rent the apartment?

(e) It is reasonable to spend up to 30% of your gross income on rent. How much money do you need to make in order to live in a 2-bedroom apartment?

# 9.4 Using Plastic Credit

Even though you may initially follow a savings program, you often want to buy a major purchase for which you don't have enough cash. Various department stores, banks, oil companies allow you to purchase goods on credit by using a credit card. You apply for a credit card and if your credit rating is good, you obtain your plastic credit card. The issuer of a credit card is interested in whether you are able to make the proper payments to eventually pay for the goods you purchased on credit. In paying your account, you usually have a choice of selecting the most suitable plan for payments. For example,

- ▶ You can pay your credit account in full by the due date of your statement. In this way you do not pay any charges for interest.
- ▶ You can choose to pay your balance in monthly amounts. Since you do not pay the entire balance you will incur a service charge, which is often a percentage of the balance owing. You will also receive a suggested schedule of minimum payments due depending on your balance.

Walter Cavanagh of Santa Clara, California has the greatest number of credit cards. He has 1173 different cards.

When you buy on credit, you are actually borrowing money. Thus, if you do not pay your balance in full at the due date, you receive a credit or service charge (also called carrying charge or interest charge).

Minimum Payment Schedule

| Unpaid Balance (dollars) | Monthly Minimum Payment (dollars) |
|---|---|
| 0–100.00 | 7.50 |
| 100.01–200.00 | 10.00 |
| 200.01–300.00 | 15.00 |
| 300.01–500.00 | 25.00 |
| 500.01–700.00 | 35.00 |
| 700.01–1000 | 45.00 |
| over $1000 | 5% of the balance |

### Example

Louis charged $265.83 on his gas card. The oil company charges 1.75% per month on the unpaid balance. If he pays $78.50 by the due date, what will the carrying charge on his account be for 1 month?

### Solution

*Step 1*: Calculate the balance of account.

| | |
|---|---|
| Charges on account | $265.83 |
| Amount Paid | $78.50 |
| Balance of Account | $187.33 |

*Step 2*: Calculate interest charged. Use $I = Prt$.
Principal $187.33, rate 1.75%/month, time 1 month

$I = Prt$
$= 187.33 \times 0.0175 \times 1$
$= 3.278275$

The carrying charge is $3.28 for the month.

## Try These

1 Refer to the minimum payment schedule on the previous page. Determine the minimum monthly payment for each balance.
(a) \$169.86 (b) \$469.75 (c) \$1425.80
(d) \$696.75 (e) \$69.80 (f) \$76.36

2 The minimum payment on the balance in each credit account is shown. What is the approximate balance?
(a) Nell, \$15.00 (b) Marie, \$45.00
(c) Maurice, \$7.50 (d) Rajah, \$35.00

3 Each person makes a payment before the due date. Determine the minimum monthly payment on the outstanding balance.

| | Person | Balance | Payment |
|---|---|---|---|
| (a) | Irene | \$643.75 | \$200 |
| (b) | Evan | \$342.86 | \$100 |
| (c) | Kevin | \$1263.29 | \$370 |
| (d) | Patrick | \$875.75 | \$400 |

## Written Exercises

**A** Remember: Estimate your answers to check whether they are reasonable.

1 Calculate. Round your answer to the nearest cent.
(a) $1\frac{1}{2}$% of \$735.60 (b) 1.75% of \$462.78
(c) 1.8% of \$325.20 (d) $1\frac{1}{4}$% of \$169.89

2 Find the missing entries.

| | Balance of account | Interest rate | Carrying charge per month |
|---|---|---|---|
| (a) | \$42.65 | $1\frac{1}{2}$%/month | ? |
| (b) | \$362.80 | 1.75%/month | ? |
| (c) | \$978.93 | 18%/annum | ? |

3 Each person does not make a payment on their credit statement before the due date. Calculate the interest charge that will occur on the next statement at $1\frac{1}{2}$%/per month.

| | Person | Previous Month's Balance | Purchases |
|---|---|---|---|
| (a) | Cecilia | \$269.35 | \$696.30 |
| (b) | Greg | \$169.20 | \$232.35, \$169.20 |
| (c) | Walt | \$186.75 | \$436.21, \$69.80 |
| (d) | Beth | \$469.83 | \$43.25, \$63.80 |

4 A cash advance can be made with some bank credit cards. Interest is payable from the date the cash advance is made. Calculate the interest payable on each cash advance for the days shown. Interest is calculated at 18% per annum.
(a) \$200, 20 days (b) \$365, 30 days
(c) \$430, 42 days (d) \$380, 65 days

5 When you make a payment on your account, you are given a credit. Find the missing entries. The service charge is calculated at 1.5% per month.

| | Previous balance | Service charge | Purchases | Credits | New balance |
|---|---|---|---|---|---|
| (a) | \$185.30 | ? | \$78.25 | \$25.00 | ? |
| (b) | \$392.75 | ? | \$263.10 | \$150.00 | ? |
| (c) | ? | \$6.06 | \$96.20 | \$100.00 | ? |

**B** Remember: Make a final statement in writing the solution to a problem.

6 Kathleen's balance from her charge account last month was \$268.95. She purchases furniture worth \$968.80. Before the due date she made a payment of \$250.00.
(a) Refer to the table on the previous page. What is her minimum monthly payment?
(b) If she makes the minimum payment what is the carrying charge, at $1\frac{3}{4}$% per month, on the balance?

7 Brenda purchases a rowing machine for the total price of $379.86. Previously the balance of her charge account was $165.85. She pays only $125.00 towards her balance. If the credit charge is calculated at 24% per annum,
(a) Calculate the amount of the credit charge.
(b) What is her minimum monthly payment?

8 Jessica purchased a windsurfer at a sale price of $962.80 using her charge account. Her previous charge account balance was $262.93. A monthly charge of $1\frac{3}{4}\%$ is charged on the unpaid balance.
(a) If she paid $200 cash and charged the remainder, what is the amount including 7% sales tax that is added to her account?
(b) On her charge account she paid an additional $175 to reduce her unpaid balance. Calculate the service charge that will be added to next month's balance.
(c) If she pays only the minimum monthly payment, calculate the unpaid balance.

---

Questions 9 to 13 require the use of the following chart. To enable the consumer to determine the service charge, some statements include a chart to show the amount of the service charge.

Monthly Service Charge

| AMOUNT | Minimum Monthly Payment | Service Charge |
|---|---|---|
| Up to 10.00 | 5.00 | 0.15 |
| 10.01 to 20.00 | | 0.30 |
| 20.01 to 30.00 | | 0.45 |
| 30.01 to 40.00 | | 0.60 |
| 40.01 to 50.00 | 6.00 | 0.75 |
| 50.01 to 60.00 | 7.00 | 0.90 |
| 60.01 to 70.00 | | 1.05 |
| 70.01 to 80.00 | 8.00 | 1.20 |
| 80.01 to 90.00 | | 1.35 |
| 90.01 to 100.00 | | 1.50 |
| 100.01 to 110.00 | 9.00 | 1.65 |
| 110.01 to 120.00 | | 1.80 |
| 120.01 to 130.00 | 10.00 | 1.95 |
| 130.01 to 140.00 | | 2.10 |
| 140.01 to 150.00 | | 2.25 |
| 150.01 to 160.00 | | 2.40 |
| 160.01 to 170.00 | | 2.55 |
| 170.01 to 180.00 | 11.00 | 2.70 |
| 180.01 to 190.00 | | 2.85 |
| 190.01 to 200.00 | | 3.00 |

| AMOUNT | Minimum Monthly Payment | Service Charge |
|---|---|---|
| 200.01 to 210.00 | 12.00 | 3.15 |
| 210.01 to 220.00 | | 3.30 |
| 220.01 to 230.00 | 13.00 | 3.45 |
| 230.01 to 240.00 | | 3.60 |
| 240.01 to 250.00 | 14.00 | 3.75 |
| 250.01 to 260.00 | | 3.90 |
| 260.01 to 270.00 | 15.00 | 4.05 |
| 270.01 to 280.00 | | 4.20 |
| 280.01 to 290.00 | 16.00 | 4.35 |
| 290.01 to 300.00 | | 4.50 |
| 300.01 to 310.00 | | 4.65 |
| 310.01 to 320.00 | | 4.80 |
| 320.01 to 330.00 | 17.00 | 4.80 |
| 330.01 to 340.00 | | 5.10 |
| 340.01 to 350.00 | 18.00 | 5.25 |
| 350.01 to 360.00 | | 5.40 |
| 360.01 to 370.00 | 19.00 | 5.55 |
| 370.01 to 380.00 | | 5.70 |
| 380.01 to 390.00 | 20.00 | 5.85 |
| 390.01 to 400.00 | | 6.00 |

9 What is the service charge for each amount?
(a) $265.30 (b) $89.60 (c) $143.25
(d) $369.20 (e) $210.11 (f) $342.76

10 When Lois received her credit card statement, her previous balance was $122.85. She made the following purchases shown on the statement: $62.75, $82.65, $36.35, $6.95, $43.25, and $16.20. She also returned items and received credits of $38.55, $16.36, and $28.23.
(a) Calculate her minimum monthly payment.
(b) Determine the service charge that will appear on her statement next month.

11 From the chart, the monthly service charge on a balance of $135.00 is $2.10. Calculate the interest rate expressed
(a) monthly (b) yearly

12 Refer to the chart. Calculate the monthly rate of interest.
(a) On a balance of $195.00 the service charge is $3.00.
(b) On a balance of $345.00 the service charge is $5.25.

What do you notice about your answers in (a) and (b)?

## C

13 (a) Create a problem based on the information given in the chart.
(b) Solve your problem in (a).

Windsurfing was developed by Schweitzer and Drake in southern California in the early 1960's. The current speed record is 51.5 km/h set on a 500-m course in 1983 at Weymouth, England by Frenchman Pascal Maka.

# 9.5 Instalment Buying

When you purchase an item, you have essentially two choices.

Choice 1: Pay cash
Choice 2: Borrow money

If you wanted to buy a canoe and do not have the cash you can apply to borrow money from one of the financial institutions, who will outline for you what they expect you to pay each month to pay off the loan. (If they approve you as a borrower).

Canada has some of the best canoeists in the world. In the 1984 Olympics Larry Cain of Toronto won the gold medal in the 500-m race with a time of 1 min 57.01 seconds.

The store from which you purchase the canoe may have allowed you to take the canoe by agreeing to pay equal amounts until the purchase is paid for. This method of payment is called an instalment plan: it allows you to pay for an item by paying equal amounts called instalment payments, over a certain number of equal time periods. Using the instalment plan, the purchaser can use or enjoy the merchandise immediately after the down payment but it is owned by the seller until the last payment is made. Buying goods on the instalment plan means that you will be paying a higher price than if you paid cash since in effect you are borrowing money and will be charged interest.

To purchase an item on the instalment plan you must understand the meaning of these words.

▶ The **principal** is the difference between the selling price (including tax) and the down payment. The down payment is a part of the price of the item. It is often required by the seller. The principal is used to calculate the interest payable.

▶ The **instalment price** is the total amount that the customer pays tor the item. It is the sum of all the instalment payments plus the down payment.

▶ The **finance charge** is the amount which is charged to the customer for the privilege of buying the item on credit. It is the difference between the instalment price and the purchase price of the item.

**Example 1**

Calculate the finance charge for a used boat selling for \$3695.00 (including tax). The monthly instalments are \$125.60 payable for 36 months.

**Solution**

*Step 1*: Calculate the amount paid by instalments.

$36 \times \$125.60 = \$4521.60$

The instalment price is \$4521.60.

*Step 2*: Finance Charge = Instalment Price − Purchase Price

$= \$4521.60 - \$3695.00$

$= \$826.60$

Thus, the finance charge is \$826.60.

In the next example, you need to calculate the amount of the monthly instalment charge.

**Example 2**

Lyle purchases a mini scooter for \$685.00. He makes a down payment of \$200 and agrees to make 10 equal monthly payments. The rate of interest charged is 18% per annum and sales tax is 8%.

(a) Calculate the finance charge.

(b) Calculate the amount of each equal monthly payment.

**Solution**

(a) *Step 1*: Purchase Price = \$685.00 + \$54.80 ← sales tax

= \$739.80

Principal = Purchase Price − Down Payment

$= \$739.80 - \$200.00$

$= \$539.80$

*Step 2*: Calculate interest payable (which is the finance charge).

Principal \$539.80  Rate 18% per annum Time 10 months

$$I = P \times r \times t$$

$$= \$539.80 \times 0.18 \times \frac{10}{12}$$

$$= \$80.97$$

The finance charge is \$80.97.

(b) $$\text{Monthly instalment payment} = \frac{\text{Principal} + \text{finance charge}}{\text{number of payments}}$$

$$= \frac{\$539.80 + \$80.97}{10}$$

$$= \$62.08 \text{ (to the nearest cent)}$$

Thus, each monthly instalment payment is \$62.08.

As a consumer, you might want to compare your instalment price with the purchase price in terms of a per cent. You would be interested to know what per cent the instalment price is more than the purchase price. To do so, you can interpret the following relationship from a different point of view.

| Instalment Price = Purchase Price + Finance Charge |
|---|

To obtain the instalment price you increased the purchase price by the finance charge.

Thus to calculate by what per cent the instalment price is more than the purchase price, you use

$$\frac{\text{finance charge}}{\text{purchase price}} \times 100\%$$

For the previous example

$$\frac{\text{finance charge}}{\text{purchase price}} \times 100\% = \frac{80.97}{739.80} \times 100\%$$

$$= 10.94485\%$$

Thus for the mini scooter, the instalment price is 10.9% more than the purchase price.

## Try These

1 To be a good consumer, you need to understand the meaning of the words used. What is meant by each term?
(a) down payment (b) purchase price
(c) instalment payments (d) instalment price
(e) interest charge (f) sales tax

2 For each purchase, a down payment of 10% is required. What is the down payment?
(a) $169.85 (b) $326.50
(c) $1268.75 (d) $932.50
(e) $683.79 (f) $13 625.86

## Written Exercises

**A** Review the meaning of the words: down payment, principal, instalment price, finance charge.

1 Calculate the instalment price for each purchase.

| | (a) | (b) | (c) |
|---|---|---|---|
| Down payment | $75.00 | $125.00 | $268.00 |
| Monthly instalment | $38.50 | $89.54 | $126.32 |
| Number of payments | 16 | 18 | 24 |

2 For each purchase, a down payment is needed. Calculate the amount of the down payment.
(a) encyclopedia set, $865.92, 15% down payment
(b) microcomputer, $1862.36, 18.5% down payment
(c) compact car, $8692.40, 25% down payment

3 What is the carrying charge for each purchase?
(a) Purchase Price $295.00; $39.50 per month for 12 months
(b) Purchase Price $1250; $119.85 per month for 12 months
(c) Purchase Price $8469.75; $236.12 per month for 48 months

4 Find the instalment price and the carrying charges for each of the following purchases. Sales tax at 7% is calculated on the cash price. The monthly payments given include sales tax.
 (a) VCR, $495.95; $48.60 per month for 12 months
 (b) Refrigerator $1250.60; 10% down payment, $36.70 per month for 36 months
 (c) Stereo Hi-Fi, $798.00, 15% down payment, $55.50 per month for 18 months

5 A snowblower is purchased with no down payment, but 16 monthly payments of $27.21. What is the instalment price?

6 A family of 8 purchased snowshoes at a cost of $318.25 including sales tax. A down payment of $125.00 was made and the balance paid in 12 monthly payments of $19. Calculate the instalment price.

7 A quality Walkman that sells for $113.28 including sales tax, can be purchased with $25 down and 10 monthly payments. Calculate the monthly payment if interest is charged at $1\frac{1}{2}$% per month.

8 A stereo can be purchased for $277.50 including sales tax or you can pay $20.04 per month for 18 months. What is the interest rate that is charged?

**B**

9 Big D Department Stores advertised colour televisions for $895.95. Sales tax is calculated at 7%. You can also purchase the T.V. set for $107.60 per month for 12 months with a $50 down payment.
 (a) What is the instalment price of the T.V.?
 (b) Calculate the carrying charge.

10 A motorbike is priced at $2450 and may be purchased on the instalment plan by making a down payment of $100 and 36 monthly payments of $89.85 each. Sales tax is 8%.
 (a) Calculate the carrying charges.
 (b) What is the instalment price?
 (c) Calculate by what per cent the instalment price is more than the cash price.

11 Beatrice purchased a chain saw priced at $476.10. She made a 20% down payment. She paid the balance in 18 equal monthly payments. Sales tax is 7% and interest is charged at 19.6% per annum.
 (a) Find the monthly instalment payments.
 (b) How much was the carrying charge?
 (c) Calculate by what per cent the instalment price is more than the cash price.

12 Holly bought a skidoo for the farm. She is financing $2950 for 30 months at 14.75% annual percentage rate.
 (a) Find the finance charge.
 (b) Find the amount of the monthly instalment payment.

**C**

13 Valerie purchased a sedan with a selling price of $9670.85. She was allowed a trade-in allowance on her previous car of $2650.00. Sales tax is calculated on the balance at 7%. She paid the balance in 36 monthly instalments of $329.50.
 (a) Find the carrying charge.
 (b) What was the rate of interest that she was charged?

## Computer Tip

- Prepare a computer program to calculate the total purchase price, $*C*, of an item including sales tax, calculated at a rate of *R*%.
- Prepare a computer program to calculate the finance charge, $*F*, for purchasing an item when the monthly instalments are given as $*N* per month.
- Prepare a computer program to calculate the monthly instalment payment $*M*, when the principal is $*P*, the finance charge $*F* is given, and *N* is the number of payments.
- Refer to the problems in this section.
 (a) Use the programs above to solve the problems.
 (b) Make any modifications to the computer programs to use the information given in the questions.

# 9.6 How much is the True Interest Rate?

In the previous section, you used instalment payments to make a purchase. In effect you are borrowing money and promising to pay it back over a period of time. As a consumer, you need to know what annual interest rate you are actually paying so you can make comparisons.

★ No money down
★ Make 12 payments of $37.96
★ Interest 1.5% per month

Refer to the ad. You decide that you want the stereo system so you
- ▶ agree to the term
- ▶ sign the contract
- ▶ pay $37.96 for 12 months

However, what is the actual or true annual rate of interest you are charged? The following calculations may help you estimate the rate of interest.

Since you are making 12 payments, the principal you pay back each month is $\frac{\$385.99}{12} = \$32.17$.

| *Step 1*: Calculate Interest based on first monthly payment |
|---|

A: Based on Monthly Payment

| | |
|---|---|
| Monthly Payment | $37.96 |
| Principal paid | $32.17 |
| Interest charged | $5.79 |

B: Based on Principal owed

Principal owed = $385.99
Interest owed = 1.5% of $385.99
= $5.79 (nearest cent)

Conclusion: For the first payment the interest charged is the same for A and B.

| *Step 2:* Calculate Interest based on second monthly payment |
|---|

A:

| | |
|---|---|
| Monthly Payment | $37.96 |
| Principal paid | $32.17 |
| Interest charged | $5.79 |

B: Principal owed = $385.99 − $32.17 (↑ principal paid in Step 1)
= $353.82

Interest owed = 1.5% of $353.82
= $5.31

Compare: You actually paid $5.79 but the interest you really owed was $5.31. You have over paid the interest based on the actual principal you really owe.

If you continue the previous calculations, you will see that each month you actually pay back more interest than you should pay based on doing the calculations with 1.5% per month. Thus, as you make payments, the actual rate of interest will be more than 1.5% per month. How much more?

To determine the actual or true interest rate, the following formula can be used.

$$r = \frac{2NI}{P(n+1)}$$

where $r$ = rate of interest per annum (expressed as a decimal)
$N$ = number of payments per year
$I$ = instalment or carrying charge (total instalment price − cash purchase price)
$P$ = principal of the loan (cash purchase price − down payment)
$n$ = total number of payments to be made

Often the true or actual rate of interest is referred to as the **effective** rate of interest.

### Example

Refer to the ad for the stereo system. Calculate the effective or true rate of interest. Express your answer to 1 decimal place.

### Solution

*Step* 1: List the given information at the start of your solution.

$N = 12 \quad P = 385.99 \quad n = 12 \quad I = 69.48$

↑ carrying charge = 18% of 385.99
= \$69.48

*Step* 2: Record the original formula before you substitute for the variables.

$$r = \frac{2NI}{P(n+1)}$$

$$= \frac{2(12)(69.48)}{385.99(12+1)}$$

$$= 0.3323163$$

← digits occurring on the display of a calculator

Thus, to one decimal place, the effective rate of interest is 33.2% per annum.

When you make a major purchase, such as a car, be sure of what you are getting yourself into before you sign the contract.

## Try These

Use the formula for the effective rate of interest to answer the following questions.

$$r = \frac{2NI}{P(n+1)}$$

1 In your own words, what is meant by each of the following?
(a) down payment
(b) cash purchase price
(c) carrying charges
(d) effective rate of interest

2 How are each of the following calculated?
(a) $I$, the instalment or carrying charges.
(b) $P$, the principal of the loan.

3 What is meant by each variable in the formula?
(a) $r$ (b) $N$ (c) $I$ (d) $P$ (e) $n$

4 What is the value of $N$ for each of the following?
(a) Payments are made monthly for 18 months.
(b) Payments are made quarterly for 3 years.
(c) Payments are made at the end of each year for 3 years.
(d) Payments are made at the end of six months for 5 years.

## Written Exercises

**A** Unless indicated otherwise, round answers to 1 decimal place.

1 Each of the following calculations occur in finding the effective interest rate $r$.
▶ What are $N$, $n$, $P$ and $I$?
▶ Do each calculation.

(a) $r = \frac{2(48)(30.50)}{700(24+1)}$ (b) $r = \frac{2(52)(17.25)}{848.30(18+1)}$

(c) $r = \frac{2(4)(49.75)}{1246.50(2+1)}$ (d) $r = \frac{2(24)(69.50)}{638.17(18+1)}$

2 Calculate the finance charge for each purchase.

| | Cash purchase price | Terms |
|---|---|---|
| (a) | \$140 | \$25 down, \$7.10 per month for 18 months |
| (b) | \$242.60 | \$50 down, \$8.50 per week for 24 weeks. |

3 Find the value of $N$, if payments are made
(a) monthly for 15 months
(b) monthly for 8 months
(c) monthly for 23 months
(d) quarterly for 2 years
(e) at the end of every 6 months for 3 years.

4 Calculate the true interest rate, $r$, for the given values.

| | $N$ | $I$ | $P$ | $n$ |
|---|---|---|---|---|
| (a) | 12 | 75 | 470 | 12 |
| (b) | 12 | 216 | 600 | 24 |
| (c) | 6 | 96 | 320 | 12 |
| (d) | 4 | 220 | 1250 | 18 |

5 Calculate the effective interest rate for each purchase.

| | Cash purchase price | Down payment | Interest charge | Number of monthly payments |
|---|---|---|---|---|
| (a) | \$640 | \$90 | \$60 | 10 |
| (b) | \$925 | \$0 | \$70 | 12 |
| (c) | \$1473 | \$250 | \$195 | 24 |
| (d) | \$2106 | \$375 | \$254 | 18 |

6 Calculate the true interest rate.

| | Purchase price | Terms |
|---|---|---|
| (a) | \$530.80 | \$100 down, \$28.10 per month for 18 months |
| (b) | \$308.00 | \$60 down, \$10.85 per week for 24 weeks |

**B** Remember. Round your answers to 1 decimal place. Read the displays on a calculator accurately!

7 Calculate the effective rate of interest for each of the following.
 (a) A video camera costs $1295 with an interest charge of $116.65, paid in 18 equal monthly payments.
 (b) A motorcycle costs $2765.90 with a carrying charge of $531.50, paid in 30 equal monthly payments.

8 A cash payment of $100 is required on a computer system which sells for $625. The balance must be paid in 24 monthly payments of $27.56.
 (a) Find the instalment charge.
 (b) Find the true interest rate.

9 Debbie purchased a new VCR costing $895 and decides to make a full payment of $1254 at the end of one year. Find the true interest rate.

10 Refer to the photo. To purchase the stereo system the terms are 20% down and $30 per week for 10 weeks. Find the true interest rate.

11 To repay the amount $1780 owing on a Honda all terrain vehicle, Darren agreed to pay 18 monthly installments of $123.50. Calculate the effective rate of interest.

12 Kathleen borrowed $1050 to buy a used car. She paid the principal of the loan as well as an interest charge of $265 in 8 monthly payments. Find the effective rate of interest.

13 A gas powered lawn mower can be bought for $349.50 (including sales tax). The terms are 30% as a down payment and $10.59 a month for 24 months. Find the effective interest rate.

14 On a contract, to purchase a brand new Cheveliar sports coupe, Jamie read the following details.

| | |
|---|---|
| Cost of Car: | $8460.70 |
| Tax & License | $612.25 |
| Total | $9072.95 |
| Down Payment | $500.00 |
| Balance | $8572.95 |

Pay $283.62/mon for 48 months.
The interest charged over 48 months is 14.7%.

 (a) Do you agree with the claim that the interest charged is 14.7% per annum?
 (b) What is really meant by the statement "The interest charged over 48 months is 14.7%"?

**C**

15 You can use the effective rate of interest formula to find the monthly payment.
 (a) A piano is purchased for $2580, including sales tax, and is to be repaid in 30 monthly payments. The effective rate of interest is 14.8% per annum. Calculate the amount of each equal monthly payment.
 (b) Create a problem of your own based on the formula.

$$r = \frac{2NI}{P(n+1)}$$

 (c) Write a solution to the problem in (b).

## Calculator Tip

Calculators are inexpensive and that allows you to have one handy when you need to do calculations to make a financial decision. Use the following calculator steps to evaluate the formula

$$r = \frac{2NI}{P(n+1)}$$ for given values of the variables.

[C] $n$ [+] 1 [=] [×] $P$ [=] [MS] 2 [×] $N$ [×] $I$ [÷] [MR] [=] output ?

**Can you do the calculator steps in a different way?**

# 9.7 Buying Bonds

In earlier sections, after you earned income you have learned methods to stretch your money, as well as ways to spend or invest your money wisely to obtain the best rate of return. However, there are other forms of investing your money. One of these is buying bonds.

> NEW ISSUE
> **Calgary Power**
> $250 000 000
> Guaranteed 9% Bonds
> to mature 1 Feb, 2000
> Price: $100.15

What are bonds? Often a city or a large company wants to raise money for a large expenditure. Since one person cannot lend all this money, the money is obtained from many sources (individuals, financial institutions, etc). The bond is a contract between the lender and the borrower. The bond shows various pieces of information:

- how much is borrowed
- the interest rate to be paid to the lender
- the terms of payment of interest
- the date by which time the loan will be repaid by the borrower

Because you agree to lend your money and receive in return a bond, your money will be invested for a longer period of time and you cannot withdraw it or cash it in as readily. For this reason, the rate of interest paid is greater than if you place your money in a bank account. There are various words used with bonds that you will need to know, such as those shown at the right.

- **Registered Bond** The bond is registered in the name of the owner. The interest is paid directly to the registered owner by cheque.
- **Unregistered Bond** The owner of the bond is not recorded on the bond.
- **Coupon Bond** Some bonds have coupons attached to the bond and are individually dated, each stating the amount of interest payable to the owner of the bond at specified dates. The interest coupons are clipped and then presented for payment.
- **Face Value** Bonds are issued with different principle amounts. The amount of a bond can vary from as little as $100 to amounts exceeding a million dollars! Thus, the face value is the amount of money borrowed and is printed on the bond. The **par value** of the bond is another name for the face value of the bond.
- **Redemption Date** This is the date on which the loan (money borrowed from you) will be repaid to you.
- **Bond Rate** Since you have lent money, you are paid interest based on the face value of the bond. If the bond rate is 11.6% per annum you will be paid $11.60 interest each year on a $100 bond. This rate of interest is called the bond rate.

On the financial pages of a newspaper, you will find a section called **Bond Market**. The bond you have obtained can be bought and sold. In other words, even though you have lent money and received a bond in return (as a contract) you can sell the bond and receive money for it. The persons to whom you sold the bond now has the contract that shows how the money has been lent. For this reason, most bonds sell at prices other than the face value. The following terms are related to buying and selling bonds.

- **Premium Bond** Bonds may sell at prices that are greater than the face value shown on the bond. The bond is said to sell at a premium, and is sold at its premium value.

- **Discount Bond** Bonds may sell at prices less than the face value. The bond is said to sell at a discount and is sold at its discounted value.
- **Market Value** The bond market prices are listed in the financial pages and a quick glance at them indicates that bonds seldom sell at the face value of the bond. The selling or buying price of a bond is dictated by the financial climate that occurs at the particular time you want to sell or buy bonds. These values are called the market values of the bonds.

The interest payable is the same regardless of what the bond sells for on the bond market.

As indicated above, bonds may sell at prices other than the face value. Often when a bond is placed on the market to sell, it may be offered at a price less than the face value to attract a buyer. For this reason, a bond with a face value of $100 might be offered for sale at $95. If the bond rate is 10%, then the actual money the buyer will make on the investment is greater than 10%. For this reason, when people invest in bonds, there are two interest rates that need to be examined.

- The **bond rate** is the rate quoted on the face or par value of the bond.
- The **yield rate** is the rate of interest you actually realize on your bond, based on how much you paid for it.

## Example

Through a broker, Jackson purchased a $1500 bond paying 11.6% with a redemption date in 5 years. The actual cost of this bond was $1380. The interest rate is payable yearly.

(a) Calculate the amount of interest Jackson will receive each year.

(b) Calculate the yield rate for the first year of the investment.

(c) Two years later Jackson buys another $1500 bond paying 11.6%, for $1620. Calculate the yield rate.

## Solution

(a) The $1500 bond pays 11.6% interest yearly.

$$\begin{aligned}\text{Interest payable} &= 11.6\% \text{ of } \$1500\\ &= 0.116 \times \$1500\\ &= \$174.00\end{aligned}$$

Each year Jackson will receive $174.00.

(b) Let r% be the rate of interest received for the investment. Use

$$\text{Interest rate per annum} = \frac{\text{Interest received}}{\text{principal}} \times 100\%$$

$$r = \frac{174}{1380} \times 100\%$$

$$= 12.60869\%$$

Thus, the yield rate of Jackson's bond is 12.6%.

(c) Let $r\%$ be the rate of interest.

$$r\% = \frac{174}{1620} \times 100\%$$

$$= 10.74074\%$$

Thus, the yield rate of this bond is 10.7%.

From the previous calculations you can note that

A: If you purchase a bond at a discount price, the yield rate will be greater than the bond rate.

B: If you purchase a bond at a premium price, the yield rate will be less than the bond rate.

Prices for bonds are quoted in prices given in the following form.

$84\frac{1}{8}$ means \$84.125 $84\frac{1}{4}$ means \$84.25 $123\frac{1}{2}$ means \$123.50

Often prices are quoted on the \$100 face value of a bond. For example,

- a quote of $82\frac{1}{2}$ means you pay \$82.50 for each \$100 face value of the bond.
- a quote of $112\frac{3}{4}$ means you pay \$112.75 for each \$100 face value of the bond.

## Try These

1 Each term is used with bonds. What is meant by each of the following?

(a) discount (b) unregistered
(c) face value (d) coupon
(e) redemption date (f) registered
(g) market value (h) premium
(i) bond rate (j) par value

2 (a) Michael purchased a bond at a discount. Will his yield rate be more than the bond rate or less? Give reasons for your answer.
(b) Jennifer purchased a bond at a premium. Will her yield rate be more than the bond rate or less? Give reasons for your answer.

## Written Exercises

### A

1 Calculate the interest payable yearly for each amount of bonds.

| | Amount | Interest Rate |
|---|---|---|
| (a) | \$500 | $9\frac{1}{2}\%$ |
| (b) | \$850 | $12\frac{1}{4}\%$ |
| (c) | \$1500 | 11.7% |
| (d) | \$2250 | 10.875% |

2 Calculate the interest payable each year for the following Government of Canada Bonds.

| | Face value | Redemption date | Rate of interest |
|---|---|---|---|
| (a) | 300 | Mar 15, 1999 | $13\frac{3}{4}\%$ |
| (b) | 500 | Dec 15, 1994 | $11\frac{1}{2}\%$ |
| (c) | 1000 | July 1, 1998 | $14\frac{3}{4}\%$ |
| (d) | 1500 | Apr 1, 1995 | $11\frac{1}{4}\%$ |
| (e) | 2000 | May 15, 1997 | $9\frac{1}{4}\%$ |

3 Calculate the interest payable each year for the following provincial bonds.

| | Face value | Redemption date | Rate of interest |
|---|---|---|---|
| (a) | \$500 Ont. Hydro | Jan 29, 2011 | 13% |
| (b) | \$2500 N.B. Electric | Feb 8, 1998 | $11\frac{3}{4}\%$ |
| (c) | \$6500 Alta | Dec 15, 2002 | $12\frac{1}{4}\%$ |

4 Calculate the interest value of a coupon that would be attached to each bond.

| | Bond | Face value | Interest rate |
|---|---|---|---|
| (a) | CPR | \$1000 | $8\frac{7}{8}\%$ |
| (b) | Gulf Oil | \$500 | $8\frac{5}{8}\%$ |
| (c) | Abitibi | \$10 000 | $9\frac{3}{4}\%$ |

5 Nadia purchased two 5-year $10\frac{3}{4}$% bonds with a face value of $500 each. The quoted value was $96\frac{1}{2}$. Identify the following information for the purchase.
(a) face value (b) discount or premium value
(c) bond rate (d) market value

6 Calculate the cost of each bond purchase.

| | Face value | Quoted value for each $100 face value |
|---|---|---|
| (a) | $500 | $79\frac{1}{4}$ |
| (b) | $1200 | $84\frac{3}{4}$ |
| (c) | $5000 | $108\frac{1}{2}$ |

**B** Be sure to check whether your answer is reasonable.

7 Sam purchased $10 000 face value of a bond series quoted at $85\frac{1}{4}$. The bond rate is $10\frac{3}{4}$%/a.
(a) What was the cost of the bonds?
(b) What is the annual yield rate?

8 Freddie purchased a $1000 bond at a discount value of $940 paying a bond rate of $10\frac{1}{4}$%.
(a) Estimate the yield rate. Will it be more or less than the bond rate?
(b) Calculate the yield rate.

9 Margo purchased a $1500 bond at a premium value of $1680, paying a bond rate of $9\frac{1}{2}$%.
(a) Estimate the yield rate. Will it be more or less than the bond rate?
(b) Calculate the yield rate.

10 When you purchase a bond you often need to pay a commission on the purchase price. The commission charges varies from sale to sale based on the commission structure established by the firm (bond broker) selling the bonds. For each purchase, calculate the yield rate for one year.
(a) A bond with face value $5000 is purchased for $4625. The bond rate is $8\frac{1}{2}$%. A commission of $\frac{1}{4}$% is charged on the sale.
(b) A bond with face value $8500 is at a premium price of $9275.86. The bond rate is $14\frac{1}{4}$%. A commission of $\frac{1}{2}$% is charged on the sale.

11 The $1000 Government of Canada $10\frac{1}{8}$% bond is quoted at a market price of 92. Brenda bought two $1000 bonds. Calculate the yield rate for her purchase if she paid $96.70 commission.

12 The $100 Canadian Utilities Bond with the redemption date July 15, 1999 is quoted at a market value of $98\frac{1}{2}$. The issue pays 10.40% interest.
(a) Calculate the cost of twelve $100 bonds.
(b) What is the yield rate?

13 Imperial Oil issued a corporate bond with a redemption date Feb 15, 1995. The market value is 98.625. Calculate the yield on 10 $1000 bonds if the bond rate is $9\frac{3}{4}$%.

14 The Government of Canada $9\frac{1}{2}$% bond issue with a redemption date June 15, 1994 is quoted at $102\frac{1}{4}$.
(a) Wynne purchased a face value of $500 of the bond. Calculate the yield rate.
(b) Todd purchased a face value of $1900 of bond. Calculate the yield rate.
What do you notice about your answers in (a) and (b)?

15 Nova issued a $17\frac{3}{4}$% bond due in Feb 15, 1997. (The redemption date is Feb 15, 1997). Calculate the yield rate if the market value is quoted as $129\frac{3}{4}$.

16 Which investment has the better yield A or B?
A Irwin Toy $14\frac{1}{2}$% bond at a quoted market price of $104\frac{1}{8}$ (redemption date Aug 15, 1992).
B Bow Valley 11% bond at a quoted market price $66\frac{1}{2}$ (redemption date Mar 1, 2001).

**Math Tip**

It is especially important in making financial decisions that you understand the vocabulary. Before you sign a contract, make sure that every term is clear.

- Make a list of all the new words you learned in this chapter.
- Provide a simple example to illustrate the meaning of each word.

# 9.8 Investing in Bonds

Whenever you invest money, there is an element of risk. To minimize the risk, you must obtain good advice and as well you must be able to interpret the advice. When you examine the financial pages, you will find tables that give you the current bond prices. The table below shows information about Government of Canada bonds.

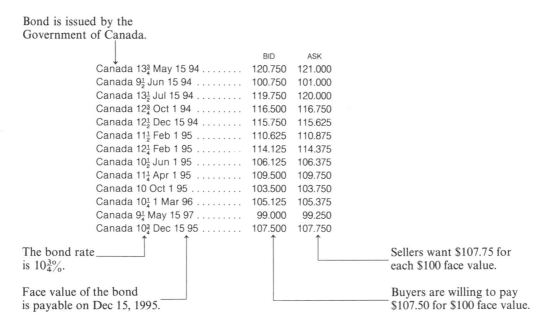

Bond is issued by the Government of Canada.

| | BID | ASK |
|---|---|---|
| Canada $13\frac{3}{4}$ May 15 94 ........ | 120.750 | 121.000 |
| Canada $9\frac{1}{2}$ Jun 15 94 ......... | 100.750 | 101.000 |
| Canada $13\frac{1}{2}$ Jul 15 94 ......... | 119.750 | 120.000 |
| Canada $12\frac{3}{4}$ Oct 1 94 ......... | 116.500 | 116.750 |
| Canada $12\frac{1}{2}$ Dec 15 94 ........ | 115.750 | 115.625 |
| Canada $11\frac{1}{2}$ Feb 1 95 ......... | 110.625 | 110.875 |
| Canada $12\frac{1}{4}$ Feb 1 95 ......... | 114.125 | 114.375 |
| Canada $10\frac{1}{2}$ Jun 1 95 ......... | 106.125 | 106.375 |
| Canada $11\frac{1}{4}$ Apr 1 95 ......... | 109.500 | 109.750 |
| Canada 10 Oct 1 95 .......... | 103.500 | 103.750 |
| Canada $10\frac{1}{4}$ 1 Mar 96 ......... | 105.125 | 105.375 |
| Canada $9\frac{1}{4}$ May 15 97 ......... | 99.000 | 99.250 |
| Canada $10\frac{3}{4}$ Dec 15 95 ........ | 107.500 | 107.750 |

The bond rate is $10\frac{3}{4}\%$.

Face value of the bond is payable on Dec 15, 1995.

Sellers want \$107.75 for each \$100 face value.

Buyers are willing to pay \$107.50 for \$100 face value.

When you buy a bond,

- ▶ you receive the interest payable on the face value of the bond.
- ▶ You hope that the price you bought the bond at will increase.

The market value of bonds fluctuates day by day, depending on many factors in the financial community. To calculate the yield rate of a bond over a longer period of time, you are able to only calculate it approximately. The term **average yield** rate is used in working with bonds, as follows.

$$\text{Average Yield Rate} = \frac{\text{average income}}{\text{average principal}} \times 100\%$$

Thus, to calculate the average yield rate, you first need to calculate the average principal for your bond purchase.

$$\text{Average Principal} = \frac{\text{face value} + \text{purchase price}}{2}$$

If you purchase a 12% bond maturing in 5 years, with a face value of $500, for only $425, then in addition to the interest payable to you, you will also earn $75 income when you cash the bond on the redemption date.

$$\underset{\text{maturity value}}{500} - \underset{\text{price you paid}}{425} = \underset{\text{income}}{75}$$

Over the 5 years you will receive $\frac{\$75}{5}$ or $15 more each year.

To calculate the average income, you use

$$\text{Average income} = \text{yearly interest} + \frac{\text{face value} - \text{purchase price}}{\text{number of years to maturity}}$$

An understanding of these principles is important, not only to people who work in a bond market but also to the consumer who may decide to invest in bonds.

## Example

Wallace purchased a corporate $9\frac{3}{4}\%$ bond to mature in 8 years. He purchased a total of $8000 face value of the bond quoted at $91\frac{1}{2}$. Calculate Wallace's average yield rate (to 2 decimal places).

## Solution

*Step 1*: Calculate the purchase price. $\$8000 = 80 \times \$100$

$$\begin{aligned}\text{Cost of 80 bonds} &= 80 \times \$91.50 \\ &= \$7320\end{aligned}$$

*Step 2*: Calculate the average principal.

$$\begin{aligned}\text{Average Principal} &= \frac{\text{face value} + \text{purchase price}}{2} \\ &= \frac{\$8000 + \$7320}{2} \\ &= \$7660\end{aligned}$$

*Step 3*: Calculate the average income.

$$\begin{aligned}\text{Average Income} &= \text{yearly interest} + \frac{\text{face value} - \text{purchase price}}{\text{years to maturity}} \\ &= \$780 + \frac{\$8000 - \$7320}{8} \\ &= \$865\end{aligned}$$

yearly interest $= 8000 \times 0.0975 = 780$

*Step 4*: Calculate the average yield rate.

$$\begin{aligned}\text{Average Yield Rate} &= \frac{\text{average income}}{\text{average principal}} \times 100\% \\ &= \frac{\$865}{\$7660} \times 100\% \\ &= 11.29242\%\end{aligned}$$

Thus, Wallace's average yield rate is 11.29% (to 2 decimal places).

## Written Exercises

**A** Remember: Bond rates are given as an annual rate.

1 Calculate the average principal for each purchase.

| | Face value | Market value (per $100 face value) |
|---|---|---|
| (a) | $800 | $92\frac{1}{4}$ |
| (b) | $1200 | $103\frac{1}{8}$ |
| (c) | $2500 | $86\frac{1}{2}$ |

2 Calculate the average income for each purchase.

| | Face value | Bond rate | Purchase price | Years to maturity |
|---|---|---|---|---|
| (a) | $100 | $9\frac{1}{4}\%$ | $89\frac{1}{4}$ | 5 |
| (b) | $100 | $10\frac{1}{2}\%$ | $92\frac{1}{2}$ | 8 |
| (c) | $500 | $12\frac{3}{4}\%$ | 112.50 | 10 |
| (d) | $1000 | 9.68% | 108.75 | 4.5 |

3 Calculate the average yield rate for each bond purchase.

| | Face value | Purchase value (per $100 face value) | Rate of interest | Years to maturity |
|---|---|---|---|---|
| (a) | $500 | 95 | $9\frac{3}{4}\%$ | 4 |
| (b) | $800 | 102 | $12\frac{1}{2}\%$ | 6 |
| (c) | $1200 | $112\frac{1}{2}$ | $14\frac{3}{8}\%$ | 8 |
| (d) | $5000 | $98\frac{3}{4}$ | $8\frac{7}{8}\%$ | 3 |

**B**

4 A $100 Province of B.C. 11% bond matures in 10 years. If the bond was purchased by Jean for $96.25, calculate her average yield rate.

5 Each $100 Norcen $11\frac{1}{4}\%$ bond was purchased at $103.50. Lois purchased 12 of the bonds. Calculate the average yield rate if the bonds mature in 8 years.

6 Dofasco issued 17% bonds maturing in 9 years. Walter paid $125.25 for each $100 bond. If he bought a face value of $5000 bonds, calculate his average yield rate.

7 Each $100 Government of Canada $10\frac{1}{2}\%$ bond will mature in 4 years. Calculate the average yield rate if Henri purchased them at the bid price of $104.25.

8 To raise money for a government project, the $13\frac{1}{4}\%$ bond was issued, payable in 5 years. Melanie used her savings and purchased 10 $100 bonds at $109.50 each. Calculate her average yield rate.

---

Questions 9 to 12 are based on the following market prices for corporate bonds.

| | BID | ASK |
|---|---|---|
| Imperial Oil $9\frac{3}{4}$ Feb 15 96. . . . . . . . . . | 96.250 | 99.250 |
| Nlld Light $11\frac{1}{4}$ Dec 1 94 . . . . . . . . . . . | 105.625 | 106.625 |
| Norcen $11\frac{1}{4}$ Aug 15 96. . . . . . . . . . . . | 106.375 | 107.375 |
| Nova $17\frac{3}{4}$ Feb 15 97 . . . . . . . . . . . . . | 129.750 | 130.750 |
| Shell Cola $9\frac{3}{8}$ Mar 15 03 . . . . . . . . . . | 94.125 | 94.625 |
| S Sears $11\frac{1}{4}$ Aug 15 94. . . . . . . . . . . . | 103.625 | 104.625 |
| Stelco $13\frac{1}{2}$ Oct 1 00 . . . . . . . . . . . . . | 119.125 | 120.125 |
| Union Gas 11 Aug 15 94. . . . . . . . . . | 103.625 | 104.625 |

9 You purchased 3 $100 bonds at the Bid price for Shell Canada.
(a) What is your cost?
(b) Calculate your average yield rate.

10 You made the following purchases.
4 $100 Sears at the Ask price
6 $100 Union Gas at the Bid price
5 $100 Stelco at the Ask price
(a) Calculate the purchase price.
(b) Calculate your income in interest per year.
(c) What is the average price you paid for your bonds?

11 Which is the better investment A or B? Remember to compare the average yield rate.
A To invest your money in Nova.
B To invest your money in S Sears.

12 (a) Create a problem based on the information in the chart.
(b) Solve your problem in (a).

# 9.9 Investing in Stocks

There have been a variety of methods that you have seen to invest your extra money: term deposits, investment certificates, bank accounts, bonds, and so on. When you invest you commit your money to earn a financial return. The house you purchase is also an investment since it may increase in value. Some people invest in art, while others may buy coins as an investment. Some people buy a hockey team, or others may buy a shopping plaza. There are many investments available to the investor to achieve financial goals, depending on how much money you have to invest and the risk you are prepared to take. Another form of investment is to buy **common** or **preferred stocks**, which you will explore in this section.

To invest in stocks as for any investment you must understand what you are getting into:

- ▶ You must ask yourself these questions: How secure is the investment? How much risk is there? Can I really afford it?
- ▶ You must also learn as much as you can about the nature of the investment before you invest. Seek advice as to whether you are doing the right thing.

To invest in stocks, as for any investment, you must have an up-to-date understanding of the vocabulary and the nature of the investment. For example, when you buy stocks you are buying a share of a company. In so doing, you expect to receive a share of the profits of this company paid to you as **dividends**. If the company's profit increases the dividends paid will increase. However, if the company's profit decreases the dividends may also decrease. Before you invest in the company you need to carefully investigate its financial picture. To do so, you acquire the company's **Financial or Annual Report**. Stocks of publicly owned companies are listed on one of the **Stock Exchanges**, such as Toronto, Vancouver, or Montreal. To purchase or sell your stocks you can do so by using the services of a **stockbroker** who arranges the business transaction for you (at one of the Stock Exchanges) and charges a **commission** for the service provided.

To obtain information about what the shares or stocks of a company currently cost you need to refer to the financial pages of the newspaper.

| STOCK | BID | ASK | LAST PRICE | CHANGE | VOLUME | HIGH | LOW |
|---|---|---|---|---|---|---|---|
| Dome Pete | 199 | 186 | 196 | +10 | 449426 | 365 | 180 |
| DPete A | $\$6\frac{1}{2}$ | 6 | $6\frac{1}{4}$ | $-\frac{1}{4}$ | 33845 | $17\frac{3}{4}$ | $5\frac{1}{8}$ |
| DPete B | $\$6\frac{1}{2}$ | $6\frac{1}{4}$ | $6\frac{1}{2}$ | +1 | 3000 | $17\frac{3}{4}$ | $5\frac{1}{2}$ |
| D Pete | 13 | 10 | 13 | +3 | 273950 | 68 | $9\frac{1}{2}$ |
| Domego | 29 | 28 | 29 | +4 | 76500 | 36 | 25 |
| D Expl | 24 | 24 | 24 | +1 | 1800 | 48 | 22 |
| D Scotish | $\$27\frac{1}{2}$ | $29\frac{1}{4}$ | $28\frac{3}{4}$ | | nt | 29 | $26\frac{1}{4}$ |
| D Textie | $\$19\frac{1}{8}$ | $18\frac{3}{4}$ | $18\frac{3}{4}$ | $-\frac{3}{8}$ | 11836 | $19\frac{1}{2}$ | 10 |
| Domtar | $\$30\frac{1}{2}$ | 30 | $30\frac{1}{8}$ | $-\frac{1}{8}$ | 12227 | $30\frac{1}{2}$ | $17\frac{5}{8}$ |

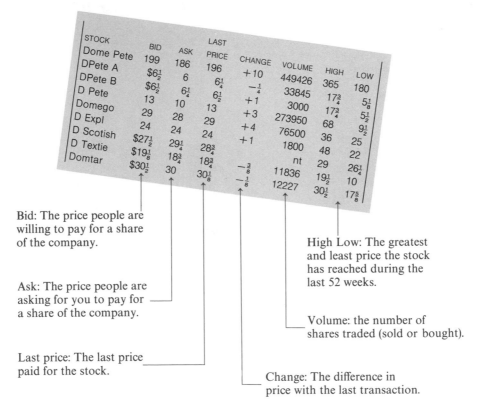

Bid: The price people are willing to pay for a share of the company.

Ask: The price people are asking for you to pay for a share of the company.

Last price: The last price paid for the stock.

Change: The difference in price with the last transaction.

Volume: the number of shares traded (sold or bought).

High Low: The greatest and least price the stock has reached during the last 52 weeks.

A company may issue two types of stocks or shares in the company. **Preferred Stocks** indicate that your shares of the company have a preference over the other shares of the company, called common stocks. A preferred stock pays a fixed dividend whereas **common stocks** allow you the opportunity to participate in the actual profit picture of the company. The stock is called preferred, because the owners of a preferred stock receive a dividend before owners of a common stock receive theirs.

The selling price of a share of the company reflects the financial condition and worth of the company. As the company improves its profits, and its value, the value of the shares reflect this and also increase in value. Thus, the purchase of stocks provides you with an opportunity to increase your net worth as the value of the stocks increase often while paying you dividends. However, the reverse may also occur, and although you thought the company was going to do well, it doesn't and the declining profits are reflected in the declining value of the shares of the company.

> Before you consider investing in the stock market, you must have a clear picture of what you are getting yourself into. You can't make wise decisions if you don't understand the nature of the investment, and the risks that occur.

To explore the stock market, complete the following studies.

## Study A — Talking about Stocks

1 What is meant by each term?

(a) Stockbroker (b) profit
(c) loss (d) common stocks
(e) dividends (f) commission
(g) preferred stocks (h) company earnings
(i) stock exchange (j) share holder

2 (a) Which investment has less risk: preferred stocks or common stocks?
(b) What are the advantages and disadvantages of purchasing preferred stocks versus common stocks?

3 (a) Refer to the yellow pages of a telephone book. Identify 5 companies listed under stock and Bond Brokers.
(b) Obtain a list of the current commission rates used for selling or buying stocks.

4 (a) Use one of the companies you listed in question 3(a). Inquire as to what printed reading materials are available to a person who wishes to invest in the stock market.
(b) What other types of investments are available to a person who wishes to invest?

## Study B — How much will you pay?

5 Refer to the financial pages of a newspaper. The share prices of various companies are listed on the Toronto Stock Exchange. For each of the following,

▶ Record the Ask Price
▶ Calculate the cost of the investment
▶ Determine the amount of commission you need to pay.

(a) 100 shares of Xerox Canada Inc.
(b) 75 shares of Shell Canada
(c) 250 shares of Lake Ontario Cement
(d) 1000 Redpath Industries
(e) 500 Genstar Corp.

6 Refer to the stock listings on the Toronto, Vancouver, or Montreal Stock Exchanges.
(a) Decide on 5 stocks you are going to buy.
(b) Calculate the cost of purchasing 1000 shares. How much commission would you pay?

7 Once you buy the stock, you can calculate the yield rate. Use the following.

$$\text{Yield Rate} = \frac{\text{amount of dividends paid yearly}}{\text{price of stock}} \times 100\%$$

(a) Shaw Industries is listed on the Toronto Stock Exchange.
▶ How much will you need to pay to purchase 100 shares?
▶ What is the yearly dividend? Calculate the yield rate.
(b) Repeat the steps in (a) for the following stocks: Crown Life; Dupont Canada; Inco Limited.
(c) When you earn income you need to pay income taxes, depending on how much income you receive. For each \$100 that Laurie earns in dividends, she pays \$35 of it in income taxes. To calculate her yield rate after taxes, use the following formula.

$$\begin{array}{c}\text{Yield Rate}\\ \text{after taxes}\end{array} = \frac{\begin{array}{c}\text{amount of yearly}\\ \text{dividend}\end{array} - \text{income tax}}{\text{price of stock}} \times 100\%$$

Calculate Laurie's yield rate after taxes for each stock in (a) and (b).

## Study C — Stock Strategy

8 (a) Choose a stock listed on the Toronto Stock Exchange. You bought 1000 shares of this company at the low price shown. What is your total purchase price including commission?
(b) You sold the stock in (a) at the high price shown. How much will you receive in all after commissions are deducted?
(c) How much money did you make in completing the transactions in (a) and (b)? (Your investment strategy is to learn when to buy at the low price and sell at the high price!)
(d) Repeat Steps (a), (b), and (c) for another stock of your choice on the Toronto, Vancouver, or Montreal Stock Exchange.

9 (a) Choose a stock. Record the daily Bid and Ask prices in a chart.

| Day | 1 | 2 | 3 | 28 | 29 | 30 |
|---|---|---|---|---|---|---|
| Bid price | | | | | | |
| Ask price | | | | | | |

(b) Draw a broken-line graph to show the fluctuations in price for 30 days. Can you predict the high and low prices for the stock based on these graphs?

## Study D — Reading the fine print

Annual or financial reports provide you with information about the financial health of the company.

10 Obtain a financial report of a company listed on the Toronto Stock Exchange. Examine each of the following sections in the Annual Report.
(a) Balance Sheet (b) Income Statement

11 (a) For the company you have chosen, what are its
(i) total assets? (ii) total liabilities?
(b) What are the current BID, ASK prices of the stocks of this company on the stock market?

12 The following terms occur in the Annual or Financial Report.
▶ What do you think is meant by each term?
▶ What is the dollar value listed for each?
(a) Accrued expenses payable
(b) Accounts payable
(c) Income taxes payable
(d) Mortgage Bonds
(e) Net Fixed Assets
(f) Inventories
(g) Cash Assets
(h) Accounts Receivable

13 (a) What is the total value of the stocks issued for the company: preferred stock? common stocks?
(b) What is the total value of the capital surplus? retained earnings?
(c) What types of graphs are used in the report to display information? Do the graphs display the information accurately?
(d) What is the value of each of the following in the report: Net Sales? Operating expenses? Total income? Net Profit?

14 (a) What is the net earnings per share listed in the financial report?
(b) What dividends are paid on this stock?
(c) Calculate the yield rate for the stock.

15 (a) Obtain an Annual report of another Canadian Company.
(b) Compare the two companies with respect to the various headings in the financial report.
(c) Which company would you interpret to be in "better financial shape?"

# Review: Practice and Problems

1 Calculate the interest for each of the balances if the rate of interest is given as follows. Each balance was invested for a year.

| | Balance | Rate of Interest |
|---|---|---|
| (a) | $744.59 | 6.5% |
| (b) | $251.03 | 9.5% |
| (c) | $1647.36 | 10.5% |
| (d) | $5043.94 | 9.5% |
| (e) | $2563.11 | 7.5% |

2 Stephanie has a savings account in which the minimum balance from June 30 to December 31 was $1856.52. If interest is paid at 9.75%/a, how much interest does she receive on her balance?

3 (a) Melinda received $1600 and invested the money in a term deposit for 179 days. How much interest did she receive if interest is paid at $10\frac{1}{2}$%?
(b) Shawn received a bonus of $1000. He deposited the money in a term deposit for 269 days. How much interest did he receive if the interest rate is $11\frac{3}{4}$%?

4 Stella's earnings last summer were $642.59. She spent $406.12 for clothes, books, and entertainment. What percent of her income did she spend?

5 Carman works after school in a grocery store earning $4.65/h for a total of 21 hours per week. After deductions, his take home pay is 86% of the earnings.
(a) Find his take home pay.
(b) He spends 21% of his take home pay on entertainment. What percent of his earnings does he spend on entertainment?

6 Calculate the interest payable on each cash advance for the days shown. Interest is calculated at 21% per annum.
(a) $450, 25 days (b) $706, 30 days
(c) $1245, 44 days (d) $952, 68 days

7 Helen's balance on her charge account last month was $672.15. She purchased a camera worth $236.95 and some clothes totalling $157.09. Before the due date she made a payment of $120.00.
(a) What is her minimum monthly payment?
(b) Find the carrying charge for one month at $1\frac{1}{2}$% per month.

8 Dominic purchased a home computer for $1795.50 and made a down payment of $500. He agrees to make 12 equal monthly payments. The rate of interest charged is 21% per annum and the sales tax is 7%.
(a) Calculate the finance charge.
(b) Calculate the amount of each equal monthly payment.

9 Angela borrowed $7500 for a car. She paid $9085 in 24 equal monthly installments. Find the
(a) amount of interest charged.
(b) amount of each installment.
(c) true interest rate.

10 Howard bought a used car for $7965.00 (including all freight charges, sales tax, etc.) He made a down payment of $1500 and agreed to make 36 equal monthly payments of $219.79. Calculate the effective rate of interest. Express your answer to 1 decimal place.

11 Rebecca purchased a $2000 bond paying 12.5% through a broker, which can be redeemed in 5 years. The actual cost of the bond was $1860. The interest rate is payable yearly.
(a) Calculate the amount of interest Rebecca will receive each year.
(b) Calculate the yield rate for the first year of investment.

12 Stelco Industries are listed on the Toronto Stock Exchange.
(a) How much money will you need to purchase 500 shares?
(b) What is the yearly dividend?
(c) Calculate the yield rate.

# A Practice Test

1 Rowena's passbook is shown.

(a) Find the missing balances.

| Date | With | Dep | Bal |
|---|---|---|---|
| 1 May | | | $1241.16 |
| 4 May | $89.17 | | ? |
| 11 May | | $256.50 | ? |
| 20 May | $121.06 | | ? |
| 1 June | $307.19 | | ? |
| 9 June | $70.56 | | ? |
| 17 June | | $63.80 | ? |
| 23 June | | $194.55 | ? |
| 30 June | | $106.80 | ? |
| 5 July | $346.17 | | ? |
| 11 July | $206.84 | | ? |
| 19 July | $90.00 | | ? |
| 26 July | | $156.37 | ? |

(b) What is the total of the withdrawals she made?

(c) Find Rowena's balance on July 26 in a different way than in (a).

2 Prescott purchased an investment certificate for $1250 that pays $9\frac{3}{4}$% per annum.

(a) Calculate the interest paid for a 120 day term.

(b) How much money will he have in 120 days to reinvest?

3 A microwave oven is advertised at $17.95 a month for 60 months. Gerry purchased the microwave for $695.00 plus sales tax. The rate of sales tax is 8%.

(a) How much will it cost if he purchased it on the monthly payment plan?

(b) Find the savings if he paid cash for the microwave.

4 Roger purchased a dishwasher for a total price of $695.95. His previous balance on the account was $252.16. He pays only $80 towards his balance. If the credit charge is calculated at 21% per annum,

(a) calculate the amount of the service charge.

(b) What is the minimum monthly payment? (Refer to the chart on page 249).

5 Refer to the ad.

| MOVIE CAMERA |
|---|
| 2-year warranty |
| $1695.00 |
| VHS—2 h tape |

If you pay 8% sales tax, 33 monthly installments of $56.50, and a $50 down payment, find

(a) the amount of interest paid.

(b) the total cost of the item.

6 Helen can buy a hi-fi in two ways. The hi-fi costs $1495 plus 8% sales tax and no down payment is required. She can pay for it in 12 equal monthly installments of $169 or 18 equal monthly installments of $128. What is the difference in interest between the two methods?

7 A van costs $12 560.00 in all and two banks offer the following installment plans for financing the van.

| Bank A | Bank B |
|---|---|
| No money down | $500 down |
| 60 monthly payments of $265.00 | 48 monthly payments of $297.00 |

Which plan offers the better true rate of interest?

8 (a) The $1000 Government of Canada $11\frac{1}{8}$% bond is quoted at market price of $95\frac{1}{2}$. Holly bought 4 $1000 bonds. Calculate the yield rate for the purchase if she paid $92.50 commission.

(b) Micro Telecommunications issued a corporate bond with a redemption date of February 15, 1999. The market value is $981.25. Calculate the yield on 15 $1000 bonds if the bond rate is $9\frac{3}{4}$%.

9 (a) Gus made the following purchase

| 15 $100 Utilities at $115.50 each |
|---|
| Earning 11.25%/a Payable in 5 years |

Calculate his average yield rate.

(b) Hazel purchased a corporate $10\frac{1}{2}$% bond to mature in 8 years. She purchased a total of $12 000 face value of the bond quoted at $94\frac{1}{2}$. Calculate her average yield rate.

# 10 Using Data: Applications and Solving Problems

the steps of statistics, collecting, organizing and interpreting data, frequency tables, stem and leaf diagrams, using graphical terms, interpreting histograms, problem-solving, cumulative frequency, applying mean, median, and mode, quartiles, percentiles, solving problems and applications

## Introduction

Whether you watch television, listen to the radio, or read the newspaper, you are confronted with much data. Often the need arises to intelligently interpret the data and make decisions. The various pieces of data are referred to as data. When you work with and analyze data you are working with statistics. The study of statistics involves three important steps.

*A* collecting data

*B* organizing the data in some way, such as graphs, charts, tables, and so on

*C* interpreting the data and using them in some useful way, to predict results

• The accumulation of data from space allows us to interpret and understand the solar system we live in better. The data allows us to embark on future space programs to obtain results to experiments that may affect us for generations.

• The compilation and study of data about the flow of vehicles allows the transportation technician to help predict and design better vehicles as well as transportation networks. Data allows us to apply better safety procedures so that incidents as in the photo can be avoided.

# 10.1 Steps of Statistics: Collecting Data

How does a large company like General Motors predict which cars to manufacture more of? The research department collects information and uses this data to make major decisions about consumer choices of colour, desirable styles, consumer tastes and dislikes. The steps followed are as follows.

*Step 1* Collect data

*Step 2* Organize and analyze the data

*Step 3* Interpret and make inferences, predictions and decisions using the data

These steps are the basis of the steps for studying statistics, a branch of mathematics.

The world's first motor car with an internal combustion engine was the 1863 Lenoir named after the Belgian engineer Etienne Lenoir. The average speed of Etienne's first trip was about 6 km/h (a little faster than walking).

Some methods used to collect data involving people are as follows.

A Personal interview, either door to door or at a shopping centre.

B Conducting polls by telephone.

C Filling out questionnaires which are mailed or handed out at various places.

D Making measurements in industry to check the quality of products coming off an assembly line.

Once the data is collected and organized you can look for patterns, and make decisions.

## Example

The following chart shows statistics concerning motor vehicle accidents involving school vehicles.

(a) In which situation do most accidents occur? *crossing road* or *within vehicle*

(b) In year 7, what percentage of the accidents occurred *within vehicle*? Express your answer to 1 decimal place.

| Motor vehicle accidents involving school vehicles: 10 consecutive years | | | | | | | | | | |
|---|---|---|---|---|---|---|---|---|---|---|
| School year | Pupils transported daily | Total number of accidents | Pupil Fatalities (F)/Personal Injuries (P.I.) | | | | | | | |
| | | | Crossing road | | Within vehicle | | Other | | Total | |
| | | | F. | P.I. | F. | P.I. | F. | P.I. | F. | P.I. |
| year 1 | 545 046 | 508 | 0 | 9 | 1 | 153 | 1 | 19 | 2 | 181 |
| year 2 | 558 549 | 542 | 0 | 9 | 0 | 233 | 3 | 18 | 3 | 260 |
| year 3 | 592 026 | 575 | 1 | 6 | 0 | 364 | 0 | 17 | 1 | 387 |
| year 4 | 578 817 | 622 | 4 | 19 | 2 | 205 | 0 | 28 | 6 | 252 |
| year 5 | 594 410 | 727 | 2 | 14 | 2 | 155 | 1 | 24 | 5 | 193 |
| year 6 | 600 082 | 793 | 0 | 10 | 0 | 247 | 1 | 10 | 1 | 267 |
| year 7 | 601 583 | 866 | 1 | 19 | 0 | 259 | 2 | 18 | 3 | 296 |
| year 8 | 599 776 | 838 | 0 | 12 | 1 | 285 | 1 | 28 | 2 | 325 |
| year 9 | 601 813 | 765 | 0 | 12 | 1 | 250 | 3 | 48 | 4 | 310 |
| year 10 | 598 096 | 847 | 1 | 20 | 0 | 191 | 0 | 18 | 1 | 229 |

## Solution

(a) From the chart, most accidents occur within the vehicle.

(b) For year 7, total number of accidents was 866. Number of accidents within vehicle was 259.

$$\text{Percentage of accidents within vehicle} = \frac{259}{866} \times 100\%$$

$$= 29.9\%$$

In year 7, 29.9% of accidents occurred within the vehicle.

## Try These

1 How would you collect data to decide
   (a) the most popular T.V. program?
   (b) the average number of girls in a classroom?
   (c) the most popular recording artist?

2 Refer to the chart on motor vehicle accidents involving school vehicles.
   (a) In which year was the greatest number of pupils transported?
   (b) In which year did the most accidents occur? Is your answer the same as in (a)?
   (c) In which year was the greatest number of students injured within the vehicle? Is your answer the same as in (a)?

## Written Exercises

**A** **Review the methods you can use to collect data. Round answers to 1 decimal place where necessary.**

1 Describe how you would collect data to find the following.
   (a) the top 5 movie stars of the year
   (b) the time required to eat lunch in the cafeteria
   (c) the strength of garbage bags
   (d) the type of vehicles crossing a particular intersection

2 To determine the most popular soft drink, a company sent out a questionnaire to a number of people.
   (a) What are some advantages of using a questionnaire to collect data?
   (b) What are some disadvantages of this method?
   (c) Suggest other ways of predicting the most popular soft drink.

3 To determine the most popular current movie a polling company conducted a telephone survey.
   (a) What are some advantages of using a telephone survey to collect data?
   (b) What are some disadvantages of this method?
   (c) Suggest other ways of determining the most popular movie.

4 You wish to start a summer house painting business with two other students. How would you collect data to help you make a decision as to whether people would be interested in using your service?

**B** **A calculator is useful in checking your work. Questions 5 to 8 are based on the data in the chart on motor vehicle accidents involving school vehicles.**

5 (a) For each year, calculate what percentage the total personal injuries are out of the total number of accidents.
   (b) Based on your results in (a), would you describe the results as
   ▶ improving? ▶ not improving?

6 For each year, what percentage of the accidents due to crossing the road were fatalities? Do you see a trend over the years? Give a reason for your answer.

7 For each year, what percentage of the injuries occurring within the vehicle were fatalities? Do you see a trend over the years? Give a reason for your answer.

8 (a) Use the data in the chart. Based on the information, create a question of your own.
   (b) Write a solution for your question in (a).

Questions 9 to 11 are based on the following experiment.
In an experiment, thumb tacks are dropped to determine the percentage of tacks that fall in each position.

 point up  sideways

Three separate experiments were performed and the following data were recorded.

| Experiment | Number dropped | Number point up | Number sideways |
|---|---|---|---|
| A | 10 | 4 | 6 |
| B | 100 | 39 | 61 |
| C | 1000 | 406 | 594 |

9 (a) Calculate the percentage of tacks that landed sideways for each experiment, A, B and C.
(b) Based on these results predict how many tacks will land sideways if you drop 500.

10 (a) Calculate the percentage of tacks that landed point up for experiments A, B, and C.
(b) How could you find your results in (a) in a different way?
(c) Predict how many thumbtacks will land point up if you drop 10 000.

11 The results for experiment A, B and C are used to obtain the figures for experiment D.

| Experiment | Number dropped | Number point up | Number sideways |
|---|---|---|---|
| D | 1217 | 423 | 794 |

(a) Calculate the percentage of tacks that land sideways in experiment D.
(b) Use your results in (a). Predict how many thumbtacks will land sideways if you drop 500. Compare your answer to the answer in question 9(b).
(c) Calculate the percentage of tacks that land point up for experiment D.
(d) Use your results in (c). Predict how many thumbtacks will land point up if you drop 10 000. Compare your answer to the answer in question 10(c).

12 The *Canadian Constitution* contains the *Charter of Rights and Freedoms.* This charter begins as follows.

> The Canadian Charter of Rights and Freedoms guarantees the rights and freedoms set out in it subject only to such reasonable limits prescribed by law as can be demonstrably justified in a free and democratic society.
>
> **Fundamental Freedoms**
>
> Everyone has the following fundamental freedoms:
> (a) freedom of conscience and religion;
> (b) freedom of thought, belief, opinion and expression, including freedom of the press and other media of communication;
> (c) freedom of peaceful assembly; and
> (d) freedom of association
>
> **Equality Rights**
>
> Every individual is equal before and under the law and has the right to the equal protection and equal benefit of the law without discrimination and, in particular, without discrimination based on race, national or ethnic origin, colour, religion, sex, age, or mental or physical disability.

Analyze the occurrence of letters in this passage.
(a) Which letter of the alphabet occurs most often?
(b) Which letter occurs the least?
(c) Which word or words occur most often?

13 Five stamps were submitted for a design contest.

(a) Which stamp do you personally like the best?
(b) Predict which stamp most people will like the best.
(c) How would you conduct a poll to determine which stamp is liked the best?

# 10.2 Organizing Data: Frequency Tables

Each year millions of dollars are spent on producing television shows. As well, the producers of these shows spend great amounts of money to collect data as to how much the audience likes the program.

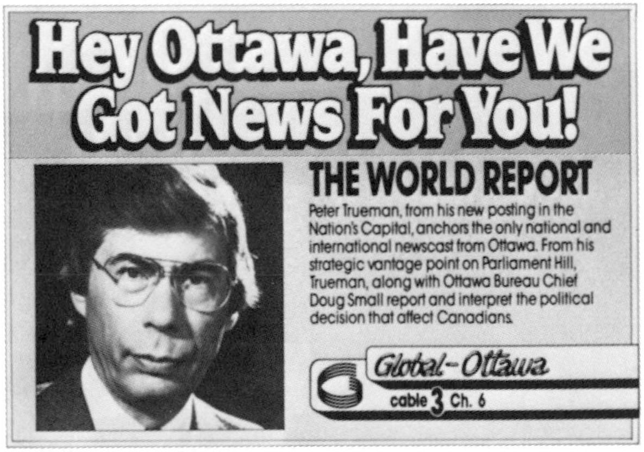
Hey Ottawa, Have We Got News For You!
THE WORLD REPORT
Peter Trueman, from his new posting in the Nation's Capital, anchors the only national and international newscast from Ottawa. From his strategic vantage point on Parliament Hill, Trueman, along with Ottawa Bureau Chief Doug Small report and interpret the political decision that affect Canadians.
Global-Ottawa
cable 3 Ch. 6

If a program is well liked, its sponsors will have to pay larger fees to advertise their products. Thus it is important to produce popular TV shows.

To make decisions, the first important step is to collect the data. For example, information about students' favourite types of programs on T.V. was gathered and recorded.

To show each type of response, letters were used to represent the programs.

Code

| | | | |
|---|---|---|---|
| S | Sports | Q | Quiz shows |
| M | Mysteries | W | Westerns |
| So | Soap Operas | A | Adventure |
| N | News | C | Comedies |

The following summary shows the data collected. In this form, it is difficult to observe any patterns.

| | | | | | | | | | | | |
|---|---|---|---|---|---|---|---|---|---|---|---|
| W | C | So | N | Q | A | M | S | M | So | A | S |
| Q | C | C | N | A | C | N | M | Q | S | So | |
| A | S | Q | A | C | S | N | Q | A | Q | S | So |
| A | A | M | S | So | W | N | C | A | C | | |

Only certain students were asked since it would be too time consuming to ask all of the student population. The students selected are a sample of the entire population of students available.

In order to easily answer questions about the data, the information needs to be organized in a useful way. One way is to use a tally chart. A stroke is used to show each student who preferred a particular type of program.

You can now use the organized data from the chart to answer questions about student viewing preferences.

Preferred T.V. Shows

| Program | Tally | Frequency |
|---|---|---|
| Sports | 𝍸 \|\| | 7 |
| Mysteries | \|\|\|\| | 4 |
| Soap Operas | 𝍸 | 5 |
| News | 𝍸 | 5 |
| Quiz shows | 𝍸 \| | 6 |
| Westerns | \|\| | 2 |
| Adventure | 𝍸 \|\|\|\| | 9 |
| Comedies | 𝍸 \|\| | 7 |

| Question | Answer |
|---|---|
| A How many students preferred soap operas? | 5 |
| B How many students liked mysteries best? | 4 |
| C How many students preferred sports? | 7 |

## Try These

Refer to the chart on Preferred TV Shows.

1 (a) What is the greatest frequency in the chart? What type of program is this?
  (b) What is the least frequency in the chart? What type of program is this?

2 (a) How many students were interviewed?
  (b) What percentage of the students liked to watch adventure programs best?

3 (a) If you want to advertise your product to high school students on TV, which type of program(s) would you choose?
  (b) Which type of programs would you not use to advertise your product to high school students?

## Written Exercises

**A** To do statistics, you must know the meaning of the words: tally, frequency.

Questions 1 to 3 are based on the following chart. The chart shows students' response to the question:
*"What is your favourite sport?"*

Favourite Sports

| Sport | Tally | Frequency |
|---|---|---|
| Swimming | 𝍸 ||| | ? |
| Skiing | 𝍸 𝍸 | | ? |
| Football | 𝍸 𝍸 || | ? |
| Basketball | 𝍸 𝍸 |||| | ? |
| Soccer | 𝍸 |||| | ? |
| Tennis | 𝍸 ||| | ? |
| Hockey | 𝍸 𝍸 𝍸 || | ? |
| Track and Field | 𝍸 𝍸 𝍸 𝍸 | ? |
| Volleyball | 𝍸 𝍸 || | ? |

1 (a) What is the frequency of each sport?
  (b) How many students were surveyed who liked tennis?
  (c) How many students preferred skiing?

2 (a) What was the most popular sport?
  (b) What was the least favourite sport?

3 (a) How many students were surveyed in all?
  (b) What percentage liked basketball best?
  (c) What percentage preferred swimming?

Questions 4 to 6 are based on the following information.

The type of soft drinks sold during one lunch period is shown.

Frequency Table

| Soft Drink | Tally | Frequency |
|---|---|---|
| Cola | 𝍸 𝍸 𝍸 || | ? |
| Ginger ale | 𝍸 𝍸 |||| | ? |
| Orange | 𝍸 |||| | ? |
| Root Beer | 𝍸 | ? |
| Soda Water | 𝍸 || | ? |
| Cream Soda | |||| | ? |

4 What was the frequency for
  (a) cola?  (b) ginger ale?
  (c) soda water?

5 Which soft drink sold
  (a) most often?  (b) least often?
  (c) How would you use the information in (a) and (b) to order supplies?

6 (a) Calculate the percentage of each type of soft drink sold.
  (b) Based on your answer in (a), how much of a monthly total of $865.80 in sales is from
    ► cola sales?  ► orange sales?

**B** Use your calculator to check your work.

Questions 7 to 12 are based on the following information obtained from a sample of students. The students were asked the following question: *"How far is it from your home to your school?"*

| Distance from home to school (in kilometres) | | | | | | |
|---|---|---|---|---|---|---|
| 2.7 | 7 | 9 | 0.8 | 4 | 5 | 6 |
| 3 | 8 | 11 | 5.5 | 6 | 3.4 | 7 |
| 10 | 1.3 | 3.8 | 6 | 4 | 1.5 | 3 |
| 9 | 12 | 7 | 5.8 | 22 | 18 | 8 |

7 Copy and complete the frequency table as started below for the data.

Frequency Table

| Distance (in kilometres) (class) | Number of students (frequency) |
|---|---|
| 0–5 | ? |
| 5–10 | ? |
| 10–15 | ? |
| 15–20 | ? |
| 20–25 | ? |

(20–25) means distances from 20 km up to but excluding 25 km

8 (a) How many students were interviewed?
(b) How many students travel 20 km or more?
(c) How many students travel less than 5 km?

9 (a) What percentage of the students live 5 km or more from school?
(b) What percentage of the students live 15 km or more from school?
(c) What is the average number of kilometres travelled from home to school?

10 From past records, the school officials estimate that 20% of the students travelling 10 km or less use their own transportation.
(a) If the school has 972 students, how many students use their own transportation?
(b) Students who travel 20 km or more to school spend about $18.50 on expenses per week. Calculate the total spent on expenses by these students each week.

11 Which statement can you more reasonably support?
A Most students travel more than 10 km from their home to school.
B Most students travel less than 10 km from their home to school.

12 Refer to the data in the chart.
(a) Create a question of your own based on the information.
(b) Write a solution to your question in (a).

---

Questions 13 to 16 are based on the following information.

In a group of 36 people, the following pulses were obtained for a time period of 1 minute.

| | | | | | | | | | | | |
|---|---|---|---|---|---|---|---|---|---|---|---|
| 62 | 67 | 66 | 61 | 71 | 53 | 79 | 64 | 67 | 83 | 81 | 73 |
| 64 | 83 | 81 | 67 | 72 | 77 | 61 | 79 | 53 | 86 | 77 | 67 |
| 56 | 67 | 62 | 56 | 82 | 96 | 72 | 77 | 64 | 67 | 56 | 82 |

13 (a) Why is it difficult to make observations about the above data in its present form?
(b) Construct a frequency chart as started below for the above information.

| Pulse rate (class) | Frequency |
|---|---|
| 50–55 | ? |
| 55–60 | ? |
| 60–65 | ? |
| 65–70 | ? |

14 (a) What was the highest pulse rate recorded?
(b) What percentage of the pulse rates were less than 75?
(c) What percentage of the pulse rates were 75 or greater?

15 (a) What is the average pulse rate for the group?
(b) Is your pulse rate above or below the average?

16 Use the data on pulse rates.
(a) Create a question of your own based on the information.
(b) Write a solution for your question in (a).

# 10.3 Organizing Data: Stem-and-Leaf Diagrams

There are different ways to record and organize data. A **stem-and-leaf diagram** is another useful way to organize data. The data below is taken from a list of marks. These marks show the results of a class test out of 100 total possible marks. A stem-and-leaf diagram is constructed for the data as shown.

| | | | | | | |
|---|---|---|---|---|---|---|
| 63 | 48 | 72 | 96 | 54 | 61 | 80 |
| 38 | 63 | 87 | 95 | 62 | 59 | 55 |
| 56 | 44 | 49 | 88 | 60 | 98 | 57 |
| 35 | 56 | 75 | 82 | 64 | 77 | 65 |

The stem is formed by the tens digit. ⟶ Tens

Units ⟵ The units digit forms the leaves.

| Tens | Units | | | | | |
|---|---|---|---|---|---|---|
| 3 | 8 | 5 | | | | |
| 4 | 8 | 4 | 9 | | | |
| 5 | 4 | 9 | 5 | 6 | 7 | 6 |
| 6 | 3 | 1 | 3 | 2 | 0 | 4 | 5 |
| 7 | 2 | 5 | 7 | | | |
| 8 | 0 | 7 | 8 | 2 | | |
| 9 | 6 | 5 | 8 | | | |

The data shown is ⟶ (row 5) 54 59 55 56 57 56

⟵ The data shown in this row (row 9) is 96 95 98

## Try These

Refer to the stem-and-leaf diagram showing the data on the marks for the class test.

1 (a) How many students wrote the test?
  (b) What is the highest mark?
  (c) What is the lowest mark?

2 (a) How many students passed?
  (b) How many students failed?
  (c) How many students obtained marks in the fifties?

3 (a) How many students obtained marks above 80?
  (b) How many students obtained marks below 70?
  (c) Arrange the marks from lowest to highest.

## Written Exercises

**A** Questions 1 to 3 are based on the following information.

The stem-and-leaf diagram shows the pulses of 26 people.

| Tens | Units | | | | | | | |
|---|---|---|---|---|---|---|---|---|
| 5 | 3 | 1 | 8 | 9 | | | | |
| 6 | 6 | 1 | 4 | 7 | 7 | 7 | 8 | 6 |
| 7 | 9 | 1 | 3 | 6 | 3 | | | |
| 8 | 6 | 1 | 7 | 6 | 6 | 2 | | |
| 9 | 0 | 1 | 3 | | | | | |

1 How many people had a pulse rate of
  (a) 67? (b) 76? (c) 81? (d) 96?

2 (a) How many people had a pulse rate of 86 or better?
  (b) How many people had a pulse rate of 67 or less?
  (c) What is the least pulse rate? the greatest pulse rate?

3 (a) Calculate the average pulse rate.
  (b) How many persons have a pulse rate above the average? Below the average?

Questions 4 to 7 are based on the following information.

A stem-and-leaf diagram can also be shown in a vertical format. The diagram shows the number of basketball throws sunk by students each taking 50 throws.

| | | | | | |
|---|---|---|---|---|---|
| | | | 7 | | |
| | | 2 | 7 | | |
| | | 8 | 6 | | |
| | | 7 | 5 | 8 | |
| 8 | 7 | 6 | 4 | 2 | |
| 9 | 7 | 7 | 4 | 2 | |
| 4 | 1 | 9 | 1 | 1 | |
| 9 | 4 | 1 | 8 | 1 | |
| 6 | 5 | 5 | 9 | 3 | |
| 3 | 2 | 3 | 2 | 2 | 0 |
| 0 | 1 | 2 | 3 | 4 | 5 |

4 (a) How many students participated?
(b) Based on the data, which students would you choose for the ideal basketball team?
(c) What assumption did you make in arriving at your answer in (b)?

5 How many students were successful on only
(a) 17 throws? (b) 22 throws?
(c) 34 throws? (d) 46 throws?

6 (a) What number of successful throws occurred most often?
(b) How many students had fewer than 22 successful throws?

7 Refer to the stem-and-leaf diagram.
(a) Create a question based on the information.
(b) Write a solution for your question in (a).

**B** Questions 8 to 12 are based on the following data. The number of points scored by a basketball team during a season was recorded as shown.

| | | | | | | | | | | |
|---|---|---|---|---|---|---|---|---|---|---|
| 66 | 78 | 62 | 42 | 74 | 75 | 59 | 109 | 73 | 96 | 58 |
| 74 | 70 | 53 | 69 | 51 | 40 | 92 | 66 | 44 | 63 | 60 |
| 57 | 88 | 68 | 60 | 67 | 76 | 87 | 102 | 64 | 66 | 87 |

8 (a) Construct a stem-and-leaf diagram to show the data.
(b) How many games were played?

9 In how many games did the basketball team score
(a) more than 56 points?
(b) fewer than 73 points?
(c) What was the most frequently occurring score?

10 In what percentage of the games did the team
(a) score more than 80 points?
(b) fewer than 60 points?

11 (a) From the stem-and-leaf diagram, estimate the average number of points scored per game.
(b) Use the data. Calculate the average number of points scored per game. How does your answer compare to that in (a)?

12 Use the data given, and your stem-and-leaf diagram.
(a) Create a question based on the data.
(b) Write a solution for your question in (a).

---

Questions 13 and 14 are based on the following data showing the times, in seconds, of 30 students running the 100-metre dash.

| | | | | | | | | | |
|---|---|---|---|---|---|---|---|---|---|
| 15.1 | 14.6 | 13.0 | 15.3 | 11.6 | 14.1 | 12.6 | 15.1 | 14.0 | 13.6 |
| 11.5 | 12.7 | 12.8 | 16.0 | 14.0 | 13.8 | 12.9 | 10.7 | 12.2 | 12.1 |
| 13.1 | 13.0 | 12.0 | 13.7 | 13.6 | 11.2 | 14.8 | 10.9 | 12.5 | 12.7 |

13 (a) Make a stem-and-leaf diagram for the data.
(b) How many students finished in less than 12 seconds?
(c) How many students finished in less than 14 seconds?

14 (a) How many students took more than 14.5 seconds to run the 100-metre dash?
(b) What was the time of the student who came in second last?

15 (a) Construct a stem-and-leaf diagram based on the following data.

Number of registered voters for each polling station

| | | | | | | | | |
|---|---|---|---|---|---|---|---|---|
| 309 | 588 | 396 | 520 | 465 | 299 | 277 | 449 | 431 |
| 235 | 324 | 241 | 625 | 351 | 406 | 425 | 605 | |
| 676 | 383 | 297 | 297 | 694 | 413 | 301 | 415 | |
| 539 | 525 | 354 | 498 | 412 | 505 | 236 | 153 | |
| 205 | 349 | 284 | 290 | 296 | 621 | 530 | 154 | |

(b) Create a question of your own based on the stem-and-leaf diagram.
(c) Write a solution for your question in (a).

# 10.4 Displaying Data: Using Graphical Terms

As you glance through a newspaper or a magazine, you will notice the variety of methods used to display information and data. The following examples illustrate some of the methods available.

**Pictographs**

Presenting information in a pictograph allows comparisons to be made visually. The pictograph shows the number of cars produced during one year. A title is used to label the pictograph.

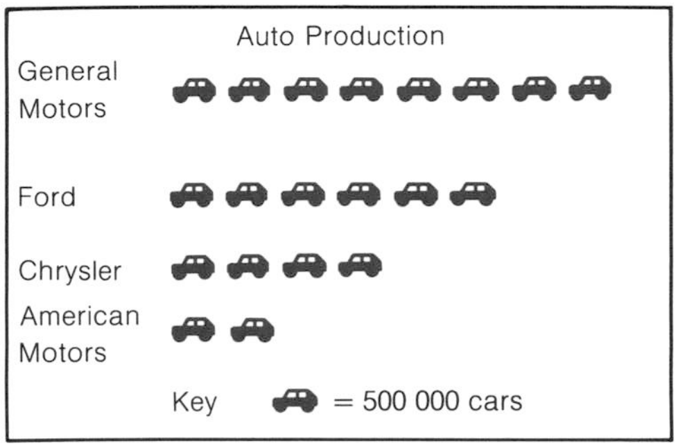


To interpret the information accurately a "key" or *legend* must be shown on the pictograph. From the pictograph you can see at a glance that:

A the greatest number of cars is produced by General Motors.

B the least number of cars is produced by American Motors.

**Bar Graphs**

In a bar graph, horizontal or vertical bars are used to show the data. The simplest type with single bars is shown.

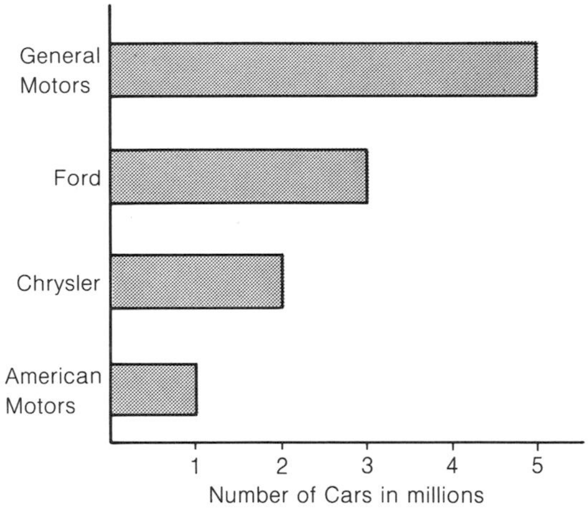


The length of the bar gives a visual representation of the data it represents. A scale is shown on one axis.

**Broken Line Graphs**

When the data relates two measures then each value can be shown by a point on a graph and the points are then joined to form a broken line. Scales are shown on both axes.

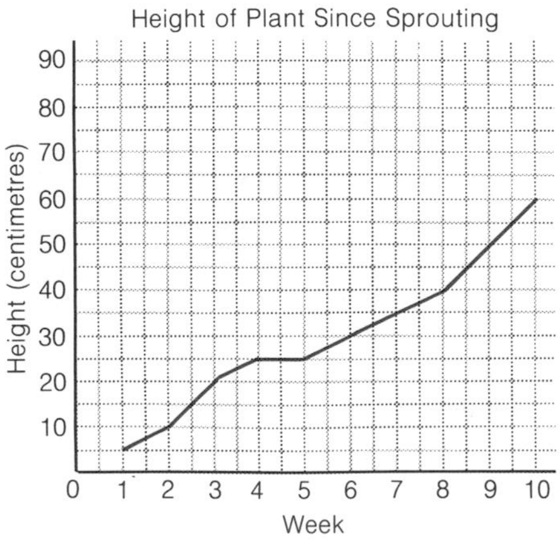

**Circle Graphs**
Circle graphs are often used to show comparisons that involve percents. For example, the amount of time spent to prepare the grounds (cut grass, plant, and so on) of the government properties is shown. Calculations are completed to prepare the circle graph.

| Property | Hours spent | Fraction of total | Percentage of total |
|---|---|---|---|
| Building A | 6 | $\frac{6}{50}$ | 12% |
| Building B | 12.5 | $\frac{12.5}{50}$ | 25% |
| Building C | 8 | $\frac{8}{50}$ | 16% |
| Main Buildings | 14 | $\frac{14}{50}$ | 28% |
| Rear Buildings | 9.5 | $\frac{9.5}{50}$ | 19% |
| Total | 50.0 | $\frac{50}{50}$ | 100% |

To show the information using a circle graph, the circle is marked into parts called *sectors*.

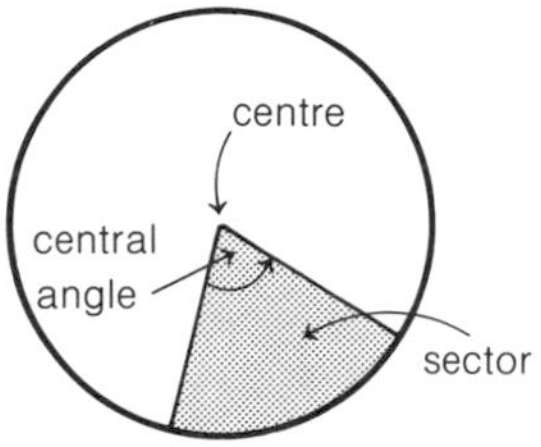


To determine what part of the circle graph should be used for each sector, per cent calculations are performed as shown.

| Property | Percentage | Measure of central angle |
|---|---|---|
| A | 12% | 12% of 360° = 43° |
| B | 25% | 25% of 360° = 90° |
| C | 16% | 16% of 360° = 58° |
| main | 28% | 28% of 360° = 101° |
| rear | 19% | 19% of 360° = 68° |
| Total | 100% | 360° |

Time Spent Maintaining Grounds

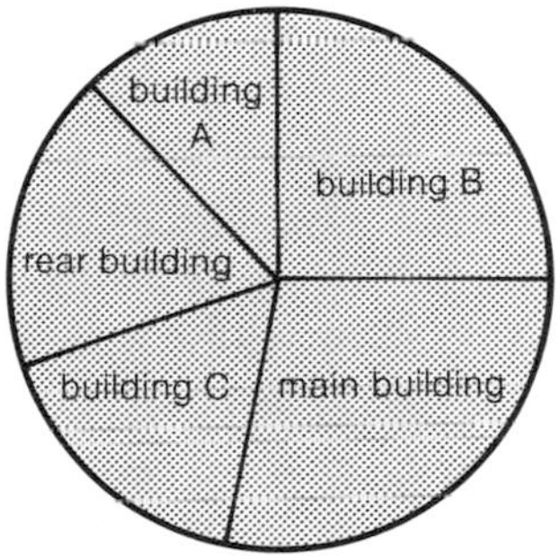


## Try These

1 Refer to the broken line graph.
  (a) What was the height of the plant by the end of the third week since sprouting?
  (b) By the end of which week had the plant grown to a height of 50 cm?
  (c) During which week did the plant not grow in height?

2 Refer to the pictograph.
  (a) How many more cars are produced by General Motors than by Chrysler?
  (b) What is the average number of cars produced by the four companies?

3 Refer to the circle graph.
  (a) Which building requires the most amount of maintenance?
  (b) Which two buildings require over half of the time available for maintenance?

## Written Exercises

**A** Round your answers to 1 decimal place as needed.

Questions 1 to 3 are based on the following pictograph.

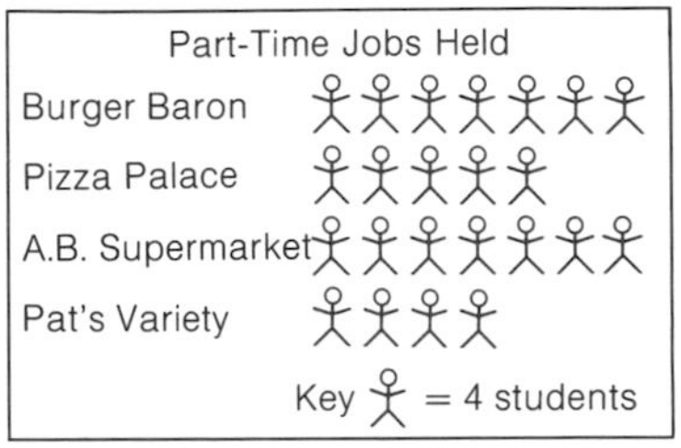


1 How many students work for each employer?
(a) Burger Baron (b) A.B. Supermarket
(c) Pat's Variety (d) Pizza Palace

2 (a) From the pictograph estimate the average number of students working at each place.
(b) Calculate the average number of students working at each place. How does your answer compare to your answer in (a)?

3 (a) How many students work altogether?
(b) What is the ratio of the number of students who work at Pizza Palace compared to the number at Pat's Variety.

4 Refer to the information shown by the circle graph.

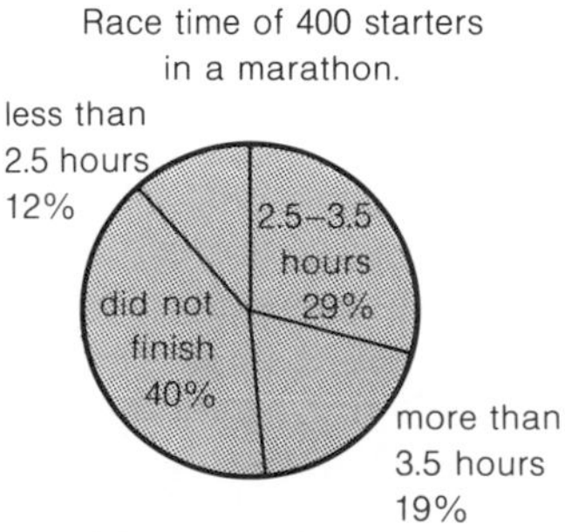


(a) What percentage of the starters finished the race?
(b) How many did not finish the race?
(c) How many finished in less than 2.5 hours?

Questions 5 to 7 are based on the following bar graph showing the number of albums sold.

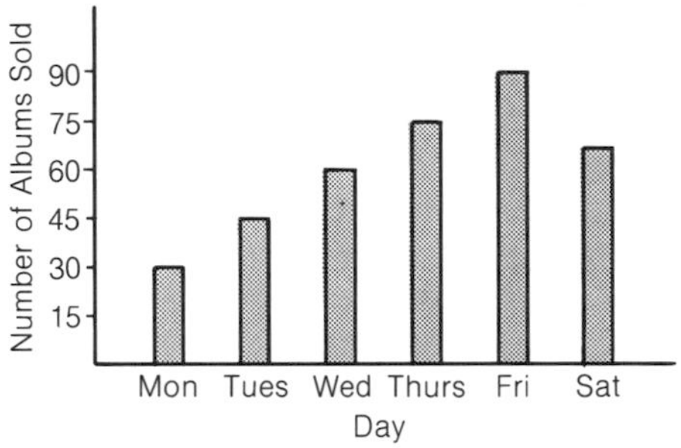


5 How many albums were sold on each day?
(a) Monday (b) Friday (c) Wednesday

6 For each pair shown, on which day were more albums sold?
(a) Thursday, Tuesday
(b) Monday, Friday
(c) Saturday, Wednesday

7 On which days were more than
(a) 50 albums sold? (b) 65 albums sold?

8 Refer to the graph.

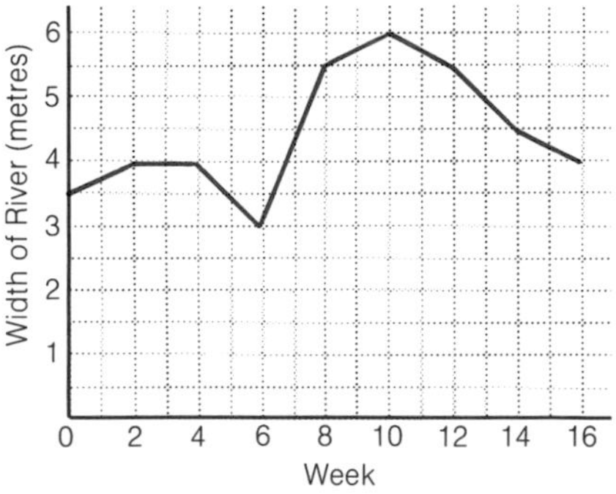


(a) During which of the weeks shown was the river least wide? What was its width that week?
(b) During which two week period would you say that the rainfall was the heaviest?
(c) From the weeks shown, what would you estimate the average width of this river to be?

**B** Questions 9 to 11 are based on the following information.

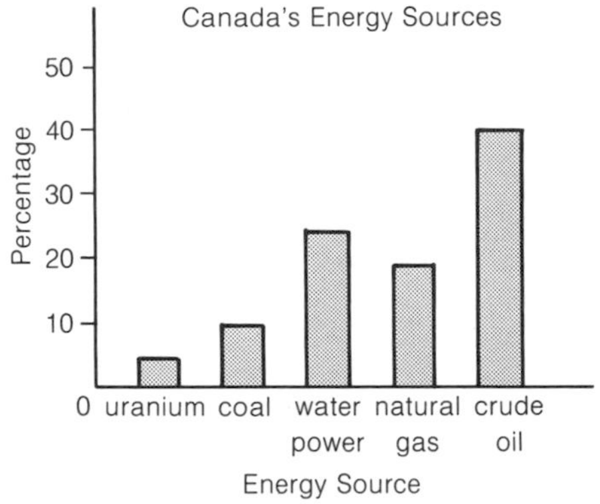


9 (a) From the bar graph, which energy is used most?
(b) Which energy source is used least?

10 What single source provides more than 30% of Canada's energy?

11 What percentage of Canada's energy comes from
(a) coal? (b) natural gas?
(c) crude oil? (d) water power?

12 Refer to the graph *Temperature of Lake Water.*

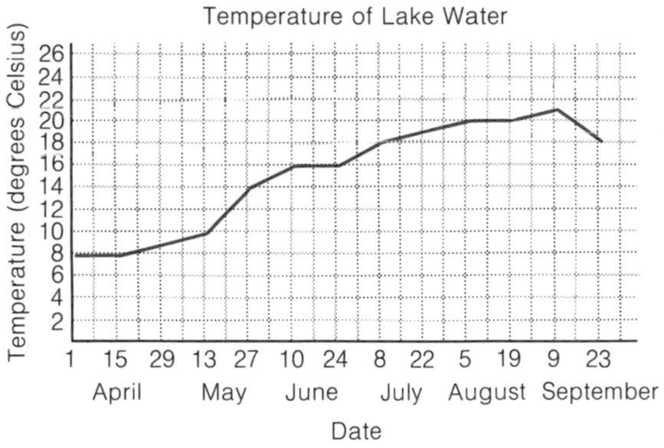


(a) On which approximate date did the lake have its warmest temperature? What was the temperature that day?
(b) At what intervals of time was the lake temperature measured?
(c) Between which two of the dates recorded did the temperature increase the most?
(d) Create a question based on the information in the graph. Write a solution to your problem.

Questions 13 to 18 are based on the following information.
Brenna is the top scorer on the volleyball team. Her scores for the regular season games are shown in the chart below.

| Game | 1 | 2 | 3 | 4 | 5 | 6 | 7 | 8 | 9 | 10 |
|---|---|---|---|---|---|---|---|---|---|---|
| Number of points | 9 | 12 | 18 | 20 | 16 | 7 | 10 | 24 | 15 | 19 |

13 Construct a pictograph to show the information.

14 In which game did Brenna score
(a) her greatest number of points?
(b) her least number of points?

15 What is the ratio of points scored
(a) in the second game to the last game?
(b) in the fourth game to the last game?

16 What percentage of her points were scored
(a) in the first half of the season?
(b) in the last half of the season?

17 (a) From your graph, estimate the average number of points that she scored per game.
(b) Calculate her average number of points scored per game. How does your answer compare to that in (a)?

18 (a) Construct a circle graph for the data shown in the chart.

| Region | Percentage of world population |
|---|---|
| Europe | 20 |
| Asia | 55 |
| Africa | 10 |
| South America | 4 |
| North America | 10 |
| Oceania | 1 |

(b) Create a problem based on the given information.
(c) Write a solution for the problem you have created in (b).

# 10.5 Interpreting Histograms

In many situations and experiments we have to deal with a large number of measurements. It is not easy to examine the chart shown, for example, and make observations about the data. We would like to present this data in a simple and informative way.

Experimental Data

| | | | | | | | | | | | | | |
|---|---|---|---|---|---|---|---|---|---|---|---|---|---|
| 2 | 15 | 48 | 18 | 6 | 7 | 69 | 66 | 55 | 2 | 6 | 79 | 51 | 23 |
| 36 | 60 | 11 | 8 | 69 | 28 | 6 | 40 | 14 | 16 | 52 | 32 | 21 | 9 |
| 94 | 48 | 64 | 70 | 37 | 41 | 51 | 26 | 56 | 56 | 36 | 9 | 42 | 22 |
| 15 | 55 | 27 | 35 | 8 | 62 | 33 | 61 | 20 | 64 | 31 | 49 | 59 | 84 |
| 12 | 68 | 34 | 29 | 41 | 2 | 47 | 17 | 74 | 50 | 7 | 66 | 1 | 43 |
| 34 | 62 | 10 | 58 | 13 | 61 | 55 | 45 | 38 | 33 | 67 | 72 | 54 | 29 |
| 87 | 52 | 19 | 38 | 3 | 81 | 8 | 47 | 57 | 85 | 16 | 58 | 42 | 93 |
| 12 | 49 | 4 | 71 | 18 | 46 | 2 | 51 | 28 | 44 | 25 | 65 | 33 | 82 |
| 74 | 63 | 93 | 9 | 39 | 61 | 52 | 24 | 21 | 19 | 73 | 53 | 48 | 30 |

In order to analyze this data, you need to organize the data. A method involving **class intervals** is useful as shown in the chart.

Experimental Data

| Class Interval | Tally | Frequency |
|---|---|---|
| 0–9 | 卌 卌 卌 \|\|\| | 18 |
| 10–19 | 卌 卌 卌 | 15 |
| 20–29 | 卌 卌 \|\|\| | 13 |
| 30–39 | 卌 卌 卌 | 15 |
| 40–49 | 卌 卌 卌 \| | 16 |
| 50–59 | 卌 卌 卌 \|\|\| | 18 |
| 60–69 | 卌 卌 卌 \| | 16 |
| 70–79 | 卌 \|\| | 7 |
| 80–89 | 卌 | 5 |
| 90–99 | \|\|\| | 3 |

← number of values in each class

Total 126

To display the data, a bar graph is drawn using the class intervals in the chart.

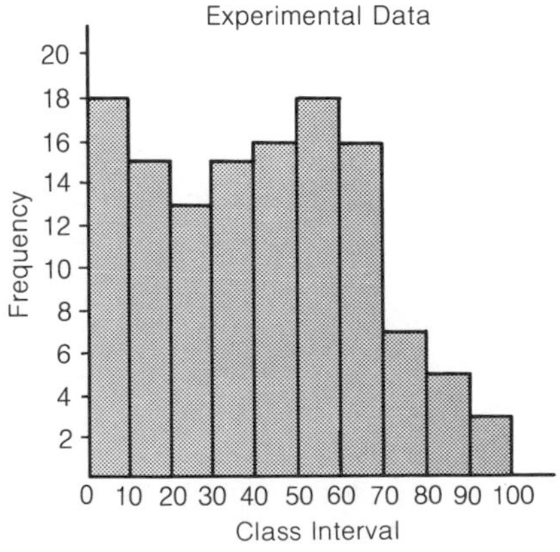


A bar graph showing the frequency in each class is called a **histogram**. Each class interval has the same length.

A **frequency polygon** is made from the histogram as follows: the midpoints of the top of each bar are connected in order. How are the histogram and the frequency polygon alike? How do they differ?

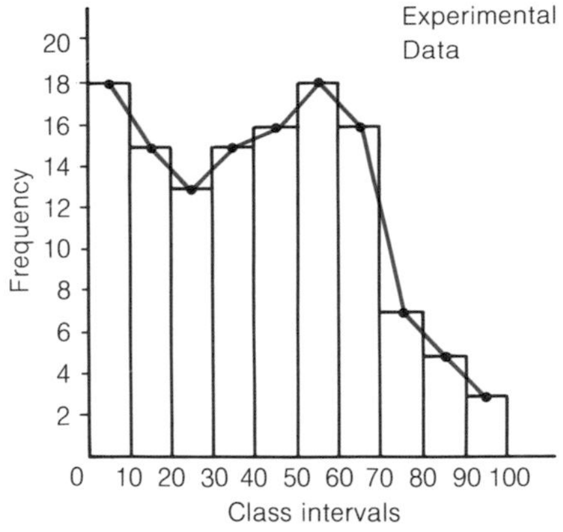


Drawing a histogram provides data in a visual way to a manufacturer such as in the following example.

## Example

The table gives data on the distribution of the "life" of light bulbs. Draw a histogram to illustrate the data.

Frequency Distribution

This interval includes the value 1000 → 1000–1100

| Life (in hours) | Frequency |
|---|---|
| 900–1000 | 10 |
| 1000–1100 | 14 |
| 1100–1200 | 19 |
| 1200–1300 | 26 |
| 1300–1400 | 35 |
| 1400–1500 | 43 |
| 1500–1600 | 49 |
| 1600–1700 | 54 |
| 1700–1800 | 39 |
| 1800–1900 | 18 |
| 1900–2000 | 12 |

## Solution

Life of light bulbs

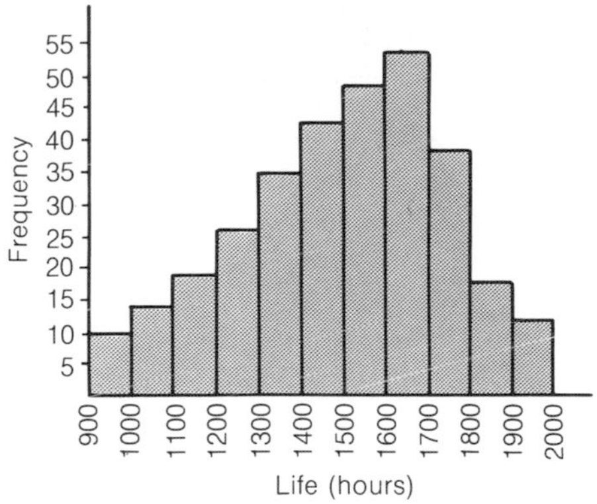


## Try These

The histogram shows the scores achieved on a test taken by high school students.

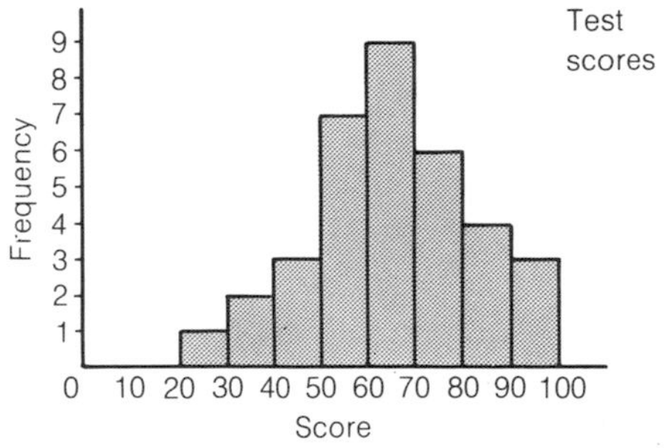


Refer to the histogram.

1 In which class interval did the greatest number of scores occur?

2 How many students scored less than 50?

3 How many more students scored in the 80–90 class interval than in the 40–50 class interval?

4 How many students had a score of 70 or more?

## Written Exercises

**A** Review the meaning of classes, class intervals, frequency and histogram.

Questions 1 to 3 refer to the following histogram.

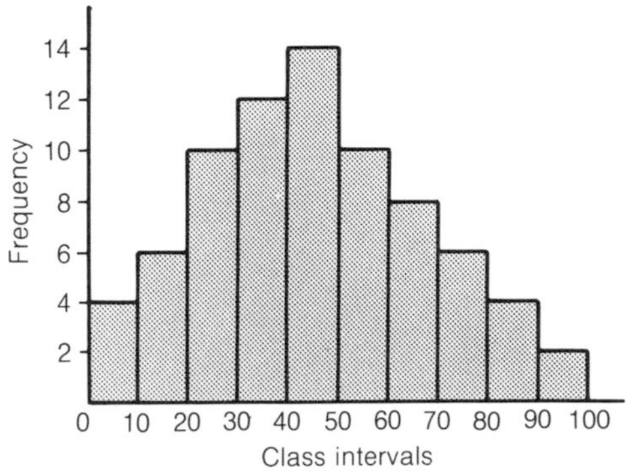


1 (a) In which class interval does the most data occur?
(b) In which class interval does the least data occur?

2 (a) How many classes are there?
(b) What are the class boundaries?

3 (a) How many values are there in the class interval 20–30?
(b) How many values are there in the classes 80 or more?

---

Questions 4 to 7 are based on the histogram shown.

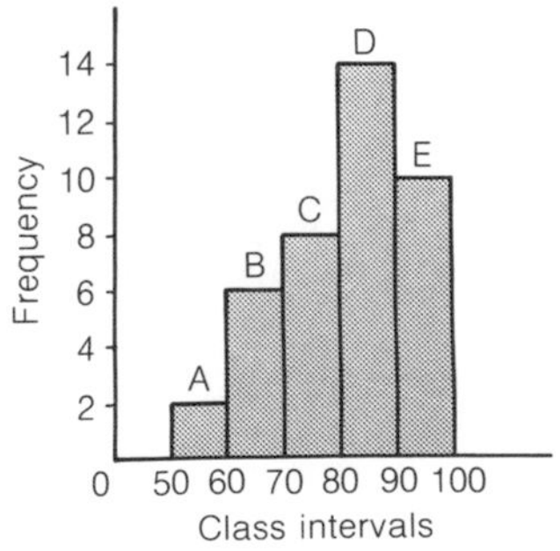


4 (a) How many classes are there?
(b) What are the class boundaries?

5 (a) How many values does the class 50–60 have?
(b) How many values does the class 80–90 have?

6 (a) Calculate the ratio, $\frac{\text{area of A}}{\text{area of B}}$

(b) Calculate the ratio,

$$\frac{\text{frequency of class 50–60}}{\text{frequency of class 60–70}}$$

(c) What do you notice about your answers in (a) and (b)?

7 (a) In which class interval do most of the values occur?
(b) In which 3 class intervals do most of the values occur?

**B** How are a histogram and a frequency polygon related? Review how their graphs are constructed.

Questions 8 to 10 are based on the following histogram. The heights of evergreens in a reforestation project were recorded.

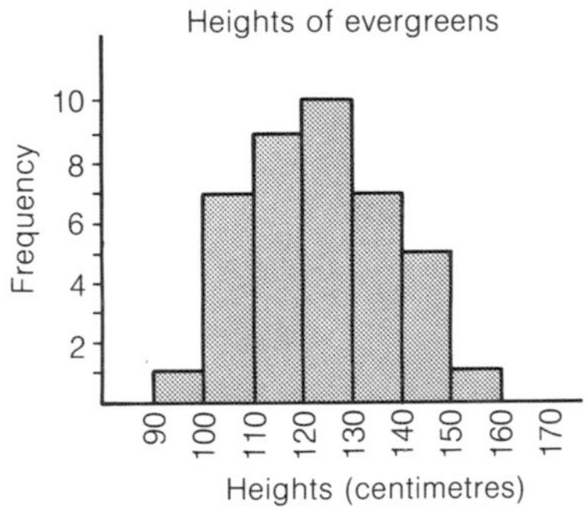


8 (a) Which height class contains the most evergreens?
(b) Which classes contain the same number of trees?
(c) How many evergreens were below 100 cm?
(d) Between which two heights are 95% of the evergreens?

9 (a) From the histogram, estimate the average height of the evergreens.
(b) The actual data used to construct the histogram is shown in the table.

| | | | | | | | | | |
|---|---|---|---|---|---|---|---|---|---|
| 101 | 123 | 148 | 133 | 139 | 99 | 112 | 126 | 120 | 103 |
| 142 | 96 | 113 | 125 | 135 | 122 | 118 | 145 | 128 | 114 |
| 105 | 117 | 132 | 131 | 125 | 111 | 100 | 115 | 156 | 129 |
| 108 | 112 | 126 | 138 | 143 | 137 | 109 | 104 | 127 | 122 |

Calculate the average height of the evergreens. How does your answer compare to your answer in (a)?

10 (a) Create a problem based on the histogram or the data.
(b) Write a solution for your problem in (a).

---

Questions 11 to 13 are based on the following information.

The B.A. Tery Company tested the lifetime of flashlight batteries. Forty flashlights are left switched on until they fail. The time in hours to failure is recorded as follows.

| | | | | | | | |
|---|---|---|---|---|---|---|---|
| 18.2 | 15.4 | 10.8 | 17.1 | 21.2 | 18.4 | 19.8 | 14.2 |
| 19.3 | 20.6 | 8.4 | 12.3 | 16.9 | 15.4 | 9.5 | 10.7 |
| 14.7 | 8.3 | 11.7 | 15.4 | 9.8 | 23.4 | 13.7 | 18.0 |
| 15.6 | 12.5 | 16.4 | 19.9 | 20.8 | 9.6 | 15.8 | 21.3 |
| 17.5 | 16.2 | 21.1 | 10.8 | 7.9 | 13.7 | 16.9 | 14.8 |

11 (a) Construct a frequency distribution using classes 0–10, 10–20, 20–30 and so on.
(b) Construct a histogram to show the data.
(c) Construct a frequency polygon for the data.

12 (a) Use your histogram. In which class does the greatest frequency occur?
(b) Estimate the average life of the battery.

13 (a) Create a question based on the data.
(b) Write a solution for the question you have created in (a).

Questions 14 to 16 are based on the following data.

A survey was conducted to determine the number of children in the average Canadian family. The following data was obtained.

| | | | | | | | | | |
|---|---|---|---|---|---|---|---|---|---|
| 2 | 1 | 3 | 7 | 3 | 2 | 5 | 1 | 1 | 4 |
| 3 | 6 | 3 | 3 | 4 | 5 | 1 | 2 | 2 | 2 |
| 5 | 4 | 3 | 7 | 8 | 2 | 5 | 5 | 6 | 6 |
| 9 | 3 | 3 | 2 | 1 | 1 | 1 | 0 | 4 | 5 |
| 0 | 2 | 1 | 3 | 0 | 3 | 3 | 4 | 2 | 2 |

14 (a) What classes would you use for the data?
(b) Complete a frequency distribution for the data.

15 (a) Construct a histogram to show the data.
(b) Construct a frequency polygon for the data.

16 Use your histogram.
(a) What percentage of the families interviewed have 3 children?
(b) What percentage have 2 or less children?
(c) Estimate the average number of children in each family.
(d) Use the data. Calculate the average number of children in each family. How does your answer compare to your answer in (c)?

17 Air pollution readings for Winnipeg are shown in the chart.

| | Class | Frequency |
|---|---|---|
| pollution parts per million | 0.00–0.05 | 4 |
| | 0.05–0.10 | 3 |
| | 0.10–0.15 | 6 |
| | 0.15–0.20 | 4 |
| | 0.20–0.25 | 2 |
| | 0.25–0.30 | 2 |
| | 0.30–0.35 | 1 |

(a) Construct a histogram for the data.
(b) Create a question based on the data. Write a solution to your question.

# 10.6 Using Cumulative Frequency

How can a manufacturer determine whether the goods mass produced are satisfactory? For example, to check the quality control of calculators, a manufacturer tests 50 calculators in every 1000 produced. Each of the 50 calculators undergoes various tests. The time taken to conduct the tests on each of the calculators is shown in the table.

Data

| | | | | | | | | | |
|---|---|---|---|---|---|---|---|---|---|
| 22 | 31 | 19 | 85 | 36 | 40 | 63 | 24 | 57 | 82 |
| 41 | 35 | 40 | 29 | 27 | 26 | 30 | 36 | 68 | 84 |
| 48 | 21 | 47 | 75 | 83 | 34 | 80 | 21 | 79 | 53 |
| 20 | 42 | 25 | 31 | 54 | 30 | 66 | 24 | 18 | 81 |
| 89 | 32 | 64 | 88 | 30 | 31 | 62 | 24 | 86 | 78 |

Frequency Table

| Time of testing (seconds) | Frequency | Cumulative frequency | |
|---|---|---|---|
| 10–20 | 3 | 3 | |
| 20–30 | 13 | 16 | ← $3 + 13 = 16$ |
| 30–40 | 7 | 23 | ← $3 + 13 + 7 = 23$ |
| 40–50 | 5 | 28 | |
| 50–60 | 4 | 32 | |
| 60–70 | 6 | 38 | |
| 70–80 | 4 | 42 | |
| 80–90 | 8 | 50 | |

A frequency table is constructed for the data. For data obtained in quality control it is also useful to know the answers to questions such as

- ▶ How many calculators were tested for less than 20 seconds?
- ▶ How many calculators were tested for more than 40 seconds?

Thus a useful piece of information about the data is the cumulative frequency. The **cumulative frequency** for any class is the cumulative sum of the frequencies that have occurred.

A cumulative frequency curve can be drawn, so that you can answer questions about quality control in a visual manner.

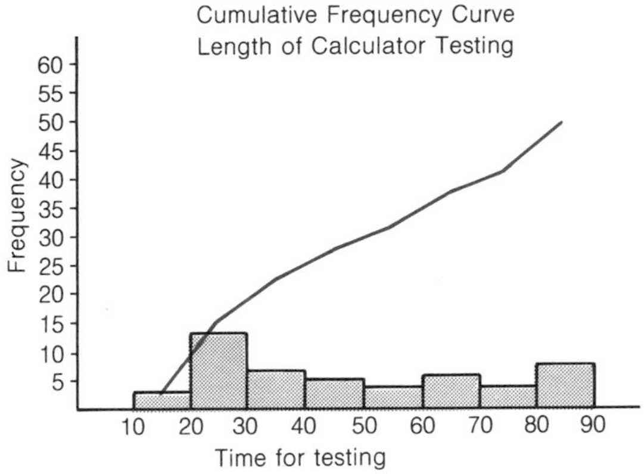


## Try These

Refer to the frequency polygon and cumulative frequency curve.

1 How many calculators were tested for
(a) less than 20 seconds?
(b) more than 40 seconds?

2 In which time interval were calculators tested
(a) most frequently?
(b) least frequently?

## Written Exercises

**A** **Review the meaning of frequency, and cumulative frequency.**

Questions 1 to 5 are based on the following table. The table shows the length of time, in seconds, of commercials in one evening on TV station PQRT.

Length of Commercials on Station PQRT

| Length (seconds) | Frequency | Cumulative frequency |
|---|---|---|
| 5–10 | 1 | ? |
| 10–15 | 1 | ? |
| 15–20 | 3 | ? |
| 20–25 | 2 | ? |
| 25–30 | 6 | ? |
| 30–35 | 8 | ? |
| 35–40 | 10 | ? |
| 40–45 | 12 | ? |
| 45–50 | 12 | ? |

1 Find the values for the cumulative frequency column in the chart for commercials on station PQRT.

2 (a) How many commercials lasted 20 seconds or more?
(b) How many commercials were 40 seconds or more in length?

3 (a) How many commercials lasted in the interval 30 seconds to 40 seconds?
(b) How many commercials were less than 20 seconds long?

4 Draw the cumulative frequency graph for the previous data.

---

Questions 5 to 8 are based on the results of an experiment in animal behaviour. The frequency table gives the time in seconds required for a mouse to find a piece of food at the end of a maze. The times for the mice are recorded.

| Time (seconds) | Frequency |
|---|---|
| 25–29 | 4 |
| 30–34 | 5 |
| 35–39 | 9 |
| 40–44 | 12 |
| 45–49 | 15 |
| 50–54 | 14 |
| 55–59 | 10 |
| 60–64 | 8 |
| 65–69 | 6 |

5 Copy the frequency table. Add a column for cumulative frequency.

6 Refer to your cumulative frequency chart.
(a) How many mice took less than 35 second to find the food?
(b) How many mice took 55 seconds or more to find the food?

7 (a) How many mice took between 35 and 50 seconds to locate the food?
(b) How many took less than 40 seconds to locate the food?

8 (a) Draw the cumulative frequency graph.
(b) Create a question based on your graph.
(c) Write a solution for your question in (b).

**B** **Remember: to construct a graph you need to record the information in an organized frequency table.**

Questions 9 to 13 are based on the following information.

The table records the number of shots on goal by the Belleville Cougars during 40 hockey games.

| | | | | | | | | | |
|---|---|---|---|---|---|---|---|---|---|
| 25 | 22 | 30 | 45 | 28 | 51 | 30 | 32 | 34 | 33 |
| 18 | 30 | 15 | 20 | 24 | 17 | 24 | 41 | 38 | 27 |
| 16 | 25 | 28 | 34 | 41 | 28 | 26 | 15 | 25 | 19 |
| 32 | 36 | 21 | 18 | 34 | 41 | 53 | 25 | 42 | 41 |

9 (a) Organize the data into 8 class intervals with boundaries 15–20, 20–25, and so on.
(b) Construct a histogram to show the data.

10 (a) Complete a cumulative frequency column.
(b) Add the cumulative frequency curve to your histogram.

11 (a) In which class interval does the least data occur?
(b) In which class interval does the most data occur?

12 (a) During how many games did the team take exactly 30 shots?
(b) During how many games did the team have fewer than 35 shots on goal?
(c) During how many games did the team have 45 or more shots on goal?

13 (a) Based on the information, create a problem
(b) Solve your problem in (a). Write a complete solution.

---

Questions 14 to 17 are based on the following information.
The table shows the masses of 60 Siberian tigers captured at random (and released after weighing).

Frequency Table

| Mass of tigers (kilograms) | Frequency | Cumulative frequency |
|---|---|---|
| 120–130 | 3 | 3 |
| 130–140 | 9 | ? |
| 140–150 | 12 | ? |
| 150–160 | 15 | ? |
| 160–170 | 16 | ? |
| 170–180 | 5 | ? |

(160–170: up to but not including 170 kg)

14 (a) Find the cumulative frequency for each class interval in the table..
(b) Construct the cumulative frequency curve.

The tiger has been admired for the qualities of beauty, mystery and strength. More than 100 years ago there were countless numbers of tigers roaming Asia. Today they number only in the thousands, and are considered an endangered species.

15 (a) How many tigers have a mass of less than 140 kg?
(b) How many tigers have a mass of 160 kg or more?
(c) How many tigers have a mass in the interval 150 kg to 160 kg?

16 (a) For the table the percentage frequency is calculated for the class 120–130:

$$\frac{3}{60} \times 100\% = 5\%$$

(3 = frequency for the class; 60 = total frequency)

Calculate the remaining percentage frequency for each of the class intervals.
(b) To calculate the percentage cumulative frequency (% CF), you use the cumulative frequency data.

$$\text{percent cumulative frequency} = \frac{\text{cumulative frequency}}{\text{total frequency}} \times 100\%$$

Calculate the percentage cumulative frequency for each class interval in the frequency table.

17 (a) Create a problem based on the tiger data.
(b) Solve your problem in (a).

## Career Tip

If you work in advertising, you will essentially work in one of these four categories.

A for the advertisers: the department stores, manufacturers, business organizations, and so on that have a product or service to sell
B for the advertising agencies: they prepare and plan the advertising copy for the groups in A
C for the advertising media: radio, television, newspapers, magazines
D for the advertising supply businesses: photographers, printing shops, material supply specialities, and so on.

# 10.7 Applications with Mean, Median and Mode

In sports, the managers and coaches are concerned with the performance of the players. During the games, data are recorded and analyzed. Then in crucial situations the data can be used to help make key decisions regarding strategies to help win the game.

In hockey, an important piece of information is to know the goals against average of goalies when they play certain teams. This information often allows a coach to decide which goalie to use against certain opposing teams.

The **mean**, **median** and **mode** are additional pieces of information about data that are useful indicators.

**Median**

To find the median for data, arrange the data in order as shown.

A: For an odd number of values, arrange the data and find the middle number.

2 2 5 6 7 8 12 15 23

(2 ↑ least; 7 ↑ the median is 7; 23 ↑ greatest)

The median of the data is 7.

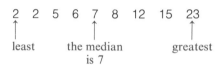

B: For an even number of values, the median is the average of the middle two numbers as shown.

2 2 5 6 7 8 12 15

The median is $\frac{6+7}{2} = 6.5$

The median is 6.5.

The median of a set of numbers is not influenced by the least or greatest numbers. For example, the following data have the same median as the data above.

2 2 5 6 7 8 12 15 68

(2 ↑ least; 7 ↑ median; 68 ↑ greatest)

**Mode**

The mode for the data is the number that occurs most often. Thus for the previous data shown the mode is 2.

2 2 5 6 7 8 12 15 68

The number 2 occurs most frequently.

The mode is also not influenced by the least and greatest numbers.

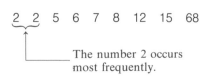

**Mean**

The arithmetic mean or average is calculated by dividing the sum of the data by the number of data. The mean for the previous data is given by the following calculations.

$$\text{mean} = \frac{2 + 2 + 5 + 6 + 7 + 8 + 12 + 15 + 68}{9}$$

$$= \frac{125}{9}$$

$$= 13.9 \text{ (to 1 decimal place)}$$

The mean is affected by extreme values. For example, the mean of the following data is affected: 2, 2, 5, 6, 7, 8, 12, 15, 16.

$$\text{mean} = \frac{2 + 2 + 5 + 6 + 7 + 8 + 12 + 15 + 16}{9}$$

$$= \frac{73}{9}$$

$$= 8.1 \text{ (to 1 decimal place)}$$

**Range**

The range is also a useful statistic. The range is the difference between the greatest and least value in the data.

2 2 5 6 7 8 12 15

$15 - 2 = 13$

The range is 13.

The median, mode, mean and range enable you to obtain additional useful information about the collected data.

## Example

The weekly wages of 10 students working part-time are \$35, \$40, \$34, \$75, \$36, \$39, \$41, \$35, \$42, \$37. Which measure (the mean, median or mode) is the best representative of the data: the typical wage?

## Solution

The data are organized

\$34 \$35 \$35 \$36 \$37 \$39 \$40 \$41 \$42 \$75

I The modal (mode) wage is \$35.
The mode is smaller than most of the wages.

II The mean wage is given by the calculation

$$\frac{35 + 40 + 34 + 75 + 36 + 39 + 41 + 35 + 42 + 37}{10}$$

$$= 41.40$$

The mean wage is \$41.40.
The mean is greater than most of the wages.

III The median wage is $\frac{\$37 + \$39}{2} = \$38$.

The median wage is the best representative of the wages.

## Try These

1 What is the mode for each set of data?
(a) 7 6 4 21 9 4 5 11
(b) 3 10 12 2 4 12 8 6 9 14

2 What is the median for each?
(a) 2 3 5 6 8
(b) 1 1 3 4 5 7

3 Find the range for the data.
(a) 2 4 5 7 8 14
(b) 10 13 19 22 38 51

4 What is the mean for each?
(a) 2 4 6 8
(b) 4 6 7 10 13

## Written Exercises

**A** Where needed round your answers to 1 decimal place.

1 Find the mode for each of the following.
(a) 0 5 15 8 6 5 19 28
(b) 41 36 0 19 8 45 16 41
(c) 121 4 68 19 24 4 89
(d) What is the range for all the data in (a) to (c)?

2 Find the mean for each of the following.
(a) 28 32 41 21 45 36
(b) 12.2 7.5 1.6 19.2 15.3
(c) 115 131 120 119 136 145 123
(d) What is the range for all the data in (a) to (c)?

3 Find the median for each set of data.
(a) 62 112 53 86 79 49
(b) 16 23 14 29 20 36 41 52
(c) 8 19 34 5 39 41 58 63 12

4 The annual salaries of six people are listed.
$18 600 $19 400 $24 000
$20 000 $21 000 $45 000
(a) Find the mean salary and the median salary.
(b) Which one in (a) is the better representative of this data? Give reasons for your answer.

5 The masses, in kilograms, of members on the school wrestling team are shown.
67 70 70 72 73 81 81 91 108
(a) Find the median, mean and mode of the masses.
(b) Which measure in (a) best represents this data?

**B** To do work with statistics, you have to clearly understand the meaning of mean, mode, median and range. Review their meanings.

6 During his baseball career, Tyson had the following batting averages rounded to 3 decimal places.

$$\text{batting average} = \frac{\text{number of hits}}{\text{number of times at bat}}$$

| | | | |
|---|---|---|---|
| 0.264 | 0.278 | 0.275 | 0.264 |
| 0.287 | 0.286 | 0.275 | 0.279 |
| 0.290 | 0.275 | 0.249 | 0.268 |

(a) Determine his median batting average, rounded to 3 decimal places.
(b) Find his mean batting average.
(c) What is the mode of the data?
(d) Which of the answers in (a) to (c) is the best representative of the data?

Remember: In using a calculator to do your work, you need
- ▶ to estimate to check whether your answer is reasonable.
- ▶ to round off your answers.

7 The chart shows the distance of various stars in light years from earth (a light year is the distance light travels in a year). Calculate the mean, median and mode for the data. What is the range?

| Star | Distance from Earth (light years) |
|---|---|
| Alpha Centauri | 4 |
| Sirius | 8 |
| Vega | 23 |
| Fomalhaut | 27 |
| Capella | 42 |
| Regulus | 70 |
| Antares | 170 |
| Deneb | 465 |
| Beta Crucis | 465 |
| Canopus | 650 |

8 During one day, Sports Shoes Unlimited sold running shoes of the following sizes.
10, 7, 7, 9, 10, 8, 11, 12, 10, 8, 10
The shoe manager says that the average size of shoe sold was 10. Which measure is the manager referring to: the mean, median or mode? Give reasons for your answer.

9 The monthly rainfall recorded at a weather station is shown in centimetres.

| J | F | M | A | M | J | J | A | S | O | N | D |
|---|---|---|---|---|---|---|---|---|---|---|---|
| 63 | 67 | 56 | 43 | 19 | 0 | 0 | 21 | 45 | 57 | 59 | 60 |

(a) Find the mean, the median, and the mode for the data.
(b) Why is the mode of the data misleading?
(c) Which of the measures in (a) best represents the data? Give reasons for your answer.

10 The salaries for the executives of a certain company are shown.

| Position | Salary |
|---|---|
| President | $125 000 |
| Vice President | $86 000 |
| Plant Manager | $71 500 |
| Accounting Manager | $53 000 |
| Personnel Manager | $41 250 |
| Research Manager | $40 975 |

(a) Find the mean, median and mode of the salaries.
(b) Which measure seems to best describe the average executive salary?
(c) Which of your answers in (a) presents misleading information?

---

Questions 11 to 14 are based as the following information.

At a plaza, certain stores recorded the number of customers each day for a week.

| | Mon | Tues | Wed | Thurs | Fri | Sat |
|---|---|---|---|---|---|---|
| Keon's Electronics | 206 | 184 | 212 | 253 | 267 | 184 |
| Computer Store | 212 | 241 | 208 | 279 | 296 | 197 |
| Jean City | 198 | 147 | 164 | 196 | 281 | 162 |
| Record Shoppe | 146 | 162 | 180 | 234 | 294 | 184 |
| A and M Dept. Store | 553 | 607 | 692 | 756 | 914 | 833 |

11 Find each of the following for Jean City.
(a) The mean number of customers per day.
(b) The median number of customers per day.
(c) How many customers should Jean City expect in one month (30 days)?
(d) On which three days do you think Jean City has to hire extra part-time help?

12 (a) Find the mean number of customers in the five stores on Thursday.
(b) Which store would you go to if you were looking for a part time job on Thursdays?

13 (a) Find the total number of customers in all five stores for the entire week.
(b) Find the mean number of customers for the week for all stores.
(c) On which days might the plaza require officers for traffic control?

14 (a) Create a problem based on the information in the chart.
(b) Write a solution for your problem in (a).

## Consumer Tip

What do you think is meant by the phrase, "Be an aware consumer"?

## Applications: The Weighted Mean

Over four weeks, Jennifer purchased gasoline at the following prices. 43¢/L 46¢/L 49¢/L 51¢/L

To find the arithmetic mean, you use your earlier skills.

$$\text{arithmetic mean} = \frac{43¢ + 46¢ + 49¢ + 51¢}{4}$$

$$= 47.25¢/\text{L (to 2 decimal places)}$$

If she purchased the same quantity of gasoline at each price, then the arithmetic mean would be accurate. If she purchased different quantities at these different prices, then she would need to calculate the **weighted mean**. For example,

Jennifer purchased 25 L at 43¢/L, 36 L at 46¢/L, 48 L at 49¢/L, and 33 L at 51¢/L. The weighted mean is given by the calculation:

$$\text{weighted mean} = \frac{25(43¢) + 36(46¢) + 48(49¢) + 33(51¢)}{142\text{ L}}$$

Total number of litres bought

$$= 47.65¢/\text{L (to 2 decimal places)}$$

---

15 During the month of September, Petrie buys 4 oranges at 30¢ each, 6 oranges at 25¢ each, 5 oranges at 28¢ each and 8 oranges at 20¢ each. Find the mean price that she paid for an orange that month.

16 Carmella invests $4500 at 9% in a savings account, $6000 at 10% in a savings certificate, $1850 at 8% in savings bonds, and $16 500 at 14% in a second mortgage. Find the weighted mean percentage rate on these investments.

17 A general building contractor earns the following amounts for different jobs.
$22.50/h for 3 hours bricklaying
$31.00/h for 2 hours plumbing
$27.95/h for 5 hours electrical work
$33.10/h for 5 hours roofing
$19.90/h for 6 hours dry-walling
$25.00/h for 7 hours framing
Find the weighted mean hourly rate.

18 The annual rate of growth for six regions is shown in the chart. Find the weighted percentage of growth over all six regions.

| Region | Present population (millions) | Annual rate of growth |
|---|---|---|
| Africa | 352 | 2.5% |
| Asia | 2001 | 2.1% |
| Europe | 459 | 0.9% |
| North America | 235 | 1.3% |
| South America | 291 | 3.1% |
| U.S.S.R. | 250 | 1.2% |

# 10.8 Quartiles and Percentiles

In today's society, we are constantly making comparisons.

- comparisons among the performance of players
- comparisons among the productivity of employees
- comparisons among individuals based on their standings on scores in aptitude tests, exam results, and so on.

People train in an attempt to achieve better and better results. In the 1928 Olympics, the high jump (for women) first occurred. Ethel Catherwood of Canada won the event with a jump of 160.0 cm. Fifty-six years later Ulrike Meyfarth of West Germany bettered the mark by 41.9 cm, an improvement of more than 25%.

A piece of information used by many institutions is a measure of an individual's *standing* or *rank* within a group. A **percentile** ranking is devised in order to provide some standardization to ranking individuals. For example, a percentile rank indicates the percentage of students who achieved *below* a particular score.

For example, suppose you were given a score of 124. This score by itself does not provide much information. However, if this score has a percentile rank of 83 this means that 83% of the individuals who also received a score, were equal to or below your score of 124. Thus a percentile rank provides useful information. In a similar way, your score of 124 with a percentile rank of 83 means that only 17% of your group had a score greater than yours. Percentiles divide the data into 100 parts and a basis of ranking can then be made.

Dividing data into parts provides a basis of comparison. For example, you have already used the median which divides data into 2 parts, a lower and an upper half.

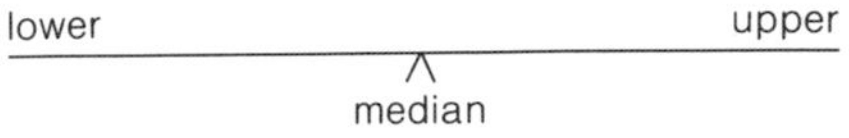


**Deciles** divide data into 10 equal parts.

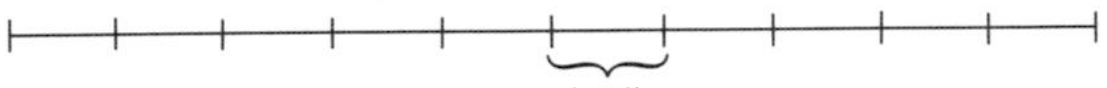


**Quartiles** divide data into 4 equal parts. Each part contains 25% of the data. The term *quartile* refers to the greatest value in each of these 4 parts.

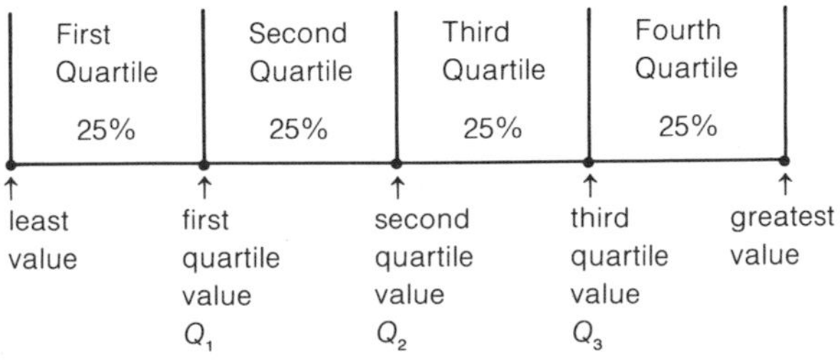

## Example

Melinda wrote an aptitude test in order to be accepted into a computer course. Her score was 48th out of 760 students. Find the percentile rank that Melinda achieved.

## Solution

*Step 1* Total number of students who wrote test was 760.
Melinda was 48th. There were 47 students who did better than her.
Number of students who achieved the same score as her or less was 760 − 47 or 713.

*Step 2* Calculate the percentage.
Melinda did as well or better than 713 students.

$$\frac{713}{760} \times 100\% = 93.8\% \text{ (to 1 decimal place)}$$

*Step 3* Write a statement answering the problem.
Melinda is in the 94th percentile.

## Try These

1 What is meant by each term?
(a) second quartile (b) 65th percentile
(c) third quartile (d) 89th percentile

2 The marks obtained on an exam are shown. What is meant by each of the percentile ranks shown in the chart?

| | Student | Mark | Percentile rank |
|---|---|---|---|
| (a) | Lorna | 75% | 81st |
| (b) | Tom | 60% | 54th |
| (c) | Ali | 89% | 93rd |
| (d) | Romka | 50% | 65th |

## Written Exercises

**A** **Round your answers to 1 decimal place where needed.**

1 $Q_1$ is used to represent the first quartile value. Data has been obtained on a test as shown.

| | | | | | | | | | |
|---|---|---|---|---|---|---|---|---|---|
| 75 | 82 | 96 | 74 | 84 | 48 | 93 | 76 | 72 | 68 |
| 79 | 80 | 97 | 70 | 72 | 85 | 74 | 91 | 73 | 87 |

Calculate each of the following.
(a) $Q_1$ (b) $Q_2$ (c) $Q_3$

2 On a test, Mike received 32 out of 40 and stood ninth highest. If there were 28 students who wrote the test, find Mike's percentile rank.

3 Sherry wrote a history exam and received a score of 27 out of 50. If out of 32 students in the class she stood 19th, what is her percentile rank?

4 Find the percentile ranks for each of the following students who wrote the mid term exams.

| | Student | Standing | Number of students writing the exam |
|---|---|---|---|
| (a) | Felicia | 56th | 428 |
| (b) | Jean | 71st | 560 |
| (c) | Guy | 63rd | 754 |
| (d) | Harvey | 88th | 910 |
| (e) | Marian | 92nd | 693 |
| (f) | Mark | 44th | 167 |

5 Out of 24 persons who wrote the geography test Lenore stood 12th. If she obtained 24 out of 35 on the test, what is her percentile rank?

**B** **Where needed round your answers to 1 decimal place.**

6 The following students wrote exams, and received a certain percentile. Find their rank or standing.

| | Student | Percentile | Number of students writing the exam |
|---|---|---|---|
| (a) | Kevin | 45th | 146 |
| (b) | Greg | 67th | 208 |
| (c) | Lesley | 98th | 615 |
| (d) | Judy | 79th | 312 |
| (e) | Doug | 86th | 464 |
| (f) | Ingrid | 33rd | 99 |

7 Applicants for a computer programming position were asked to write a computer awareness test. For the 25 applicants writing the test, the scores are shown out of 100.

| | | | | | | | | |
|---|---|---|---|---|---|---|---|---|
| 56 | 41 | 50 | 42 | 42 | 50 | 60 | 46 | 34 |
| 29 | 36 | 45 | 22 | 26 | 44 | 44 | 52 | 34 |
| 20 | 37 | 40 | 31 | 57 | 32 | 41 | | |

Calculate the percentile rank for the applicants who received scores of
(a) 26 (b) 52 (c) 46
(d) Based on the results, would you classify the test as easy, medium or hard?

---

Questions 8 to 12 are based on the following information.
The table shows the scores out of 40 on an English test written by 50 students.

| | | | | | | | | | |
|---|---|---|---|---|---|---|---|---|---|
| 28 | 37 | 27 | 12 | 40 | 31 | 18 | 25 | 34 | 15 |
| 29 | 22 | 35 | 32 | 17 | 19 | 26 | 29 | 17 | 34 |
| 38 | 28 | 21 | 24 | 16 | 30 | 25 | 22 | 31 | 23 |
| 20 | 13 | 32 | 23 | 10 | 28 | 35 | 29 | 37 | 19 |
| 31 | 26 | 36 | 24 | 19 | 29 | 24 | 33 | 28 | 35 |

8 (a) Calculate the mean.
(b) Calculate the median.
(c) Find each quartile value $Q_1$, $Q_2$, $Q_3$.
(d) For the quartiles, the interquartile range is defined as the difference between the values of the first and third quartiles.
Interquartile range $= Q_3 - Q_1$.
Find the interquartile range for the data.

9 (a) Stephan received a score of 32 on the test. What is his percentile rank?
(b) Nancy scored 27 on this exam. What is her percentile rank?
(c) With a score of 40 Jackson was elated. What is his percentile rank?

10 On the test, Meg received a score that placed her in the 58th percentile. What was her score?

11 Wilf's ranking was the 92nd percentile. What score did he obtain in order to be placed in this ranking?

## Computer Tip

Run the following program on a computer. What is the program designed to do?

```
10 DIM H (100)
20 READ N
30 FOR I = 1 TO N
40 READ H(I)
50 NEXT I
60 LET T = 0
70 FOR I = 1 TO N
80 IF H(I) > T THEN 100
90 GO TO 120
100 LET T = H(I)
110 LET Q = I
120 NEXT I
130 PRINT "THE TALLEST IS STUDENT"; Q
140 PRINT "THE STUDENT IS"; T; "CM TALL"
150 DATA 20
160 DATA 168, 172, 163, 166, 171, 169, 173
170 DATA 159, 168, 175, 170, 169, 173, 174
180 DATA 178, 170, 171, 159, 164, 171
190 END
```

- Modify the program so that you can input 25 measures. Run the program.
- Modify the program so that data from a class can be used.

# Review: Practice and Problems

Questions 1 to 4 refer to the following data. The time taken to run the 100-m dash was recorded for the students (in seconds).

| | | | | | | |
|---|---|---|---|---|---|---|
| 14.2 | 12.8 | 11.9 | 16.0 | 19.2 | 16.4 | 12.8 |
| 21.4 | 15.3 | 14.4 | 14.5 | 15.7 | 15.8 | |
| 11.8 | 10.1 | 11.7 | 14.7 | 17.5 | 13.2 | |
| 19.0 | 14.6 | 15.2 | 17.8 | 18.3 | 11.7 | |

1 Construct a frequency table for the data.

2 What percentage of the students took at least 16.0 seconds to run the 100-m dash?

3 What percentage of the students took less than 12 seconds to run the 100-m dash?

4 A student running the 100-m dash in less than 13.6 seconds is given an excellent rating while a student running in more than 14.2 seconds is given a poor rating. What percentage of the students were given
A: an excellent rating? B: a poor rating?

5 The rainfall for a region is shown in the centimetres for various months.

| | | | | | |
|---|---|---|---|---|---|
| 72 | 81 | 35 | 18 | 0 | 12 |
| 51 | 58 | 63 | 70 | 62 | 58 |

(a) How many months had a rainfall of
A 58 cm? B 62 cm? C 70 cm?
(b) How many months had a rainfall of
A greater than 63 cm?
B less than 63 cm?
(c) During how many months did it rain?

6 Josephine's activities during an eight hour school day is shown by the circle graph.

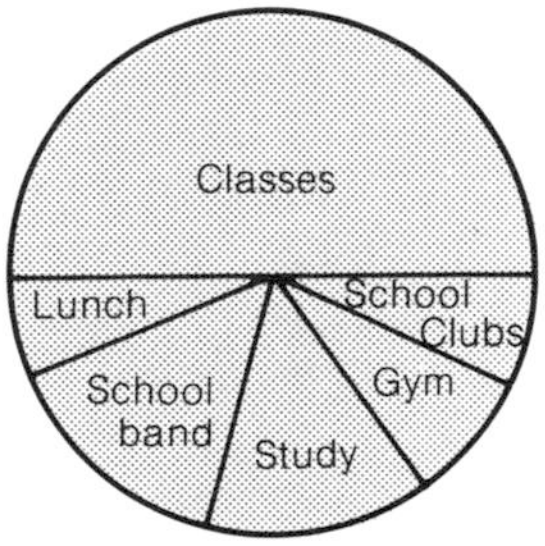


(a) What percent is spent in class?
(b) Apart from her classes, where does Josephine spend the most time?
(c) How many hours are spent on studying?
(d) How many hours are spent for gym?

7 The marks obtained in mathematics test at the beginning of a term are shown below.

| | | | | | | | |
|---|---|---|---|---|---|---|---|
| 51 | 76 | 83 | 48 | 79 | 93 | 61 | 57 |
| 66 | 82 | 54 | 63 | 88 | 98 | 59 | 71 |
| 75 | 70 | 44 | 59 | 72 | 60 | 64 | 85 |

(a) What class intervals would you use to organize the data?
(b) How many classes will there be?
(c) Draw a histogram for the data.

8 The list below shows the number of goals scored per game by the Calgary Flames during part of a season.

| | | | | | | | | | | | |
|---|---|---|---|---|---|---|---|---|---|---|---|
| 3 | 2 | 4 | 2 | 5 | 4 | 6 | 0 | 1 | 1 | 4 | 2 |
| 3 | 4 | 5 | 0 | 1 | 4 | 1 | 2 | 2 | 0 | 3 | |

(a) Find the mean, median, and mode.
(b) What measure is the best indicated of the above data?

9 Find the percentile rank for each student.

| | Student | Standing | Number of students writing |
|---|---|---|---|
| (a) | Benjamin | 38th | 503 |
| (b) | Ralph | 79th | 688 |
| (c) | Terry | 94th | 863 |
| (d) | Sharon | 56th | 159 |

10 The average salaries of firemen in Lowe City, Franklin Township, York County, Mertle City, and South Bay were respectively \$26 800, \$31 090, \$28 130, \$25 941 and \$29 475. Each town had respectively 36, 19, 40, 25, and 31 people on the payroll. Find the mean of the above salaries.

### Consumer Tip

Consult the bulletin board of a supermarket or restaurant. You can often obtain much information on articles for sale, people providing services, vacation planning, government consumer information, career suggestions, and so on.

# A Practice Test

1 The following table shows the weekly wages of 170 students employed after school.

| Wages | Frequency |
|---|---|
| $15.00–19.99 | 2 |
| 20.00–24.99 | 6 |
| 25.00–29.99 | 10 |
| 30.00–34.99 | 18 |
| 35.00–39.99 | 22 |
| 40.00–44.99 | 28 |
| 45.00–49.99 | 35 |
| 50.00–54.99 | 25 |
| 55.00–59.99 | 14 |
| 60.00–64.99 | 10 |

(a) How many students receive less than $45 per week?
(b) How many students receive more than $34.99 per week?
(c) What is the percentage of employee's receiving more than $49.99 per week?
(d) What is the percentage of employees receiving less than $30.00 per week?

2 The number of basketball free throws sunk by 38 students each taking 50 throws is shown in the table below.

| | |
|---|---|
| 0 | 3 6 9 4 9 8 |
| 1 | 2 5 4 1 7 7 |
| 2 | 3 5 1 9 7 6 7 8 2 |
| 3 | 2 9 8 1 7 4 5 6 7 7 |
| 4 | 2 3 1 1 2 8 |
| 5 | 0 |

(a) How many students were successful at
(i) 17 throws? (ii) 42 throws?
(b) What was the most frequently occurring number of successful throws?
(c) How many had fewer than 22 successful throws?
(d) How many students had a perfect number of throws?

3 For the data shown in the chart.
(a) Decide on the type of graph you would use to display the information.

| Region | Europe | Asia | Africa | South America | North America | Other |
|---|---|---|---|---|---|---|
| Percent of total world population | 20% | 55% | 10% | 4% | 10% | 1% |

(b) Draw a graph.

4 The following are results of a final exam for the students in one class.

| | | | | | | | |
|---|---|---|---|---|---|---|---|
| 61 | 84 | 92 | 59 | 46 | 66 | 72 | 88 |
| 55 | 75 | 67 | 82 | 69 | 54 | 63 | 74 |
| 79 | 67 | 71 | 60 | 52 | 43 | 96 | 57 |
| 87 | 61 | 58 | 78 | 72 | 50 | 83 | 70 |

(a) What classes would you use for the data?
(b) Construct a frequency distribution for the data.
(c) Draw a histogram using the data.

5 At a fast food outlet, the number of "Chicken Nuggets" sold each day for one month was recorded.

| | | | | | | | |
|---|---|---|---|---|---|---|---|
| 96 | 85 | 114 | 93 | 141 | 87 | 131 | 137 |
| 105 | 103 | 125 | 129 | 125 | 95 | 106 | 109 |
| 97 | 108 | 115 | 125 | 87 | 105 | 138 | |
| 123 | 99 | 134 | 130 | 101 | 117 | 120 | |

(a) Organize the data into classes with intervals 80 — 90, 90 — 100, and so on.
(b) Construct a histogram to show the data.
(c) Complete a cumulative frequency column.
(d) Construct a cumulative frequency curve.
(e) In which class interval does the most data occur?

6 The masses, in kilograms, of the Bears wrestling team are shown below.

67, 70, 70, 72, 73, 81, 81, 91, 108

(a) Find the median, mode, and mean.
(b) Which measure best describes this data?

7 A T.V. manufacturer is interested in knowing how often customers need repairs during their first year after purchasing a T.V. The following are the number of times that customers require repairs.

3 2 0 0 4 5 7 3 2 1
1 3 6 4 8 3 10 4 0 2

(a) Find the mean, median, and mode.
(b) What measure is the best indicator of the need for repairs?

8 Salem wrote an entrance exam in order to enter an apprenticeship program. He ranked fiftieth out of 1231 students. Find his percentile rank.

# 11 Applications with Geometry and Graphing

vocabulary of geometry, using geometric properties, applying construction skills, Pythagoras, working with ordered pairs, drawing graphs, curve of best fit, problem solving, extrapolation, interpolation, slope and distance on the plane, solving problems, and applications

## Introduction

Concepts and skills with geometry are used in many ways as shown by the stamps displayed on this page. What aspects of geometry can you recognize on the stamps?

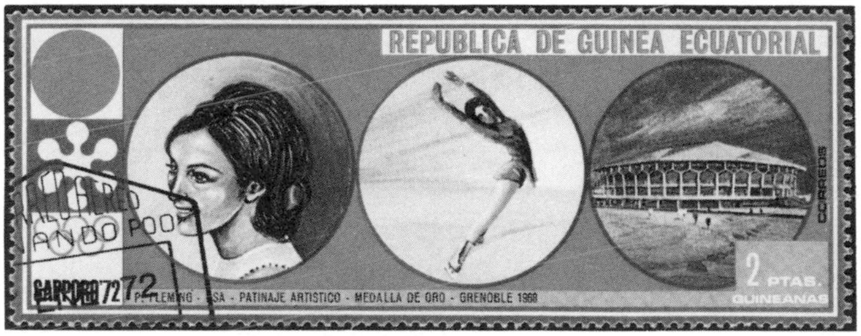

Skills with geometry are applied when you work with co-ordinates on the plane. Concepts and skills with co-ordinates are essential when you work with computer technology in the design of new buildings, automobiles and even in drawing efficient transportation networks.

In any career that is pursued it is important to learn the vocabulary of the skills and concepts of that career. Similarly, to work with geometry and graphing, you need to learn the essential vocabulary. They are important tools for solving problems.

# 11.1 Vocabulary of Geometry

If you learn how to sail, you first learn all the names of special parts of the boat and sails. Similarly to work with geometry you must first know the special terms used to describe angles and triangles. Different sizes of angles affect the shape of triangles and so they have special names, as shown in the charts that follow.

Skills with geometry are used in constructing sleek hulls as well as efficient sails. To plot your course also requires skills with geometry.

**Classification of Angles**

| | | |
|---|---|---|
| Acute angle |  | Angle measures less than 90° |
| Right angle | 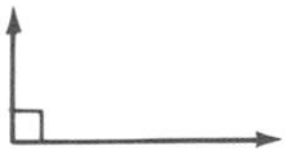 | Angle measures exactly 90° |
| Obtuse angle |  | Angle measures greater than 90° but less than 180° |
| Straight angle |  | Angle measures exactly 180° |
| Reflex angle |  | Angle measures greater than 180° |

**Classification of Triangles**

| | | |
|---|---|---|
| Acute triangle | 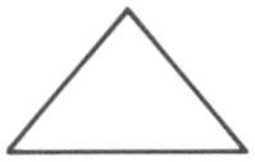 | All three angles are acute |
| Right triangle | 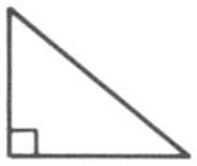 | One angle is 90° |
| Obtuse triangle |  | One angle is obtuse |

Triangles can also be classified according to the measures of their sides.

| | | |
|---|---|---|
| Scalene triangle | 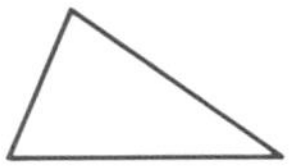 | All sides have different measures |
| Isosceles triangle |  | Two sides are equal |
| Equilateral triangle |  | All three sides are equal |

### Naming angles and triangles

Upper case letters are used to label the vertices of a triangle. The triangle shown is named △KLM. Three letters are used to describe angles. For example, the angle at vertex L is named ∠KLM.

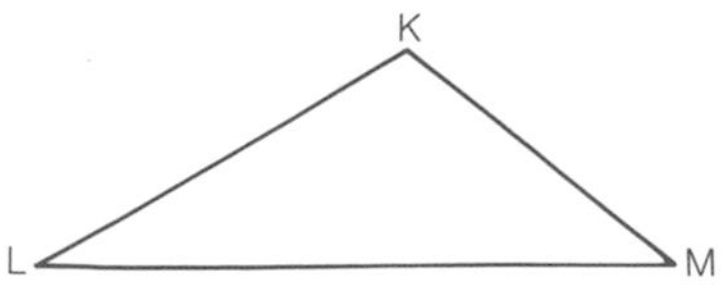

## Try These

1 Classify each angle as acute, right, obtuse, straight or reflex.

(a) (b) (c)

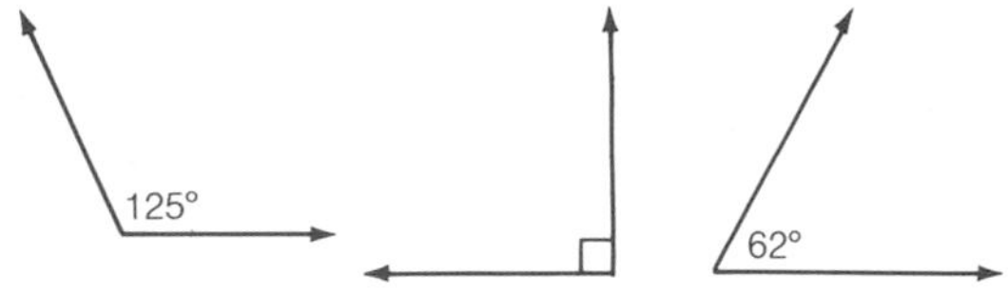


(d) (e)

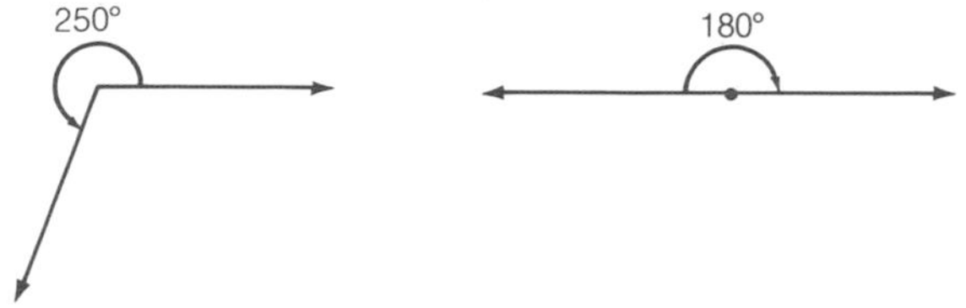


2 Which of the triangles shown is
   (a) a right triangle?
   (b) an obtuse triangle?
   (c) an acute triangle?

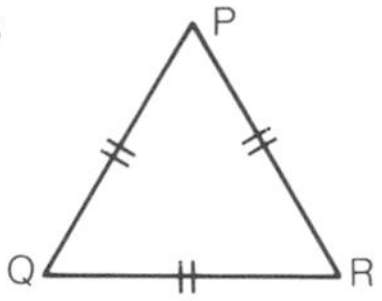


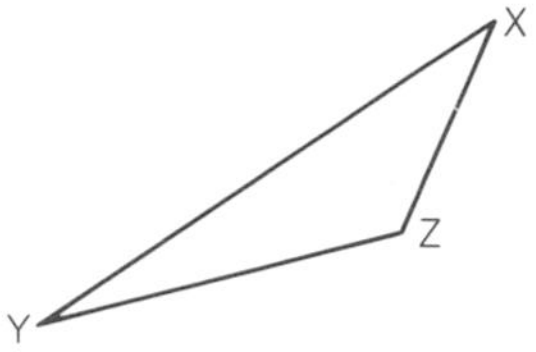


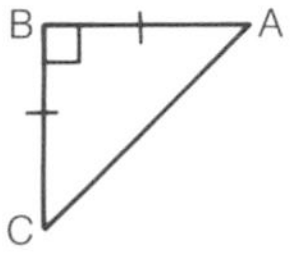


3 Which triangle in the previous question is
   (a) scalene? (b) isosceles?
   (c) equilateral?

## Written Exercises

**A** To work with geometry, you need to learn the vocabulary. Review the meanings of the terms.

1 Refer to the diagram. What type of angle is each of the following?
   (a) $\angle AOE$ (b) $\angle BOA$
   (c) $\angle COA$ (d) $\angle DOA$
   (e) $\angle DOB$ (f) $\angle BOC$

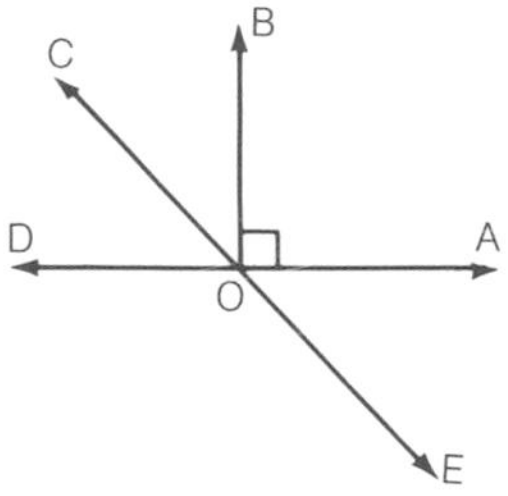


2 Use the diagram. Name two of each type of angle.
   (a) acute (b) obtuse
   (c) right (d) straight

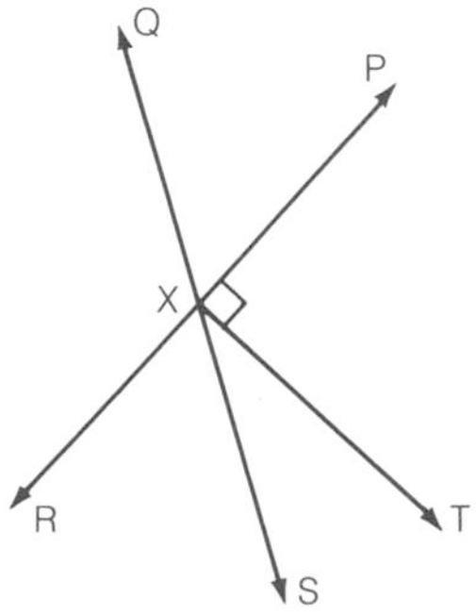


3 (a) What type of angle is $\angle LMN$?
   (b) Classify $\triangle LMN$ according to its angles.
   (c) Which sides of $\triangle LMN$ have equal measure?
   (d) Classify $\triangle LMN$ according to its sides.

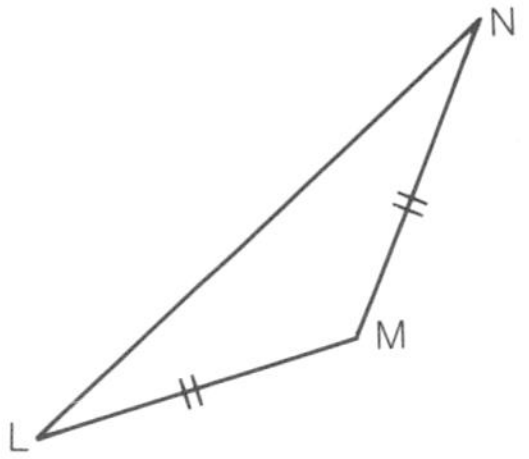

4 (a) Classify $\triangle VWT$ according to its sides.
   (b) Classify $\triangle VWT$ according to its angles.
   (c) What type of angle is $\angle WTV$?

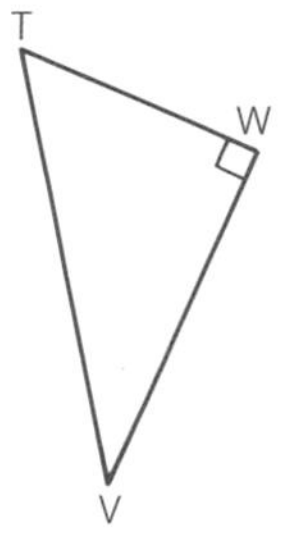

5 (a) Classify $\triangle PQR$ according to its sides.
(b) Classify the triangle according to its angles.

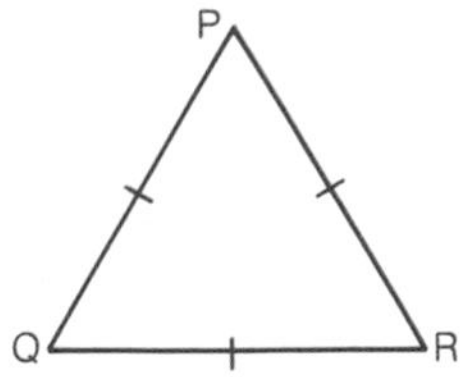


6 Classify each angle.

(a) 52° (b) 105° (c) 90° (d) 215°
(e) 90° (f) 173° (g) 300° (h) 68°

**B** **Review the meaning of each of these words that describe triangles: acute, obtuse, right, isosceles, equilateral, scalene.**

7 What type of triangle classified by the angles, is suggested by each situation?

(a)

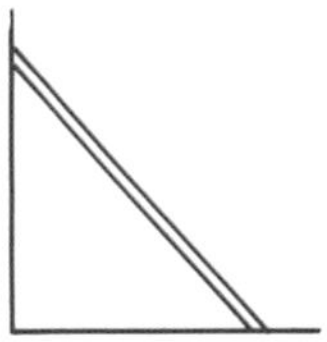

(b)

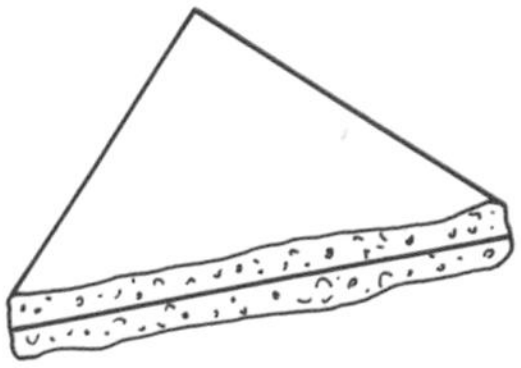

8 What type of triangle, classified by the sides, is suggested by each situation?

(a)

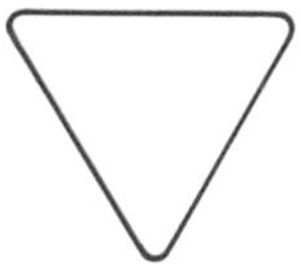

(b)

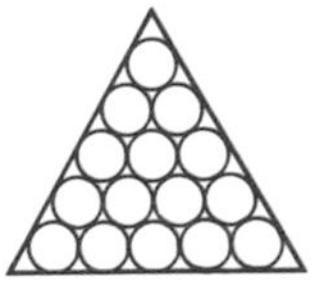

9 Brian is an artist who makes stained glass windows. The diagram shows a design he is planning.

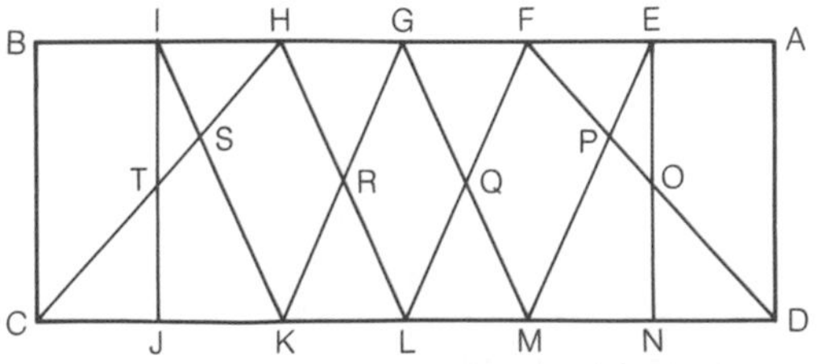


(a) Name two acute angles in the design.
(b) Name two right triangles in the design.
(c) Name an obtuse angle.
(d) Name an obtuse triangle.

10 In the figure, name
(a) an acute triangle
(b) a right triangle
(c) an obtuse triangle

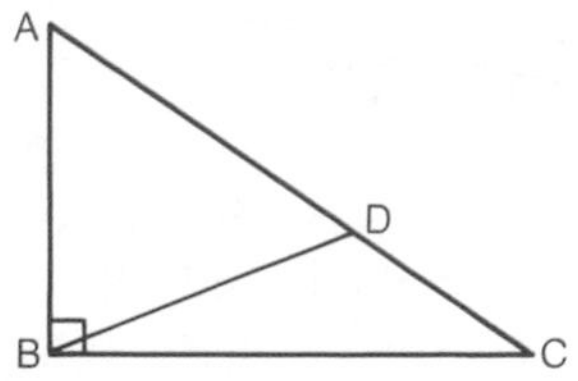


11 In the figure, $PQ = QR = RP$ and $PT = TQ$.
Name
(a) an equilateral triangle
(b) an isosceles triangle
(c) three right triangles

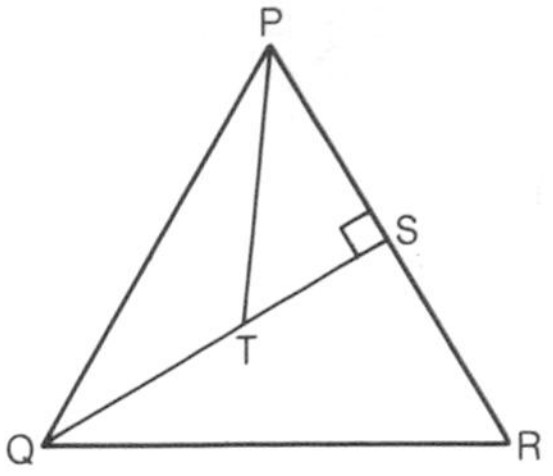


12 In the figure, $AB = BC = CD = DA = BD$. (ABCD is a rhombus).

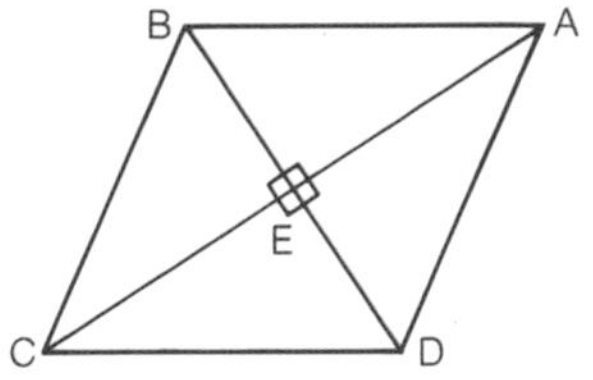


Name
(a) two isosceles triangles that are also obtuse
(b) two equilateral triangles
(c) two scalene triangles

## Career Tip

An aircraft maintenance engineer undergoes a very rigourous training course since the least error can result in tragedy. Learning the meanings of the vocabulary in this field, as in mathematics, is essential in order to perform accurately.

- Some of the words learned in this field are variable pitch, generator, airframe, avionics, hydraulics. Use a dictionary. What is meant by these terms?
- List the type of skills in mathematics you think are needed by an aircraft maintenance engineer.

## Problem Solving: Relationships Among Angles

The basic measuring tools of geometry are: a **protractor** to measure angles and a **ruler** to measure length of sides. Use a protractor, ruler and sharp pencil to complete the following investigations.

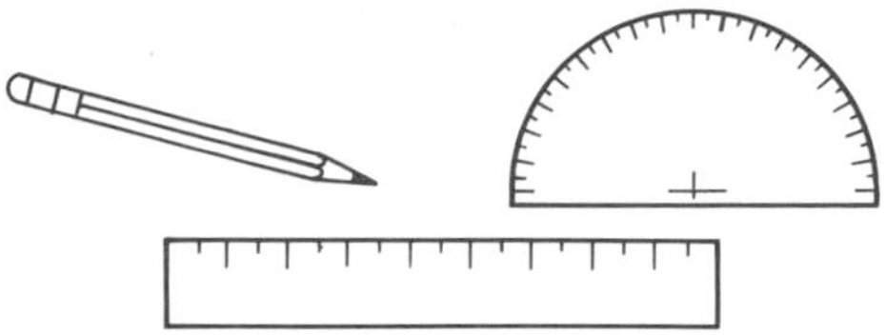

13 Draw two intersecting lines. Measure each of the four angles formed at the point at which the lines intersect.

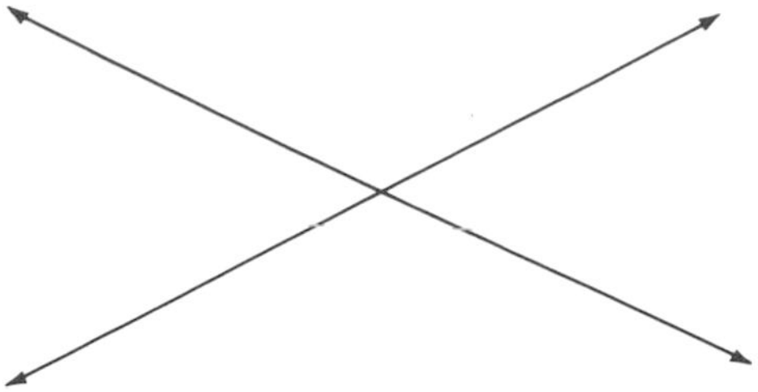

(a) How are the measures of the opposite pairs of angles related?

(b) How are the measures of each pair of angles that are adjacent to each other related?

14 (a) Draw a triangle. Measure each of its angles. What is the sum of the three angles?

(b) Extend one side of the triangle. Measure the exterior angle of the triangle How is its measure related to the opposite interior angles?

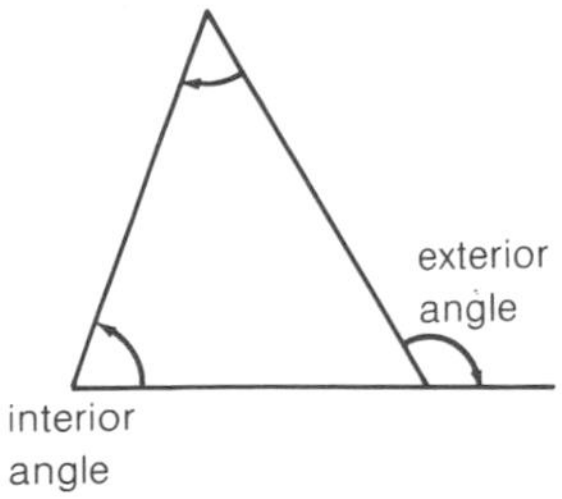


15 (a) Repeat the steps of the previous question, using a different shaped triangle.

(b) What conclusion seems to be true about the sum of the three angles in a triangle?

(c) What conclusion would you make about the measure of the exterior angle and the two opposite interior angles?

16 Draw two line segments of equal length with a common endpoint. Join the lines to complete an isosceles triangle. Measure the angles formed at the base of the triangle. What do you notice?

17 (a) Repeat the steps of the previous question, using a different sized triangle.

(b) What relationship do your results suggest for the base angles in an isosceles triangle?

18 (a) Draw two line segments of equal length with the angle between these sides measuring 90°. Join the lines to make a triangle.

(b) Predict the measure of the other two angles.

(c) Measure to check your prediction.

19 (a) Draw a line AB measuring 5 cm.
At A, draw the $\angle CAB$ measuring 50°
At B, draw the $\angle CBA$ measuring 40°

(b) What do you think $\angle ACB$ will measure?

(c) Measure to check your prediction.

### Calculator Tip

Some calculators have a key labelled DRG. This key allows you to compute with angles that are measured in degrees, radians or grades. Both degrees and radians are commonly used in trigonometry. (See Chapter 15). Radians are related to degrees. (Look ahead to page 422). Grades are not commonly used, but 100 grades = 90°.

# 11.2 Using Properties

### Angle properties

**Complementary Angles**

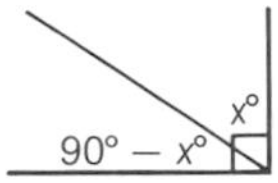


Two angles whose sum is 90°

**Supplementary Angles**

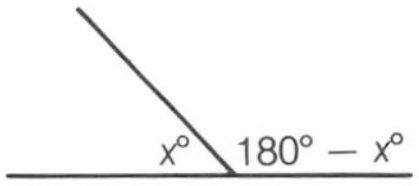


Two angles whose sum is 180°

**Vertically Opposite Angles**

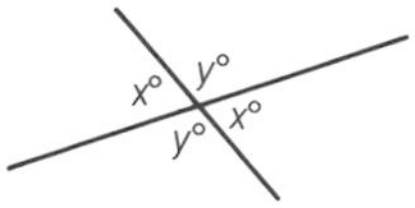


Vertically opposite angles are equal.

### Triangle properties

**Angle sum of a triangle**

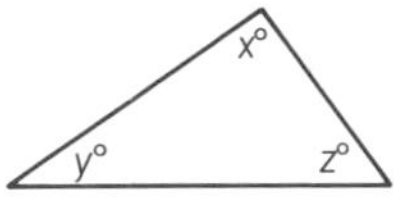


$x° + y° + z° = 180°$

The sum of the angles of a triangle is 180°

**Exterior angle of a triangle**

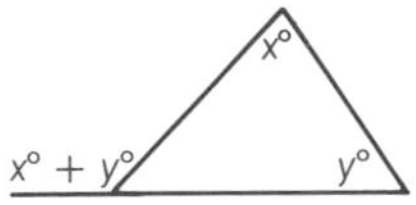


The exterior angle of a triangle is equal to the sum of the interior opposite angles.

**Isosceles triangle**

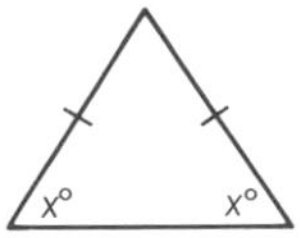


Base angles are equal.

You can use the basic properties of angles and triangles to find missing information in a diagram.

## Example

Find the values of the variables.

(a)

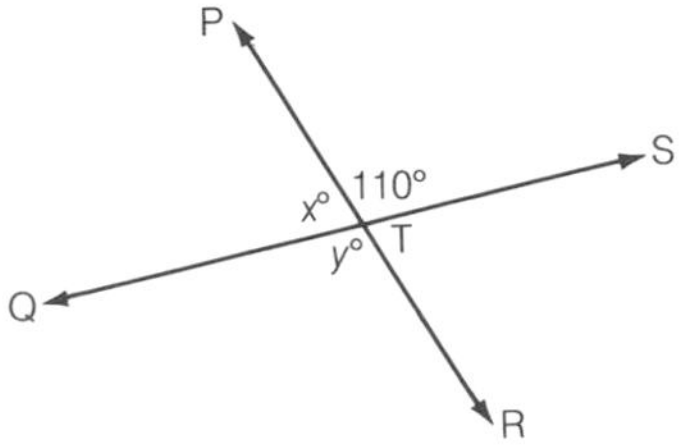


(b)

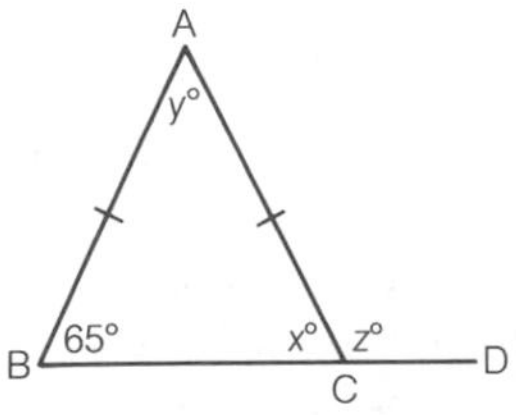


## Solution

(a) ∠STP and ∠PTQ are supplementary so

$x° + 110° = 180°$
$x° = 180° - 110°$
$x° = 70°$

∠QTR is vertically opposite ∠STP, so $y° = 110°$

(b) △ABC is isosceles, so

$x° = 65°$

then,

$65° + x° + y° = 180°$
$65° + 65° + y° = 180°$
$130° + y° = 180°$
$y° = 180° - 130°$
$y° = 50°$

and,

$x° + z° = 180°$
$65° + z° = 180°$
$z° = 180° - 65°$
$z° = 115°$

## Try These

1 What is the measure of each angle marked $x°$? Which property did you use?

(a)

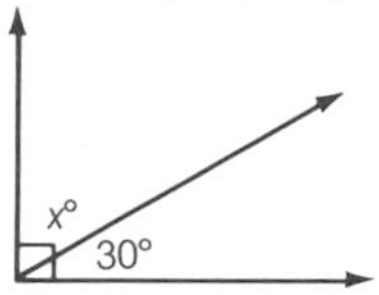


(b)

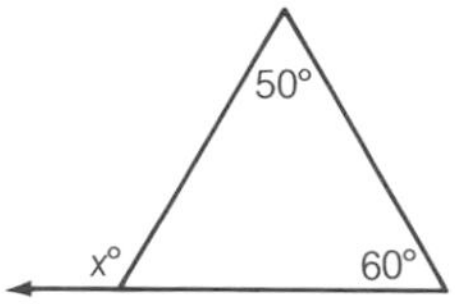


(c)

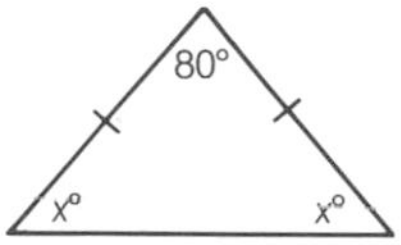


(d)

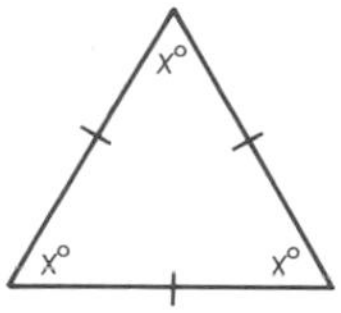


2 In each diagram which other angle is equal to the angle marked $n°$. Which property did you use?

(a)

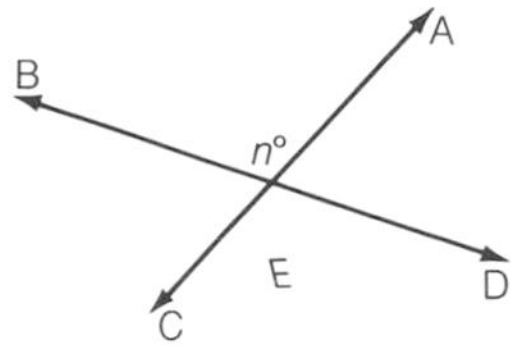


(b)

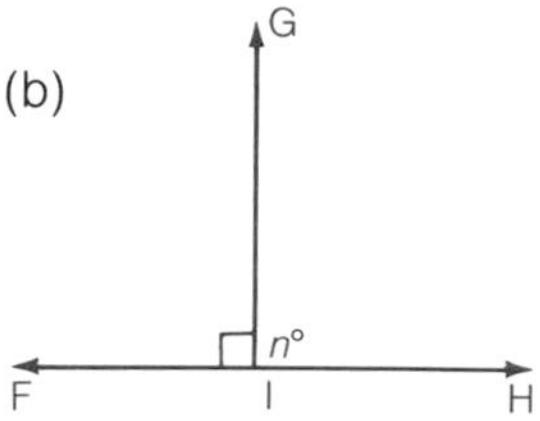


(c)

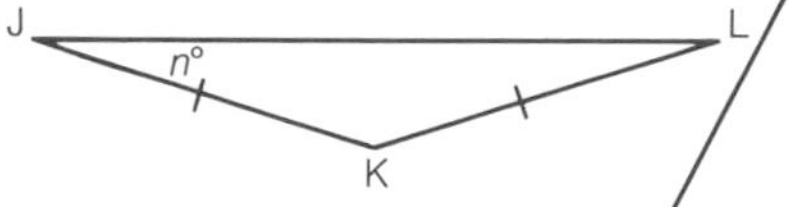


(d)

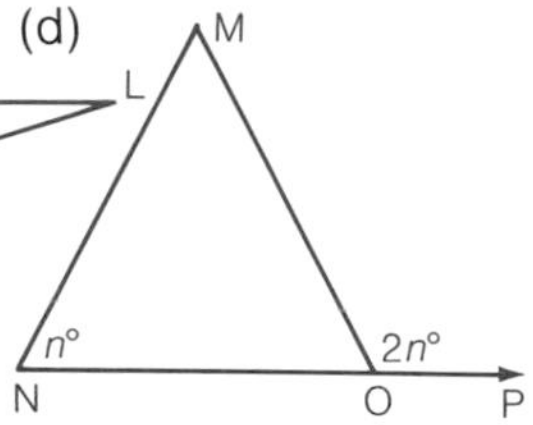


## Written Exercises

**A** Review the properties of angles and triangles summarized in this section.

1 (a) What type of angle is ∠KOL?
(b) Find the measure of ∠KOM. What type of angle is this?

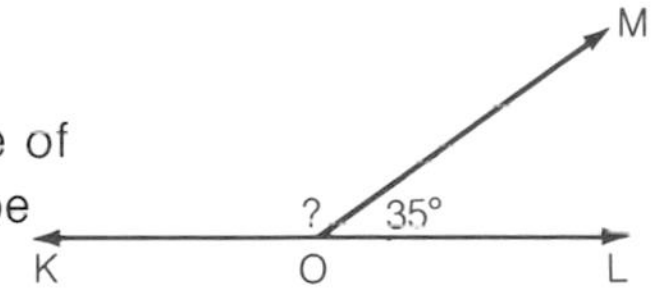


2 (a) What type of angle is ∠VWX?
(b) Find the measure of ∠YWX. What type of angle is this?

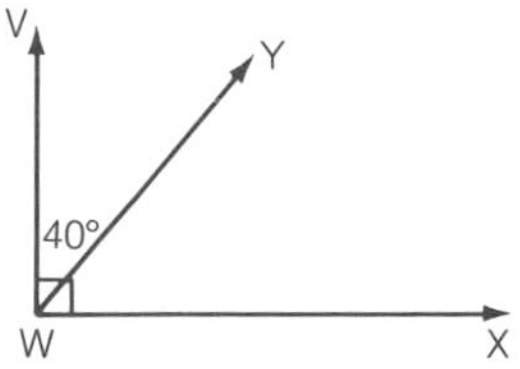


3 (a) Write an equation for the sum of the angles of △ABC.
(b) Find the measure of ∠ABC.
(c) What type of triangle is this?

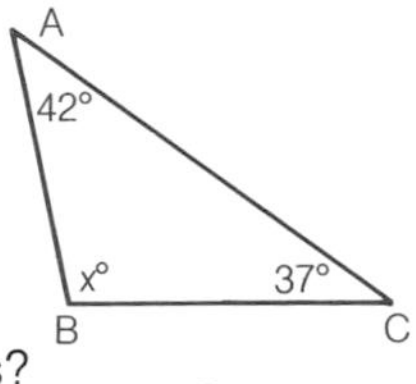


4 (a) What type of triangle is △DEF?
(b) What is the measure of ∠DFE?
(c) Find the measure of ∠FDE.

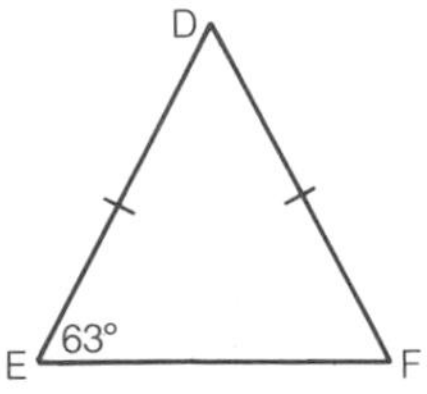


5 Find each missing measure.

(a)

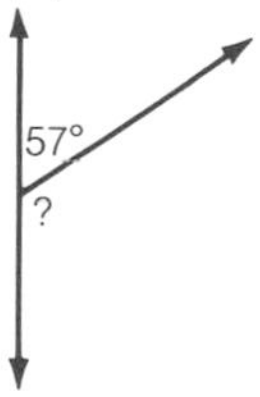


(b)

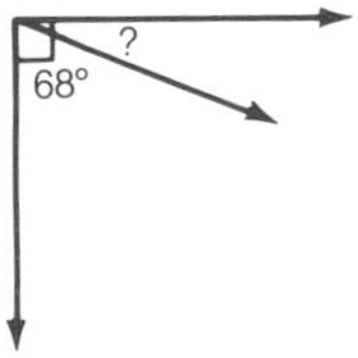


(c)

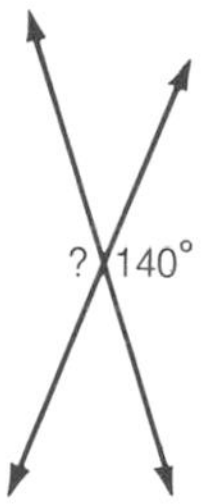


6 Find the missing measures.

(a)

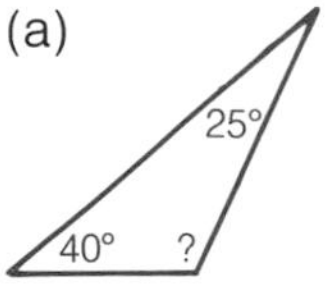


(b)

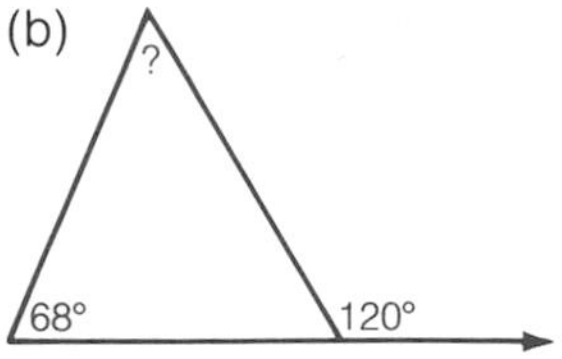


(c)

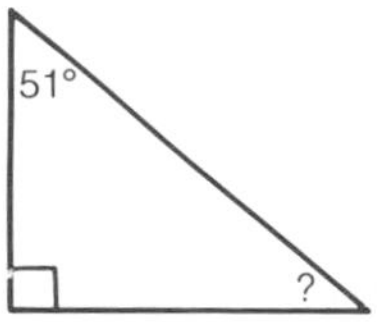


(d)

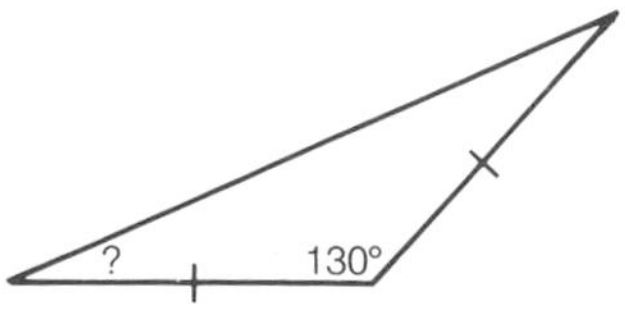

**B** Review the meaning of complementary, supplementary, and vertically opposite angles.

7 (a) An angle measures 63°. What is the measure of its complement?
(b) An angle measures 63°. What is the measure of its supplement?
(c) An angle measures 117°. What is the measure of its supplement?

8 Find the number of degrees represented by the variables in each diagram.

(a)

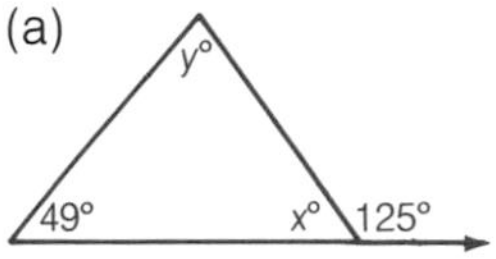


(b)

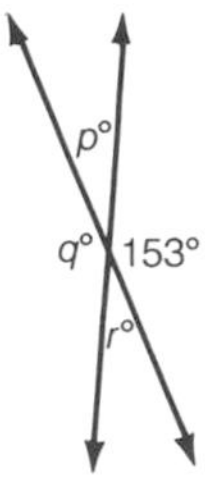


(c)

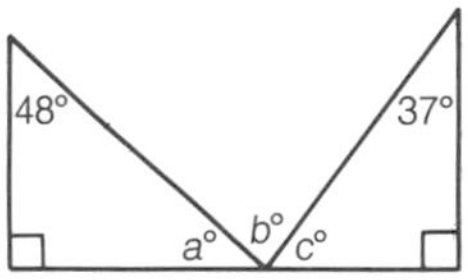


(d)

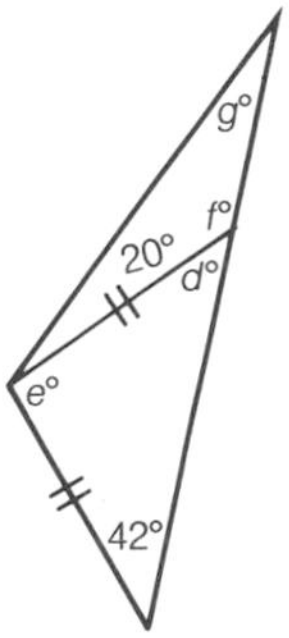


9 Two of the angles of a triangle measure 40° and 70°.
(a) Find the measure of the third angle.
(b) What type of triangle is this?

10 (a) In a right triangle, one of the acute angles measures 33°. What is the measure of the other acute angle?
(b) In a triangle, one angle measures 56°. The other two angles have equal measures. Find the measures of the other angles.

11 The diagram shows a cross section of the taper on a screwdriver. Find the measure of the angle $y°$ at the tip of the screwdriver.

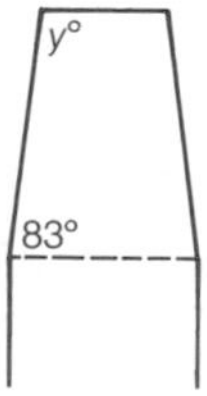


12 Refer to the diagram.

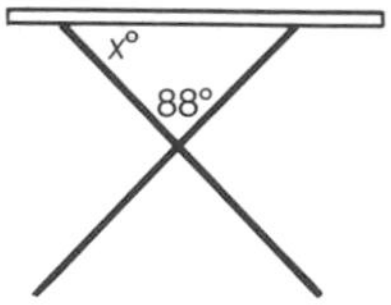


(a) Find the size of the angle $x°$ between the leg and the horizontal surface of the ironing board.
(b) The position of the legs is changed so that the angle between them is increased to 106°. What does the angle between the board and the leg change to? Is the board higher or lower than in (a)?

13 (a) Write an equation to relate the measures of the angles in △GHI.

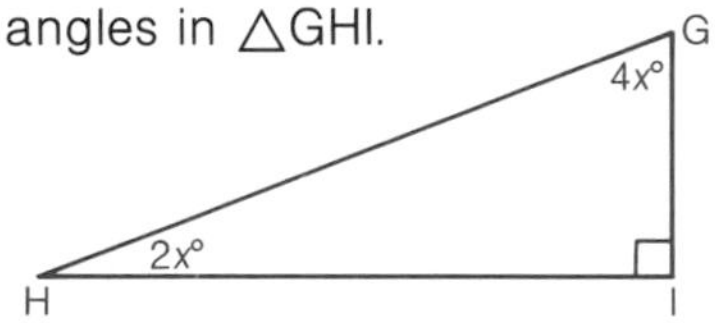


(b) Solve the equation in (a).
(c) What is the measure of each angle in △GHI?

14 Find $p$, $q$, and $r$.

(a)

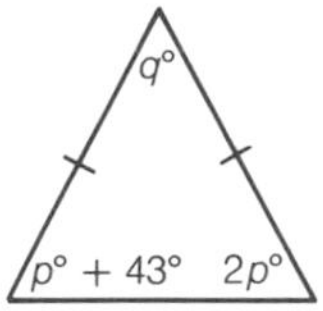


(b)

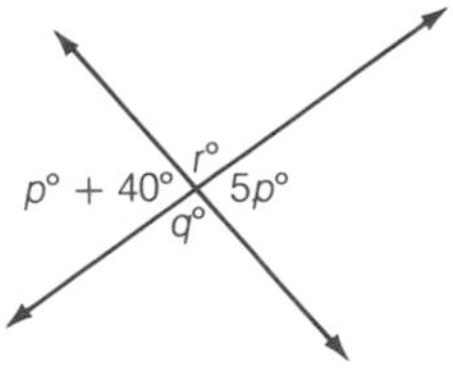


(c)

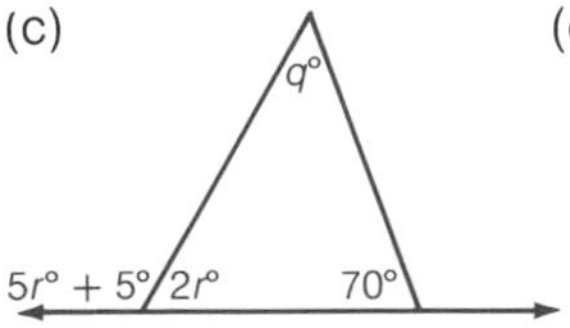


(d)

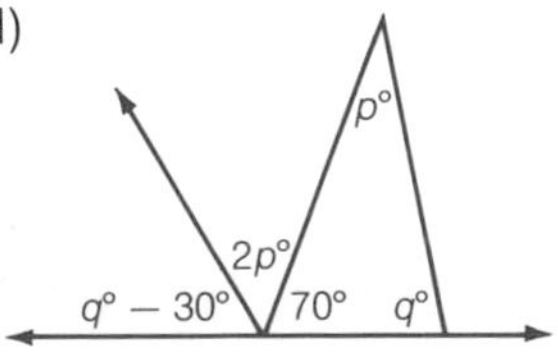


**C**

15 An engineer has determined that a triangular machine part must have these properties. The largest angle is 12° less than five times the measure of the smallest angle. The other angle is double the measure of the smallest angle. Find the angles.

# 11.3 Solving Problems Using Construction Skills

In some situations, skills with accurate construction are needed to solve a problem. There are certain basic constructions that you can make using a pair of compasses and a straightedge. An important skill in doing mathematics is being able to describe your work to someone else. The descriptions to do any construction must be accurate, so that the same result is obtained by others who follow your instructions.

**Bisecting an angle:**

To bisect $\angle ABC$.

*Step 1*
With centre B, and suitable radius, draw an arc to cut BA and BC at M and N.

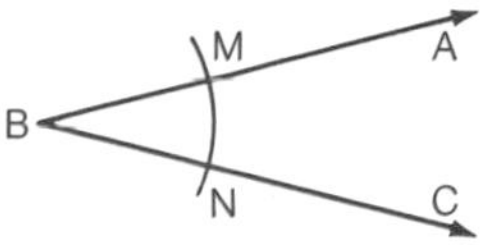


*Step 2*
With centres M and N and the same radius, draw arcs to intersect at P.

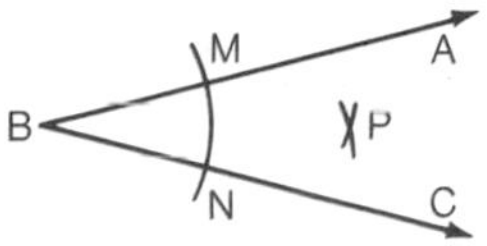


*Step 3*
Join BP.
Check: By measurement.
$\angle ABP = \angle PBC$.
BP is the bisector of $\angle ABC$.

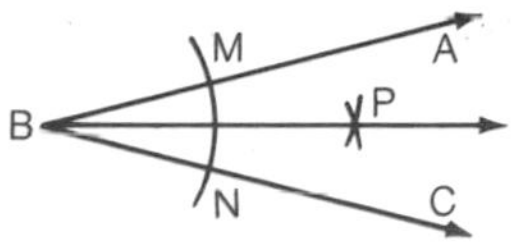


**Constructing a perpendicular:**

***A: At a given point on a line***

To construct a perpendicular at D.

*Step 1*
With centre D, and a suitable radius, make arcs cutting the line at E and F.

*Step 2*
With centres E and F, and the same radius (longer than ED), make two arcs to intersect at C.

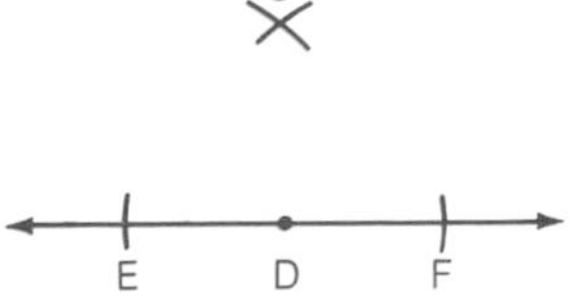


*Step 3*
Join CD.
Check: By measurement,
$\angle EDC = \angle CDF = 90°$
CD is perpendicular to the line through E and F.

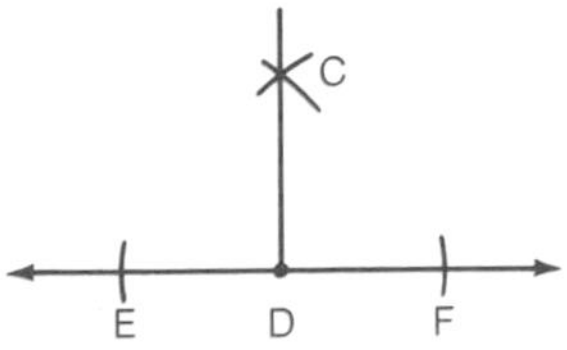

### *B: From a given point to a line*

To construct a perpendicular from P to the line.

*Step 1*
With centre P and a suitable radius, make arcs cutting the line at Q and R.

*Step 2*
With centres Q and R, and a suitable radius, draw arcs on the other side of the line to intersect at S.

*Step 3*
Join P and S. PS is perpendicular to the line through Q and R.

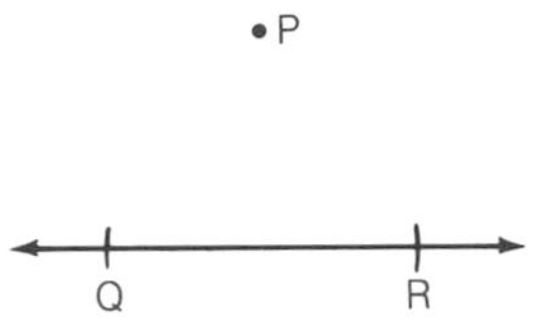


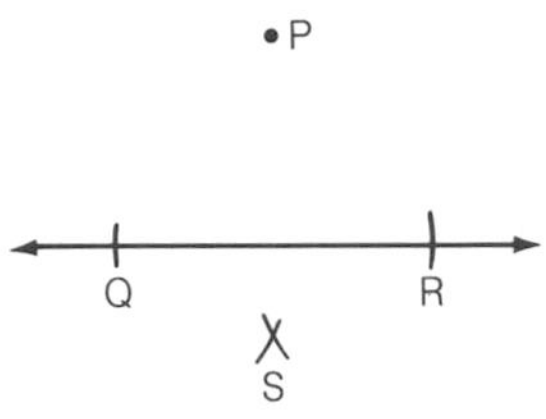


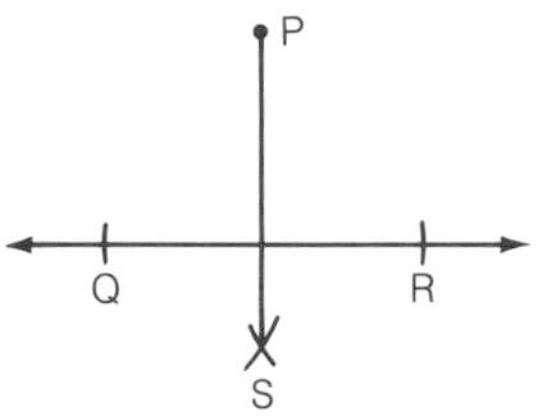


Investigations done using the above constructions have led to the discovery of important properties. For example, when you bisect each of the angles of a triangle the three bisectors meet at a single point. This single point is very special as it is the centre of gravity for the triangle. This means it is the point at which the triangle will balance.

In the exercises that follow you will use construction skills to investigate for yourself some properties of polygons.

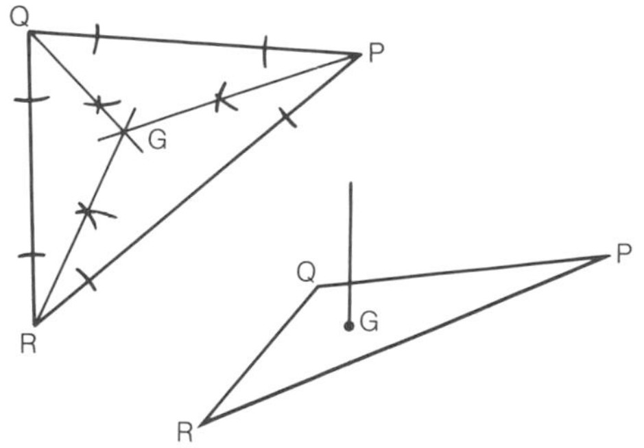


## Try These

1 In each diagram
- ▶ which angle has been bisected?
- ▶ which line is the angle bisector?

(a)

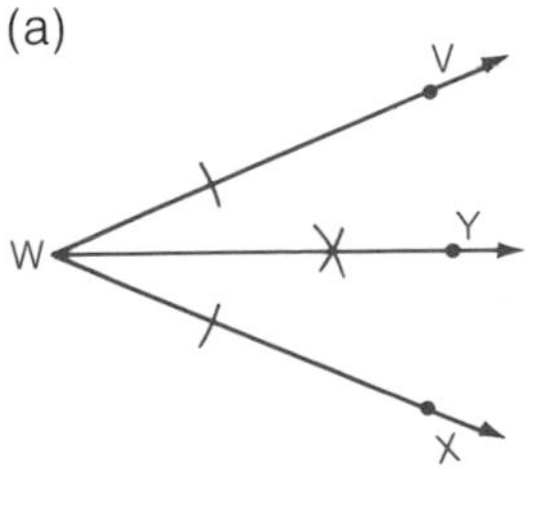


(b)

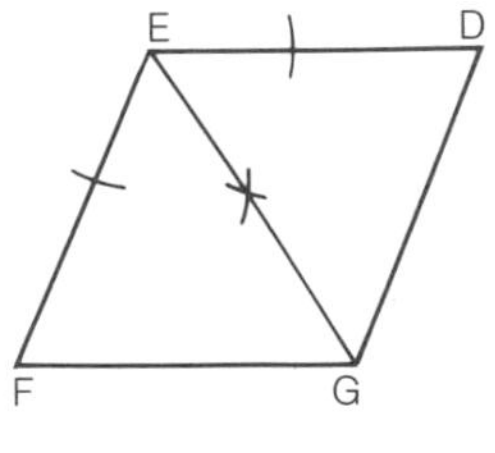


2 In △ABC, describe the steps used to construct the perpendicular, AD, from the vertex, A, to the side BC.

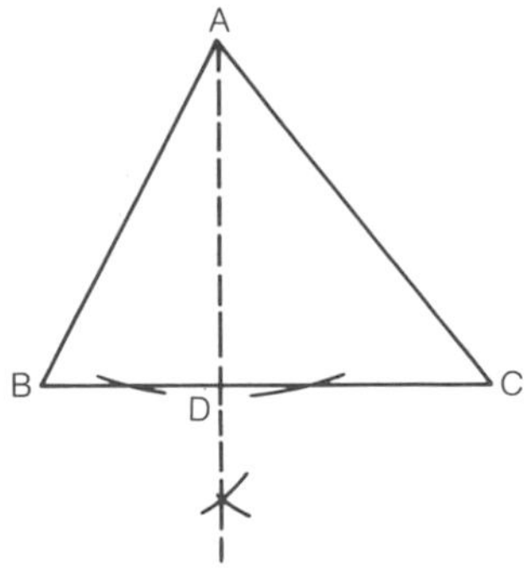

## Written Exercises

**A** In drawing accurate construction diagrams, a sharp pencil should be used. Dull pencils are boring!

1 Draw each angle. Construct its bisector.
(a) an acute angle (b) a right angle
(c) an obtuse angle (d) a straight angle

2 Draw an acute triangle. Bisect each of its angles. Label the centre of gravity G.

3 Draw an obtuse triangle. Bisect each of its angles. Label the centre of gravity.

4 Draw a line about 8 cm in length. Mark a point near the middle of the line. Construct the perpendicular at this point. Check by measuring the angles using a protractor.

5 Draw a line about 8 cm in length. Mark a point not on the line. Construct the perpendicular from the point to the line. Check by measuring.

**B** Remember: to describe a construction you must be precise. Each person should obtain the same drawing following your instructions. Follow all instructions carefully.

6 Draw a line and mark two points on it, P and Q.
(a) Construct angles measuring 90° at P and at Q.
(b) Bisect the 90° angle at Q. Extend the bisector to meet the perpendicular from P at the point R. What is the measure of ∠PQR? What type of triangle is △PQR?

7 Refer to the previous question.
(a) Describe the steps you would use, to provide instructions for someone else to obtain your results.
(b) Have someone use your instructions to do the construction.

8 (a) Draw a line and mark two points A and B about 6 cm apart. Construct the perpendicular at A and at B.
(b) Use compasses centre A and radius AB. Cut the perpendicular at D.
(c) Use compasses centre B and radius BA. Cut the perpendicular at C.
(d) Join C and D. What special name would you give to quadrilateral ABCD?

Remember: a *tri*angle has 3 sides; a *quad*rilateral has 4 sides.

9 Use the quadrilateral ABCD that you constructed in the previous question.
(a) Bisect each of the vertices of the quadrilateral. What do you notice?
(b) Label the point at which the bisectors intersect E. Measure AE, BE, CE and DE. What do you notice?
(c) Measure ∠AEB, ∠BEC, ∠CED and ∠DEA. What do you notice?

10 (a) Draw a line and mark two points G and H about 8 cm apart. Construct the perpendicular at G and at H.
(b) Use compasses centre G and radius about 6 cm. Cut the perpendicular at J. Keep the same radius and with centre H, cut the other perpendicular at I.
(c) Join I and J. What special name would you give to quadrilateral GHIJ?

11 Use the quadrilateral GHIJ that you constructed in the previous question.
(a) Join the opposite vertices: GI and HJ.
(b) Label the point at which the diagonals intersect K. Measure GK, HK, IK and JK. What do you notice?
(c) Measure ∠GKH, ∠HKI, ∠IKJ, and ∠JKG. What do you notice?

12 (a) Draw an accurate diagram of the parallelogram shown.

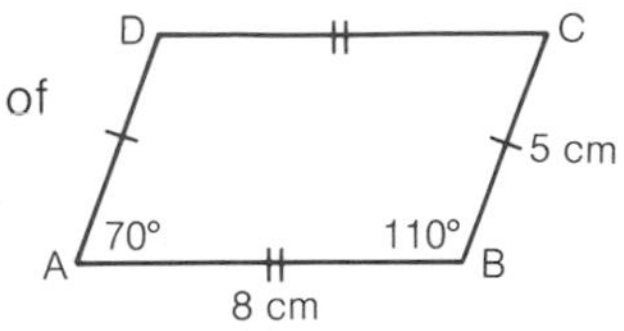


(b) Write the instructions needed to do the steps of the construction.

(c) Use your instructions in (b). Have someone follow your instructions. Did they construct the figure ABCD as shown?

13 Refer to the previous question.

(a) Join the diagonals, BD and AC.

(b) Label the point at which the diagonals intersect M. Measure AM, MC, BM and MD. What do you notice?

14 A parallelogram in which all four sides have equal measure is called a rhombus.

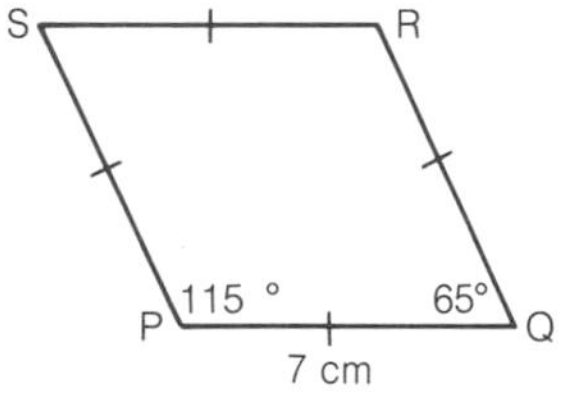


(a) Draw an accurate diagram of rhombus shown.

(b) Bisect each of its angles. What do you notice?

(c) Label the point at which the bisectors intersect T. Measure ∠PTQ, ∠QTR, ∠RTS and ∠STP. What do you notice?

15 Based on your results in the previous questions, which of the following statements are probably true?

(a) The diagonals of a parallelogram bisect each of the angles at the vertices.

(b) The diagonals of a parallelogram intersect at the midpoints.

(c) The diagonals of a rhombus intersect at right angles.

(d) The diagonals of a rectangle intersect at right angles.

(e) The diagonals of a square intersect at right angles.

16 (a) Draw any triangle. Construct the perpendicular from each vertex to the opposite side. What do you notice?

(b) Label the point at which the perpendiculars intersect O. Using compasses with centre O and radius to any vertex, draw a circle. What do you notice?

17 Repeat the steps of the previous question using

(a) an acute triangle (b) a right triangle

(c) an obtuse triangle

Describe how to find the centre of the circle passing through the vertices of a triangle.

## C

18 The sketch shows a cross section of a metal shelf. Use accurate construction to find the diameter of the smallest cylindrical package that the shelf would fit into.

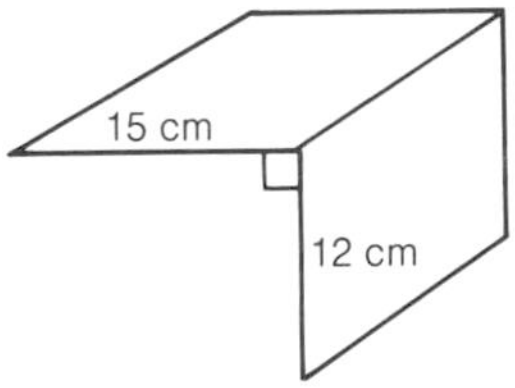


### Math Tip

Often in solving a problem, you need to look at the problems in different ways. For example, try this problem.

Draw 9 points as shown.

Start with one of the points. Draw at most 4 line segments to pass through all of the points once and only once. Once you start to draw you cannot lift your pen off the paper.

### Calculator Tip

Remember, it is easy to press the wrong key on a calculator.

- Always estimate your answer.
- Always check, when you have finished computing, whether your answer is reasonable.

(You wouldn't want to charge for 10 m² of sod and have to deliver 100 m²: zero counts!)

# 11.4 Pythagoras and Right Triangles

Pythagoras was a Greek mathematician whose name is associated with an important property that relates the hypotenuse to the other two sides in a right triangle.

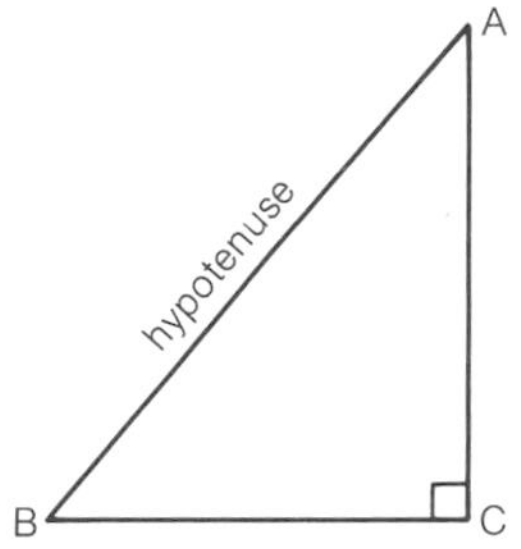


For the triangle shown, $(AB)^2 = (BC)^2 + (CA)^2$

This property is known as the **Pythagorean Property** or the **Pythagorean Theorem.** The property is very useful for finding the third side of a right triangle when you know two sides.

### Example

Calculate the length of the third side in each.

(a)

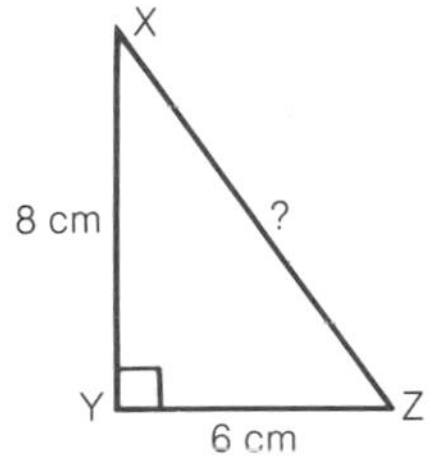


(b)

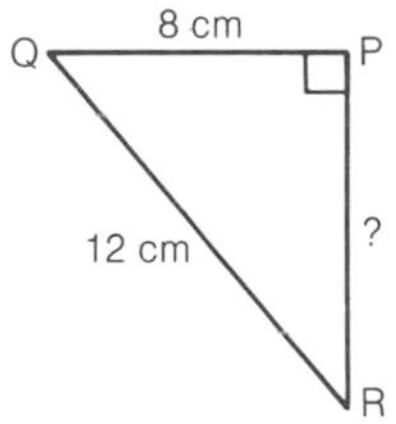


### Solution

(a)
$$\begin{aligned} (XZ)^2 &= (XY)^2 + (YZ)^2 \\ &= 8^2 + 6^2 \\ &= 64 + 36 \\ &= 100 \\ XZ &= \sqrt{100} \\ &= 10 \end{aligned}$$

Refer to a calculator. Does it have a square root function?

The length of XZ is 10 cm.

(b)
$$\begin{aligned} (QR)^2 &= (RP)^2 + (PQ)^2 \\ 12^2 &= (RP)^2 + 8^2 \\ 144 &= (RP)^2 + 64 \\ 144 - 64 &= (RP)^2 \\ 80 &= (RP)^2 \\ \text{or } (RP)^2 &= 80 \\ RP &= \sqrt{80} \\ &= 8.9 \text{ (to 1 decimal place)} \end{aligned}$$

The length of RP is about 8.9 cm.

## Try These

1 Use the Pythagorean Property. What equation relates the sides of each triangle?

(a)

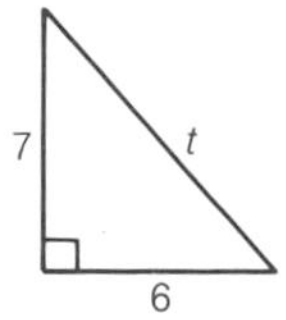


(b)

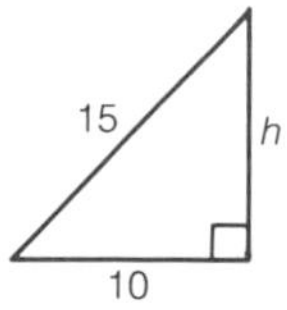


(c)

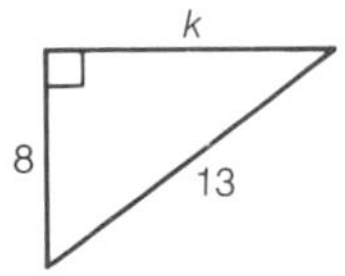


2 Find the missing measure in each triangle.

(a)

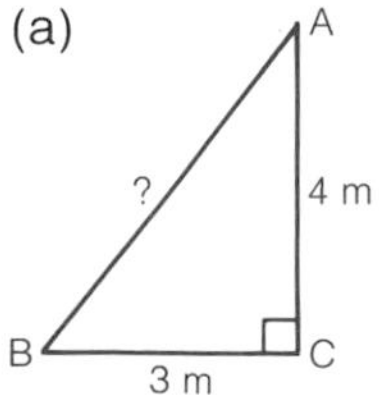


(b)

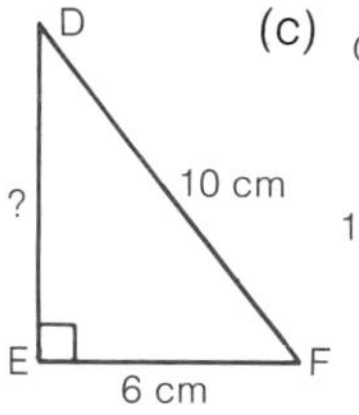


(c)

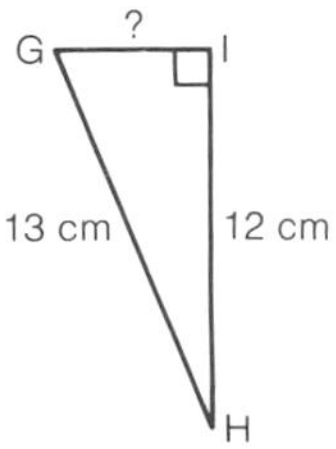

## Written Exercises

**A** Express your answers correct to 1 decimal place.

1 Calculate each hypotenuse.

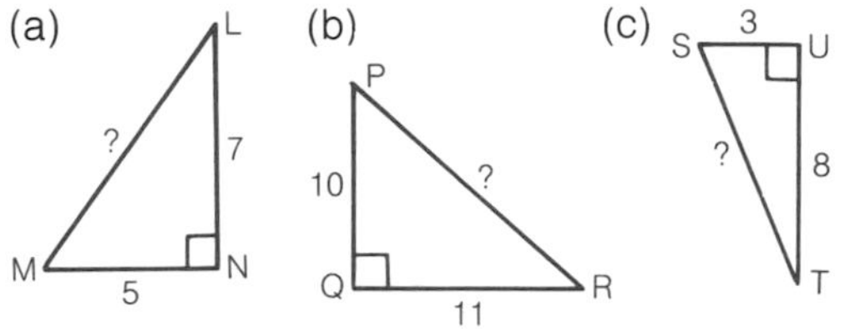


2 Right triangles are shown on a grid. Calculate the length of the hypotenuse of each. Each □ represents one square centimetre.

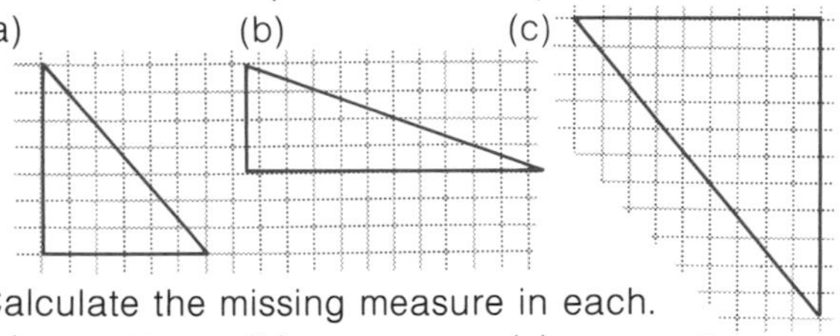


3 Calculate the missing measure in each.

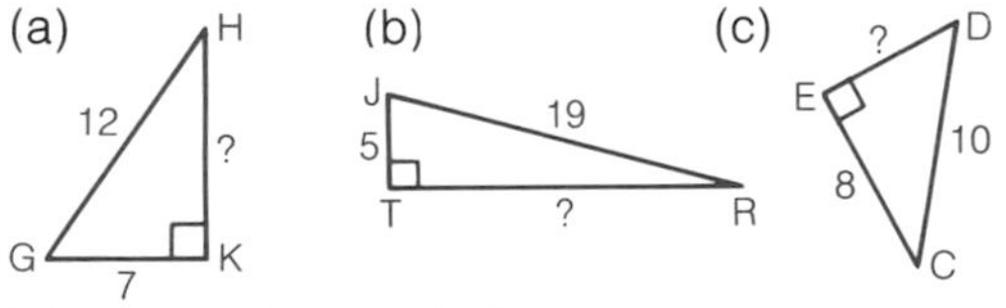


4 The foot of a 4-m ladder is placed 1.2 m away from a wall. How high up the wall does the ladder reach?

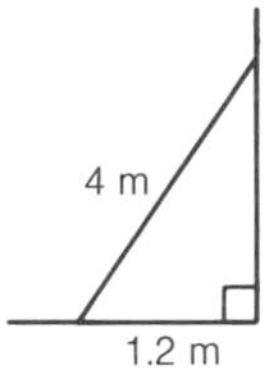


5 The back of a truck is 0.9 m above the ground. Find the length of ramp needed to reach from the back of the truck to a point A shown on the ground 2.5 m away.

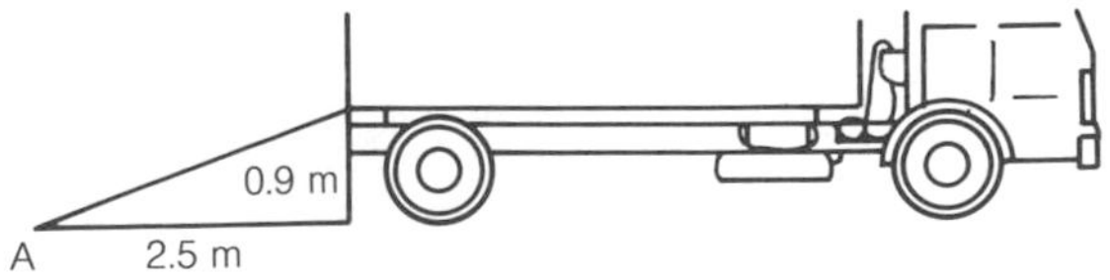


6 The size given for a T.V. or monitor screen is usually the length of the diagonal. Find the size of the monitor shown.

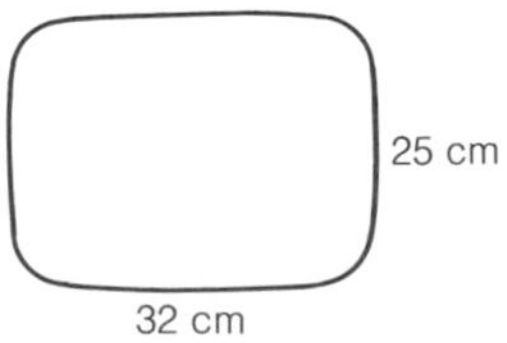


**B** Check your answers. Use a calculator.

7 Find the length, $x$, in each.

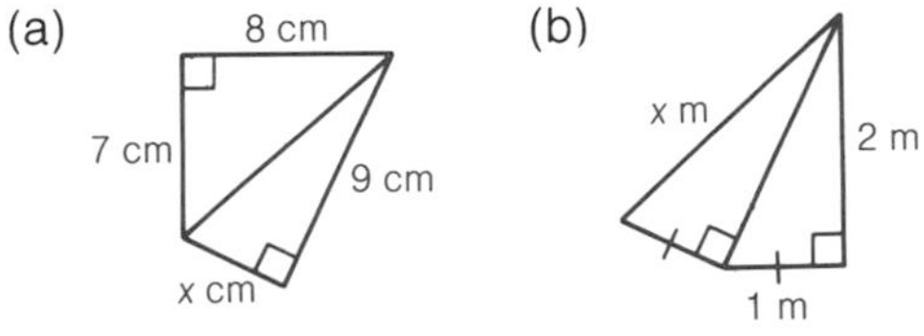


8 (a) A rectangle measures 15.2 cm by 8.8 cm. What is the length of its diagonal?
(b) Each side of a square measures 0.75 m. Find the length of the diagonal of the square.

9 The length of the hypotenuse of a right isosceles triangle is 20 cm. Find the length of each of the other sides of the triangle.

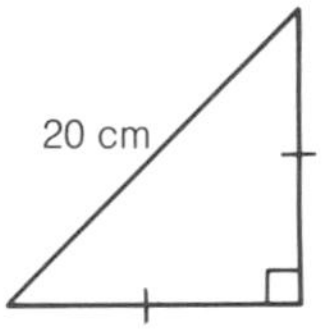


10 The span of a roof is 4.6 m. The height of the peak is 3.1 m above the eaves. Find the length of the roof from the peak to the eaves.

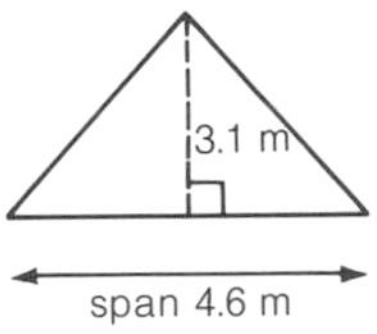


11 Diagonal braces are used to strengthen a bookshelf. Find the length of one of the braces.

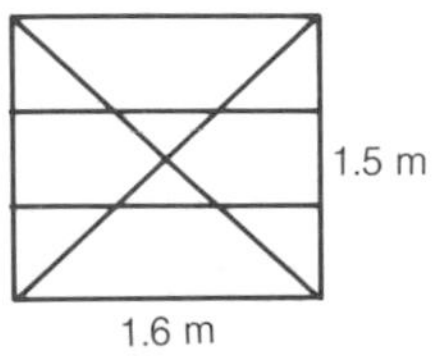


12 A groove is chiselled into a piece of wood as shown. Find the depth, $d$, of the groove. The slanting sides both measure 2.8 mm.

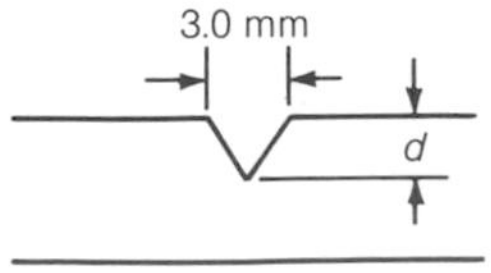

# 11.5 Graphing Ordered Pairs

To describe a location on a map you need to have two pieces of information: a horizontal and a vertical reference.

On the map, Doverport is located in square B2.

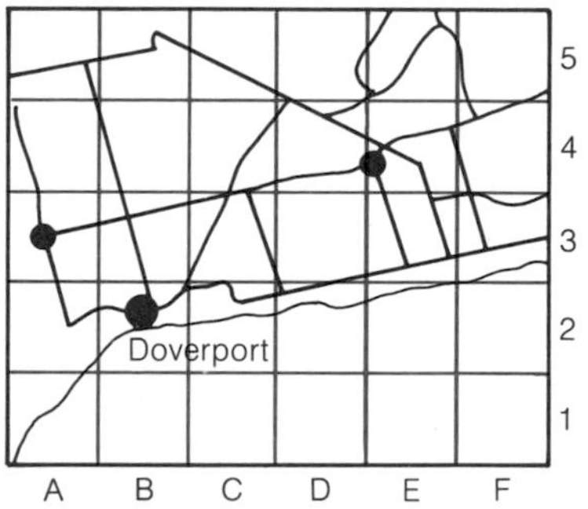


Similarly in mathematics, you can describe the position of points on the plane by referring to 2 pieces of information: to a horizontal and a vertical axis. By convention, when you are describing the location of a point you always give the horizontal reference first.

For example, the **co-ordinates** of the point P are given as an order pair: P(5,4).

The ordered pair (5,4) means that to plot (locate) the point P you start at the origin (0,0) and move horizontally 5 units to the right and then move vertically 4 units up.

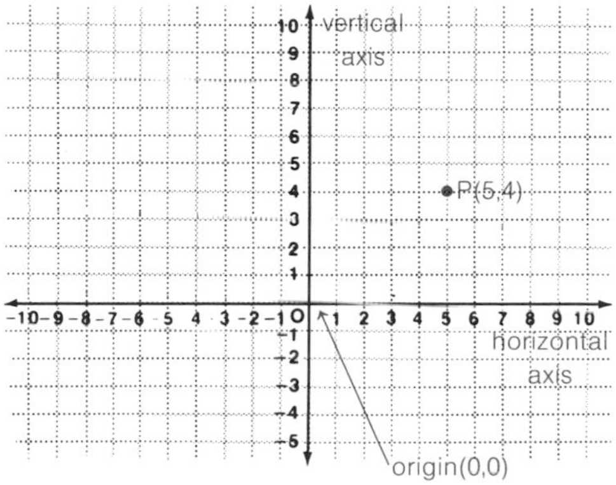


## Example

Plot the following points.
A(3,8), B(−4,2), C(0,−5), D(7,−4), E(6,0), F(−6,−6)

## Solution

Draw and label the axes. Then plot the points.

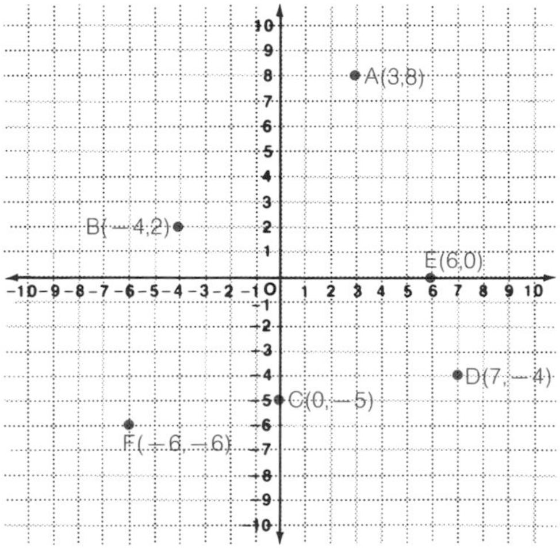

The co-ordinate axes divide the co-ordinate plane into 4 regions called quadrants which are numbered as shown.

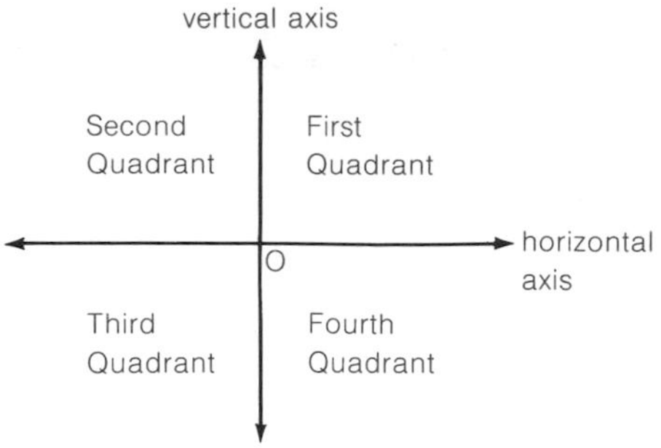


The plane with a pair of intersecting axes and a grid is often referred to as a **Cartesian plane** after the French mathematician René Descartes who developed many of the ideas in this branch of mathematics.

## Try These

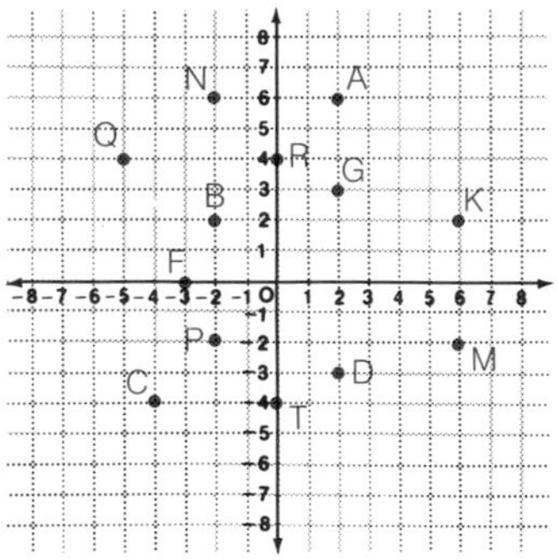


1 Refer to the diagram.
(a) What points are located at these co-ordinates?
(2,3) (6, −2) (−2,2) (0, −4)
(b) What are co-ordinates of these points?
K, D, Q, F
(c) Which points have first co-ordinate −2?
(d) Which points have second co-ordinate 2?

## Written Exercises

**A** Questions 1 to 7 are based on this diagram.

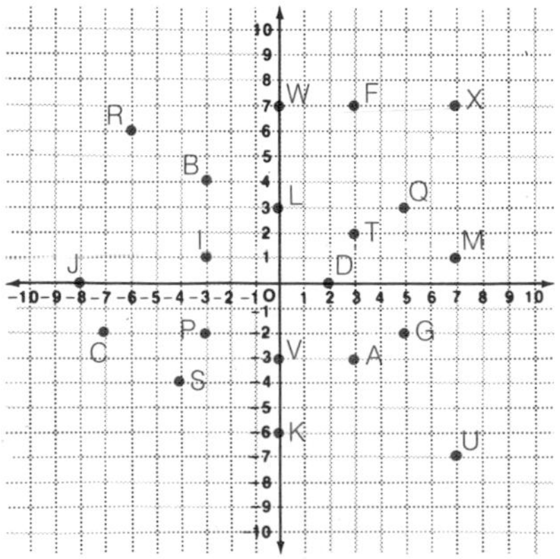


1 What are the co-ordinates of each point?
(a) L (b) C (c) K (d) J
(e) Q (f) G (g) B (h) U

2 What point is named by each ordered pair?
(a) (−3, −2) (b) (−6,6) (c) (0, −3)
(d) (5,3) (e) (−3,4) (f) (3, −3)
(g) (3,7) (h) (2,0) (i) (−7, −2)

3 (a) What are the co-ordinates of these points?
(i) T (ii) F (iii) A
(b) What do these three points have in common?

4 (a) Which points have first co-ordinate −3?
(b) Which points have second co-ordinate −3?

5 (a) Which points are on the horizontal axis?
(b) What do these points have in common?

6 (a) Which points lie on the vertical axis?
(b) What do these points have in common?

7 Which points have the same first and second co-ordinates?

**B** Often a problem is solved incorrectly because it has been incorrectly read. Read carefully.

8 (a) Plot the following points.

| | | |
|---|---|---|
| A(8,10) | B(−8,2) | C(4,1) |
| D(2,−8) | E(1,6) | F(8,−6) |
| G(−4,−3) | H(−3,10) | I(4,3) |
| J(−4,5) | K(4,−7) | L(−2,−2) |
| M(−6,5) | N(−6,−3) | |

(b) Which points are in the first quadrant?
(c) Which points are in the fourth quadrant?
(d) Which quadrant is the point B in?
(e) If both co-ordinates of a point are negative, which quadrant is the point in?

9 Use your diagram from the previous question.
(a) Join the following points in order: GJMN. What type of figure have you drawn?
(b) Join the following points in order: GDKL. What type of figure is this?
(c) Join the three points BCI. What type of triangle is this? Give reasons for your answer.

10 The points P(−3,2), Q(5,−8) and R(4,9) are the vertices of a triangle. Which quadrant is each vertex in?

11 (a) Plot the following points.
P(5,3) Q(−2,3) R(−2,−5)
(b) Locate the point S in your diagram so that PQRS is a rectangle. What are the co-ordinates of S?

12 (a) Plot the following points
A(1,3) B(1,−3) C(7,−3)
(b) Locate a fourth point D so that ABCD is a square. What are the co-ordinates of the point D?
(c) How do you know that your figure ABCD is a square?

13 The following points are three of the vertices of a square.
H(4, −3) I(3, 4) J(−4,3)
(a) Predict the co-ordinates of the fourth vertex, S.
(b) Plot the points H, I and J. Use your diagram to locate the fourth vertex S of the square. Was your prediction correct? What are the co-ordinates of S?

14 Belinda stored the results of an experiment as ordered pairs in her microcomputer. When she went for lunch her mischievous little brother tried to ruin her results by inserting some ordered pairs that he made up. Following is the list of ordered pairs that Belinda came back to.

| | | | |
|---|---|---|---|
| A(5,2) | B(−3,0) | C(7,4) | D(−3,8) |
| E(1,−2) | F(0,0) | G(−2,−5) | H(−4,−2) |
| I(2,−1) | J(7,−7) | K(0,6) | L(4,1) |

Help Belinda sort out her own data by plotting the points. Which points do you think her brother inserted?

## Computer Tip

To write a computer program, you need to first know the formula or steps in mathematics. For example, if you know the co-ordinates of the vertices of a triangle on the Cartesian plane, you can calculate its area. The computer program is written for the general co-ordinates shown.

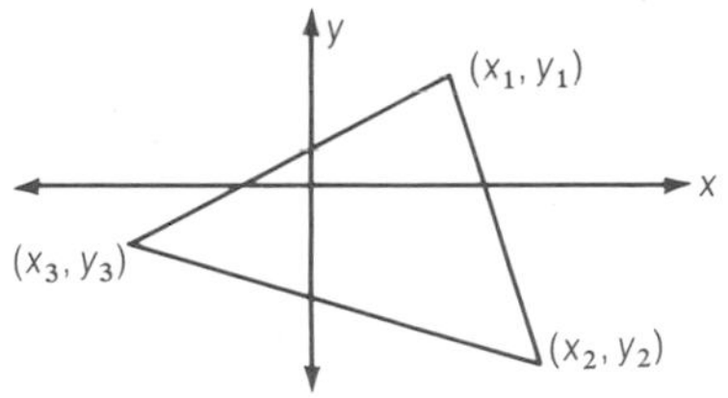


```
10 INPUT X1, Y1, X2, Y2, X3, Y3
20 LET D = X1 * Y2 + X2 * Y3 + X3 * Y1
30 LET U = X2 * Y1 + X3 * Y2 + X1 * Y3
40 LET A = ABS(D − U)/2
50 PRINT "AREA OF TRIANGLE IS"; A
60 END
```

A Calculate the area of each triangle.
△XYZ: X(4,3), Y(0,1), Z(−1,1)
△ABC: A(−4,2), B(6,−3), C(−3,5)

B (a) Choose a triangle of your own. Use the above formula to calculate its area.
(b) What effect is there on the area if you double each co-ordinate?
(c) Try some experiments of your own based on the previous computer program.

# 11.6 Drawing Graphs

The Cartesian plane provides a very useful tool for showing relationships between two variables. The horizontal axis is used to represent the first variable, and the vertical axis is used to represent the second variable. The two variables used most often are $x$ and $y$.

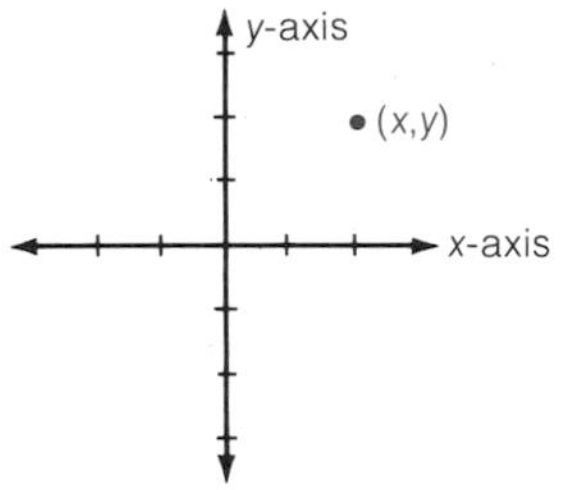


### Example 1

Use the equation $y = 3x - 1$. Construct a table of values and graph the relation between $x$ and $y$.

### Solution

*Step 1*: To construct a table of values, choose values for $x$ and use the given formula to find each corresponding value for $y$.

| x | y |
|---|---|
| 2 | 5 |
| 1 | 2 |
| 0 | −1 |
| −1 | −4 |
| −2 | −7 |

$$y = 3x - 1 = 3(2) - 1 = 6 - 1 = 5$$

$$y = 3(-1) - 1 = -3 - 1 = -4$$

*Step 2*: Read the table of values as ordered pairs. Plot the points. Since $x$ can be any number, you can draw the line through the points. Label the line. Record its equation $y = 3x - 1$.

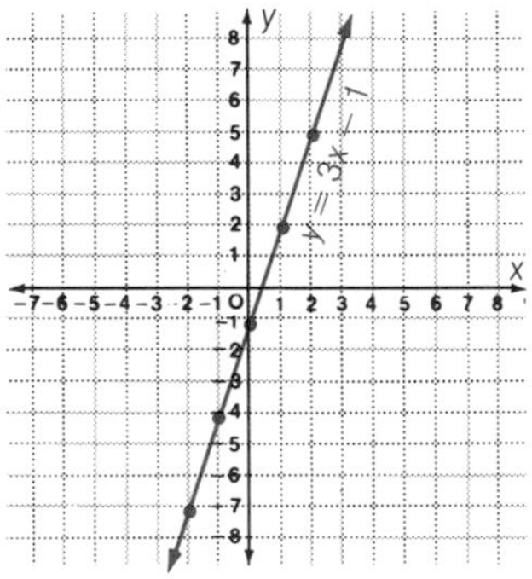


The relation $y = 3x - 1$ is a **linear relation** because its graph is a straight line.

The following example shows a relation that is non-linear.

### Example 2

Graph the relation given by the equation
$y = 5 - x^2$.

### Solution

*Step 1:* Construct a table of values for selected values for $x$.

Choose values for $x$ so that you obtain representative points of the graph.

The choice of 3, and −3 for $x$ was used so that you can show the relation in the third and fourth quadrants.

| x | y |
|---|---|
| 3 | −4 |
| 2 | 1 |
| 1 | 4 |
| 0 | 5 |
| −1 | 4 |
| −2 | 1 |
| −3 | −4 |

*Step 2*: Graph the ordered pairs. Since $x$ can be any number, you can draw a smooth curve through the points.

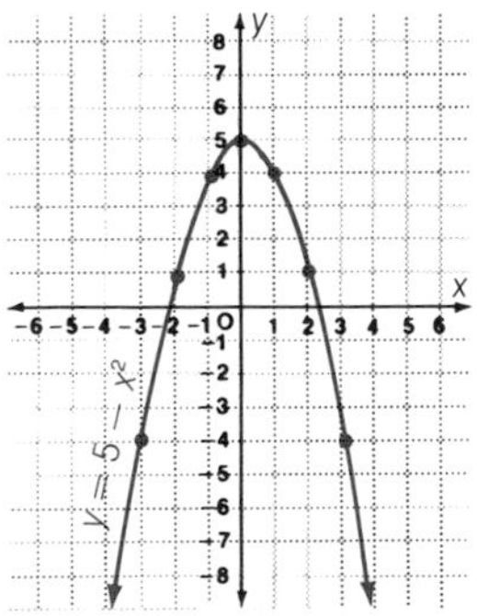


## Try These

1 For each relation, what are the missing values in the table?

(a) $y = 3x$

| $x$ | $y$ |
|---|---|
| 2 | 6 |
| 1 | ? |
| 0 | ? |
| −1 | −3 |
| −2 | ? |

(b) $y = 2x^2$

| $x$ | $y$ |
|---|---|
| 2 | 8 |
| 1 | ? |
| 0 | ? |
| −1 | ? |
| −2 | ? |

(c) $y = 6 - 2x$

| $x$ | $y$ |
|---|---|
| 2 | ? |
| 0 | ? |
| −2 | 10 |
| −4 | ? |
| −6 | ? |

2 Points have been plotted for each relation. Which are linear relations? Which are non-linear?

(a) $y = 3x - 2$

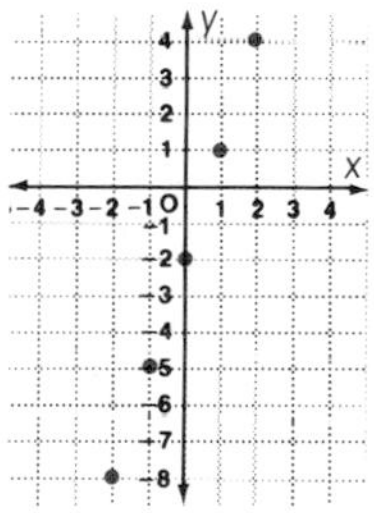

(b) $y = 2^x$

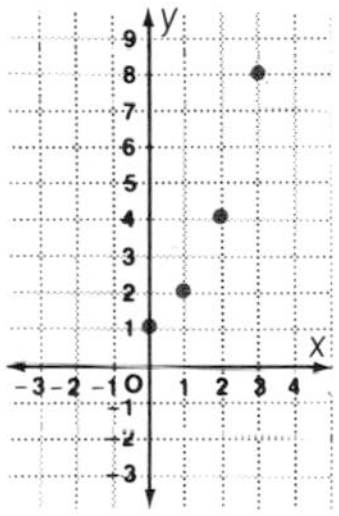

(c) $y = x^2 - 3$

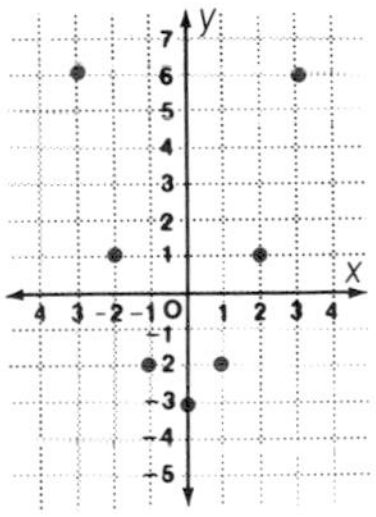

## Written Exercises

**A** Remember: to sketch the graph you need to record a table of values.

1 What ordered pairs are shown in each table of values?

(a)

| $x$ | $y$ |
|---|---|
| 2 | 2 |
| 1 | 0 |
| 0 | −2 |
| −1 | −4 |

(b)

| $x$ | $y$ |
|---|---|
| 2 | 0 |
| 1 | 3 |
| 0 | 4 |
| −1 | 3 |
| −2 | 0 |

(c)

| $x$ | $y$ |
|---|---|
| 4 | 1 |
| 2 | 3 |
| 0 | 5 |
| −2 | 7 |
| −4 | 9 |

2 The graph for the equation $y = x - 4$ is shown. The following are co-ordinates of points on the line. Find each missing co-ordinate.

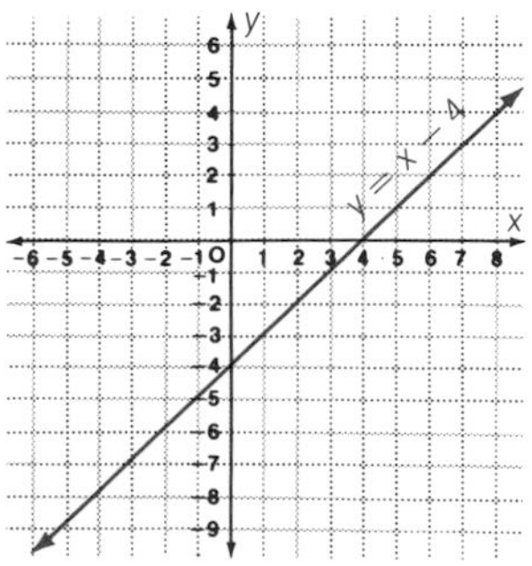


(a) (4,?) (b) (−2,?)
(c) (?,1) (d) (?,−8)

3 The graph of the equation $y = 5 - x^2$ is shown. Write the co-ordinates of each of the following points on the graph.

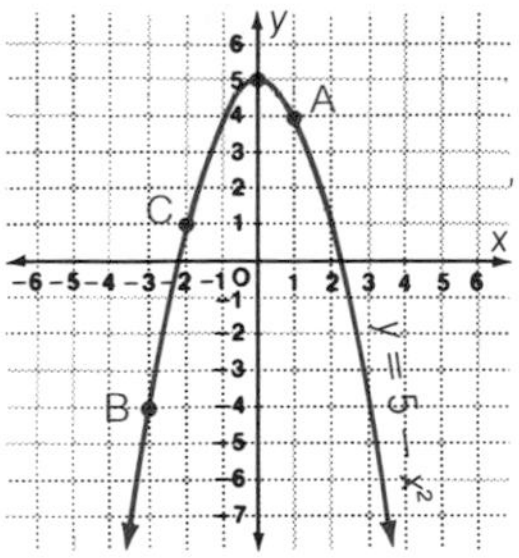

(a) A (b) B (c) C

Check that each of your ordered pairs satisfies the equation.

4 Copy and complete each table of values.

(a) $y = 5x$

| x | 2 | 1 | 0 | −1 | −2 |
|---|---|---|---|---|---|
| y | ? | ? | ? | ? | ? |

(b) $y = x^2 + 1$

| x | 2 | 1 | 0 | −1 | −2 |
|---|---|---|---|---|---|
| y | ? | ? | ? | ? | ? |

(c) $y = x - 5$

| x | −2 | 0 | 2 | 4 | 6 |
|---|---|---|---|---|---|
| y | ? | ? | ? | ? | ? |

5 Use the table of values to graph each relation.

(a) $y = 1 - x^2$ (b) $y = 1 - 2x$ (c) $y = 2x^2 - 1$

| x | y |
|---|---|
| 2 | −3 |
| 1 | 0 |
| 0 | 1 |
| −1 | 0 |
| −2 | −3 |

| x | y |
|---|---|
| 2 | −3 |
| 1 | −1 |
| 0 | 1 |
| −1 | 3 |
| −2 | 5 |

| x | y |
|---|---|
| 2 | 7 |
| 1 | 1 |
| 0 | −1 |
| −1 | 1 |
| −2 | 7 |

6 Which of the relations in the previous question are linear?

**B** **To draw a graph, you need to obtain representative points. Join these points with a line or a smooth curve.**

7 Two points for the relation $y = 4 - 3x$ are (1,1) and (2,−2).
(a) Graph the two points given. To complete the graph what other values would you choose for $x$?
(b) Find four more ordered pairs for the relation and show them on a graph.
(c) Is the graph linear?

8 The graph shows two points for the relation $y = x^2 - 4x$

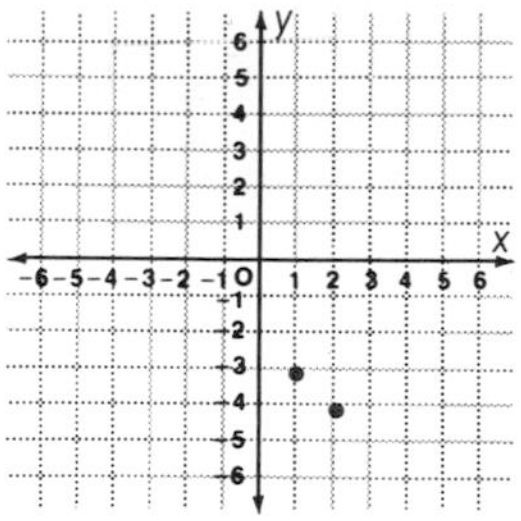

(a) To complete the graph what other values would you choose for $x$?
(b) Complete a table of values for the relation and graph the ordered pairs.
(c) Is the graph linear?

9 To find ordered pairs for the relation $y = \frac{1}{2}x + 3$
(a) would you prefer to choose odd numbers or even numbers for $x$? Explain.
(b) Construct a table of values and graph the relation.

10 For each relation
- ▶ construct a table of values
- ▶ plot the points
- ▶ draw a line or smooth curve through the points
- ▶ classify each graph as linear or non-linear

(a) $y = 3x$ (b) $y = -3x$
(c) $y = 3x + 2$ (d) $y = -3x + 2$
(e) $y = \frac{1}{2}x - 1$ (f) $y = 8x + 1$

11 Graph each of the following. Is the graph linear or non-linear?

(a) $y = -x^2$ (b) $y = \frac{3}{2}x^2$
(c) $y = x^2 - 1$ (d) $y = 3 - x^2$
(e) $y = x - x^2$ (f) $y = 3x^2 - 5$

12 Draw a graph for each equation. Classify each graph as linear or non-linear.

(a) $y = 6 - 5x$ (b) $y = x^2 + 2x$
(c) $y = -\frac{1}{2}x^2 + 8$ (d) $y = 3(x - 1)$
(e) $y = 2 - x + x^2$ (f) $y = \frac{1}{x}$

## A Useful Strategy: Renaming the Axes

A graph is a very useful way of illustrating a relationship between two variables. For example, when you throw a baseball, the height $h$ of the ball above the ground is related to the time $t$ since it was thrown by the equation

$h = -5t^2 + 20t + 1$

where $t$ is the time in seconds and $h$ is the height in metres. You can construct a table of values for $t$ and $h$.

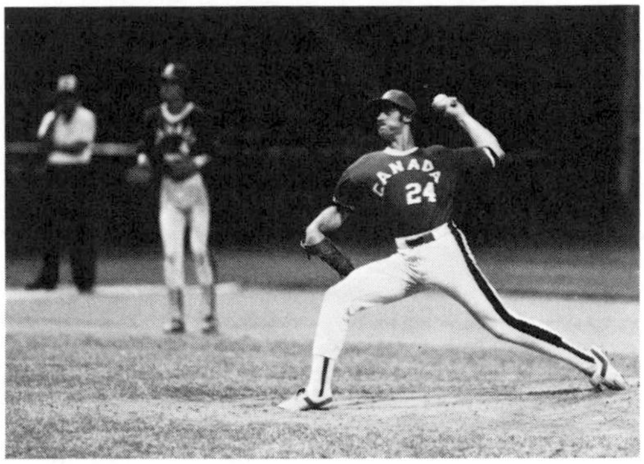

| $t$ | 0 | 1 | 2 | 3 | 4 | 5 |
|---|---|---|---|---|---|---|
| $h$ | 1 | 16 | 21 | 16 | 1 | −24 |

Since $t$ represents time since throwing the ball, you only need positive values of $t$

When you graph the points, label the horizontal axis the $t$-axis and the vertical axis the $h$-axis.

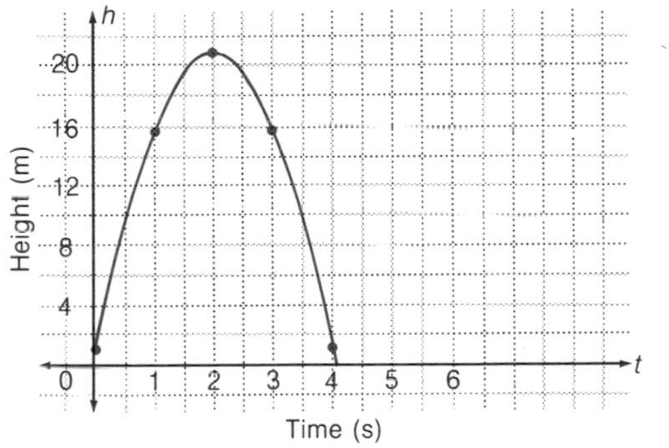


For each of the following
- ▶ construct a table of values
- ▶ graph the relation using appropriate labels for the axes
- ▶ classify the graph as linear or non-linear

13 The cost for renting a canoe is given by the equation

$c = 10 + 2n$

where $n$ represents the number of hours that the canoe is rented for.

14 The distance, $d$, in metres, of a snowmobile from a cottage is given by $d = 12t + 5$ where $t$ is the time in seconds.

15 The distance that a skydiver falls can be found using the formula $d = 5t^2$ where $t$ is the time in seconds of falling and $d$ is the distance fallen in metres.

16 The circumference, $C$, of a circle is given by $C = \pi d$, where $d$ is the diameter.

17 The area, $A$, of a circle is related to its radius, $r$, by the formula $A = \pi r^2$.

18 The height of an eagle above the ground is given by the equation

$h = 3.5t + 45$

where $t$ is the time, in seconds, since it started climbing and $h$ is the height in metres.

19 The approximate distance that you can see when looking out from a tall building is given by

$d = 4\sqrt{h}$

where $h$ is the height in metres that you are looking out from and $d$ is the distance in kilometres.

# 11.7 Curves of Best Fit

The research department at a car manufacturing plant is testing the length of time that a car takes to start from cold at different temperatures below zero. The results of ten such tests are recorded in the table.

| Temperature (°C) | −4 | −8 | −2 | −6 | −10 | −5 | −8 | −3 | −1 | −4 |
|---|---|---|---|---|---|---|---|---|---|---|
| Starting time (s) | 5 | 7 | 5 | 7 | 8 | 6 | 8 | 5 | 4 | 6 |

The data can be shown on a Cartesian plane, where the horizontal axis represents temperature and the vertical axis shows starting time.

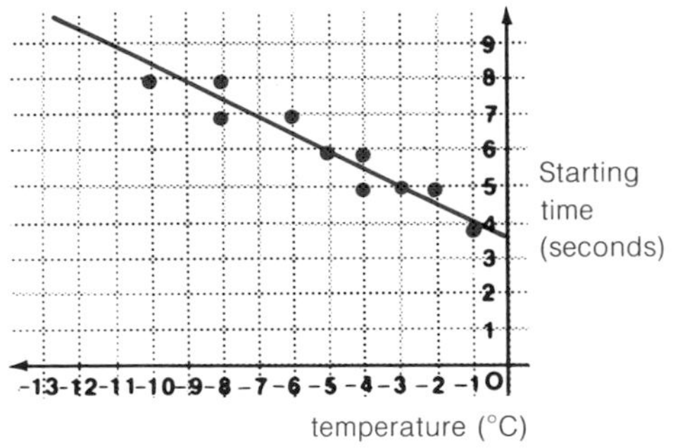


As you can see, the pattern of the points is almost linear. The line that can be drawn that is the least distance from most of the points is called the **line of best fit**.

In other cases, the data when graphed falls into a non-linear pattern which can be shown by a **curve of best fit**.

## Example

The data shows as ordered pairs the percent profit obtained delivering parcels with different distances. The distance, in kilometres, to be covered is given first.

(18,17), (10,14), (22,16), (16,18), (36,8),
(12,16), (24,16), (28,14), (2,7), (32,11), (6,12),
(20,18)

Plot the data. Draw a curve of best fit.

## Solution

Plot the points. Then draw a smooth curve that approximately fits most of the data.

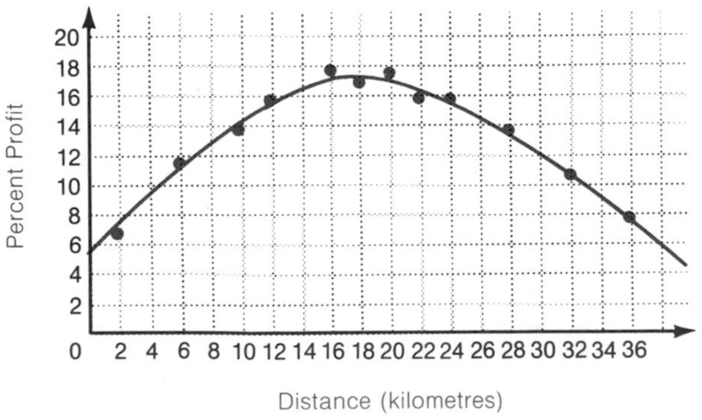


Remember: the curve is drawn so that it is the least distance from most of the points.

## Try These

1 In each, related data has been graphed. Would you say that the data has
- ▶ a line of best fit?
- ▶ a curve of best fit?
- ▶ neither of the above?

(a)

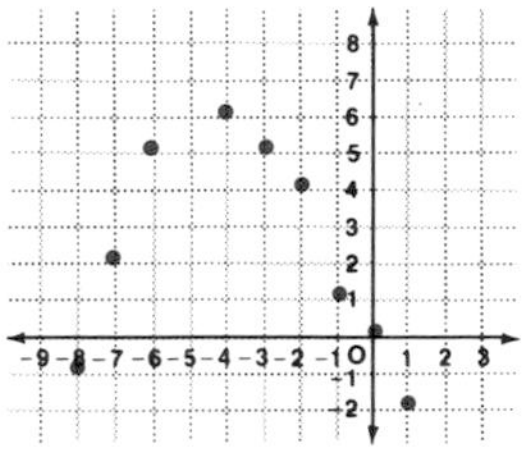

(b)

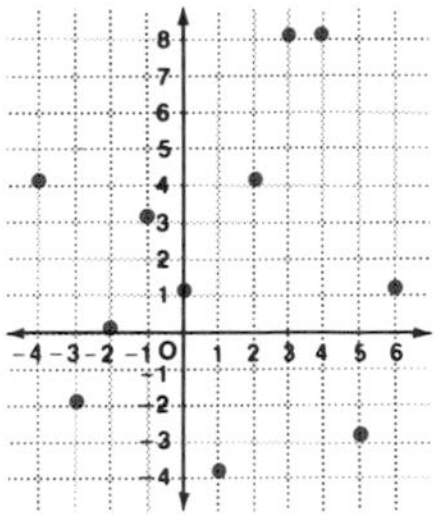

(c)

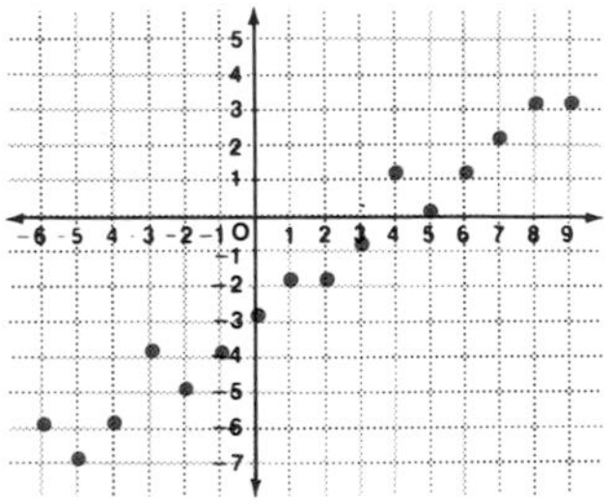

## Written Exercises

**B** **In question 1–7, graph the data and draw a line or curve of best fit.**

1 The height of a firework was estimated in metres each second after it was fired.

| time (s) | 1 | 2 | 3 | 4 | 5 | 6 | 7 | 8 |
|---|---|---|---|---|---|---|---|---|
| height (m) | 200 | 400 | 450 | 525 | 500 | 425 | 350 | 100 |

2 At a medical lab, a technician records the number of bacteria in a sample.

| number of bacteria | 6 | 30 | 45 | 80 | 105 | 160 | 200 | 310 | 500 |
|---|---|---|---|---|---|---|---|---|---|
| time (hours) | 0 | 1 | 2 | 3 | 4 | 5 | 6 | 7 | 8 |

3 To find out how far its signal is reaching, a radio station asks listeners who are driving away from the city to send in to the station information on where they lose the signal. They use a Cartesian grid over a map of their region to record the listener's data. The following points were gathered.

(8,6), (2,9), (−3,9), (−8,−5), (0,−10), (6,7), (7,−7), (−5,9), (4,−9), (−3,−9), (9,4), (2,−10), (1,10), (−7,8), (8, −7), (−10,1), (9,−4), (−5,−8), (10,−1), (−9,3)

4 On a trip, Ben kept a record of the quantity of gas he bought and the cost.

| Quantity (L) | 20 | 47 | 50 | 10.2 | 48 | 32 |
|---|---|---|---|---|---|---|
| Cost ($) | 9.06 | 20.00 | 23.25 | 5.00 | 20.88 | 14.98 |

Will the line of best fit pass through the origin? Explain.

5 Cathy gathered data on the model of car she is considering to buy. She recorded the resale price of the model of previous years. She used ordered pairs to record the age in years followed by the price in dollars.

(1,8500), (5,1000), (7,750), (2,5800), (3,3200), (2,6000), (4,1750), (1,8000), (4,2250), (6,800), (2,5500), (3,3500)

6 Mark goes to his bank each Friday. The table shows the balance, to the nearest dollar, in his account at the end of each week.

| Week | 1 | 2 | 3 | 4 | 5 | 6 | 7 | 8 |
|---|---|---|---|---|---|---|---|---|
| Balance | 356 | 284 | 247 | 270 | 230 | 180 | 180 | 110 |

7 Eileen is trying to quit smoking. She records as ordered pairs the number of cigarettes she smokes each day.

(1,30), (2,25), (3,22), (4,24), (5,20), (6,17), (7,16), (8,12), (9,9), (10,9)

8 In a chemistry experiment, students were asked to measure the volume of a liquid as it is heated. They recorded the temperature followed by the volume in millilitres as ordered pairs. (20,50), (30,50), (40,51), (50,52) (60,65), (70,60), (80,65), (90,67)

(a) Graph the data.

(b) The students are told that their results should be approximately linear. Draw the line of best fit.

(c) Which piece of data do you think was recorded incorrectly? Suggest what the reading might have actually been.

# 11.8 Interpreting Graphs: Interpolation, Extrapolation

In the previous two sections you have learned how to draw a graph of a relationship by plotting ordered pairs related by an equation or formula, or were the results of an experiment. Once you have drawn the graph you can often use it to find other facts about the relation.

For example, the graph shows how the height of a helicopter is related to the time since takeoff.

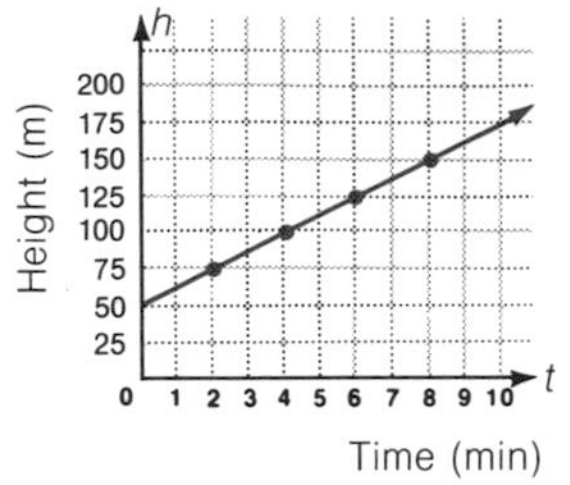


From the graph you can tell that the height after 5 min is 112.5 m. This process of reading new information located between the given points is described as **interpolation**.

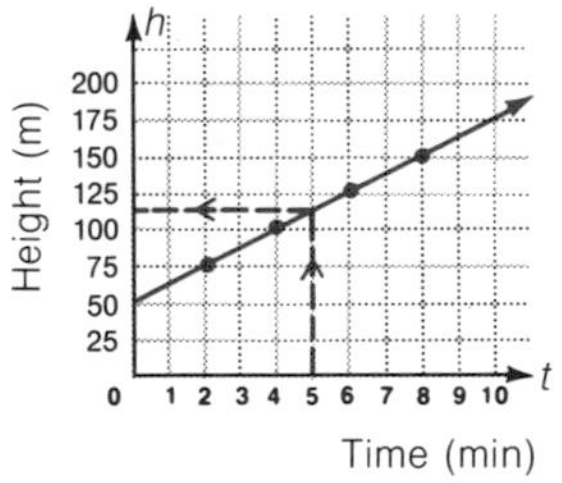


The process of reading information beyond the given points is described as **extrapolation**. For example, the helicopter will reach a height of 175 m after a time of 10 min.

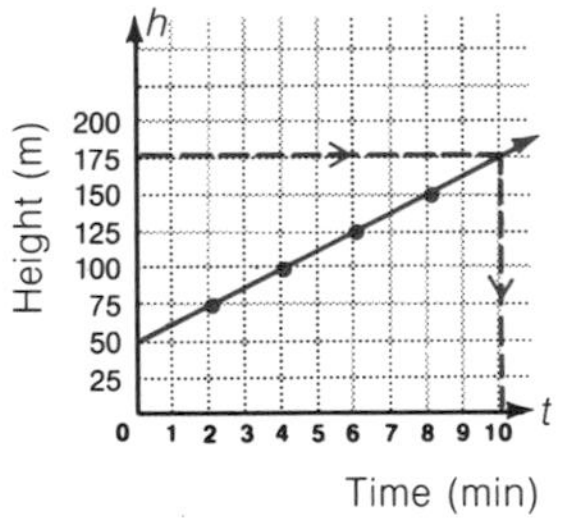


## Try These

Refer to the graph showing how the height of a football is related to the time since it was kicked.

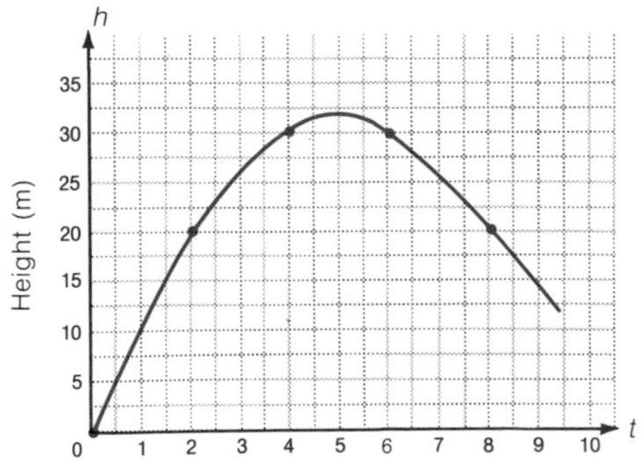


1 What is the height of the football after each time?
(a) 3 s (b) 7 s (c) 1 s

2 After what length(s) of time is the ball at each height?
(a) 15 m (b) 35 m (c) 25 m

3 Extrapolate to find the time at which the ball will be back on the ground.

4 Interpolate to find the time at which the ball reaches its greatest height. What is the height?

## Written Exercises

**A** Review the meaning of interpolation and extrapolation.

1 The graph shows how the value of a rare record album is increasing with time.

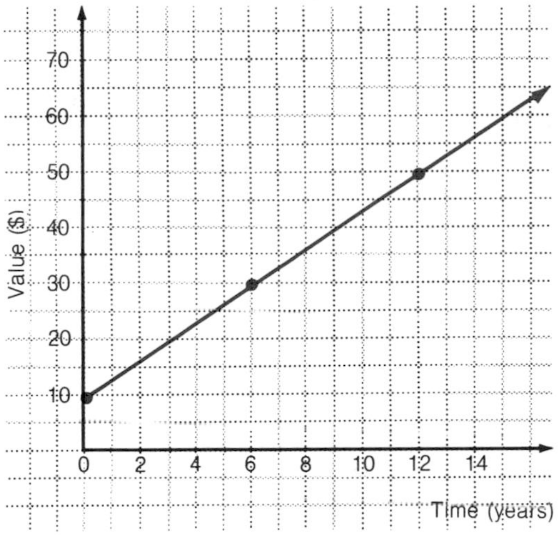


(a) What is the value of the record after
▶ 10 years ▶ 14 years

(b) After how many years is the record worth
▶ $20 ▶ $60

2 The depth of water in a ditch varies with time as shown on the graph. Estimate the missing values in the following ordered pairs.
(a) (1,?) (b) (?,7.0) (c) (3,?) (d) (?,4.0)

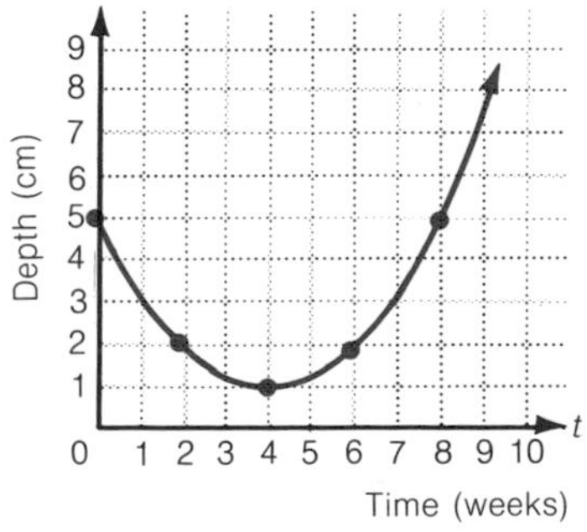


3 The distance that a car takes to stop increases with the speed of the car. The graph shows the relationship for a car on a concrete road surface.

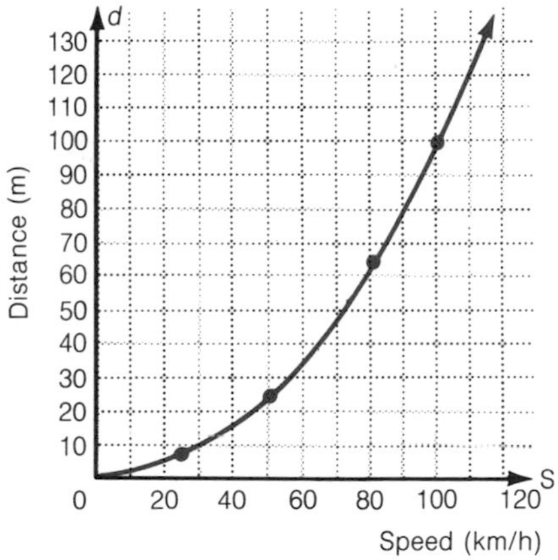


(a) About how many metres does it take for a car to stop when it is travelling at
▶ 40 km/h ▶ 70 km/h ▶ 110 km/h

(b) When the police are investigating accidents, they measure the length of skid marks to estimate how fast the cars were travelling. Estimate the speed of cars whose stopping distance is
▶ 30 m ▶ 60 m ▶ 90 m

**B** To draw the graphs, decide which variable is shown on the horizontal axis, and which is on the vertical.

4 The distance that a helicopter travels at its cruising speed varies with time as shown in the table.

| time (hours) | 0 | 2 | 4 | 6 |
|---|---|---|---|---|
| distance (km) | 0 | 180 | 360 | 540 |

(a) Draw a graph to show the data.

(b) Use your graph to estimate how far the helicopter travels in
▶ 5 hours ▶ 7 hours ▶ 3.5 hours

(c) Estimate how long it will take the helicopter to travel
▶ 250 km ▶ 600 km ▶ 1000 km

5 The time that a train takes to travel a distance of 500 km varies with its speed. The table shows some values for the relationship.

| time (h) | 2 | 4 | 5 | 8 | 10 |
|---|---|---|---|---|---|
| speed (km/h) | 250 | 125 | 100 | 62.5 | 50 |

(a) Show the data as points on the Cartesian plane. Use a smooth curve to show the relation.

(b) Use your graph to estimate the average speed of the train when the trip takes
▶ 6 h ▶ 9 h

(c) About how long does the journey take on a train that travels at
▶ 175 km/h ▶ 80 km/h

(d) Refer to the graph. Create a problem based on the information. Solve the problem.

6 Did you know that you can tell the temperature by the number of times a cricket chirps? (Summer only, of course!) The temperature, $t$, in degrees Celsius, is related to the number, $n$, of chirps per minute by the equation

$$t = \frac{n}{6.3}$$

(a) Construct a table of values for the relation. Use $n = 10$, $n = 20$ and $n = 30$.

(b) Draw a graph of the relation.

(c) Use your graph to estimate the temperature if you count 100 chirps in a minute.

(d) If you hear 16 chirps in 10 seconds what is the approximate temperature?

(e) When the temperature drops to 5°C, how many times will a cricket chirp in a minute?

(f) Refer to your graph. Create a problem based on the information. Write a solution for your problem.

7 The approximate area, $A$, of a circle is related to its radius, $r$, by
$A = 3r^2$.

(a) Make a table of values using $r = 1$, $r = 2$, $r = 5$ and $r = 10$.

(b) Graph the relation.

(c) From your graph, what is the approximate area of a circle with radius
▶ 4 cm ▶ 12 cm

(d) If a circle has an area of about 200 $cm^2$, estimate its radius.

8 The table shows the price of chocolate bars with different masses.

| mass | 35 g | 50 g | 75 g | 100 g | 200 g |
|---|---|---|---|---|---|
| price | 45¢ | 59¢ | 79¢ | $1.09 | $2.09 |

(a) Plot the data using Cartesian co-ordinates. Draw a line of best fit.

(b) Use the line of best fit, to estimate how much a chocolate bar with mass 150 g would cost.

(c) If a new size of bar is to sell for 99¢, estimate what its mass will be.

## Career Tip

Commercial artists are often called upon to draw graphs. They need to interpret visually many communication problems. This can include the preparation of a package design, an advertisement, or a display in a newspaper or magazine. Commercial artists work in a variety of related fields, such as

| | |
|---|---|
| advertising designer | layout designers |
| illustrator | assembly artist |
| technical artist | typographic designer |
| medical illustrator | |

What type of skills do you think are required by each of the fields? What skills in mathematics do you think are necessary?

## Math Tip

In any field you work in, it is important to know the vocabulary of your specialty. In mathematics, you cannot solve problems if you don't know what the clues are.

- Make a list of all the words you have learned in this chapter.
- Provide a simple example to illustrate the meaning of each word.

# 11.9 Slope on the Plane

When you graph linear relations, it is sometimes useful to have ways to compare the lines. One characteristic that is frequently used is the **slope**. The slope of any line is defined as follows:

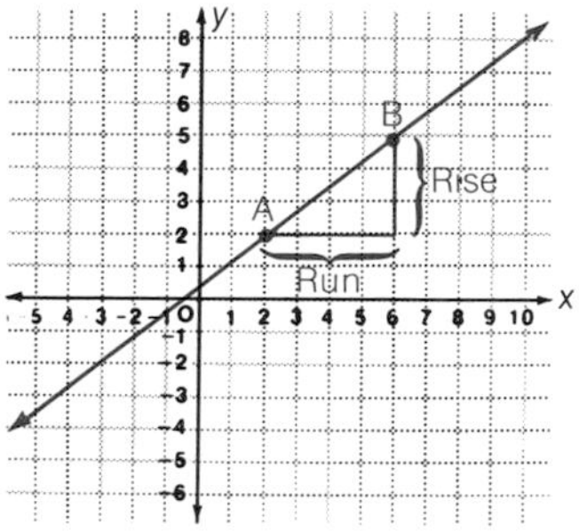


$$\text{slope} = \frac{\text{rise}}{\text{run}}$$

The slope of the line shown, passing through points A and B is given by

$$\text{slope} = \frac{3}{4}$$
3 ← the rise from A to B is 3 units up
4 ← the run from A to B is 4 units to the right

You can use the co-ordinates of two points to find the slope of the line passing through those points.

### Example

Find the slope of the line passing through the points C(7,1) and D(−3,6).

### Solution

Show the given information on a diagram. For CD,

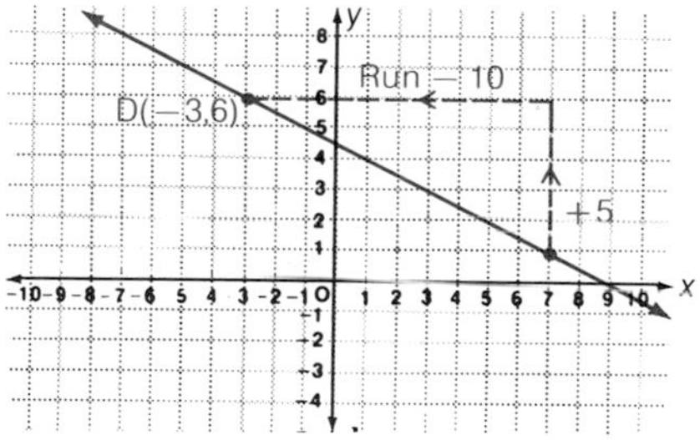


$$\text{slope} = \frac{\text{rise}}{\text{run}}$$

$$= \frac{6-1}{-3-7}$$
6 − 1 ← Calculate the rise.
−3 − 7 ← Calculate the run.

$$= \frac{5}{-10} \text{ or } \frac{-1}{2}$$

## Try These

1 What is the slope of each line segment shown?

(a)

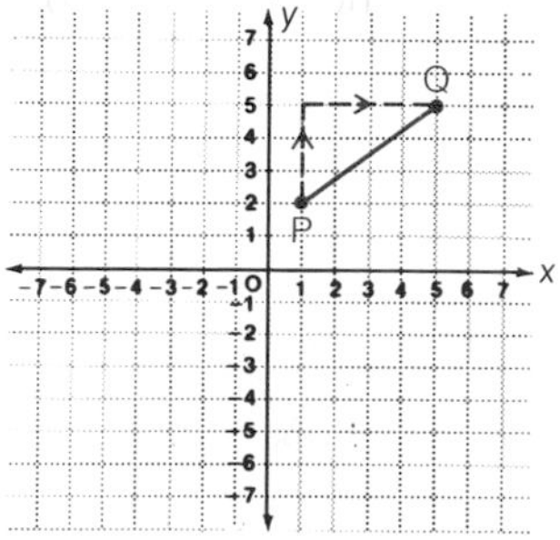


(b)

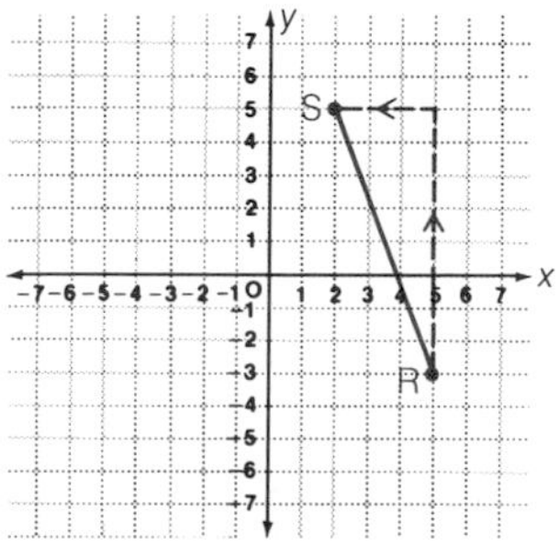


(c)

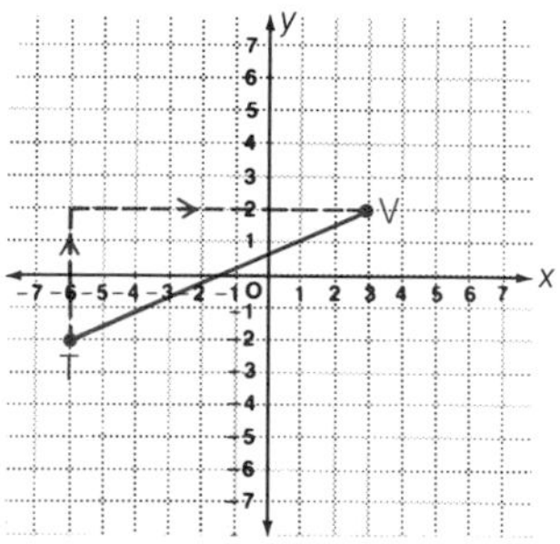

## Written Exercises

**A** Review the meaning of rise, run, and slope.

1 Refer to the diagram. For the line segment XY,
(a) what is the rise?
(b) what is the run?
(c) what is the slope?

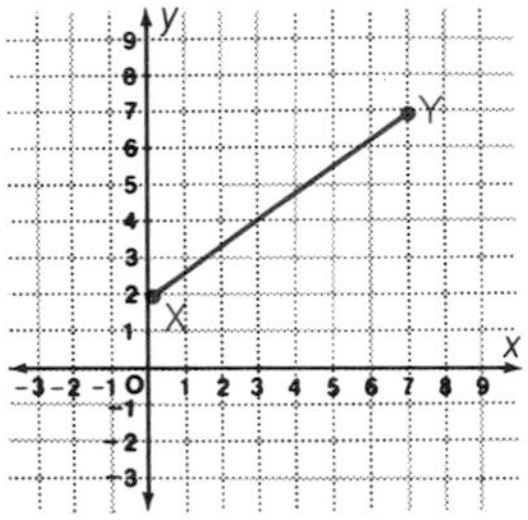


2 For the line segment GH, calculate
(a) the rise
(b) the run
(c) the slope.

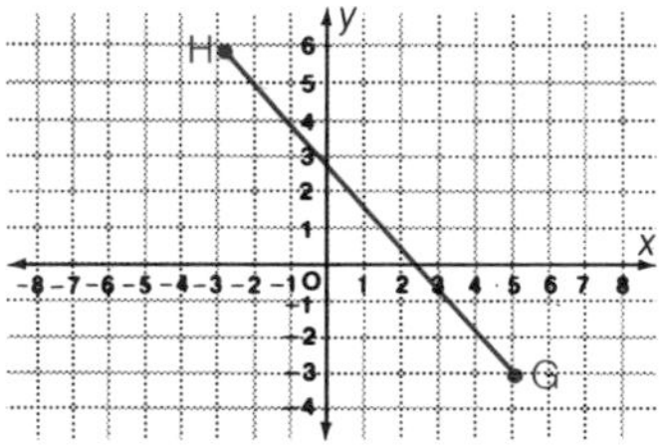


3 Find the slope of the line passing through each pair of points marked.

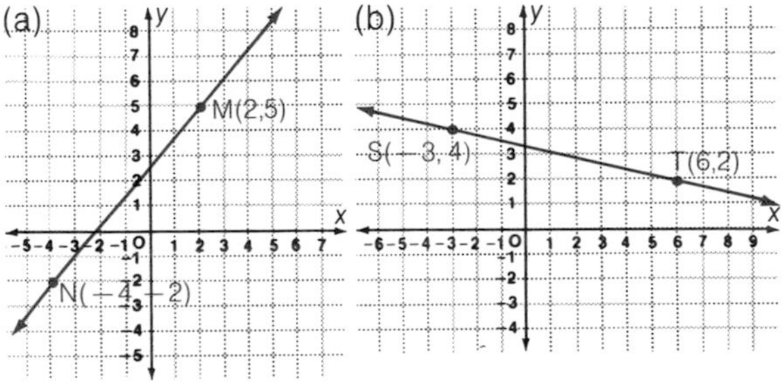


4 Refer to the diagram.
(a) Which line segments do you expect to have positive slopes?

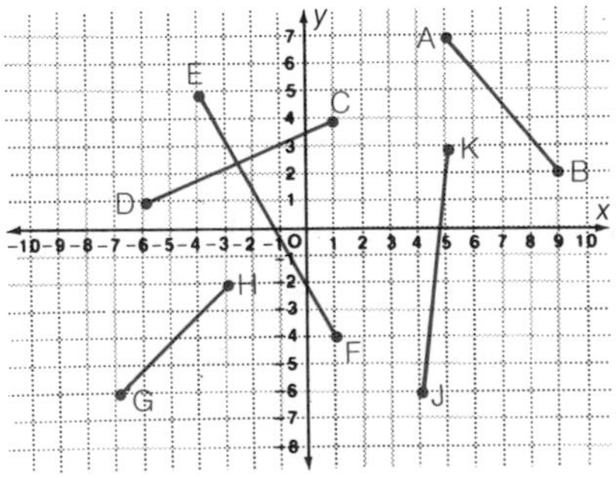


(b) Which do you expect have negative slopes?
(c) Calculate the slope of each line segment shown to check your answers in (a) and (b).

5 A line passes through the points A(3, −4) and B(−2, −5).
(a) Draw a diagram to show the line.
(b) Find the slope of the line.

**B** To find slope, you need to use the formula

$$\text{slope} = \frac{\text{rise}}{\text{run}}.$$

6 Find the slope of the line passing through each pair of points.
(a) A(−1,1), B(5, −2) (b) C(2, −2), D(6,4)
(c) E(3, −4), F(−1,3) (d) G(3,2), H(−5, −5)

7 (a) Find the slope of the line joining J(1,2) and K(−5,2)
(b) Explain the meaning of your result from (a) in terms of a diagram.

8 (a) Find the slope of the line joining P(−3, −4) and Q(−3,7).
(b) Explain your result from (a) using a diagram.

9 (a) Find the slope of the line passing through A(−3,2) and B(3,5).
(b) Find the slope of the line passing through C(3,1) and D(9,4).
(c) Compare your results in parts (a) and (b). Explain using a graph.

10 (a) Find the slope of the line passing through E(3, −7) and F(−2, −3).
(b) Find the slope of the line passing through G(5,2) and H(0,6).
(c) How do your results in parts (a) and (b) compare? Explain using a graph.

**C**

11 For each line, the slope and one point on the line is given. Draw the graph.

(a) P(2,5), slope $-\frac{1}{2}$ (b) R(6, −3), slope $-\frac{3}{4}$

# 11.10 Distance on the Plane

Often in mathematics, skills that you have learned in one part of your work are later found to apply in a new but different situation.

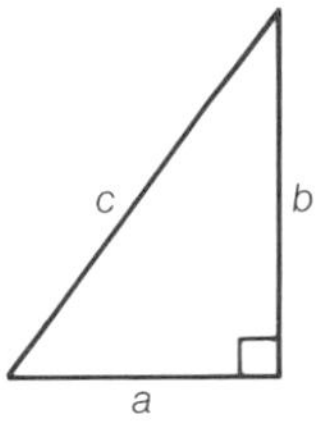


Previously you used the Pythagorean relation to find the length of the hypotenuse of a right triangle:

$c^2 = a^2 + b^2$

You can use this same relationship to find the distance between two points on the Cartesian plane.

## Example

Find the distance between the points A(5,6) and B(1,−4).

## Solution

Sketch a diagram. Draw a right triangle, △ABC, as shown.

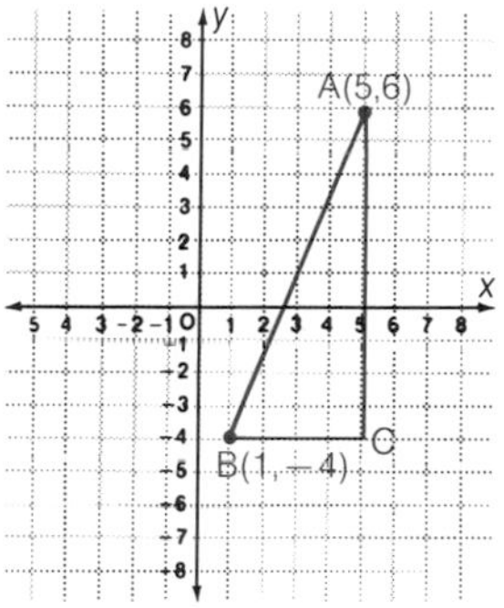


The vertical distance is from −4 to 6, or $6 - (-4)$ which is 10 units.

$(AB)^2 = (BC)^2 + (AC)^2$

$(AB)^2 = \begin{pmatrix}\text{horizontal}\\ \text{distance}\end{pmatrix}^2 + \begin{pmatrix}\text{vertical}\\ \text{distance}\end{pmatrix}^2$

$(AB)^2 = (5 - 1)^2 + (6 - (-4))^2$

$= 4^2 + 10^2$

$= 16 + 100$

$= 116$

So $AB = \sqrt{116}$ From a calculator or square root table.

$= 10.8$ (to one decimal place)

Thus the distance between A and B is 10.8 units.

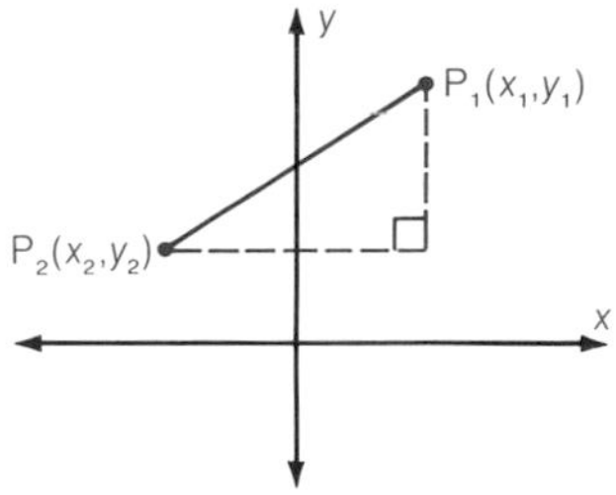


In general, the distance between the points $P_1(x_1,y_1)$ and $P_2(x_2,y_2)$ is given by the formula

$$P_1P_2 = \sqrt{(x_1 - x_2)^2 + (y_1 - y_2)^2}$$

## Try These

Refer to the diagram.

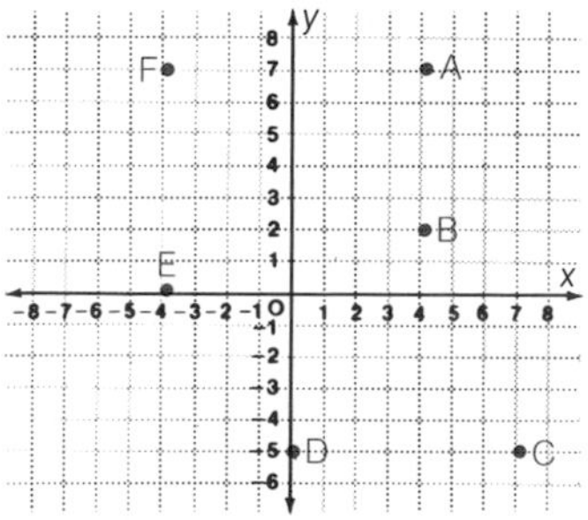


1 What is the distance between the following points?
(a) A and B (b) C and D (c) E and F

2 For each pair of points,
▶ What is the horizontal distance?
▶ What is the vertical distance?
(a) B and C (b) E and B
(c) D and A (d) F and B

## Written Exercises

**A** Round your answers to 1 decimal place.

1 Use the line segment PQ.
   (a) What is the horizontal distance?
   (b) What is the vertical distance?
   (c) Calculate the distance between P and Q.

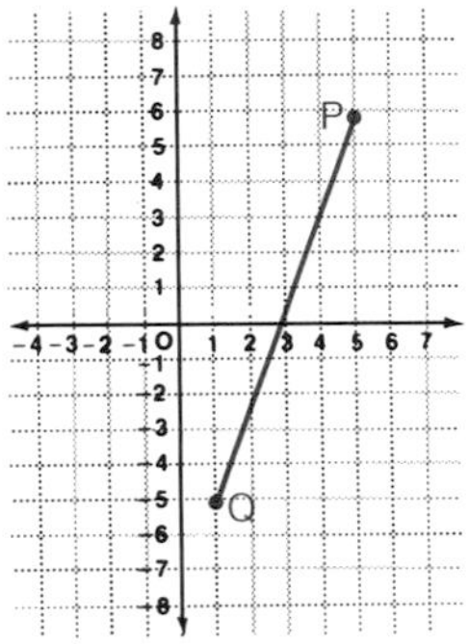

2 Use the line segment MN.
   (a) What is the horizontal distance?
   (b) What is the vertical distance?
   (c) Calculate the length.

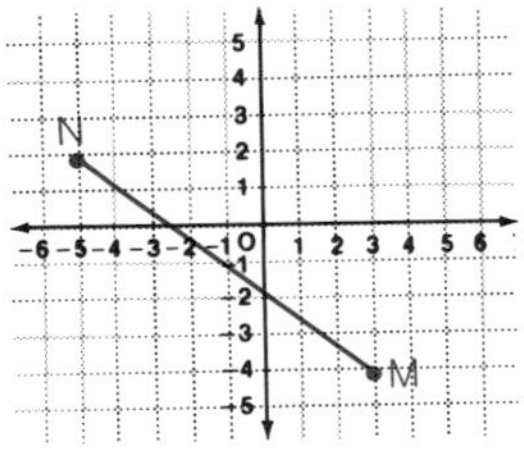

3 Calculate the distance between each of the following pairs of points.
   (a) D and K
   (b) R and D
   (c) W and R
   (d) T and K

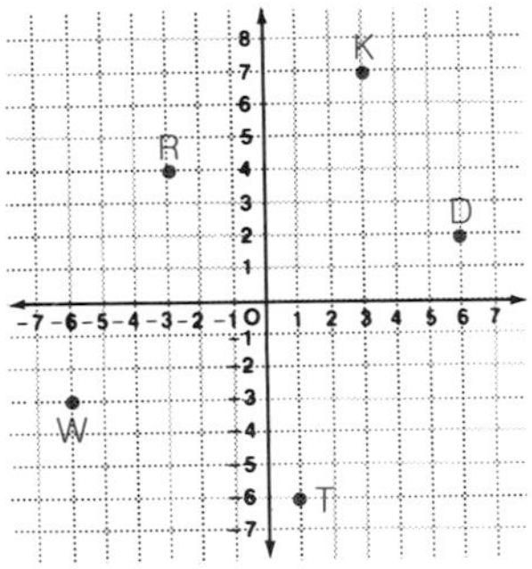

4 Show each of the following pairs of points on a diagram and calculate the distance between them.
   (a) A(2,6), B(5,1)
   (b) C(−3,4), D(3,2)
   (c) E(0,−7), F(1,3)
   (d) G(−3,−3), H(5,−4)

Throughout this section, use a calculator to evaluate the distance given by $\sqrt{(x_1 - x_2)^2 + (y_1 - y_2)^2}$.

**B** Review the meaning of each variable occurring in the Formula to find the distance between points on the plane.

5 The following points are the vertices of triangles. Draw each triangle on the Cartesian plane. Predict whether the triangle is scalene, isosceles or equilateral. Calculate the length of each side to check your prediction.
   (a) A(3,3), B(−1,2), C(0,−2)
   (b) D(2,−3), E(−2,−4), F(6,−6)
   (c) G(−1,3), H(−2,−2), I(2,0)

6 Three points are plotted on the Cartesian plane:
   X(2,8), Y(−4,−7), Z(5,−6).
   Which point is the least distance from the origin?

7 A grid system is used to design an automated machine for assembling watches. For each watch a main arm holding the watch casing moves along a path given by the following sequence of points.
   A(4,0), B(4,5), C(1,2), D(4,−4)
   E(6,0), F(1,−2), G(3,2), H(0,−1)
   (a) Calculate, to the nearest tenth, what distance the main arm covers in the assembly of one watch.
   (b) Past records show that the arm needs service after it has moved a distance of 5000 units. After how many watches should the arm be serviced?

8 For the points A(1,1), B(3,5) and M(2,3).
   (a) Draw a diagram showing the three points.
   (b) Calculate the distance from A to M and from B to M. What do you notice?
   (c) Compare the co-ordinates of A, B and M. How is the first co-ordinate of M related to those of A and B? How is the second co-ordinate of M related to those of A and B?

9 In the previous question you found that M was the point equidistant from A and B. In general, the co-ordinates of the midpoint, M, between the points $P_1(x_1,y_1)$ and $P_2(x_2,y_2)$, are given by

$$\left(\frac{x_1 + x_2}{2}, \frac{y_1 + y_2}{2}\right).$$

Find the co-ordinates of the midpoint of the line segment joining the following points:
(a) A(3,2), B(1,7)
(b) C(0, −3), D(−2, −1)
(c) E(5, −3), F(−2,3)
(d) G(−6,7), H(9, −5)

10 The following points are the vertices of a square.
R(3,4), S(−1,1), T(2, −3), U(6,0)
(a) Show the points on a diagram.
(b) Calculate the perimeter of the square.
(c) Calculate the length of each diagonal. What property of a square have you shown?
(d) Calculate the co-ordinates of the midpoint of each diagonal.

11 A space probe is located at the midpoint between planets at co-ordinates $P_1(-10,13)$ and $P_2(15,8)$. The space probe needs fuel supplies which are available either on the planet $P_1$ or from a space station at S(−7, −9) What is closer to the space probe?

12 A co-ordinate grid is placed over the map which shows the route of the "Polar Bear Express." This train carries tourists from Cochrane to Moosonee. 1 unit represents 60 km.

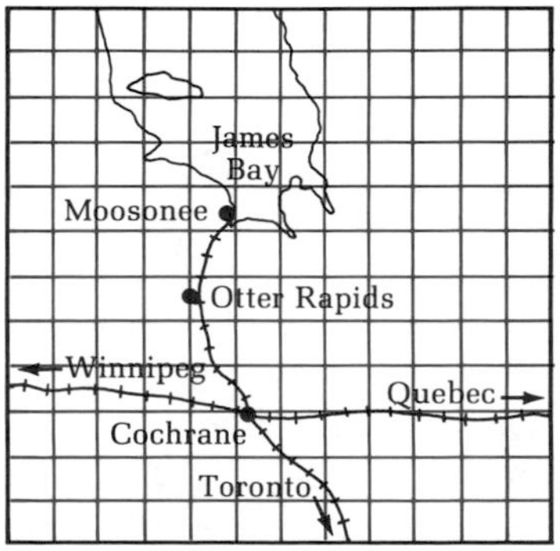


(a) Calculate the distance from Moosonee to Otter Rapids.
(b) Calculate the distance from Otter Rapids to Cochrane.
(c) What is the direct distance if you flew from Cochrane to Moosonee?

13 An architect is using a grid to help design a cottage. The diagram shows a side view plan.

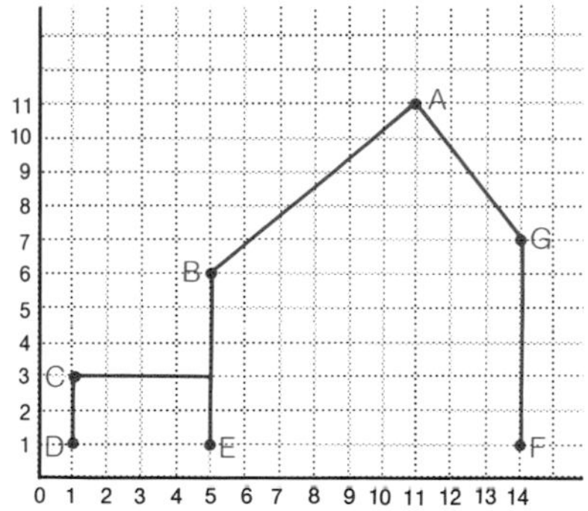


(a) The architect knows that if the length of a roof is more than 18 units it will need additional rafters for support. Calculate the distances AB and AG. Will these roofs need extra support?
(b) A round window is to be located at the midpoint of the line BG. Find the co-ordinates of the point at which the window will be placed.

## Computer Tip

If you know the co-ordinates of 2 points, you can use a computer program to find the distance between $A(x_1,y_1)$ and $B(x_2,y_2)$.

```
 10 PRINT "FOR THE FIRST POINT:"
 20 INPUT "GIVE THE X CO-ORDINATE"; X1
 30 INPUT "GIVE THE Y CO-ORDINATE"; Y1
 40 PRINT "FOR THE SECOND POINT:"
 50 INPUT "GIVE THE X CO-ORDINATE"; X2
 60 INPUT "GIVE THE Y CO-ORDINATE"; Y2
 70 REM FIND THE DISTANCE
 80 LET D = SQR((X1 − X2) ↑ 2 + (Y1 − Y2) ↑ 2)
 90 PRINT "THE DISTANCE IS"; D
100 END
```

Choose points on the plane. Use their co-ordinates to find the distance between them.

## Review: Practice and Problems

1 Construct $\triangle ABC$ where BC = 7.2 cm, $\angle B = 54°$, $\angle C = 56°$.
(a) Construct the perpendicular from C to AB.
(b) Measure the altitude in (b).

2 (a) Find the missing measures in each triangle.

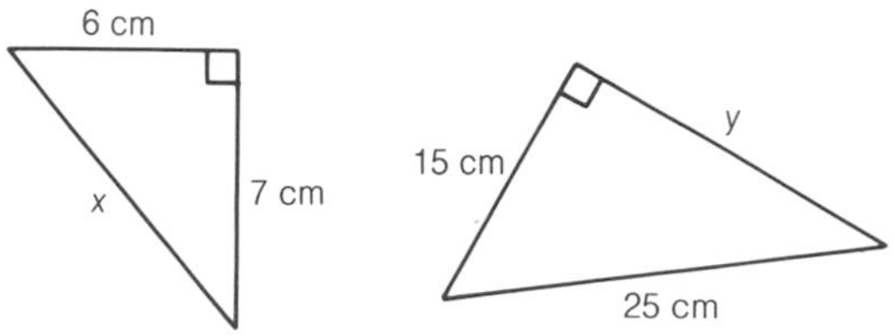


(b) Find the dimensions of the largest square that will fit into a circular pipe of diameter 18.4 cm.

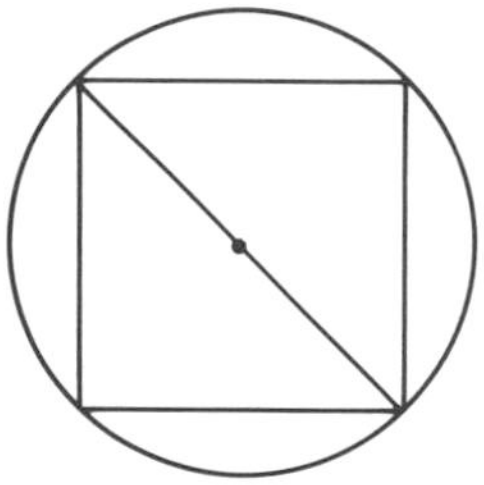

3 A line passes through the points, P(−4,6) and Q(5,−1).
(a) Draw a diagram to show the line.
(b) Find the slope of the line.

4 The following points are vertices of a rectangle A(−1,1), B(7,7), C(0,0).
(a) Show the points on a diagram.
(b) What are coordinates of the fourth vertex, D?
(c) What is the length of the diagonal CD?
(d) Calculate the co-ordinates of the midpoint of diagonal CD.

5 (a) The table below shows the distance, *d*, in metres, a water skier travels for each time, *t*, in seconds. Draw a graph of the data.

| *t* | 1 | 2 | 3 | 4 | 5 | 6 | 7 | 8 |
|---|---|---|---|---|---|---|---|---|
| *d* | 3 | 6 | 10 | 16 | 29 | 41 | 59 | 85 |

(b) Create a problem based on the data in (a). Solve the problem.

## A Practice Test

1 (a) An angle measures 71°. What is the measure of its supplement?
(b) Find the number of degrees represented by the variables in each diagram.

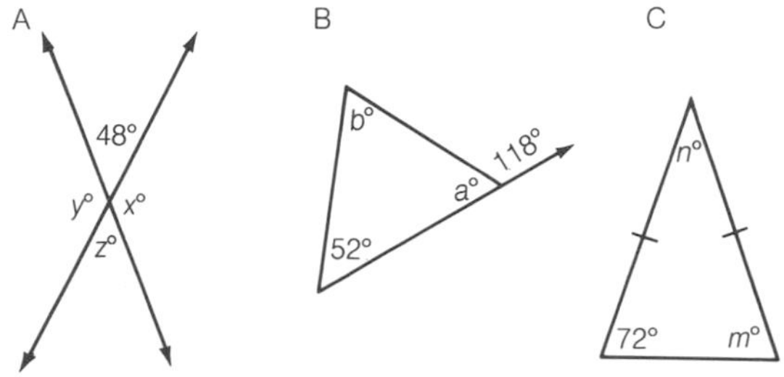


2 The following points are the three vertices of a parallelogram.
A(−5,−1) B(−5,−6) C(3,1)
(a) Find the co-ordinates of the fourth vertex.
(b) How would you check to see if your answer is correct?

3 An 8 m ladder is leaned against a wall with the base of the ladder 1.3 m from the wall. Find the height that the ladder reaches.

4 The vertices of a triangle are A(1,5), B(−4,−2), and C(6,−2).
(a) Find the length of AB, BC, and AC.
(b) What type of triangle is this?

5 Draw a graph for each equation. Indicate whether your graph is linear or non-linear.
(a) $y = -2x + 5$ (b) $y = x^2 - 3x$

6 The table shows the cost of coffee sweetener with different masses.

| Mass (grams) | 5 | 10 | 15 | 20 | 25 | 50 | 100 | 200 |
|---|---|---|---|---|---|---|---|---|
| Price (cents) | 8 | 15 | 22 | 28 | 38 | 70 | 1.35 | 256 |

(a) Plot the data shown.
(b) Draw a line of best fit.
(c) Estimate the cost of 150 g of sweetener.
(d) Find the mass of sweetener if the cost is $1.07.

# 12 Working with Straight Lines

properties of lines, interpreting slope, parallel and perpendicular lines, using intercepts, patterns for $y = mx + b$, drawing graphs of straight lines, equations for lines, solving a system of two linear equations, problem solving, useful strategies, solving problems, and applications

## Introduction

Properties of straight lines and their graphs can be used to interpret and visualize concepts that are around us.

- Have you ever noticed, how much steeper the slope of a roof is, in places that have a lot of snow?

- Have you ever heard of a near miss? When a plane approaches too close, a pilot may report a near miss to the Department of Transportation.

In your study of mathematics, or any subject, there is often a pattern that you follow. If you look for patterns they will help you remember material. In many careers, the people are trained to look for patterns, and based on these patterns, they make decisions.

*I* Earlier in your work in mathematics you followed this procedure.

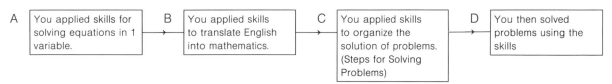

A [You applied skills for solving equations in 1 variable.] → B [You applied skills to translate English into mathematics.] → C [You applied skills to organize the solution of problems. (Steps for Solving Problems)] → D [You then solved problems using the skills]

*II* In this chapter you will follow this pattern in a similar way. You will learn the skills of this chapter in a parallel way.

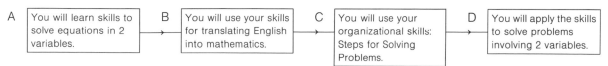

A [You will learn skills to solve equations in 2 variables.] → B [You will use your skills for translating English into mathematics.] → C [You will use your organizational skills: Steps for Solving Problems.] → D [You will apply the skills to solve problems involving 2 variables.]

An essential skill for a pilot, a transportation engineer, a forest ranger, or an economist, is to understand the properties of straight lines and their graphs.

# 12.1 Properties of Lines: Slope

In your earlier work, you have found the slope of a line using the relationship

$$\text{slope} = \frac{\text{rise}}{\text{run}}.$$

To find the slope of a line, choose 2 points on the line and use the relationship for slope, as shown in the following example.

**Example 1**

From the diagram, find the slope of the line given by $5x + 8y = 17$.

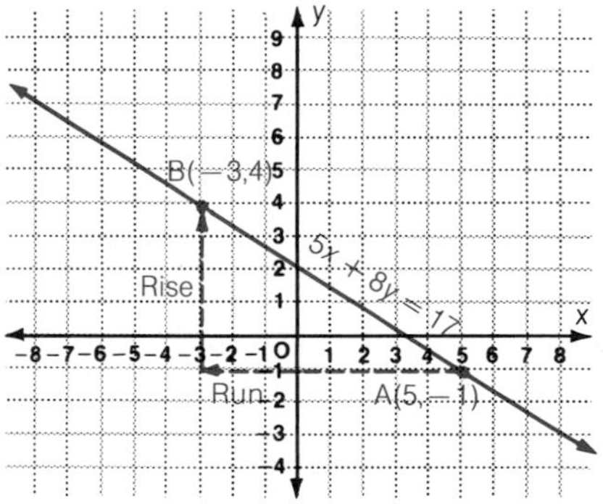


**Solution**

Think:
Use the co-ordinates of the points A, B to calculate the slope.

$$\text{slope} = \frac{\text{rise}}{\text{run}}$$ ← Use the co-ordinates of the points, A and B to calculate the run and the rise.

$$= \frac{4 - (-1)}{-3 - 5}$$

$$= \frac{5}{-8} \text{ or } \frac{-5}{8}$$

Thus the slope of the line is $\frac{-5}{8}$.

In doing mathematics, often the question "What if . . .?" is asked. In particular, "What if different points are chosen on a line to find the slope, will the slopes be equal?" Refer to the next example.

**Example 2**

Find the slope of the line given by $4x - 3y = 7$. Use different pairs of points.

**Solution**

Sketch the graph to help you choose different pairs of points.

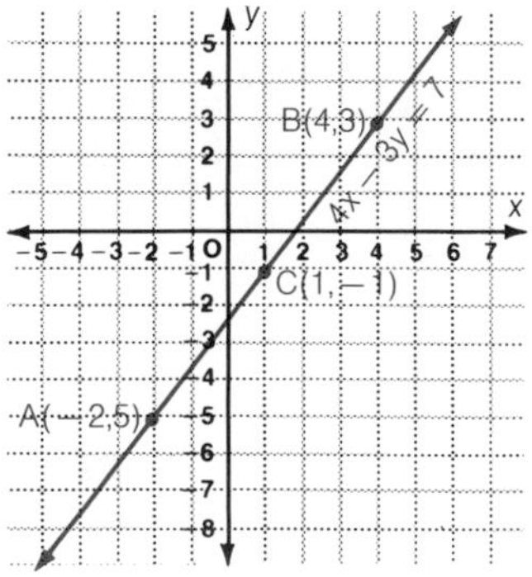


Use points B, C.

$$\text{slope} = \frac{3 - (-1)}{4 - 1}$$

$$= \frac{4}{3}$$

Use points A, C.

$$\text{slope} = \frac{-1 - (-5)}{1 - (-2)}$$

$$= \frac{4}{3}$$

The previous results suggest that the slope is the same no matter which two points of the line you choose. To find the slope of a line you can choose any two points on the line. Often, you choose two points that can be readily obtained.

Often in doing mathematics, you examine your results and look for any other useful information. For example, in the previous solution you can express the slope relationship as a formula.

For any two points $P_1$ and $P_2$ the slope of $P_1P_2$ is expressed by the formula

$$\text{slope} = \frac{\text{difference in } y \text{ co-ordinates}}{\text{difference in } x \text{ co-ordinates}} \qquad \text{slope} = \frac{y_2 - y_1}{x_2 - x_1}$$

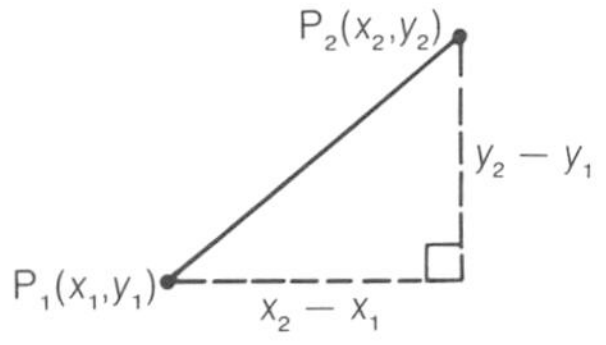


## Try These

1 What is the slope of each line?

(a)

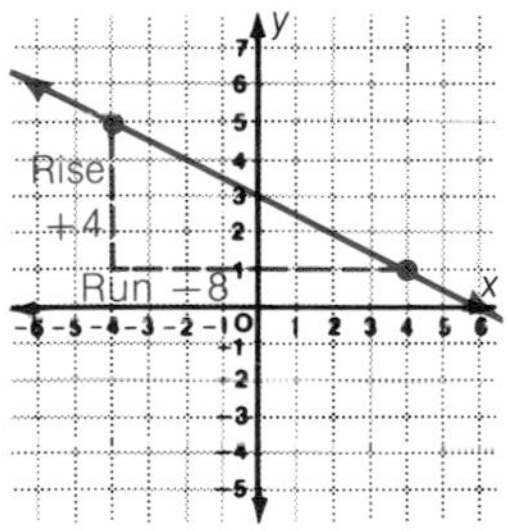


(b)

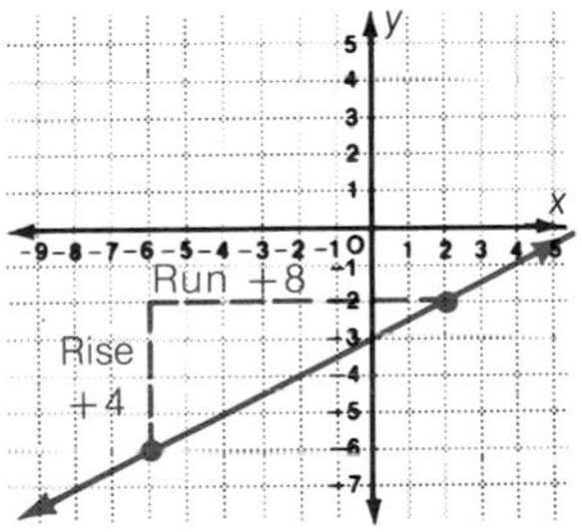


2 What is the slope of each line?

(a)

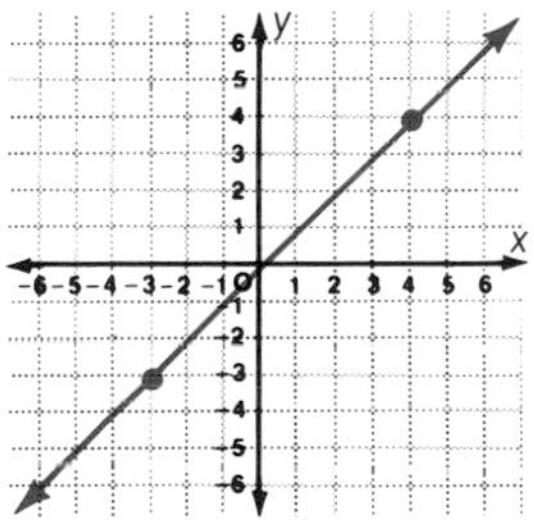

(b)

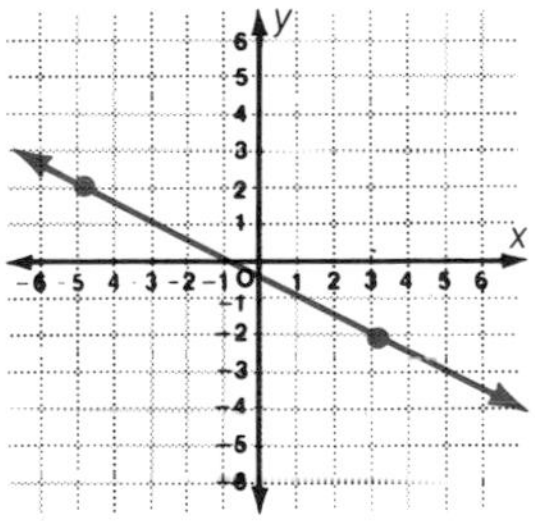

## Written Exercises

**A** Review the formula for finding slope. What do $y_2 - y_1$, and $x_2 - x_1$ represent?

1 Refer to the line shown.

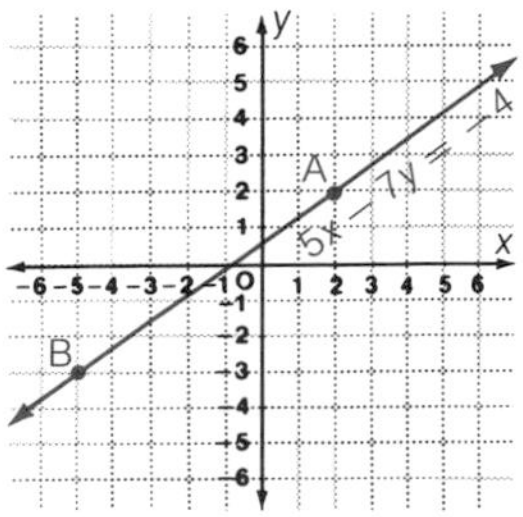


(a) Calculate the rise.

(b) Calculate the run.

(c) What is the slope of the line?

(d) Choose another pair of points on the line. Find the slope. What do you notice?

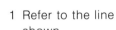

2 The graph of $5x + 7y = -18$ is shown.

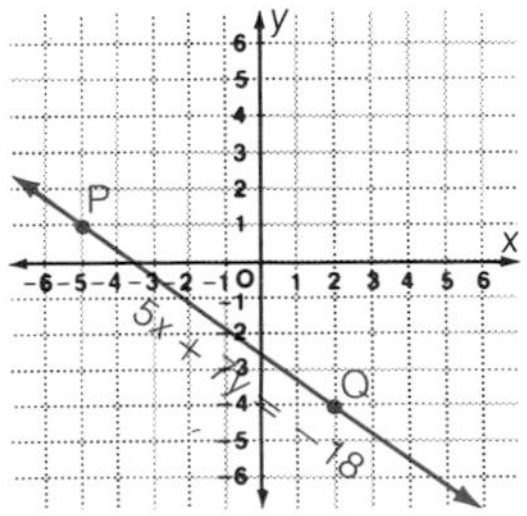


(a) Use the points P and Q to calculate the rise, the run, and the slope.

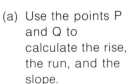

(b) Use another pair of points to calculate the slope of the line. What do you notice?

3 The graph of $2x - 3y = 6$ is shown.

(a) Choose points on the line and calculate the rise, the run, and the slope.

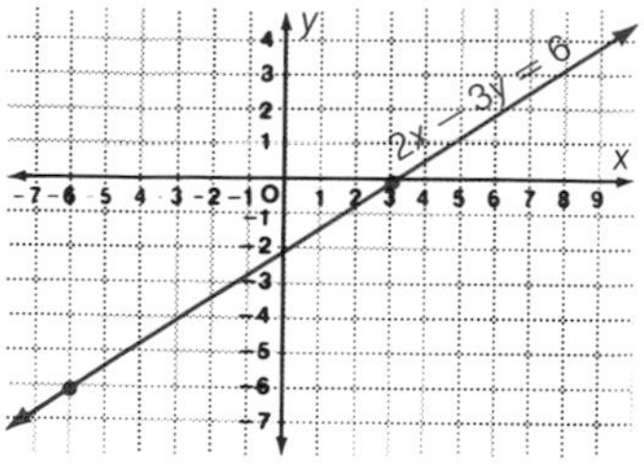


(b) Choose another pair of points. Calculate the rise, run and slope. What do you notice?

4 Refer to the graph. Calculate the slope of the line using each pair of points.

(a) A,B (b) C,D
(c) B,C (d) A,D

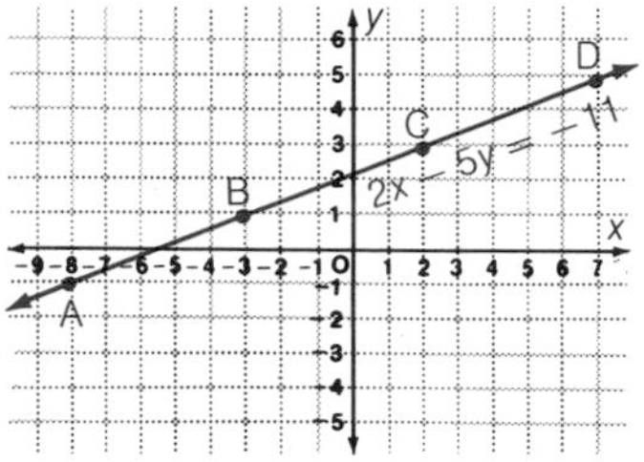


What do you notice about your answers?

5 Two points are chosen on the equation of each line. Find the slope of the line.

| | equation | points on the line |
|---|---|---|
| (a) | $5x + 8y = -4$ | A(4, −3), B(−4, 2) |
| (b) | $x - y = 6$ | C(−2, −8), D(2, −4) |
| (c) | $5x + 11y = -20$ | E(−4, 0), F(7, −5) |
| (d) | $x + 2y = -6$ | G(4, −5), H(−6, 0) |
| (e) | $3.5x + 6.4y = 29.4$ | J(2, 3.5), K(8.4, 0) |

6 A line is given by the equation $y = 2x - 4$

(a) Find two points that are on the line by choosing a value for $x$ and calculating the corresponding value for $y$.

(b) Use your answer in (a). Find slope of the line.

**B** Remember: the value of the slope of a line is the same regardless of the points you choose.

7 For each line, choose two points on the line. Then calculate the slope.

(a) $3x - y = 2$ (b) $x - 3y = 6$
(c) $2x + y = 4$ (d) $y = 2x + 3$
(e) $2x - 5y = 0$ (f) $x = 3y - 1$
(g) $y + 3x = 6$ (h) $2x = 3y - 1$
(i) $y - 4.2x = 10.7$ (j) $2.5x - y = 20$

8 A line is given by the equation $2x + 3y = 6$.

(a) Draw a graph of the equation.
(b) What is the slope of the line?
(c) Decide which points are on the line.
A(6, −2) B(5, −1) C(−9, 8)

9 (a) Draw the graph of $3x - 2y = 12$.
(b) What is the slope of the line?
(c) Decide which points are on the line.
P(−6, −15) Q(8, 6) R(−8, 18)

10 For each line, the slope and a point on the line are given. Draw the graph of each line.

(a) slope $= \frac{1}{2}$, A(2, 1) (b) slope $= \frac{3}{4}$, B(−4, 3)

(c) slope $= -\frac{3}{4}$, C(5, −1)

11 A scuba diver is descending on a path that has slope $-\frac{3}{5}$ and that passes through the point (−10, −11). Which of the following equations describes the diver's path?

A $5y + 6x = 15$
B $5y - 3x = -25$
C $5y + 3x = -85$

12 A Cessna piper cub, on a linear path with slope $\frac{2}{3}$, passes through the point (4, −1). Through which of these other points will it pass?

(a) Mount Aetna with co-ordinates (1, −3)
(b) supply depot at a point with co-ordinates (−5, −7)
(c) a stranded camper at co-ordinates (16, 7)

13 A weather balloon is rising on a path that has slope 0.8 and passes through the point (85.5, 120).

(a) Which of the following equations describes the path of the balloon?
A $y - 0.8x = 51.6$
B $1.5y + 1.2x = 77.4$

(b) Will the balloon pass through the point (10, 43.6)?

## Applications: Interpreting Slope

A car travels at a constant speed from Edmonton to Winnipeg. The graph shows how the distance of the car from Winnipeg is related to the time it has been travelling. From the graph, you can see that

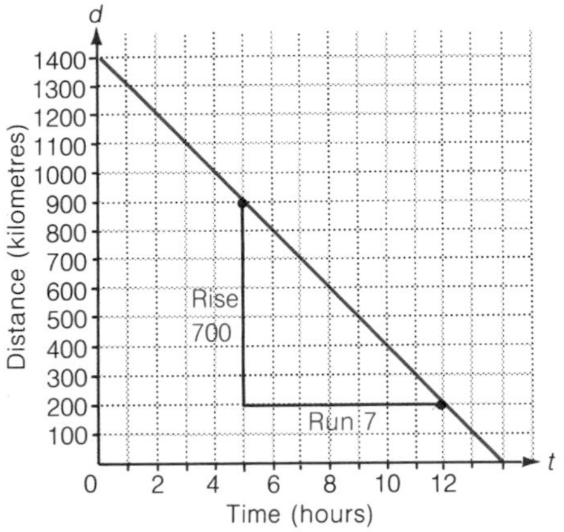


- The distance from Winnipeg to Edmonton is approximately 1350 km.
- The total travelling time is 14 h.
- The slope of the line is given by

$$\text{Slope} = \frac{\text{Rise}}{\text{Run}}$$

$$= \frac{700}{7} = 100$$

For this application all slopes are considered to be positive.

- You can interpret what the slope means. The slope represents the speed.

  Thus, the car was travelling at a constant speed of 100 km/h.

---

14 Refer to the graph shown.

(a) Find the slope of the line.

(b) Interpret what the slope represents.

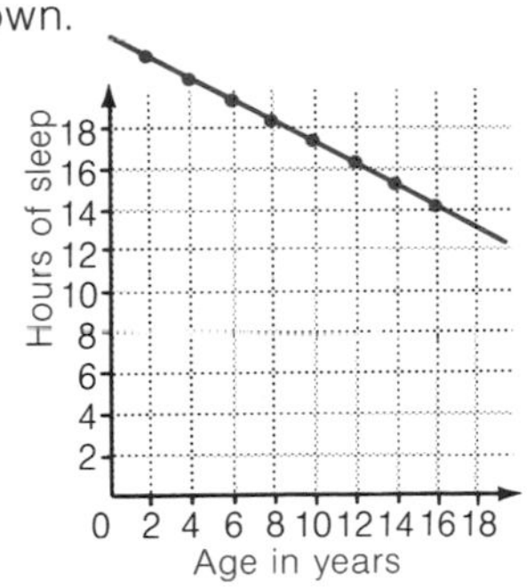


15 Sally works in a department store during the summer and is paid by the hour. Her earnings are shown by the graph.

(a) Find the slope of the line.

(b) What does the slope represent?

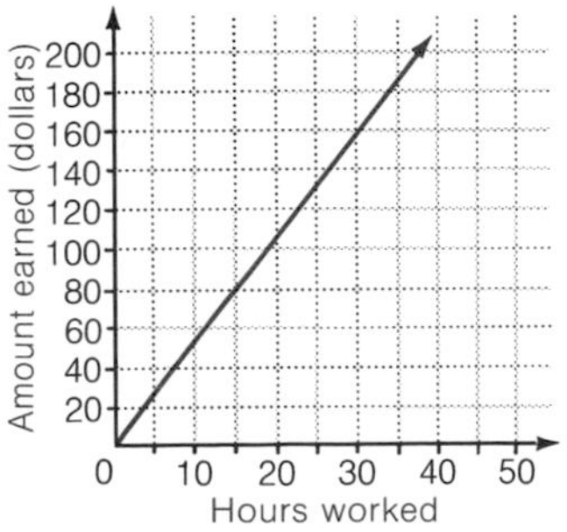


16 For each of the following graphs.
What is the slope of the line?
Interpret what each slope represents.

(a) The amount of gasoline a car consumes.

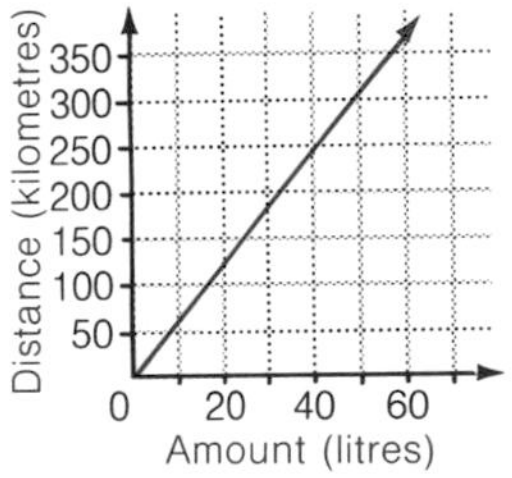


(b) Hiring a guard for a school dance.

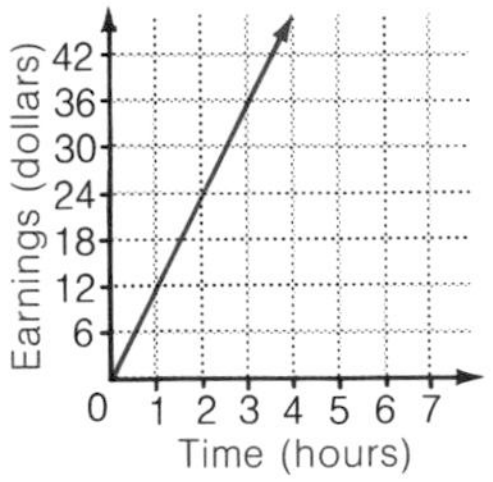


(c) Renting a computer.

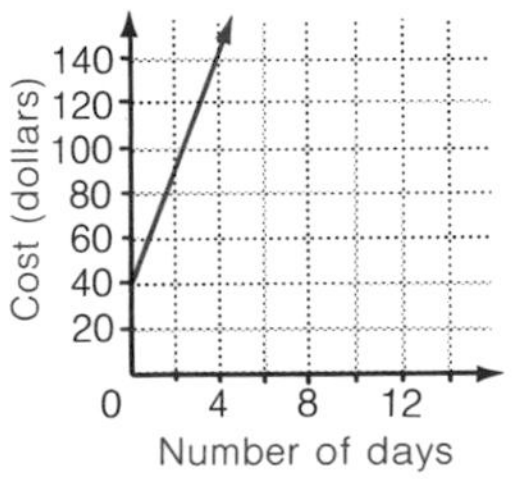


(d) Printing a school newspaper.

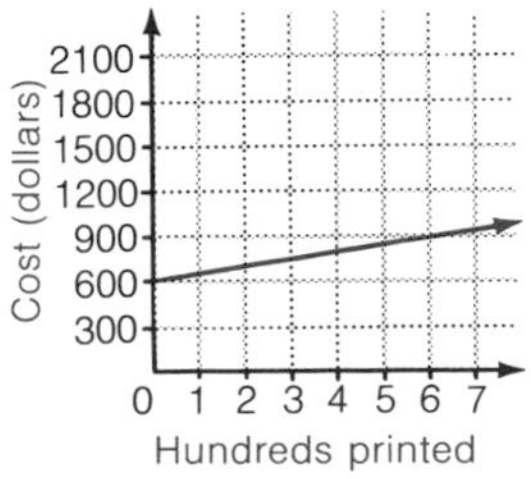

# 12.2 Parallel and Perpendicular Lines

Calculations in mathematics often reveal patterns. For example, by calculating slope for different lines you find the following pattern.

positive slope

$$\frac{y_2 - y_1}{x_2 - x_1}$$

$$= \frac{5 - (-3)}{2 - (-3)}$$

$$= \frac{8}{5}$$

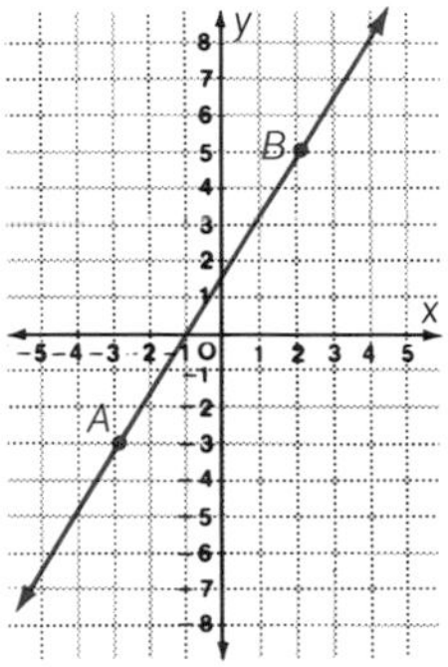


negative slope

$$\frac{y_2 - y_1}{x_2 - x_1}$$

$$= \frac{-5 - 4}{2 - (-4)}$$

$$= \frac{-9}{6} \text{ or } \frac{-3}{2}$$

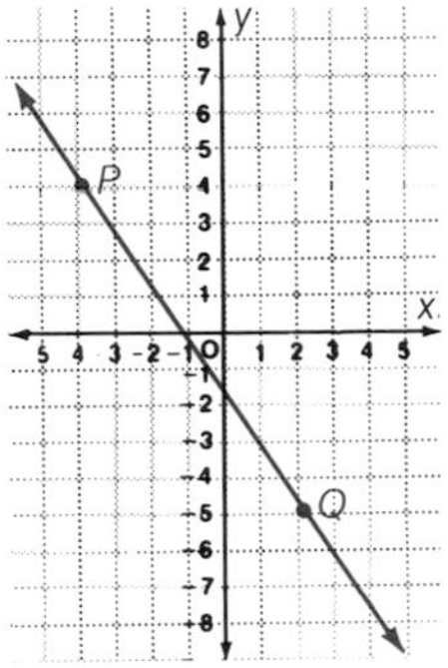


slope of zero

$$\frac{y_2 - y_1}{x_2 - x_1}$$

$$= \frac{-3 - (-3)}{4 - (-3)}$$

$$= \frac{0}{7}$$

$$= 0$$

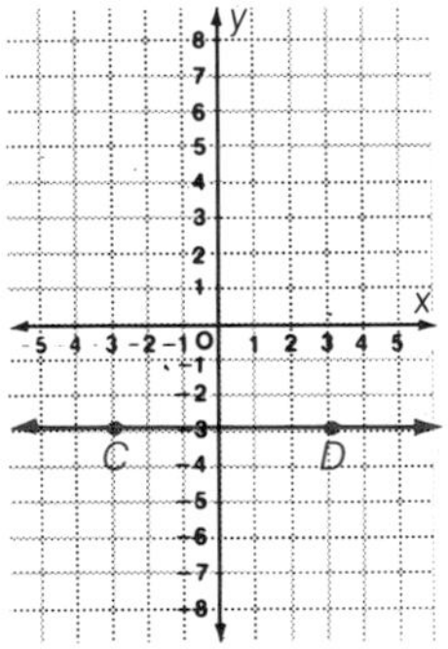


undefined slope

$$\frac{y_2 - y_1}{x_2 - x_1}$$

$$= \frac{-5 - 2}{-4 - (-4)}$$

$$= \frac{-7}{0}$$

You cannot divide by zero. The slope is said to be undefined.

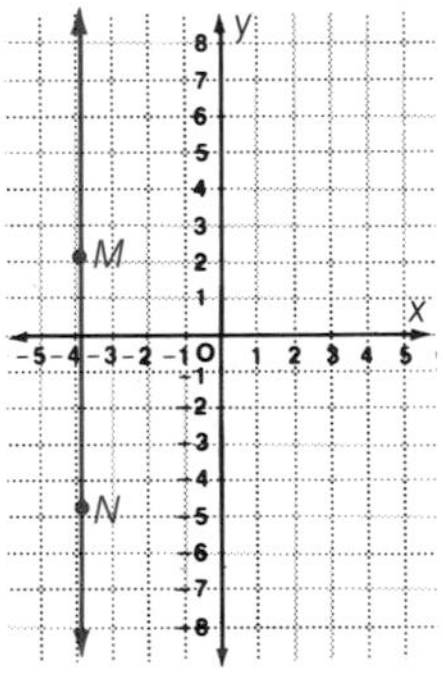


You can also use the slope of lines to tell whether the lines are parallel or perpendicular.

Two lines are drawn on the graph. They are parallel.

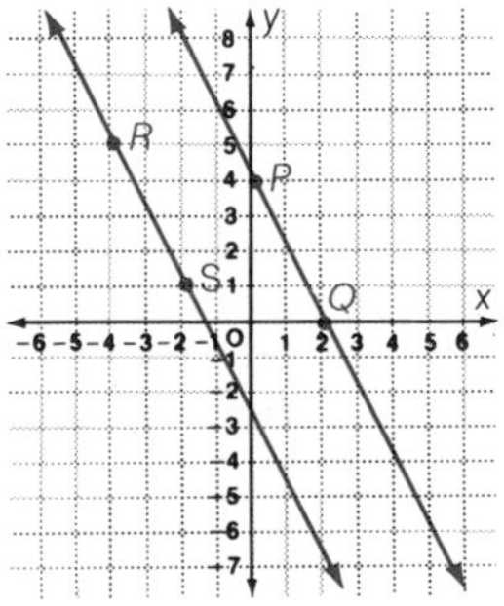


$$\text{slope RS} = \frac{5 - 1}{-4 - (-2)}$$

$$= \frac{4}{-2}$$

$$= -2$$

$$\text{slope PQ} = \frac{4 - 0}{0 - 2}$$

$$= \frac{4}{-2}$$

$$= -2$$

Lines that are parallel have slopes that are equal. The slope of both PQ and RS is $-2$. Thus PQ $\parallel$ RS.

the symbol means "is parallel to"

Two lines are drawn on the graph. They are perpendicular to each other.

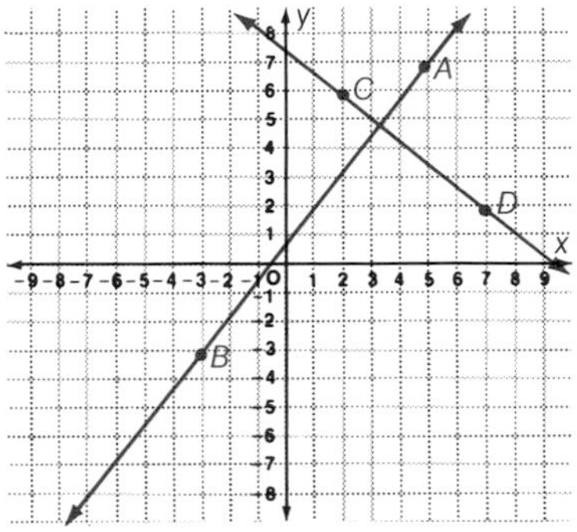

$$\text{slope AB} = \frac{7-(-3)}{5-(-3)} = \frac{10}{8} \text{ or } \frac{5}{4}$$

$$\text{slope CD} = \frac{6-2}{2-7} = \frac{4}{-5}$$

The slope of AB is $\frac{5}{4}$. The slope of CD is $-\frac{4}{5}$. The product of the slopes is $-1$.

$$\frac{5}{4} \times \frac{-4}{5} = -1$$

From examples such as the above, we find that lines that are perpendicular have slopes whose product is $-1$. Since the product of their slopes is $-1$, we say that the slopes are negative reciprocals. Thus AB ⊥ CD.

⊥ is perpendicular to

You can use the previous results to show whether lines are parallel or perpendicular. Refer to the next example.

## Example

Show that the line through P(1,3) and Q(−2,−1) is perpendicular to the line through R(6,5) and S(10,2).

## Solution

$$\text{For PQ, slope} = \frac{3-(-1)}{1-(-2)} = \frac{4}{3}$$

$$\text{For RS, slope} = \frac{5-2}{6-10} = \frac{3}{-4}$$

$$\text{Product of the slopes} = \frac{4}{3} \times \frac{3}{-4} = -1$$

Thus, the lines through PQ and RS are perpendicular.

## Try These

1 The slope of two lines AB and CD is shown. In each, decide whether the lines are parallel, perpendicular or neither.

| | (a) | (b) | (c) | (d) |
|---|---|---|---|---|
| Slope of AB | $-5$ | $\frac{3}{2}$ | $\frac{1}{2}$ | $\frac{1}{4}$ |
| Slope of CD | $\frac{1}{5}$ | $-\frac{2}{3}$ | $\frac{1}{2}$ | 4 |

2 The following slopes have been calculated.

slope of AB $= \frac{1}{5}$ slope of CD $= -3$

slope of EF $= \frac{-2}{3}$ slope of GH $= \frac{1}{4}$

What is the slope of a line that is
(a) parallel to AB?
(b) perpendicular to GH?
(c) parallel to EF?
(d) perpendicular to CD?

## Written Exercises

**A** What do you know about the slopes if two lines are parallel? perpendicular?

1 The slope of a line is $\frac{4}{9}$. What is the slope of a line that is parallel to this line?

2 The slope of a line is $-\frac{2}{3}$. What is the slope of a line that is perpendicular to this line?

3 The slopes of two line segments are given. Which line segments are perpendicular?

(a) slope of PQ $= \frac{4}{7}$, slope of RS $= \frac{-7}{4}$

(b) slope of AB $= 3$, slope of CD $= \frac{1}{3}$

(c) slope of EF $= -5$, slope of FG $= \frac{1}{5}$

(d) slope of RV $= \frac{-1}{8}$, slope of XY $= -8$

4 The slopes of two line segments are given. Are the lines parallel, perpendicular, or neither?

(a) $\frac{1}{2}, \frac{1}{2}$ (b) 4, 5 (c) $\frac{3}{4}, -\frac{4}{3}$

(d) 8, $-8$ (e) $\frac{5}{6}, -\frac{6}{5}$ (f) $-1, \frac{1}{2}$

(g) 17, $-17$ (h) $\frac{8}{9}, \frac{9}{8}$ (i) $\frac{36}{7}, -\frac{7}{36}$

5 The slope of certain line segments is given. What is the slope of a line segment that is perpendicular to each line?

(a) $\frac{3}{5}$ (b) $-\frac{1}{2}$ (c) $-5$

**B** 6 In each what is the slope of lines that are parallel to PQ?

(a)

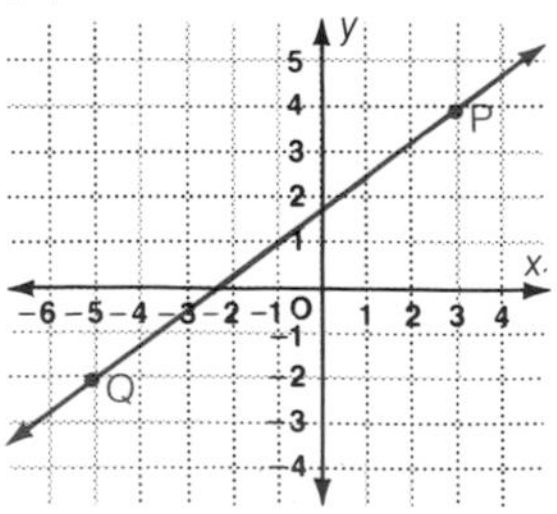


(b)

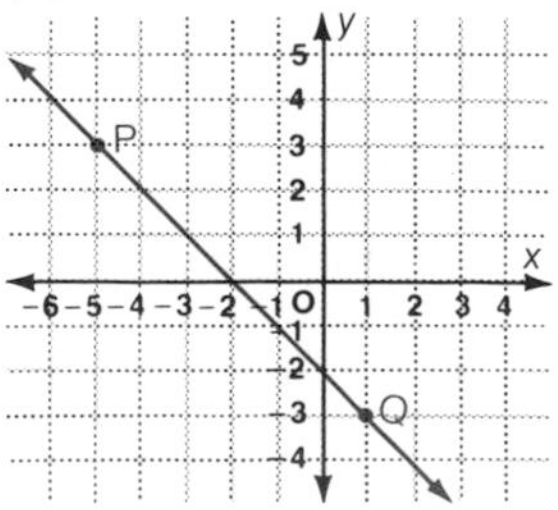

7 In each what is the slope of lines that are perpendicular to MN?

(a)

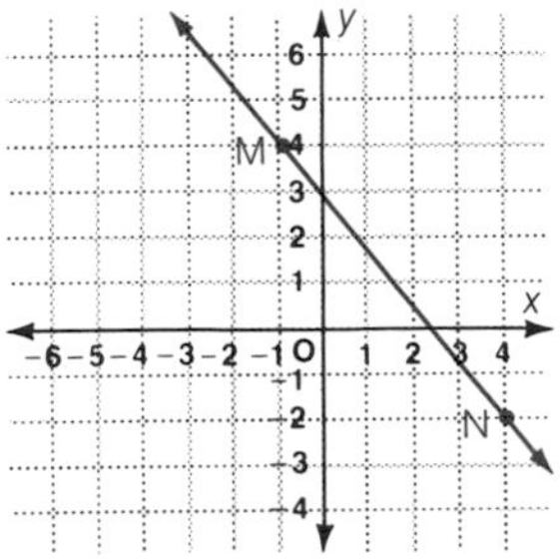


(b)

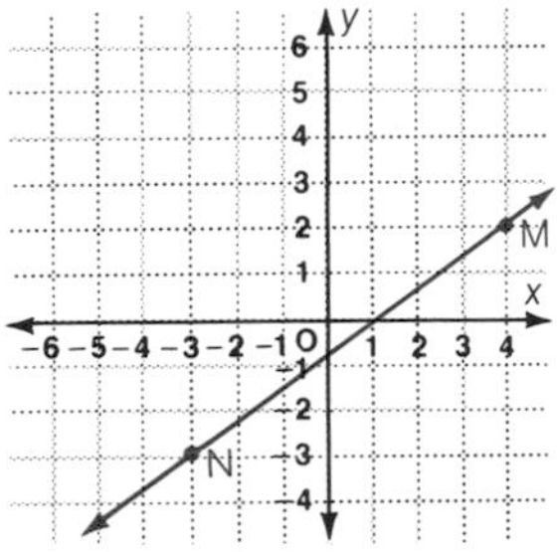


8 Line segment PQ is given by P(6,2), Q(−1,−5). What is the slope of a line segment that is
(a) parallel to PQ? (b) perpendicular to PQ?

9 (a) Plot the following points
P(−1,−3) Q(4,7) R(−3,2) S(5,−2)
(b) Draw the line segments PQ and RS. What do you notice?
(c) Find the slopes of the line segments. What can you conclude about the lines?

10 (a) Plot the following points
A(−1,6) B(2,3) C(4,−4) D(−2,2)
(b) Draw the line segments AB and CD. What do you notice?
(c) Find the slopes of the line segments. What can you conclude about the lines?

11 Find the slope of the line passing through each pair of points.
(a) A(6,2) B(−4,1)
(b) C(−4,−9) D(4,7)
(c) E(−10,8) F(−3,−6)
(d) G(4,8) H(5,−2)
(e) Which lines are parallel?
(f) Which are perpendicular?

12 Find the slope of the line passing through each pair of points.
(a) M(3.7,3.4), N(2.5,−1.4)
(b) P(−4.2,5), Q(2.8,2.5)
(c) R(−5,2.8), S(−7.4,−6.8)
(d) T(−2.2,0.3), V(0.3,0.1)
(e) Which lines are parallel?
(f) Which are perpendicular?

13 Find the slope of lines that are perpendicular to the line passing through each pair of points.
(a) P(4,−1) Q(7,2)
(b) R(0,−5) S(6,−9)
(c) T(3,−6) U(−8,−9)
(d) V(−1,7) W(5,0)

14 During a cross-country race, a skier is on a path that passes through the points J(2,5) and K(6,6). An old railroad track runs through the points L(7,−4) and M(3,−5). Will the skier cross the railroad track?

15 Rose is an electrical engineer. She is designing the layout of a circuit board for a new type of colour photocopier. She has a wire running from X(−3,5) to Y(7,2). She wants to continue this circuit to a point Z, so that XY is perpendicular to YZ. If she puts Z at the point (4,−8), will she have the arrangement that she wants?

## Math Tip

It is important to clearly understand the vocabulary of mathematics when solving problems.
- Make a list of all the new words you meet in this chapter.
- Provide a simple example to illustrate each word.

## Computer Tip

The following computer program can be used to find the slope of line segments given the co-ordinates of two points $(x_1,y_1)$ and $(x_2,y_2)$ on the line.

```
10 PRINT "INPUT X1, Y1, X2, Y2 IN THIS ORDER"
20 INPUT X1, Y1, X2, Y2
30 IF X1 = X2 THEN 70
40 LET M = (Y2 − Y1)/(X2 − X1)
50 PRINT "THE SLOPE IS"; M
60 GO TO 80
70 PRINT "THE SLOPE IS NOT DEFINED"
80 END
```

Find the slope of each line segment.
AB: A(−6,3), B(12,8)
CD: C(12.6,−9.3), D(18.3,−3.4)

# 12.3 Working with Intercepts

Imagine you are designing a computer game in which targets moved on different linear paths. The player can only fire when a target crosses a horizontal or vertical axis. As the computer programmer you will need to know where each linear path crosses the axis.

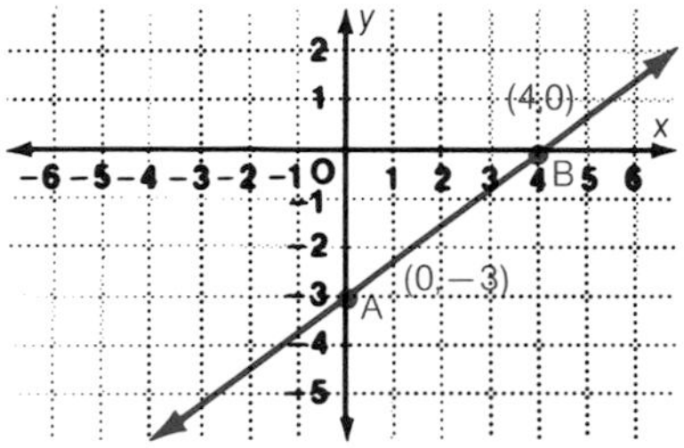


- The $y$ intercept is the directed distance from the origin to the point where the graph crosses the $y$ axis. In the diagram, the $y$ intercept is shown by OA and is $-3$ units.
- The $x$ intercept is the directed distance from the origin to the point where the graph crosses the $x$ axis. In the diagram, the $x$ intercept is 4 units.

You can use your earlier skills with algebra to find the values of the $x$ and $y$ intercepts as shown in the following example.

### Example 1

Find the $x$ and $y$ intercepts for the line given by $x + 2y = 8$.

### Solution

To find the $x$ intercept, let $y = 0$.

$$x + 2y = 8$$
$$x + 2(0) = 8$$
$$x = 8$$

The $x$ intercept is 8.

To find the $y$ intercept, let $x = 0$

$$x + 2y = 8$$
$$0 + 2y = 8$$
$$y = 4$$

The $y$ intercept is 4.

You can apply your earlier skills with slope, and your new skill with intercepts to draw the graph of a line if you know

- ▶ the slope of the line
- ▶ and one of the intercepts.

### Example 2

The $x$ intercept of a line is $-3$. The slope of the line $\frac{1}{2}$.

Graph the line.

### Solution

*Step 1*: The $x$ intercept is $-3$. Thus the graph crosses the $x$-axis at the point A($-3$,0).

*Step 2*: From the point A, mark another point B. Use the information about the slope as shown.

*Step 3*: Draw the graph of the line.

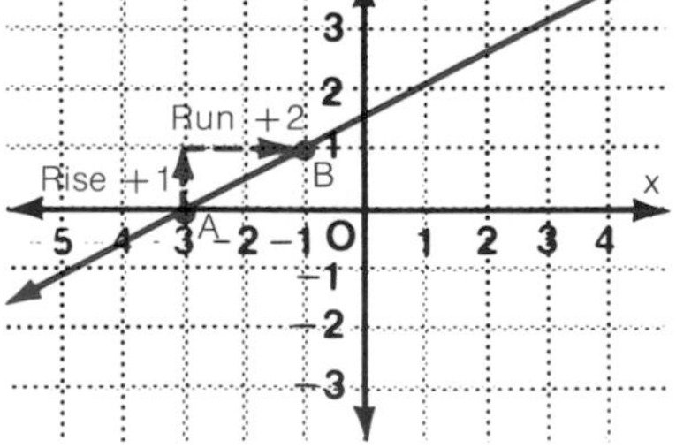

## Try These

1 Refer to the graphs. What are the $x$ and the $y$ intercepts of each line?

(a)

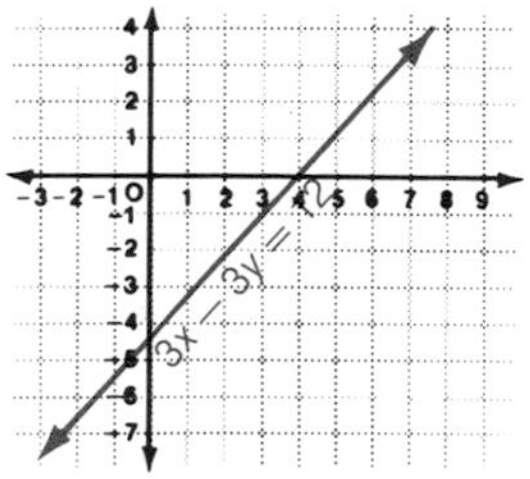


(b)

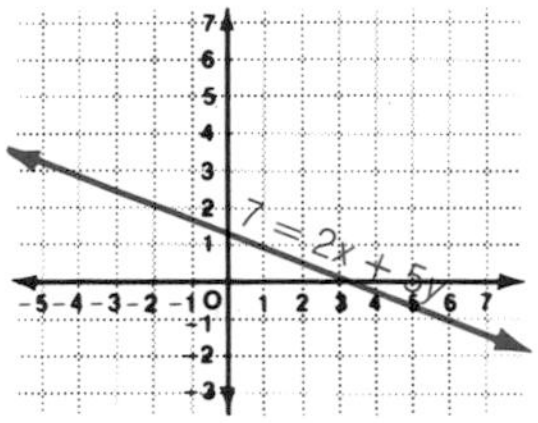


2 For each line, an equation is shown. What are the intercepts of each line?

(a) $x + y = 6$ (b) $x - y = 8$

(c) $2x - y = 8$ (d) $x + 3y = 6$

## Written Exercises

**A** Review the meaning of $x$ and $y$ intercept.

1 Refer to the graphs. For each what is the value of

▶ the $x$ intercept? ▶ the $y$ intercept?

▶ the slope?

(a)

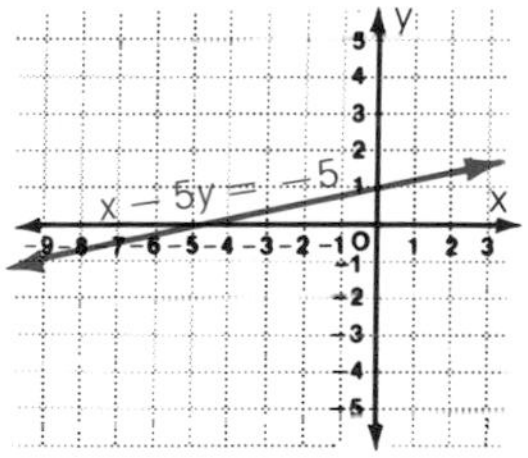


(b)

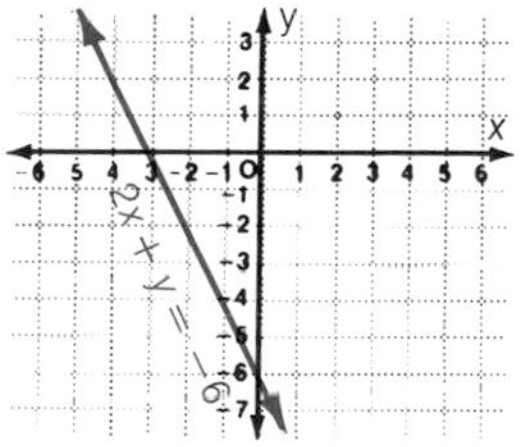


(c)

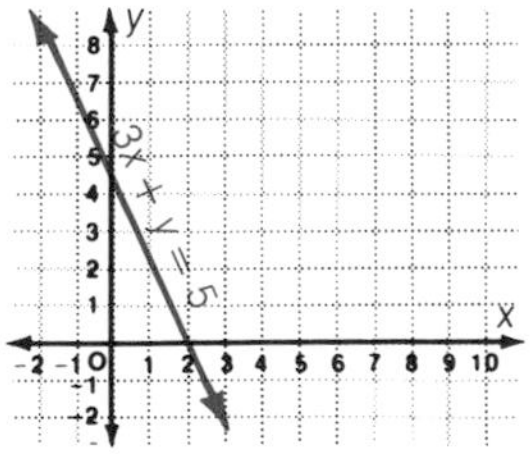


(d)

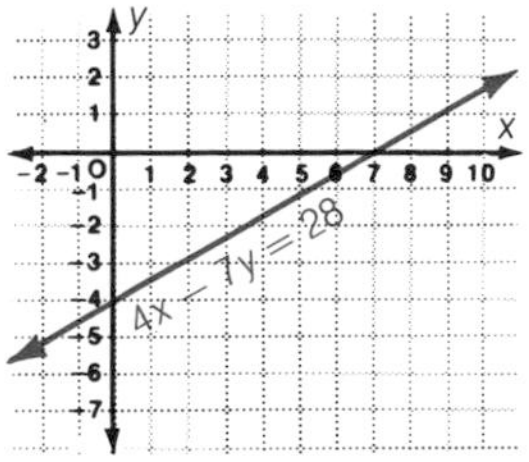


2 (a) Draw the graph of $3x + y = 6$. Label the point A where the graph crosses the $x$-axis.

(b) What is the value of the $x$ intercept?

(c) What are the coordinates of the point A?

3 (a) Draw the graph of $x - 3y = 9$. Label the point B where the graph crosses the $y$ axis.

(b) What is the value of the $y$ intercept?

(c) What are the coordinates of the point B?

4 (a) Draw the graph of $4x - y = 8$

(b) What is the slope?

(c) What are the values of the intercepts?

(d) What are the coordinates of the points where the graph of $4x - y = 8$ crosses each axis?

5 Refer to each graph.

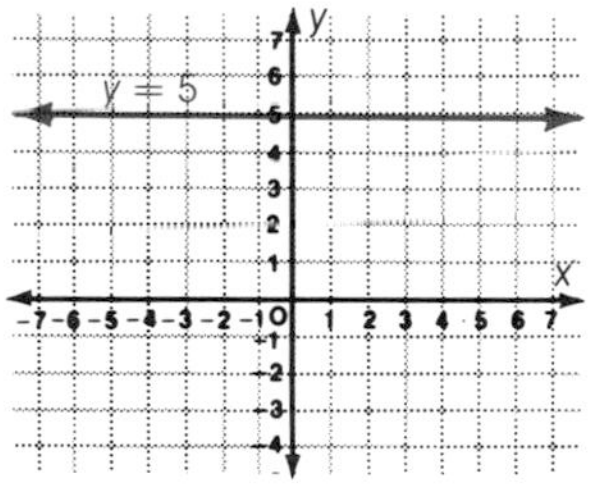


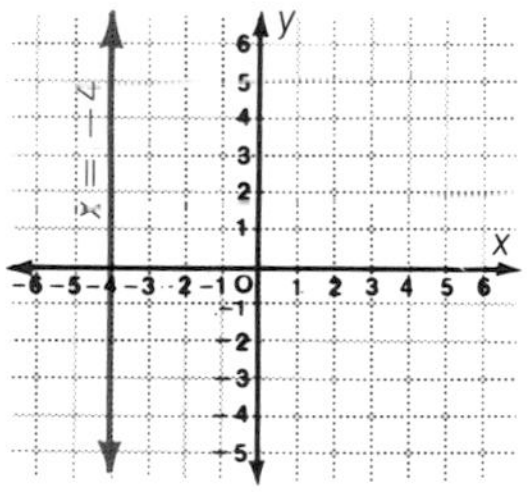


(a) What is the $x$ intercept?

(b) What is the $y$ intercept?

(c) What do you notice about your answers?

**B** Remember: use your skills with algebra to find the intercepts of a graph.

6 Find the $x$ intercept for each line.

(a) $x + y = 10$ (b) $2x - y = 10$

(c) $3x + y = 6$ (d) $\frac{1}{2}x + y = 5$

(e) $4x - y - 16 = 0$ (f) $y - 5x = 15$

(g) $8y - 0.4x = 2.6$ (h) $5.2x - 6.5y = 11.96$

7 Find the $y$ intercept for each line.
(a) $4x - y = 12$ (b) $2x = 6 + y$
(c) $3x + y + 5 = 0$ (d) $5x = 2y - 6$
(e) $y - 2x - 11 = 0$ (f) $5y + x = 5$
(g) $1.9x + 4.7y = 84.6$ (h) $0.2x - 0.5y = 1.8$

8 For each equation
▶ find the $x$ and the $y$ intercepts
▶ then use the intercepts to draw the graph.
(a) $x + 2y = 4$ (b) $2x - y = 6$
(c) $3x - 4y = 12$ (d) $2x + y = 6$
(e) $y = 3x - 3$ (f) $x - 4y + 8 = 0$
(g) $y = \frac{1}{2}x + 4$ (h) $\frac{x}{3} - \frac{y}{4} = 2$

9 (a) Draw the graph of the line which passes through the point (4,0) and has slope $\frac{2}{3}$.
(b) What is the $x$ intercept of the line?
(c) What is the $y$ intercept of the line?

10 (a) Draw the graph of the line which passes through the point $(0,-4)$ and has slope $\frac{-3}{4}$.
(b) What is the $y$ intercept of the line?
(c) What is the $x$ intercept of the line?

11 Draw the graph of each line.
(a) $x$ intercept 3, slope 2
(b) $y$ intercept $-1$, slope $\frac{1}{2}$
(c) $x$ intercept $\frac{1}{2}$, slope $-4$
(d) $y$ intercept 5, slope $-\frac{3}{4}$

12 The path of an aircraft has slope $\frac{1}{2}$ and $y$ intercept $-3$.
(a) Draw the graph of the path.
(b) What is the $x$ intercept?
(c) Will the aircraft pass over a shipwrecked crew at a point with coordinates (10,2)?

13 A deep sea diver is descending on a path that has slope $-\frac{2}{3}$ and $x$ intercept $-5$.
(a) Draw the graph of the path.
(b) What is the $y$ intercept?
(c) Will a shark that is resting around the point $(-6,-9)$, be on the diver's path?

14 A hovercraft is on a course that has $x$ intercept $-2$ and $y$ intercept 6.
(a) Draw the graph of the course.
(b) What is the slope of the course?
(c) A pickup of passengers at an island with co-ordinates (2,10) is to be made. Is the hovercraft off course?

15 In a warehouse, the path of a fork-lift truck has $x$ intercept 12 and $y$ intercept $-9$.
(a) Draw the graph of the truck's path.
(b) What is the slope of the path?
(c) Is the fork-lift truck on the correct path to pick up a box that is stored at the point with co-ordinates (20,6)?

16 The graph shows the profit $P$, in dollars, of a business with time $t$, in years. At time $t = 0$ the current owners bought the business.

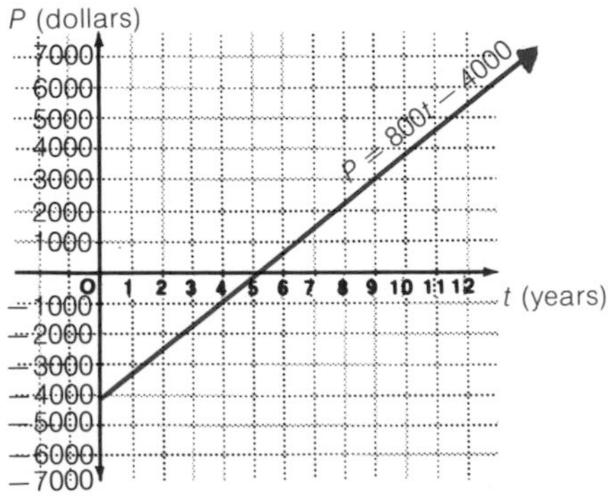


(a) When the current owners bought the business, was it making a profit or a loss? How much?
(b) During which year did the current owners break even?

# 12.4 Finding Patterns: $y = mx + b$

Often in your study of mathematics, you explore patterns and apply them to simplify your calculations. In your work with equations, patterns are useful to help you draw the graphs of lines. For example, from graphs such as these you notice a pattern.

graph

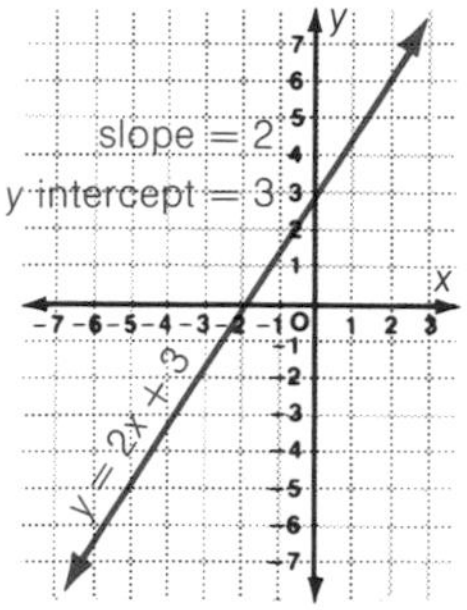


equation

$y = 2x + 3$

graph

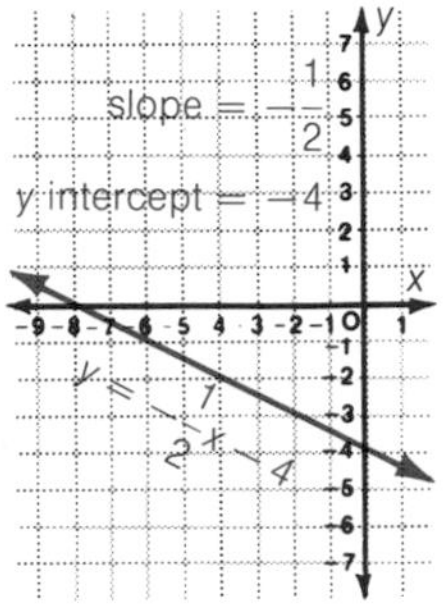


equation

$y = -\frac{1}{2}x - 4$

graph

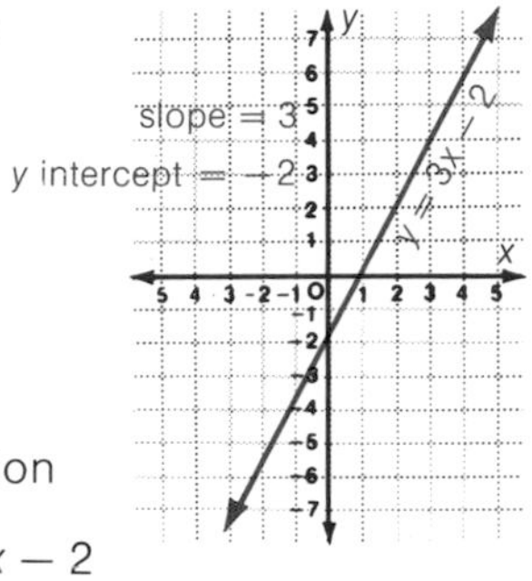


equation

$y = 3x - 2$

These examples suggest a useful form of the equation. From the equation written in this form, the slope and $y$ intercept can be found.

$$y = mx + b$$

$m$ ↑ slope  $b$ ↑ $y$ intercept

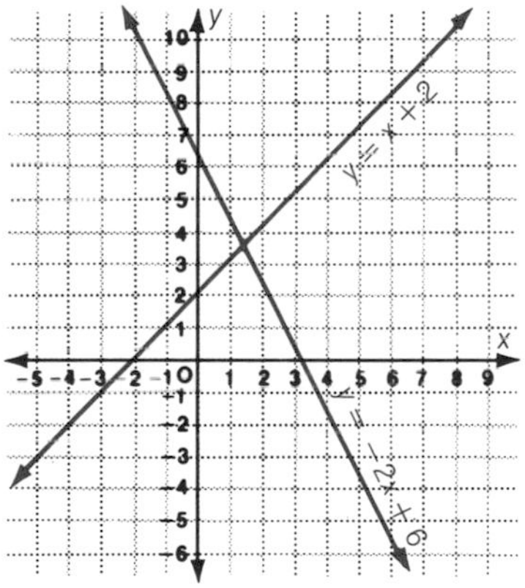


Refer to the diagram.
For the line $y = x + 2$, the slope is 1 and the $y$ intercept is 2.
For the line $y = -2x + 6$, the slope is $-2$ and the $y$ intercept is 6.

If the equation is not written in the $y = mx + b$ form, then you need to rearrange it first.

### Example 1

Find the slope and the $y$ intercept of the lines given by each equation.
(a) $2x + 5y - 30 = 0$  (b) $-3y = 7x$

### Solution

(a) $2x + 5y - 30 = 0$

$5y = -2x + 30$

$y = -\frac{2}{5}x + \frac{30}{5}$ ← Think: Compare with $y = mx + b$.

$y = -\frac{2}{5}x + 6$  $m = -\frac{2}{5}$  $b = 6$

The slope is $-\frac{2}{5}$ and the $y$ intercept is 6.

(b) $-3y = 7x$

$y = -\frac{7}{3}x$ ← Think: compare with $y = mx + b$

$m = -\frac{7}{3}$  $b = 0$

The slope is $-\frac{7}{3}$ and the $y$ intercept is 0.

You can also work backwards. For example, if you know the slope and the $y$ intercept then you can write the equation of the line.

### Example 2

For the line with slope $\frac{4}{5}$ and $y$ intercept $-2$

(a) write the equation of the line in the form $y = mx + b$, (b) graph the line.

### Solution

(a) In $y = mx + b$ use $m = \frac{4}{5}$ and $b = -2$.

The equation is $y = \frac{4}{5}x - 2$.

(b) *Step 1*: The $y$ intercept is $-2$. Mark the point A(0, −2).
*Step 2*: Use point A to locate point B. Use the slope to locate the point B.
*Step 3*: Draw the graph of the line. Label the line by writing its equation.

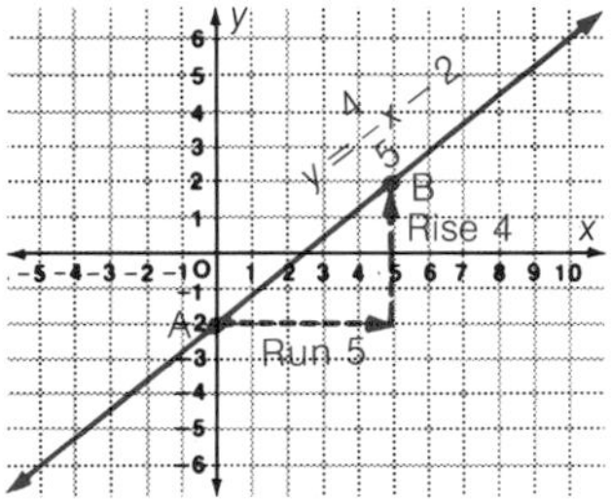


## Try These

1 What is the slope of each line?

(a) $y = 3x - 2$ (b) $y = -\frac{2}{3}x + 5$

(c) $y = -x + \frac{7}{3}$ (d) $y = \frac{3}{5}x$

2 What is the $y$ intercept of each line?

(a) $y = 5x - 1$ (b) $y = -\frac{2}{3}x + 4$

(c) $y = -x - 7$ (d) $y = -\frac{1}{2}x$

## Written Exercises

### A

1 The diagram shows the line given by $y = 2x - 5$.
(a) What is the value of $m$ in the equation?
(b) What is the value of $b$ in the equation?
(c) What is the slope of the graph?
(d) What is the $y$ intercept of the graph?

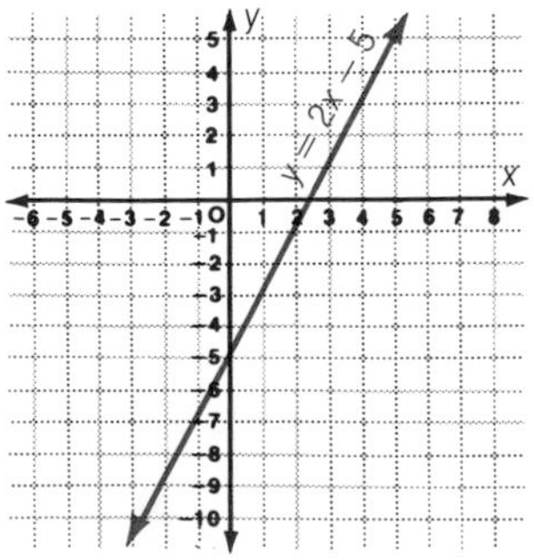


2 The diagram shows the line given by $y = -3x + 1$.
(a) From the equation, what are the values of $m$ and $b$?
(b) What is the slope of the graph?
(c) What is the $y$ intercept of the graph?

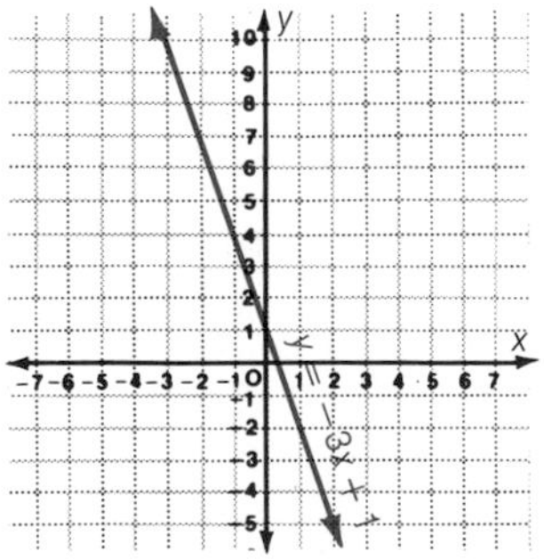

3 A line passes through the point A(0, −5) with slope $\frac{5}{2}$.

(a) What is the $y$ intercept of the line?
(b) Write an equation of the line.
(c) Draw its graph.

4 For each line, a point on the line and the slope are given. Find the equation of each line.

(a) P(0, −4), slope 4 (b) Q(0,1), slope −1

(c) R(0, −2), slope $\frac{4}{5}$ (d) $S\left(0, \frac{5}{2}\right)$, slope 0

(e) T(0,0), slope $-\frac{1}{2}$ (f) V(0, −3.5), slope −1

5 For each graph

▶ find the slope and the $y$ intercept
▶ write the equation of the line.

(a)

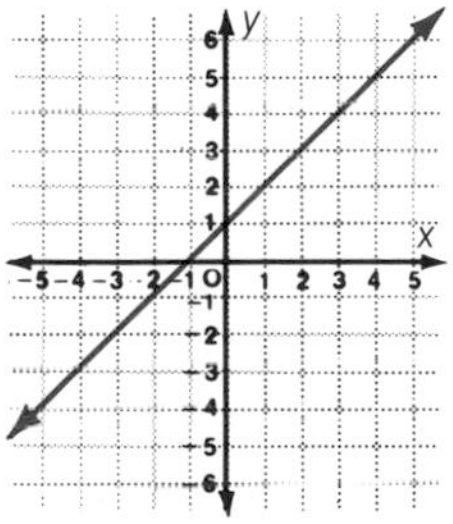

(b)

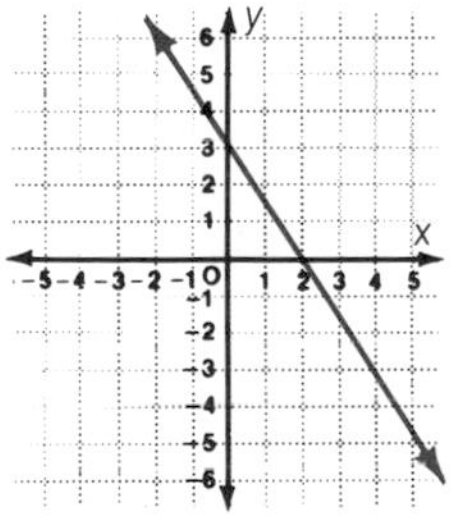

(c)

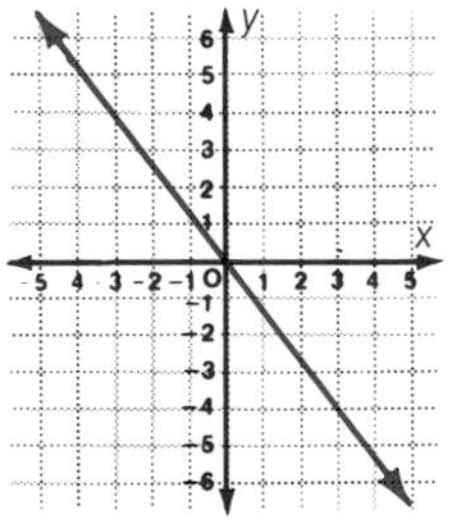

(d)

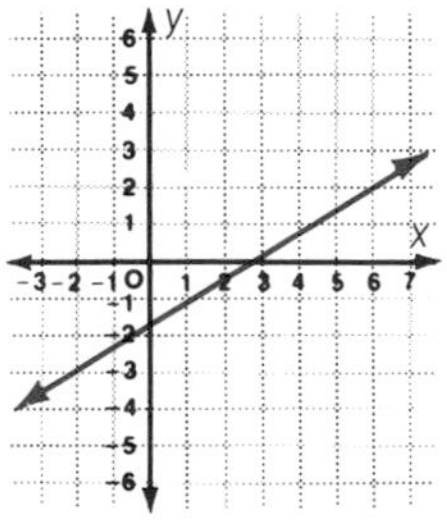

6 The values of $m$ and $b$ for lines whose equations are given in the form $y = mx + b$ are shown. Graph and label each line.

(a) $m = 2, b = -3$ (b) $m = -4, b = 1$

(c) $m = \frac{1}{2}, b = -4$ (d) $m = -\frac{2}{3}, b = 6$

**B** Remember: to read the slope and $y$ intercept from an equation you need to express the equation in the form $y = mx + b$.

7 The equation of a line is given by $3x + y = 4$.

(a) Write the equation in the form $y = mx + b$.
(b) What is the slope of the line?
(c) What is the $y$ intercept of the line?

8 For each of the following lines

▶ write the equation in the form $y = mx + b$.
▶ what is the slope and the $y$ intercept?

(a) $y - 2x = 3$ (b) $y - \frac{2}{3}x = 7$
(c) $2x + 5y = 10$ (d) $3x - 2y = 12$
(e) $-4x + 3y = 15$ (f) $2x - 5y - 15 = 0$

9 The graph shows the path of a water pipeline, where A is the location of the pumphouse by the lake and B is the kitchen tap.

(a) What is the slope of the pipeline?

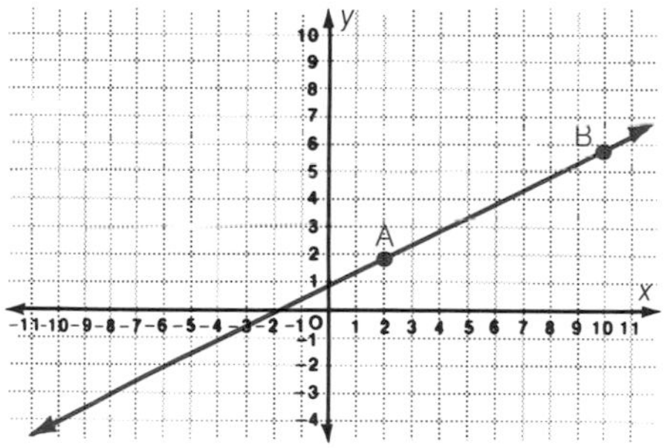


(b) What is the equation of the path of the pipeline?

10 At a research station in the Arctic a co-ordinate grid is used to record the path of icebergs. On May 25 the path of an iceberg crossed the $y$ axis at −3. The slope of its path was $-\frac{3}{5}$.

(a) What is the equation of the path of the iceberg?
(b) Draw the graph of the path.

11 Lines with slope 3 are represented by the equation $y = 3x + b$. Find the value of $b$ and write the equation of the line when
(a) the $y$ intercept is $-5$.
(b) the line passes through the point (0,4).
(c) the line passes through the origin.

12 Refer to the line shown.
(a) What is the slope?
(b) What is the $y$ intercept?
(c) What is the equation of the line?

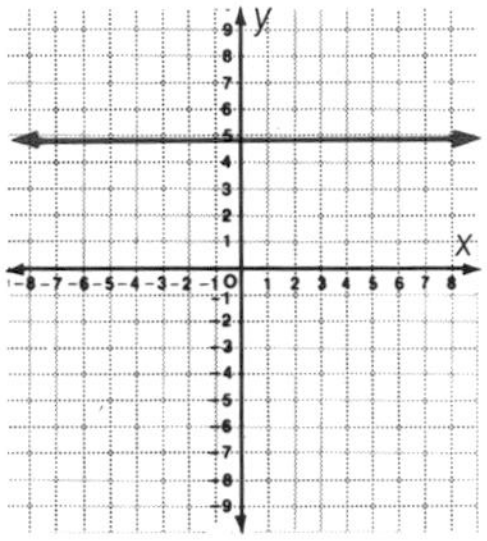


13 Refer to your results in the previous question. Write the equation of the line that is parallel to the $x$ axis and has $y$ intercept at
(a) 7 (b) $-4$ (c) $-9$

14 Refer to the graph.
(a) What is the slope?
(b) What is the $y$ intercept?
(c) What is the equation of the line?

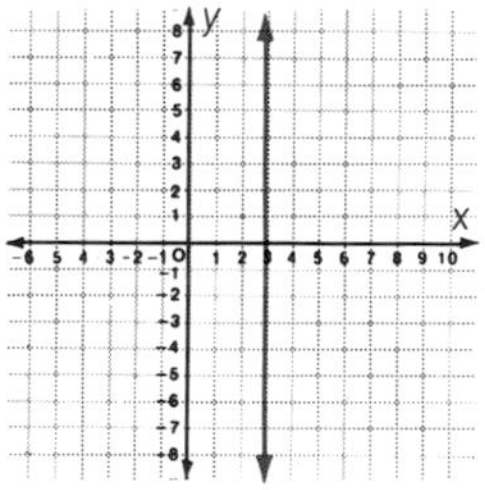


15 Refer to your results in the previous equation. Write the equation of the line that is parallel to the $y$ axis and
(a) has $x$ intercept $-5$.
(b) passes through the point (2,7).
(c) passes through the origin.

16 (a) What is the slope of each line?

A: $y = -3x + 5$ B: $y = \frac{1}{3}x + 5$

(b) Are the lines perpendicular? Give reasons for your answer.

17 For each pair of lines, decide whether the lines are parallel, perpendicular or neither.
(a) $y = 4x - 1$, $y = -4x + 1$
(b) $y = -\frac{1}{5}x + 4$, $y = 5x - 1$
(c) $y = -x - 2$, $y = x + 2$
(d) $y = 3x - \frac{1}{2}$, $y = 3x + 4$
(e) $y = \frac{2}{3}x + 6$, $y = \frac{3}{2}x - 1$

18 (a) Write each equation in the form $y = mx + b$.
A: $4x - 5y = -25$ B: $4x - 5y = 15$
(b) Determine whether the lines are parallel.

## C

19 Indicate which of the following lines are
▶ parallel. ▶ perpendicular.

(a) $3x - y = -7$ (b) $x - 3y = -7$
(c) $x - 5y = 4$ (d) $5x + y = 4$
(e) $2x + 3y = 6$ (f) $3x - 2y - 8 = 0$
(g) $-x + 4y = -4$ (h) $5y - x = 10$

### Math Tip

You have probably heard of people having an invention named after them: Goodyear Tires, Celsius Thermometers, Levi Jeans. In mathematics, a similar procedure is often used. Skills of graphing have their roots in the work of Rene Descartes (1596–1650). His contribution was honored by having the *Cartesian* plane named after him.

### Calculator Tip

The earth's path around the sun is not circular, but rather elliptical (a flattened circle). The formula for $e$ shows how much an orbit is "off" from a true circular form.

$$e = \frac{\sqrt{a^2 - b^2}}{a}$$

$e$ is called the eccentricity of the orbit.

Use a calculator to find the eccentricity of the orbit of earth if $a = 149.515 \times 10^6$ and $b = 149.494 \times 10^6$.

# 12.5 Writing Equations for Lines: Making Decisions

In your earlier work you drew a straight line on the co-ordinate plane if you knew either

- two points on the line or
- the slope and one point on the line

Once you know either of these facts you can also find the equation of a line. You make use of the fact that the equation of any line can be written in the form $y = mx + b$ and use the given facts to find the specific values of $m$ and $b$. These steps are shown in the following example.

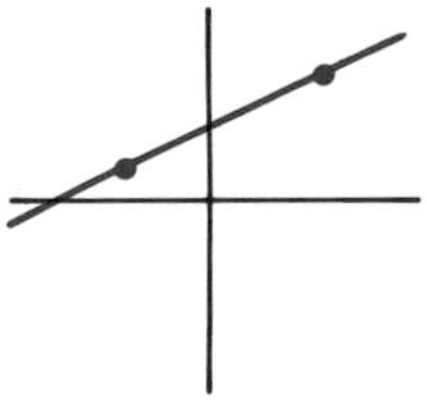

two points

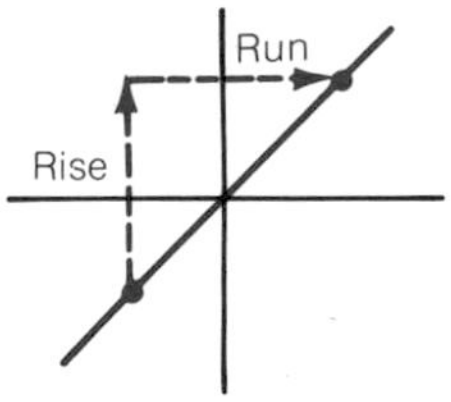


one point and slope

### Example 1

Find the equation of the line

(a) with slope $-2$ and passing through the point A$(4, -3)$.

(b) with slope $\frac{3}{4}$ and $x$ intercept 5.

### Solution

(a) *Step 1*: Use $y = mx + b$.
Substitute the slope, $m = -2$.
Thus $y = -2x + b$

*Step 2*: Find the value of $b$. The co-ordinates of $(4, -3)$ satisfy the equation.
Use $x = 4$ and $y = -3$. in

$y = -2x + b$ — The co-ordinates of the point are $(4, -3)$.

$$-3 = -2(4) + b$$
$$-3 = -8 + b$$
$$-3 + 8 = b$$
$$5 = b$$

*Step 3*: Write the equation of the line.
The equation is $y = -2x + 5$

(b) Think of the steps to do the following question.

In $y = mx + b$, use $m = \frac{3}{4}$.

Thus $y = \frac{3}{4}x + b$

Substitute $x = 5$, $y = 0$ — The $x$ intercept is 5, so $(5,0)$ is a point on the line.

$$0 = \frac{3}{4}(5) + b$$

$$0 = \frac{15}{4} + b$$

$$-\frac{15}{4} = b$$

The equation is $y = \frac{3}{4}x - \frac{15}{4}$.

If you are given two points on the line, then you have an extra step to do. First you use the two points to find the slope of the line, as shown in the following example.

### Example 2

On a grid, a new section of a highway is shown through the point A(−1,4) and B(2,3). Find the equation of the line shown.

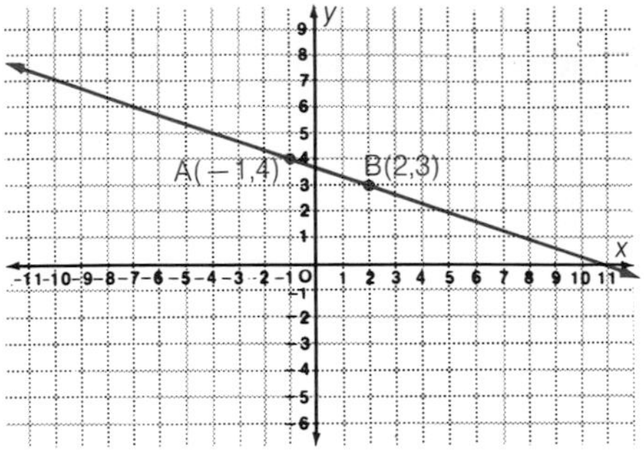


### Solution

*Step 1*: Find the slope.

$$\text{slope} = \frac{\text{difference of } y \text{ co-ordinates}}{\text{difference of } x \text{ co-ordinates}}$$

$$= \frac{4-3}{-1-2}$$

$$= \frac{1}{-3} \text{ or } -\frac{1}{3}$$

In $y = mx + b$, use $m = -\frac{1}{3}$.

$$y = -\frac{1}{3}x + b$$

*Step 2*: Use one of the points to find the value of $b$.

In $y = -\frac{1}{3}x + b$ use $x = 2$, $y = 3$. ← Use the point with co-ordinates B(2,3)

$$3 = -\frac{1}{3}(2) + b$$

$$3 = -\frac{2}{3} + b$$

$$3 + \frac{2}{3} = b$$

$$\frac{11}{3} = b$$

*Step 3*: Write the equation.

$$y = -\frac{1}{3}x + \frac{11}{3}$$

Sometimes it is convenient to rewrite the equation in the *general form* by eliminating any fractions and placing all the terms on the left side.

$$y = -\frac{1}{3}x + \frac{11}{3}$$

$$3y = 3\left(-\frac{1}{3}x\right) + 3\left(\frac{11}{3}\right)$$ ← Multiply by 3 to eliminate the fractions. Remember: you must multiply *each* term by 3.

$$3y = -x + 11$$

$$x + 3y - 11 = 0$$ ← This is the equation in general form.

## Try These

1 What is the equation of the line in the form $y = mx + b$ for the following values of $m$ and $b$?

(a) $m = 2, b = 3$ (b) $m = \frac{1}{2}, b = 1$

(c) $m = -\frac{3}{4}, b = 5$ (d) $m = -1, b = -\frac{5}{2}$

2 For each equation what is the value of
- ▶ the slope, $m$?
- ▶ the $y$ intercept, $b$?

(a) $y = 3x - 7$ (b) $y = -\frac{1}{2}x + 8$

(c) $y = -x - \frac{9}{2}$ (d) $y = -\frac{2}{3}x + 1$

(e) $y = \frac{1}{5}x + 7$ (f) $y = -3x$

## Written Exercises

**A** Review the meaning of the slope $y$ intercept form of the equation. What is meant by the general form?

1 For each line the $y$ intercept and a point, P, are shown.
- ▶ What is the slope?
- ▶ What is the $y$ intercept?
- ▶ Write the equation of the line.

(a)

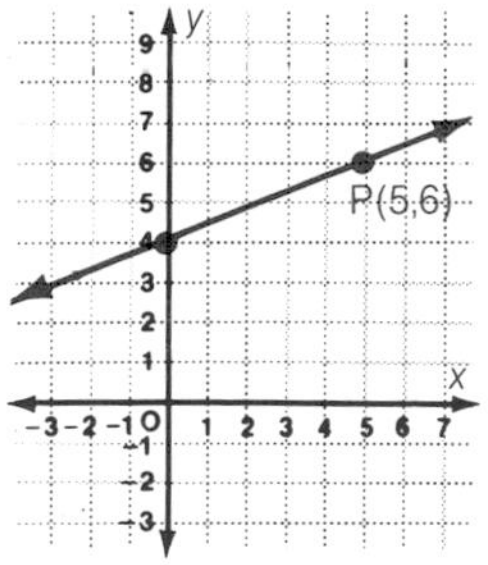


(b)

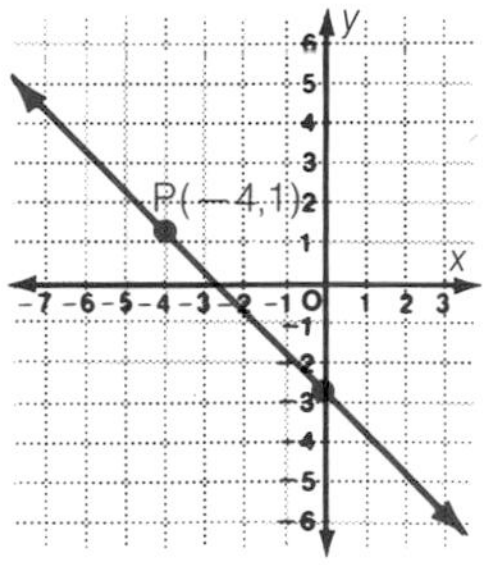


(c)

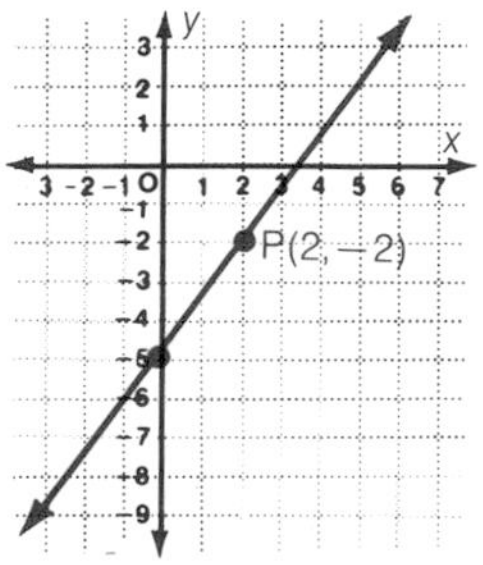


(d)

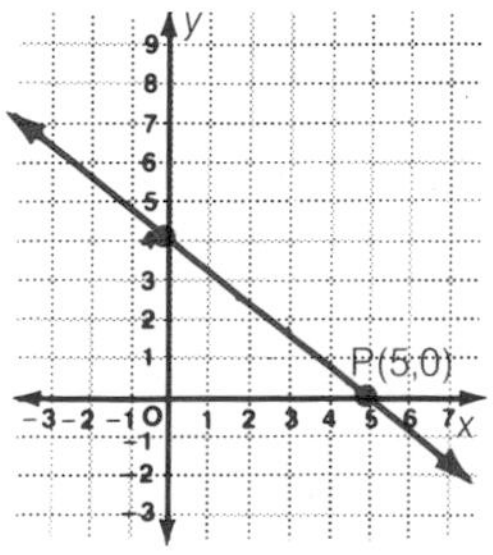


2 Write each equation in the general form.

(a) $y = 3x - 5$ (b) $y = -x$

(c) $y = \frac{2}{3}x + 1$ (d) $y = -\frac{3}{4}x - 2$

(e) $y = \frac{1}{4}x - \frac{1}{2}$ (f) $y = \frac{5}{8}x + \frac{5}{2}$

(g) $\frac{4}{5}x = 1$ (h) $y = -\frac{7}{3}$

3 A line has slope $-2$ and passes through the point K(1,3).
- (a) Write the equation of this line in the form $y = mx + b$. What is the value of $m$?
- (b) Find the value of $b$.
- (c) Write the equation of the line in the general form.

4 A helicopter is on a path that passes through the point $(4, -9)$. The slope of the path is $\frac{3}{5}$.
- (a) Draw a diagram to show the given information.
- (b) From the diagram, what is the slope?
- (c) Use (a) and (b). What is the equation of the path of the helicopter.
- (d) Check your answer in (c) by substituting the co-ordinates $(4, -9)$ in your equation.

5 A line passes through the points G(1,7) and H(−4,3).
(a) What is the slope of the line?
(b) Write the equation of the line in the form $y = mx + b$. What is the value of $m$?
(c) Find $b$.
(d) What is the equation of the line? How can you check your answer?

**B** Remember: to write the equation of a line, you need to know the values of the slope $m$, and the $y$ intercept $b$.

6 A line joins the points M(−3,8) and N(5,5).
(a) What is the slope of the line?
(b) Find the equation of the line.

7 Find the equation of the line passing through each pair of points. Express the equations in the slope $y$ intercept form.
(a) A(5,2), B(0,−4)
(b) P(−1,−1), Q(−7,10)
(c) F(4,−2), G(−1,0)
(d) K(−3,−5), L(0,0)

8 Find the equation of the line which passes through the given point and has the slope shown. Express the equations in the slope $y$ intercept form, $y = mx + b$.
(a) A(−4,3), slope 3 (b) B(8,5), slope $\frac{2}{3}$
(c) C(5,−2), slope −4 (d) D(−7,−7), slope $-\frac{3}{4}$

9 Express in general form the equation of each of the following lines.
(a) passing through K(−1,6) with slope $-\frac{3}{5}$
(b) passing through L(8,2) with slope −1
(c) passing through M(−3,0) with slope $\frac{3}{2}$
(d) passing through N(0,4) with slope $-\frac{5}{8}$

10 A lighthouse keeper uses a co-ordinate grid to keep a record of ships passing in her area. She spots a ship at the point S(12,−7), sailing on a course with slope $\frac{5}{3}$. What is the equation of the course of the ship?

11 Co-ordinate geometry is used when the program for a computer game is being written. The programmer wants to light up a path between the points A(−3,−8) and B(5,−1). Find the equation of this path.

12 Rowena has summer employment as a fire-watcher. She uses a co-ordinate grid to make a map of her observation area around her fire tower. A power line runs through the point (10,−15) with a slope of $-\frac{3}{4}$. Find the equation of the path of the power line.

**C**

13 On a map the township line runs straight from the point X(−10,8) to the point Y(15,5). What is the equation to this line?

14 The equation of a line in the slope $y$ intercept form is given by $y = mx + b$. The general equation of a line is given by
$Ax + By + C = 0$
(a) Express the slope $m$ in terms of $A$, $B$, and $C$.
(b) Express the $y$ intercept $b$ in terms of $A$, $B$, and $C$.

## Math Tip

If you are given two points on a line, you can compute the slope of the line. The following form shows the equation of the line in a general form.

$$\frac{y - y_1}{x - x_1} = \frac{y_2 - y_1}{x_2 - x_1}$$

use one of the points (points to $x_1$)
shows the slope of the line (points to $\frac{y_2 - y_1}{x_2 - x_1}$)

Find the equation of the line passing through the pairs of points.
A (4,3)(2,−1) B (3,−2)(−4,0)
C (6,3)(5,−2) D (−3,5)(−3,−5)

# 12.6 Solving Pairs of Equations: Using Graphs

Many problems in business and engineering result in solving equations. In fact, a pair or system of linear equations occurs often in the business world. Mathematicians and computer scientists have spent much time and energy on finding methods for their solutions. You can use your previous graphing skills to solve a pair of equations.

For example, the graph shows two linear equations that are involved in the production process at a paint factory. The best quality of paint requires both equations to be satisfied. This is true at the point where the two lines intersect: at (5,4). Thus using the graph, the solution to the pair of equations $x + y = 9$ and $x + 5y = 25$ is when $x = 5$ and $y = 4$. To check your answer you need to substitute into both equations.

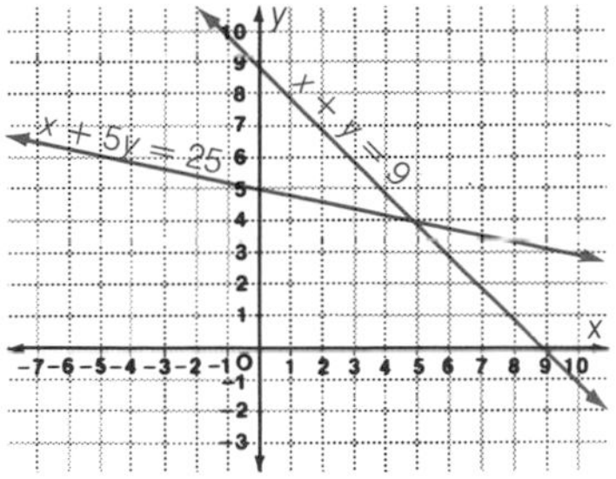


Use $x = 5$, $y = 4$.

$x + y = 9$
L.S. $= x + y$
$= 5 + 4$
$= 9$
$=$ R.S. checks ✓

$x + 5y = 25$
L.S. $= x + 5y$
$= 5 + 5(4)$
$= 5 + 20$
$= 25$
$=$ R.S. checks ✓

You can use the properties of lines that you have learned earlier to graph the lines, as shown in the following example.

### Example

Find the co-ordinates of the point of intersection of the lines $x + y = 5$ and $x + 5y = 7$.

### Solution

Think: Find convenient points to graph.

for $x + y = 5$

| x | y |
|---|---|
| 0 | 5 |
| 5 | 0 |
| 3 | 2 |

for $x + 5y = -7$

| x | y |
|---|---|
| 3 | −2 |
| −7 | 0 |
| −2 | −1 |

← Check the graph. Choose a third point.

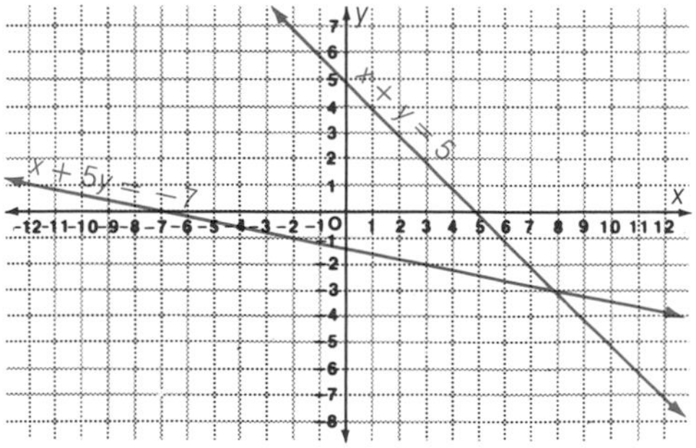


From the graph, the point of intersection is P(8, −3).

Check by substituting the co-ordinates of P into the equations.

$x + 5y = 8 + 5(-3)$
$= 8 - 15$
$= -7$ ✓checks

$x + y = 8 + (-3)$
$= 5$
✓checks

## Try These

1 What is the point of intersection of each pair of lines?

(a)

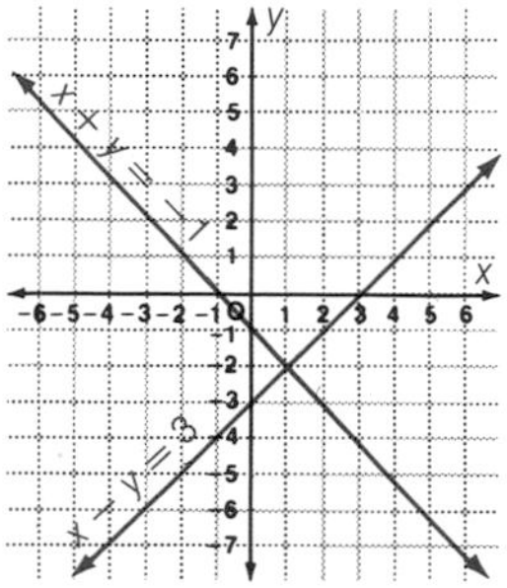


(b)

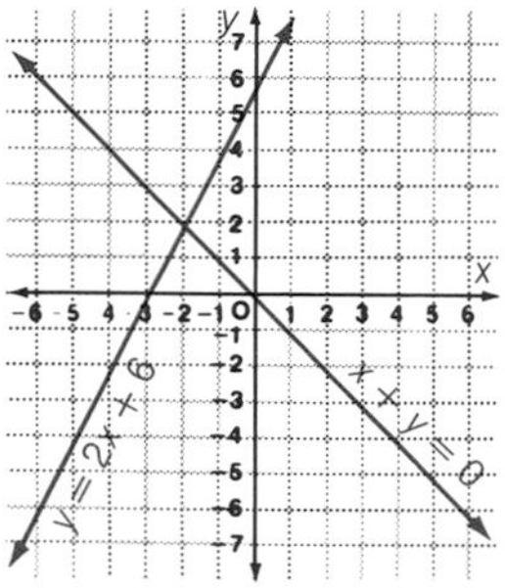


2 Which point, A or B, is on both lines?

(a) $x + y = 6$, $x - y = 2$ — A(4,2) or B(5,1)

(b) $x + y = 10$, $x - y = 4$ — A(10, −3) or B(7,3)

(c) $x + 2y = 5$, $x - y = -1$ — A(1,2) or B(3,4)

(d) $x - 3y = 2$, $x + y = 6$ — A(4,2) or B(5,1)

## Written Exercises

**A** Remember: check the co-ordinates of the intersection point in both equations.

1 The graph of the equation $x + y = 4$ is drawn. Which of the following points are on the line?

(a) (2,2) (b) (0,4)
(c) (6,1) (d) (4,0)
(e) (1,3) (f) (−1,5)

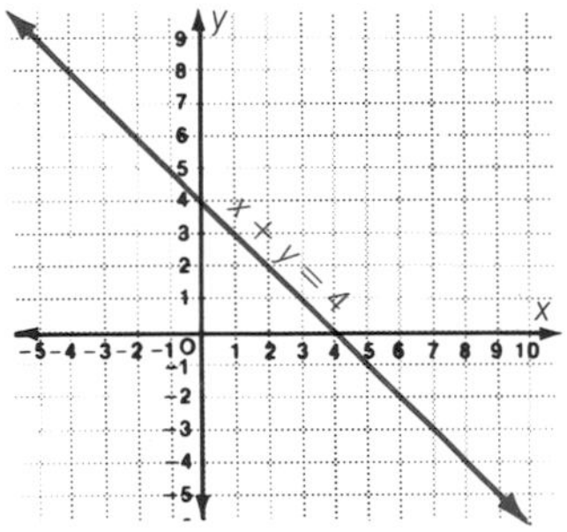


2 Which of the given points satisfy the equation?

(a) $x + y = 8$ A(6,2) B(0,8) C(9,6)
(b) $y = 2x - 3$ D(0,5) E(1, −1) F(2,1)
(c) $2x + y = 7$ G(0,7) H(−3, −3) I(5, −3)

3 Refer to the graph.

(a) What is the point of intersection of the lines?
(b) What is the solution for the pair of equations $2x + y = 8$ and $4x - 5y = 30$?
(c) Check your answer in (b).

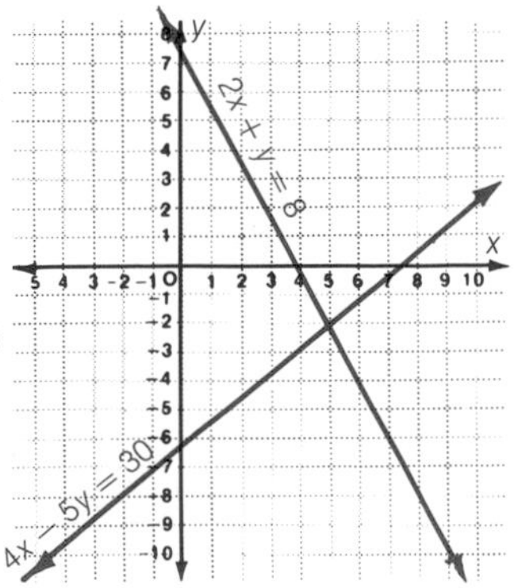


4 (a) Copy and complete the table of values for each equation.

A: $2x - y = 8$

| x | y |
|---|---|
| 0 | ? |
| ? | 0 |

B: $x - 3y = 4$

| x | y |
|---|---|
| 0 | ? |
| ? | 0 |

(b) Suggest a reason for finding another pair of values for each table.
(c) Draw the graph for A and B.
(d) What is the solution of the pair of equations? How can you check your answer?

5 (a) For the line $y = x - 3$ what is
▶ the $y$ intercept? ▶ the slope?
(b) For the line $y = x + 2$ what is
▶ the $y$ intercept? ▶ the slope?
(c) Use your results in (a) and (b) to graph the lines. What are the co-ordinates of their point of intersection?
(d) Check that your solution.

Remember: choose convenient co-ordinates when you draw a graph.

## B

**Remember: once you draw the graph of a line, check your graph.**

6. Use the graphs shown.
   ▶ Find the point of intersection for each of the following pairs of equations.
   ▶ Then check your solution.

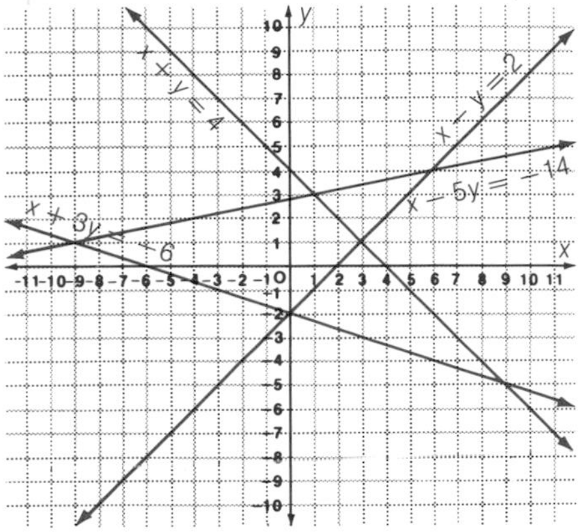


(a) $x + y = 4$
$x - y = 2$

(b) $x - 5y = -14$
$x + 3y = -6$

(c) $x - y = 2$
$x - 5y = -14$

(d) $x + 3y = -6$
$x - y = 2$

7 (a) Draw the graph of each equation.
$y = x + 3 \qquad y = 5 - x$
(b) At what point do the lines intersect?
(c) Check your solution.

8 (a) Draw the graph of each equation.
$x + y = 5 \qquad 3x - y = -1$
(b) What are the co-ordinates of the point of intersection of the lines?
(c) Check that your solution satisfies both equations.

9 Use a graphical method to solve each of the following pairs of equations.

(a) $y = x - 3$
$y = 6 - 2x$

(b) $y = 3x - 15$
$y = 1 - x$

(c) $y = 2x$
$y = 12 - 2x$

(d) $y = x - 4$
$y = -x + 8$

(e) $2x - y = 7$
$x + 2y = 1$

(f) $x + 2y = 20$
$x - y = 2$

(g) $5x - y = 9$
$x = y - 3$

(h) $x - 2y = 10$
$x + y = 4$

10 The paths of two submarines are given by the following equations.
Submarine A $\quad 3x + y = 7$
Submarine B $\quad x - y = 1$
At what point do their paths cross?

11 A train is on a path given by the equation $y = x - 5$. A chipmunk is travelling on a path given by $y = 2x - 14$.
(a) What are the co-ordinates of the point at which the paths cross?
(b) Will the train hit the chipmunk? Why or why not?

12 The path of a gas pipeline into a house is given by the equation $2x + y = 12$. The water pipe into the house follows the line given by the equation $3x + y = 17$.
(a) What are the co-ordinates of the location where the two lines cross.
(b) If you dug a hole at this point, which pipeline do you think you would reach first? Why is this?

## C

13 The straight line path from Steve's home to the mall is given by the equation $2x + 3y = 18$. From Cassie's home the straight line path to the same mall is given by the equation $8x - 5y = -64$.
(a) Find the co-ordinates of the mall.
(b) If the straight line path from Steve's home to Cassie's is given by the equation $10x - 19y = 22$; what are the co-ordinates of each person's home?

### Computer Tip

If a formula is used to do a problem, then it can be programmed for a computer. To find the co-ordinates of the midpoint $(M_1, M_2)$ of a line segment you need only know the co-ordinates of its end points $(x_1, y_1)$ and $(x_2, y_2)$. Run the following program.

```
10 INPUT X1, Y1, X2, Y2
20 LET M1 = (X1 + X2)/2
30 LET M2 = (Y1 + Y2)/2
40 PRINT "MIDPOINT IS ("; M1,", ",M2;")"
50 END
```

# 12.7 Using Algebra: Solving Pairs of Equations

In the previous section, you solved pairs of equations by graphing the lines and then locating the point of intersection. The co-ordinates of the intersection point gave you the solution to the pair of equations.

Because the method of graphing is time consuming and does not always give an accurate answer, other methods have been developed. One algebraic method uses your substitution skills, as shown in the following example.

From the graph, you cannot tell the exact point of intersection. Is it (2.6,2) or (2.5,2.1) or . . . ?

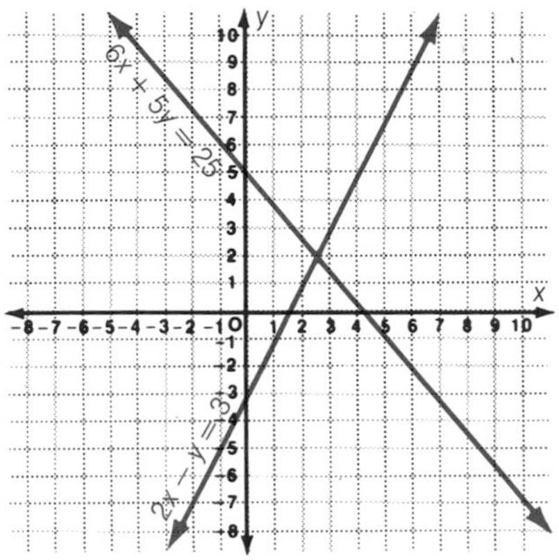


### Example

Find the point of intersection of the lines given by $2x - y = 3$ and $6x + 5y = 25$.

### Solution

*Step 1* Record the given information.

$$2x - \ y = 3 \quad ①$$
$$6x + 5y = 25 \quad ②$$

*Step 2* Use equation ①. Express $y$ in terms of $x$.

$$2x - y = 3$$
$$-y = -2x + 3$$
$$y = 2x - 3 \quad ③$$

*Step 3* Use the result ③. Substitute the expression for $y$ in ②.

$$6x + 5y = 25$$
$$6x + 5(2x - 3) = 25$$
$$6x + 10x - 15 = 25$$
$$16x = 25 + 15$$
$$16x = 40$$

You now have one equation in one variable. You have solved this type of equation earlier.

$$x = \frac{40}{16} \text{ or } 2\frac{1}{2}$$

*Step 4* Use the value $x = 2\frac{1}{2}$ in ① to find the corresponding value for $y$.

$$2x - y = 3$$
$$2\left(2\frac{1}{2}\right) - y = 3$$
$$5 - y = 3$$
$$y = 2$$

Thus the co-ordinates of point of intersection are $\left(2\frac{1}{2}, 2\right)$.

Check:

Use $x = 2\frac{1}{2}$ and $y = 2$ in the second equation to check your answer.

$$\text{L.S.} = 6x + 5y$$
$$= 6\left(2\frac{1}{2}\right) + 5(2)$$
$$= 15 + 10$$
$$= 25 = \text{R.S.} \quad \text{checks} \checkmark$$

With practice you will be able to decide quickly which of the two equations to use first to express one of the variables.

## Try These

1 For each pair of equations
- ▶ decide which equation to use first
- ▶ decide which variable to express in terms of the other

(a) $x + 2y = 8$
$3x - 2y = 7$

(b) $3x - 4y = 5$
$2x + y = 1$

(c) $3k - t = 2$
$2k - 5t = -1$

(d) $6m + 4n = 3$
$3m - n = 2$

2 Use $x = 1$, find the corresponding value of $y$.
(a) $y = 2x$ (b) $y = 3x + 1$
(c) $y = x - 2$ (d) $y = 4x - 4$

3 Use $y = 2$, find the corresponding value of $x$.
(a) $x = 2y$ (b) $x = 2y - 1$
(c) $x = -3y$ (d) $x = -3y + 6$

## Written Exercises

**A** Remember: decide which variable to express in terms of the other.

1 Express $y$ in terms of $x$.
(a) $y + 1 = x$ (b) $y - 1 = 2x$
(c) $y + x = 13$ (d) $-2x + y = 8$

2 Express $x$ in terms of $y$.
(a) $x + 3y = 6$ (b) $x - 5y = 10$
(c) $5y + x = -12$ (d) $4y = -8 + x$

3 Find the value of $x$ in each of the following equations; use $y = -1$.
(a) $2x + y = 9$ (b) $3x - y = 2$
(c) $x + 3y = -10$ (d) $y = 4x - 13$

4 Find the value of $y$ in each of the following equations; use $x = 3$.
(a) $2x + 2y = 24$ (b) $3x - y = -12$
(c) $-x + 3y = -42$ (d) $x + 3y - 18 = 0$

5 A pair of lines are given by the equations
$5x + y = -16$ $3x - 4y = -5$
(a) Use the first equation to express $y$ in terms of $x$.
(b) Substitute your expression for $y$ into the second equation. Solve for $x$.
(c) Use your answer in (b). Solve now for $y$.
(d) Check your answers.
(e) What is the point of intersection of the two lines?

6 (a) Graph the equations $x + y = 7$ and $x - 2y = 1$.
(b) What is the point of intersection of the lines in (a)?
(c) Solve the pair of equations in (a) using the substitution method.
(d) Compare your answers in (b) and (c).

7 A pair of lines are given by
$2x - y = 5$
$3x + y = 5$
(a) Solve the equations graphically.
(b) Solve the equations by using the substitution method.
(c) Compare your solutions in (a) and (b).

8 (a) Graph the equations $x + 4y = 18$ and $2x + 9y = 27$.
(b) What is the solution in (a)? Why is it difficult to give an answer?
(c) Solve the pair of equations using the substitution method.

9 Use the equations
$y = 2x$ $3x + y = 15$
(a) What is your first step in solving the equations? Solve the equations.
(b) Check your solution.

10 Use the equations

$x = 2y \qquad 5x + 3y = 52$

(a) What is your first step in solving the equations? Solve the equations.

(b) What are the co-ordinates of the intersection point?

**B** Remember: the solution you obtain **must** satisfy both equations.

11 For each of the following pairs of equations decide

- ▶ which equation to use first and
- ▶ whether to express $x$ in terms of $y$ or $y$ in terms of $x$.

Solve the system of equations.

(a) $2x + 3y = 0$, $x + 4y = -3$

(b) $3x + y = 12$, $2x + 3y = 8$

(c) $2y = 3x + 6$, $4x - y = 3$

(d) $3x - 2y = 6$, $y = 3x$

(e) $5x - 3y = 7$, $4x - y = 7$

(f) $x = \frac{1}{2}y$, $2x - 3y = 8$

12 Solve and verify.

(a) $x - 2y = 7$, $x + 3y = -8$

(b) $x = y + 8$, $2y = x - 6$

(c) $3x - y = 10$, $x + 3y = 0$

(d) $3x - 4y = 6$, $x + y = 23$

13 Find the co-ordinates of the point of intersection of the lines given by the following pairs of equations.

How can you check your answers?

(a) $x - 3y = 2$, $x + 2y = -8$

(b) $2x + y = 18$, $3x - y = 22$

(c) $x + y = 9$, $3x - y = 7$

(d) $5x - y = -11$, $x - 3y = -5$

14 The paths of two ships are given by the equations.

A: $x + 2y = 14 \qquad$ B: $x - 3y = -11$

Their paths intersect at a port. Find the co-ordinates of the location of the port.

15 The paths of two air balloons are given by $4x - 5y = -22$ and $y = 3x + 7$.

(a) What are the co-ordinates of the point at which their paths intersect?

(b) Will the balloons collide? Why or why not?

16 The following linear equations occurred in an experiment:

$3x - 2y = 2$

$x + y = 14.$

What is the solution to the pair of equations?

17 A chocolate manufacturer has found by consumer research the most popular mix of hard and soft centred chocolates. The best profit is given by the equations

$3s - 2h = 41 \quad$ and $\quad 2s + h = 53$

where $s$ is the number of soft-centred chocolates and $h$ the number with hard centres. Solve the equations to find the number of each kind of chocolate.

**C**

18 The number of reserved-seat tickets, $r$, and the number of general admission tickets, $g$, for a baseball game is given by the equations

$r + g = 47\,300$

$15r + 10g = 668\,000$

How many tickets of each type were sold?

## Consumer Tip

Principles in mathematics were used to develop the universal product code to identify products. You have probably seen this symbol before.

034560

These numbers and lines identify the product; its name, size, colour, flavour, quality, grade and so on.

An optical scanner can read the product code, check the current price encoded in the computer, and show price on a computerized receipt.

- How are all product codes alike?
- How do product codes differ?

# 12.8 Another Strategy: Solving Pairs of Equations

By comparing the steps in the substitution method with the original equations, a short cut can be found. This short cut leads to another method for solving pairs of equations: the method of elimination (or often called the add or subtract method).

Compare the following methods to solve the equations $x + y = 3$ and $2x - y = 6$

**Method of Substitution**

$x + y = 3$ ①
$2x - y = 6$ ②

Use equation ①. Express $y$ in terms of $x$.

$y = 3 - x$

Substitute for $y$ in ②.

$2x - (3 - x) = 6$
$2x - 3 + x = 6$
$3x - 3 = 6$
$3x = 9$ ③
$x = 3$

**Method of Elimination**

Look for a shortcut. You could obtain the equation ③ directly from the original equations by adding as shown:

$x + y = 3$ ①
$2x - y = 6$ ②
$3x = 9$ ① + ②
$x = 3$

As before, find the corresponding value for $y$ by substituting $x = 3$ in ①

$3 + y = 3$
$y = 0$

In using the method of elimination you must decide whether to add or to subtract in order to eliminate one of the variables, and obtain an equation with just one variable.

## Example

Find the point of intersection of the lines given by $2x + 3y = -17$ and $x - 4y = 8$.

## Solution

$2x + 3y = -17$ ①
$x - 4y = 8$ ②

Remember: label the equations

Multiply ② by 2, so the numerical coefficients of the variable $x$ are the same in both equations.

$2x + 3y = -17$ ①
$2x - 8y = 16$ ③
$11y = -33$ ① − ③
$y = -3$

Subtract so that $x$ is eliminated.

Substitute $y = -3$ in ②.

$x - 4(-3) = 8$
$x + 12 = 8$
$x = 8 - 12$
$= -4$

Check: Use $(-4, -3)$ in ①
L.S. $= 2(-4) + 3(-3)$
$-8 + (-9)$
$-17 =$ R.S. ✓

The co-ordinates of the point of intersection are $(-4, -3)$.

## Try These

1 For each of the following, what number has the equation A been multiplied by to obtain the equation B?

| | A | B |
|---|---|---|
| (a) | $2x - y = 5$ | $4x - 2y = 10$ |
| (b) | $3x - 2y = -7$ | $6x - 4y = -14$ |
| (c) | $-x + 2y = 8$ | $3x - 6y = -24$ |
| (d) | $5x - 3y = -2$ | $-10x + 6y = 4$ |

2 In each pair of equations, would you add or subtract to eliminate one of the variables? Which variable is eliminated?

(a) $x + y = 7$
$2x - y = 2$

(b) $m + 2n = 3$
$-m + 7n = -4$

(c) $3p + 3q = 4$
$2p + 3q = -10$

(d) $6a - 3b = 1$
$-6a + 5b = 3$

(e) $7k - 7m = 2$
$7k + 8m = -1$

(f) $4v - w = 8$
$7v - w = 3$

## Written Exercises

**A** Remember: decide whether to eliminate *x* or *y*. Solve the equations.

1 (a) In order to eliminate *x*, should you add or subtract the following equations?

$x + 2y = 10$
$x - 3y = 5$

(b) Complete the solution to solve the pair of equations.

2 A pair of equations is shown.

$x + y = 8$ ①
$3x - y = 12$ ②

(a) What is the first step in solving the pair of equations:
- ▶ add ① and ② or
- ▶ subtract ② from ①?

(b) Solve the pair of equations.

3 Two lines are given by the equations:

$4x - 2y = -10$ ①
$x + 2y = 0$ ②

(a) Which variable can you eliminate?
(b) Complete the solution to find the point of intersection of the two lines.
(c) Graph the lines to check your result.

4 A pair of equations is shown

$x + 3y = -14$ ①
$4x - 2y = 0$ ②

(a) As the first step towards eliminating the variable *x*, multiply equation ① by 4. Label your new equation ③.
(b) Would you add or subtract ② and ③ to eliminate *x*?
(c) Complete the solution.

5 Describe what you would do to eliminate
- ▶ the variable *x* in part (a)
- ▶ the variable *y* in part (b).

Solve each pair of equations.

(a) $x + 3y = 4$
$3x - 2y = 1$

(b) $-x + 2y = -5$
$15x - 4y = 23$

6 To solve some pairs of equations, you need to multiply both equations.

$3x - 4y = 5$ ①
$2x - 3y = 4$ ②

(a) To eliminate the variable *x*, you need to make the coefficient of *x* the same in both equations. To do this multiply ① by 2 to give equation ③, and multiply ② by 3 to give equation ④.
(b) Decide whether to add or to subtract equations ③ and ④ and complete the solution, check your answer by substituting into equations ① and ②.

**B** Remember: always check your solution. Substitute into the *original* equations.

7 To solve each pair of equations
- ▶ decide which variable is more easily eliminated
- ▶ multiply one of the equations if necessary
- ▶ remember to check your solution by substituting back into the original equations.

(a) $x + 3y = -7$, $x - y = -3$ (b) $5x + 2y = -11$, $3x - 2y = -13$
(c) $x + 4y = 1$, $2x - y = -7$ (d) $m - 4n = 7$, $2m + 3n = 3$
(e) $5x - 3y = -16$, $x - 3y = 4$ (f) $5x - y = -10$, $x - 3y = -16$

8 To find the point of intersection of the lines given by the following pairs of equations
- ▶ decide which variable you want to eliminate
- ▶ multiply one or both of the equations if necessary
- ▶ complete and check the solution.

(a) $3x - 2y = 1$, $2x + 3y = 5$ (b) $5p - 4q = 1$, $3p + 2q = 5$
(c) $4a - 5b = -1$, $5a + 4b = 9$ (d) $2x - 3y = 2$, $6x - 8y = 10$
(e) $-3x - 5y = 67$, $4x - 3y = -12$ (f) $7x - 3y = 6$, $-4x + 6y = 18$

9 (a) Use the method of elimination to find the point of intersection of the lines given by
$2x + 5y = -1$ and $3x + 4y = 9$.
(b) Check your result in (a) by graphing the lines.

10 (a) What would be the first step in solving the following pair of equations by the method of elimination?
$3x + 6 = 4y$ $5y + x = 17$
(b) Solve the pair of equations.

11 The paths of two cargo planes are given by the following equations.
A: $4x - 5y = -11$ B: $3x = 4y + 8$
Find the co-ordinates of the point at which the paths intersect.

12 The number of falcons, $f$, and the number of eagles, $e$, observed at a bird sanctuary, are given by the solution of the equations:
$2f + e = 5$ $3f + 2e = 8$.
Solve the equations to find the number of each type of bird.

## Computer Tip

To write a program, you often first need to do some mathematics. For example, to design a program to solve a pair of equations in 2 variables, you need to develop the mathematics so that you can organize the steps needed to list the instructions for the computer to follow.

| Equations | Solution |
|---|---|
| $Ax + By = C$ | $x = \frac{CE - BF}{AE - BD}$, $AE \neq BD$ |
| $Dx + Ey = F$ | $y = \frac{CD - AF}{BD - AE}$, $BD \neq AE$ |

The following BASIC program will solve any systems of 2 linear equations in 2 variables.

```
10 PRINT "SOLVE TWO EQUATIONS IN TWO
   VARIABLES"
20 INPUT A, B, C
30 INPUT D, E, F
40 LET Q = A * E - B * D
50 IF Q = 0, THEN 90
60 LET X = (C * E - B * F)/(A * E - B * D)
70 LET Y = (C * D - A * F)/(B * D - A * E)
80 PRINT X; Y
90 INPUT "INPUT MORE VALUES? YES (TYPE 1) OR
   NO (TYPE 0)"; P
100 IF P = 1 THEN 20
110 END
```

What does this computer line allow you to do? (refers to line 100)

1 What are the values of A, B, C, D, E, F in the system $5p - 4q = 1$, $3p + 2q = 5$? Run the computer program.

2 Solve each system. Use the computer program.
(a) $x - 4y = 7$, $2x + 3y = 3$ (b) $4x - 5y = -11$, $3x - 4y = 8$

3 Use the program to solve the following.
(a) $6y - 4x = 18$, $7x = 3y + 6$ (b) $5y + 67 = -3x$, $3y - 12 = 4x$

4 Choose pairs of equations of your own. Solve them using the computer program.

# 12.9 Applying Skills: Solving Problems

Some problems can be solved by translating the problem into a pair of equations with two variables. Use the *Steps for Solving Problems* to help you organize your thinking.

> *Steps for Solving Problems*
> Step A Do I understand the problem?
> I. What information am I asked to find?
> II. What information am I given?
> Step B Decide on a method. (Write two equations using two variables)
> Step C Find the answer. (Solve the equations.)
> Step D Check my answer in the original problem.
> Step E Write a final statement to answer the question

### Example

A minor league hockey team has played 15 games so far without a loss. They have 24 points. If 2 points are awarded for a win and 1 point for a tie, find the number of games that the team has won.

Did you know that most professional hockey players are Canadian? In 1893 the Stanley Cup was first presented to the team winning the championships in Canada.

### Solution

Think Step A: Analyze the given information. What are you asked to find?

Let $w$ represent the number of games won. Let $t$ represent the number of games tied.

Think Step B: Write two equations using the information given.

$w + t = 15$ games won + games tied = 15 games played

$2w + t = 24$ 2 points for a win + 1 for a tie = 24 points

Think Step C: Solve the pair of equations. Here, the elimination method is used. The method of substitution would work equally well.

$$w + t = 15 \quad ①$$
$$2w + t = 24 \quad ②$$
$$-w = -9 \quad ① - ②$$
$$w = 9$$

Use $w = 9$ in ①.

$$9 + t = 15$$
$$t = 6$$

Think Step D: Check your solution.

Use $w = 9$, $t = 6$ in ②

L.S. $= 2(9) + 6$
$= 18 + 6$
$= 24$
$=$ R.S. ✓ checks

Think Step E: Make a final statement.

The team has won 9 games.

## Try These

1 If $h$ represents the cost of a hamburger and $f$ represents the cost of an order of fries, give an equation for each of the following statements.
   (a) Two hamburgers and three orders of fries cost \$5.65.
   (b) The charge for an order of fries and three hamburgers is \$4.20.
   (c) The difference between the price of a hamburger and an order of fries is \$0.95.

2 If $p$ represents the cost in cents of a peach and $k$ represents the cost in cents of a kiwi fruit, explain in words what the following equations represent.
   (a) $3p + 2k = 150$ (b) $p - k = 10$ (c) $4p = 3k$

## Written Exercises

**A**

1 A jar contains a mixture of nails and screws. Use $n$ to represent the number of nails and $s$ to represent the number of screws. Write an equation for each of the following statements.
   (a) The total number of nails and screws in the jar is 520.
   (b) Each nail has a mass of 7 g and each screw has a mass of 5 g. The mass of all the nails and screws in the jar is 485 g.
   (c) The difference between the mass of all the nails and the mass of all the screws is 74 g.

2 The refreshment bar at a movie theatre sells popcorn in two different sizes. The regular size costs \$1 and the large size costs \$2.
   (a) One evening 120 containers of popcorn were sold. Choose two variables to represent the number of each size sold and write an equation.
   (b) If the total cash received from the sale of popcorn that evening was \$165, write a second equation.
   (c) Use your equations from (a) and (b). Solve them to find the number of each size of popcorn sold.

3 On a ferry there is a charge for each car plus a charge for each person in the car.
   (a) The charge for one car with four persons is \$16. Write an equation to represent this statement.
   (b) For another car with five persons the charge is \$18. Use this statement to write a second equation.
   (c) Solve the equations from (a) and (b) to find the charge for a car and for each person.

**B** Remember: organize your solution. Refer to the *Steps for Solving Problems* to help you.

To solve each of the following problems
- ▶ choose variables and record what each represents.
- ▶ Write two equations using the information given in the problem.
- ▶ Use the method of substitution or the method of elimination to solve the equations. Be sure to check your work.
- ▶ Write a statement to answer the problem.

4 Tickets for a school play are \$3 for students and \$5 for adults. The 500 seats available were all sold and receipts totalled \$2074. How many of each type of ticket was sold?

5 At Snippers quick haircut salon, the haircutters are paid an hourly rate plus a bonus for each customer that they serve. Martin worked an 8 h shift and served 46 customers. His pay was \$109. Julia cut 30 customers' hair in her 6 h shift. Her pay was \$75. Find the hourly rate of pay and how much the bonus is per customer.

6 At the cafeteria three hamburgers and three colas cost \$6.90. Two hamburgers and one cola cost \$4.10. What is the cost of a hamburger? What is the price of a cola?

7 The sum of the measures of two angles of a triangle is 140°. The difference of the measures of the angles is 50°. Find the size of each angle.

8 In the winter, a florist prices her bouquets according to the number of roses and carnations used. A bouquet containing 8 roses and 5 carnations costs \$44. A bouquet with 6 roses and 6 carnations costs \$42. Find the cost of a single stem of each type of flower.

9 At a bowling alley, bowlers are charged an hourly rate for using the lane, plus a charge for each game played per person. Marina and Bob played for 2 h and completed 3 games. They were charged \$15. Daniel and three friends played for an hour and completed 2 games. They were also charged \$15. What is the hourly rate and what is the charge per person for each game?

10 A contractor knows that he can complete a job in a day. If he hires 3 carpenters plus 2 students he will have to pay out \$700 in wages. If he hires 2 carpenters plus 3 students, wages will cost him \$600. How much does he pay a carpenter per day? How much does he pay a student per day?

11 The deposit on pop bottles is 30¢ for large bottles and 15¢ for small bottles. Janice took 18 bottles back and received \$4.65. How many of each size of bottle did she return?

## C

12 Carmen invests an amount of money at 8% and another at 10%. If the total annual interest is \$496 and the total amount invested is \$5200, how much did Carmen invest at each rate?

## Career Tip

Each of the following on the list displays a number of "firsts", and illustrates a type of career. For each

- What type of career is involved? In what field is most of the work done?
- Find out about the requirements to pursue each career.

1 The first animated cartoon film occurred on August 12, 1906.
2 The first escalator was installed at Coney Island in the autumn of 1896.
3 The first newspaper advertisement appeared on October 14, 1612.
4 The first policewoman was appointed to the Los Angeles Police Department on September 12, 1910.
5 The first telephone was patented on March 9, 1876.
6 The first elastic band was patented on March 17, 1945.
7 The first jeans were made in 1850 by Levi Strauss.
8 The first photograph in colour was developed on May 17, 1861.
9 The first motor car was built in May, 1862.
10 The first disc jockey went on the air on July 7, 1927.
11 The first fire insurance was issued on December 3, 1591.
12 The first police force was established in March, 1667 in Paris.

## Review: Practice and Problems

1 A line is given by the equation $3x - 4y - 10 = 0$.
(a) Draw its graph.
(b) What is the slope of the line?
(c) Find which of the following points are on the line. A(−1,2) B(2,−1) C(0,−2.5)

2 The slopes of two line segments are given. Are the lines parallel (I), perpendicular (II), or neither (III)?
(a) $6, \frac{1}{6}$ (b) $-4, -\frac{1}{4}$ (c) $\frac{3}{4}, \frac{-4}{3}$ (d) $-1,1$

3 (a) Draw the graph of $3x - 2y - 10 = 0$.
(b) Find the slope of the line.
(c) Find the $x$ and $y$ intercepts.

4 (a) A tanker passes through the points P(6,5) and Q(−12,7). Find the equation of this path.
(b) Show that the path of a sailboat through P(−2,8) and S(−4,−10) is perpendicular to the tanker's path.

5 A line passes through the points A(−2,8) and B(3,−7)
(a) What is the slope of the line?
(b) Write the equation of the line through the two points. Use $y = mx + b$.
(c) What is the value of $m$?
(d) What is the value of $b$?

6 Solve each of the following pairs of equations.
(a) $x + 4y = -10$, $x - y = 8$
(b) $3x + 2y = -12$, $2x + 3y = 1$
(c) $x + y = 4$, $x - 2y = 10$
(d) $3x - 2y = 5$, $4x + 14y = 15$

7 A ship is sailing on a path given by the equation $4x - 3y - 6 = 0$. A weather balloon is flying on a path given by the equation $2x + 3y = 12$. Find the co-ordinates of the point at which the weather balloon flies over the ship.

8 The perimeter of a rectangular parking lot is 96 m. The length is 12 m more than the width. Find the dimensions of the parking lot.

## A Practice Test

1 For each line, the slope and a point on the line are given. Draw their graphs.
(a) slope $= \frac{3}{4}$, A(−4,3) (b) slope $= -2$, B(5,−1)

2 A barge is travelling along the path through the points A(2,−4) and B(3,0). A row boat is following a path through the points C(2,3) and D(−4,1). Will their paths cross?

3 Draw the graph of each line given by the data.
(a) $x$ intercept 4, slope $-\frac{1}{2}$.
(b) $y$ intercept $\frac{1}{2}$, slope $\frac{4}{5}$.

4 Indicate which of the following lines are parallel and which are perpendicular.
(a) $y = 3x - 1$
(b) $y = -3x + 7$
(c) $2x - y = 10$
(d) $x = 2y - 5$
(e) $3x - y = -13$
(f) $x + 2y - 23 = 0$
(g) $x - 3y = 0$
(h) $-2x + y = 11$

5 Express in general form the equation for each line.
Line A: passing through M(4,−7) with slope $-\frac{2}{3}$.
Line B: passing through N(−8,0) with slope $\frac{3}{8}$.

6 Solve the following by drawing a graph.
$3x - y = 1$ $x + 2y = 12$

7 A bicycle is travelling on the path given by $3x - y = 8$. A scooter is travelling on a path given by $y = 4x - 5$.
(a) What are the co-ordinates of the point at which the paths cross?
(b) Will the scooter hit the bicycle? Why or why not?

8 Solve each pair of equations.
(a) $2x - 5y = 11$, $3x + 4y = 5$
(b) $3m - 2n - 10 = 0$, $2m + 5n = 13$

# Update: A Cumulative Review

1 Simplify each of the following.
(a) $3a + 4 - 2(a - 5)$
(b) $-2(6 - m) - m + 12$
(c) $4(x - 7) + (3x + 4)^2$

2 Find the interest for the following.
(a) Principal of \$2550 for 4 years at $12\frac{1}{2}\%$.
(b) Loan of \$925 for 8 months at $14\frac{3}{4}\%$.

3 An elevator has dimensions 2.2 m by 3.1 m by 2.4 m.
(a) Find the volume of the elevator.
(b) The elevator shaft measures 2.5 m by 3.5 m by 42.3 m. Find the volume of the elevator shaft.
(c) What is the difference in the volumes in (a) and (b)?

4 A lot of land has the shape shown. Calculate the perimeter of the lot.

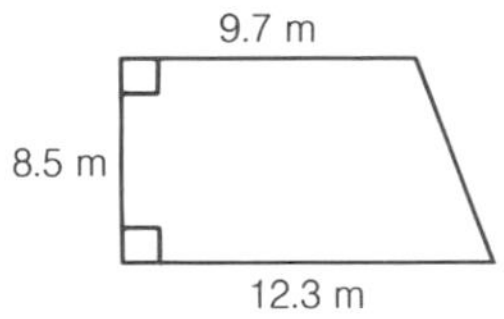


5 Nell can purchase the car of her dreams for a total of \$8640.69 (including all charges, sales tax). She makes a down payment of \$1200 and signs the contract for 36 equal monthly payments of \$264.80. Calculate the effective rate of interest. Express your answer to 1 decimal place.

6 Factor.
(a) $10ab - 24abc$ (b) $100 - p^2$
(c) $x^2 + 7x + 10$ (d) $14mn^2 - 2mn$
(e) $r^2 - 6r + 9$ (f) $18m^2 - 2$
(g) $m^2n^2 - 1$ (h) $3p^2q - 6p^2q^2$
(i) $5m^2 + 55m + 150$ (j) $16a^2 - 36b^2$
(k) $(p - 3q)^2 - 9r^2$

7 Which equation describes the path of a jet on a course with slope $\frac{4}{3}$ and passing through the point with co-ordinates $(-3,1)$?
A $3x - 4y = 5$ B $3y - 4x = 15$
C $4x + 3y = 9$

8 Simplify. Express your answer in scientific notation.
(a) $\dfrac{2.56 \times 10^{14}}{9.31 \times 10^{17}}$ (b) $\dfrac{4.09 \times 10^{-8}}{5.63 \times 10^{-5}}$
(c) $(1.33 \times 10^{8})^2 \div (5.903 \times 10^{11})$

9 Simplify.
(a) $\dfrac{p^2 + 5p}{p^2 - 36} \times \dfrac{p^2 - 6p}{p^2 - 25}$
(b) $\dfrac{x^3y + x^2y^2}{x^2y - xy^2} \div \dfrac{3x^3y - 3xy^3}{x^3 + 2x^2y + xy^2}$

10 Money invested at 11% doubles approximately every 7 years. How long would it take an investment of \$1000 to reach a million dollars? (Hint: Use a calculator).

11 The slope of a line is $-\frac{3}{4}$ and passes through the points $A(x,-4)$ and $B(-3,7)$. Find the value of $x$.

12 The value, $V$, of a tractor after $t$ years, where $P$ is the purchase price and $r$ is the annual rate of depreciation as a decimal is given by the formula,
$$V = P(1 - r)^t$$
The original cost of a tractor was \$42 000. If the tractor depreciates at an average rate of 20%/a, find the value of the tractor after 4 years.

14 Michael sells appliances for a large department store and earns 8.5% commission on all sales. Find the amount of commission received if the sales for the week were \$5 482.00.

15 (a) Use the data below to construct a broken-line graph.
(b) Create a problem based on the given information.
(c) Write a solution for the problem you created in (b).

Marathon Race

| Time (hours) | Distance run |
|---|---|
| 1 | 15 km |
| 2 | 28 km |
| 3 | 40 km |

# 13 Applications: Ratio, Rates and Variation

essential skills with ratio and rate, using scale diagrams, skills and graphs of direct variation, problem solving, calculator skills, using inverse variation, applications with partial variation, solving problems and applications

## Introduction

An important skill in learning content is to compare one topic with another and ask yourself
- How are the topics alike? How are the skills and strategies similar?
- How are the topics not alike? How do the skills and strategies differ?

By noticing similarities and differences you are in better shape to learn either.

For example
- In correcting a problem with two-cycle boat engines or a two-cycle lawnmower engine, the same principles are followed to correct the problem.
- To mass produce tents or garments involve the same principles of business.

In studying rate, ratio and variation,
- look for similarities
- look for differences

- To the people fighting a fire, the rate at which the fire creeps through the forest is of great importance, especially if a town is in the path of the fire. The rate at which an aircraft can "pick up water" off the top of a lake and drop it at the fire source may mean the difference between success and failure.

- At a hydro electric instalation, the rate at which power is consumed is watched carefully by the operator to avoid a power blackout. The study of the variation in power consumption at different time periods throughout a day, week, or year, is an important study.

# 13.1 Inventory: Skills with Ratio

We often make comparisons in different situations.

- ▶ we compare prices
- ▶ we compare performances
- ▶ we compare fuel efficiency
- ▶ we compare people

When we compare, we often compare numbers. A comparison of one number with another is a ratio.

The fuel efficiency of cars is expressed as the number of litres of gas used in driving 100 km. The size of the engine and the mass of the car affect the efficiency.

A trial jury consists of twelve people chosen at random from the voters list. A two-term ratio can be used to compare the number of men chosen with the number of women.

7:5

7 is the first term of the ratio — compared to — 5 is the second term of the ratio

Skills with ratios occur in many different subject areas.

The following examples review skills for working with ratios.

**Example 1**

The length of wire solder on a roll is 6 m. The solder is 3 mm in diameter.

(a) Write a ratio to compare the length to the diameter.

(b) Express the ratio in lowest terms.

**Solution**

(a) Length is 6 m.
Diameter is 3 mm.

Think: To write a ratio, the quantities to be compared must be expressed in the same units. 1 m = 1000 mm

6 m = 6 × 1000 mm
= 6000 mm

The ratio of the length to the diameter is 6000:3.

(b) 6000:3 = 2000:1

Divide both terms by 3.

The ratio is in *lowest terms*. The only common factor of both terms is 1.

Three term ratios can be used to compare quantities, as shown in the next example.

### Example 2

The ratio of fiction to non-fiction to reference books in a public library is 24:10:9.←This is a three-term ratio.

(a) Write a ratio to compare the number of fiction books to the number of reference books.
(b) Write two other pairs of equivalent ratios for the ratio in (a).

### Solution

(a) fiction:non-fiction:reference = 24:10:9
fiction:reference = 24:9

(b) 24:9 = 8:3 also 24:9 = 48:18

Divide both terms by 3. Multiply both terms by 2.

The ratios 24:9, 8:3 and 48:18 are pairs of equivalent ratios.

When you write a statement that two ratios are equal, such as 24:9 = 8:3 you are writing a proportion. You can use your equation solving skills to find the missing term in a proportion, and thus solve a problem.

### Example 3

At a radio station the ratio of Canadian records played to other nationalities played is 2:9. If 34 Canadian records were played one day, how many records of other nationalities were played that day?

### Solution

Let $n$ represent the number of records of other nationalities that were played.

$2:9 = 34:n$ ← Think: First step, write the proportion.

$\frac{2}{9} = \frac{34}{n}$ ← Think: Second step, write the ratio in fractional form. Then solve the equation for $n$.

Multiply both sides by $9n$:

$9n\left(\frac{2}{9}\right) = 9n\left(\frac{34}{n}\right)$ ← Think: $\overset{1}{\cancel{9}}n\left(\frac{2}{\underset{1}{\cancel{9}}}\right) = 9\overset{1}{\cancel{n}}\left(\frac{34}{\underset{1}{\cancel{n}}}\right)$

$2n = 306$ ← Think: $\frac{2n}{2} = \frac{306}{2}$

$n = 153$

The number of records of other nationalities played was 153.

## Try These

1 Use this guitar chord progression.
G B A B D A B G G B
Write a ratio to compare the number of
(a) G chords to A chords
(b) A chords to D chords
(c) A chords to B chords to G chords.

2 Express each ratio in lowest terms.
(a) 6:2 (b) 9:12 (c) 10:15:20

3 Which ratio is not equivalent to the others?
(a) 3:5, 9:15, 6:12
(b) 6:2, 8:3, 9:3, 24:8

## Written Exercises

**A** Express ratios in lowest terms.

1 Write a ratio in lowest terms to compare the diameters of the ball used in each sport:
(a) soccer compared to golf
(b) baseball compared to squash
(c) golf compared to baseball compared to soccer

| Sport | Diameter of ball |
|---|---|
| baseball | 72 mm |
| golf | 42 mm |
| soccer | 222 mm |
| squash | 63 mm |

2 Find the missing term.
(a) 3:2 = ■:4 (b) 15:5 = 3:■
(c) 1:6 = 5:■ (d) 2:5:■ = 6:15:24

3 Write two equivalent ratios for each ratio.
(a) 1:2 (b) 6:4 (c) 2:3:5

4 Write each comparison as a ratio in lowest terms.
(a) 5 min to 60 min (b) 8 cm to 120 cm
(c) 200 g to 45 g (d) 18 L to 10 L
(e) 27¢ to $1.50 (f) 150 m to 2 km
(g) 15 min to 2 h (h) 3.6 cm to 8 mm

5 The diagrams show the dimensions of a standard flat-top acoustic guitar.

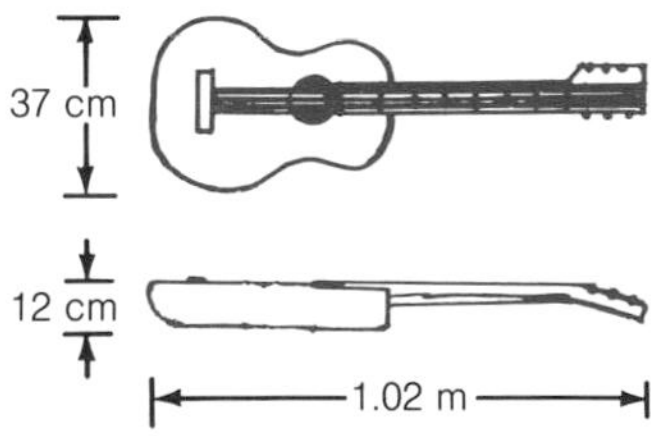


Write a ratio in lowest terms to compare
(a) the width to the depth
(b) the width to the length
(c) the width to the depth to the length.

**B** Review your skills with solving equations: these skills are used to find missing terms in ratios, as well as to solve problems.

6 Find the missing term in each proportion.
(a) $5:8 = n:20$ (b) $3:k = 5:12$
(c) $x:10 = 3:4$ (d) $240:100 = 18:a$
(e) $15:t = 8:3$ (f) $80:35 = m:56$

7 The ratio of oil to gasoline for an outboard engine is 1:40. What volume of oil should be mixed with 1.5 L gasoline?

8 In a bathroom, the ratio of plain tiles to patterned tiles is 25:3. Charlene counted 24 patterned tiles in the bathroom.
(a) How many plain tiles are there?
(b) How many tiles are there altogether?

9 The ratio of reserved seats to general admission tickets sold for a concert is 5:2. If 4750 reserved seat tickets were sold, how many general admission tickets were sold?

10 The ratio of the length to the width of a photograph is 8:5. If the photo is enlarged so that its length is 25 cm, what will the width of the enlargement be?

11 The win-loss-tie ratio for a hockey team is 5:4:1. So far this season they have won 30 games.
(a) How many games have they lost?
(b) How many games have they played so far this season?

12 For a pastry recipe, the ratio of flour to shortening to water is 15:2:1.
(a) If 300 g of flour are used, what mass of shortening is needed? What mass of water?
(b) If you have 50 g of shortening, what mass of flour should you combine it with? How much water should you use?

## Applications: Partnerships and Proportions

Often people participate as partners in buying a store, starting a business venture, or sharing the cost of a lottery ticket. Each person that invests money receives a return payment in proportion to the amount invested by them. For example,

Steve, Maria and Ben used their savings to open a Video-rental store. The amounts invested were in the ratio 8:7:5. If their profits at the end of the first year were $3000, how much should each person receive?

They invested in the ratio 8:7:5
Let $\$8n$, $\$7n$, and $\$5n$ represent each person's share of the profit.

$$8n + 7n + 5n = 3000$$
$$20n = 3000$$
$$n = 150$$

| Steve's share | Maria's share | Ben's share |
|---|---|---|
| $\$8n = \$8(150)$ | $\$7n = \$7(150)$ | $\$5n = \$5(150)$ |
| $= \$1200$ | $= \$1050$ | $= \$750$ |

Steve should receive $1200, Maria $1050 and Ben $750.

---

13 Laura and Mike agree to share the costs of running their car in proportion to the time they each use it. The ratio of Laura's time of use to Mike's time of use is 5:4. If their costs were $216, how much should each person pay?

14 Mohamed, Inga and Tien invested in the ratio 2:7:3 to buy lottery tickets. If they won $3000 how much should each person receive?

15 In an insurance office, the management decided to share the overhead costs in proportion to the number of employees in each department. The property department has 20 employees, the vehicle department 25 and the life insurance department 15 employees. If the overhead costs for December were $4200, how much should each department pay?

16 Sarah and Carla are renting an apartment. They agree to share the rent in proportion to the ratio of the area of their bed-rooms. Sarah's room measures 3.8 m by 3.5 m. Carla's room is 5.2 m long and 2.5 m wide. If the rent is $500, how much does each person pay?

17 Four students started a summer contracting business. They agreed to share the earnings in proportion to the amount of time they each worked. After expenses, they made $1500 to finish a basement. Hannah worked 20 h, Armand 42 h, Sue 35 h and Larry 28 h. How much money should each person receive?

18 When Arviv and Regine were married their families agreed to share the cost of the reception in proportion to the number to guests that each family invited. The total cost of the reception was $2176.20. Arviv's family invited 82 guests and Regine's family invited 74 guests. How much should each family pay?

# 13.2 Applications with Scale Diagrams

A scale diagram is a very useful way of showing an accurate picture of a large or small object.

You can use the scale factor to calculate dimensions of the actual object. For example, to find the length of the car shown, first measure the length on the diagram. Then use the scale factor to write a proportion.

$$1:75 = 6:l$$

6 ← length on scale diagram; $l$ ← actual length

$$1:75 = 6 \times 1:6 \times 75$$
$$= 6:450$$

Now solve (compare the terms)

$$1:75 = 6:l$$
$$l = 450$$

The length of the actual car would be 450 cm.

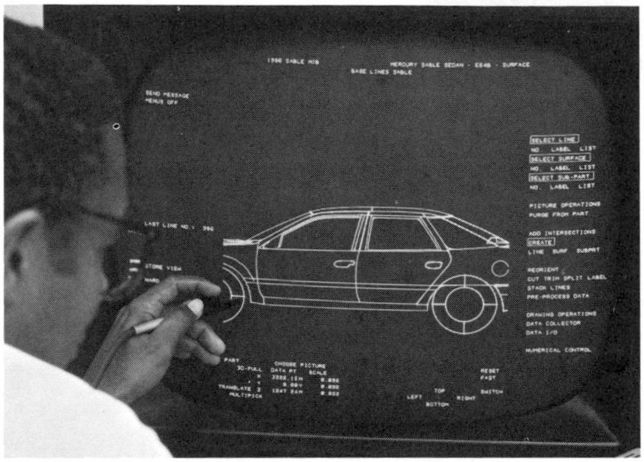

Computers are used to help design new cars.
Scale Factor 1:75

**Example**

The scale drawing is of a "no-see-um", a small biting midge.
Find the actual length of the midge from the head to the tip of the abdomen.

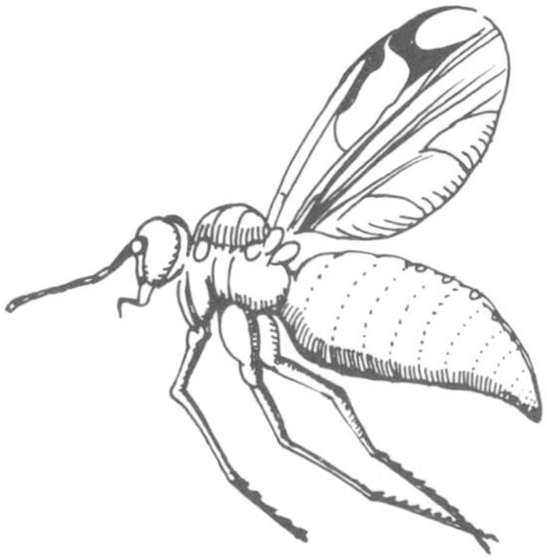

Scale factor 20:1

**Solution**

The scale can be expressed as
20 mm represents 1 mm.

20 mm ← measure on the diagram; 1 mm ← actual measure of the midge

Let $n$ represent the actual length of the midge.
The length on the diagram is 38 mm.

equation is expressed in ratio form:

$$20:1 = 38:n \text{ or } \frac{20}{1} = \frac{38}{n}$$ ← equation is expressed in fractional form

$$20n = 38$$
$$n = \frac{38}{20}$$
$$= 1.9$$

The midge is 1.9 mm long.

## Try These

1 The scale on a diagram of a vehicle is 1:20. What actual length do the following diagram lengths represent?
(a) 1 cm (b) 10 cm (c) 0.5 cm

2 The scale on a diagram of a flea is 50:1. What is the actual length for each length on the diagram?
(a) 50 mm (b) 20 mm (c) 1 cm

3 The scale to be used on a floor plan of a shopping mall is 1:250. How many centimetres should be used to represent each of the following actual lengths?
(a) 250 cm (b) 5 m (c) 10 m

## Written Exercises

**A** **Where necessary, express your answers to one decimal place.**

1 The scale of a model train is 1:50. Find the actual length of each measure on the model.
(a) 3 cm (b) 10 cm (c) 0.8 cm

2. For the same model train set, what length on the model would represent the following actual measures?
(a) 25 m (b) 100 cm (c) 70 cm

3 When an artist is designing a piece of jewelry she draws her ideas on paper using a scale of 10:1. Find the actual length of the following measures on the design.
(a) 20 cm (b) 5 mm (c) 2.5 cm

4 For a second design, the artist uses the same scale as given in the previous question. What length on the design would represent the following actual measures?
(a) 5 mm (b) 1.5 mm (c) 0.8 cm

5 The scale used on a map is 1:20 000.
(a) How many centimetres on the earth's surface does each centimetre on the map represent?
(b) How many metres does each centimetre represent?
(c) How many centimetres on the map would represent an actual distance of 1 km?

6 Express the scale for each of the following as a ratio in lowest terms

| | Actual measure | Measure on diagram |
|---|---|---|
| (a) | 250 cm | 5 cm |
| (b) | 0.1 mm | 20 mm |
| (c) | 15 m | 0.2 m |
| (d) | 2 m | 10 cm |
| (e) | 15 km | 5 cm |

7 A photograph shows a silicon chip magnified by a factor of 40.

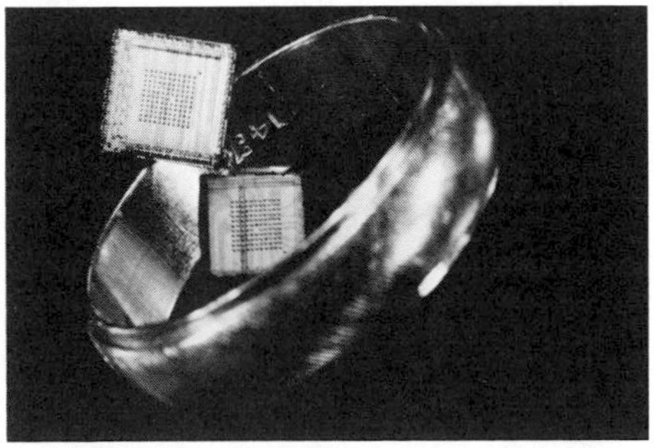

(a) Write the scale factor in ratio form.
(b) What length on the actual chip is shown by a length of 4 cm on the photo?
(c) What length on the photo would show a length of 0.5 mm on the actual chip?

8 A method used by artists to change the size of a design is to cover the design with a grid of a different size. Use measurements to find the scale factor in each of the following. Express the scale as a ratio in lowest terms.

(a)

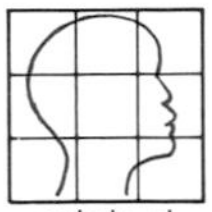

original

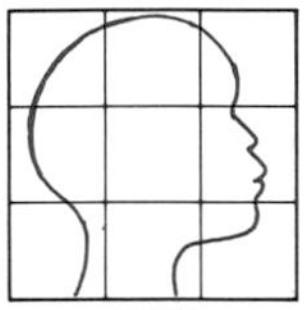

copy

(b)

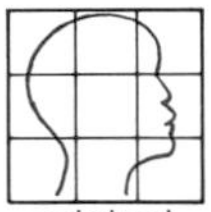

original

copy

**B** Express your answers to 1 decimal place. Use a calculator to check your work.

9 The diagram is of a machine part.

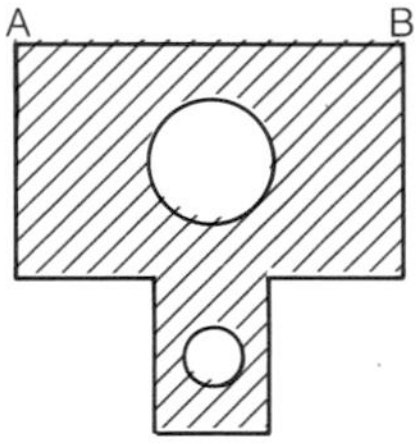


(a) If the length AB on the actual machine part is 25 cm, what is the scale factor of the diagram?
(b) What is the diameter of the larger hole on the actual machine?
(c) What is the actual shortest distance between the two holes?
(d) What is the circumference of the smaller hole on the actual machine part?

10 The diagram is of a mange mite, a small insect that attacks the skin of many animals.

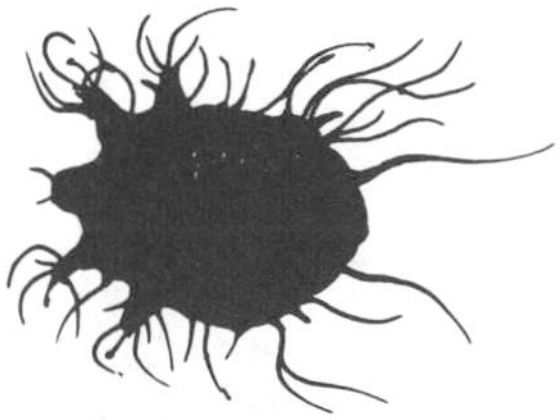

This is the bug that makes a dog "mangy".

(a) The actual mange mite is 0.3 mm long. What is the scale factor of the diagram?
(b) What is the actual width of the mange mite's body?

11 The diagram is of a sailboat in the flying Dutchman class.

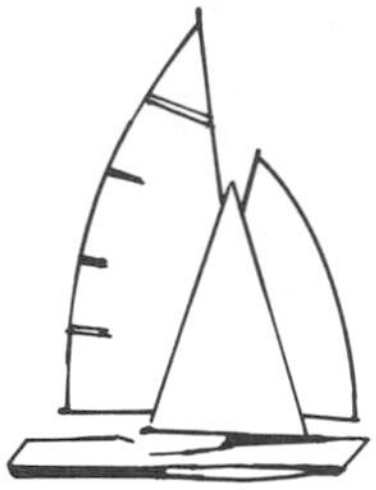

Scale factor 1:274

(a) What is the length of the actual sailboat?
(b) What is the height of the tallest sail?
(c) A person who has a height of 1.8 m is drawn standing on the deck. How tall would this person be in the diagram?

12 The diagram shows the lot plan for a new housing development.

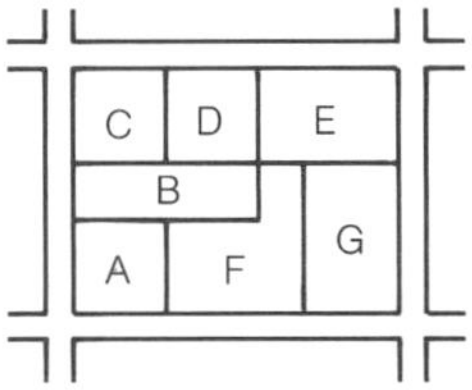


Scale factor 1:2000

(a) Find the area in square metres, of lot A.
(b) Which has the greater area, lot F or G? How much greater?
(c) If you were buying one of these lots, which would you prefer? Why?

13 Refer to the map.

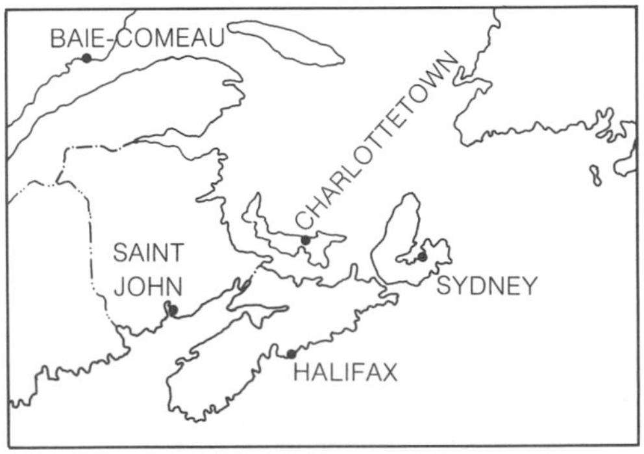


SCALE FACTOR 1: 16 650 000

(a) What is the air-line distance from Charlottetown, Prince Edward Island, to Halifax, Nova Scotia?
(b) If a seagull flies directly from Baie-Comeau, Québec, to Sydney on Cape Breton Island what distance does the bird travel?

## Applications: Consumer Planning

The blueprint shows the ground floor of a new house. You can use the plan to calculate measurements in the actual home and to plan its furnishings. Some of these calculations are not as straightforward as they might seem as you have to make special allowances for the way in which the item is sold. For example, when calculating the area of carpeting needed, you should add 0.1 m to the measured length and width to allow for fitting into doorways and for the fact that most rooms are not exactly rectangular. Most carpeting is cut from large rolls that are 3.66 m wide. You must decide what length you need from the roll to fit your room. Each metre of the length cut from the roll is referred to as a running metre. The following questions refer to the house plan shown.

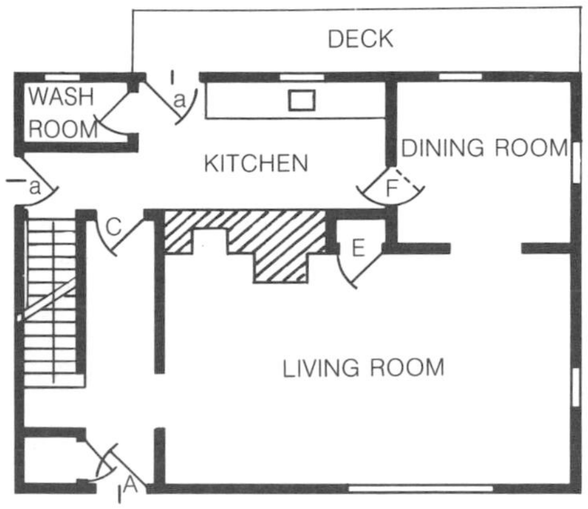


14 (a) If the actual living room is 6.3 m long, what scale is used on the blueprint?
(b) Find the area of the living room.
(c) Carpeting that costs \$69.95/running metre is on sale with 15% off. Underpadding costs \$8.95/m². Find the cost of having this carpet and underpadding laid wall-to-wall in the living room. Include sales tax at 7%.
(d) The carpet-layer charges a basic fee of \$50, plus \$18/h to install wall-to-wall carpeting. If it took $1\frac{1}{2}$ h to complete the job in this living room, how much does the bill for having the carpet laid amount to?
(e) What is the total cost of putting the carpeting in the living room?

15 Oak parquet flooring is sold in packages for \$19.99. Each package covers 0.93 m².
(a) Find the area of the dining room.
(b) Increase your answer from (a) by 10% to find the area of parquet that should be bought.
(c) How many packages will you need to buy?
(d) Find the cost of the parquet including 8% sales tax.

16 The deck is to be covered with indoor-outdoor carpeting.
(a) Use the scale to find the length and width allowing 0.1 m extra on each dimension.
(b) Indoor-outdoor carpeting comes in precut sizes. Which of the following should be bought to cover the deck? Explain your answer.

| | | |
|---|---|---|
| A | 6.70 m × 3.66 m | \$171.38 |
| B | 5.50 m × 3.66 m | \$140.56 |
| C | 4.00 m × 3.66 m | \$102.32 |

17 (a) The carpet-runner chosen for the stairs is 67 cm wide. What width of each stair will be left uncovered?
(b) Each stair has a 18 cm riser and a 27 cm tread. What length of carpet runner is needed for both sets of stairs? (There are 26 stairs in all.)

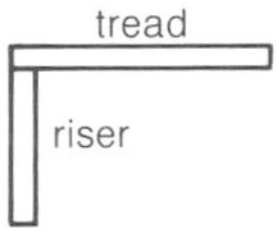


(c) The runner costs \$13.99/metre. What is the cost for both sets of stairs with 9% sales tax?
(d) What is the vertical distance between the basement floor and the ground floor?

# 13.3 Rates for Everyday

A rate is used to compare quantities that are measured in different units.

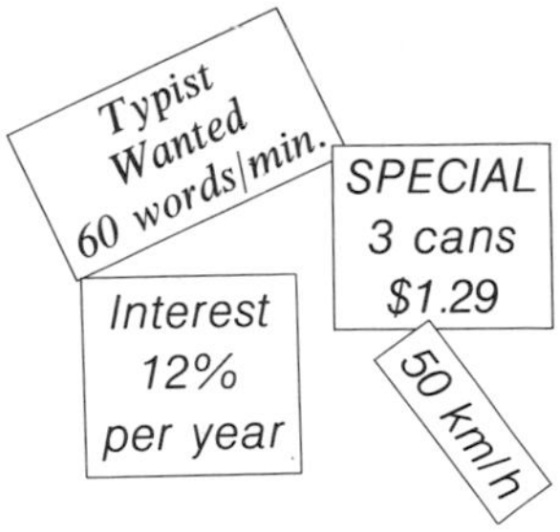


Rate is often used to compare a quantity to a unit of time.

| | |
|---|---|
| Denise earned $34.20 in 6 h. | In 6 h she earned $34.20 |
| | So in 1 h she earned $\frac{\$34.20}{6}$ or $5.70. |
| | Thus Denise's rate of pay is $5.70/h. |

To use rate in some problems you need to change the units of measure.

### Example

A snail takes 5 min to travel 4 m.

(a) Express the snail's pace in metres per minute.

(b) What is the snail's rate of travel in kilometres per hour?

When you compare movement to "a snail's pace", what speed are you really talking about?!

### Solution

(a) The snail's rate is 4 m in 5 min.

In 1 min the snail travels $\frac{4}{5}$ m or 0.8 m.

Thus, the snail's pace is 0.8 m/min.

(b) In 1 min the snail travels 0.8 m. In 1 h the snail travels 0.8 × 60 m

Then in 1 h the snail travels $\frac{0.8 \times 60 \text{ km}}{1000}$ ⟵ Divide by 1000 to convert metres to kilometres

or 0.048 km.

The snail's rate is 0.048 km/h.

## Try These

1 Express each rate as a rate per hour.
  (a) $24 for 4 h work
  (b) 1 bus every 10 min
  (c) 180 km travelled in 3 h
  (d) 80 words typed in 1 min

2 Ken has a part-time job that pays $8/h.
  (a) How much does he earn in 6 h?
  (b) How long does it take him to earn $100?

3 During a thunderstorm, 10 mm of rain fell in 5 min.
  (a) How much rain fell per minute?
  (b) If it continued to rain at the same rate, how many millimetres of rain would fall in 1 h?
  (c) How many centimetres would fall in 1 h?

## Written Exercises

**A**

1 Mark earned $50 in 8 h, while Arlene earned $39 in 6 h. Which person had the better rate of pay?

2 Oranges are $1.29 per dozen. At this rate, how much will 50 oranges cost?

3 At the fair, Kurt paid $4.25 for 8 ride tickets. How many ride tickets can Shelley buy with $12.75?

4 A bus travels 10 km in 25 min. At this rate, how far will the bus travel in one hour?

5 Petra cycled 30 km in 1.5 h. If she continues at the same rate, what distance will she travel in 7 h?

6 Each winter Montreal spends $33 000 000 to clear the snow from 1700 km of its streets.
(a) How much is spent per kilometre, to the nearest dollar?
(b) How many centimetres does each dollar clear?

7 Modern container ports such as Saint John can unload a 500-container ship in 24 h.
(a) At this rate how many containers are unloaded each hour?
(b) How many containers can be unloaded in a week?

**B** Remember: organize your written solution. Refer to the *Steps for Solving Problems.*

8 The surface of a rectangular swimming pool measures 4.0 m by 10.0 m. Water is hosed into the pool at the rate of 0.5 $m^3/h$. How long will it take to fill the pool to a depth of 1 m?

9 The directions on a can containing 270 mL of weed-killer for lawns say that 6 mL of the chemical are to be mixed with 1 L of water. This mixture is to be spread over 20 $m^2$ of grass.
(a) How many litres of water should the whole can of weed-killer be mixed with?
(b) What area will the mixture in (a) cover?

10 When Katherine was born she had a mass of 3.4 kg. During her first two months her mass increased at the rate of 4.5 kg each week.
(a) What was her mass when she was 8 weeks old?
(b) If she continued to grow at this rate, what would her mass be on her first birthday?

11 A record album is played at 33 rev/min. Side one of the record lasts 21 min.
(a) How many times does the record turn in each playing of side one?
(b) The diameter of the record is 30 cm. What is its circumference?
(c) How far does a point on the edge of the record travel in one playing of side one?
(d) What is the speed of the edge of the record, in kilometres per hour?

12 Joanne was checking her phone bill. She was charged $4.05 for a 3 min call to Halifax and $10.32 for a call to Trois-Rivieres that lasted 8 min. Which call was charged at the higher rate per minute?

13 The heaviest snowfall in one day in Canada occurred on Dec. 18, 1972 at Kitimat, British Columbia when 112 cm fell.
(a) How much snow fell per hour that day?
(b) If it snowed for the whole month of December at the same rate, how many metres of snow would have fallen that month?

14 The amount of water flowing over the Horseshoe Falls at Niagara is $5.4 \times 10^6$ L/s
(a) How much water flows over the Horseshoe Falls each hour? Express your answer in scientific notation.
(b) The volume of Lake Erie is about $1.0 \times 10^{15}$ L. How many hours does it take for this amount of water to pass over the Horseshoe Falls?
(c) Express your answer from (b) in days.

How come Lake Erie isn't empty?

## Applications: Olympic Records

The rate of speed achieved by Olympic athletes is quite remarkable. For example, in winning the gold medal in the 1000-m speed-skating event, Gaetan's time was 1 min 15.8 seconds. He skated 1 km in 1.263 min.

$$15.8 \text{ seconds} = \frac{15.8}{60} \text{ min}$$
$$= 0.263 \text{ min}$$

At this rate, in 1 hour Gaetan would skate $\frac{60}{1.263} \times 1$ km, or 47.5 km.

Thus Gaetan Boucher won the 1000 m race by skating at 47.5 km/h.

Gaetan Boucher won 2 gold medals for Canada in the 1984 winter Olympics in Sarajevo, Yugoslavia.

---

15 Gaetan, of Charlesbourg, Québec, won his second gold medal for the 1500-m speed-skate. His time was 1 min 58.36 seconds.
- (a) Express this rate of skating in kilometres per hour.
- (b) How much slower is this than his rate in the 1000 m race described above?

16 At the 1968 Olympics in Mexico City, Maureen Caird of Australia won the 80-m hurdles in a time of 10.3 seconds. At what rate was Maureen travelling in kilometres per hour?

17 Canada was very successful in the swimming events of the 1984 Olympic Games. Victor Davis took the gold medal in the 200-m breaststroke race with a time of 2 min 13.34 seconds. Express Victor's rate of swimming in kilometres per hour.

18 Canada won a gold medal in the women's 200-m breaststroke. Anne Ottenbrite was first with a time of 2 min 30.38 seconds.
- (a) What was Anne's rate in kilometres per hour?
- (b) At that rate, how long would it take Anne to swim across Lake Ontario from Toronto to the mouth of the Niagara River, a distance of 48 km?

19 Swimmer Alex Baumann earned two gold medals. He won the 200-m individual medley in 2 min 10.42 seconds and the 400-m event in 4 min 17.41 seconds.
- (a) Express his rate of swimming in each race in metres per second.
- (b) How far did he swim in one minute in each race?

20 In the 1984 Winter Olympics, Thomas Wassberg of Sweden won the 50 km cross-country skiing event with a time of 2 h 16 min. What was his average rate in kilometres per hour?

21 In 1984, Ernesto Canto of Mexico set the record for the 20-km walk with a time of 1 h 23 min 13.2 s.
- (a) How many kilometres per hour was he "walking"?
- (b) How many minutes did it take him to walk 1 km?

# 13.4 Direct Variation

Mark pays \$30 for 3 h of driving lessons. For 5 h of lessons he pays \$50. The table shows the cost for different hours.

| Number of hours | 1 | 2 | 3 | 4 | 5 | 6 |
|---|---|---|---|---|---|---|
| Cost in dollars | 10 | 20 | 30 | 40 | 50 | 60 |

The cost of insurance is reduced considerably when a student has successfully completed a driver education program. If the ownership of a car is in the name of a young driver, the insurance costs increase significantly. Check it out!

The cost of lessons is directly related to the number of hours. You can also say that the cost of driving lessons **varies directly** with the amount of time. From the chart, these calculations are made.

$$\frac{10}{1} = 10 \quad \frac{20}{2} = 10 \quad \frac{30}{3} = 10 \quad \frac{40}{4} = 10 \text{ and so on.}$$

(cost → 10, hours → 1)

Thus $\dfrac{\text{cost}}{\text{hours}} = \text{constant.}$

The cost, $C$, is related to the time, $t$, by the equation:

$\dfrac{C}{t} = k$ where $k$ is the constant of variation. (In this case it is the hourly rate of the lessons.)

or

$C = kt$

If you know one pair of values of $C$ and $t$ that are in direct variation, then you can find other values as shown in the following example.

## Example

The time between seeing a flash of lightning and hearing the thunder varies directly with the distance away that the storm is. When the storm is 4 km away, the time between the lightning and the thunder is 12 seconds.

(a) How far away is the storm when the time between the lightning and the thunder is 15 seconds?

(b) If a storm is 10 km away, how many seconds will there be between observing the lightning and hearing the thunder?

## Solution

Let $d$ represent the distance in kilometres and $t$ represent the time in seconds.

$\dfrac{t}{d} = k$, where $k$ is constant

$\dfrac{12}{4} = k$ or $k = 3$

Thus $\dfrac{t}{d} = 3$

Think:
*Step 1* Write the variation statement.
*Step 2* Find the constant of variation.

See solution on next page.

(a) $\frac{t}{d} = 3$ ⟵ Think: use $t = 15$. Find $d$.

$\frac{15}{d} = 3$ or $3d = 15$

$d = 5$

When the time taken is 15 seconds, the storm is 5 km away.

(b) $\frac{t}{d} = 3$ ⟵ Think: use $d = 10$. Find $t$.

$\frac{t}{10} = 3$

$t = 30$

When the storm is 10 km away, the time between the thunder and the lightning is 30 seconds.

In the previous example, time elapsed, $t$, varied directly with distance, $d$, expressed by

$$\frac{t}{d} = k \quad \text{or} \quad t = kd$$

Sometimes the variation symbol, $\propto$, is used to write the statement of direct variation. For instance, the variation statement can be shown as

$t \propto d$ ⟵ means $t$ varies directly with $d$

If $t_1$, $d_1$ and $t_2$, $d_2$ are two pairs of values that satisfy this direct variation statement then you can write

$$\frac{t_1}{d_1} = k \quad \text{and} \quad \frac{t_2}{d_2} = k$$

Thus $\frac{t_1}{d_1} = \frac{t_2}{d_2}$ where $t_1$, $t_2$ are lengths of time and $d_1$, $d_2$ are the corresponding distances.

## Try These

1 The amount that Nathan earns varies directly with the number of hours that he works. He earns $24 for 4 h work.
  (a) How much does Nathan earn in 1 h?
  (b) How much does he earn in 6 h?
  (c) How many hours does he work to earn $54?
  (d) What is the constant of variation, $k$?

2 At a constant speed, the distance travelled is directly proportional to the time.
  (a) What are the missing values in the following chart for a train travelling at constant speed?

| distance | 160 km | 1600 km | ? |
|---|---|---|---|
| time | 2 h | ? | 5 h |

  (b) What is the value of the constant of variation?

## Written Exercises

**A** Review the meaning of direct variation. Remember you often express the same statement in different ways as shown in exercises 1 and 2.

1 $m$ varies directly as $p$.
(a) Write an equation to express the direct variation.
(b) If $m = 24$ when $p = 4$, find the constant of variation.

2 $t$ is directly proportional to $m$.
(a) Write an equation to express the direct variation.
(b) If $t = 144$ when $m = 8$, find the constant of variation.

3 $t$ varies directly with $v$.
(a) Write an equation to express the direct variation.
(b) If $t = 25$ when $v = 2.5$, find the constant of variation.
(c) Use your answer in (b). If $t = 19$, find the value of $v$.

4 $p$ is directly proportional to $q$.
(a) Write an equation to express the direct variation.
(b) If $p = 255$ when $q = 15$, find the constant of variation.
(c) Use your answer in (b). If $q = 12$, then find the value of $p$.

5 For each of the following find the missing value.
(a) $y \propto x$ When $y = 225$, $x = 25$. When $x = 5$, $y = ?$
(b) $p$ varies directly as $q$. When $p = 80$, $q = 160$. When $p = 15$, $q = ?$
(c) $k$ is directly proportional to $d$. When $k = 0.8$, $d = 2$. When $k = 0.5$, $d = ?$
(d) $m \propto n$. When $m = 4500$, $n = 25$. When $m = 3060$, $n = ?$

6 A direct variation $y \propto x$ may be shown by the proportion $\frac{y_1}{x_1} = \frac{y_2}{x_2}$.
Find the missing value for each direct variation.
(a) $x_1 = 6$, $y_1 = 14$, $x_2 = 30$, $y_2 = ?$
(b) $x_1 = 8$, $y_1 = 32$, $x_2 = ?$, $y_2 = 56$
(c) $x_1 = ?$, $y_1 = 12$, $x_2 = 36$, $y_2 = 144$

7 The number of words that Don types varies directly with the amount of time spent typing. He types 220 words in 4 minutes.
(a) Use $w$ to represent the number of words and $t$ to represent the corresponding time. Write a proportion that relates $w$, $t$, and the given information.
(b) Use the proportion in (a) to find the number of words Don types in 5 minutes.
(c) How long does it take him to type a 1430-word essay?

**B** Remember: to solve problems about direct variation you need to find the constant of variation.

8 The amount of garbage collected each day from a picnic area varies directly as the number of people in the picnic area. If there are 450 people in a picnic area the garbage collected is 134 kg. How many kilograms of garbage would you collect if there are (a) 125 people? (b) 280 people? (c) 620 people?

9 The amount of water formed when snow melts varies directly with the depth of snow. A depth of 125 cm of snow melts to give 14 cm of water.
(a) What depth of water would 75 cm of snow melt to?
(b) An early snowfall soon melted to give 2.1 cm of water. What depth of snow had fallen?

10 At the same time in the same location, the length of the shadow of an object varies directly with the height of the object. Marlene is 1.5 m tall and she casts a shadow that is 1.1 m long. At the same time, the shadow of the apartment building is 16.5 m long. How high is the apartment building?

11 The electrical resistance in a wire is directly proportional to the length. A 15 cm length of copper wire has a resistance of 4.5 Ω.
   (a) What is the resistance of 2 cm of this wire?
   (b) What length of wire would need to be used to achieve a resistance of 12 Ω?

12 Hassan discovered that the exposure time needed for making an enlargement from a negative varies directly as the area of the enlargement. An enlargement measuring 6 cm by 8.5 cm requires 12 seconds of exposure time.

Have you ever wondered how prints are made larger from photographic negatives? A technician uses the equipment to flash another picture on larger photographic paper to obtain the enlargement. Many mathematical skills are used to obtain precise enlargements.

   (a) If an enlargement requires 20 seconds of exposure time, what is its area?
   (b) What length of exposure should be used for an enlargement measuring 20 cm by 25.4 cm.

13 The volume of carbon monoxide put out by a car's engine while it is idling varies directly with time. The engine puts out $6.1 \times 10^4$ cm³ of carbon monoxide while it is left idling for 2 min.
   (a) What volume of carbon monoxide does the engine put out if it is left idling for 5 min?
   (b) To the nearest minute, how long would the engine have to idle to put out 1 m³ of carbon monoxide?

14 Deep sea diving without any breathing apparatus is extremely dangerous because of the pressure that forces the air out of the lungs. The pressure, in kilopascals (kPa), varies directly with depth. At 3 m below sea level the pressure is 130 kPa. The record for a breath-held dive is 86 m by Jacques Mayol of France. What was the pressure to the nearest kilopascal, on Jacques at the lowest point of his dive?

## Computer Tip

A computer program can be very useful to do repetitive calculations. For example, this equation needs to be solved in doing problems with direct variation: $\frac{x_1}{y_1} = \frac{x_2}{y_2}$.

1 Use the computer program

```
10 INPUT X2, Y1, Y2
20 IF Y2 = 0 THEN 60
30 LET X1 = X2 * Y1/Y2
40 PRINT "THE SOLUTION IS"; X1
50 GO TO 10
60 END
```

Choose different values of $x_2$, $y_1$ and $y_2$ to solve for $x_1$.

2 Refer to the question 5 and 6 in the previous exercise. Use inputs from these questions in the computer program. (You may need to modify the computer program.)

3 Write a program to solve for $X_1$ in each of the following.

(a) $\frac{X_1}{Y_1^2} = \frac{X_2}{Y_2^2}$ (b) $Y_1 \times X_1^2 = Y_2 \times X_2^2$

# 13.5 Using Graphs of Direct Variation

When filling a swimming pool, the depth of water varies directly with the length of time that the hose is running. At one pool, after 2 h the depth of water was 25 cm.

You can organize a table of values for the direct variation and then graph the relation.

| depth | 25 cm | 12.5 cm | 50 cm | 75 cm |
|---|---|---|---|---|
| time | 2 h | 1 h | 4 h | 6 h |

Use your skills with direct variation to calculate other pairs of values.

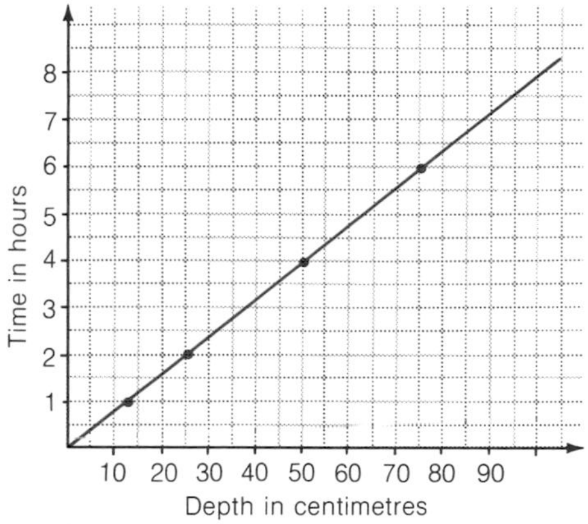


The graph of the direct variation is a linear one: the depth increases with time. You can use the graph to interpolate other values. For example, after about $3\frac{1}{4}$ h the depth is 40 cm.

After 5 h the depth is about 63 cm.

## Try These

Refer to the direct variation above.

1 Use your skills with direct variation to calculate
(a) the time when the depth is 100 cm
(b) the time when the depth is 125 cm
(c) the depth when the time is 3 h
(d) the depth when the time is 0.5 h

2 Use the graph of the direct variation to estimate
(a) the time when the depth is 20 cm
(b) the time when the depth is 70 cm
(c) the depth when the time is 7 h
(d) the depth when the time is 4.5 h

## Written Exercises

**A** Review your skills for working with graphs.

Questions 1 and 2 refer to the graph showing how the depth of water in a pool varies directly with time.

1 (a) Use the graph to interpolate the depth when the time is 2.5 h.
(b) Use your skills with direct variation to calculate the depth when the time is 2.5 h.
(c) Compare your answers in (a) and (b). How close was your estimate in (a)?

2 (a) Use the graph to extrapolate the time when the depth is 110 cm.
(b) Use your skills with direct variation to calculate the time when the depth is 110 cm.
(c) Compare your answers in (a) and (b). How close was your estimate in (a)?

Questions 3 and 4 refer to the following graph.

The graph shows how the cost of speaker-wire varies directly with the length bought.

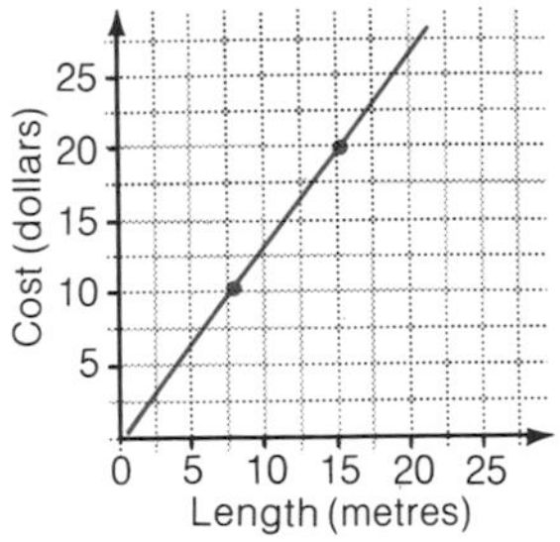


3 (a) What is the cost of 15 m of the speaker-wire?

(b) Use your answer in (a) to find the constant of variation.

4 (a) Use the graph to estimate what length of wire can be bought for $15.

(b) Use your skills with direct variation to calculate the length that can be bought for $15.

**B** Remember: your skills with co-ordinate graphing are useful to solve problems about direct variation.

Questions 5 to 7 are based on the following information.
The number of hot dogs sold at a baseball game is directly proportional to the number of people at the ball park. When 500 hot dogs were sold the attendance was 4000.

5 (a) Calculate the number of hot dogs sold when the attendance is
▶ 2000 ▶ 8000

(b) Find the number of people at the game when the number of hot dogs sold is
▶ 100 ▶ 300

6 (a) Use the results in the previous question to construct a table of values.

(b) Graph the points from your table of values. Draw a line that shows the direct variation.

7 (a) Use your graph to find the number of hot dogs sold when 5500 people are at the game.

(b) If 1300 hot dogs are sold, how many people are at the game?

Questions 8 to 10 are based on the following information.
For average highway driving, a compact car uses 32 L of gas in 4 h. The amount of gas used varies directly with the time.

8 (a) Choose 3 more values for one of the variables and calculate the corresponding values of the other variable. Organize your results in a table of values.

(b) Graph the direct variation.

9 (a) Use your graph to estimate how much gas the car will use if it is driven for $9\frac{1}{2}$ hours.

(b) The gas tank on the car has a capacity of 45 L. About how long could the car be driven for on one tank-full of gas?

10 (a) Create a problem of your own based on the information.

(b) Solve your problem in (a).

---

Questions 11 and 12 are based on the following information.
The amount that "chest-expanders" stretch by is directly proportional to the force used to pull them. A force of 10 N stretches the expander 3 cm.

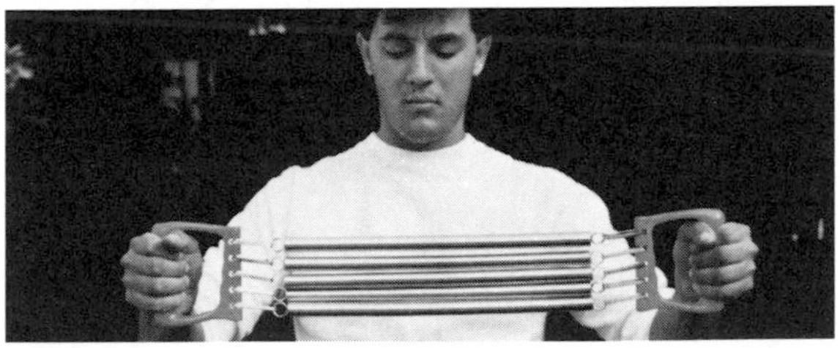

11 (a) Show this direct variation in a graph.

(b) Use your graph to estimate what distance the expander stretches when a force of 12 N is used.

12 (a) When Gary started training he could only stretch the expander 2 cm. What force was he using?

(b) After six months training, Gary could stretch the expander 10 cm. By what amount of force has his pull strength increased?

# 13.6 Inverse Variation

With 6 people helping, a basement is cleaned in 3 h. If only 2 people work, the job takes 9 h. The constant factor in this situation is that there are 18 h of work to be done. The number of people, $N$, is related to the time, $t$, that the job takes as follows.

$Nt = 18$ Think: $6 \times 3 = 18$
$2 \times 9 = 18$

In general, you write

$Nt = k$ where $k$ is the constant of variation

or $N = k\left(\frac{1}{t}\right)$

In this form, $N$ is said to vary inversely, or $N$ is inversely proportional to $t$. The variation statement is used to solve problems about inverse variation as shown in the following example.

**Example**

The temperature of the air varies inversely with the height above sea level. At 400 m above sea level the temperature is 12°C.

(a) What is the temperature at 1200 m above sea level?

(b) At what height is the temperature 10°C?

Part of being a park warden in a Canadian National Park is to look after the park's visitors that get injured or lost. The Banff park wardens in Banff National Park in Alberta are probably the best trained and equipped for mountain rescue in North America, performing about 80 rescues a year. The picture shows two wardens raising a victim by using a cable hauling system that was perfected in Europe.

**Solution**

Let $t$ represent the temperature, in degrees Celsius, and $h$ represent the height above sea level, in metres.

$th = k$, where $k$ is constant
$12 \times 400 = k$
$4800 = k$

Thus $th = 4800$.

Think: *Step 1.* Write the variation statement. *Step 2.* Find the constant of variation.

(a) $th = 4800$ ⟵ Think: Use $h = 1200$, find $t$.
$t(1200) = 4800$
$t = \frac{4800}{1200}$
$= 4$

The temperature at 1200 m is 4°C.

(b) $th = 4800$ ⟵ Think: Use $t = 10$, find $h$.
$10(h) = 4800$
$h = \frac{4800}{10}$
$= 480$

The temperature is 10°C at 480 m above sea level.

In the previous example, temperature $t$ varied inversely with height $h$, expressed by

$$th = k \quad \text{or} \quad t = k\left(\frac{1}{h}\right)$$

Using the variation symbol to show that $t$ and $h$ vary inversely, you would write $t \propto \frac{1}{h}$.

↑ means $t$ varies inversely with $h$

If $t_1$, $h_1$ and $t_2$, $h_2$ are two pairs of values that satisfy this inverse variation statement then you can write

$t_1h_1 = k$ and $t_2h_2 = k$

thus $t_1h_1 = t_2h_2$ where $t_1$ and $t_2$ are temperatures and $h_1$ and $h_2$ are the corresponding heights

## Try These

1 The value of a car varies inversely with its age. When the car is 2 years old it is worth $8000.
(a) What is the constant of variation?
(b) When the car is 4 years old what is it worth?
(c) How old is the car when its value is $2000?

2 To charter a bus for a trip, the cost for each person varies inversely with the number of people sharing the cost.
(a) What are the missing values in the chart?

| | | | |
|---|---|---|---|
| cost per person | $20 | ? | $15 |
| number of people | 30 | 20 | ? |

(b) What is the value of the constant of variation?

## Written Exercises

**A** Review the meaning of inverse variation. Remember that you can express the same statement for inverse variation in different ways as shown in exercises 1 and 2.

1 $m$ varies inversely as $n$.
(a) Write an equation to express the inverse variation.
(b) If $m = 11$ when $n = 20$, find the constant of variation.

2 $d$ is inversely proportional to $f$.
(a) Write an equation to express the inverse variation.
(b) If $d = 5$ when $f = 41$, find the constant of variation.

3 $x$ varies inversely as $y$.
(a) Write an equation to express the inverse variation.
(b) If $x = 4$ when $y = 25$, find the constant of variation.
(c) Use your answer in (b). If $x = 5$, find the value of $y$.

4 $p$ is inversely proportional to $v$.
(a) Write an equation to express the inverse variation.
(b) If $p = 30$ when $v = 40$, find the constant of variation.
(c) Use your answer in (b). If $v = 25$, find the value of $p$.

5 The inverse variation $p \propto \frac{1}{q}$ may be shown by the equation $p_1q_1 = p_2q_2$. Find the missing values in each of the following inverse variations.

(a) $p_1 = 4$, $q_1 = 60$, $p_2 = 12$, $q_2 = ?$
(b) $p_1 = 10$, $q_1 = 14$, $p_2 = ?$, $q_2 = 16$
(c) $p_1 = 80$, $q_1 = 60$, $p_2 = ?$, $q_2 = 32$
(d) $p_1 = 1.2$, $q_1 = 1.2$, $p_2 = 1.6$, $q_2 = ?$

6 For each variation, find the missing value.

(a) $y$ is inversely proportional to $x$. When $y = 1.5$, $x = 12$. Find $x$ when $y = 0.75$.
(b) $q$ varies inversely as $p$. When $q = 90$, $p = 10$. Find $q$ when $p = 45$.
(c) $m \propto \frac{1}{n}$. When $m = 4$, $n = 35$. Find $m$ when $n = 15$.

7 The time required to travel a fixed distance varies inversely with the speed. At 80 km/h it takes 5 h to travel from Ferguson's Cove to Ryan's Landing.

(a) Use $t$ to represent the time in hours and $s$ to represent the corresponding speed in kilometres per hour. Write an equation to relate $t$ and $s$.
(b) What is your speed if you can travel the same route in 4 h?
(c) If the bus takes 8 h for the same route, what is its average speed?

**B** Remember: to solve problems about inverse variation, you need to find the constant of variation.

8 The amount of time that it takes to earn enough to buy a bike varies inversely with the rate of pay. Bev is paid \$5/h and it takes her 30 h to earn the required amount. How long would it take to earn the required amount if your rate of pay is

(a) \$6/h? (b) \$10/h? (c) \$7.50/h?

9 The time required for harvesting the apple orchard varies inversely with the number of people employed. When 64 persons are employed the work takes 15 days.

(a) How many people should be hired if the harvest is to be completed in 10 days?
(b) If only 30 people are hired, how long will the harvest take?

10 With each skein of knitting wool, the length of a scarf that can be knitted varies inversely with the number of stitches across the width. With 80 stitches a length of 15 cm can be completed.

(a) If the width is increased to 100 stitches, what length can be knitted?
(b) If you want to knit a length of 25 cm, how many stitches should you have across?

11 The force needed to pry open a can of paint varies inversely with the length of screwdriver used. A force of 1.5 N (Newtons) is needed when an 18 cm long screwdriver is used.

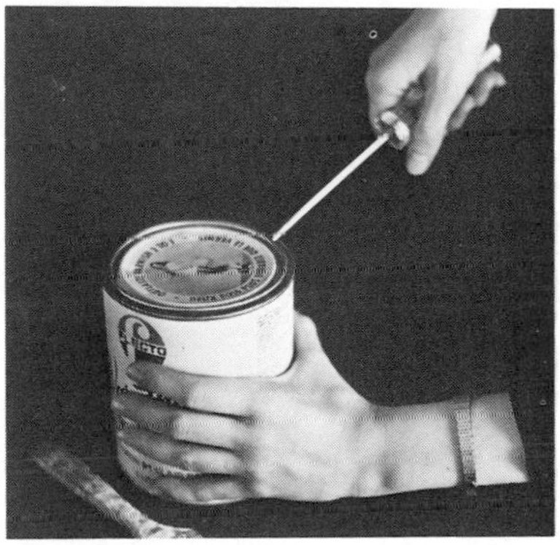

(a) What force is needed when only a 12 cm screwdriver is available?
(b) If a 24 cm long screwdriver is used, what force is required?

12 The amount of money that needs to be invested to yield a given annual income varies inversely with the rate of interest. When Maria inherited some money, she decided to invest part of it to yield enough interest to pay her annual fitness club membership. She can obtain the required amount if she invests \$5000 in an account paying 8%/a interest.

(a) If she can only invest \$4000, what rate of interest will she need?
(b) If the interest rate goes up to 15%, how much will she need to invest to raise the same amount of interest?

# 13.7 Graphs of Inverse Variation

A vendor of T-shirts at a concert has found that the number sold is inversely proportional to the price. When the price is $6, they sell 500 T-shirts. If they increase the price to $8, the sales drop to 375.

You can make a table of values for this inverse variation and then graph the relation.

| Number | 500 | 375 | 300 | 600 | 1000 |
|---|---|---|---|---|---|
| Price | $6 | $8 | $10 | $5 | $3 |

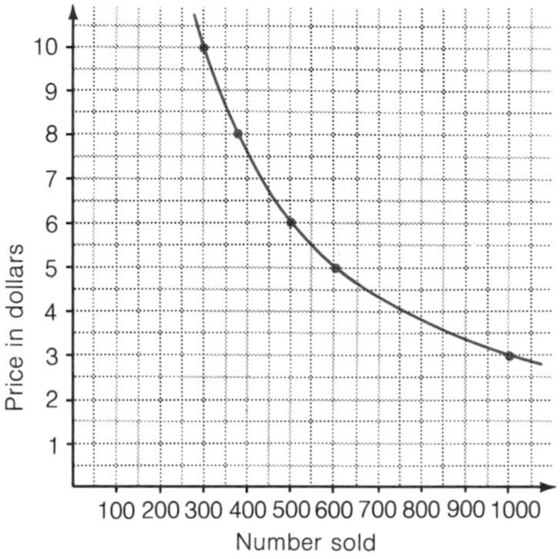


The graph of the inverse variation is non-linear.

Once you have drawn the graph you can use it to estimate other values.

If the price is $7, about 425 T-shirts are sold. To increase sales to 800, about $3.75 would have to be charged.

## Try These

Refer to the inverse variation above.

1 Use your skills with inverse variation to calculate
  (a) the price when 250 T-shirts are sold
  (b) the price when 1500 T-shirts are sold
  (c) the number of T-shirts sold when the price is $20
  (d) the number of T-shirts sold when the price is $2.50

2 Use the graph of the inverse variation to estimate
  (a) the price when 700 T-shirts are sold
  (b) the price when 400 T-shirts are sold
  (c) the number of T-shirts sold when the price is $4
  (d) the number of T-shirts sold when the price is $6.50.

## Written Exercises

**A** Review your skills for working with graphs.

Questions 1 and 2 refer to the graph showing how the number of T-shirts sold varies inversely with the price.

1 (a) Use the graph to interpolate the price when 450 T-shirts are sold.
  (b) Use your skills with inverse variation to calculate the price, to the nearest cent, when 450 are sold.
  (c) Compare your answers in (a) and (b). How close was your estimate?

2 (a) Use the graph to extrapolate the number of T-shirts sold when the price is $11.
(b) Use your skills with inverse variation to calculate the number sold when the price is $11.
(c) Compare your answers in (a) and (b). How close was your estimate in (a)?

Questions 3 and 4 refer to the following graph.

The graph shows how the time taken for a journey varies inversely with the speed.

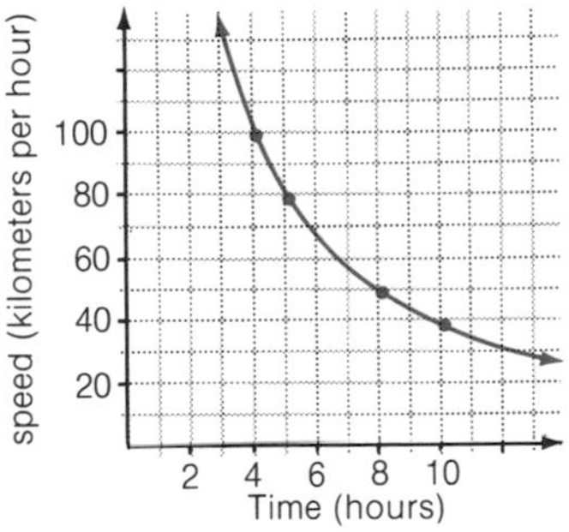


3 (a) How long does the journey take at a speed of 80 km/h?
(b) Use your answer in (a) to find the constant of variation.

4 (a) Use the graph to estimate how long the journey takes at a speed of 90 km/h.
(b) Use your skills with inverse variation to calculate how long the journey takes at 90 km/h.

**B** Questions 5 to 7 are based on the following information.
The gas efficiency of a car varies inversely with the mass of the car. A family-size car with a mass of 1500 kg obtains a gas efficiency of 6 km/L.

5 (a) What is the gas efficiency of
▶ a compact car with a mass of 720 kg?
▶ a mid-size car with a mass of 1000 kg?
(b) Find the mass of a car, if its gas efficiency is ▶ 8 km/L ▶ 5 km/L

6 (a) Organize your results from the previous question to construct a table of values. Graph the inverse variation.
(b) Use your graph to estimate the mass of a car that has a gas efficiency of 7 km/L.

7 (a) Helen's car has a mass of 1250 kg. Use your graph to estimate the gas efficiency of her car.
(b) If Helen uses her car to pull a trailer that has a mass of 300 kg, by how much will her gas efficiency decrease?

8 The value of a stereo set varies inversely with its age in months. Tony's stereo set is worth $2000 after 12 months.
(a) Construct a table of values for this inverse variation. Graph the relation.
(b) Use your graph to estimate the value of Tony's stereo after 14 months.
(c) After about how many months will the stereo set have depreciated to $1300?

Questions 9 to 11 are based on the following information.
The speed, in metres per second, of a runner in a race varies inversely with the amount of time, in seconds, taken. At a speed of 12 m/s a runner takes 22 seconds to complete the race.

9 Complete a table of values and graph the relation.

10 (a) Find the speed of a runner whose time is 24.5 seconds.
(b) How long would it take to complete the race at a speed of 9 m/s?

11 (a) Create a problem of your own based on the information.
(b) Solve your problem in (a).

12 The time required to make a Hungarian stew in a pressure cooker varies inversely with the pressure. The stew is ready in 60 min when the pressure is 125 kPa.
(a) Graph this inverse relation.
(b) If the pressure is decreased to 110 kPa, about how long will the stew take?
(c) If you only have 50 min in which to get the stew ready, what pressure will you need to use?

# 13.8 Applications with Partial Variation

When you record the expenses for running a car, there is a fixed cost and a cost that varies depending on how much you drive the car. The cost involves the fixed costs of the licence, insurance and so on, plus the variable costs which depend on the distance driven. You can express the variation as

$C = F + kd$ which $C$ is the cost, $F$ is the fixed costs, $d$ is the distance driven and $k$ the constant of variation.

The cost of running a car is an example of a partial variation. You can use the variation statement to solve problems about partial variation.

**Example**

Lesley knows that the weekly cost for her car's licence and insurance is \$9. Past experience has shown that the actual running costs are \$0.75/km.

(a) Write an equation to show the cost for a week, driving $d$ kilometres.

(b) Find the cost for a week in which she drove 120 km.

**Solution**

(a) $C = 9 + 0.75d$

↑ fixed cost — This part varies directly with the distance, $d$.

(b) Use $d = 120$

$C = 9 + 0.75(120)$
$= 9 + 90$
$= 99$

Lesley's cost for the week is \$99.00.

You can also show partial variation on a graph.

Use the relation $C = 9 + 0.75d$ to make a table of values.

Choose some other values for the distance, $d$, and work out their corresponding cost, $C$.

| distance | 120 | 0 | 100 | 10 | 50 |
|---|---|---|---|---|---|
| cost | \$99 | \$9 | \$84 | \$16.50 | \$46.50 |

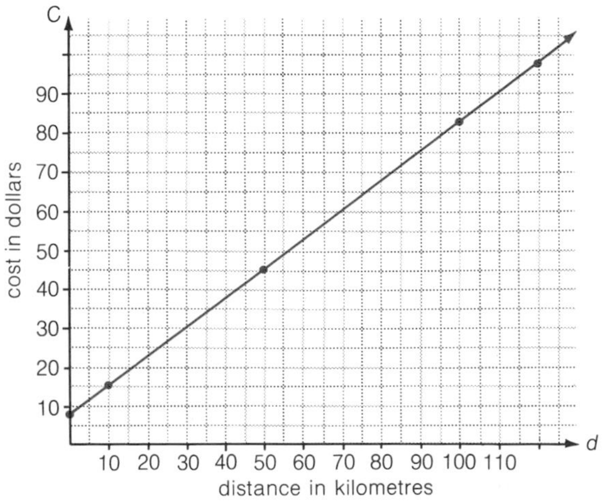


When you have plotted several points, you will notice that the graph of the partial variation is linear. You can join the points using a straight line. You can use the graph to find other values. For example, in a week in which her total costs were \$50, Lesley drove about 56 km.

## Try These

1 The cost $C$ of renting skis includes a fixed cost and a charge per hour. The rental cost is given by the equation

$C = 5 + 2t$ where $t$ is the time in hours.

(a) What is the fixed part of the cost?

(b) How much does it cost to rent the skis

▶ for 1 h? ▶ for 3 h? ▶ for 5 h?

2 The graph shows the relation between the mass and the cost for shipping a parcel by bus from Toronto to Halifax. The cost is given by $C = 12 + 0.25n$, where $n$ is the mass of the parcel.

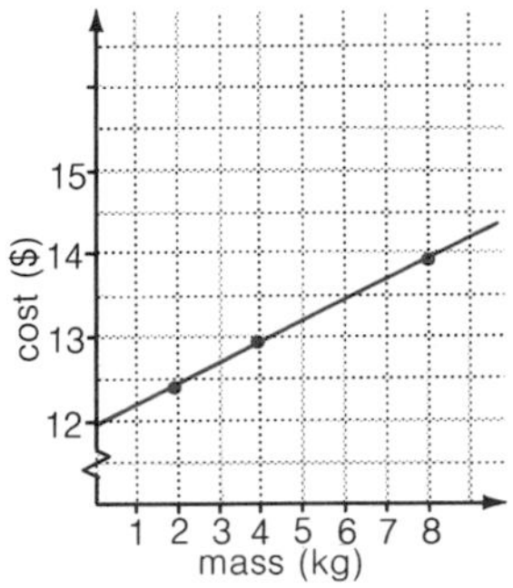


(a) What is the fixed charge? How is this value related to the graph?

(b) Use the graph to estimate the cost for a 7 kg parcel.

## Written Exercises

**A** Review the meaning of partial variation. Remember to include the fixed and the variable part.

1 A partial variation is given by $C = 20 + 3n$. Find $C$ for

(a) $n = 1$ (b) $n = 4$ (c) $n = 15$

2 The equation for a partial variation is

$R = 8.5 + 0.8s$.

Find $R$ for

(a) $s = 1$ (b) $s = 10$ (c) $s = 100$

3 The cost of manufacturing video games is given by

$C = 25 + 10n$ where $n$ represents the number of games.

Find the cost of making

(a) 1 game (b) 8 games (c) 500 games

4 For each of the following, write an equation for the partial variation.

(a) The cost, $C$, of renting a hall for a dance is \$300 plus \$25/h for the time, $t$, that it is used.

(b) The total cost, $T$, in dollars, of printing a magazine consists of a fixed cost of \$500 and a cost that varies directly with the number, $n$, of magazines printed.

(c) The fuel, $f$, in litres, in a car is partly constant, $C$, and partly varies directly, with the distance, $d$, travelled.

**B** To solve each problem, you need to write a statement for the partial variation. Use suitable choices for the variables.

5 A pizza store charges \$5.10 for a basic medium sized pizza plus 50¢ for each additional topping (mushrooms, pepperoni, green peppers, etc.)

(a) Use $C$ to represent the cost in dollars and $t$ to represent the number of toppings chosen. Write an equation to show this partial variation.

(b) Find the cost of a pizza with two toppings.

(c) Find the cost if you had 5 toppings.

(d) How many toppings did you order if the cost was \$8.10?

6 The length of time, $t$, in minutes, needed to roast a turkey is 30 minutes plus 45 minutes per kilogram.
(a) Use $m$ to represent the mass of the turkey in kilograms. Write an equation to represent this partial variation.
(b) Complete a table of values and graph the relation.
(c) Use your graph to estimate how long a 7.5 kg turkey should be roasted.

7 A carpet installer charges a minimum of \$30. To this basic charge she adds \$15/h for the labour.
Use $C$ to represent the charges in dollars, and $t$ to represent the time in hours.
(a) Write an equation to represent the relation between the charge and the time.
(b) How much would the carpet installer charge for a call which took 6 h?
(c) If the charge for installing some carpeting was \$75, how long did the job take?

8 The cost of a person-to-person phone call to Yellowknife is \$3.50 for the first 3 minutes plus 0.65 for each additional minute.
(a) Write an equation to show how the cost, $C$ in dollars, is related to the time, $t$ in minutes, of the phone call.
(b) What is the cost for an 8 minute phone call?
(c) If the charge for a call is \$11.30, for how long were the parties talking?

9 As a salesperson Sheilagh earns a basic salary of \$200 per week. She also earns 5% commission on the goods that she sells.
(a) Use $E$ to represent her total earnings in dollars and $S$ to represent her sales in dollars. Write an equation to show how $E$ and $S$ are related.
(b) Find Sheilagh's earnings in a week in which she sells \$800 worth of goods.
(c) In her best week so far, her total earnings were \$325. What value of goods did she sell that week?

10 The cost of renting a van for a day consists of a fixed cost of \$32 and a variable cost of 8 ¢/km.
(a) Write an equation that shows the cost of renting the van.
(b) Complete a table of values and graph the relation.
(c) Use your graph to find the cost of driving 710 km in one of these rented vans.

**C**

11 The cost of sending the school hockey team to Montreal is partly constant and partly varies with the number of students that attend. The cost for 20 students is \$6480 and the cost for 28 students is \$8860.
(a) Write the equation for the partial variation.
(b) Find the constant of variation.
(c) Find the cost for 24 students to attend.

## Calculator Tip

You have already learned a formula to calculate the area of a triangle. A calculator is an invaluable tool to do the computation, if you are just given the measures of the sides of the triangle. The formula for the area of a triangle given only the sides is the following.

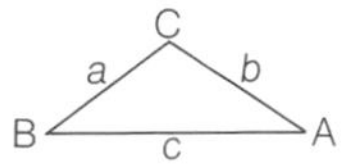


*Step 1* Calculate $s = \dfrac{a + b + c}{2}$

*Step 2* Calculate the area, $A$.
$A = \sqrt{s(s - a)(s - b)(s - c)}$

Use this formula to calculate the area of a triangular island with sides measuring 14.5 km, 18.8 km and 12.6 km.

## Consumer Tip

The rate at which a car uses gasoline is important to the consumer. Cars are rated for fuel economy by showing how many litres are used for 100 km. 5.4 L/100 km means 5.4 L are used to drive 100 km. If you want to check the fuel efficiency of a car, obtain a copy of the *Guide to Fuel Economy* published by *Transport Canada.*

# 13.9 Problem Solving: Using Principles

When you learn skills in mathematics, you often use the same principles applied to different problems. For example, the principles that you have learned in the previous sections about direct, inverse and partial variation can be applied to solving problems that involve other types of variation as shown in the following example.

The fastest speed recorded for a hockey puck is by Bobby Hull when he played for the Chicago Black Hawks. The puck was measured to "fly" at a speed in excess of 190 km/h.

### Example

The distance that a hockey puck travels on ice varies directly as the square of its speed. A puck travelling at 4 m/s travels 160 m before stopping. How far will a puck travelling at 6 m/s go?

Remember: look for the principles that you have used earlier to solve a problem about variation.

### Solution

| Think: | | Record the solution. |
|---|---|---|
| *Step 1*: Organize the given information. | → | (table below) |

| distance | 160 m | $d$ m/s |
|---|---|---|
| speed | 4 m/s | 6 m/s |

*Step 2*: Write an equation for the given type of variation. Find the constant of variation. → Let $d$ represent the distance in metres, and $s$ the speed in metres per second

$$\frac{\text{distance}}{(\text{speed})^2} \text{ is constant.}$$

$$\frac{d}{s^2} = k \quad \text{or} \quad d = ks^2$$

*Step 3*: Solve the problem. →

$$\frac{160}{4^2} = k \quad \text{or} \quad k = 10$$

$$\frac{d}{s^2} = 10 \qquad \text{Use } s = 6, \text{ find } d.$$

$$\frac{d}{6^2} = 10$$

$$d = 360$$

*Step 4*: Make a final statement. → A puck travelling at 6 m/s will go 360 m.

## Try These

1 The volume of water flowing out of a pipe varies directly as the square of the radius of the pipe.

(a) What are the missing values in the chart?

(b) What is the constant of variation.

| | | | |
|---|---|---|---|
| Volume (kilolitres) | 400 | 100 | ? |
| Radius (centimetres) | 10 | ? | 2 |

2 The value of a microcomputer varies inversely as the square of its age.

(a) What are the missing values in the chart?

| | | | |
|---|---|---|---|
| Value (dollars) | 1000 | ? | 250 |
| Age (years) | 2 | 1 | ? |

(b) What is the constant of variation?

## Written Exercises

**A** Review the principles you have learned to solve problems about variation.

1 $h$ varies directly as the square of $t$.

(a) Write an equation to express the direct squared variation.

(b) If $h = 3$ when $t = 4$, find the constant of variation.

2 $p$ varies inversely as the square of $q$.

(a) Write an equation to express the inverse squared variation.

(b) If $p = 5$ when $q = 2$, find the constant of variation.

3 $m$ varies directly as the square of $n$.

(a) Write an equation to express the direct squared variation.

(b) If $m = 12$ when $n = 2$, find the constant of variation.

(c) Use your answer in (b). If $n = 5$, find the value of $m$.

4 $x$ varies inversely as the square of $y$.

(a) Write an equation to express the inverse squared variation.

(b) If $x = 24$ when $y = 5$, find the constant of variation.

(c) Use your answer in (b). If $x = 150$, find the value of $y$.

5 In each of the following variations set up the appropriate equation based on the type of variation. Then solve for the missing value.

(a) $T$ varies inversely as the square of $m$.

| | | |
|---|---|---|
| $T$ | 18 | ? |
| $m$ | 3 | 6 |

Remember: This is an inverse variation so $Tm^2$ is constant.

(b) $S$ varies directly as the square root of $d$.

| | | |
|---|---|---|
| $S$ | 10 | 15 |
| $d$ | 4 | ? |

Use $\frac{S}{\sqrt{d}} = k$.

**B**

6 Skydivers know that the distance travelled by a falling object varies directly as the square of the time it has been falling. A person falls 22 m in 2 seconds.

(a) What distance will a person free-fall in 6 seconds?

(b) How many seconds does it take to fall a distance of 352 m?

7 The mass of a metal sphere varies directly as the cube of its diameter. A sphere with mass 60 g has a diameter of 4 cm. What is the mass of a sphere with radius 4 cm?

8 The time taken for one swing of a pendulum is directly proportional to the square root of its length. It takes 3 seconds for a pendulum that is 1 m long to make one swing. How long would it take for each swing of a pendulum that is 64 cm long?

9 The intensity of sound varies inversely as the square of the distance from its source. At a rock concert, if you are standing 24 m away from the speakers the sound has an intensity of 160 units. What is the intensity of the sound for a person who is 60 m away from the speakers?

10 The distance needed to stop a car varies directly as the square of its speed. When a car is travelling at 16 km/h it can stop in 7 m.
(a) When the same car is travelling at 40 km/h, what distance does it need to stop?
(b) If the car needed 175 m to come to a stop, what speed was it travelling at?

11 The value of a diamond varies directly as the square of its mass. (The mass of precious stones is most often given in carats, where 1 K (carat) = 0.2 g). A diamond with a mass of 1.8 K is valued at $1500. What would the value be of a diamond of similar quality and with mass 2.7 K?

12 A satellite must maintain the proper velocity in order to stay in orbit. The velocity varies inversely as the square root of its distance from the centre of the earth. A satellite that is travelling at a distance of 1200 km above the earth's surface has a velocity of 8.5 km/s. Find the velocity of another satellite that is 1800 km above the earth's surface (the radius of the earth is 6400 km).

13 The resistance in a wire varies inversely as the square of the radius of the wire. A wire with radius 0.4 mm has a resistance of 8 $\Omega$ (ohms). What would be the resistance of the same type of wire with a radius of 0.5 mm?

**C**

14 The amount that the length of a steel bar increases when heated varies directly as the product of the original length and the actual rise in temperature. A section of railroad track that is 20 m increases 0.5 cm when the temperature rises from 0°C to 20°C. What would the length of this section of track increase to if the temperature continues to rise up to 30°C?

## Career Tip

The skills in this chapter are of particular importance to a cartographer. A cartographer works with specialized information provided by many people: geologists, agriculturalists, surveyors, hydrographers, foresters, geographers, engineers. To design and compile a map requires the use of skills with scale, projection and variation. There are many precise measurements and computations to be made, as well as data to be interpreted before a map is published. Cartographers and computer programmers work as a team in adapting mathematical skills into map production.
A number of careers related to cartography are shown by the list: aerial photographer, film processor, hydrographer, computer programmer, surveyor, printer, lithographer, research assistant, production manager, editor, sales person. Obtain information on a career that might be of interest to you. Explore what steps you need to take to start to work towards this career.

## Consumer Tip

Often a source of information is available that may save you a lot of inconvenience as well as money. If you want to protect yourself, when you make a major purchase of services or goods investigate the rating of the firm by contacting the local branch of the Better Business Bureau or a department of the consumer protection branch of a provincial government. The information provided to you will help you make a better decision.

## Review: Practice and Problems

1 The ratio of tickets sold for adults, students, and children is 16:12:5.
  (a) If 560 adult tickets were sold, how many student tickets were sold?
  (b) If tickets cost \$5.50 for adults, \$3.50 for students, and \$2.00 for children, how much money was collected?

2 The scale on a diagram is 1:50.
  (a) The distance on a diagram is measured to be 5.5 cm. Find the actual length of the object.
  (b) An actual length on the object is 32 cm. What is the distance shown on the scale diagram?

3 $m$ is proportional to $n$.
  (a) Write an equation to express the direct variation.
  (b) If $m = 325$ when $n = 25$, find the constant of variation.
  (c) Use your answer in (b). If $n = 48$, then find the value of $m$.

4 The amount of gasoline a bus uses varies directly with the distance driven. Mila uses 33.5 L of gas for a trip of 230 km.
  (a) Write an equation relating the amount of gasoline used and the distance travelled.
  (b) Draw the graph of the relationship in (a).
  (c) Mila travelled 745 km during one week. How much gasoline was used for this week?

5 $D$ varies inversely as $E$ and when $E = 90$, then $D = 55$.
  (a) Write an equation to express the variation.
  (b) Find the constant of variation.
  (c) Find $D$ when $E = 40$.

6 The total cost of renting a car is \$49 for the first day and \$35 for each additional day.
  (a) Write an equation that describes the relationship between cost and time rented.
  (b) Find the cost of renting the car for 8 days.

## A Practice Test

1 What is the value of the missing term?

  (a) $4:5 = 12:x$ (b) $\frac{3}{7} = \frac{m}{84}$ (c) $3:7:d = 9:21:15$

2 The scale on a map is 1:12 000.
  (a) How many centimetres on the earth's surface does each centimetre on the map represent?
  (b) How many centimetres on the map would represent an actual distance of 1 km?

3 Rocky typed an essay for English in 2 h 15 min. The essay contained 4000 words. Find the rate of typing, expressed in words per minute.

4 (a) If $p$ varies inversely as $q$, write an equation to express the inverse variation.
  (b) If $p = 86$, when $q = 38$, find $p$ when $q = 20$.

5 The gas efficiency of a firetruck varies inversely with the mass of the truck. An 8600 kg fire truck obtains a gas efficiency of 5 km/L.
  (a) Write an equation relating the gas efficiency to the distance travelled.
  (b) Construct a graph of the relationship.
  (c) Find the gas efficiency of a fire truck with a mass of 14 200 kg.

6 The time needed to fill a tank varies inversely with the square of the diameter of the hose. With a 4 cm hose it takes 5 min to fill the tank. How long will it take to fill the tank with a hose with diameter 5.5 cm?

### Math Tip

Regardless of the career you choose, you will need to learn a specialized vocabulary for that career. To learn the vocabulary, you can follow a procedure you have used to learn vocabulary in mathematics.

- Make a list of any special new words.
- Provide a simple example of your own to illustrate the meaning of each word.

# 14 Exploring with Geometry: Skills and Applications

inventory of language, exploring constructions, congruent triangles, organizing steps, working with quadrilaterals, properties of parallel lines, problem-solving, exploring angles in circles, chords in circles, applying skills, solving problems and applications

## Introduction

In many careers such as navigation, map making, weather forecasting, conservation, urban planning, upholstery, and so on, various principles of geometry are used to solve particular problems. The vocabulary of the careers may differ since you may in one career talk about latitude or longitude and in another talk about a residential unit, or even wildlife management. However, the mathematics used to solve similar problems in any career have similarities. Thus, the same skills in mathematics can often be applied in different situations. For each photo, what skills in mathematics or geometry might play a role in the particular career?

- in upholstry

- in weather forecasting

- in rescue work

- in wild-life management

# 14.1 Inventory: Words and Properties

Often the success of following instructions, or solving a problem, hinges on your clear understanding of the words. To do geometry, you must have a clear understanding of the language used. To help you remember and understand the meanings of words, you have seen how new words in mathematics build on earlier ones. If, in the following inventory, you do not remember the meaning of any of the words, refer to the index to look up the pages on which you studied the word.

## Inventory

1 Each of the following descriptions are used for angles. What type of angles have each measure?
  (a) less than 90°
  (b) greater than 90° but less than 180°
  (c) equal to 90°
  (d) equal to 180°
  (e) between 180° and 360°

2 What type of triangle is described by each of the following?
  (a) all three sides have equal measures
  (b) all sides have different measures
  (c) all measures of angles are less than 90°
  (d) one angle is 90°
  (e) two sides have equal measures
  (f) one angle is more than 90°

3 For each of the following, sketch a diagram to illustrate the geometric information.
  (a) two angles are said to be supplementary if their sum is 180°
  (b) the base angles of an isosceles triangle are equal
  (c) two angles are said to be complementary if their sum is 90°
  (d) the sum of the angles of a triangle is 180°
  (e) vertically opposite angles are equal

4 Each diagram illustrates an important geometric property. What is the property? (Express the property in your own words.)

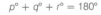

(a)

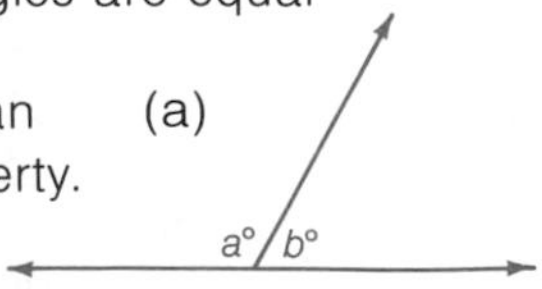


$a° + b° = 180°$

(b)

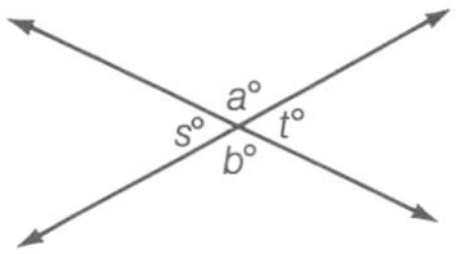


$a° = b°,\ s° = t°$

(c)

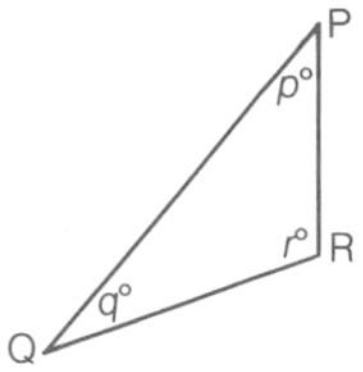


$p° + q° + r° = 180°$

(d)

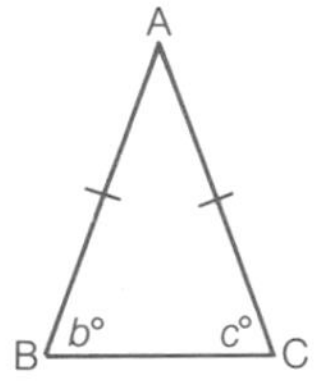


$b° = c°$

(e)

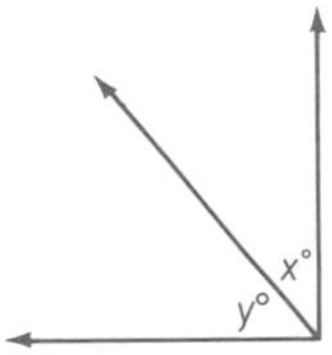


$x° + y° = 90°$

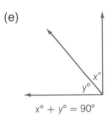

5 Find the missing measures. List the geometric facts you used.

(a)

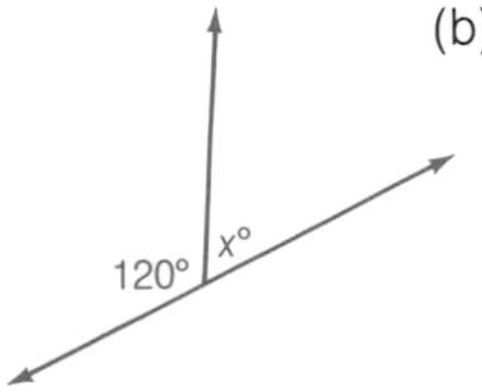


(b)

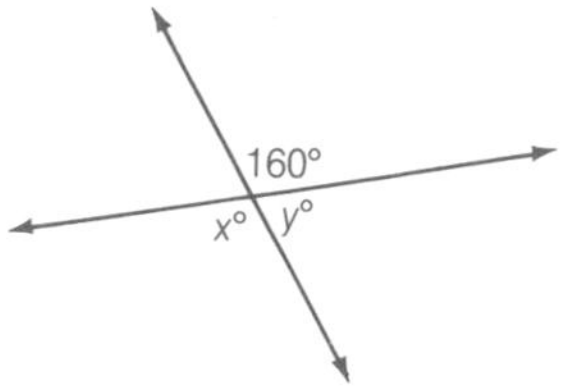


(c)

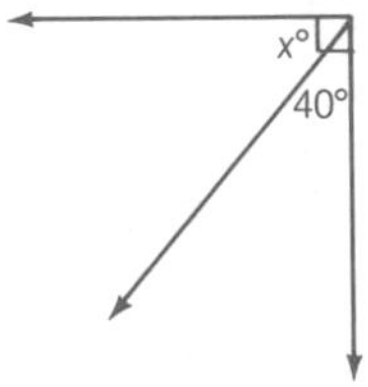


(d)

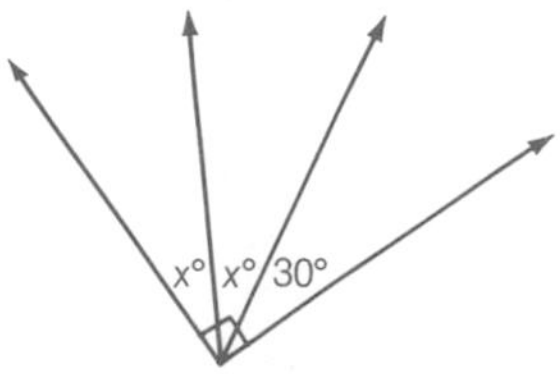

6 Find each missing measure. List the geometric facts you used.

(a)

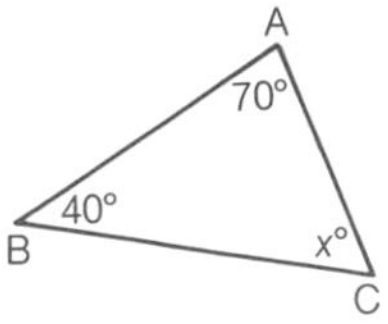


(b)

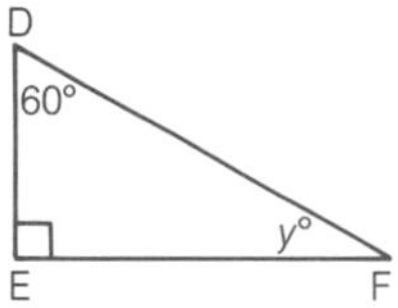


(c)

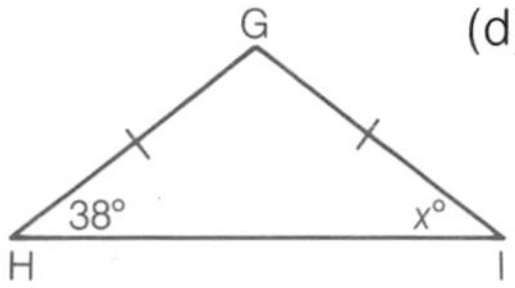


(d)

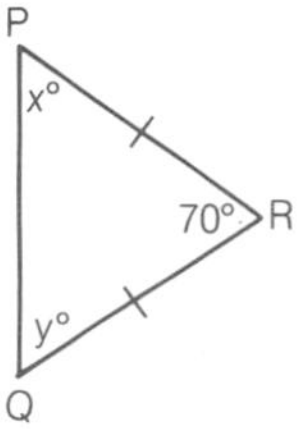


(e)

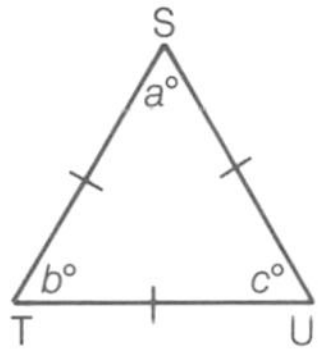


(f)

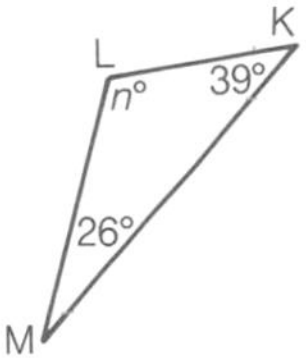


7 Find each missing measure. List the geometric facts you used.

(a)

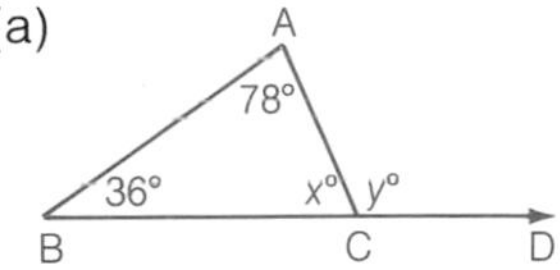


(b)

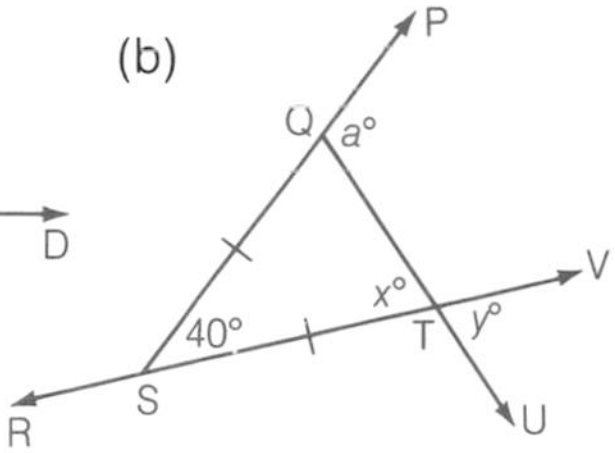


(c)

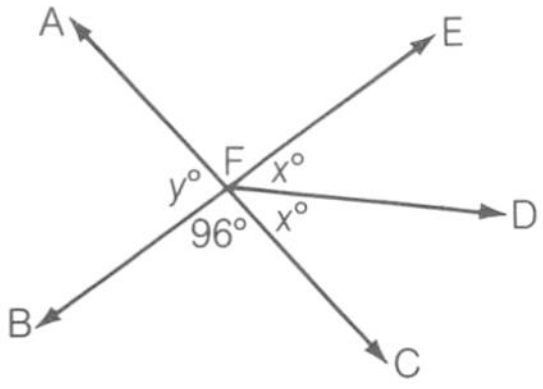


(d)

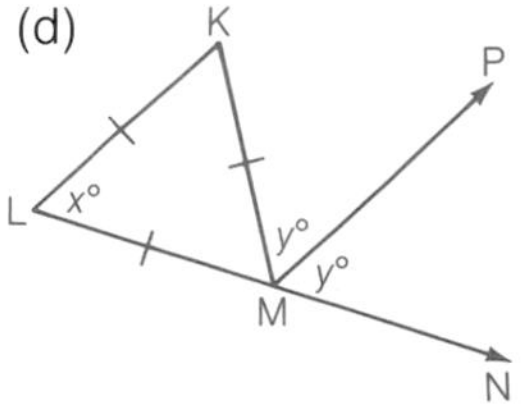


(e)

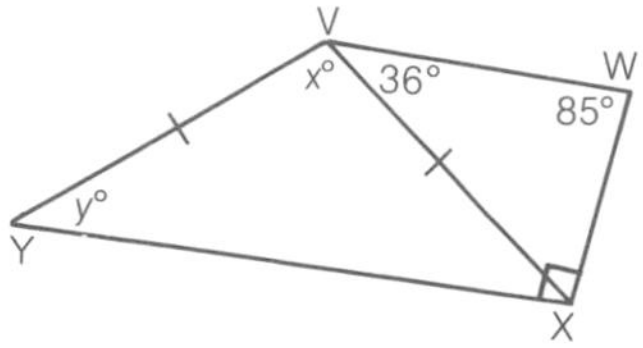


8 To find the measures of the angles,

- write an equation
- solve equation
- find the missing measures.

(a)

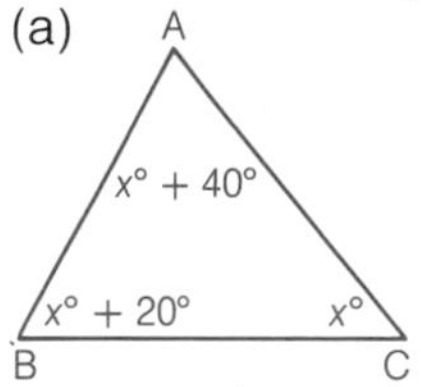


(b)

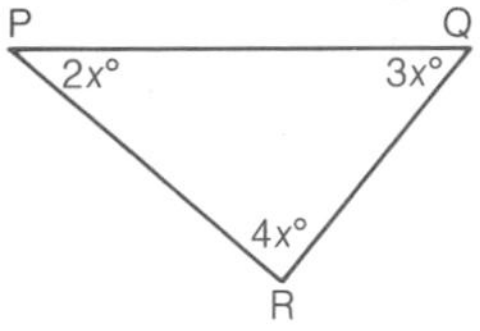


(c)

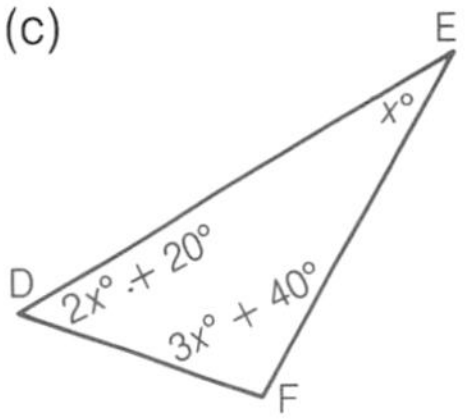


(d)

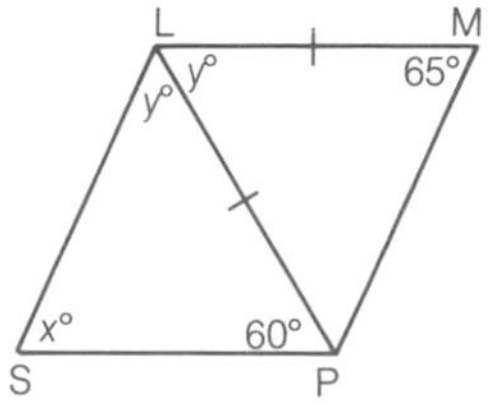


(e)

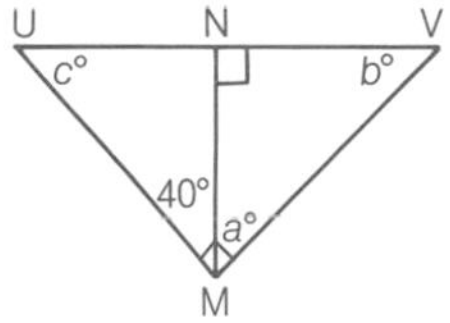


(f)

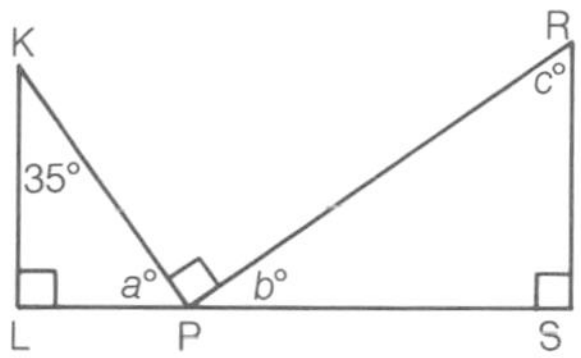


9 Now that you have completed the inventory, you know that each of the following words has an important meaning in geometry. For each word

- write its meaning in your own words.
- Use your own example and sketch a diagram to illustrate the meaning of each.

(a) right triangle
(b) perpendicular
(c) obtuse angle
(d) scalene triangle
(e) reflex angle
(f) straight angle
(g) complementary angles
(h) perpendicular bisector
(i) isosceles triangle
(j) angle bisector
(k) obtuse triangle
(l) acute triangle
(m) equilateral triangle
(n) right angle
(o) acute angle
(p) supplementary angles
(q) base angles
(r) midpoint
(s) sum of the angles of a triangle
(t) vertically opposite angles

## Exploring Constructions

What if you are given only some of the parts of a triangle? Can you construct a unique triangle? In the exercise, you will explore how many parts are needed to construct a triangle.

10 For each sketch measures are shown.
- ▶ For which sketches can you construct a unique triangle? Did you use all measures?
- ▶ For which sketches can you not construct a unique triangle?

(a)

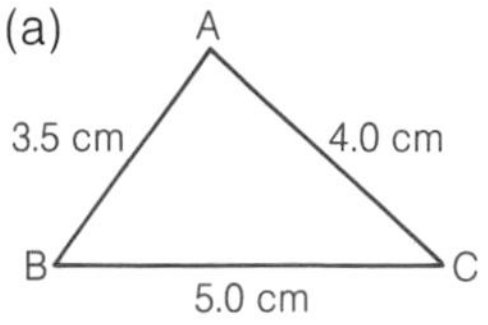


(b)

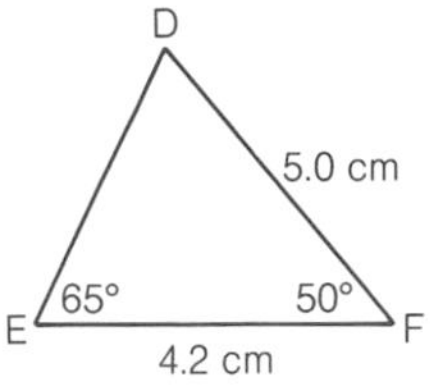


(c)

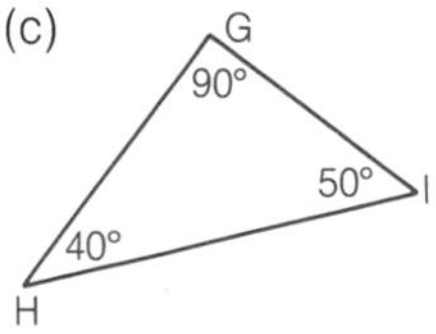


(d)

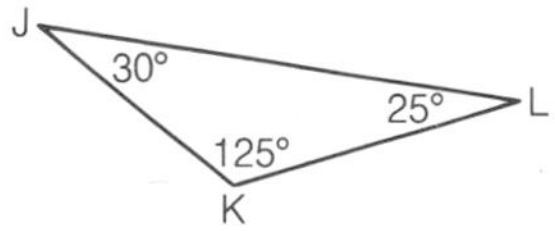


(e)

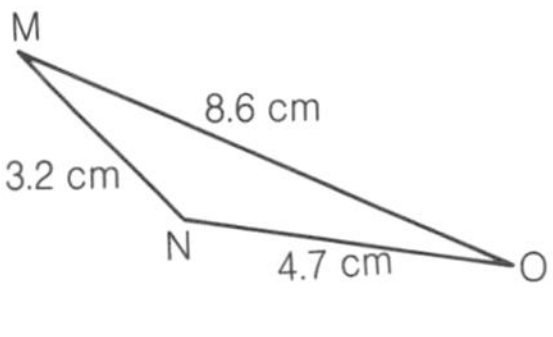


(f)

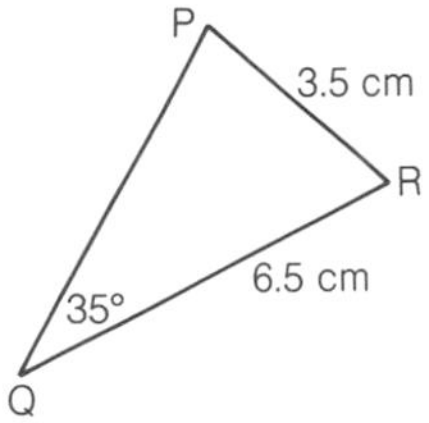


(g)

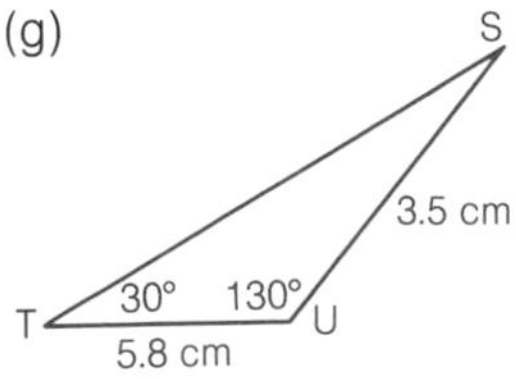


(h)

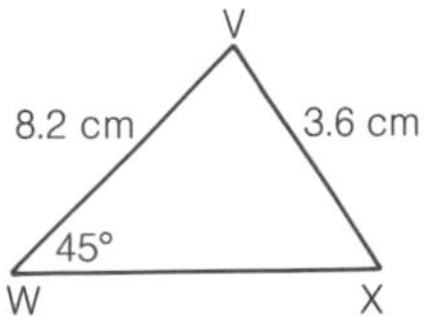


(i)

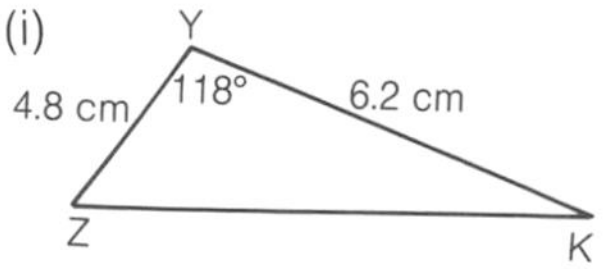


(j)

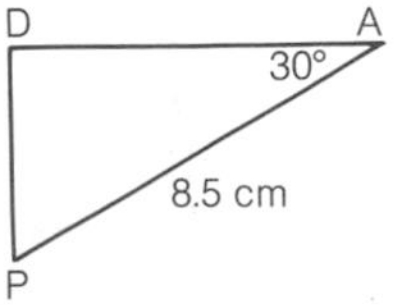


11 Construct each of the following triangles. For which of the following measures can you obtain A: a unique triangle, B: more than one triangle, C: no triangle?

(a) △MLK, ∠M = 40°, ML = 5 cm, KL = 6 cm
(b) △RQT, RQ = 3 cm, TR = 2 cm, TQ = 5 cm
(c) △VQW, ∠W = 45°, WQ = 7 cm, VQ = 8 cm
(d) △PMN, MN = 8 cm, PM = 5 cm, PN = 9 cm
(e) △WVX, WV = 5 cm, XV = 4 cm, ∠W = 75°
(f) △ABC, AB = 6.1 cm, ∠B = 30°, BC = 5.2 cm
(g) △SAB, ∠S = 105°, ∠A = 30°, ∠B = 45°
(h) △DEF, FD = 8 cm, ED = 6 cm, FE = 6 cm
(i) △GHP, ∠P = 60°, ∠H = 45°, HP = 5 cm
(j) △QAR, QA = 4 cm, RA = 2 cm, ∠Q = 45°
(k) △RAQ, RA = 5.9 cm, ∠R = 30°, AQ = 5.1 cm
(l) △DAF, ∠D = 30°, ∠F = 30°, FA = 8 cm
(m) △SRW, SR = 6.1 cm, WR = 7.5 cm, ∠W = 45°

12 △ABC is constructed with the following measures. Decide which give
A: one triangle,
B: more than one triangle.

(a) 3 sides
(b) 2 angles and a side
(c) 3 angles
(d) 1 angle and two sides
(e) 2 angles and a contained side
(f) 2 sides and a contained angle

Under what conditions will the above measures give no triangle?

13 Use your results in questions 10 to 12.

(a) What measures for a triangle can be used to construct a unique triangle?
(b) What measures for a triangle might yield more than one triangle.
(c) What type of measures for angles or sides would yield no triangle?

# 14.2 Congruent Triangles

Whenever you replace an item such as a

- ▶ window in a house
- ▶ bolt of a wheel
- ▶ fender of a car
- ▶ sleeve of a coat

you are using congruence. When you replace the above items you want them to be identical in shape, as well as in size.

In geometry, two triangles are said to be congruent if they are identical in shape and size.

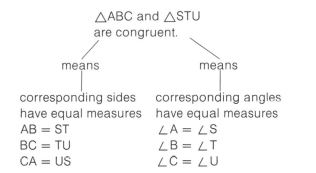

△ABC and △STU are congruent.

| means | means |
|---|---|
| corresponding sides have equal measures | corresponding angles have equal measures |
| AB = ST | ∠A = ∠S |
| BC = TU | ∠B = ∠T |
| CA = US | ∠C = ∠U |

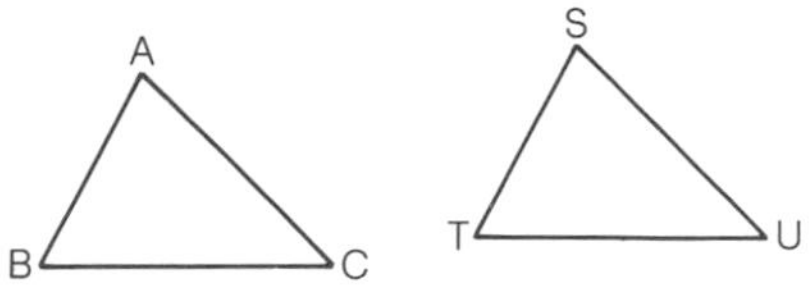


△ABC ≅ △STU

means

△ABC is congruent to △STU

If all the corresponding angles and sides of one triangle are equal to those of another, then we know the triangles are congruent. We have seen that for certain conditions, triangles can be congruent even if not all angles and sides are known. Three congruence conditions can be used, described as follows.

**SSS: Side Side Side Condition for Congruence**

If 3 sides of one triangle are equal to 3 sides of another triangle, then the triangles are congruent.

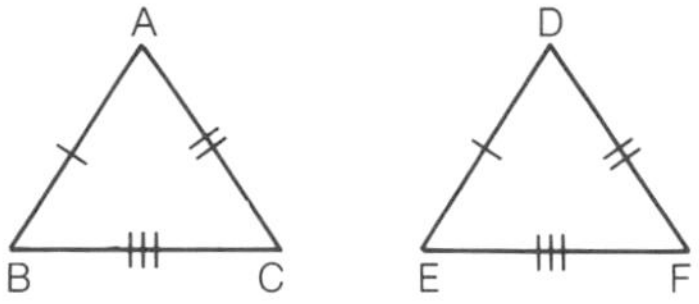


In △ABC, △DEF

AB = DE
AC = DF
BC = EF

means ⇨

△ABC ≅ △DEF
thus ∠A = ∠D
∠B = ∠E
∠C = ∠F

**SAS: Side Angle Side Condition for Congruence**

If 2 sides and the contained angle of one triangle are equal to the corresponding sides and angle of another triangle, then the triangles are congruent.

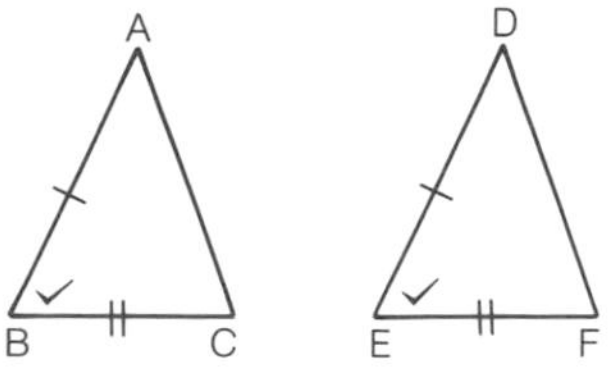


In △ABC, △DEF

AB = DE
∠B = ∠E
BC = EF

means ⇨

△ABC ≅ △DEF
thus AC = DF
∠A = ∠D
∠C = ∠F

**ASA: Angle Side Angle Condition for Congruence**
If 2 angles and the contained side of a triangle are equal to the corresponding side and angles of another triangle, then the triangles are congruent.

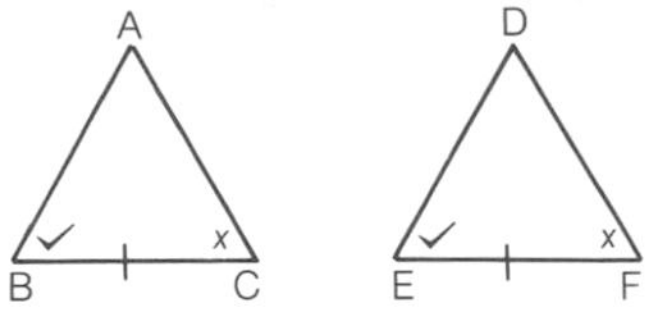


In △ABC, △DEF

| | | |
|---|---|---|
| ∠B = ∠E<br>BC = EF<br>∠C = ∠F | means ⇒ | △ABC = △DEF<br>thus AB = DE<br>AC = DF<br>∠A = ∠D |

## Try These

Which pairs of triangles are congruent? Give reasons for your answer.

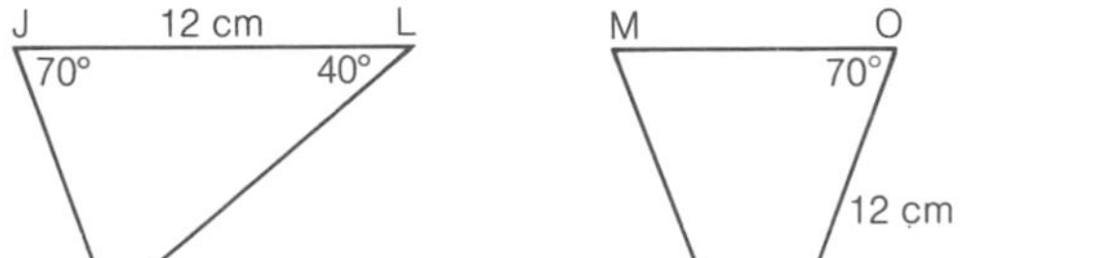


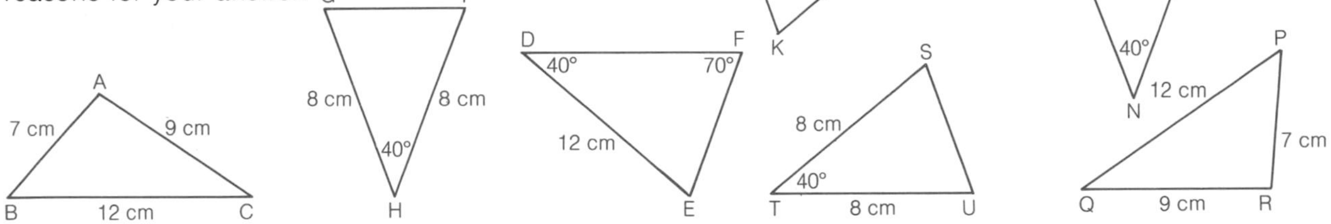


## Written Exercises

**A** Review the conditions for congruence: SSS, SAS, ASA.

1 Refer to △PQR, △STV.

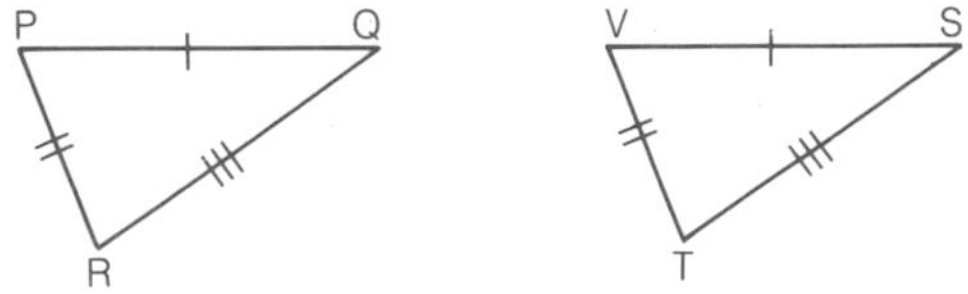


(a) Which sides are equal?
(b) Why are the triangles congruent?
(c) What other parts are equal?

2 Refer to △MNP, △DEF.

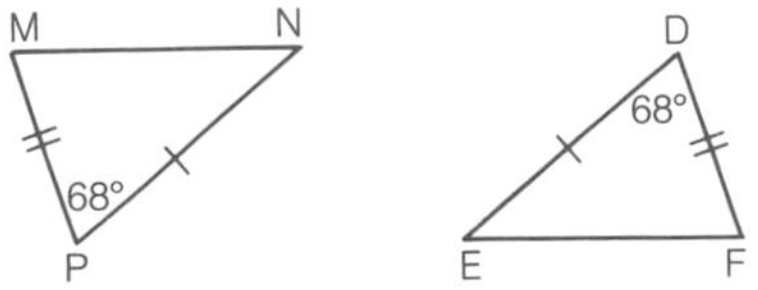


(a) Which sides, angles are equal?
(b) Why are the triangles congruent?
(c) What other parts are equal?

3 Refer to △PQR, △BCD.

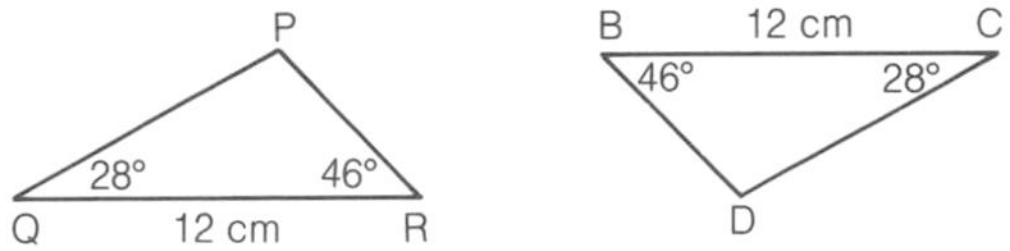


(a) Which sides, angles are equal?
(b) Why are the triangles congruent?
(c) What other parts are equal?

4 Refer to △PST, △ABC.

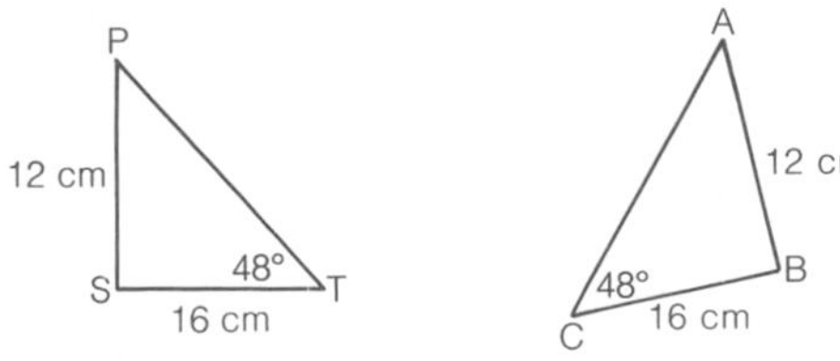


(a) Which sides, angles are equal?
(b) Why are the triangles not congruent?
(c) What other parts are equal?

5 What additional information do you need so that each pair of triangles is congruent?

(a)

(b)

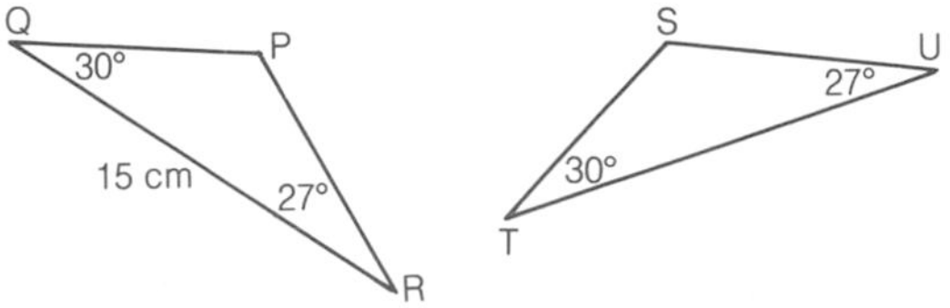


(c)

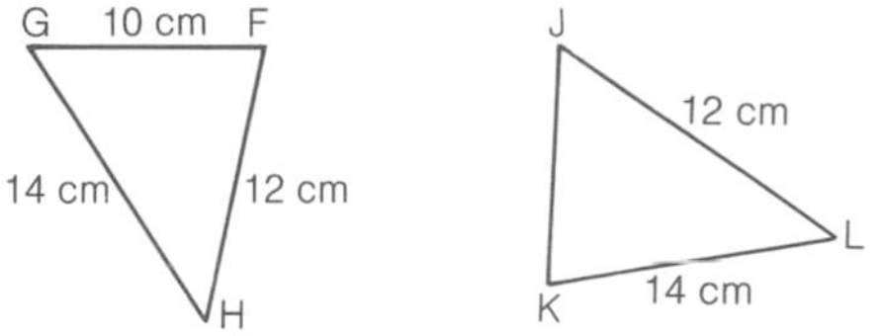


(d)

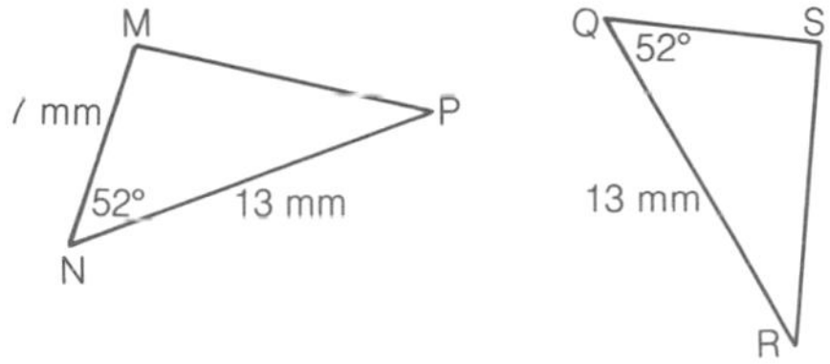


**B Remember, to show triangles are congruent, you must interpret diagrams correctly.**

6 For the following triangles,
- ▶ which pairs are congruent?
- ▶ Give reasons for your answer.

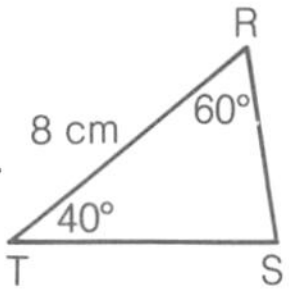


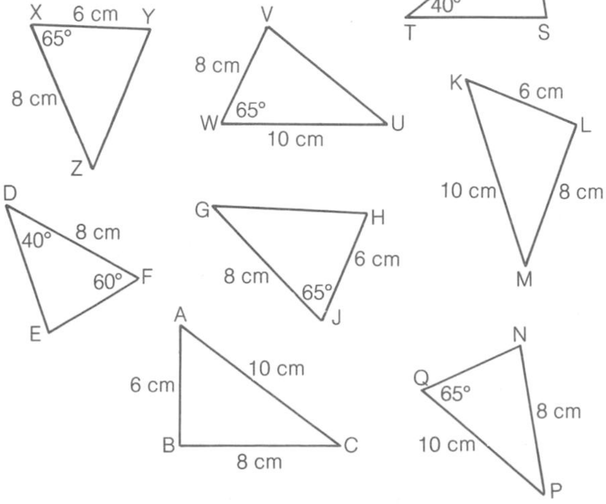


7 A collection of triangles are shown with information missing. Match pairs of triangles. Include the missing information that show the condition for congruence.

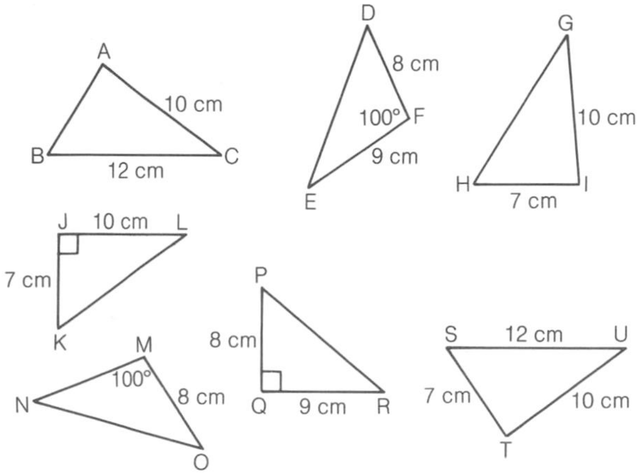


8 For each diagram,
- ▶ decide which triangles are congruent.
- ▶ Give reasons for your answer.

(a)

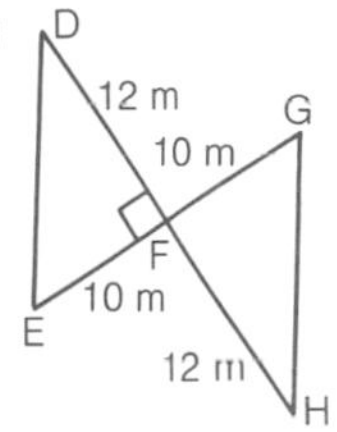


(b)

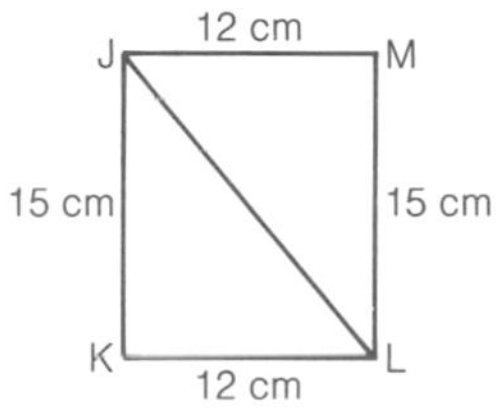


(c)

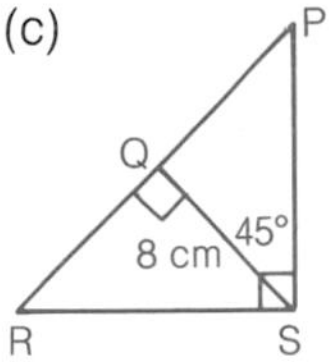


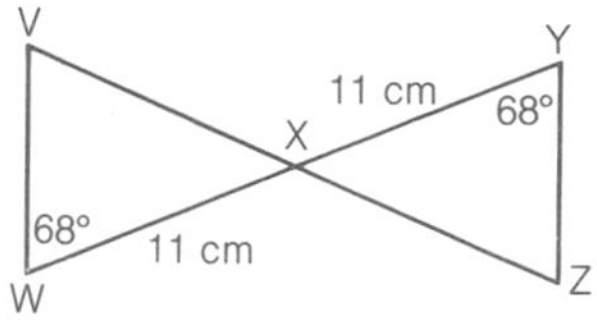


9 For each diagram,
- ▶ which triangles are congruent?
- ▶ Give reasons for your answer.
- ▶ What is the missing measure?

(a)

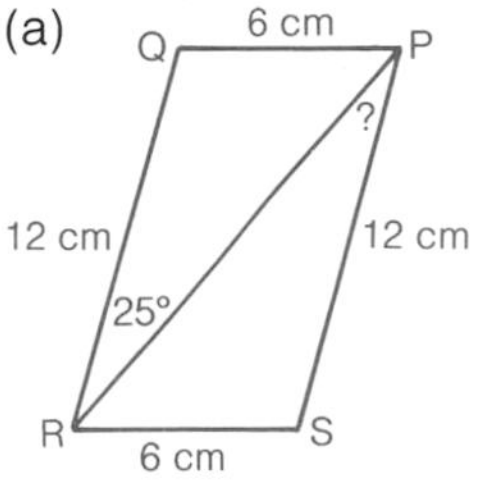


(b)

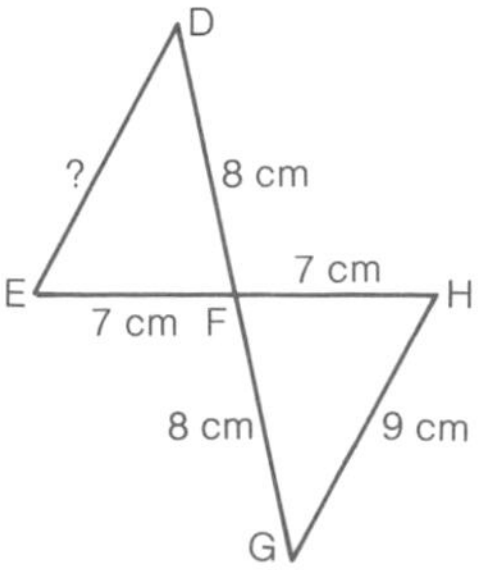

# 14.3 Organizing Steps

Often when you make statements, you will be asked to justify your answer. In writing a report the steps you organize, or the information you provide, are listed so that another person reading your work will come to the same conclusion.

The need to organize your steps is also important in arriving at conclusions in geometry. You can use these conditions for congruence to arrive at conclusions.

Condition for congruence: *SSS*
*side–side–side*
△ABC ≅ △PQR

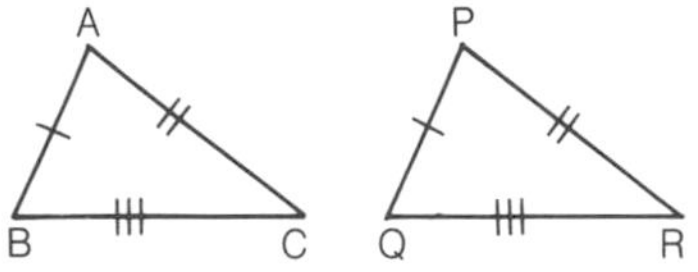


Condition for congruence: *SAS*
*side–angle–side*
△ABC ≅ △PQR

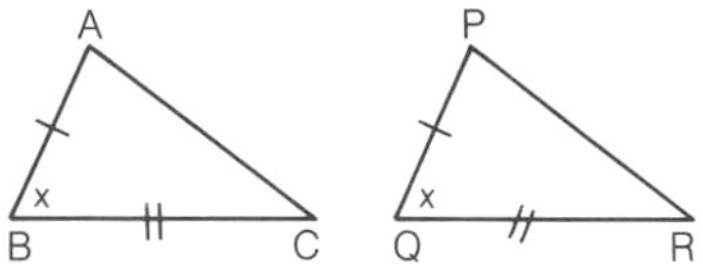


Condition for congruence: *ASA*
*angle–side–angle*
△ABC ≅ △PQR

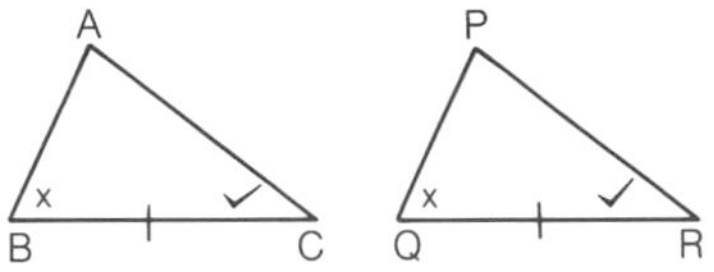


You can use these conditions for congruence to obtain useful information. For example, in the following diagram, triangles are constructed. PQ represents the width of a river. From the measurements on land in △SRT, you can measure the inaccessible distance PQ.

### Example

Use the diagram. What is the width of the river, PQ?

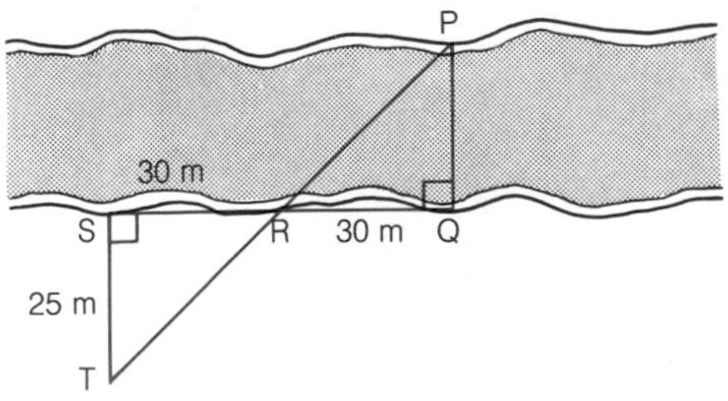


### Solution

Since ∠SRT and ∠PRQ are vertically opposite angles, then
∠SRT = ∠PRQ
In △PQR and △TSR

| | |
|---|---|
| ∠TSR = ∠PQR = 90° | (angle) |
| SR = RQ = 30 m | (side) |
| ∠SRT = ∠PRQ | (angle) |

Use the ASA condition for congruence.
△PQR = △TSR
Thus
PQ = TS = 25 m

The width of the river is 25 m.

## Try These

For each pair of triangles, what are the missing measures? Give reasons for your answer.

(a)

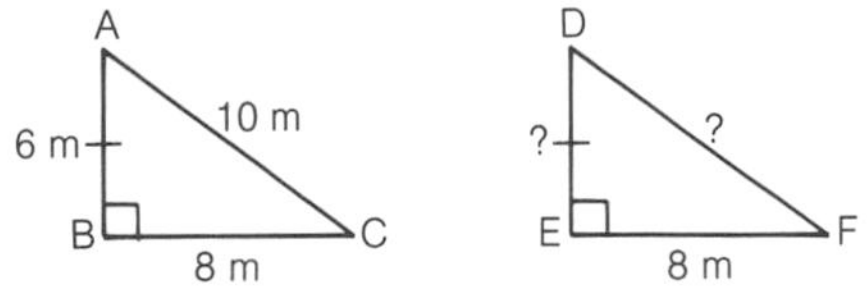


(b)

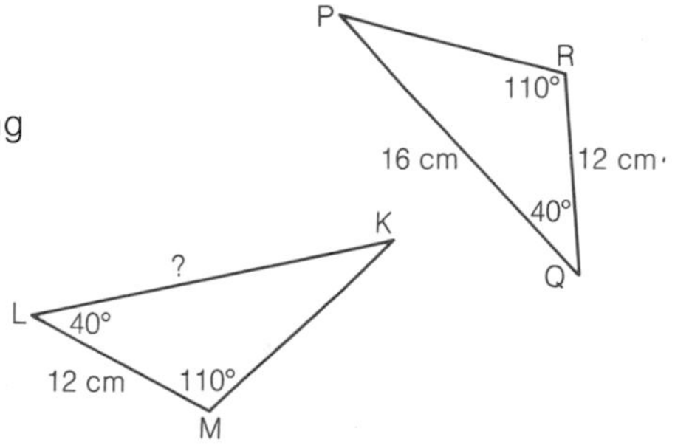


(c)

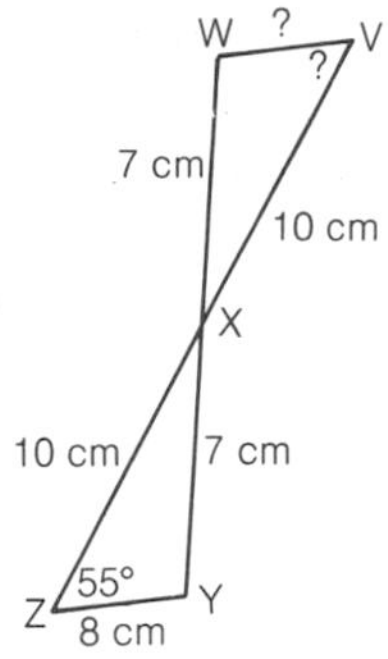


## Written Exercises

**A** Review the conditions for congruence.

1 For each diagram, which angles have equal values? Give reasons for your answers.

(a)

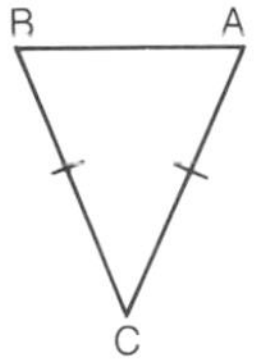


(b)

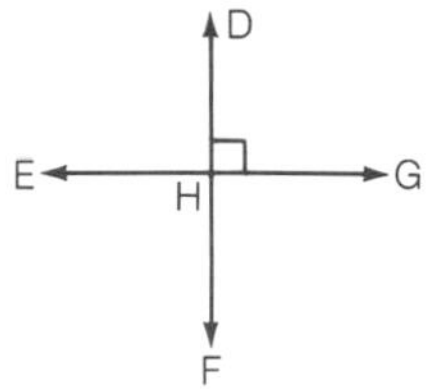


(c)

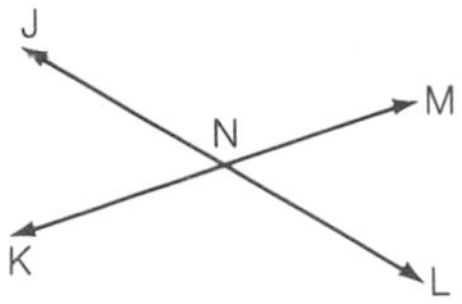


(d)

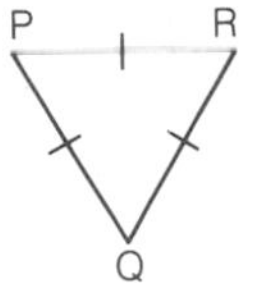


(e) $a° = b°$

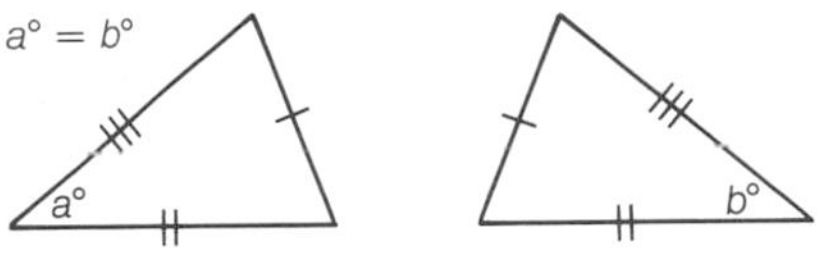


2 Give reasons for each result.

(a) $a° + b° = 180°$

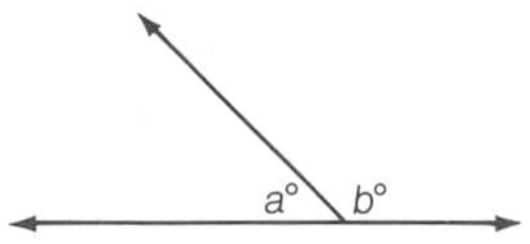


(b) $a° = b°$

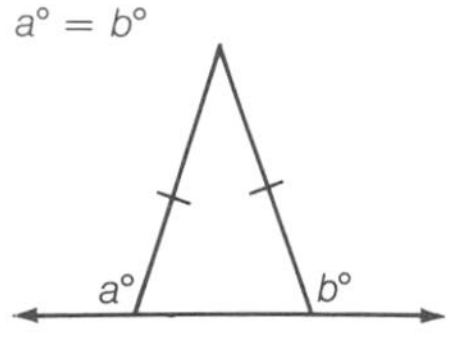


(c) $a° = b° = 45°$

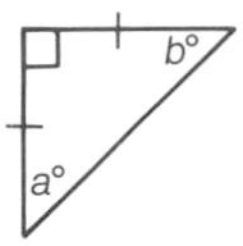


(d) $a° = b°$

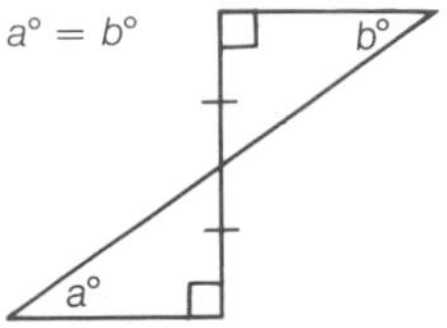


3 Refer to the diagram.
(a) Which parts are equal?
(b) Why is $\triangle BPA \cong \triangle BCA$?
(c) Why is $\angle PBA = \angle CBA$?

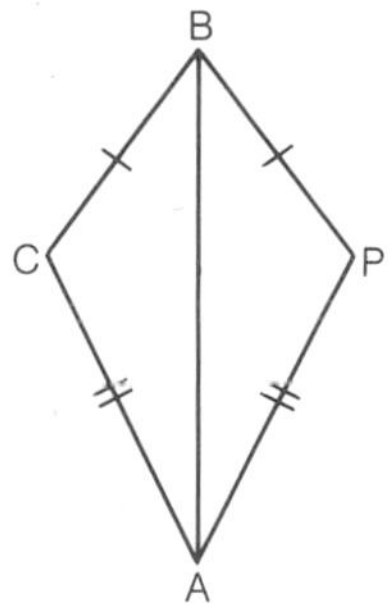


4 Refer to the diagram.
(a) Which parts are equal?
(b) Why is $\triangle DEF \cong \triangle AEG$?
(c) Why is EF = EG?

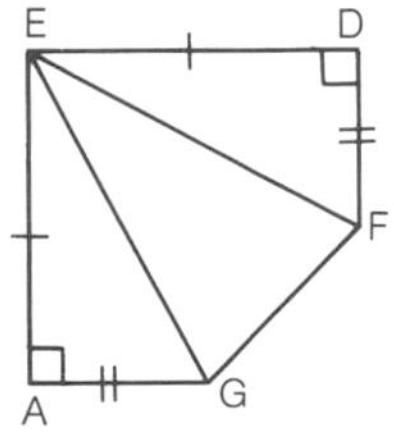


5 Refer to $\triangle PQR$, $\triangle PSR$.
(a) Which parts are equal?
(b) Why is $\triangle PQR \cong \triangle PSR$?
(c) Why is QR = SR?

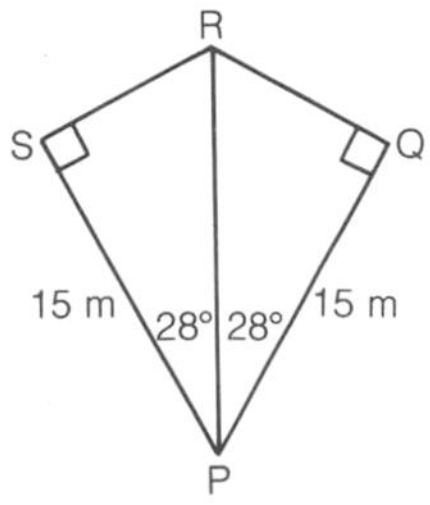

6 Refer to △SUV, △AUT.
(a) Which parts are equal?
(b) Why is △SUV ≅ △AUT?
(c) Why is SV = AT?

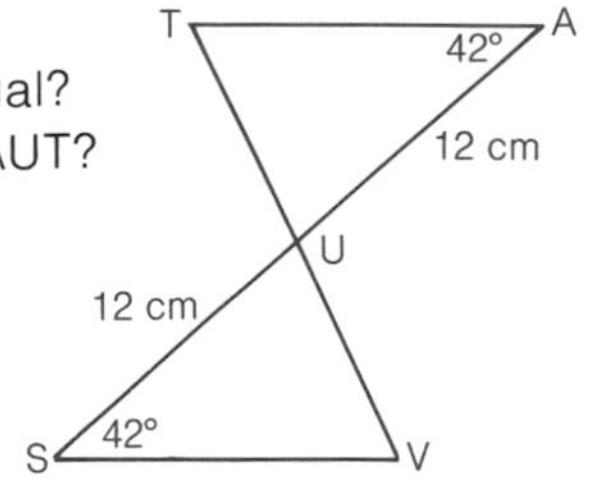


**B** Remember. Justify your answers. List the condition for congruence: *SSS*, *SAS*, or *ASA*.

7 Refer to the diagram.
(a) Which parts are equal?
(b) Why is △PQS ≅ △RSQ?
(c) Why is ∠PQS = ∠QSR?
(d) What other parts are equal?

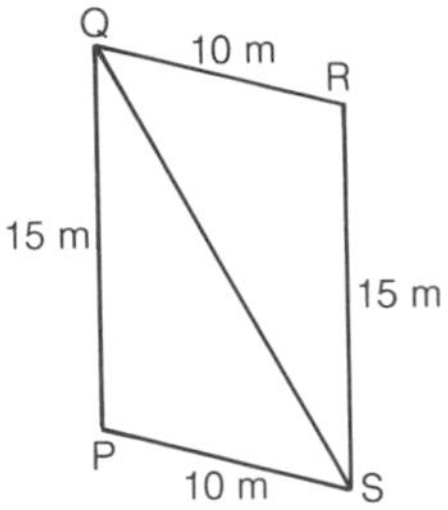


8 In △ABC, ∠A has been bisected as shown.
(a) Which parts are equal?
(b) Why is △ABD ≅ △ACB?
(c) Why is BD = DC?
(d) Why is ∠ADB = 90°?

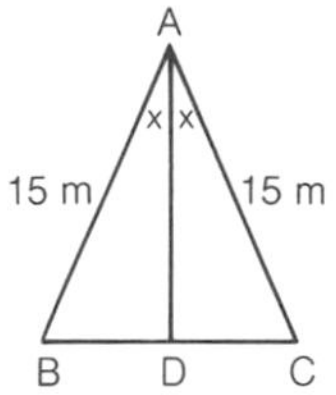


9 In the diagram, show why ∠CDE = 49°.

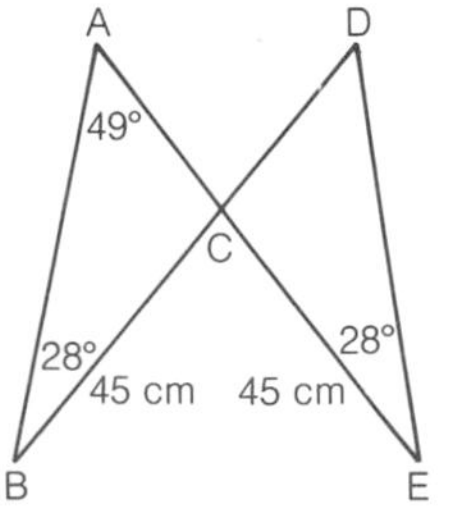


10 Show that BM = 12 cm.

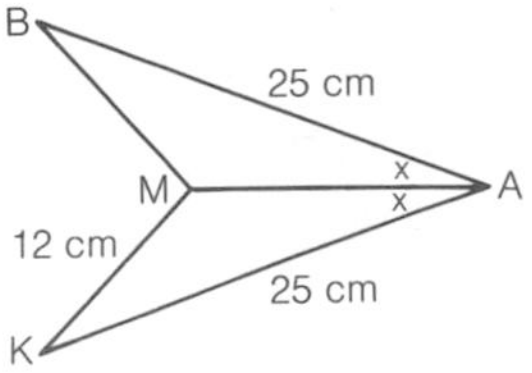


11 For each diagram,
▶ find the missing measures.
▶ Give reasons for your answer.

(a)

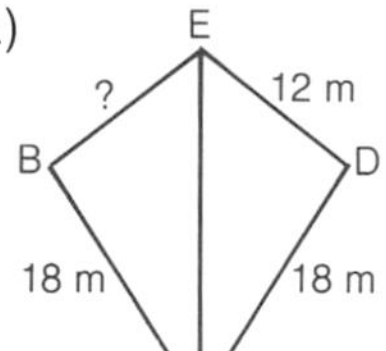


CE bisects ∠BCD

(b)

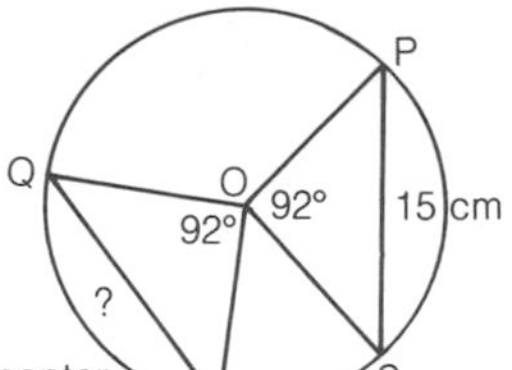


O is the center of the circle.

(c)

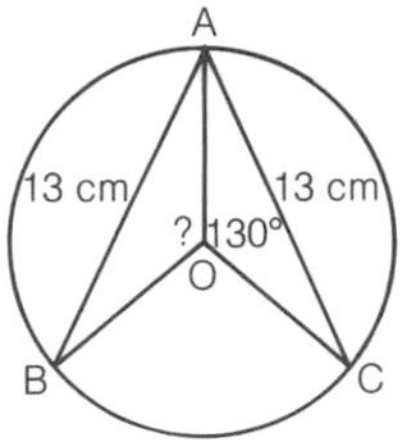


The radius OA bisects ∠BAC.

(d)

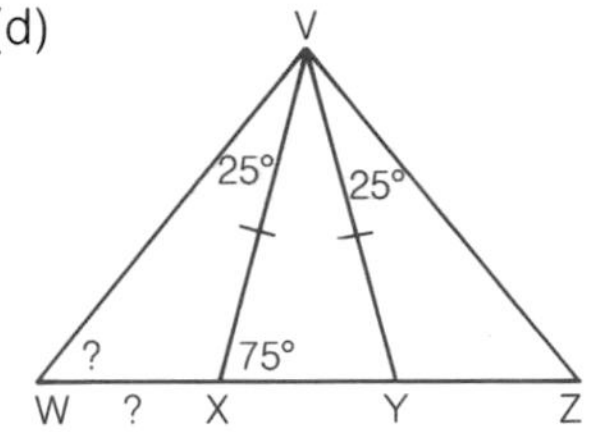


YZ = 10 cm

12 The diagram is used to find the width TW of a river.

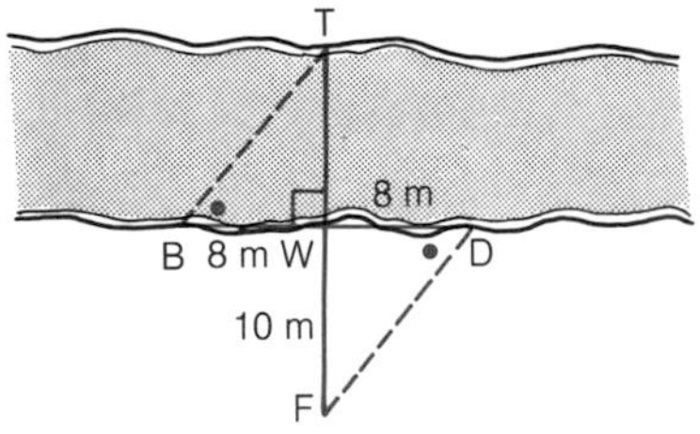


What is the width of the river?

13 To find the length, TP, of a pond measurements were made and recorded on a diagram.

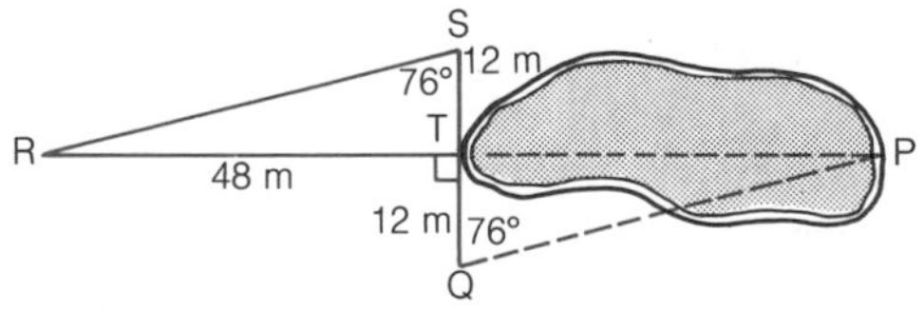


What is the length of the pond?

# 14.4 Working with Quadrilaterals

When you are given instructions to do construction, whether a building or a suit, you must understand the meanings of the words in order to correctly follow the instructions.

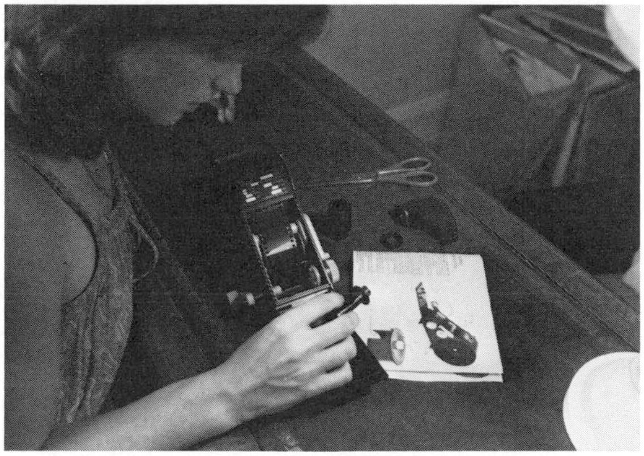

To learn mathematics, look for strategies to help you remember. For example, to work with geometry you also need to carefully learn the words. Often if you learn how words are related you more easily remember the meanings of words.

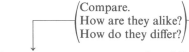

(Compare.
How are they alike?
How do they differ?)

| Triangle | Quadrilateral |
|---|---|
| A triangle is a closed figure with 3 sides. | A quadrilateral is a closed figure with 4 sides. |

For triangles, special words were used to describe triangles with a particular property. For quadrilaterals, special words are also used to describe quadrilaterals with a particular property.

In mathematics, the skills you learn can be often be extended to new situations.

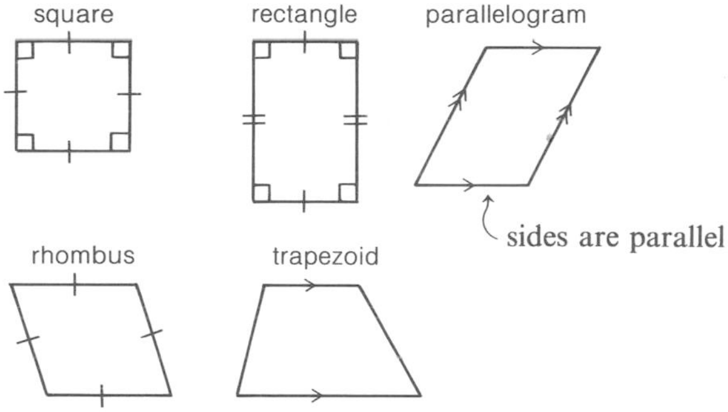


Triangle

$a^\circ + b^\circ + c^\circ = 180^\circ$

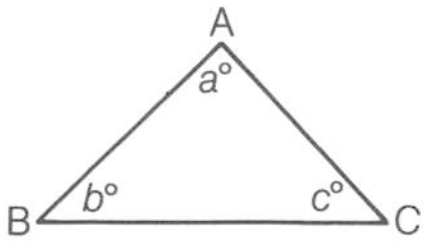


Quadrilateral

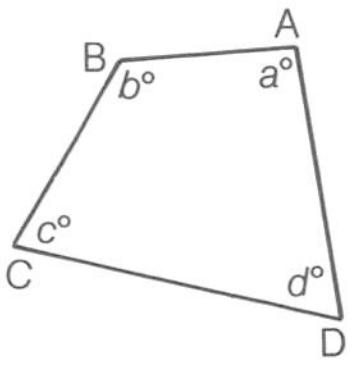


$a^\circ + b^\circ + c^\circ + d^\circ = ?$

What is the sum of the angles of a quadrilateral?

To find the sum you can use the properties of triangles

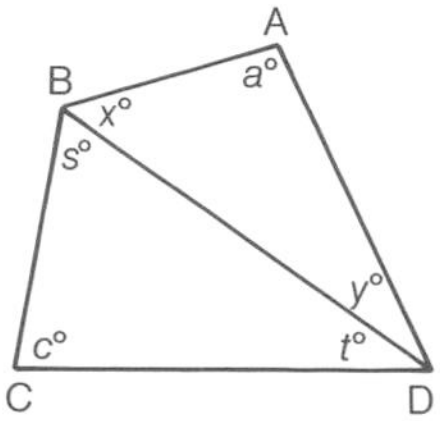


In $\triangle$ABD, $a^\circ + x^\circ + y^\circ = 180^\circ$
In $\triangle$BCD, $s^\circ + c^\circ + t^\circ = 180^\circ$

$a^\circ + x^\circ + y^\circ + s^\circ + c^\circ + t^\circ = 360^\circ$

represents $b^\circ$ represents $d^\circ$

Thus $a^\circ + b^\circ + c^\circ + d^\circ = 360^\circ$.

You can use this property to find missing angles in a quadrilateral.

### Example

Use the information in the diagram.
Find the measures of the angles.

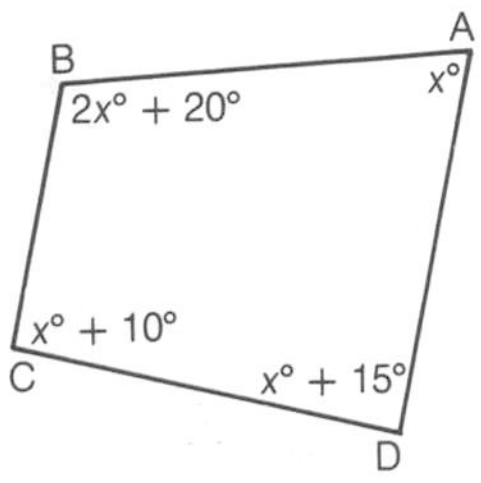


### Solution

*Step 1* Use the property to write an equation.

$x + (2x + 20) + (x + 10) + (x + 15) = 360$

*Step 2* Solve the equation. Find the missing values.

$x + 2x + 20 + x + 10 + x + 15 = 360$

$5x + 45 = 360$

$5x = 315$

$x = 63$

$\angle A = 63°$

$\angle B = 146°$ ← $2x + 20 = 2(63) + 20 = 146$

$\angle C = 73°$ ← $x + 10 = 63 + 10 = 73$

$\angle D = 78°$ ← $x + 15 = 63 + 15 = 78$

Think: Check your work.
$63 + 146 + 73 + 78 = 360$

## Try These

What is the missing measure in each quadrilateral?

(a)

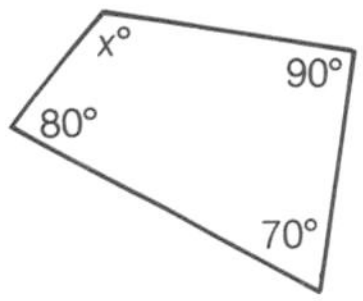


(b)

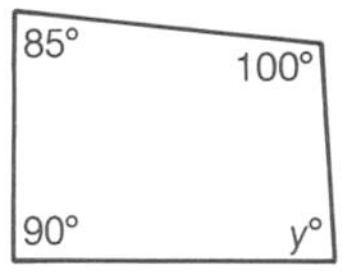


(c)

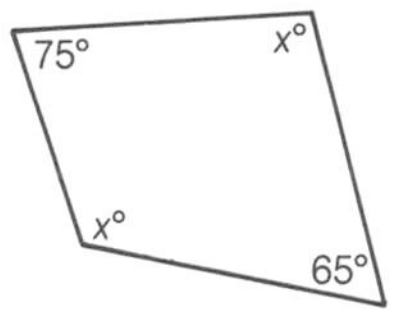


(d)

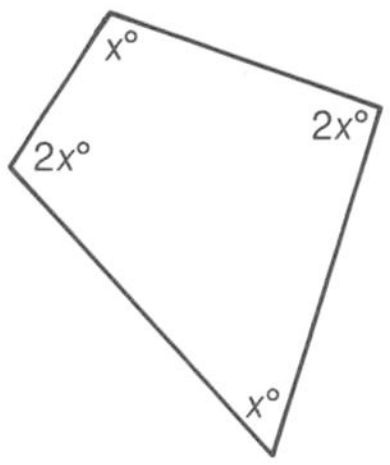


## Written Exercises

**A** Learn the special words used for quadrilaterals.

1 What are the special properties of each quadrilateral? What is its special name?

(a)

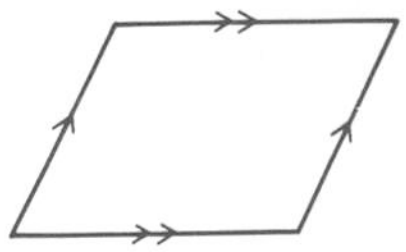

(b)

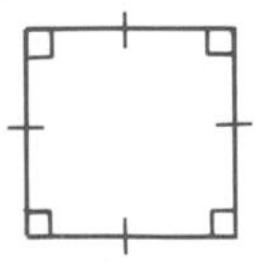

(c)

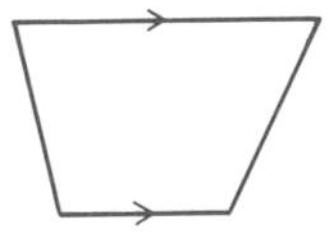

(d)

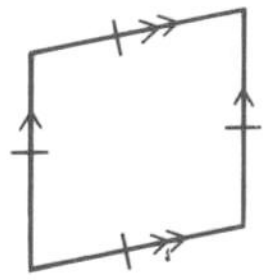

(e)

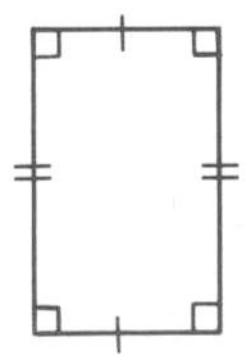

(f)

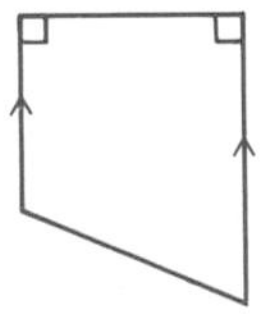

2 Find the missing measures.
▶ Write an equation.
▶ Solve the equation to find the missing measures. Be sure to check your answers.

(a)
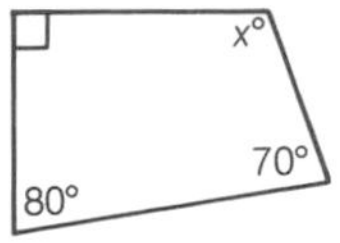


(b)
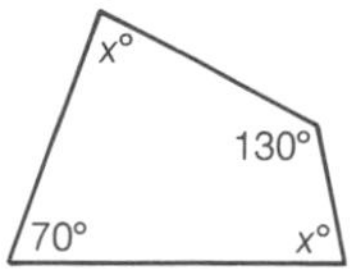


(c)
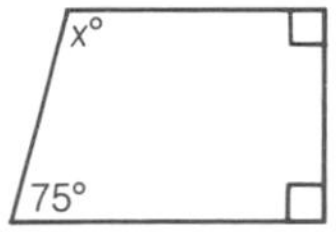


(d)
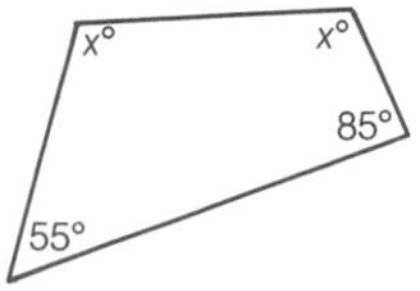


3 ▶ Write an equation to show the sum of the angles of each quadrilateral.
▶ Find the measures of each angle.

(a)
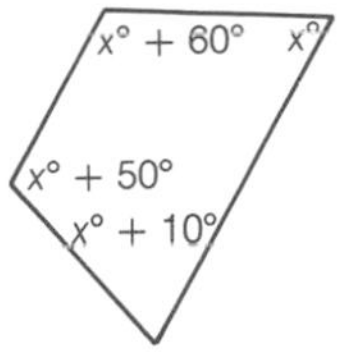


(b)
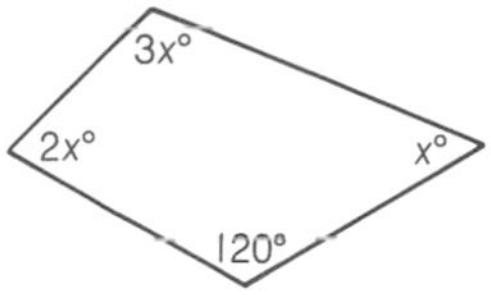


(c)
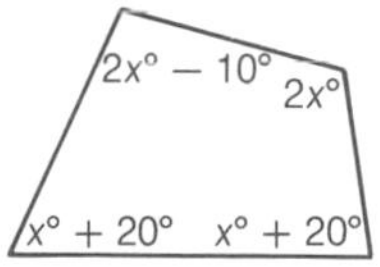


(d)
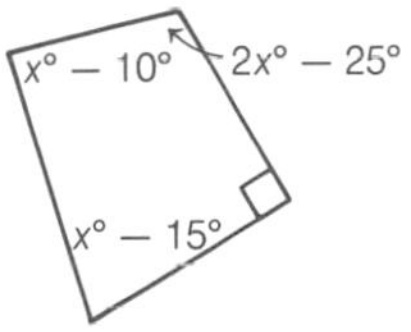


**B** To construct some quadrilaterals, you need to use the angles property of quadrilaterals. For questions 4 to 6 decide on a strategy to check the accuracy of your construction.

4 (a) Construct quadrilateral STUV with
UT = SV = 2.8 cm
UV = 6.8 cm
∠V = ∠U = 90°.

Remember: draw a rough sketch to record the information.

(b) What type of quadrilateral is STUV?

5 (a) Construct quadrilateral ABCD with
∠D = 120°   ∠C = 60°   AD = BC = 4.2 cm
DC = 8.6 cm
(b) What type of quadrilateral is ABCD?

6 (a) Construct quadrilateral PQRS with
∠S = ∠R = 45°   SR = 5.2 cm
PS = QR = 3.1 cm
(b) What type of quadrilateral is PQRS?

7 A sketch is shown of a quadrilateral. To construct JKLM you need to find the missing measure.
(a) What is the missing measure?
(b) Construct the quadrilateral.

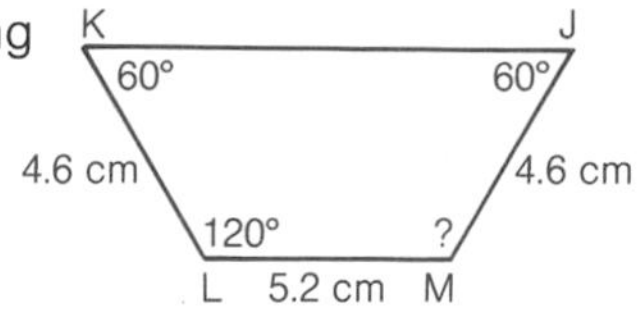


8 A figure PQRS is drawn from a blueprint. A support QS on the blueprint measures 9.8 cm.
(a) What other information do you know about the quadrilateral?
(b) What is the measure of ∠QPS?
(c) Construct the quadrilateral.

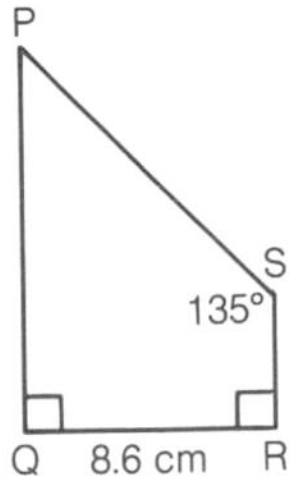


9 ▶ Find the missing angles on each blueprint.
▶ Construct an accurate copy of each.
▶ Measure the missing sides.

(a)
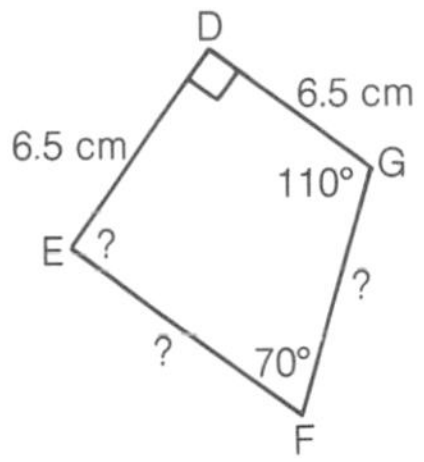


(b)
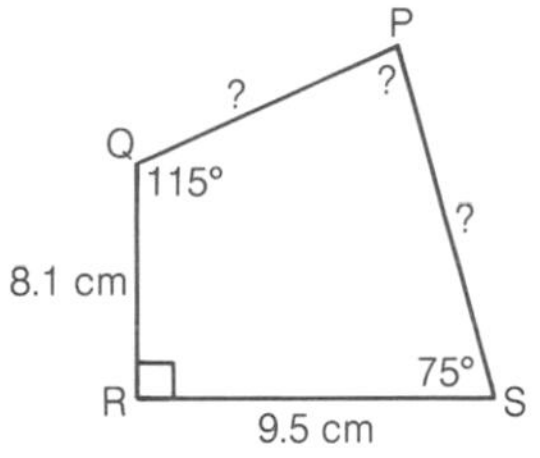


10 The surface of a machine part is in the shape of a quadrilateral. PQRS is described by
PQ = 6.9 cm   ∠P = ∠Q = 75°   QR = 3.6 cm
∠S = ∠R.
(a) Make a sketch of the quadrilateral.
(b) Construct a copy of PQRS.

11 The plan of a courtyard is drawn to scale in the shape of a quadrilateral ABCD.
AB = AD = 6.5 cm   ∠A = 60°   ∠B = 105°
BC = CD
(a) Use your sketch. What other information do you know?
(b) Construct the quadrilateral.
(c) If 1 cm represents 2.1 m, what is the length of CD?

# 14.5 Properties of Parallel Lines

**Parallel lines** are lines in the same plane that do not intersect. Quadrilaterals with special properties are related to parallel lines.

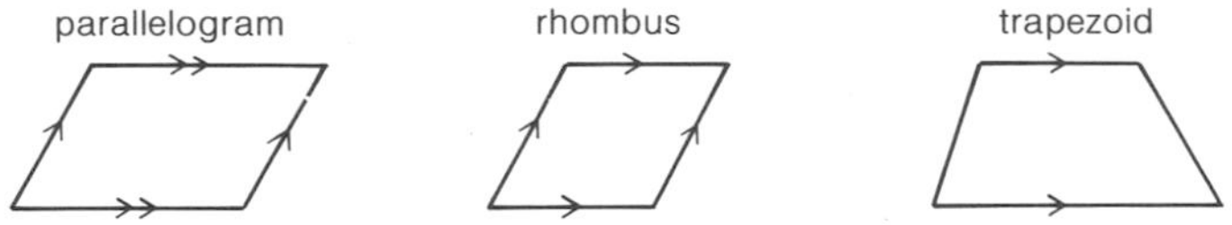


Special words are associated with parallel lines. For example, if a **transversal** PQ intersects AB and CD at R and S, certain pairs of angles are formed.

∠ARS and ∠DSR are called **alternate angles**.

∠ARP and ∠CSR are called **corresponding angles**.

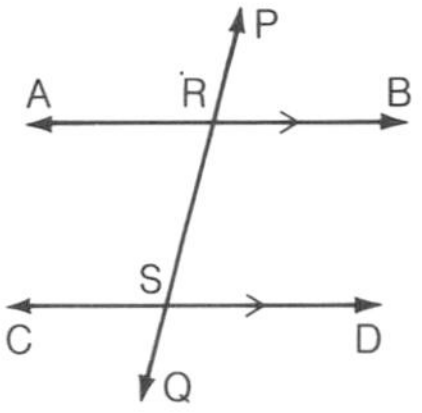


Other alternate angles occur as shown. They are pairs of equal angles.

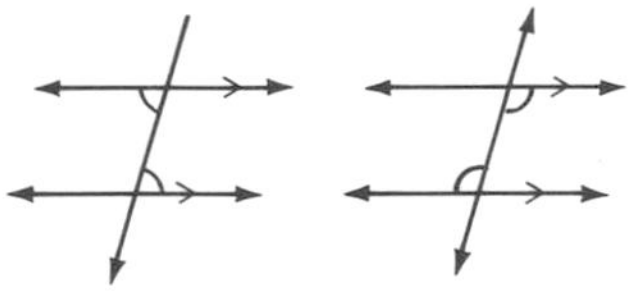

They also occur as shown. They are pairs of equal angles.

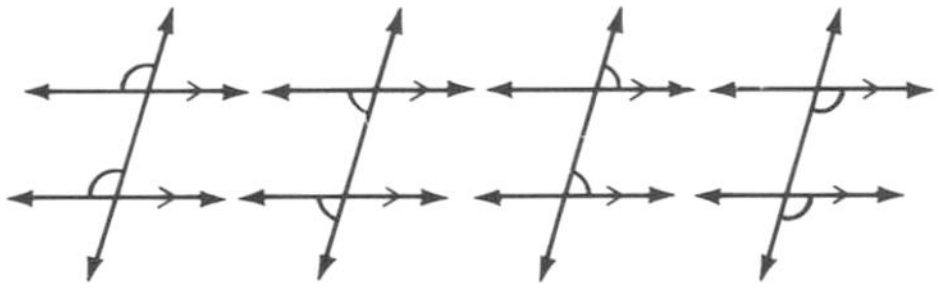

∠BRS and DSR are called **interior angles** on the same side of the transversal. They occur as shown. They are pairs of supplementary angles.

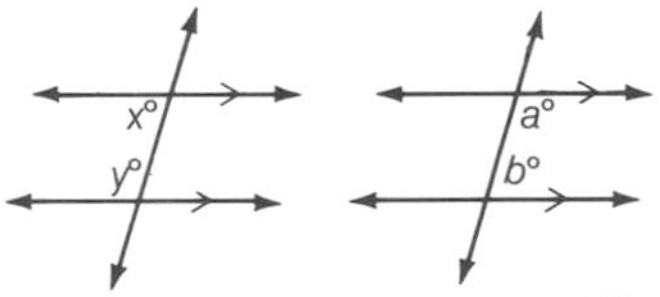


$x° + y° = 180°$ $a° + b° = 180°$

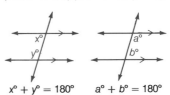

The properties of angles related to parallel lines are used to find missing measures.

## Example

Find the missing measures.

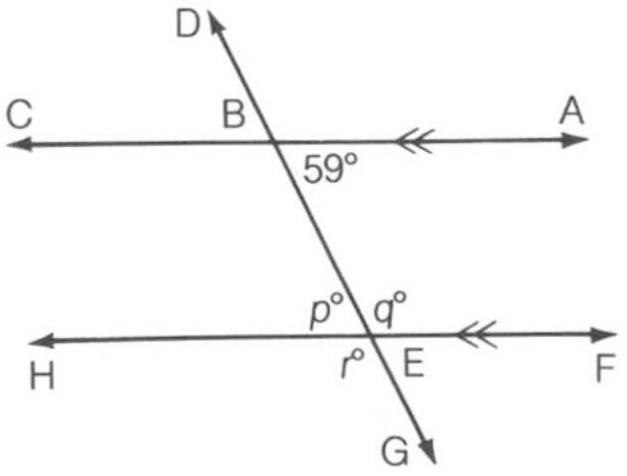


## Solution

∠ABE, ∠BEH are alternate angles.
∠BEH = ∠ABE
$p° = 59°$

∠HEB, ∠FEB are supplementary
∠HEB + ∠FEB = 180°
59° + ∠FEB = 180°
∠FEB = 121°
$q° = 121°$

∠BEF and ∠HEG are vertically opposite angles
∠HEG = ∠BEF
$r° = 121°$

## Try These

1 Refer to the diagrams. Which pairs of angles are
   (a) alternate angles?
   (b) corresponding angles?
   (c) interior angles on the same side of the transversal?

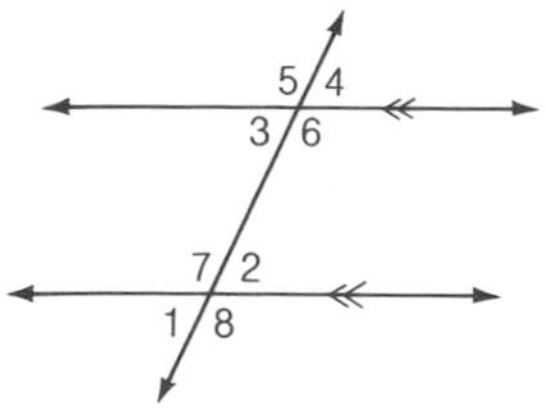


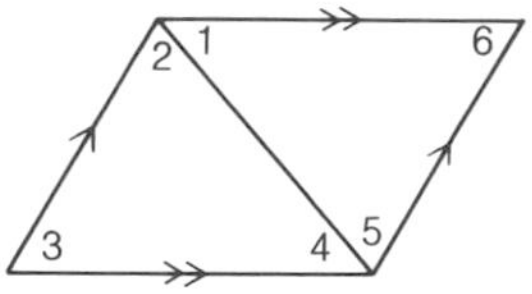


## Written Exercises

**A** Remember: Learn the meaning of alternate, corresponding, and interior angles.

1 Refer to the diagram. Name the type of angles shown by each pair.

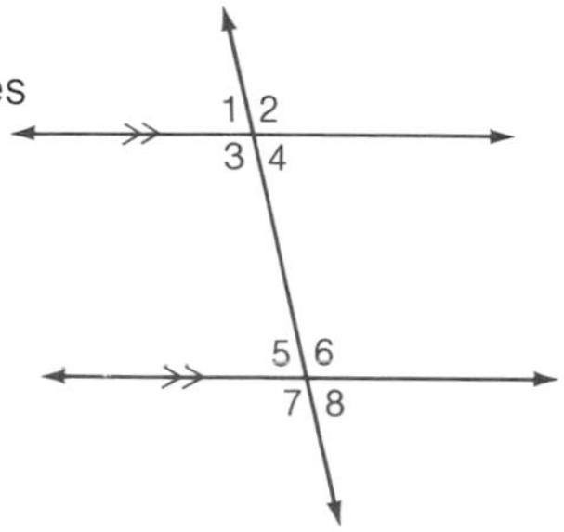


(a) ∠1, ∠5 (b) ∠4, ∠5 (c) ∠4, ∠6
(d) ∠7, ∠3 (e) ∠8, ∠4 (f) ∠2, ∠3
(g) ∠6, ∠3 (h) ∠5, ∠6 (i) ∠8, ∠5

2 Refer to the diagram. List pairs of
   (a) alternate angles
   (b) corresponding angles
   (c) interior angles on the same side of the transversal.

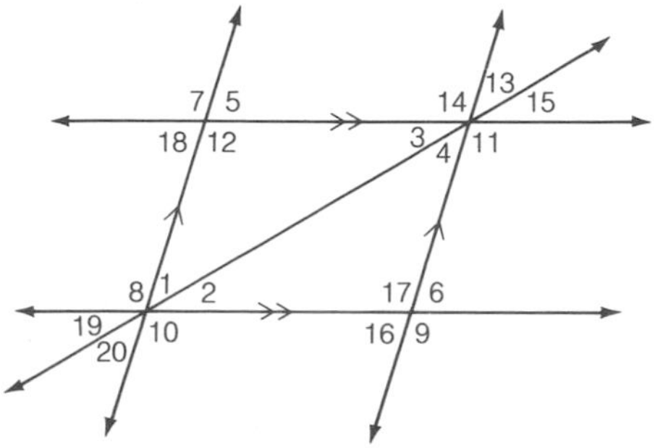


3 (a) What types of angles are shown?
   (b) What is the value of $p$?
   (c) What is the value of $q$?

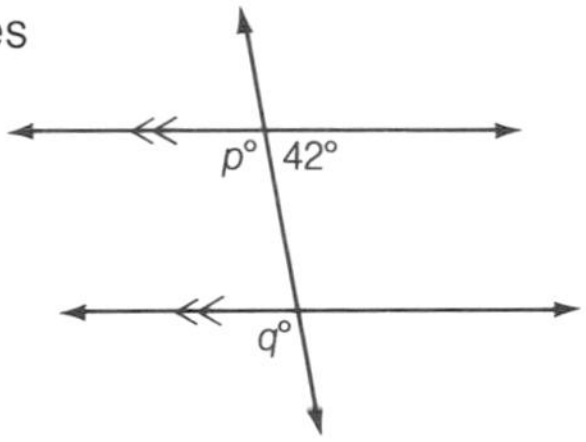


4 (a) What types of angles are shown?
   (b) Find the missing values for the angles.

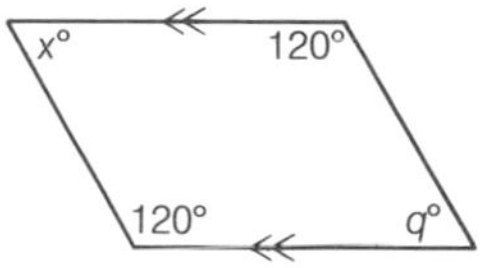


5 To solve some problems in geometry, you often need to use more than one fact. Refer to the diagram.
   (a) What fact do you know about ∠P, ∠Q and ∠R? Use this fact to find ∠PRT.

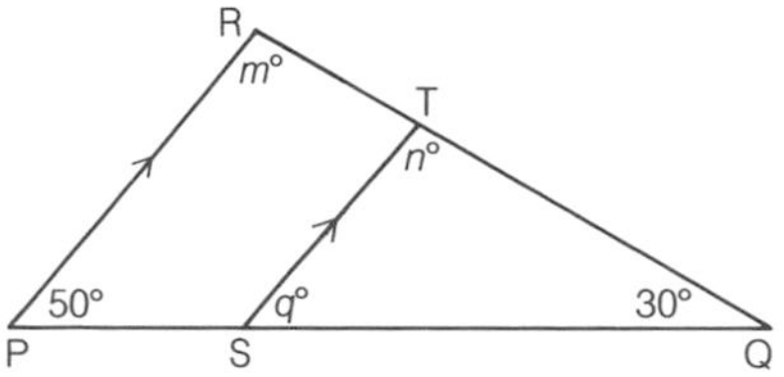


   (b) How are $m°$, $n°$ related? Use this fact to find ∠STQ.
   (c) Find the value of $q°$.

**B** When you find values for the missing measures, be sure you can justify your answer.

6 Find the missing measures. Give reasons for your answers.

(a)

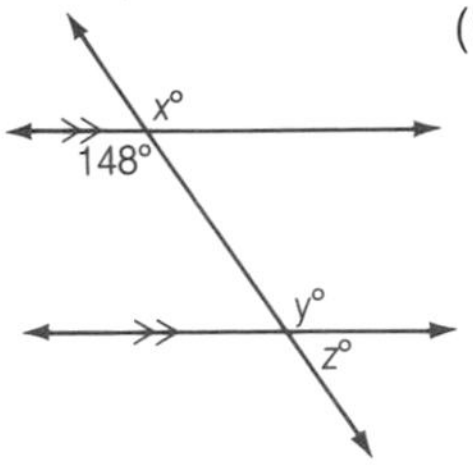


(b)

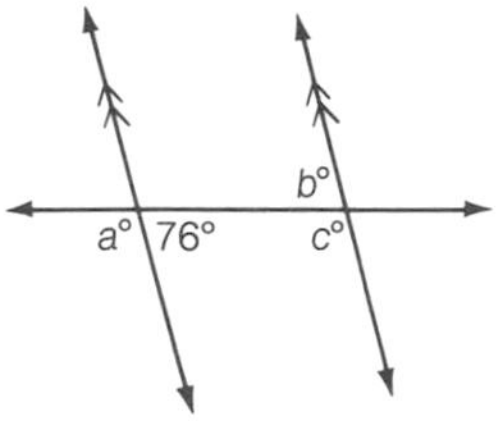


(c)

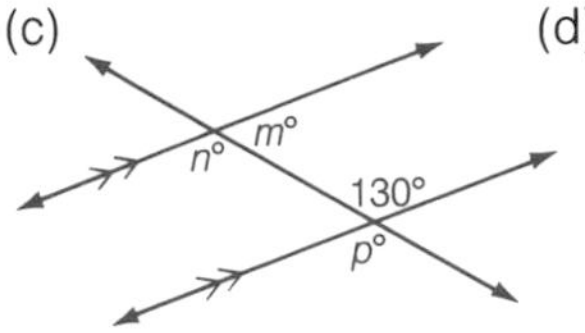


(d)

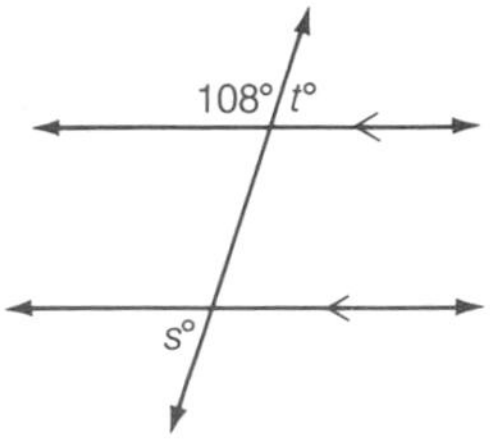


(e)

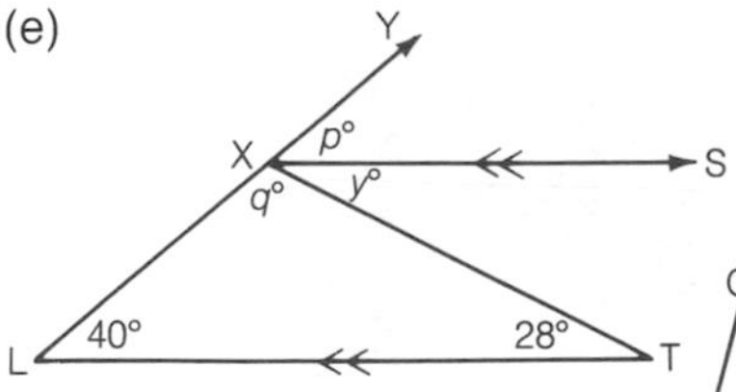


(f)

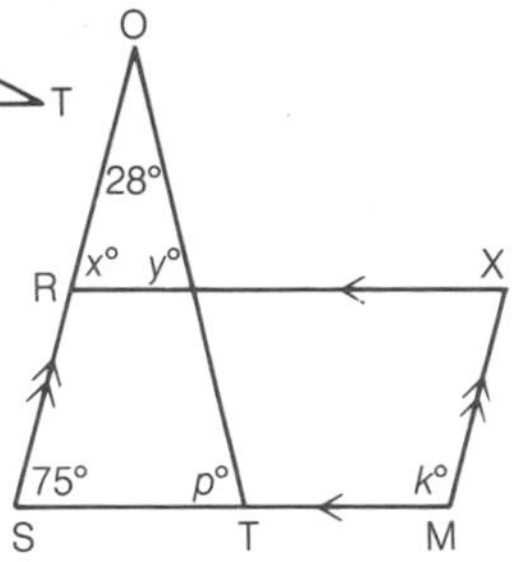


7 Find the missing measures.

(a)

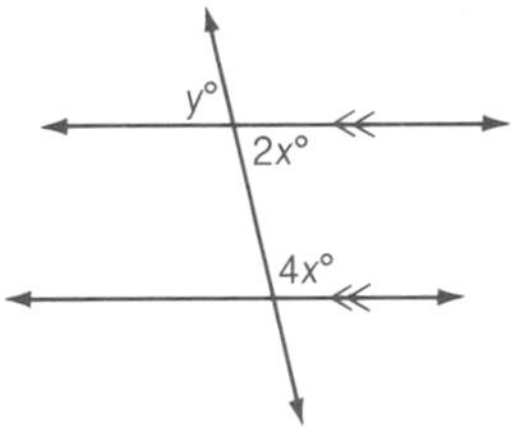


(b)

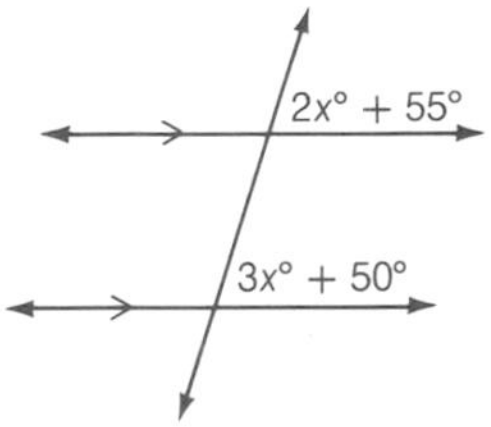


8 Find the missing measures.

(a)

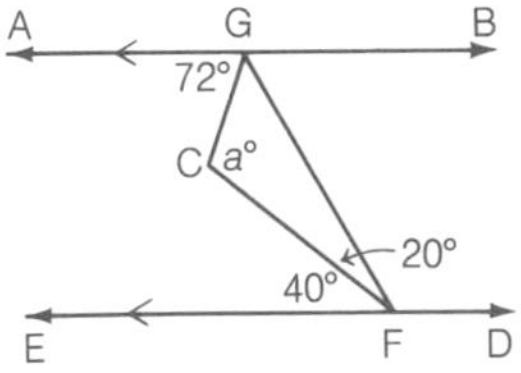


(b)

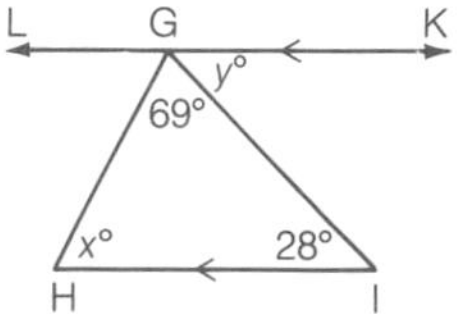


(c)

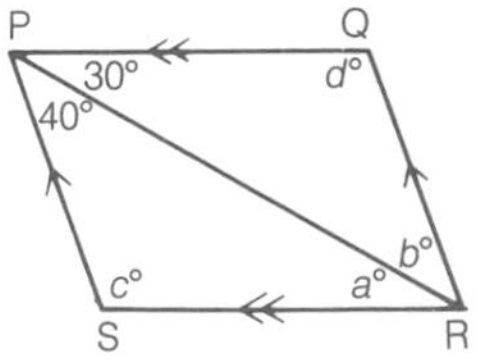


(d)

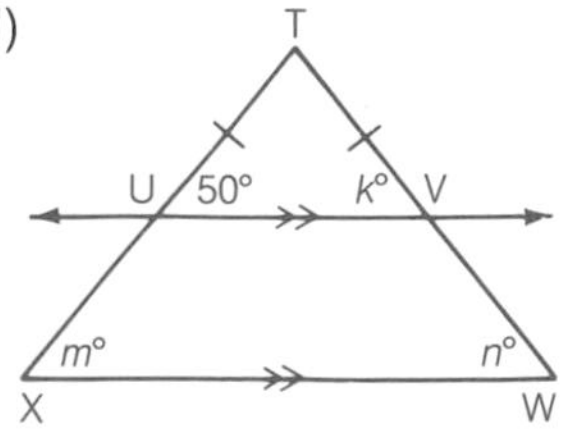


9 In the diagram showing some construction, the braces are used to support the wall. Find the missing measures.

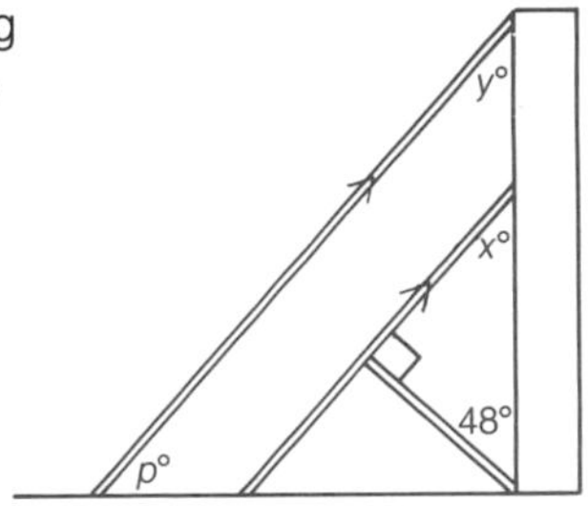


10 The diagram shows a car designer's plan for the geometry of the side windows. If CE = ED, find the missing measures.

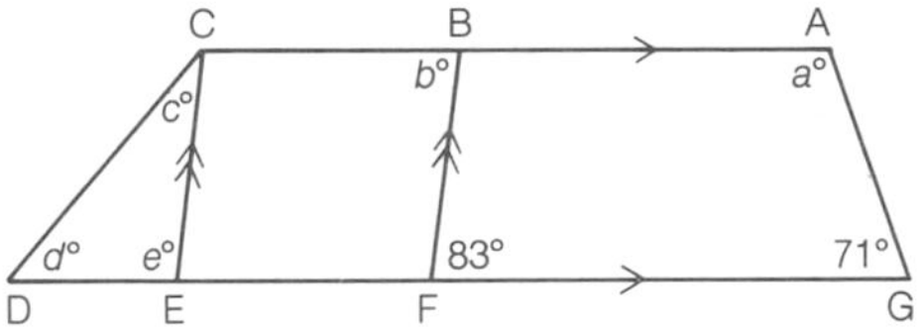


**C**

11 (a) List various ways in which parallel structures occur in constructing buildings.

(b) Find various ways parallel lines are used in design. Use newspapers, magazines, fabric, wallpaper design.

## Career Tip

Civil engineering technicians use many skills in mathematics. They are often asked to interpret information on diagrams, analyze reports, as well as conduct tests on various construction materials.

# Applications: Art and Perspective

Artists try to overcome the difficulty of showing three-dimensional objects on a two-dimensional surface by using the principle of perspective. This technique was discovered in Italy during the Renaissance, at the beginning of the fifteenth century. It became generally accepted after Leonardo da Vinci wrote about the technique of perspective and used it in his paintings.
Lines that are parallel in the real world are made to intersect at a vanishing point in a painting.
To use perspective, the artist selects one, two or three "vanishing points" on his canvas and draws a real life picture.

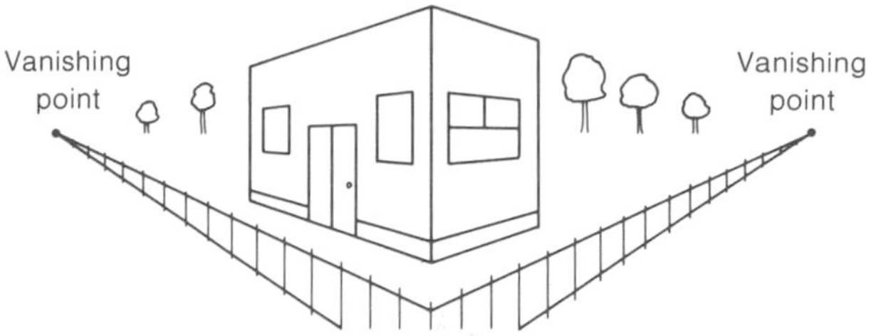


The early artists had no knowledge of perspective. Their paintings did not appear life like. In the above painting, the artist uses perspective to make the subject of the painting appear life like.

You can use perspective to create interesting letters.

Select a letter and a vanishing point.

Draw construction lines to the vanishing point.

Draw parallel lines as shown.

Erase the construction lines. You have a three dimensional letter E.

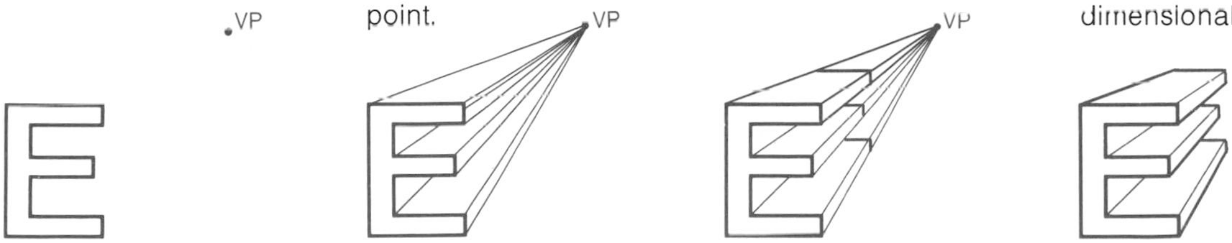


12 Use perspective to create three dimensional letters.
(a) (b) (c)

13 A vanishing point was used to create the three dimensional title.

(a) Where is the vanishing point?
(b) Reconstruct a copy of your own for the above title.

14 Use perspective to put your name in three dimensional block letters. Remember you must choose a vanishing point.

15 Vanishing points are used in the following artists' drawings of a turntable. Various points are marked for reference. In each
- ▶ which point(s) is a vanishing point?
- ▶ Name two lines that are parallel on the real turntable.

(a)

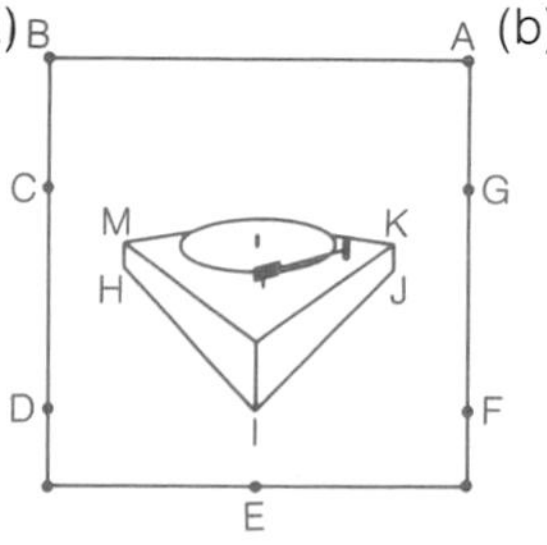


(b)

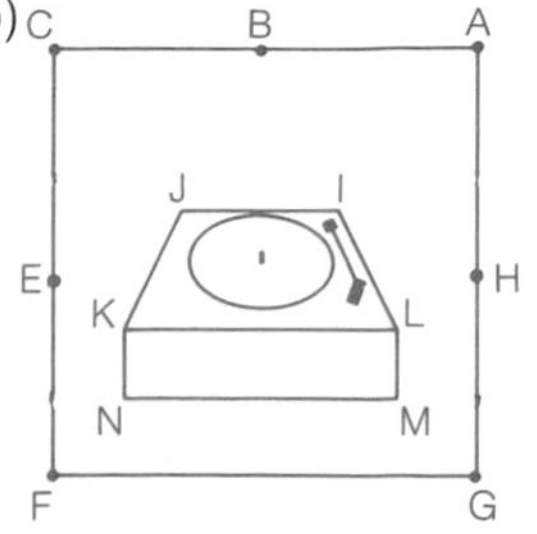

# 14.6 Exploring Angles in Circles

To explore the properties of circles, you need to review the names of its parts.

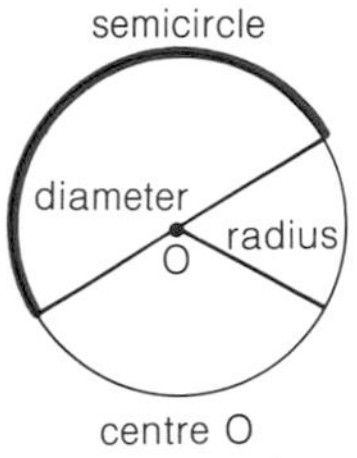


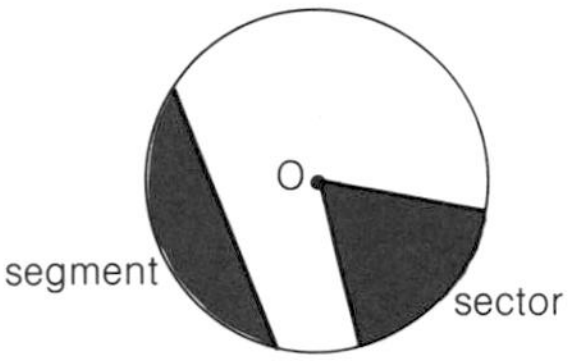


Special names are given to certain line segments and angles related to circles.

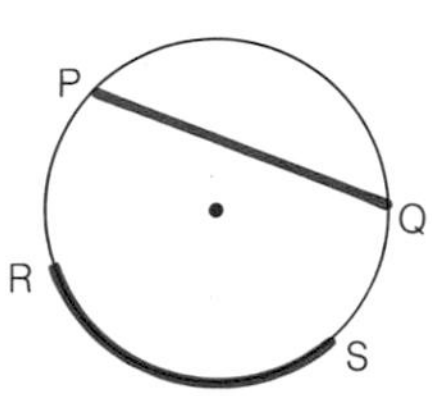


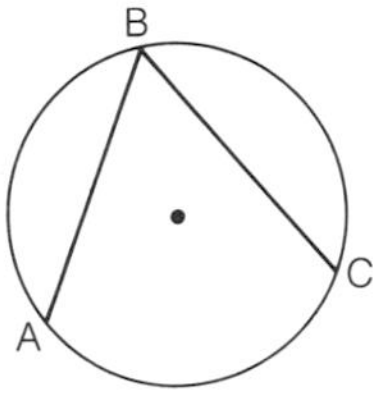


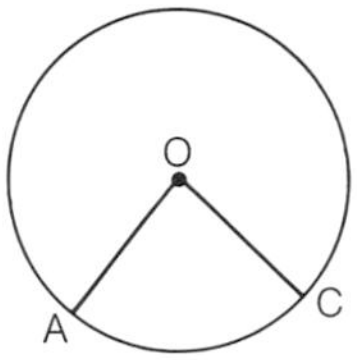


PQ is a **chord**. RS is an **arc**

∠ABC is an **inscribed angle** on arc AC.

∠AOC is a central, or **sector angle** on arc AC.

Whenever you do an assignment, on a job site or in school, you need to follow instructions carefully and precisely. When you solve a problem in mathematics, or explore a diagram, you also need to follow instructions carefully. The following provide practice not only in geometric skills, but also in following instructions.

---

### Explore A: Inscribed angle on the diameter of a circle

1 (a) Refer to the sketch. Construct a copy of the diagram. O is the centre.
  (b) Measure ∠SPQ, which is drawn on the diameter of the circle.

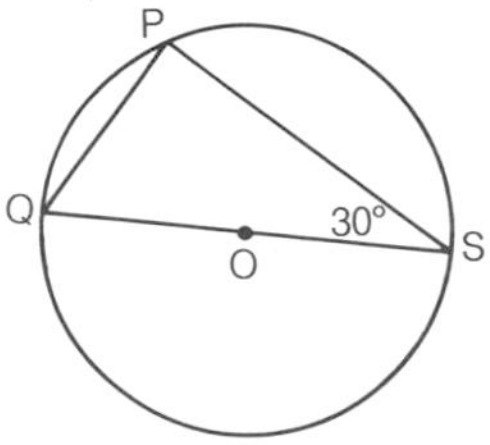


2 Follow these steps.
  *Step 1* Construct a circle with diameter 6 cm. Mark its center 0. Show a diameter of the circle, labelled SQ.
  *Step 2* Choose any point P on the circumference. Mark ∠SPQ in your diagram.
  *Step 3* Measure ∠SPQ. What is its measure?

3 (a) Repeat the steps in question 2 for other points P on the circle.
  (b) Measure each ∠SPQ. What is its measure?

4 (a) Construct any circle with center O. Draw a diameter AB for the circle.
  (b) Choose any point P on the circumference. Measure ∠APB. What is its measure?
  (c) Repeat steps (a) and (b) for other points P on the circumference of the circle.

5 Use your results in questions 1 to 4. What appears to be the measure when an angle is subtended by the diameter?

## Explore B: Inscribed angles of a circle

6 (a) Refer to the sketch. Construct a copy of the diagram. O is the centre. The radius of the circle is 4 cm. CD = 5 cm.

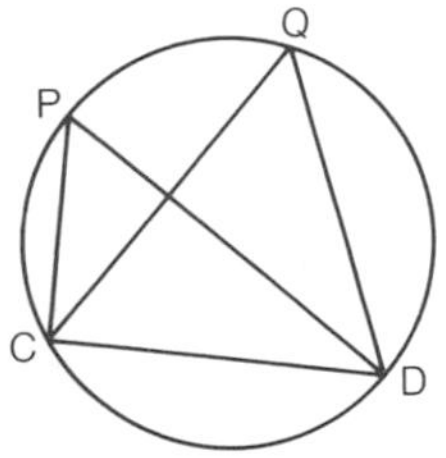


∠P and ∠Q are said to be subtended by the chord CD.

(b) Measure ∠P, ∠Q. What do you notice about their measures?

7 (a) Refer to the diagram in the previous question. Construct a circle with radius 5.5 cm. Construct a chord CD = 3 cm in the circle.

(b) Mark points P and Q on the circle. Measure ∠CPD and ∠CQD. What do you notice about their measures?

8 Repeat the steps in the previous question for each circle.

(a) diameter 9 cm, CD = 4 cm

(b) radius 6 cm, CD = 5.5 cm

9 Use your results in the previous questions, 6 to 8. What appears to be true about inscribed angles on the same chord?

## Explore C: Inscribed and central angles

10 (a) Refer to the sketch. Construct a copy of the diagram. 0 is the centre. The radius of the circle is 3 cm. Chord QR is 3.5 cm.

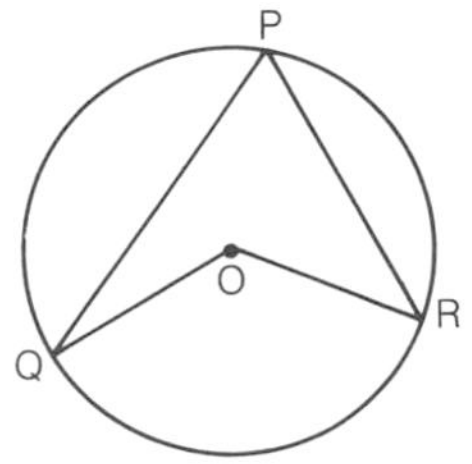


∠QPR is an inscribed angle
∠QOR is a central angle

(b) Measure ∠QPR and ∠QOR. What do you notice about their measures?

11 (a) Refer to the diagram in the previous question. Construct a circle with diagram 10 cm. Construct chord QR = 5 cm in the circle. Mark angles ∠QPR and ∠QOR.

(b) Measure ∠QPR and ∠QOR. What do you notice about their measures?

12 Repeat the steps in question 11 for each circle.

(a) diameter 11 cm, QR = 6 cm

(b) radius 6.2 cm, QR = 5.3 cm

13 Use your results in the previous questions, 10 to 12. What appears to be the relationship between the measures of an inscribed and central angle on the same chord?

## Explore D: Inscribed quadrilaterals

14 Quadrilateral ABCD is inscribed in the circle with center O. ∠A and ∠C are called *opposite angles of quadrilateral* ABCD.

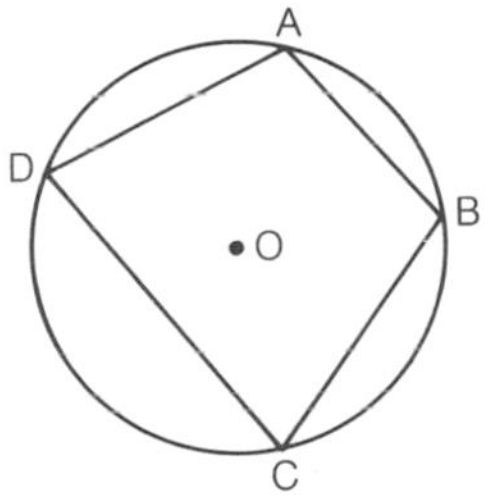


Follow these steps.

*Step 1* Construct a circle with center O and radius 4 cm. Construct quadrilateral ABCD inscribed in the circle. CD = 4.5 cm.

Step 2 Measure ∠A and ∠C. Find their sum, to the nearest degree.

*Step 3* Measure ∠B and ∠D. Find their sum, to the nearest degree.

What do you notice about your answers in Step 2 and Step 3?

15 Repeat the steps in the previous question for the following circles.

(a) radius 3.2 cm, AD = 4.5 cm

(b) diameter 9.6 cm, BC = 3.4 cm

16 Refer to your results in questions 14 and 15. What appears to be true about the opposite angles of an inscribed quadrilateral?

# 14.7 Finding Measures: Angles in Circles

In many fields of study, important discoveries are made by exploring. In the study of geometry, important properties can be found by again exploring. In the previous section, you explored angles in circles and obtained the following results.

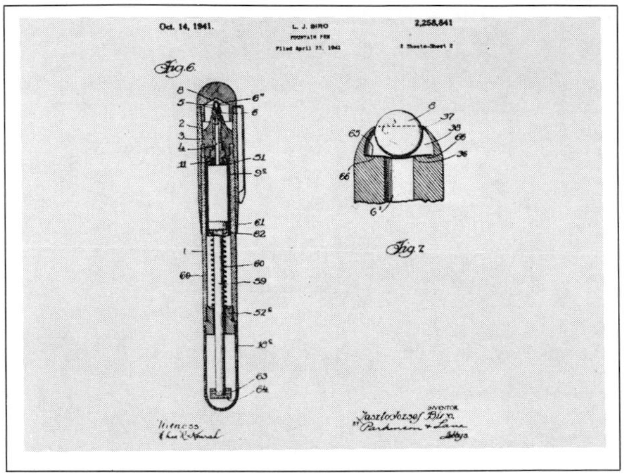


Did you know that the first ballpoint pen was devised in 1938. Laslo Biro, the inventor, explored a variety of ways to prevent his first ballpoint from blotting. By 1944 he had perfected his pen and that year 30 000 were made. Since that time, more than a billion ballpoint pens have been manufactured, used and discarded.

**Angle Property I**
The Inscribed Angle drawn on a diameter is a right angle.

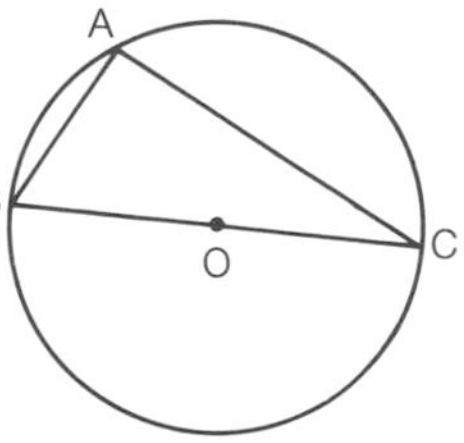


BC diameter
$\angle A = 90°$

**Angle Property II**
Inscribed Angles drawn on the same chord have equal measures.

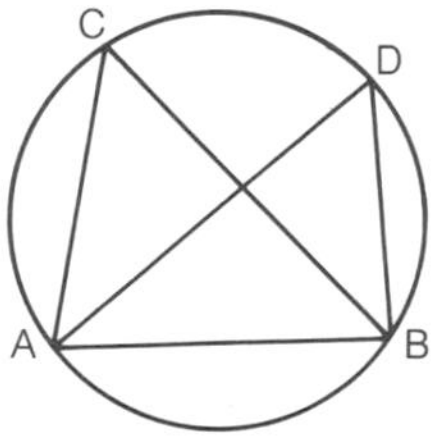


$\angle C$ and $\angle D$ are inscribed on the same chord AB.
$\angle C = \angle D$

**Angle Property III**
The measure of a central angle in a circle is twice the inscribed angle drawn on the same chord.

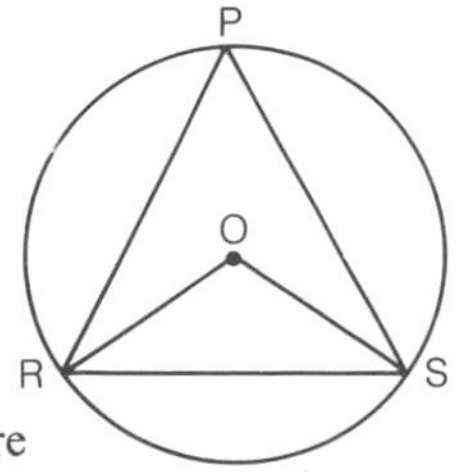


$\angle P$ and $\angle ROS$ are inscribed on the same chord RS.
$\angle P = \frac{1}{2}\angle ROS$ or $\angle ROS = 2\angle P$

**Angle Property IV**
The opposite angles of an inscribed quadrilateral are supplementary (their sum is 180°).

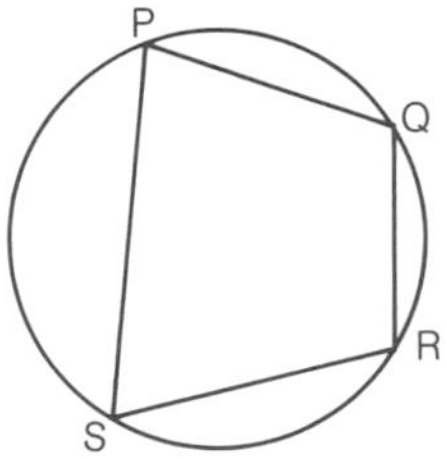


PQRS is an inscribed quadrilateral.

| | |
|---|---|
| $\angle P$ and $\angle R$ are opposite. | $\angle Q$ and $\angle S$ are opposite |
| $\angle P + \angle R = 180°$ | $\angle Q + \angle S = 180°$ |

Based on these properties you can find the measures of angles inscribed in a circle.

### Example

Find the missing measures. Give reasons for your answers.

(a)

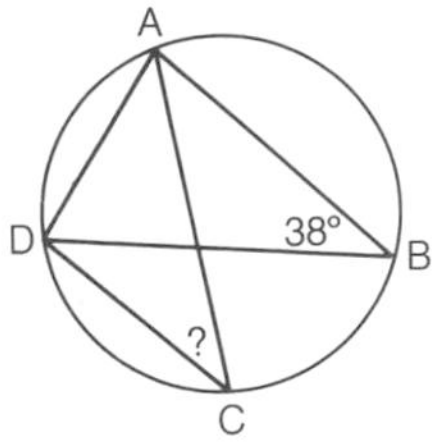


(b)

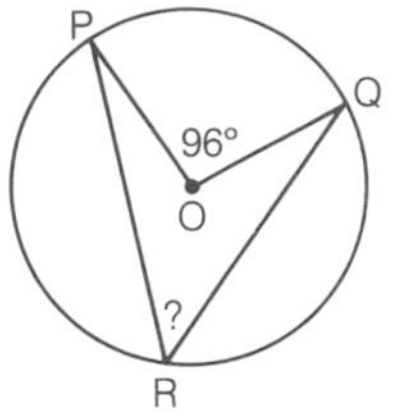


### Solution

(a) ∠ABD, ∠ACD are inscribed angles on the same chord. *Give a reason for your work.*

$\angle ACD = \angle ABD$ But $\angle ABD = 38°$

Thus $\angle ACD = 38°$

(b) ∠POQ is a central angle and ∠PRQ is an inscribed angle on the same arc.

$\angle PRQ = \frac{1}{2}\angle POQ$ *Give a reason.*

$= \frac{1}{2}(96°) = 48°$

## Try These

1 Refer to the diagram. Identify each angle.
   (a) a central angle on a chord
   (b) an inscribed angle on a chord
   (c) a central angle on an arc
   (d) an inscribed angle on an arc
   (e) an inscribed angle on a semicircle
   (f) an inscribed quadrilateral
   (g) a pair of opposite angles

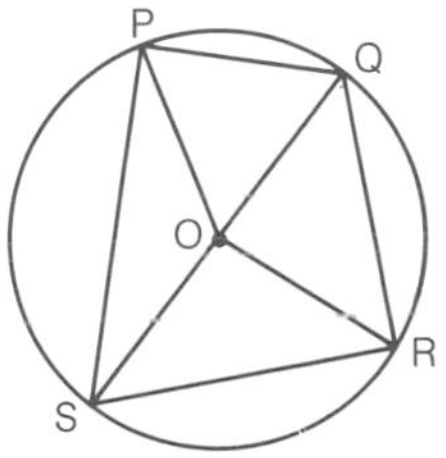


2 Each diagram shows a property about angles on circles. What is the property?

(a)

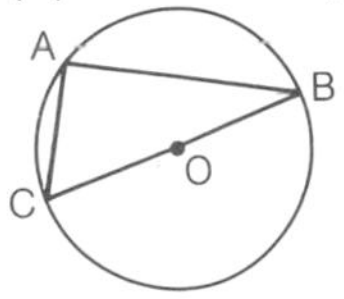


(b)

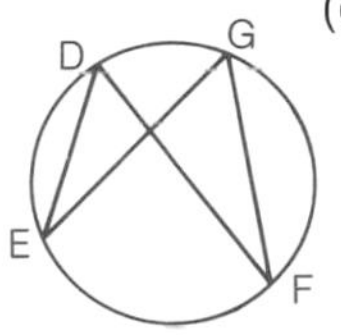


(c)

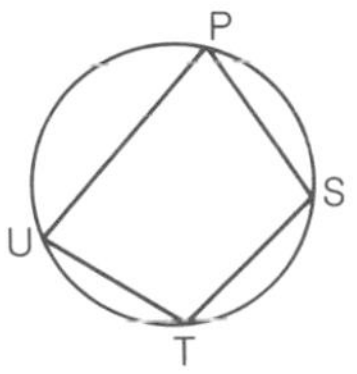


(d)

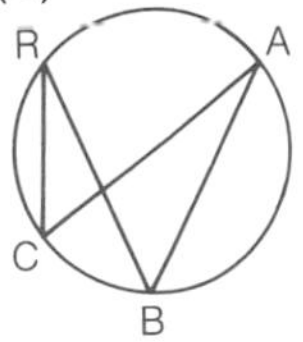


(e)

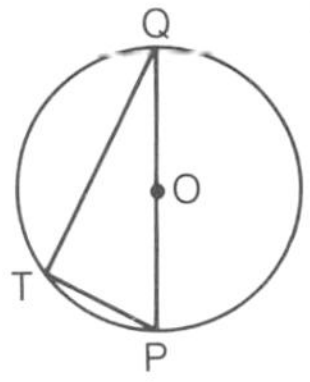


(f)

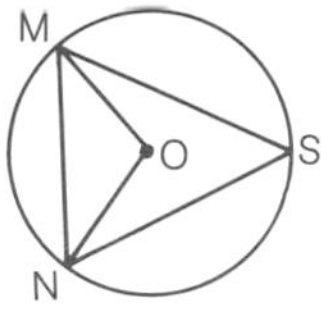


## Written Exercises

**A** Review the 3 properties of inscribed angles in a circle.

1 Refer to the circles. Name the following parts in the circles shown. The centres are marked by O.

(a) a radius
(b) a diameter
(c) a chord
(d) a semicircle
(e) an arc
(f) a sector
(g) a segment
(h) an inscribed angle on a chord
(i) a central angle on a chord

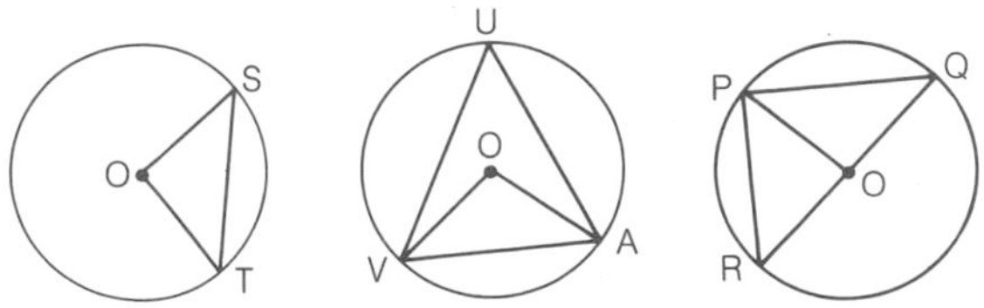

2 For each of the diagrams, name the inscribed angles; central angles.

(a)

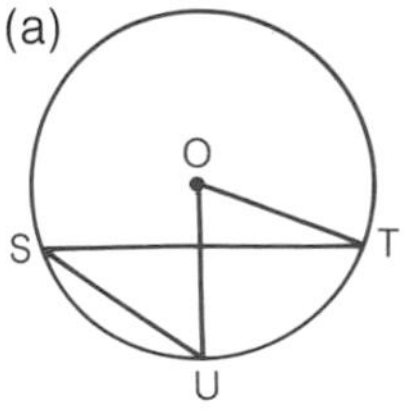


(b)

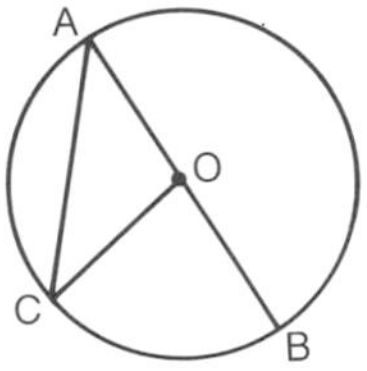


(c)

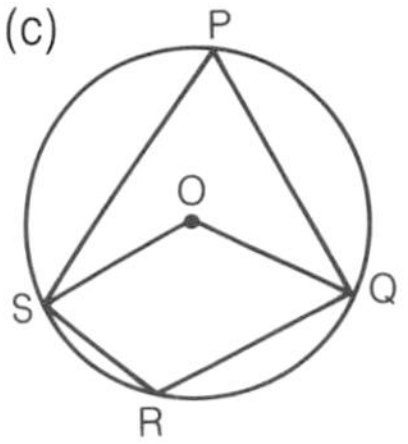


(d)

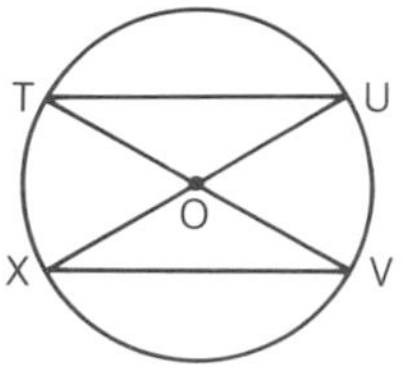


3 How are angles P and A related in each diagram?

(a)

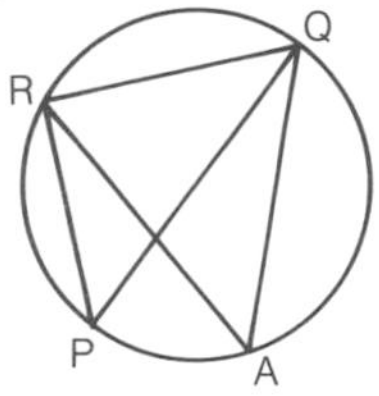


(b)

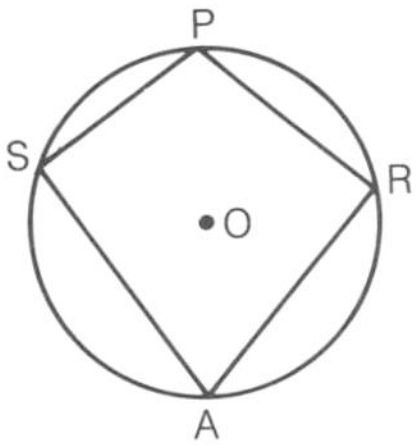


(c)

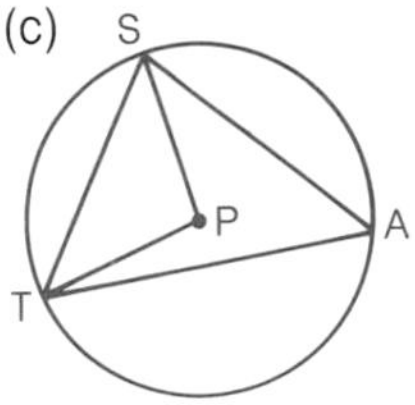


(d)

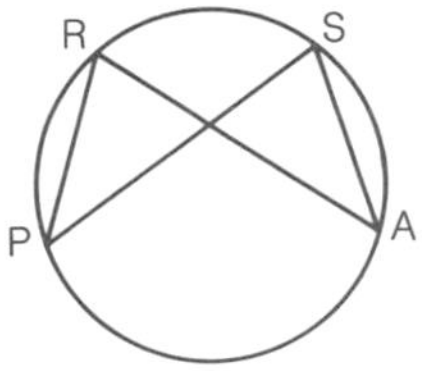


4 Refer to each diagram

(a) Why is ∠A = ∠B? What is the value of *m*?

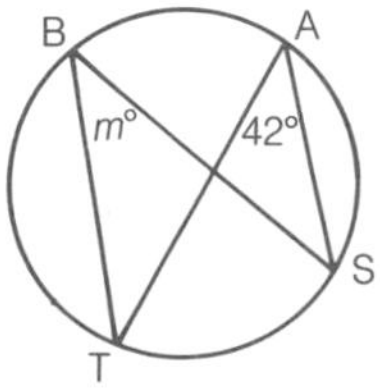


(b) What type of line segment is PQ? What is the measure of ∠S?

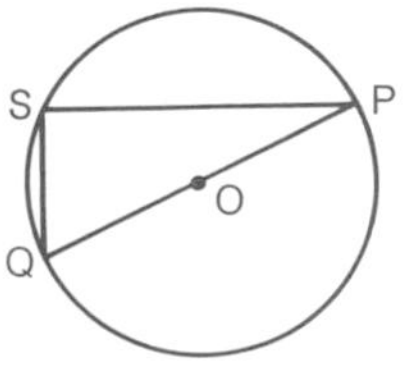


(c) Which angle in the diagram is a central angle; an inscribed angle? What is the measure of ∠POQ?

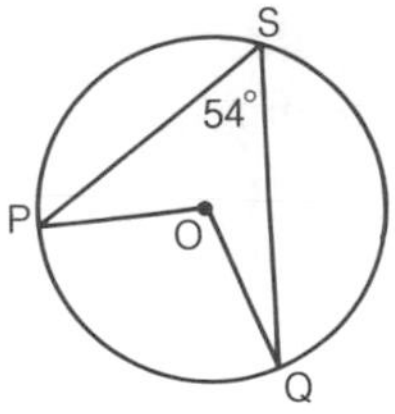

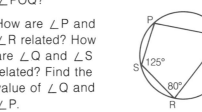

(d) How are ∠P and ∠R related? How are ∠Q and ∠S related? Find the value of ∠Q and ∠P.

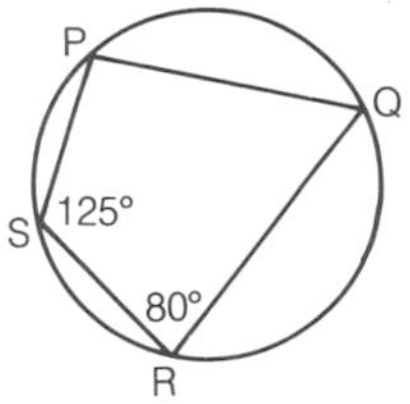

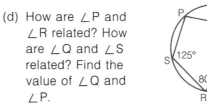

5 An arc subtends each angle at the circumference. What is the measure of the corresponding central angle?

(a) 20° (b) 40° (c) 100°

6 An arc subtends each angle at the centre of the circle. What is the measure of the corresponding inscribed angle at the circumference?

(a) 80° (b) 50° (c) 110°

**B** For the following exercises, remember the following.

- To find the missing measures in some problems, you need to use other properties of geometric figures.
- Carefully examine a diagram involving circles to decide which angles are equal or related.

7 For each diagram, which angles are equal?

(a)

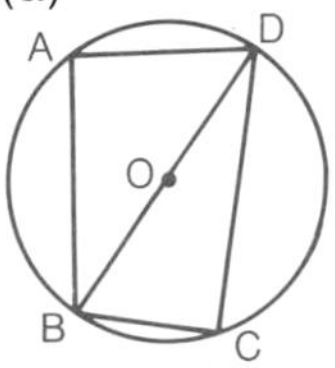


(b)

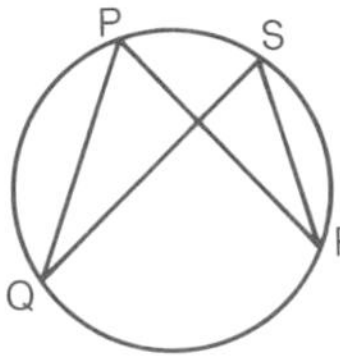


(c)

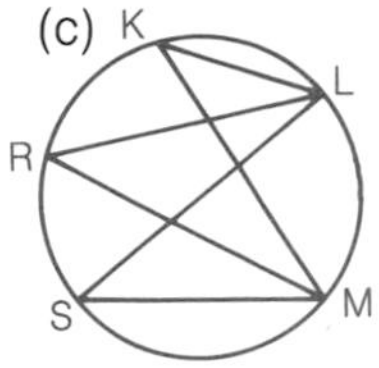


8 Which property of angles in a circle is used to find each measure? Find each missing measure. Give reasons for your answers.

(a)

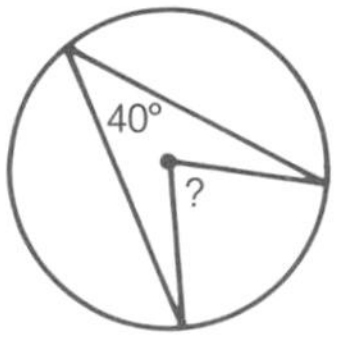


(b)

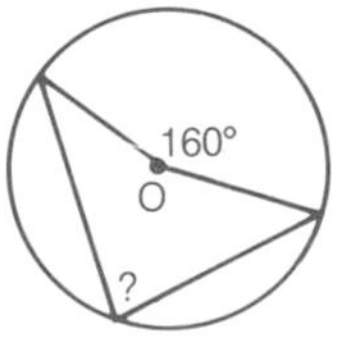


(c)

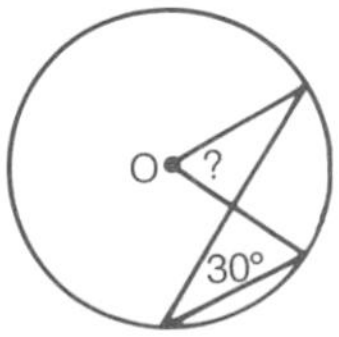

9 Which property of angles in a circle is used to find each measure?

(a)

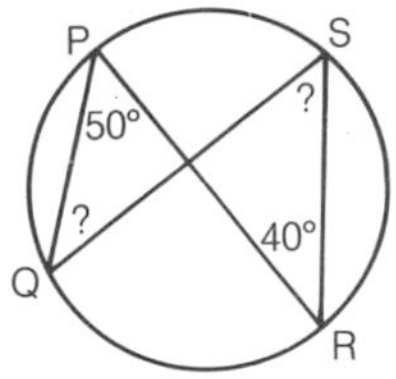


(b)

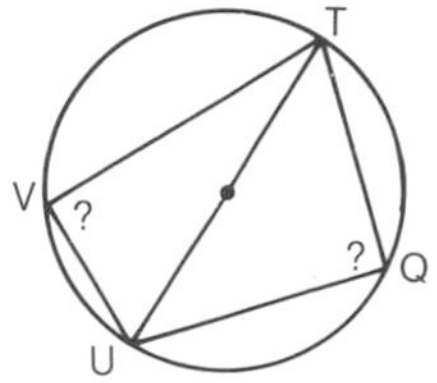


10 Find the missing measures. Do not use your protractor.

(a)

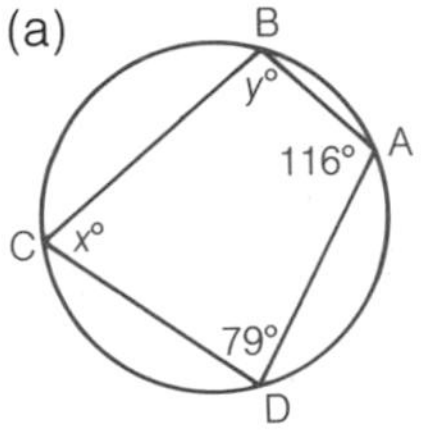


(b)

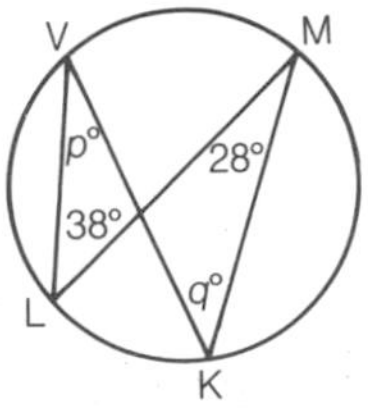


(c)

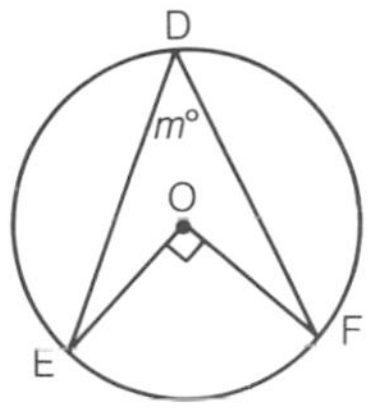


(d)

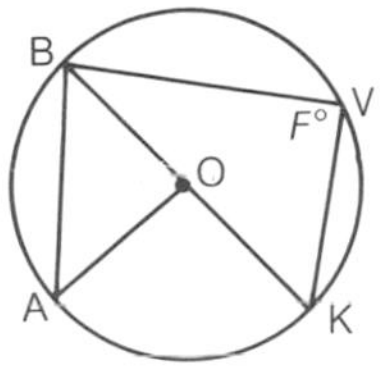


(e)

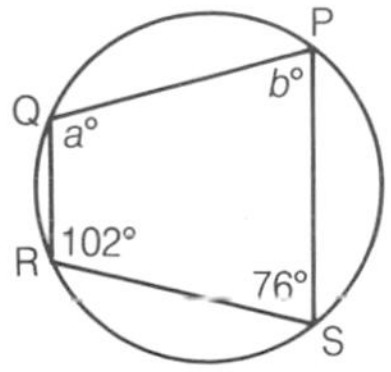


(f)

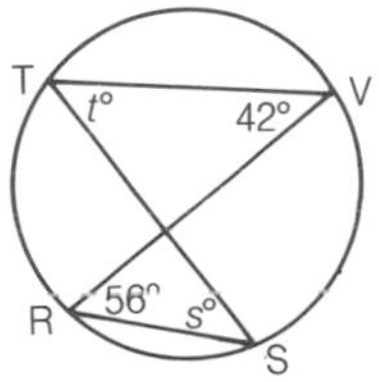


(g)

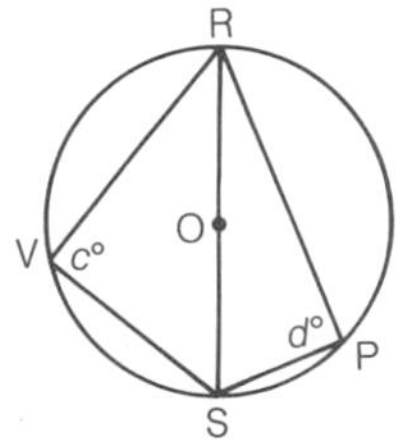


(h)

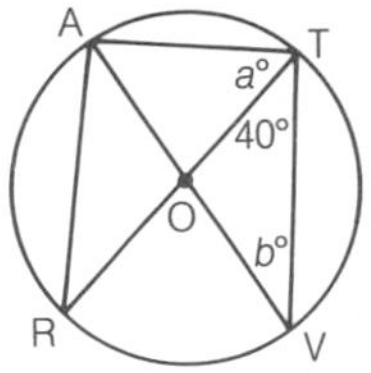


To solve some problems you may need to use more than one geometric fact.

11 (a) How are the angles in $\triangle$PQR related?
(b) Find the missing measures.

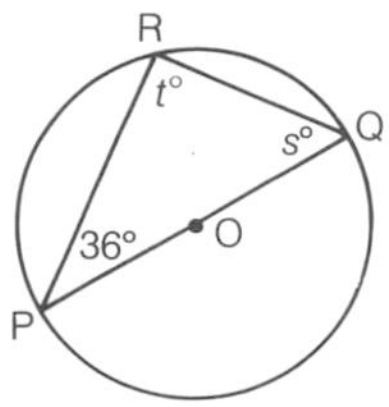


12 (a) Which angles in the diagram are equal?
(b) Find the missing measures.

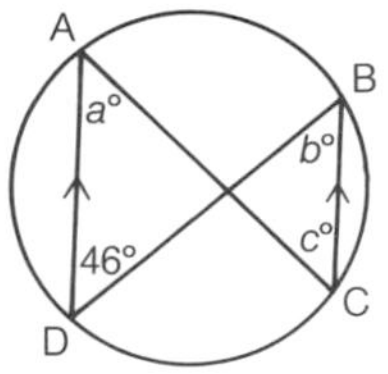


13 (a) Which angles are supplementary?
(b) Find the missing measures.

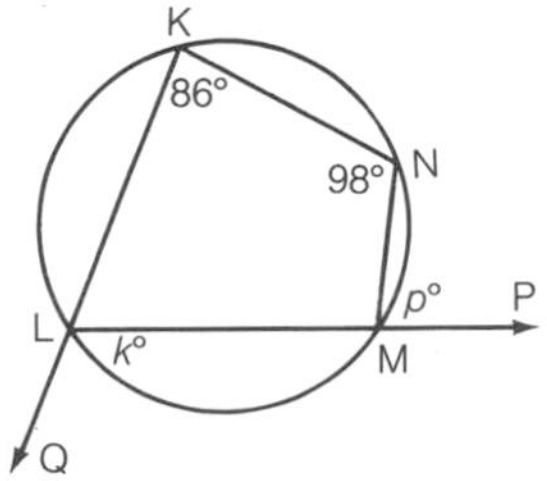


14 Find the missing measures. (Remember, you may need to use more than one property about geometric figures.)

(a)

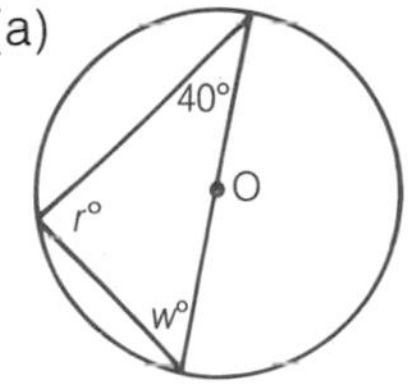


(b)

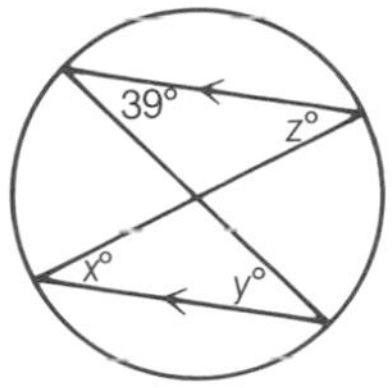


(c)

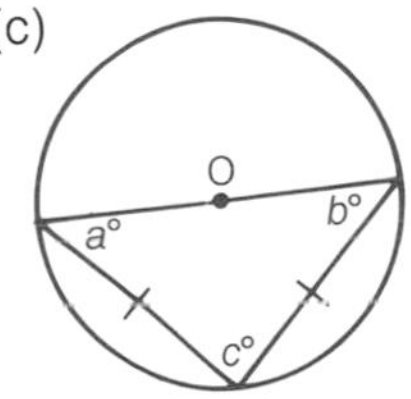


(d)

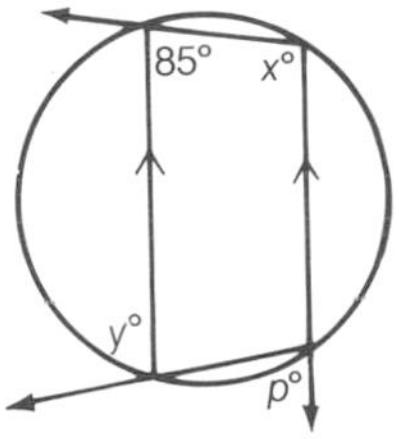


(e)

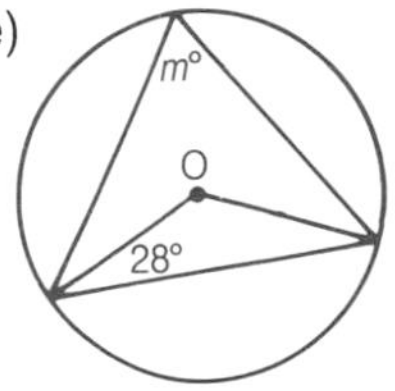


(f)

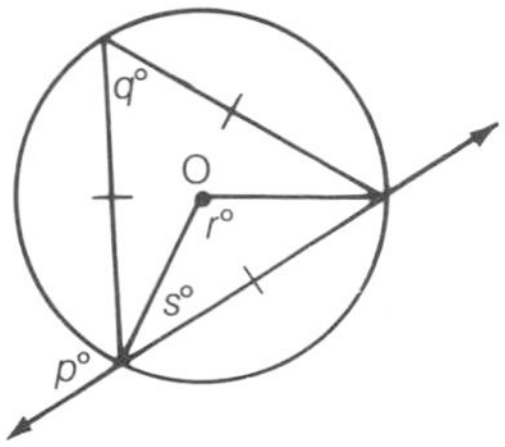


(g)

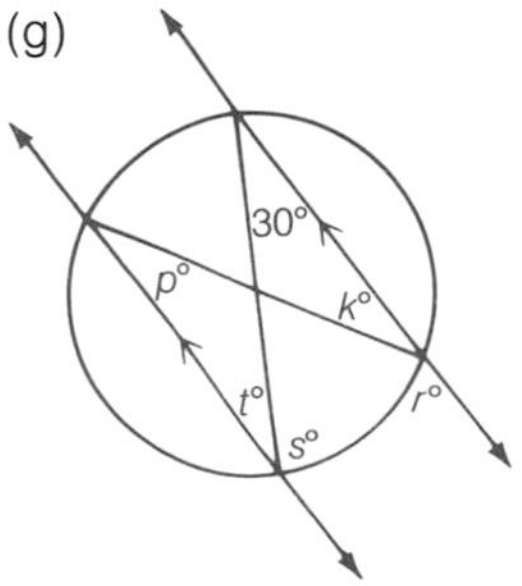


(h)

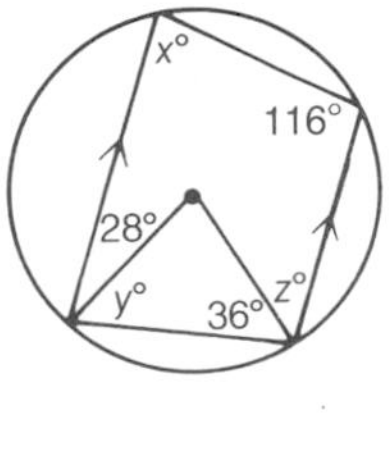

## Measuring Angles: Radians

In your previous work with angles, you measured angles using degrees. The notion of measuring in terms of degrees is based on a complete rotation.

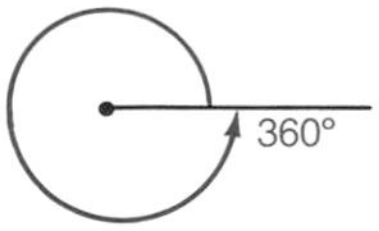


One complete rotation or revolution = 360°

Another system of measuring angles is also based on using a circle, and arcs of circles.

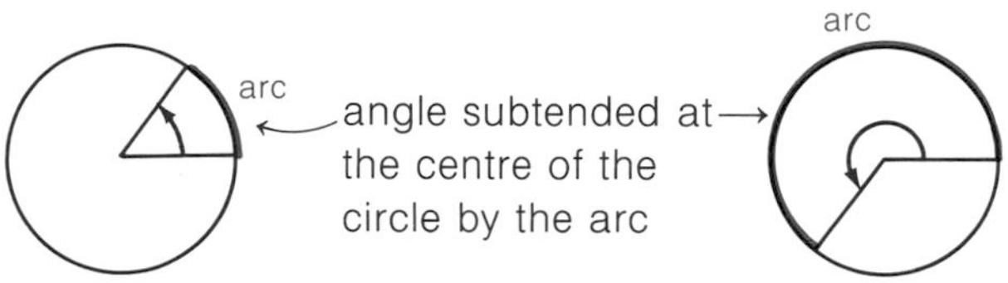


When the arc on the circumference of the circle is equal in length to the radius, you obtain an angle for which the measure is 1 radian.

A radian is the measure of the angle subtended at the centre of the circle by an arc equal in length to the radius of the circle.

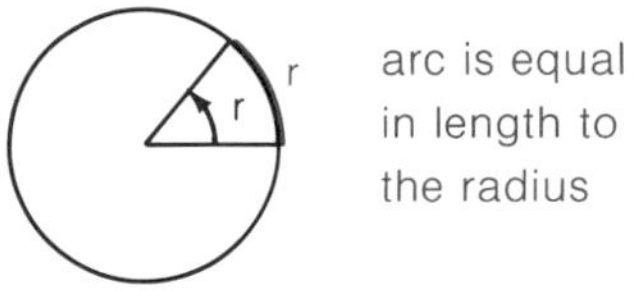


The relationship between degrees and radians is shown by the diagram. Use a radius of one unit.

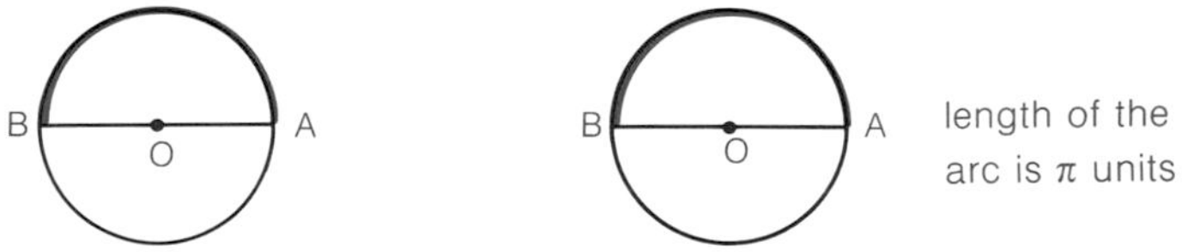


$\angle AOB = 180°$ degrees $\qquad \angle AOB = \pi$ radians

$180°$degrees $= \pi$ radians

Thus 1 degree $= \dfrac{\pi}{180}$ radians $\qquad$ 1 radian $= \dfrac{180}{\pi}$ degrees

$= 0.017\,453\,2$ radians $\qquad = 57.295\,78$ degrees

---

15 Write each radian measure as a degree measure.

(a) $\frac{\pi}{2}$ (b) $\frac{\pi}{3}$ (c) $\frac{\pi}{4}$ (d) $\frac{\pi}{6}$

(e) $\frac{3}{4}\pi$ (f) $\frac{2}{3}\pi$ (g) $\frac{3}{2}\pi$ (h) $2\pi$

16 Write each degree measure as a radian measure.

(a) 30° (b) 60° (c) 90° (d) 45°

(e) 52° (f) 65° (g) 75.3° (h) 143°

17 For each radian measure, find the degree measure to the nearest degree.

(a) 1.5 radians (b) 0.65 radians (c) 0.46 radians (d) 2.3 radians

18 (a) Show why

1 complete revolution $= 2\pi$ radians.

(b) A wheel makes 5 complete revolutions every second. Express this speed as radian per second.

19 Express each rate as radians per second.

(a) 10 revolutions per second

(b) 5.3 revolutions per second

(c) 160 revolutions per second

# 14.8 Exploring Chords in Circles

The steps in doing mathematics repeat often as follows.
*Step 1* You learn new facts, properties, etc in mathematics.
*Step 2* You apply these facts, properties, etc to solve problems.

In this section you will explore the properties of chords in circles. In the next section you will apply them to solve problems.

## Explore A: Chords and perpendicular bisectors

1 (a) Construct a circle with radius 4.5 cm. Indicate the centre as O.
(b) Construct a chord CD, 5 cm in length.
(c) Construct the perpendicular bisector of CD. Through what point in the circle does the perpendicular bisector pass?

2 (a) Construct a circle of your choice with centre O. Record the radius of the circle to the nearest tenth of a centimetre.
(b) Draw any two chords CD and PQ in the circle. Construct the perpendicular bisector of each chord CD and PQ.
(c) What point in the circle do the perpendicular bisectors pass through?
(d) Repeat the previous steps (a), (b), (c), for circles of your own choice. Record the measures of the radii and the chords in each case.

3 Use your results in the previous questions 1 and 2. What appears to be true about the perpendicular bisector of any chord in the circle?

## Explore B: Chords and centres

4 Follow these steps.
*Step 1* Construct a circle with centre O and radius 4.3 cm.
*Step 2* Construct a chord CD 3.2 cm in the circle.
*Step 3* From O construct the perpendicular OF to the chord CD. F is a point on the chord.
*Step 4* Measure FC, FD. What do you notice?

5 Repeat the steps 1 to 4 in the previous question for each of the following measures.
(a) radius of circle 5.8 cm; chord CD = 4.3 cm
(b) diameter of circle 9.6 cm; chord CD = 3.8 cm
(c) Choose measures of your own for the diameter and the chord.

6 Use your results in questions 4 and 5. What appears to be true?

## Explore C: Midpoints and Centres

7 Follow these steps.
*Step 1* Construct a circle with centre O and radius 6.1 cm.
*Step 2* Construct a chord CD = 4.4 cm in the circle.
*Step 3* Find the midpoint M of the chord.
*Step 4* Measure $\angle$OMC and $\angle$OMD. What do you notice?

8 Repeat steps 1 to 4 in the previous question for each of the following measure.
(a) diameter 10.6 cm; chord CD = 5.4 cm
(b) radius 5.4 cm; chord 6.2 cm
(c) Choose measures of your own for the diameter and the chord.

9 Use your results in questions 7 and 8. What appears to be true?

### Math Tip

It is important to understand clearly the vocabulary of mathematics when solving problems.

- Make a list of all the new words you used in this chapter.
- Provide an example to illustrate each word.

# 14.9 Applying Skills: Chords and Circles

By exploring chords in circles in the previous section, you have learned these properties about chords.

**Chord Property I**
The perpendicular bisector of a chord passes through the centre of a circle.

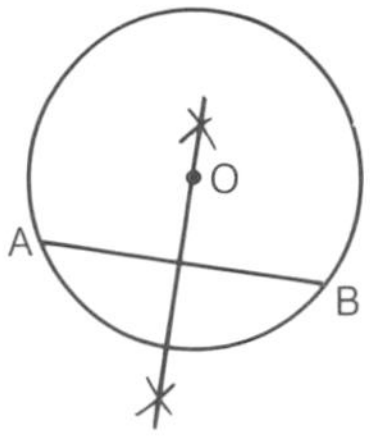


**Chord Property II**
A line drawn perpendicular to a chord from the centre bisects the chord.

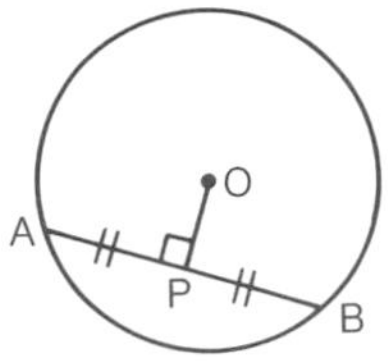


AP = PB

**Chord Property III**
The line segment drawn from the centre of a circle to the midpoint of the chord is perpendicular to the chord.

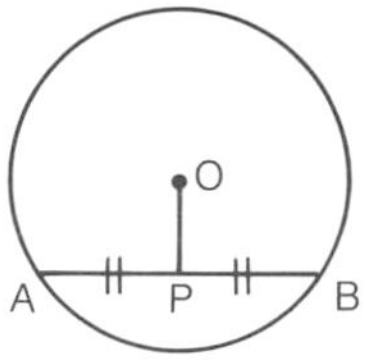


∠OPA = 90°

These properties of chords combined with other geometric properties are used to solve problems about circles.

## Example

A chord, 16.8 cm in length, is drawn in a circle with diameter 21 cm. How far is the chord from the centre of the circle?

## Solution

*Step 1* Sketch a diagram. Record the given information. Construct OP ⊥ DE.

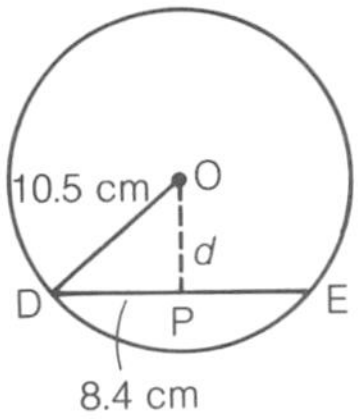


*Step 2* Find the missing measure, $d$. In right triangle OPD

$OP^2 + PD^2 = DO^2$

$d^2 + (8.4)^2 = (10.5)^2$

$d^2 = (10.5)^2 - (8.4)^2$

$d = 6.3$ ⟵ Use a calculator to find the answer efficiently.

[C] 8.4 [$x^2$] [MS] 10.5 [$x^2$] [−] [MR] [=] [√]

The chord is 6.3 cm from the centre of the circle.

## Try These

Each diagram shows properties about chords related to circles. What is the property?

(a)

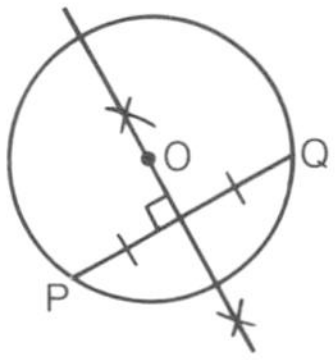


(b)

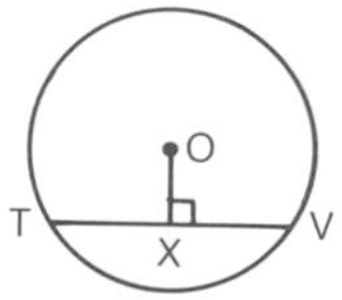


TX = XV

(c)

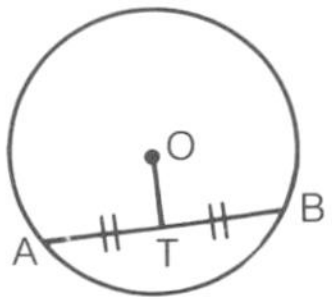


∠OTB = 90°

(d)

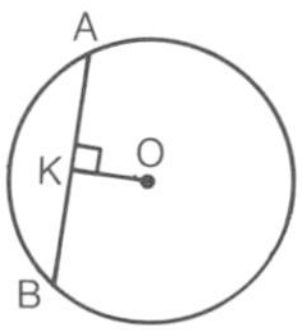


AK = KB

(e)

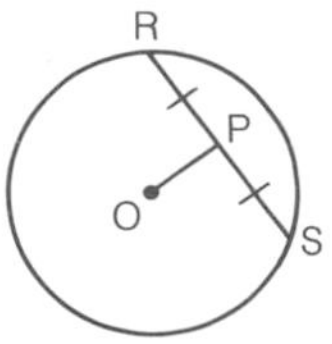


∠OPS = 90°

(f)

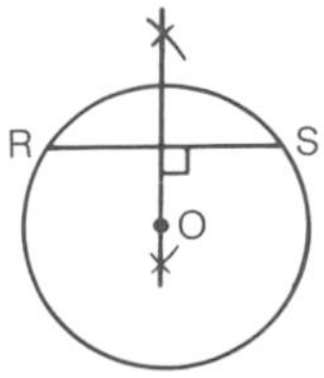

## Written Exercises

**A** Remember: to find missing measures, you can use the properties of chords.

1 (a) Construct a circle with diameter 7 cm and centre O. Draw a chord CD that is 5 cm in length.
(b) Construct a perpendicular OM to chord CD.
(c) How are the lengths CM, DM, related? Measure CM and DM.
(d) What property of chords is shown by (a)—(c).

2 (a) Construct a circle with radius 4.2 cm and centre O. Construct chord ST which measures 5 cm.
(b) Mark the centre C of chord ST. (Use the perpendicular bisector).
(c) How are ∠SCO and ∠TCO related?
(d) What property of chords is shown by (a)—(c).

3 Use the diagram. Find the length of the chord PQ. Justify your answer.

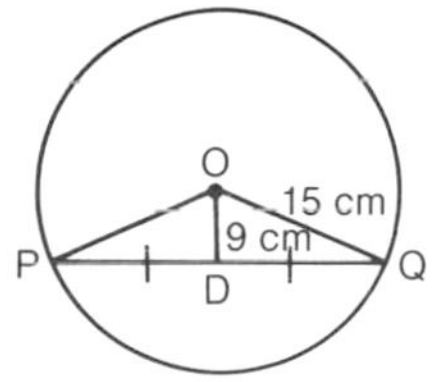


4 Find the length of the perpendicular OT.

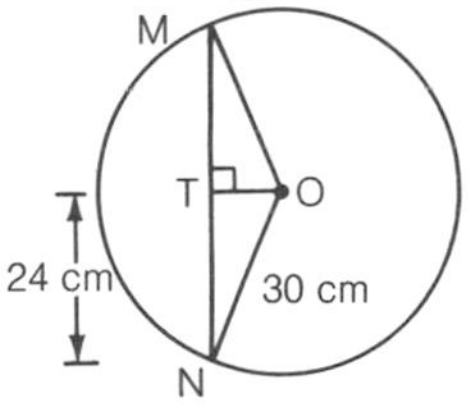


5 (a) Follow these steps.
*Step 1* Trace the base of a circular object such as a can.
*Step 2* Construct two chords AB, CD in the circle. AB and CD are not parallel.
*Step 3* Construct the perpendicular bisectors of each chord. Extend them to intersect at O.
(b) What is special about the point O?

6 Use the steps in the previous question.
(a) Trace the base of a circular cup. Locate the centre of the circle.
(b) Trace any circular object. Locate the centre of the circular object.
(c) A circular garden is placed in a park. A flag-pole is to be placed at its centre. How would you locate the centre of the garden?

**B** Express your answers to 1 decimal place. Use efficient procedures on a calculator.

7 Use the diagram. Find the length of the chord PQ. O is the centre of the circle.

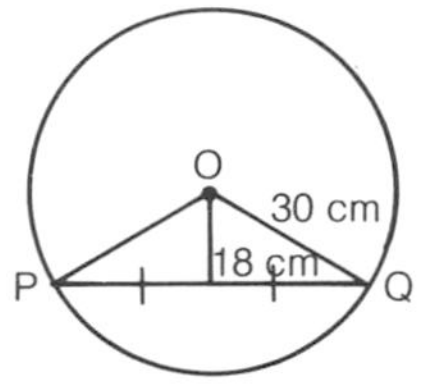


8 In each diagram, find the missing measure.

(a)

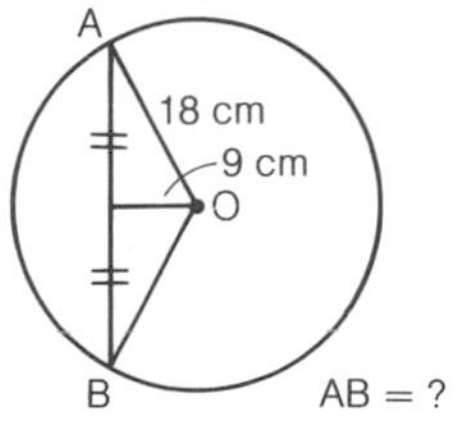


(b)

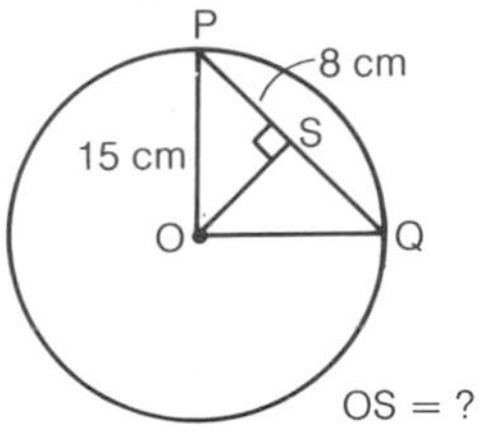


(c)

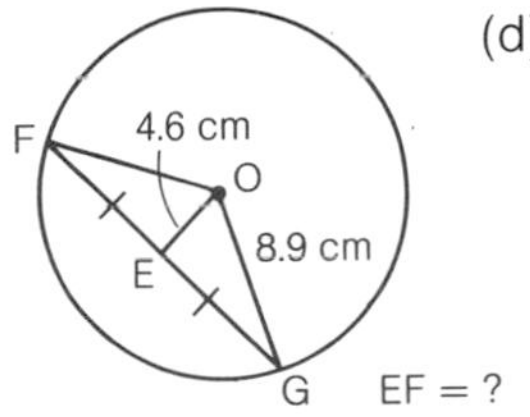


(d)

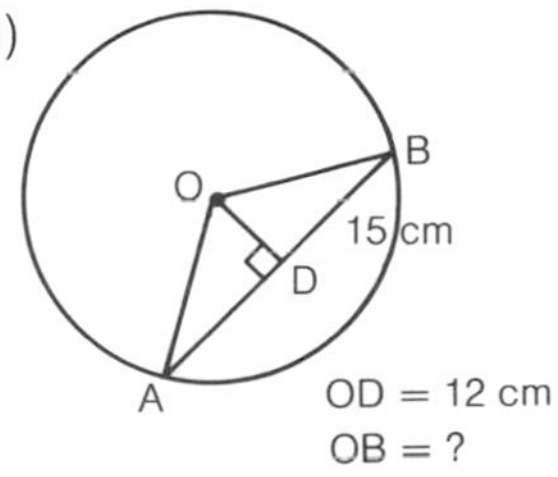


9 A chord PQ, 8.0 cm in length is drawn in a circle with radius 6.5 cm. How far is the chord from the centre of the circle?

10 The diameter of a circle is 10.6 cm, and a perpendicular is drawn to a chord. The perpendicular distance to the chord is 3.2 cm. What is the length of the chord?

11 The distance from the centre of a circle to a chord is 2.4 cm. If the radius is 4.3 cm, how long is the chord?

12 At the hydro plant, the surface of a circular pipe is to be reconditioned. To give a base to work on, a scaffold is built as shown. If the radius of the pipe is 8.4 m, how high is the top of the pipe from the scaffold?

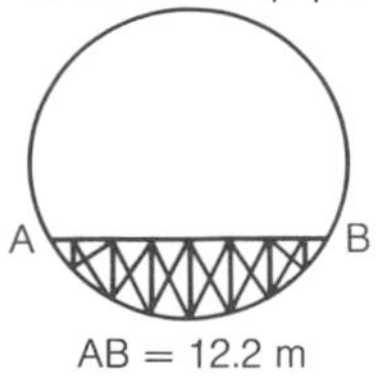

# 14.10 Problem Solving: Interpretation

Often in solving a problem you need to interpret the problem in a different way and use your earlier skills. For example, how would you solve the following problem?

### Problem

How could you draw a circle so that the vertices of △ABC lie on the circumference?

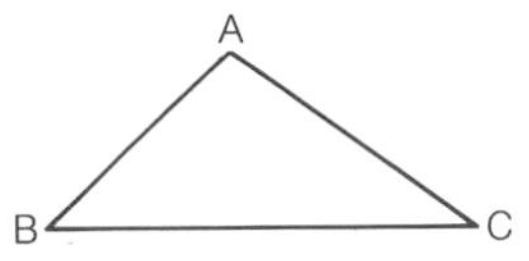


### Solution

To do so, interpret the sides of the triangles to be chords. Construct the perpendicular bisectors of the chords. The intersection is the centre of the required circle.

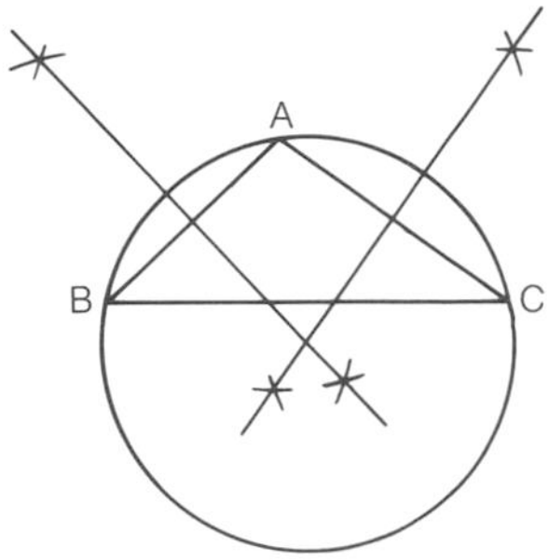


The circle drawn above is given a special name. The **circumcircle** of a triangle is the circle that passes through all the vertices of the triangle. △ABC is said to be inscribed in the circle.

## Written Exercises

You will need to use your construction skills to complete the following exercises.

1 (a) Construct triangle ABC with the following sides: 8 cm, 5 cm, 9 cm.
(b) Construct the circumcircle of △ABC.

2 (a) Use the sketch. Construct △STU.
(b) Construct the circumcircle of △STU.

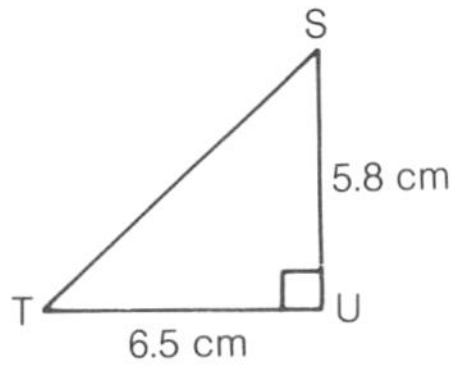


3 (a) Construct a triangle of your own choice.
(b) Construct the circumcircle of the triangle.

4 (a) Mark any 3 points P, Q, R, on a piece of paper, not all in a straight line.
(b) Locate the point S that is equidistant from P, Q, and R.

5 You know the following property of angles in a circle.
"The inscribed angle drawn on a diameter of a circle measures 90°."
(a) Use this geometric fact to develop a method for locating the centre of any circle.
(b) Test your method in (a). Trace a circular object. Locate the centre of the circle based on your method in (a).

6 These statements are made about chords in a circle.
I Chords that are the same distance from the centre of a circle are equal in length.
II Chords that are equal in length are the same distance from the centre of a circle.
(a) Do these statements seem to be reasonably true?
(b) Use different circles and chords. Use constructions to show whether statements I and II appear to be confirmed by your construction.

# Review: Practice and Problems

1 Find each missing measure.

(a)

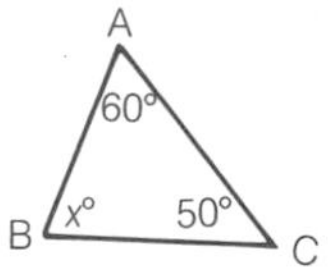


(b)

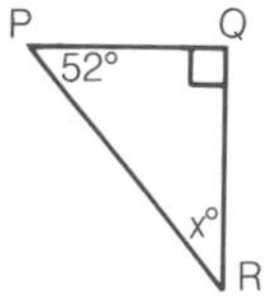


(c)

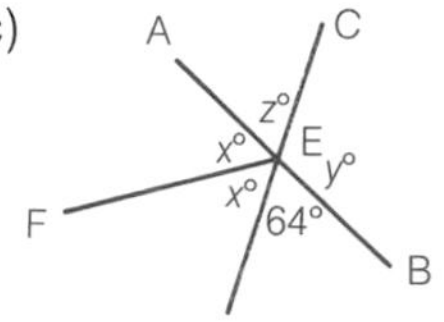


(d)

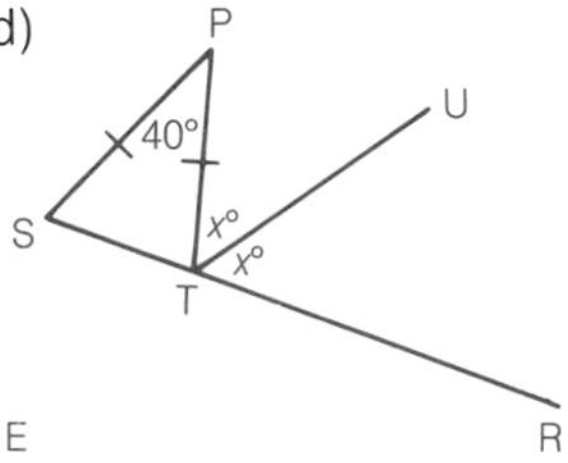


(e)

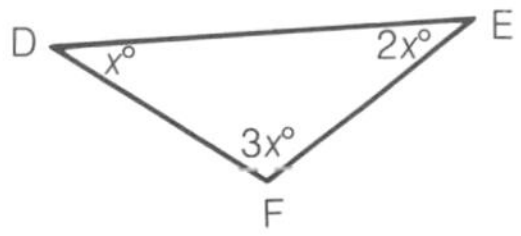

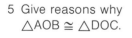

2 Construct each triangle.

(a) $\triangle ABC$, $\angle A = 46°$, $AB = 6$ cm, $BC = 7$ cm

(b) $\triangle PQR$, $\angle R = 62°$, $\angle Q = 41°$, $QR = 6$ cm

(c) $\triangle LMN$, $\angle L = 108°$, $\angle M = 34°$, $\angle N = 38°$

3 Find the missing measures in each figure.

(a)

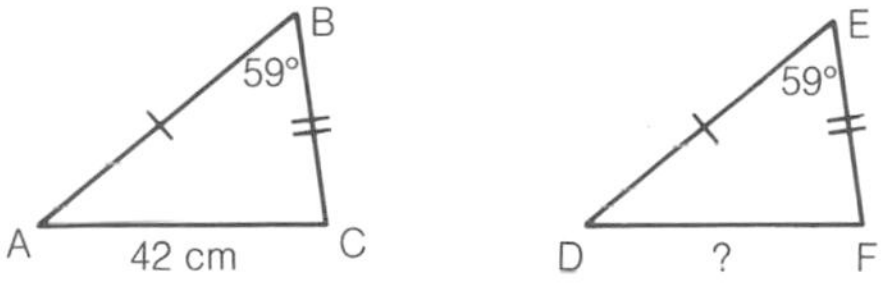


(b)

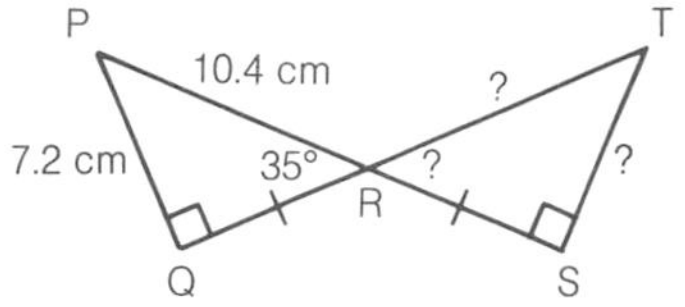


4 (a) Use the diagram shown.

(b) What information do you know?

(c) Write the congruence relations in the diagram.

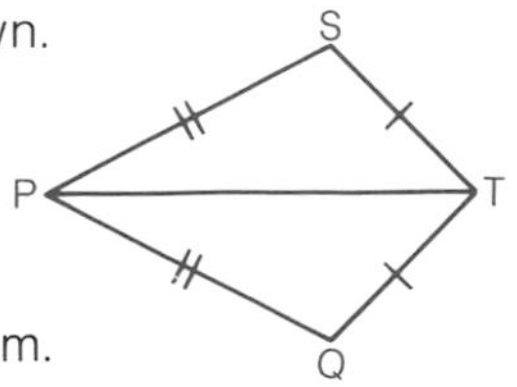


5 Give reasons why $\triangle AOB \cong \triangle DOC$.

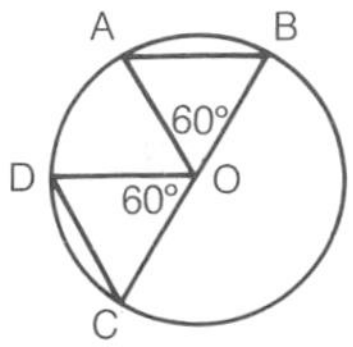


6 Use the information in the diagram to find the missing measures.

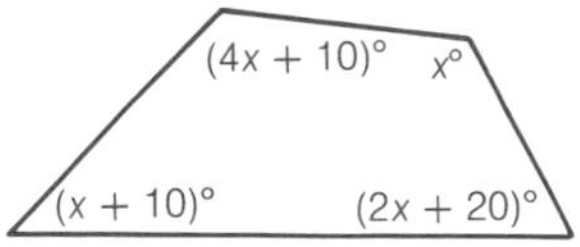


7 A plaza is drawn to scale in the shape of a quadrilateral PQRS.

$PQ = PS = 7.5$ cm $\angle P = 64°$ $\angle Q = 108°$

$QR = RS$

(a) What other information do you know about the quadrilateral?

(b) Construct the quadrilateral.

(c) If 1 cm represents 8.2 m, what is the length of RS?

8 Find the missing values.

(a)

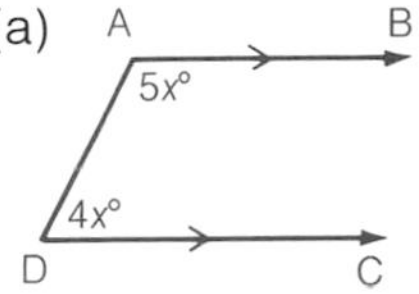


(b)

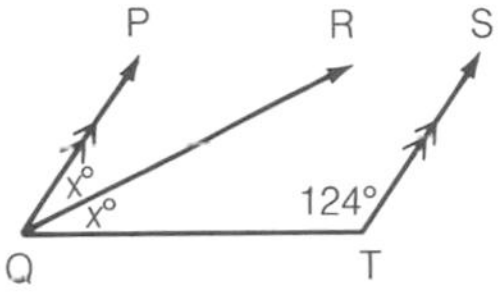


9 (a) Construct a circle with diameter 16 cm. Construct a chord $AB = 7$ cm in the circle. Mark angles $\angle ACB$ and $\angle ADB$ for points C and D on the circle.

(b) Measure $\angle ACB$ and $\angle ADB$. What do you notice about their measures?

10 Find the missing measures. Give reasons for your answer.

(a)

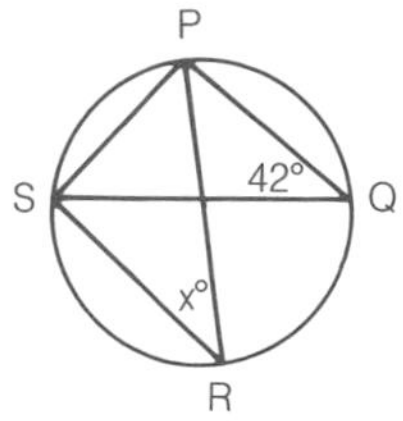


(b)

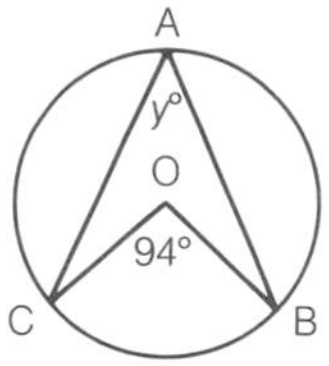


11 Find the length of the chord PQ.

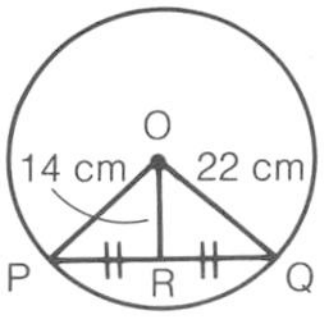


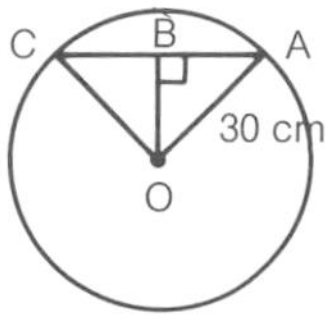


Find the length of the perpendicular OB if $AC = 56$ cm.

# A Practice Test

1 A sketch is drawn for $\triangle PQR$.

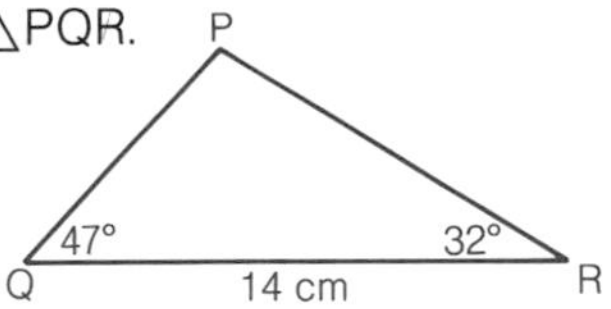


(a) Construct $\triangle PQR$.
(b) What would you expect the measure of $\angle QPR$ to be?
(c) Measure $\angle QPR$. What did you find?

2 Use the diagram shown.

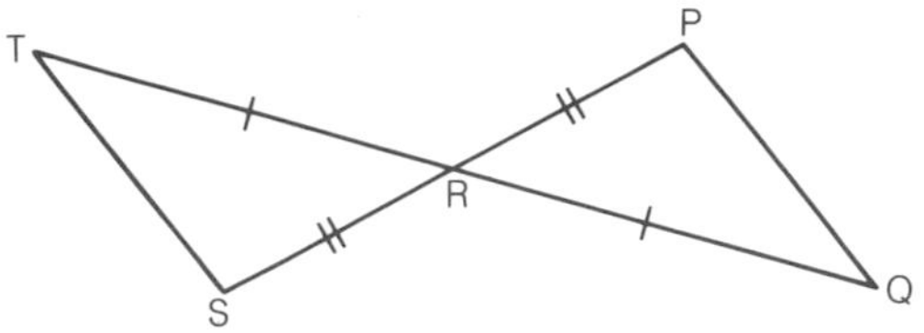


(a) Why is $\angle PRQ = \angle TRS$?
(b) Give reasons why the two triangles are congruent.
(c) Why is PQ $\|$ ST?

3 Use the diagram to find the width of the river. Justify your results.

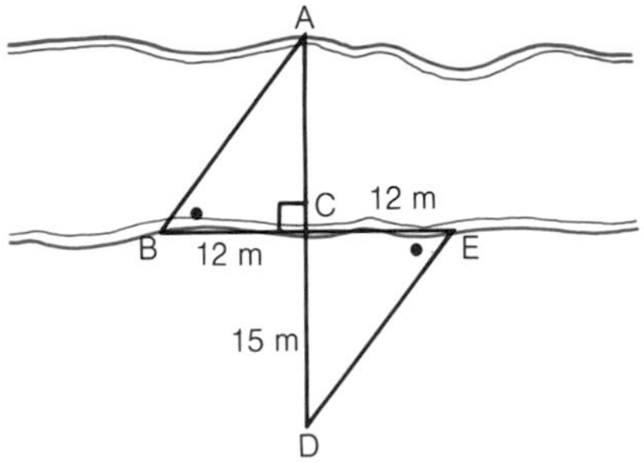


4 Construct each of the following. Be accurate!
(a)

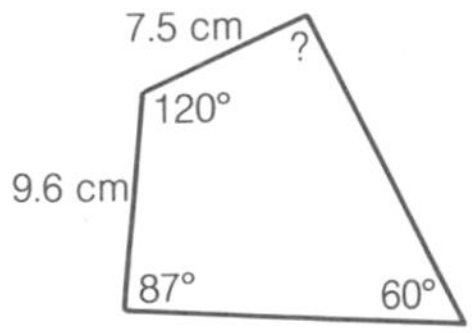


(b)

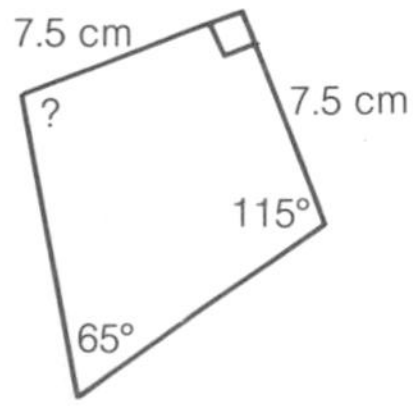


5 Find the missing measures.
(a)

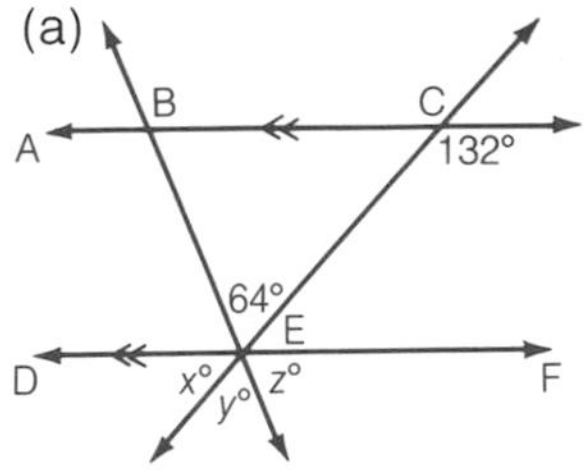


(b)

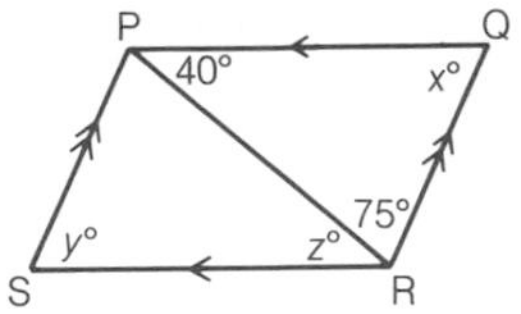


6 (a) Construct a circle with diameter PQ = 12 cm
(b) Choose a point R on the circumference of the circle. Draw chords from P and Q to meet at R.
(c) Find the measure of $\angle PRQ$.

7 Find the missing measures.
(a)

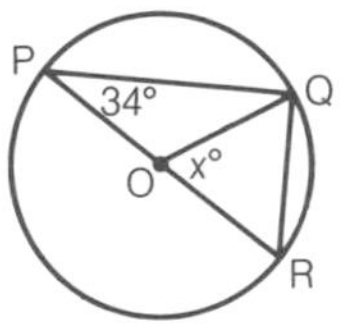


(b)

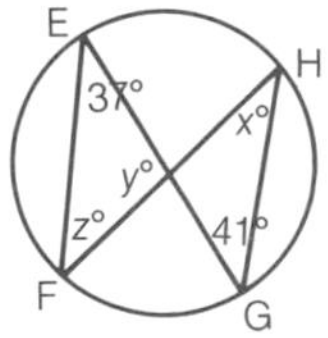


(c)

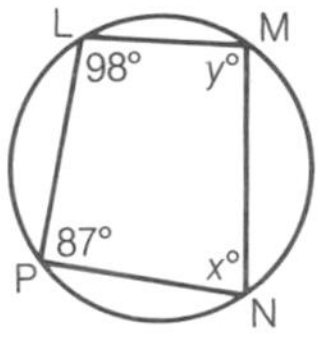


(d)

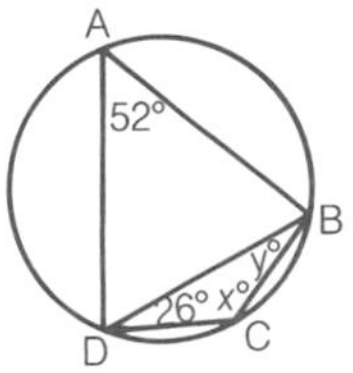


8 (a) Construct a circle with centre O and radius 5 cm.
(b) Construct a chord AB = 4.2 cm for the circle.
(c) From O construct the perpendicular OC to the chord AB. C is a point on the chord.
(d) Measure AC, BC, what do you notice?

9 Use the diagram shown. Find the length of the chord AC.

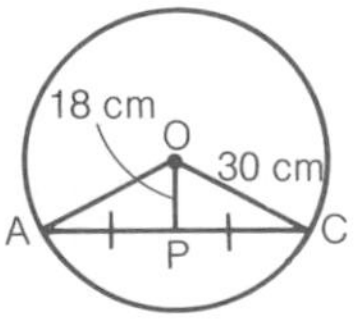


10 A circular racing track is used for go-cart racing. A tower is to be placed at its centre. How would you locate the position of the tower for the track?

# 15 Essentials of Trigonometry

properties and problems with similar triangles, concepts of trigonometry, finding lengths, using trigonometry, using calculators, problem solving, technical problems, angles of depression and elevation, solving problems and applications

## Introduction

Many of the skills you have learned previously are applied in the study of the skills and concepts about trigonometry. The roots of trigonometry occurred in ancient times. Since then it has flourished as an important branch of mathematics. For example, the ancient Greeks used the study of angles and sides to solve problems involving triangles. The word trigonometry is derived from their vocabulary.

tri gono metry

tri-three gonia-angle metria-measurement

The first application of trigonometry is the solution of problems involving distances. The early astronomers used the concepts in trigonometry to aid their work. Today, trigonometry is still used in finding distances, but the skills and concepts have expanded to many unrelated fields, such as the following.

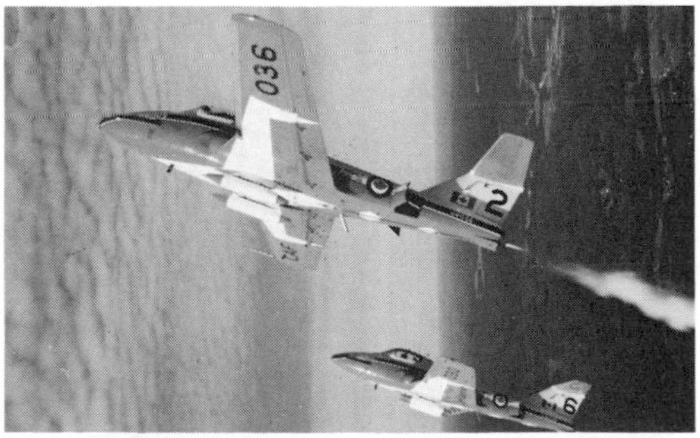

• In navigation

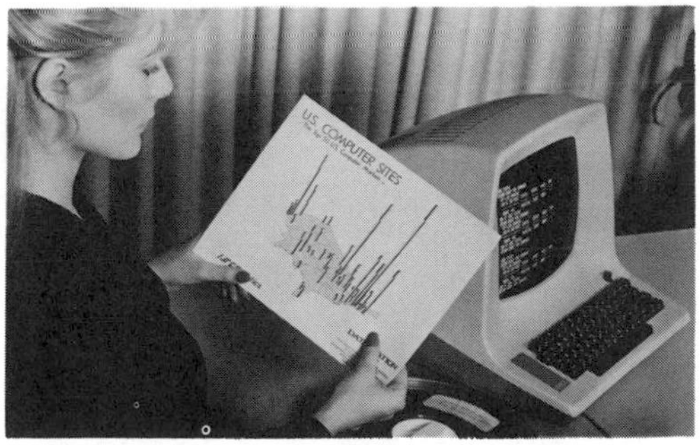

• In economics

• In electrical work

• In surveying

# 15.1 Skills with Similar Triangles

Often words in everyday use have a very special meaning in mathematics. For example, the word similar . . . How are these stamps alike? How are they different?

The figures have the same shape but are different in size. The following triangles are similar.

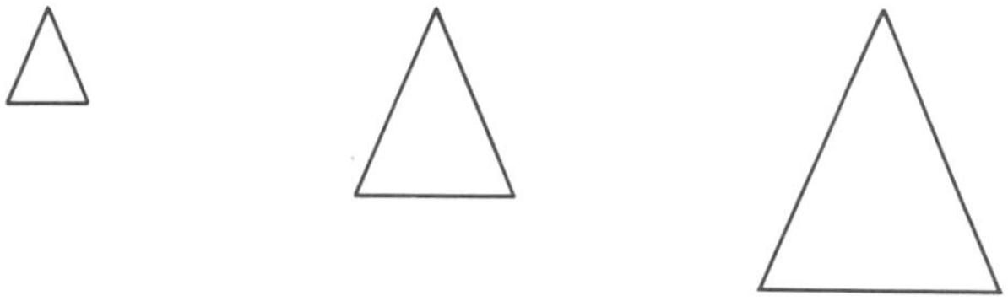

They have the same shape, but they differ in size. Similar triangles have the following properties.

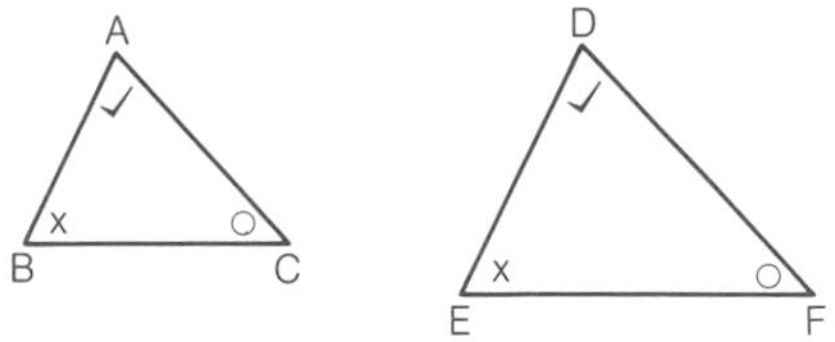


- Corresponding pairs of angles are equal.

$\triangle ABC \sim \triangle DEF$ ($\sim$ means is similar to)

$\angle A = \angle D$
$\angle B = \angle E$
$\angle C = \angle F$

- Corresponding pairs of sides are proportional.

$\triangle ABC \sim \triangle DEF \qquad \frac{AB}{DE} = \frac{AC}{DF} = \frac{BC}{EF}$

For example, $\triangle PQR$ is similar to $\triangle LMN$. The ratios for the corresponding sides are shown.

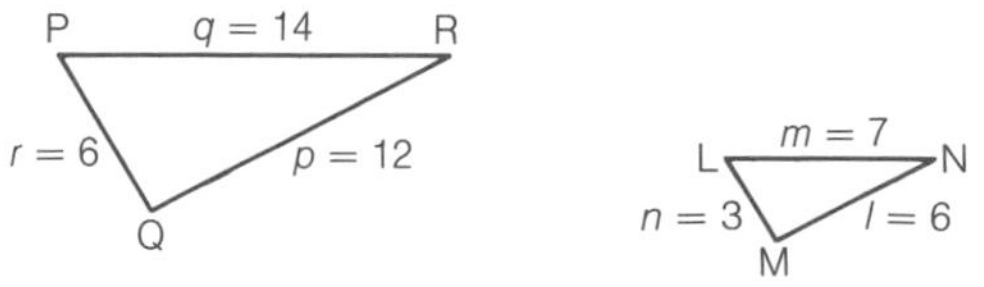


| corresponding sides | Sides are proportional |
|---|---|
| $q$ and $m$ | $\frac{q}{m} = \frac{14}{7} = 2$ |
| $r$ and $n$ | $\frac{r}{n} = \frac{6}{3} = 2$ |
| $p$ and $l$ | $\frac{p}{l} = \frac{12}{6} = 2$ |

To solve problems about similar triangles, you need to use your earlier skills with equations.

**Example**

$\triangle ABC \sim \triangle DEF$. Find the missing measures, in centimetres.

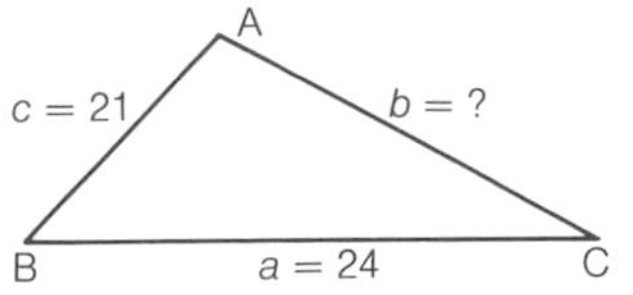


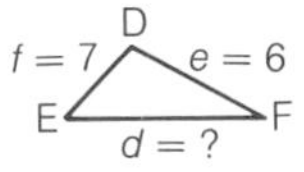


**Solution**

Think: $\triangle ABC \sim \triangle DEC$.
Write the corresponding sides.

$$\frac{a}{d} = \frac{b}{e} = \frac{c}{f}$$

$$\frac{a}{d} = \frac{c}{f}$$ Record the proportion

$$\frac{24}{d} = \frac{21}{7}$$

$$d = 8$$

Thus EF = 8 cm

To find AC, use the proportion

$$\frac{e}{b} = \frac{d}{a} \quad \text{or} \quad \frac{6}{b} = \frac{8}{24}$$

$$b = 18$$

Thus AC = 18 cm

To solve problems about similar triangles you will use these two properties.

*Property 1*: If the corresponding angles of two triangles are equal then the triangles are similar.

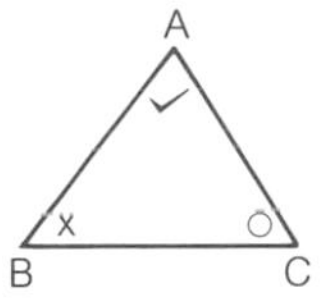


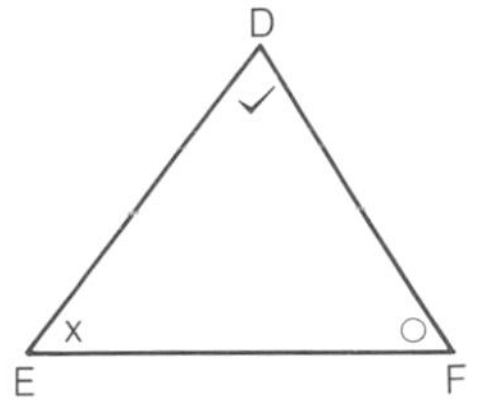


| If we know | Then we know |
|---|---|
| $\angle A = \angle D$<br>$\angle B = \angle E$<br>$\angle C = \angle F$ | $\triangle ABC \sim \triangle DEF$<br>$\frac{AB}{DE} = \frac{AC}{DF} = \frac{BC}{EF}$ |

*Property 2*: If the corresponding sides of two triangles are proportional, then the triangles are similar.

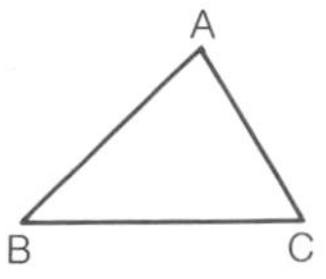


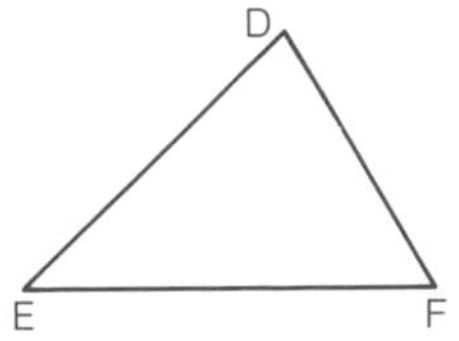


| If we know | Then we know |
|---|---|
| $\frac{AB}{DE} = \frac{AC}{DF} = \frac{BC}{EF}$ | $\triangle ABC \sim \triangle DEF$<br>$\angle A = \angle D$<br>$\angle B = \angle E$<br>$\angle C = \angle F$ |

In working with similar triangles, you will use many of your earlier skills in geometry, as well as the various skills you have learned to solve problems.

*Step 1*: *Record the given information.*
In △ABC, △DEF
∠A = 45° ∠D = 45°
∠B = 60° ∠E = 60°

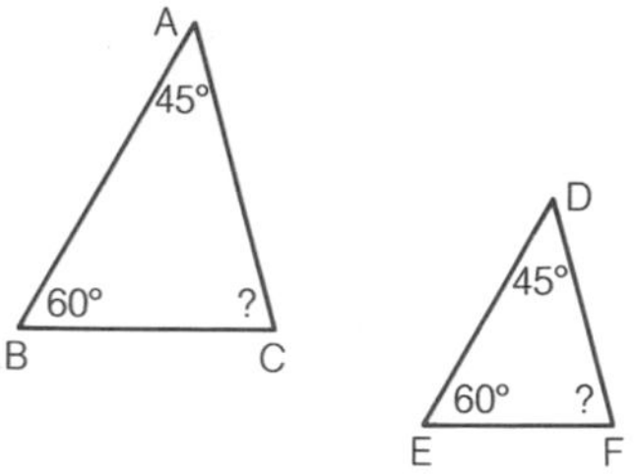


Record the given information on a diagram.

*Step 2*: *Record any other information you know.*
In △ABC, △DEF, two corresponding angles are equal.
Thus ∠C = ∠F = 75°

Remember: the sum of the angles of a triangle is 180°.

*Step 3*: *Write a concluding statement.*
Thus △ABC and △DEF are similar.

Remember: If the corresponding angles of two triangles are equal, then the triangles are similar.

## Try These

1 Which triangles are similar?

(a)

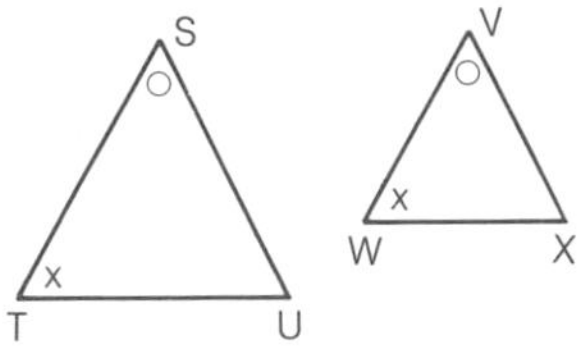


(b)

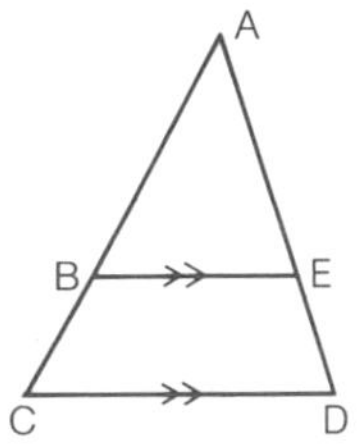


(c)

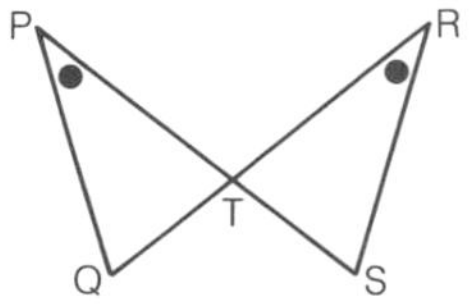


(d)

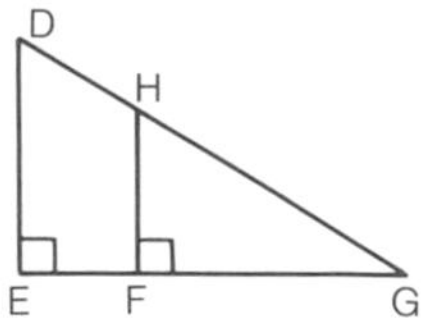


2 What is the missing information in the chart?

| If you know | Then you know |
|---|---|
| (a) △PQR ~ △TUV | ? |
| (b) △RST ~ △ABC | ? |

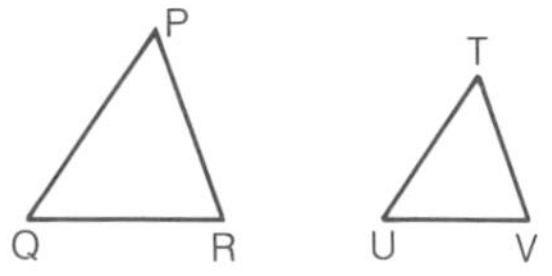


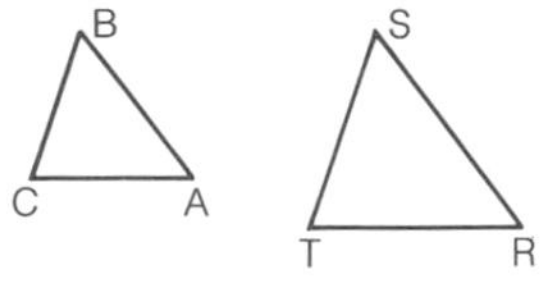

## Written Exercises

**A** Review the meaning of similar triangles. Where necessary, round your answers to decimal place.

1 Find the missing parts.
(a) If $\triangle ABC \sim \triangle DEF$ then
▶ side AB is proportional to side ▨
▶ side BC is proportional to side ▨
▶ side AC is proportional to side ▨.
(b) If $\triangle LMN \sim \triangle PQR$ then
$\angle L = ?$ $\angle M = ?$ $\angle R = ?$

2 $\triangle STU$ is similar to $\triangle PQR$.
(a) Which angles are equal?
(b) Write the equations for proportional sides.

3 Which triangles are similar to $\triangle ABC$? Give reasons for your answer.

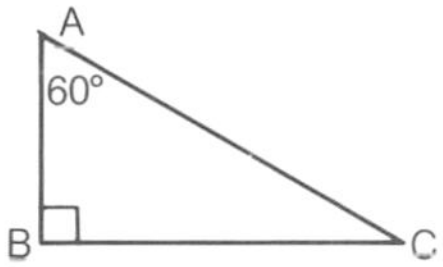


(a)
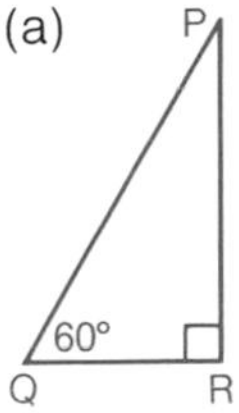


(b)
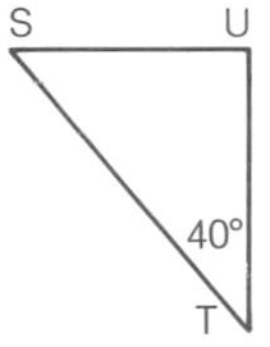


(c)
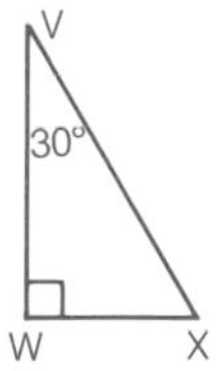


4 In each triangle, there are missing measures. Find the missing measures.
(a) $\triangle STU \sim \triangle PQR$

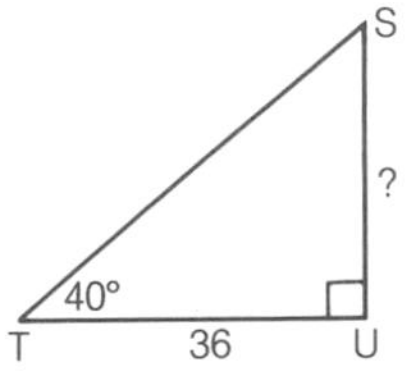


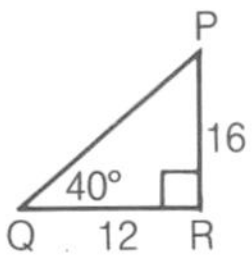


(b) $\triangle ABC \sim \triangle MPS$

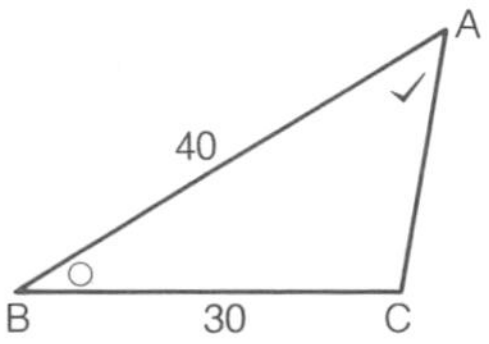


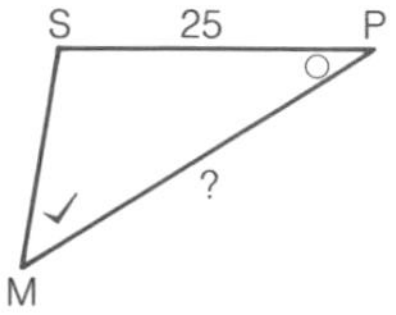


5 Refer to the diagram.
(a) Which triangles are similar?
(b) Why is $\frac{k}{45} = \frac{8}{12}$? Find the value of $k$.

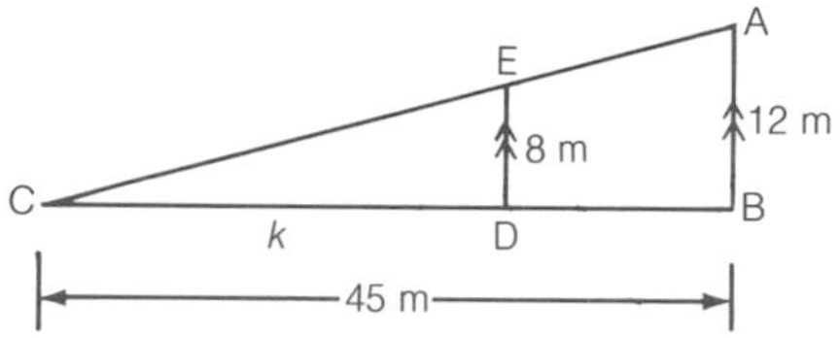


6 Refer to the diagram.
(a) Which triangles are similar?
(b) How is this equation obtained from the diagram?

$$\frac{a + 15}{15} = \frac{24}{18}$$

Find the value of $a$.

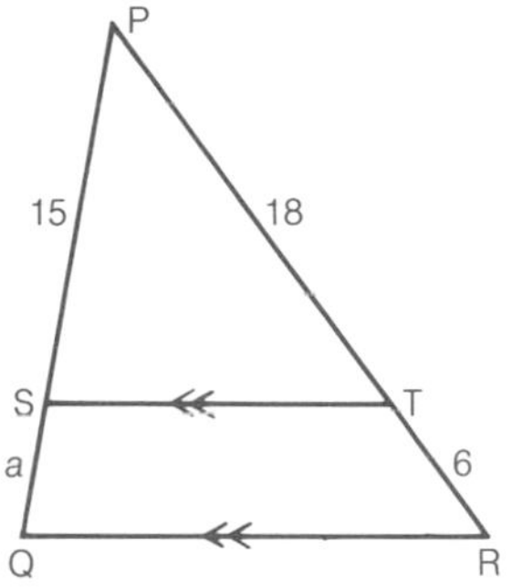


**B** To find missing measures in triangles, you need to find pairs of similar triangles. Remember: record the given information on the diagram.

7 (a) Which triangles are similar? Give reasons for your answer.

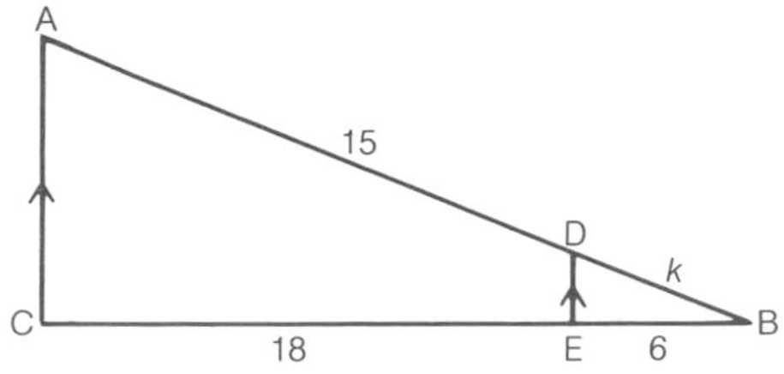


(b) Write an equation. Find the value of $k$.

8 (a) Which triangles are similar? Give reasons for your answer.

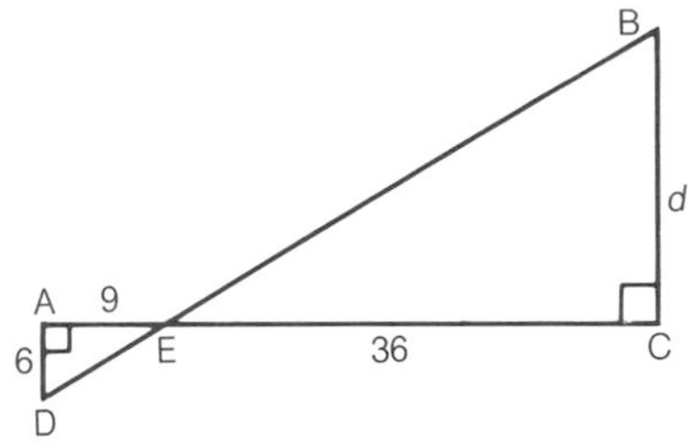


(b) Write an equation. Find the value of *d*.

9 Find the missing measures.

(a)

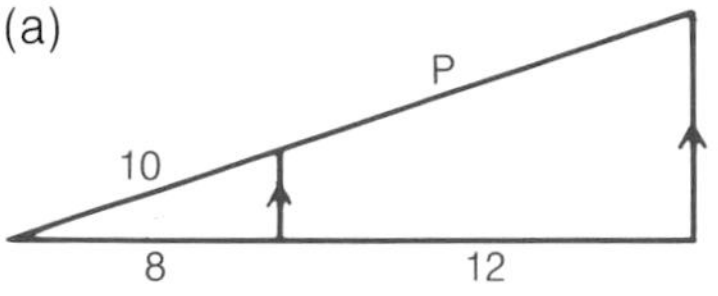


(b)

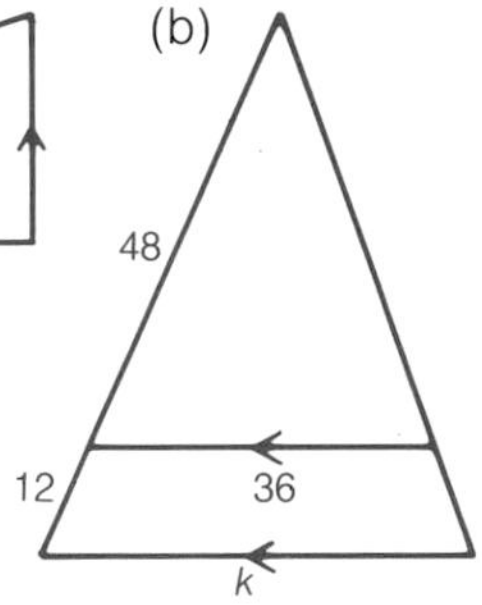


(c)

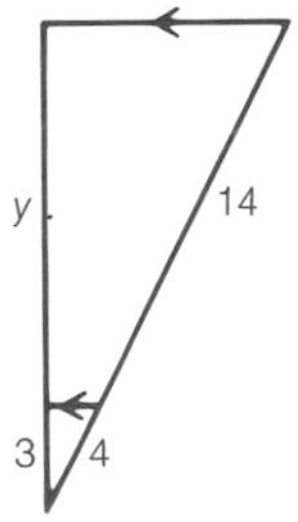


(d)

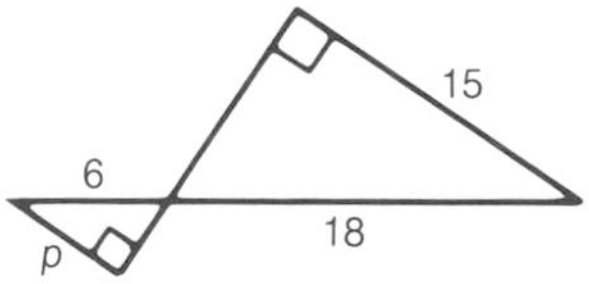


10 (a) Make a sketch of the diagram. Record the given information on the diagram.
BC = 36.8 m
CE = 16.2 m
DE = 8.6 m

(b) Find the measure of AB, to 1 decimal place.

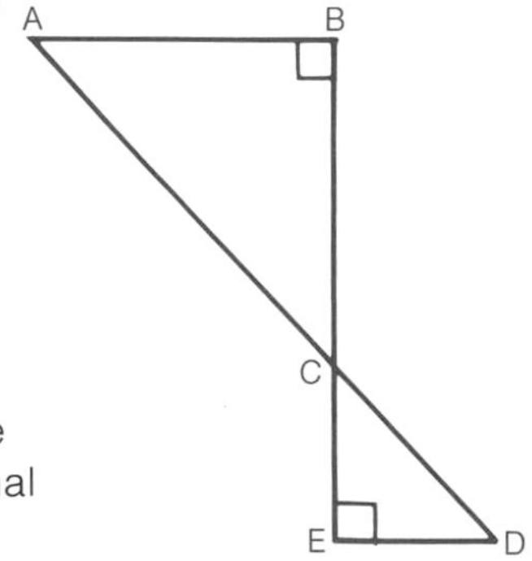


11 For each diagram
- ▶ record the given information on a sketch of your own
- ▶ find the missing measure.

(a) In the diagram, TR = 9.6 m, QS = 40.2 m, RS = 28.6 m. ∠PQR = ∠TRS = 90°. Find PQ.

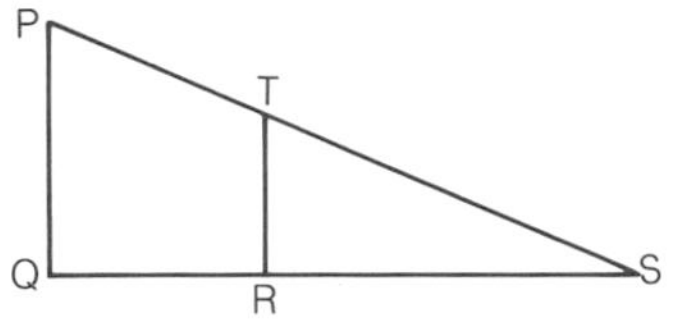


(b) In the diagram
UY = 6.8 m,
YX = 9.3 m,
VW = 5.4 m,
UV || YW.
Find VX.

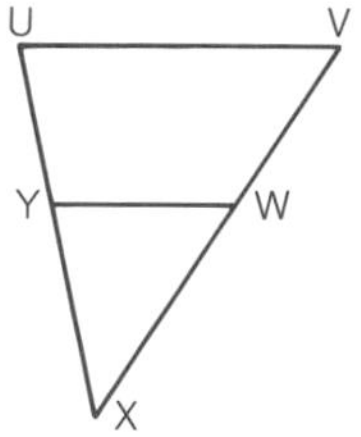


(c) In the diagram TA ⊥ AB, CD ⊥ BC, CD = 6.2 cm, BC = 9.6 cm, AB = 18.5 cm. Find TA.

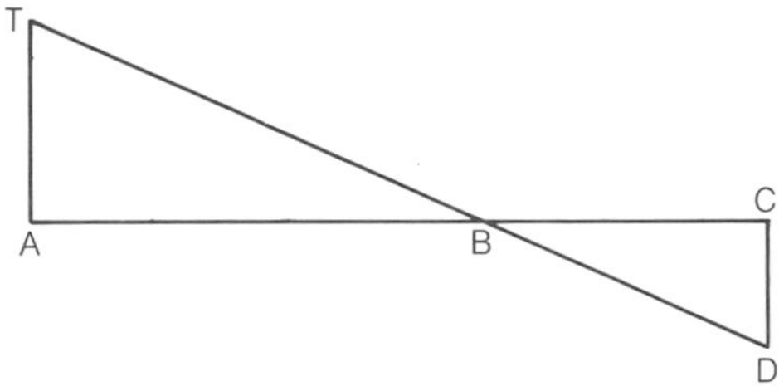


## Career Tip

Each of the following careers require the use of skills with trigonometry.

Forest technician
Meteorological technician
Forest technician
Civil engineering technician
Electrical engineering technician
Industrial engineering technician
Mining engineering technician

Explore the requirements to prepare for any of the careers listed above that may be of interest to you.

# 15.2 Solving Problems: Similar Triangles

In your study of mathematics, you often do the following steps.

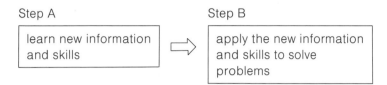

| Step A | | Step B |
|---|---|---|
| learn new information and skills | ⇨ | apply the new information and skills to solve problems |

In the previous section, you learned new information and skills about similar triangles. In this section, you will apply these skills to solve problems. To organize your work, refer to the steps for solving problems.

To measure some distances, you can do so by using indirect measurement. For example, to measure the height of a tree or tower you would not use a tape measure and climb to the top. You will use your skills with similar triangles to solve problems that use indirect measurement, as shown in the following problem.

| *Steps for Solving Problems* | |
|---|---|
| Step A | Do I understand the problem?<br>I What information am I asked to find?<br>II What information am I given? |
| Step B | Decide on a method (sketch a diagram. Use similar triangles.) |
| Step C | Find the answer. (Solve the equation.) |
| Step D | Check my answer in the original problem. |
| Step E | Write a final statement to answer the question. |

### Example

A tower casts a shadow 30.4 m in length. At the same time, a gate that is 1.5 m high casts a shadow 4.5 m in height. Calculate the height of the tower to 1 decimal place.

### Solution

Think: sketch a diagram.
Record the given information on your sketch.

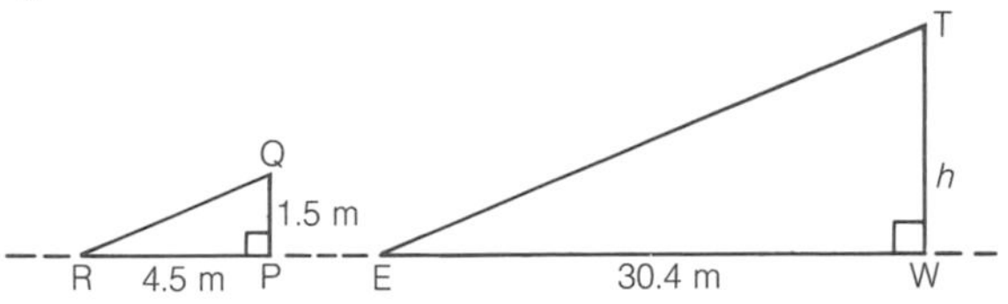


Use $h$, in metres, to represent the height of the tower.

From the diagram,
△QPR is similar to △TWE.

Why are the triangles similar?

Thus $\frac{TW}{QP} = \frac{EW}{RP}$ $\quad \frac{h}{1.5} = \frac{30.4}{4.5}$

$$h = \frac{(1.5)(30.4)}{4.5}$$ Use a calculator

$$= 10.13 \text{ (to 2 decimal places)}$$

The height of the tower is 10.1 m
(to 1 decimal place)

To solve problems involving indirect measurement, you will combine various skills:

- use your skills for solving equations
- use your skills about similar triangles
- refer to the *Steps for Solving Problems* to plan your solution.

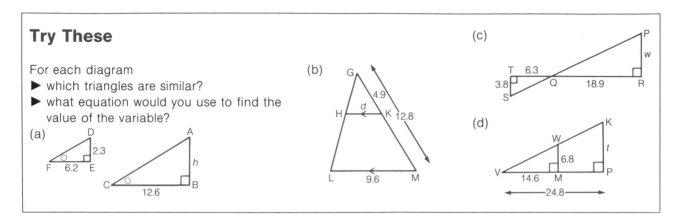

## Try These

For each diagram

- which triangles are similar?
- what equation would you use to find the value of the variable?

(a)

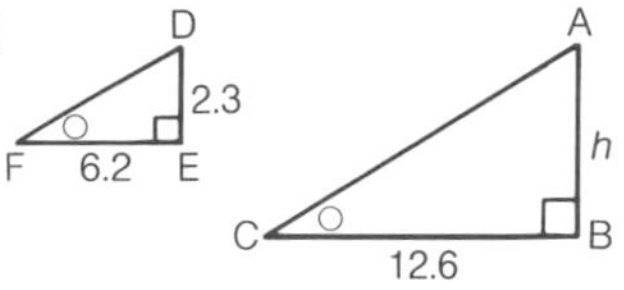


(b)

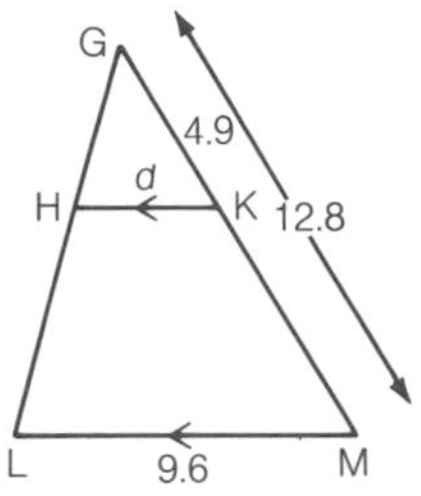


(c)

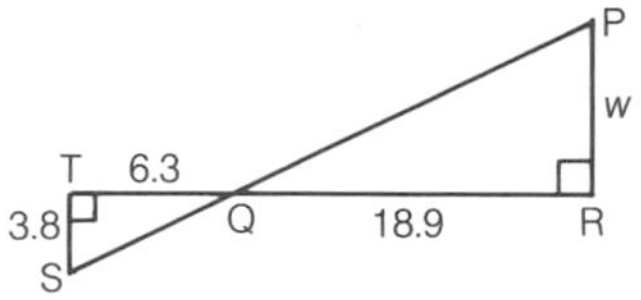


(d)

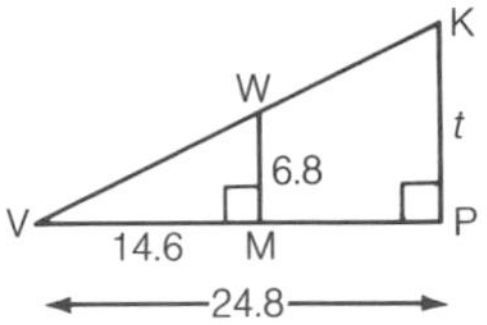


## Written Exercises

**A** Express your answer to one decimal place in each of the following problems.

1 To find the height of a tree, $h$, in metres, use the diagram.

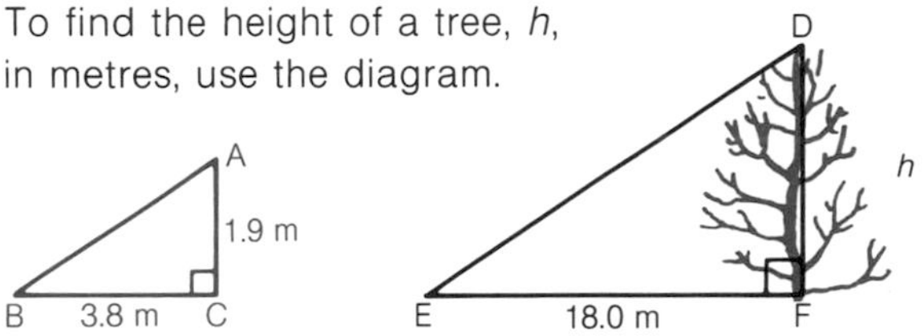


(a) Which triangles are similar?
(b) Write the equation to solve for $h$.
(c) Solve the equation in (b).
(d) What is the height of the tree?

2 The width, $w$ in metres, of a channel is shown in the diagram.

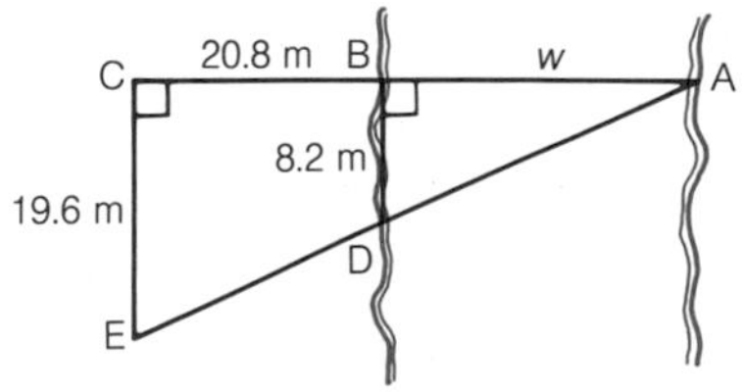


(a) Which triangles are similar?
(b) Write the equation to solve for $w$.
(c) Solve the equation in (b).
(d) What is the width of the channel?

3 To calculate the length of a lake in metres, measurements are recorded on the diagram.

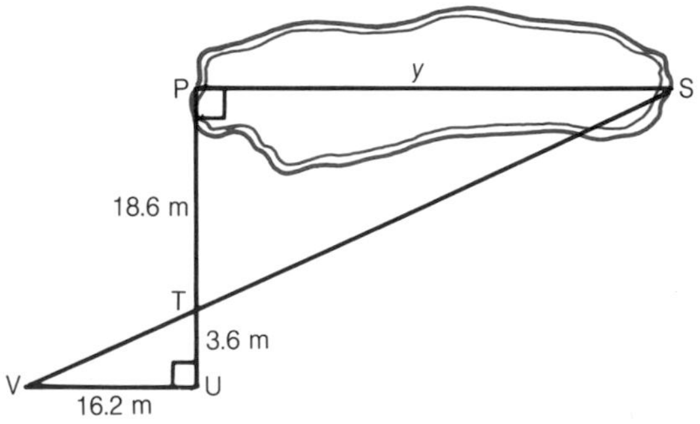


(a) Which triangles are similar?
(b) Write the equation to solve for $y$.
(c) Solve the equation in (b).
(d) What is the length of the lake?

**B** For each of the following problems, sketch a copy of the diagram. Record the given information. Solve the problem.

4 To calculate the height of a tree, AB, the following measurements were made.
CD = 3.0 m
AD = 12.0 m
DE = 1.0 m
Calculate the height of the tree.

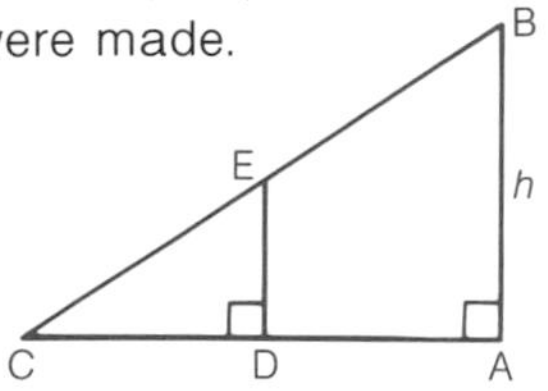


5 In the diagram, PQ represents the width of a river. Use the measurements to find the width of the river.

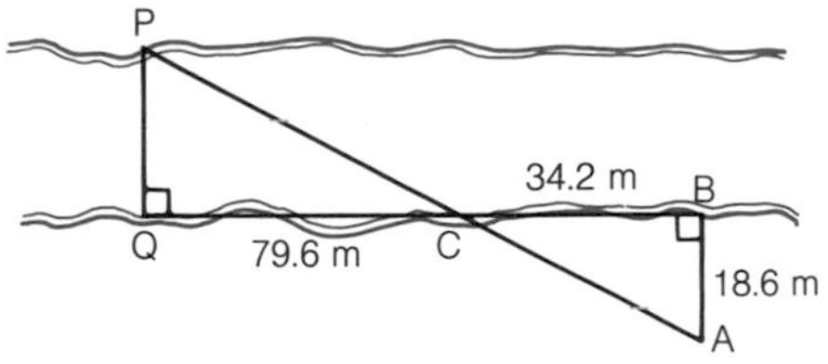


6 To calculate the length of a trout pond, the following measurements are made.
AB = 17.1 m
AC = 15.2 m
CE = 39.8 m
Use the diagram. Calculate the length of the pond.

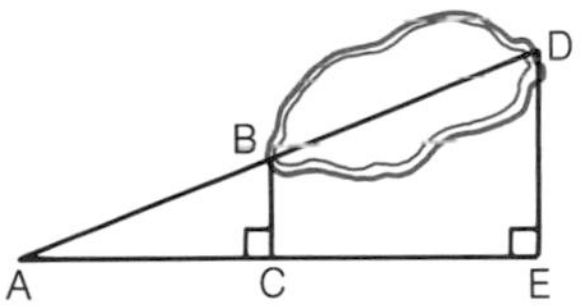


7 A mirror is placed on the ground to calculate the height of a building. Jennifer places the mirror so that she sees the reflection at the top of the building.

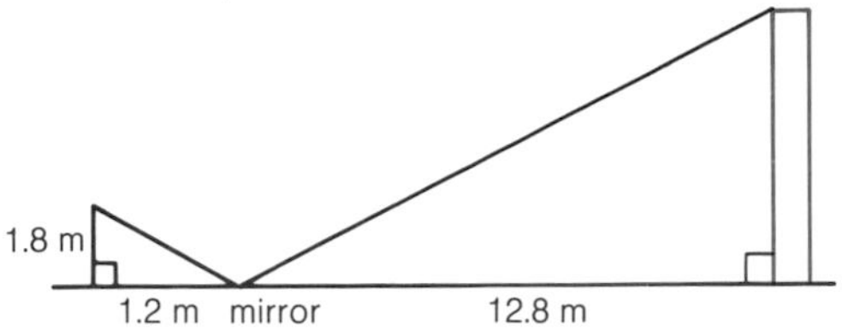


Use the diagram. Calculate the height of the building.

8 In a camera, similar triangles occur as shown. Use the information in the diagram. Calculate the height of the tree.

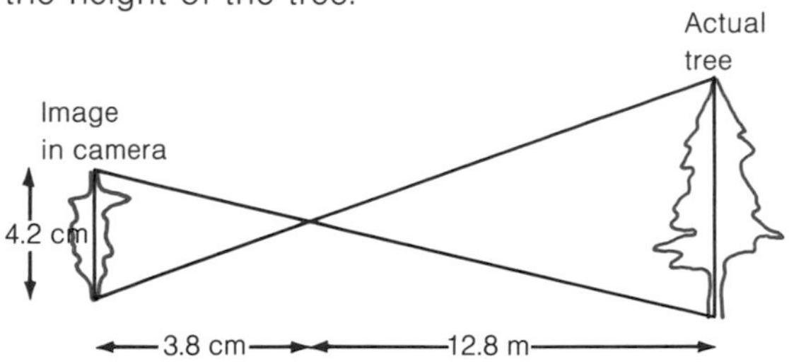


9 On a sunny day, John's shadow is 2.9 m long, while the shadow of a tower is 11.3 m long. If John is 1.8 m tall, calculate the height of the tower.

10 The shadow of a metre stick is 2.7 m long while the shadow of a monument is 18.6 m in length. Find the height of the monument.

11 A ski tow rises 40.2 m for a horizontal distance of 120.8 m. How high are you if you have travelled 785.2 m horizontally?

12 A road rises 3.8 m for a horizontal distance of 100.0 m. How far have you gone horizontally, if you have risen 32.3 m?

## Math Tip

In measuring angles, you will often obtain parts of a whole degree. These parts are measured in seconds as shown.

1 degree = 60 minutes
$1° = 60'$
1 minute = 60 seconds
$1' = 60''$

Write 16.3° in degrees and minutes.
$16.3° = 16°18'$ ← Think: $0.3 \times 60 = 18$

Write 16.12° in degrees, minutes and seconds.
$16.12° = 16°7'12''$
$0.12 \times 60 = 7.2$ $\quad 0.2 \times 60 = 12$

Express each measure in degrees, minutes and seconds.

(a) 23.4° (b) 46.5° (c) 75.6°
(d) 123.3° (e) 18.36° (f) 36.23°
(g) 81.78° (h) 118.43°

# 15.3 Problem Solving: Exploring Triangles

In solving problems involving similar triangles, you need to make at least 3 measurements. If you were out in the woods, you might have difficulty in doing the measurements needed to calculate the height of a cliff. For this reason, the question is asked whether the widths and heights of various objects can be calculated with fewer measurements. If you examine the diagram used to calculate lengths you will soon notice that many of them involve right angles.

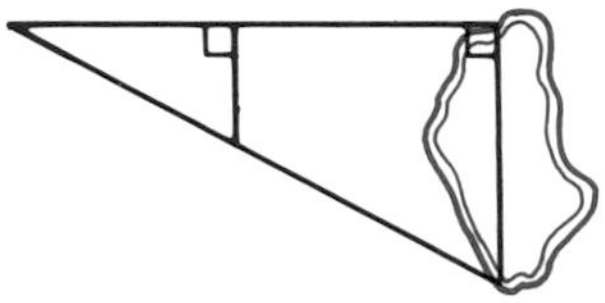

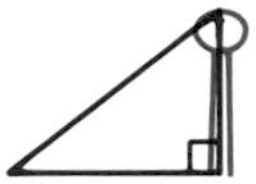

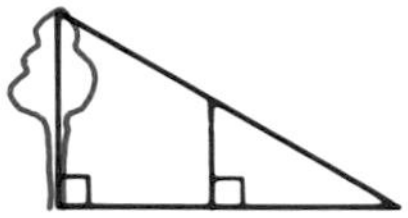

The properties of similar triangles with right angles are explored in this section. Special words are used to refer to the sides of a right triangle.

Side BC is said to be opposite to ∠A.
Side AC is said to be adjacent to ∠A.

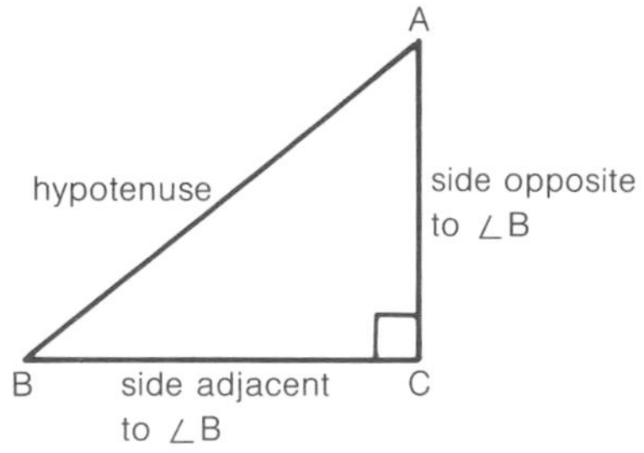


## Try These

1 Refer to the diagram.
   (a) Which triangles are similar?
   (b) Which ratios are equal?

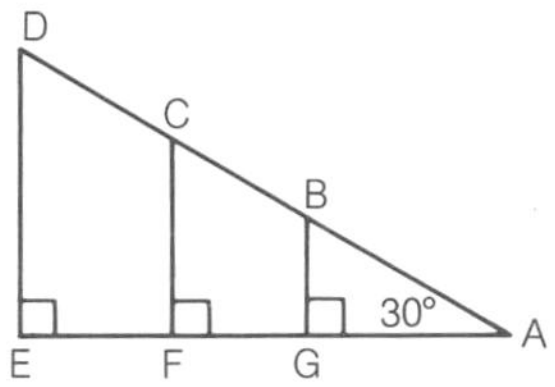


2 Refer to the diagram.
   (a) Which triangles are similar?
   (b) Which ratios are equal?

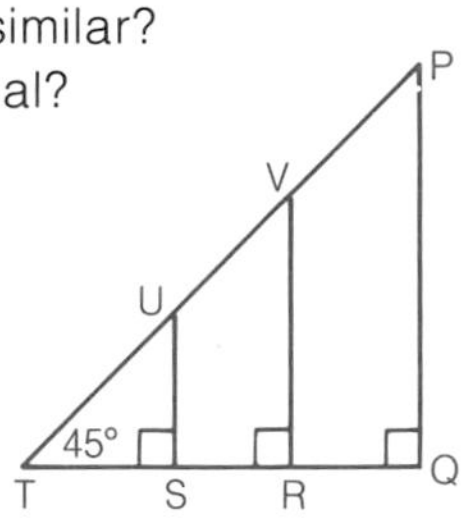


## Written Exercises

**B** Throughout the exercise, construct accurate diagrams.

1 Refer to △ABC.

   (a) Measure AC, BC, AB.
   (b) Calculate $\frac{AC}{BC}, \frac{AC}{AB}, \frac{BC}{AB}$. Express your answers to 2 decimal places.

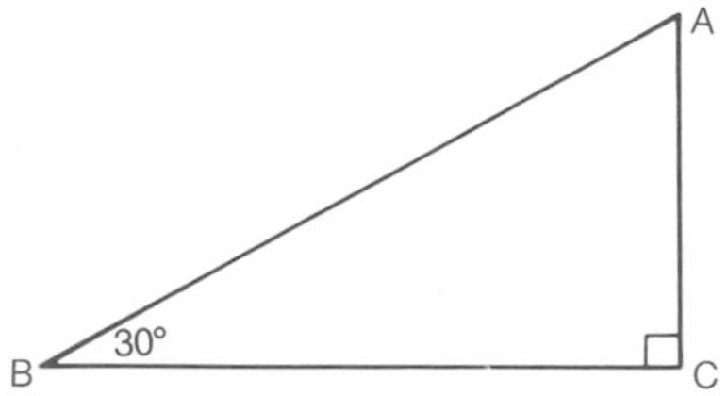

2 Use the diagram.

(a) Which triangles are similar?

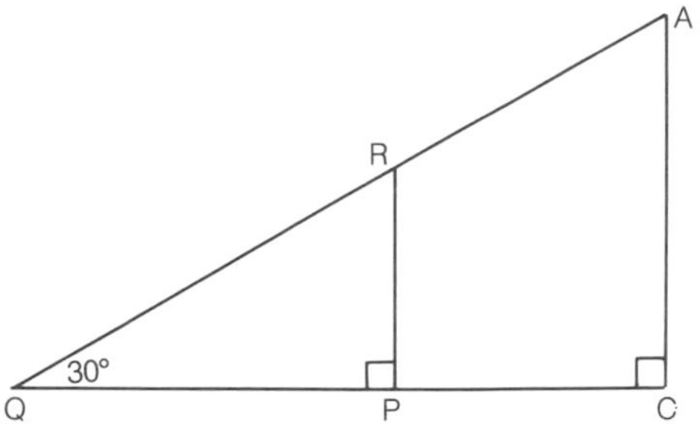


(b) Measure AC, RP, AQ, RQ, QC, QP.

(c) Calculate these pairs. Express your answers to 2 decimal places.

$\frac{AC}{QC}, \frac{RP}{QP}; \quad \frac{AC}{QA}, \frac{RP}{QR}; \quad \frac{QC}{QA}, \frac{QP}{QR}$

3 Refer to your answers in the previous questions.

(a) Which calculations have approximately the same values?

(b) Construct a triangle of your own as shown by the sketch.

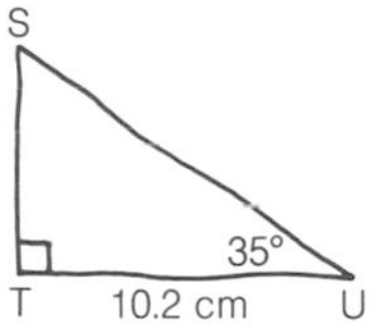


(c) Calculate $\frac{ST}{UT}, \frac{ST}{SU}, \frac{TU}{SU}$. How do your answers compare to your earlier calculations?

4 (a) Repeat the steps of question 3. Use the following sketches.

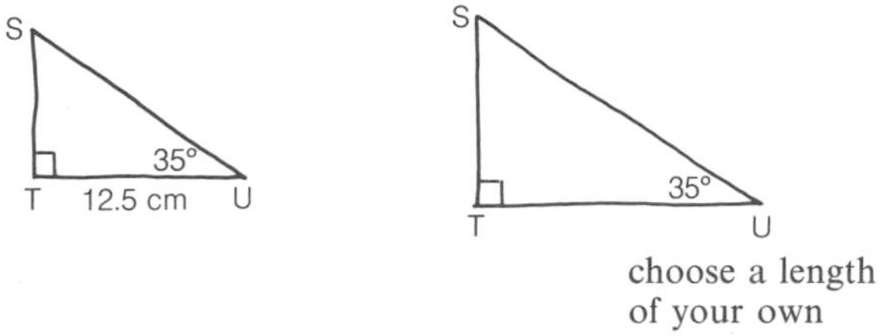


(b) What do you notice about your calculations?

5 Refer to the diagram.

(a) Calculate each of the following to 2 decimal places for ∠F.

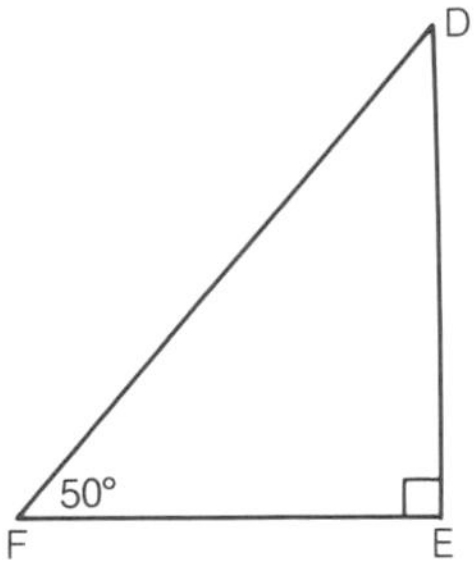


Step A: $t = \frac{\text{measure of side opposite to } \angle F}{\text{measure of side adjacent to } \angle F}$

Step B: $s = \frac{\text{measure of side opposite to } \angle F}{\text{measure of hypotenuse}}$

Step C: $c = \frac{\text{measure of side adjacent to } \angle F}{\text{measure of hypotenuse}}$

(b) Construct each triangle. Use the sketches shown. Then repeat steps A, B and C.

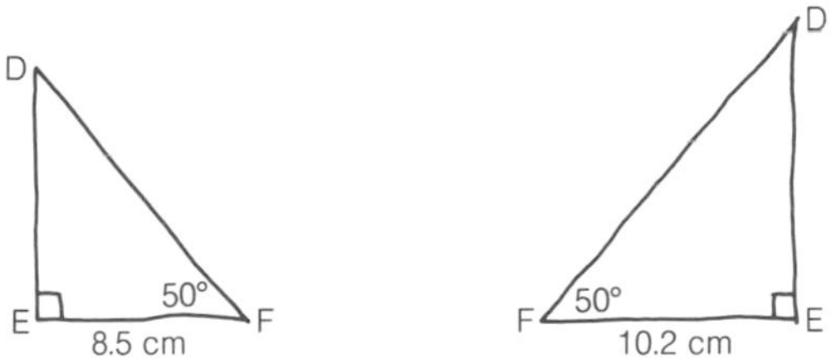


(c) Based on your results, what are the values of $t$, $s$, and $c$ expressed to 2 decimal places?

6 Repeat the steps of the previous questions to complete the following table of values. Express your calculations to 2 decimal places.

| | measure of ∠B | value of $t$ | value of $s$ | value of $c$ |
|---|---|---|---|---|
| (a) | 10° | ? | ? | ? |
| (b) | 20° | ? | ? | ? |
| (c) | 25° | ? | ? | ? |
| (d) | 30° | ? | ? | ? |
| (e) | 35° | ? | ? | ? |
| (f) | 40° | ? | ? | ? |
| (g) | 45° | ? | ? | ? |
| (h) | 50° | ? | ? | ? |
| (i) | 60° | ? | ? | ? |
| (j) | 70° | ? | ? | ? |
| (k) | 80° | ? | ? | ? |

# 15.4 Applying Skills: Finding Lengths

The results of your work in the previous section will allow you to find lengths in a much simpler way. A part of your table is reproduced here for the calculation of *t*.

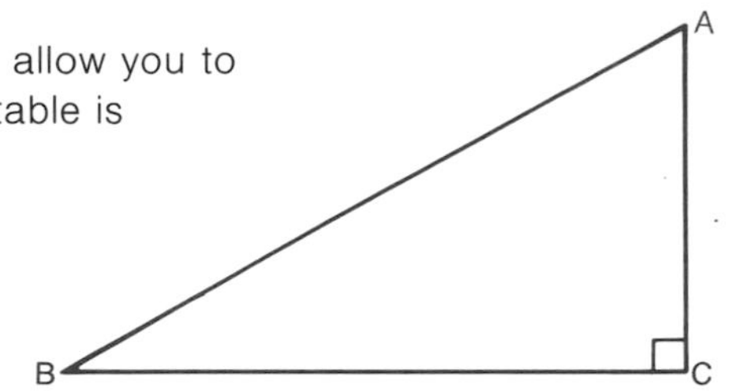


For $\angle B \quad t = \dfrac{\text{measure of opposite side}}{\text{measure of adjacent side}}$

| Measure of ∠B | 10° | 20° | 25° | 30° | 35° | 40° | 45° | 50° | 60° | 70° | 80° |
|---|---|---|---|---|---|---|---|---|---|---|---|
| Value of *t* | 0.18 | 0.36 | 0.47 | 0.58 | 0.70 | 0.84 | 1 | 1.19 | 1.73 | 2.75 | 5.67 |

Once you have calculated these values for *t*, you can use your results and apply them to solve problems for which you need only know the measure of one angle and one side.

For example to measure a cliff you make these measurements.

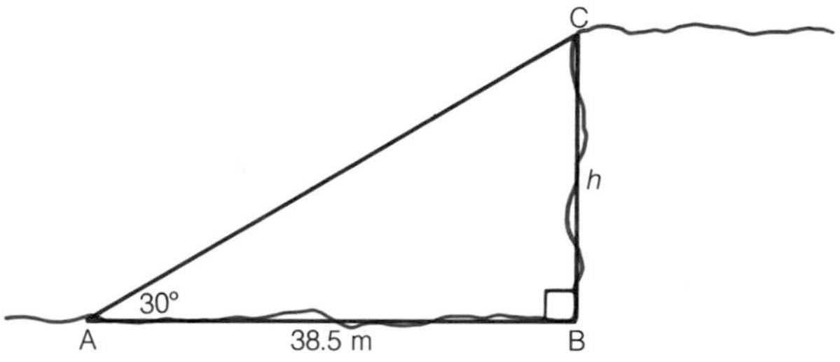


One Angle:
∠CAB = 30°

One Side:
AB, distance from base of cliff is 38.5 m

From the measurements, you can calculate the height *h*.

From the diagram $\dfrac{h}{38.5} = 0.58$ ← The value of *t* when the angle is 30°

$$h = 38.5\,(0.58)$$
$$= 22.3 \text{ (to 1 decimal place)}$$

Based on the calculations, the height of the cliff is 22.3 m.

The advantage of the previous method is that you can often more easily obtain the measure of an angle than you can the measure of 2 or more sides, as shown in the following example.

## Example

Certain measurements related to height of an eagle's nest are shown in the diagram. Calculate how high the eagle's nest is, to the nearest metre.

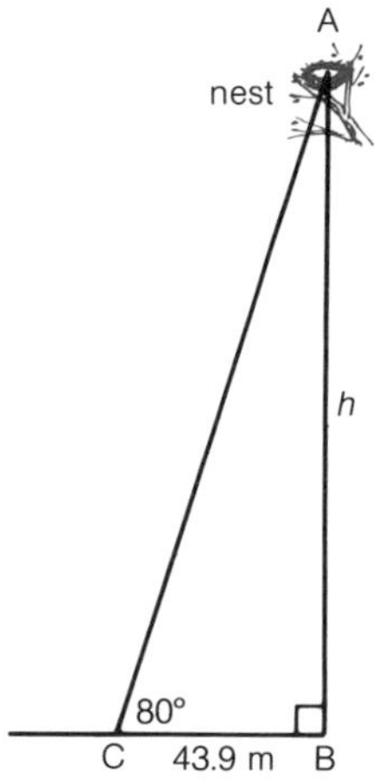


## Solution

From the diagram

$$\frac{\text{measure of opposite}}{\text{measure of adjacent}} = \frac{h}{43.9}$$

From your earlier work for 80°

$$\frac{AB}{CB} = \frac{\text{measure of opposite}}{\text{measure of adjacent}}$$
$$= 5.67$$

$$\frac{h}{43.9} = 5.67$$

$$h = 43.9(5.67)$$
$$= 248.9 \text{ (to 1 decimal place)}$$

Thus the height of the eagle's nest is 249 m, to the nearest metre.

## Try These

1 For each triangle, which is the adjacent side and which the opposite side for angle B?

(a) (b) (c) (d) (e)

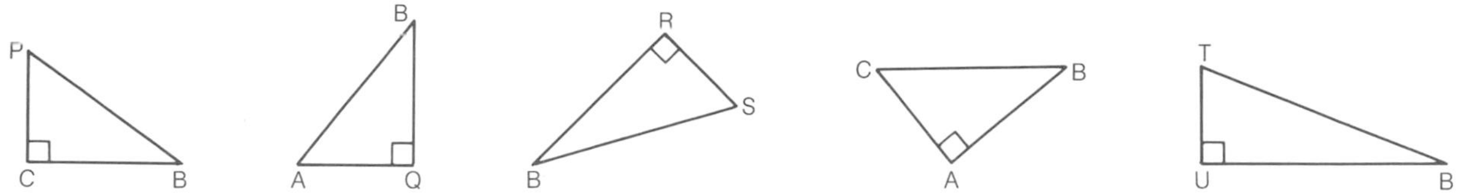


## Written Exercises

**A** Throughout the exercise, the value of $t$ is obtained as shown for ∠B.

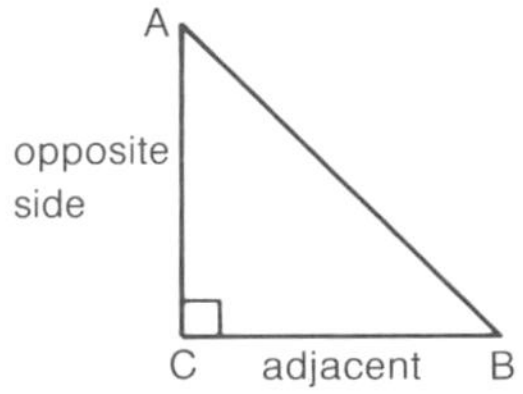


$$t = \frac{\text{measure of opposite side}}{\text{measure of adjacent side}}$$

1 For an angle of 15°, the value of $t$ is given by $t = 0.27$.
Calculate the height $h$.

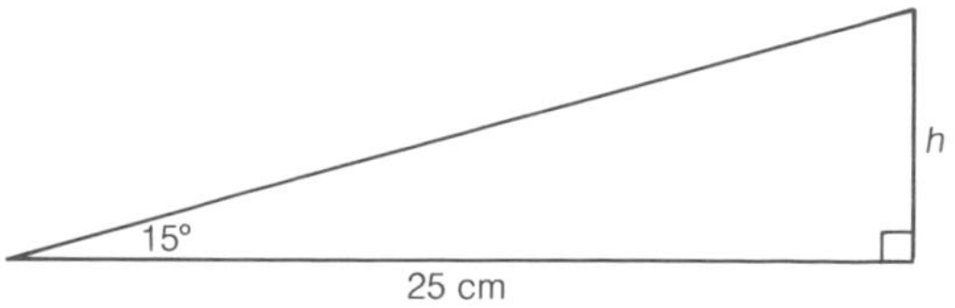

2 For each triangle, the value of $t$ is shown for the measured angle. Calculate the value of $h$ to 1 decimal place.

(a)

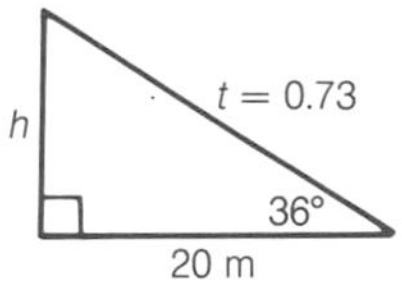


(b)

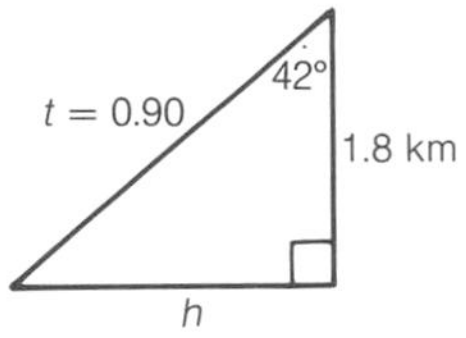


(c)

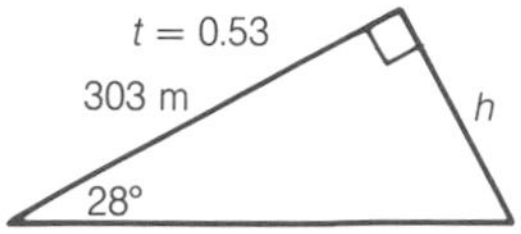


(d)

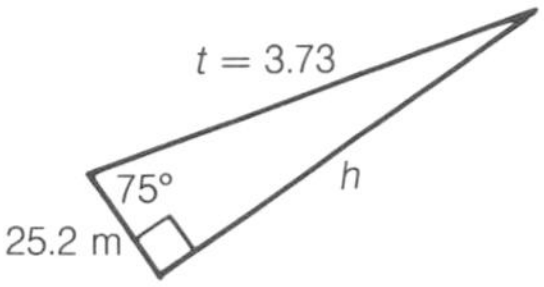


(e)

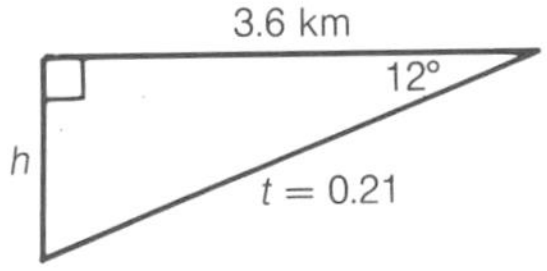


**B** For each of the following problems, the values of $t$ for each angle were calculated by constructing triangles. The results for the values of $t$ are given for each problem.

3 An angle is measured to determine the height of a tree. Use the value $t = 0.70$ for an angle of 35°. Find the height of the tree.

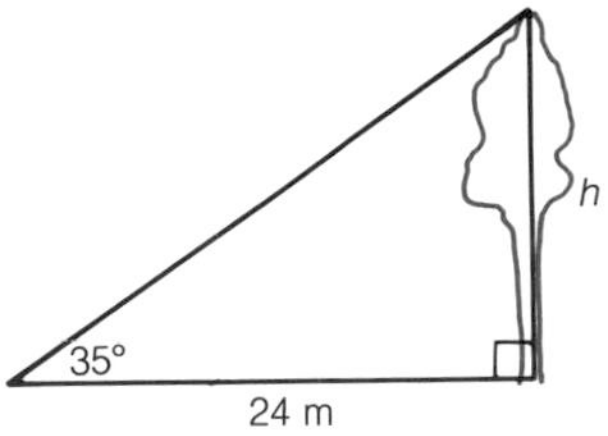


4 To calculate the width of a crater the measurements are made. Calculate the distance CR across the crater. Use $t = 0.62$ for an angle of 32°.

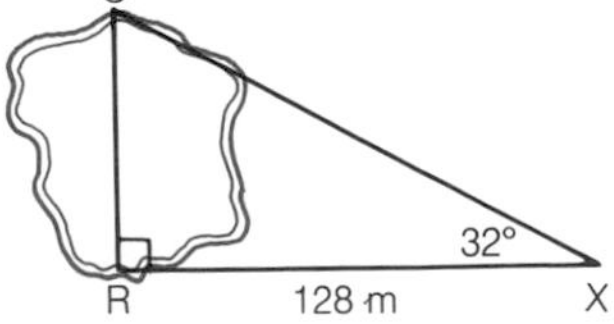


5 A weather balloon is located at position B. At that moment measurements are made as shown. Calculate the height of the balloon. Use $t = 0.32$ for angle of 18°.

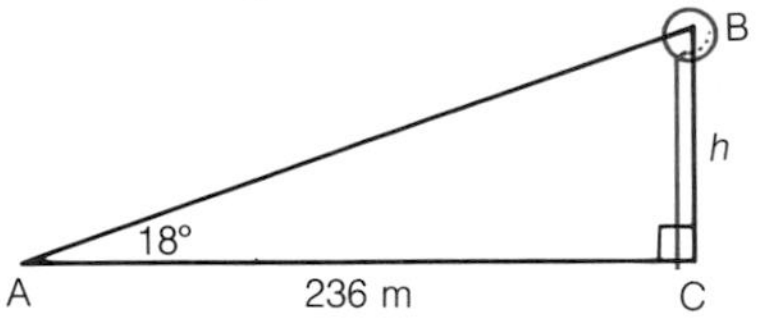


For each of the following problems
- ▶ Draw a diagram to record the information.
- ▶ Use the value of $t$ as given.
- ▶ Solve the problem. Find the missing lengths.

6 A ladder is placed against a wall making an angle of 63° with the ground. The base of the ladder is 2.3 m from the wall. How high up does the ladder reach? Use $t = 1.96$ for an angle of 63°.

7 A pole casts a shadow 18.5 m in length. The sun's rays meet the ground at an angle of 36°. Find the height of the pole, if the value of $t$ for an angle of 36° is $t = 0.73$.

8 A wire is supporting a TV antenna and makes an angle of 40° with the flat roof. If the guy wire is attached 12.3 m from the base of the antenna, how high is the antenna? Use $t = 0.84$ for an angle of 40°.

9 From a point 68 m from the base of a cliff, Jeremy measures the angle to the top of the cliff to be 53°. Find the height of the cliff. Use $t = 1.33$ for an angle of 53°.

10 An airplane takes off at an angle of 15° with the ground and continues on this path. When the plane is 2.5 km, measured along the ground, from the airport, what is its vertical height above the ground?

**Consumer Tip**

Before you make a purchase, be sure to ask what the "return policy" is? *Ask now, and don't be sorry later.*

# 15.5 Using Trigonometry

You have often seen people at the roadside working with equipment as they survey roads. They are using skills with trigonometry to solve problems about surveying. Trigonometry is an important branch of mathematics. The word trigonometry is obtained from the following words.

| tri | gono | metry |
|---|---|---|
| three | angle | measurement |

The study of trigonometry that you will use is based on the measures of the sides of triangles, and of the angles. In the previous section, you used a particular ratio, called the tangent of an angle. With values of the tangent you were able to solve problems making only the angle measurement and one measurement of a side. To obtain skills that apply to any problem solving situation, other ratios are introduced.

In your previous work with a right triangle, the sides were given names with respect to ∠A as shown.
These ratios are introduced for ∠A.

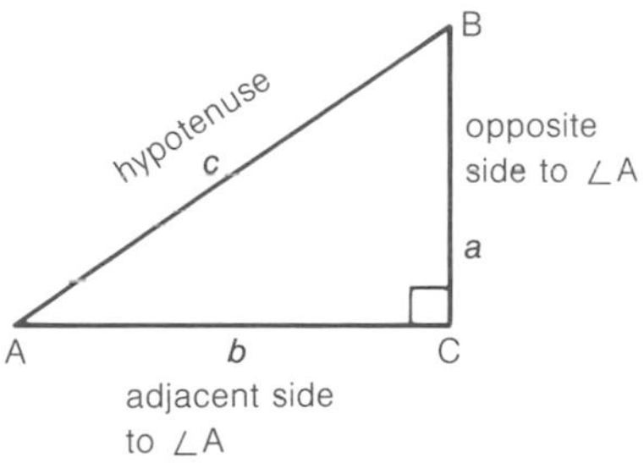


$$\text{sine of } \angle A = \frac{\text{opposite side to } \angle A}{\text{hypotenuse}}$$

$$\text{cosine of } \angle A = \frac{\text{adjacent side to } \angle A}{\text{hypotenuse}}$$

$$\text{tangent of } \angle A = \frac{\text{opposite side to } \angle A}{\text{adjacent side to } \angle A}$$

We call these ratios the primary trigonometric ratios.

| Name of ratio | Abbreviation | Meaning |
|---|---|---|
| sine of ∠A | sin A | $\frac{\text{side opposite to } \angle A}{\text{hypotenuse}}$ |
| cosine of ∠A | cos A | $\frac{\text{side adjacent to } \angle A}{\text{hypotenuse}}$ |
| tangent of ∠A | tan A | $\frac{\text{side opposite to } \angle A}{\text{side adjacent to } \angle A}$ |

You can use the values of the trigonometric ratios to find missing measures in a triangle.

**Example 1**

Find the length of CD.
Use $\cos 63° = 0.4540$.
Express your answer to the nearest metre.

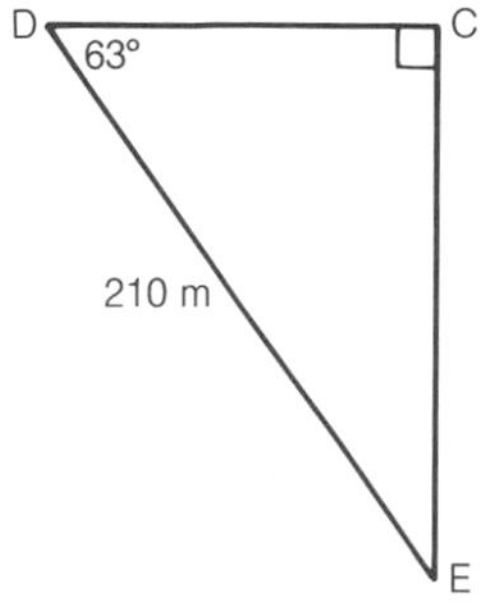


**Solution**

Let $h$, in metres, represent the length of CD. From the diagram

$$\frac{CD}{DE} = \cos 63°$$

$$\frac{h}{210} = 0.4540$$

$$h = 210(0.4540)$$
$$= 95.3 \text{ (to 1 decimal place)}$$

Remember:

$$\cos \angle D = \frac{\text{adjacent side}}{\text{hypotenuse}} = \frac{CD}{DE}$$

Thus, the length of CD is 95 m to the nearest metre.

If you know the measures of 2 sides of a right triangle, you can calculate the values of the trigonometric ratios. To do so, you need to use your earlier skills with the Pythagorean Property of triangles.

**Example 2**

In $\triangle ABC$, find the values of the primary trigonometric ratios of $\angle A$ and $\angle B$.

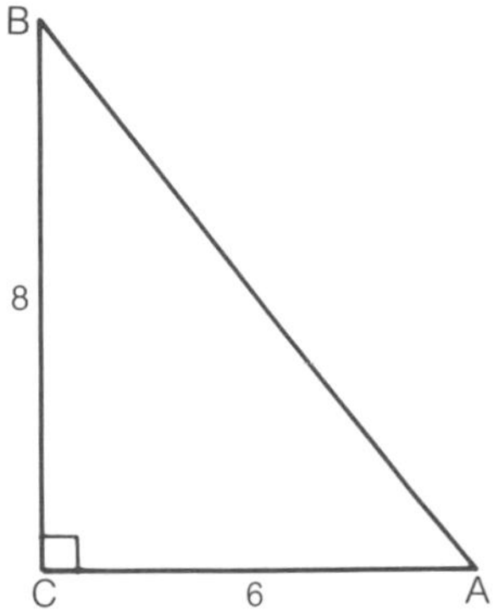


**Solution**

Think: To find the primary trigonometric ratios, we must first calculate the hypotenuse AB.

*Step 1*: Find AB.

$$(AB)^2 = 6^2 + 8^2$$
$$= 36 + 64$$
$$= 100$$
$$\text{Thus } AB = \sqrt{100}$$
$$= 10$$

*Step 2*: Write the values.

$$\sin A = \frac{8}{10} = \frac{4}{5} \qquad \sin B = \frac{6}{10} = \frac{3}{5}$$

$$\cos A = \frac{6}{10} = \frac{3}{5} \qquad \cos B = \frac{8}{10} = \frac{4}{5}$$

$$\tan A = \frac{8}{6} = \frac{4}{3} \qquad \tan B = \frac{6}{8} = \frac{3}{4}$$

## Try These

For triangle PQR, what is the length of
(a) the hypotenuse?
(b) the side opposite ∠R?
(c) the side opposite ∠P?
(d) the side adjacent ∠R?
(e) the side adjacent ∠P?

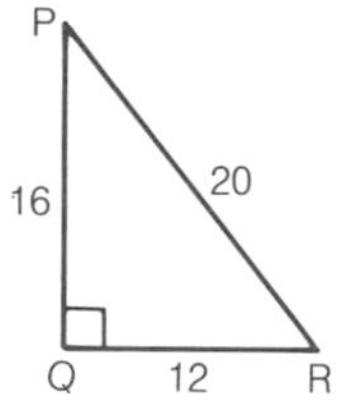


2 What are the sine, cosine and tangent ratios for ∠B in each triangle?

(a)
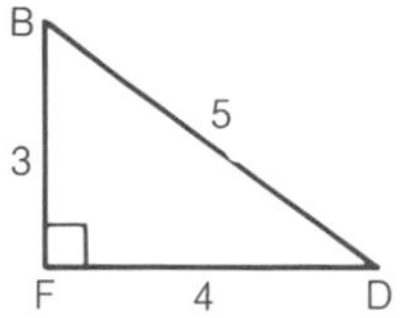


(b)
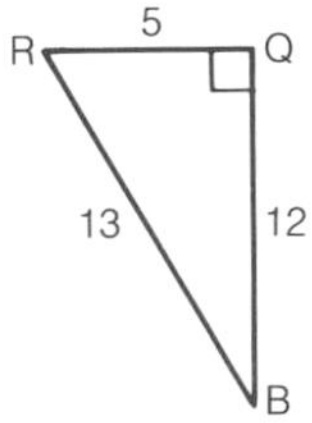


## Written Exercises

**A** You can only use trigonometry if you know the meaning of sin, cos and tan. Review the meanings of these words.

1 Refer to △ABC. Which of the following are true?

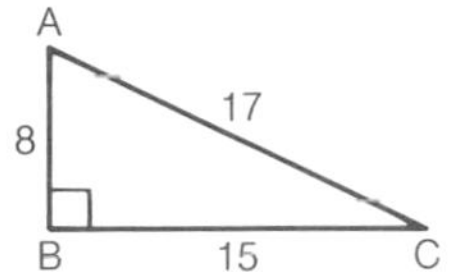


(a) $\sin C = \frac{15}{17}$ (b) $\cos A = \frac{17}{15}$

(c) $\tan A = \frac{15}{8}$ (d) $\sin A = \frac{8}{15}$

2 Refer to △EFG. Which of the following are true?

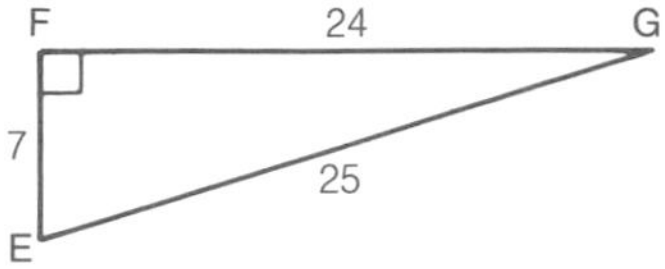


(a) $\cos E = \frac{7}{25}$ (b) $\tan G = \frac{7}{24}$

(c) $\sin E = \frac{25}{24}$ (d) $\cos G = \frac{24}{25}$

3 Use △PQR. What is each ratio?

(a) sin R (b) cos R
(c) tan R (d) sin P
(e) cos P (f) tan P

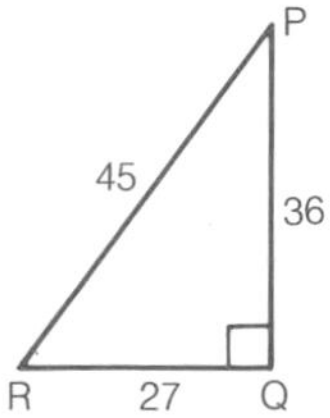


4 Use △ABC to find the following.

(a) sin A (b) sin B
(d) cos A (d) cos B
(e) tan A (f) tan B

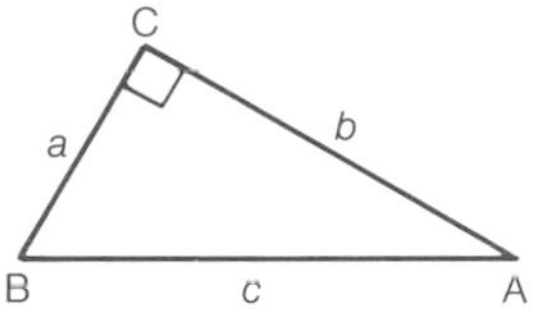


5 For each triangle, find the trigonometric ratio shown.

(a)
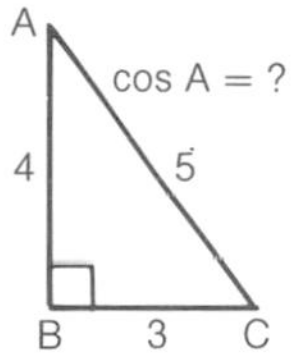


(b)
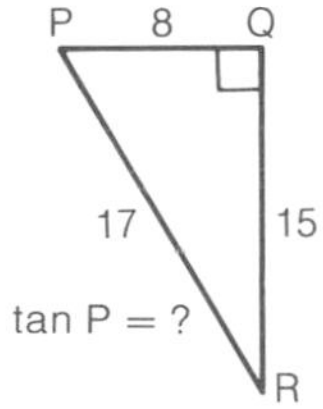


6 Find the value of the missing side. Then find the value of sin A, cos A and tan A for each triangle.

(a)
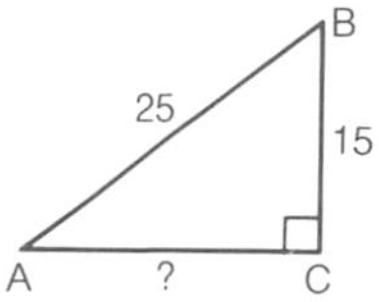


(b)
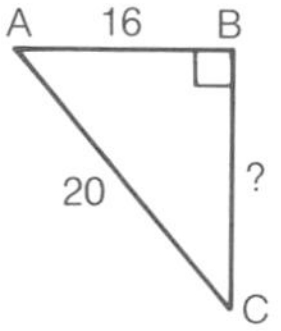


(c)
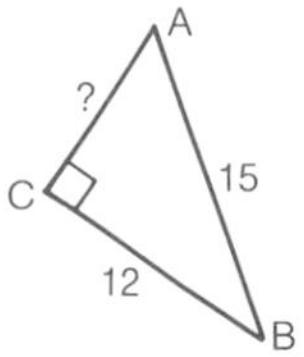


(d)
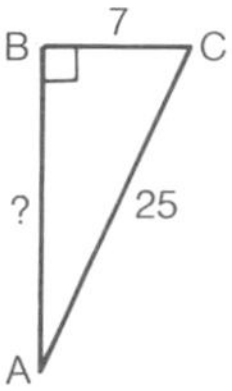

**B** Where needed, sketch a diagram. Then record the given information on your diagram.

7 In each triangle, find the primary trigonometric ratios for both acute angles.

(a)

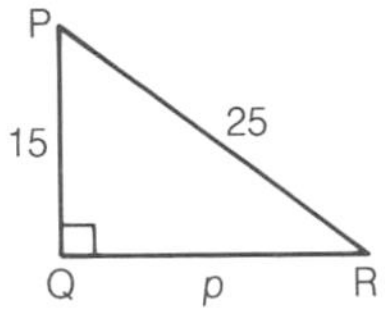


(b)

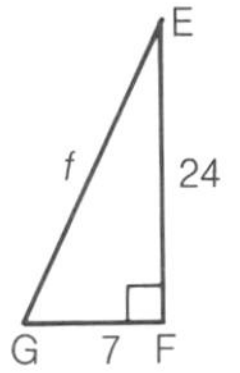


(c)

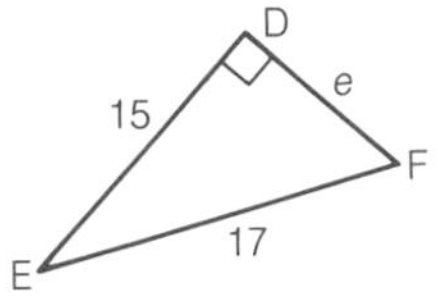


(d)

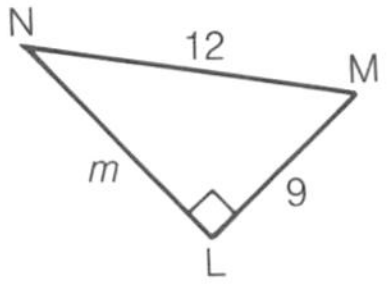


8 In $\triangle ABC$, $\angle B = 90°$, $AB = 5$, and $AC = 13$.
(a) Draw a sketch of the triangle.
(b) Find cos A.
(c) Find sin C.

9 For each triangle, use the information given to find the primary trigonometric ratios of both acute angles.
(a) In $\triangle PQR$, $\angle Q = 90°$, $PQ = 5$, $QR = 12$.
(b) In $\triangle LMN$, $\angle L = 90°$, $LM = 20$, $MN = 25$.
(c) In $\triangle XYZ$, $\angle X = 90°$, $XY = 15$, $XZ = 8$.

10 From earlier calculations, these values were found to 2 decimal places.
$\sin 32° = 0.53$ $\cos 32° = 0.85$ $\tan 32° = 0.62$
$\sin 58° = 0.85$ $\cos 58° = 0.53$ $\tan 58° = 1.60$
Use these values to find the length $h$ in each triangle.

(a)

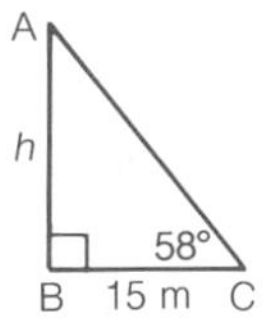


(b)

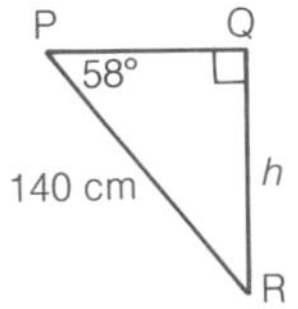


(c)

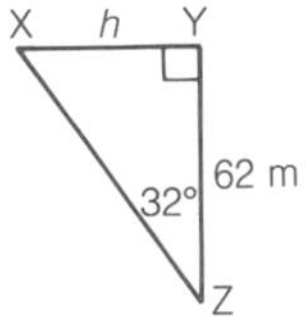


(d)

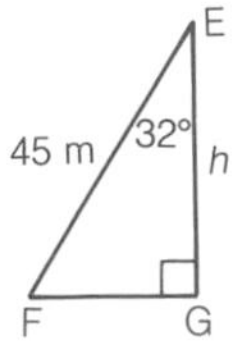


By constructing triangles, the values of the following ratios were calculated to 2 decimal places.

| | | |
|---|---|---|
| sin 21° = 0.36 | sin 29° = 0.48 | sin 47° = 0.73 |
| cos 21° = 0.93 | cos 29° = 0.87 | cos 47° = 0.68 |
| tan 21° = 0.38 | tan 29° = 0.55 | tan 47° = 1.07 |
| sin 34° = 0.56 | sin 37° = 0.60 | sin 66° = 0.91 |
| cos 34° = 0.83 | cos 37° = 0.80 | cos 66° = 0.41 |
| tan 34° = 0.67 | tan 37° = 0.75 | tan 66° = 2.25 |

Use the values in the chart to find the missing lengths.

11 Find the height of the monument AB using the information in the diagram.

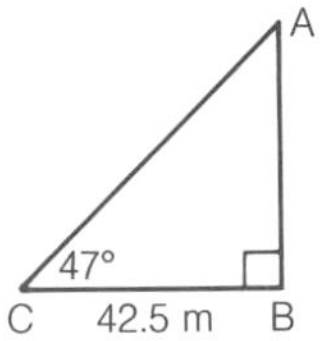


12 A kite is shown by the height $h$. How high is the kite?

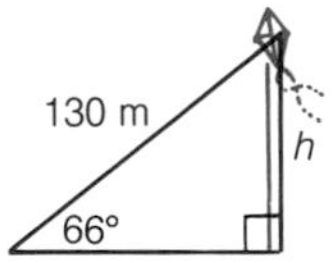


13 The width of a river, PQ, is shown in the diagram. Calculate the width.

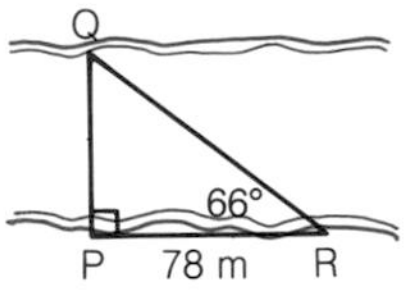


14 A boat is shown offshore from a cliff PQ. How high is the cliff?

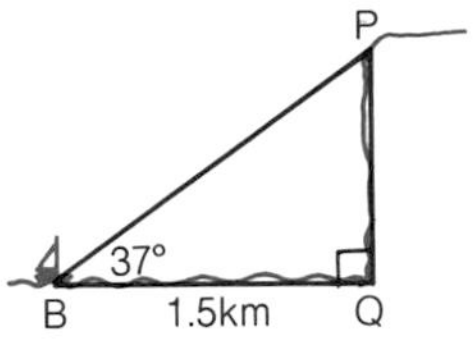


15 A guy wire RS holds the antenna RT in place. Calculate the length of the guy wire.

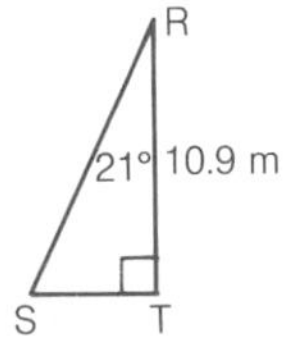


16 Calculate the length of the lake CD using the data given in the diagram.

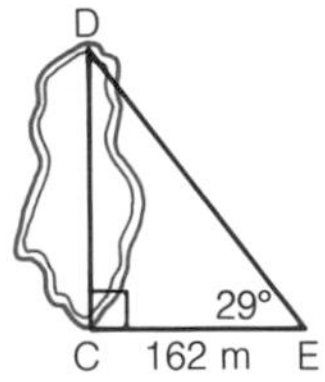

# 15.6 Using Tables: Trigonometry

In your previous work, you have calculated the values of the primary ratios in trigonometry using diagrams. In surveying problems, you often require high degrees of accuracy to obtain answers.

For this reason, computers are used to generate the values of trigonometric ratios. The values shown in the chart to the right are expressed correct to 4 decimal places.

### Example 1

Use the table of trigonometric values to find

(a) cos 36° (b) sin 52°
(c) tan 8° (d) cos 84°

### Solution

(a) cos 36° = 0.8090
(b) sin 52° = 0.7880
(c) tan 8° = 0.1405
(d) cos 84° = 0.1045

You can also obtain trigonometric values on a calculator. For example, to find cos 36°, you follow these steps.

[CE/C] 36 [cos] Display
0.809017

cos 36° = 0.809 017

Since calculators vary, refer to the manual provided with the calculator.

Once you obtain the value from a calculator, you need to decide how many decimal places you need to record.

From the tables, you can also reverse the process: if you are given the value of a primary ratio, you can determine the angle, as shown in the following example.

**Table of Trigonometric Values: Sine A, Cosine A, Tangent A**

| ∠A degrees | sin A | cos A | tan A | ∠A degrees | sin A | cos A | tan A |
|---|---|---|---|---|---|---|---|
| **1** | 0.0175 | 0.9998 | 0.0175 | **46** | 0.7193 | 0.6947 | 1.0355 |
| **2** | 0.0349 | 0.9994 | 0.0349 | **47** | 0.7314 | 0.6820 | 1.0724 |
| **3** | 0.0523 | 0.9986 | 0.0524 | **48** | 0.7431 | 0.6691 | 1.1106 |
| **4** | 0.0698 | 0.9976 | 0.0699 | **49** | 0.7547 | 0.6561 | 1.1504 |
| **5** | 0.0872 | 0.9962 | 0.0875 | **50** | 0.7660 | 0.6428 | 1.1918 |
| **6** | 0.1045 | 0.9945 | 0.1051 | **51** | 0.7771 | 0.6293 | 1.2349 |
| **7** | 0.1219 | 0.9925 | 0.1228 | **52** | 0.7880 | 0.6157 | 1.2799 |
| **8** | 0.1392 | 0.9903 | 0.1405 | **53** | 0.7986 | 0.6018 | 1.3270 |
| **9** | 0.1564 | 0.9877 | 0.1584 | **54** | 0.8090 | 0.5878 | 1.3764 |
| **10** | 0.1736 | 0.9848 | 0.1763 | **55** | 0.8192 | 0.5736 | 1.4281 |
| **11** | 0.1908 | 0.9816 | 0.1944 | **56** | 0.8290 | 0.5592 | 1.4826 |
| **12** | 0.2079 | 0.9781 | 0.2126 | **57** | 0.8387 | 0.5446 | 1.5399 |
| **13** | 0.2250 | 0.9744 | 0.2309 | **58** | 0.8480 | 0.5299 | 1.6003 |
| **14** | 0.2419 | 0.9703 | 0.2493 | **59** | 0.8572 | 0.5150 | 1.6643 |
| **15** | 0.2588 | 0.9659 | 0.2679 | **60** | 0.8660 | 0.5000 | 1.7321 |
| **16** | 0.2756 | 0.9613 | 0.2867 | **61** | 0.8746 | 0.4848 | 1.8040 |
| **17** | 0.2924 | 0.9563 | 0.3057 | **62** | 0.8829 | 0.4695 | 1.8807 |
| **18** | 0.3090 | 0.9511 | 0.3249 | **63** | 0.8910 | 0.4540 | 1.9626 |
| **19** | 0.3256 | 0.9455 | 0.3443 | **64** | 0.8988 | 0.4384 | 2.0503 |
| **20** | 0.3420 | 0.9397 | 0.3640 | **65** | 0.9063 | 0.4226 | 2.1445 |
| **21** | 0.3584 | 0.9336 | 0.3839 | **66** | 0.9135 | 0.4067 | 2.2460 |
| **22** | 0.3746 | 0.9272 | 0.4040 | **67** | 0.9205 | 0.3907 | 2.3559 |
| **23** | 0.3907 | 0.9205 | 0.4245 | **68** | 0.9272 | 0.3746 | 2.4751 |
| **24** | 0.4067 | 0.9135 | 0.4452 | **69** | 0.9336 | 0.3584 | 2.6051 |
| **25** | 0.4226 | 0.9063 | 0.4663 | **70** | 0.9397 | 0.3420 | 2.7475 |
| **26** | 0.4384 | 0.8988 | 0.4877 | **71** | 0.9455 | 0.3256 | 2.9042 |
| **27** | 0.4540 | 0.8910 | 0.5095 | **72** | 0.9511 | 0.3090 | 3.0777 |
| **28** | 0.4695 | 0.8829 | 0.5317 | **73** | 0.9563 | 0.2924 | 3.2709 |
| **29** | 0.4848 | 0.8746 | 0.5543 | **74** | 0.9613 | 0.2756 | 3.4874 |
| **30** | 0.5000 | 0.8660 | 0.5774 | **75** | 0.9659 | 0.2588 | 3.7321 |
| **31** | 0.5150 | 0.8572 | 0.6009 | **76** | 0.9703 | 0.2419 | 4.0108 |
| **32** | 0.5299 | 0.8480 | 0.6249 | **77** | 0.9744 | 0.2250 | 4.3315 |
| **33** | 0.5446 | 0.8387 | 0.6494 | **78** | 0.9781 | 0.2079 | 4.7046 |
| **34** | 0.5592 | 0.8290 | 0.6745 | **79** | 0.9816 | 0.1908 | 5.1446 |
| **35** | 0.5736 | 0.8192 | 0.7002 | **80** | 0.9848 | 0.1736 | 5.6713 |
| **36** | 0.5878 | 0.8090 | 0.7265 | **81** | 0.9877 | 0.1564 | 6.3138 |
| **37** | 0.6018 | 0.7986 | 0.7536 | **82** | 0.9903 | 0.1392 | 7.1154 |
| **38** | 0.6157 | 0.7880 | 0.7813 | **83** | 0.9925 | 0.1219 | 8.1443 |
| **39** | 0.6293 | 0.7771 | 0.8098 | **84** | 0.9945 | 0.1045 | 9.5144 |
| **40** | 0.6428 | 0.7660 | 0.8391 | **85** | 0.9962 | 0.0872 | 11.4301 |
| **41** | 0.6561 | 0.7547 | 0.8693 | **86** | 0.9976 | 0.0698 | 14.3007 |
| **42** | 0.6691 | 0.7431 | 0.9004 | **87** | 0.9986 | 0.0523 | 19.0811 |
| **43** | 0.6820 | 0.7314 | 0.9325 | **88** | 0.9994 | 0.0349 | 28.6363 |
| **44** | 0.6947 | 0.7193 | 0.9657 | **89** | 0.9998 | 0.0175 | 57.2900 |
| **45** | 0.7071 | 0.7071 | 1 | **90** | 1 | 0 | Not defined |

**Example 2**
Find ∠A given that
(a) $\cos A = 0.3584$
(b) $\sin A = 0.5736$
(c) $\tan A = 4.7046$

**Solution**
(a) $\cos A = 0.3584$
∠A = 69°
(b) $\sin A = 0.5736$
∠A = 35°
(c) $\tan A = 4.7046$
∠A = 78°

Think: find 0.3584 in the column of cosine values.
0.3584 = cos 69°

On a calculator you can also find the angle if you are given the values of any primary ratio.

Find ∠A if sin A = 0.9781

[CE/C] 0.9781 [Inv] [sin]   Display shows 77.986889

Rounded to the nearest degree
∠A = 78°

On some calculators [$\sin^{-1}$] has the same function. Refer to the manual to use the function.

If you have the measures of the sides of a triangle, you can determine the angles, as shown in the following example.

**Example 3**
Find the measure of ∠A and ∠B.

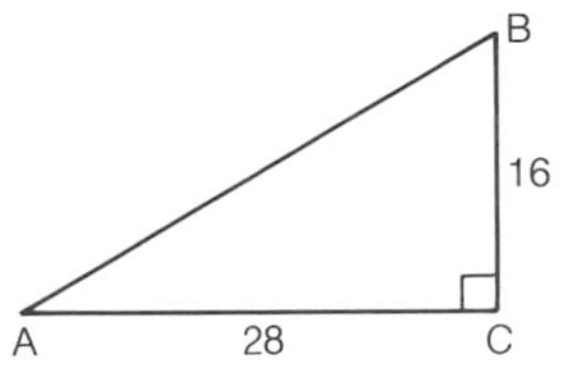


**Solution**
In △ABC

$$\tan B = \frac{28}{16}$$
$$= 1.75$$

To the nearest degree
∠B = 60°
∠A = 90° − 60°
= 30°

From the tables, or with a calculator
tan 60° = 1.7321
tan B = 1.75
tan 61° = 1.8040

## Try These

1 What is each value?
(a) cos 32° (b) sin 56° (c) tan 78°
(d) tan 62° (e) sin 79° (f) cos 17°
(g) sin 53° (h) cos 4° (i) tan 88°

2 What is the angle for each value?
(a) sin A = 0.2419 (b) cos A = 0.9877
(c) cos C = 0.9945 (d) tan X = 1.3270

3 Which is greater?
(a) sin 60° or cos 60°
(b) sin 45° or cos 45°
(c) tan 30° or tan 60°
(d) sin 60° or tan 40°

## Written Exercises

**A** Refer to the table of trigonometric values or use a calculator. Express angles to the nearest degree.

1 Find the value of each trigonometric ratio.

| | | |
|---|---|---|
| (a) tan 28° | (b) sin 53° | (c) cos 19° |
| (d) tan 63° | (e) sin 84° | (f) cos 24° |
| (g) sin 60° | (h) cos 4° | (i) tan 13° |
| (j) sin 45° | (k) sin 79° | (l) cos 56° |

2 Find the value of each ∠A.

| | |
|---|---|
| (a) sin A = 0.2588 | (b) cos A = 0.5150 |
| (c) tan A = 1.7321 | (d) tan A = 1.2349 |
| (e) sin A = 0.9976 | (f) sin A = 0.7193 |
| (g) cos A = 0.1564 | (h) cos A = 0.9994 |
| (i) cos A = 0.9336 | (j) tan A = 28.6363 |

3 Which is greater in value?

(a) sin 42° or cos 42° (b) cos 58° or sin 58°
(c) tan 30° or tan 50° (d) sin 85° or tan 71°

4 Use a calculator. Find the sine of each angle.

12° 18° 36° 40° 70° 85°

Round your answers to 4 decimal places. Compare your answers to those in the trigonometric tables.

5 Use a calculator. Find the cosine of each angle.

8° 15° 26° 38° 53° 62° 70°

Round your answers to 4 decimal places. Compare your answers to those in the trigonometric tables.

**B** When necessary, express angles to the nearest degree and lengths to 1 decimal place.

6 For each diagram, find the measures of ∠A and ∠B to the nearest degree.

(a)

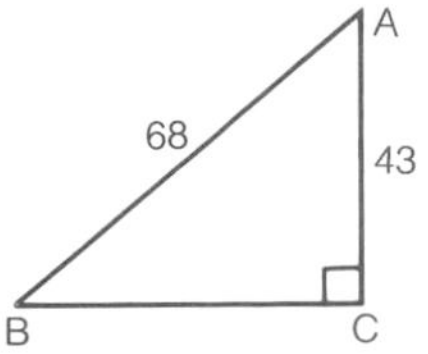


(b)

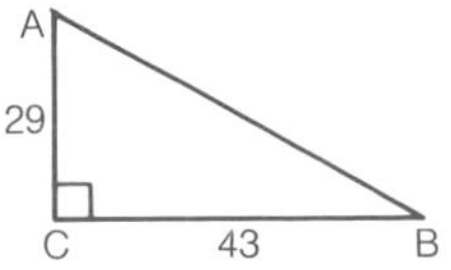


7 For each diagram, find the missing length. Express your answer to 1 decimal place.

(a)

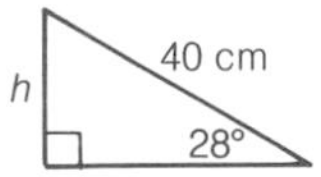


(b)

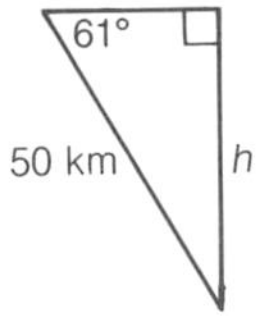


(c)

(d)

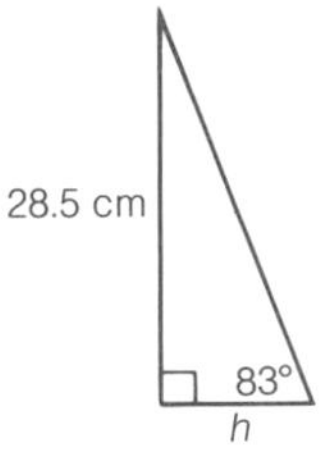


8 Use the diagram to find the height of the tree.

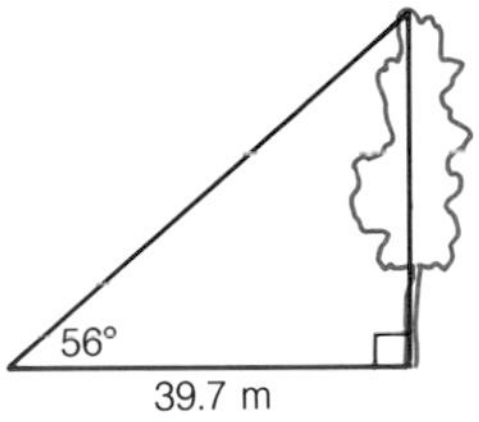


9 A cloud is shown in the diagram.

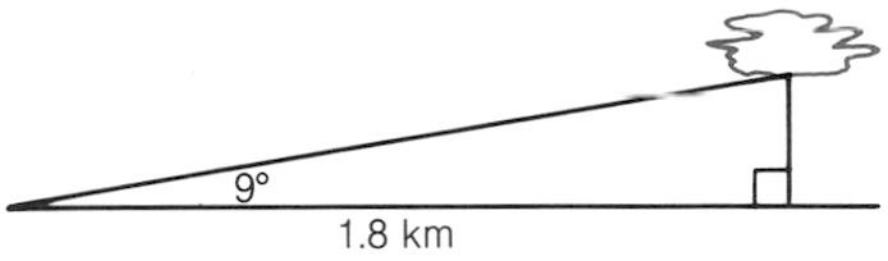


Calculate the height of the clouds.

10 A rectangular lot is surveyed. The measurements are shown. How long is the lot?

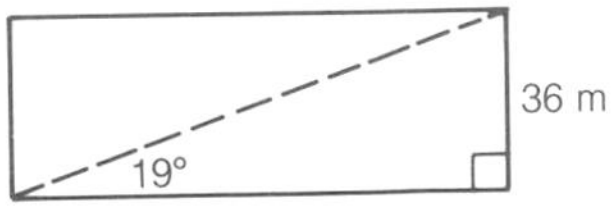


11 A ladder 9 m long leans against a wall so that it makes an angle of 54° with the ground. How high from the ground does the ladder reach?

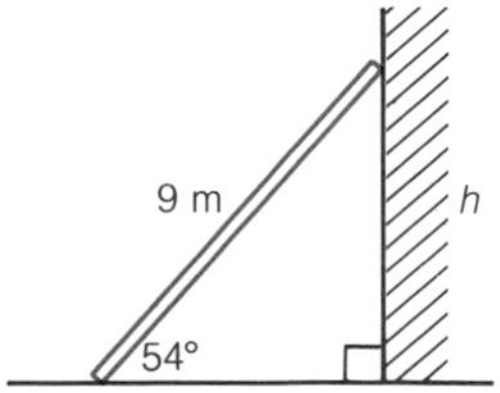

# 15.7 Solving Problems: Trigonometry

In the previous exercises, you have already solved some problems involving diagrams. In this section, you will solve a variety of problems using trigonometry. In using mathematics to solve problems, you have noticed frequently that to solve a problem you must know the answers to these two important questions.

*I What information am I asked to find?*
*II What information do I know?*

Whether you are solving a problem about a car, a bridge or a bank account, you need to know the answers to questions I and II.

To organize your solution, refer to the *Steps for Solving Problems*. In the chart, the missing parts are the skills you have learned about trigonometry.

Steps For Solving Problems

| | |
|---|---|
| Step A | Do you understand the problem?<br>I What information am I asked to find?<br>II What information am I given? |
| *Step B* | Decide on a method. |
| *Step C* | Find the answer. |
| *Step D* | Check your answer in the *original* problem. |
| *Step E* | Write a final statement to answer the problem. |

### Example 1

An office building casts a shadow that is 46 m in length. The rays of the sun strike the ground at an angle of 59°. Calculate the height of the building to 1 decimal place.

### Solution

Let $h$ represent the height of the building, in metres.

Think: sketch a diagram to record the information.

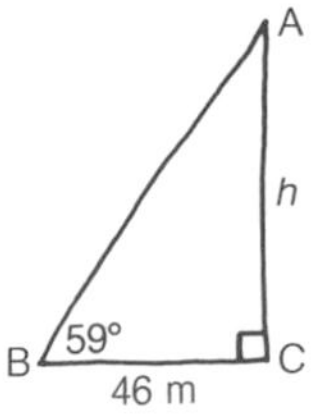


From the diagram

$$\frac{AC}{BC} = \tan 59°$$

$$\frac{h}{46} = \tan 59°$$

$$h = 46(1.6643)$$
$$= 76.56 \text{ (to 2 decimal places)}$$

The height of the building is 76.6 m (to 1 decimal place).

You can also use your skills to calculate angles.

**Example 2**

At a construction site, the brace used to retain a wall is 10.6 m in length. The distance from the wall to the lower end of the brace (on the ground) is 5.9 m. Calculate the angle at which the brace meets the wall.

**Solution**

*Step 1* Sketch a diagram to show the given information.

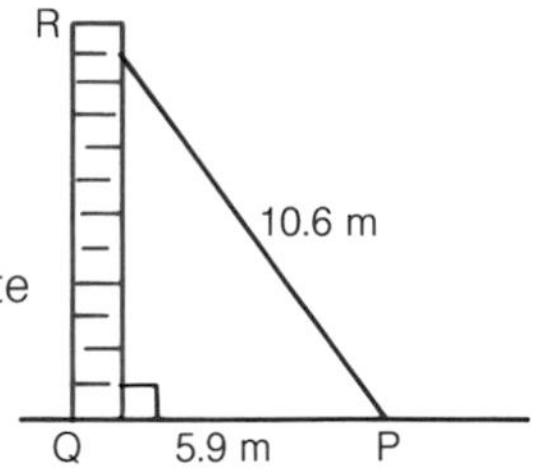


*Step 2* Use the diagram. Write an equation.

$$\sin R = \frac{PQ}{RP}$$

$$= \frac{5.9}{10.6}$$

$$= 0.5566 \text{ (to 4 decimal places)}$$

From the tables, $\angle R = 56°$ (to the nearest degree)

Thus the brace meets the wall at an angle of 56°.

## Try These

1 For each diagram, which trigonometric ratio would you use to find the value of *h*?

(a)

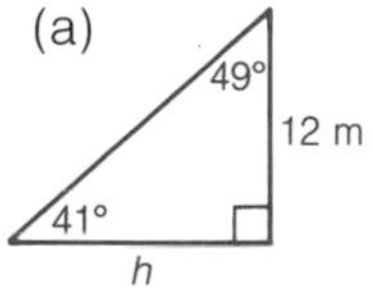


(b)

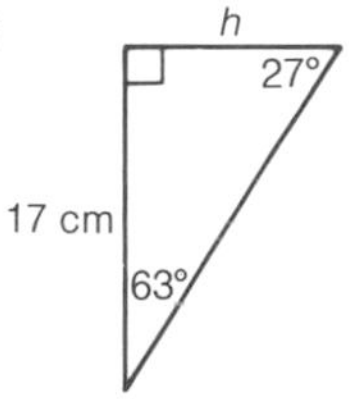


(c)

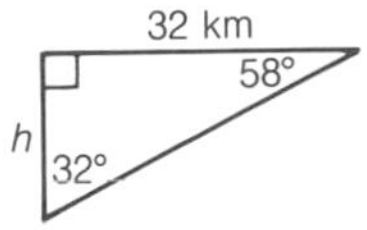


(d)

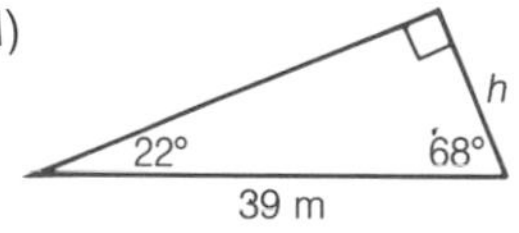


(e)

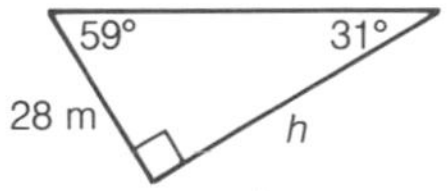


## Written Exercises

**A** Express your answers to 1 decimal place for lengths, and to the nearest degree for angles.

1 For each diagram
- ▶ decide on the trigonometric ratio you will use to find *h*;
- ▶ solve the problem.

(a)

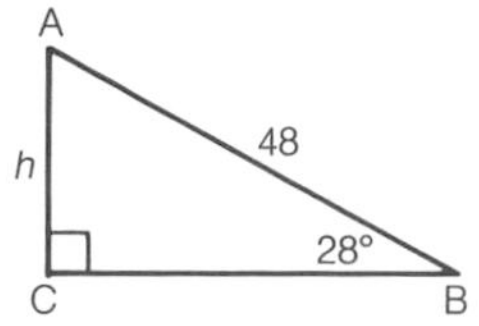


(b)

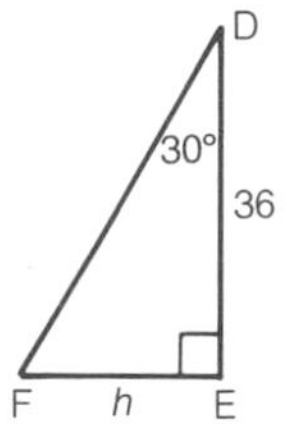


(c)

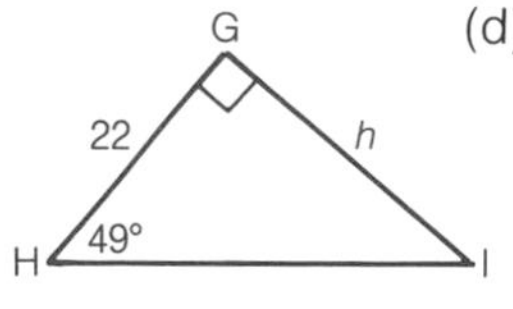


(d)

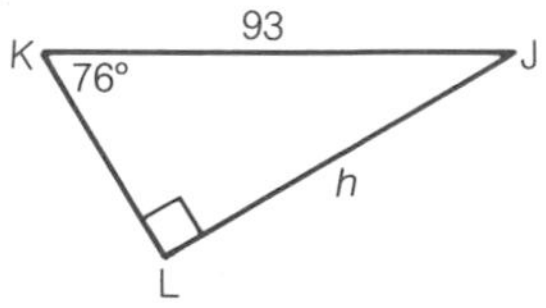


(e)

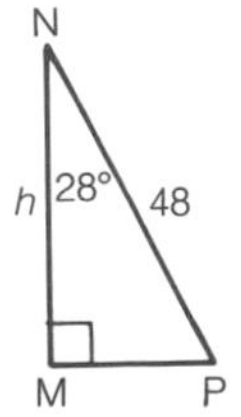


(f)

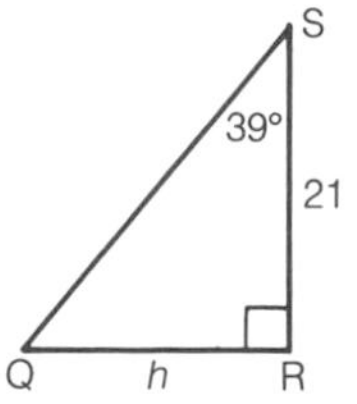

2 For each diagram
- ▶ decide on which trigonometric ratio you will use to find the missing angle;
- ▶ find the missing angle.

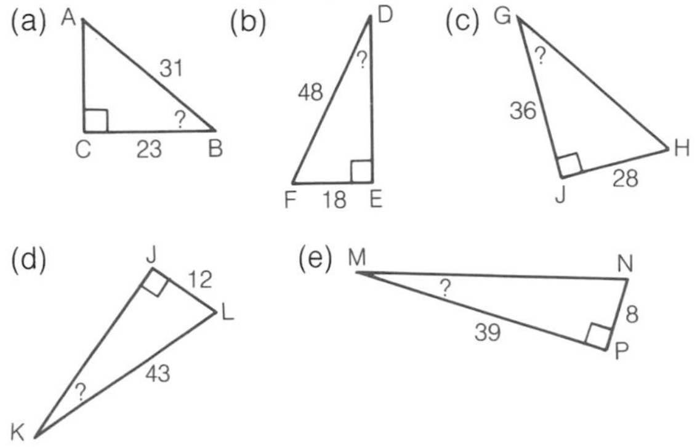


3 For each triangle, various measures are given. Find the remaining measures.

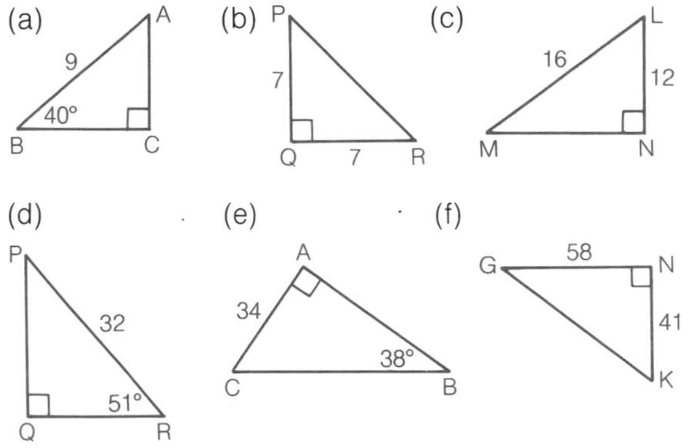


4 For each triangle
- ▶ draw a sketch of the triangle;
- ▶ record the information on the sketch;
- ▶ find the remaining measures.

(a) $\angle Q = 90°$, $\angle R = 62°$, PQ = 8 cm
(b) $\angle R = 90°$, $\angle Q = 46°$, PR = 12 m
(c) $\angle P = 90°$, $\angle Q = 77°$, PR = 4 mm
(d) $\angle Q = 90°$, $\angle P = 25°$, QR = 15 cm

**B** For each problem, sketch a diagram. Then record the given information on the diagram.

5 A 12 m ladder is leaned against a wall, with the foot of the ladder 1.4 m from the wall. Find the angle between the ladder and the ground.

6 (a) From the diagram, calculate the angle between the guy wire supporting the sign and the top of the sign.
(b) How long is the supporting wire, TB?

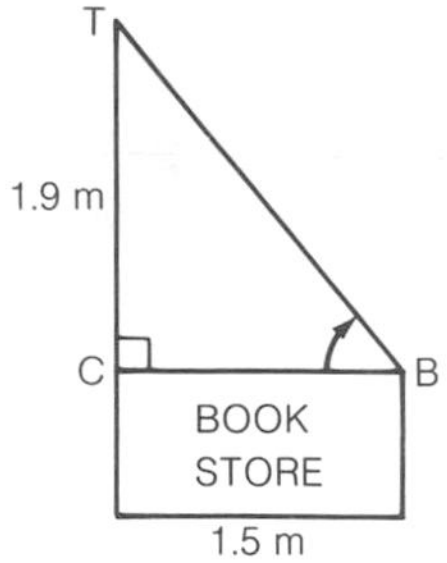


7 A tree 12 m high casts a shadow 17 m long. Calculate the inclination of the sun to the horizontal at this time of day.

8 A flagpole is held vertical by means of 2 guy wires each 35 m long. If the wires make an angle of 76° with the ground, find the horizontal distance along the ground between the two wires.

9 A roof rafter, BC, is 8 m long. The rise, CD, is 2.6 m. Find $\angle B$ and the length of the support, AB.

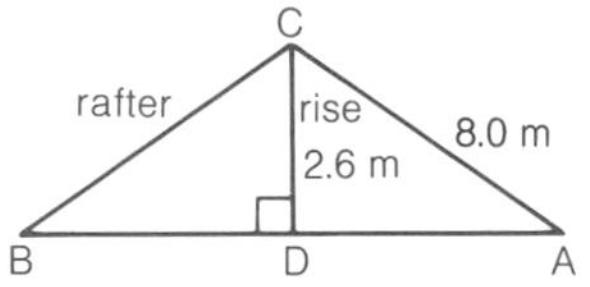


10 A ship passes a lighthouse as shown, at a speed of 12.5 km/h. In 15 min the ship is opposite the lighthouse. Calculate how close the ship comes to the shore.

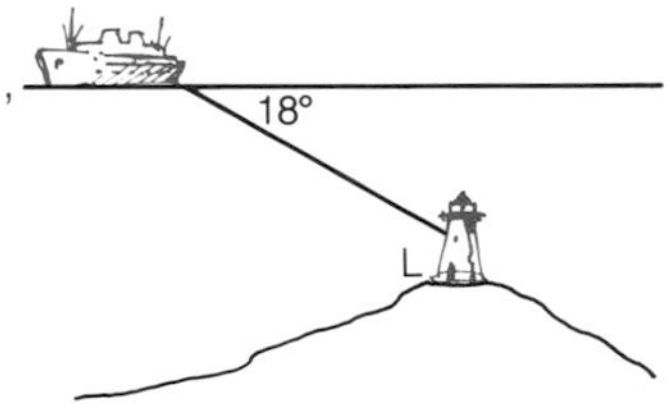


## Computer Tip

A computer can be used to explore properties of numbers. These numbers have a special property,

$(7,24,25) \rightarrow 7^2 + 24^2 = 25^2$

Run the following program to test for other "Pythagorean triples."

```
10 INPUT A, B, C
20 LET D = A ↑ 2 + B ↑ 2 − C ↑ 2
30 IF D = 0 THEN 60
40 PRINT A, B, C, "IS NOT A TRIPLE"
50 GO TO 70
60 PRINT A, B, C, "IS A TRIPLE"
70 END
```

## Applications: Technical Problems

Each problem occurs in some aspect of construction or in an industry. Use the information given to find the answer.

11 Find the length of the rafter of the deck roof shown in the diagram.

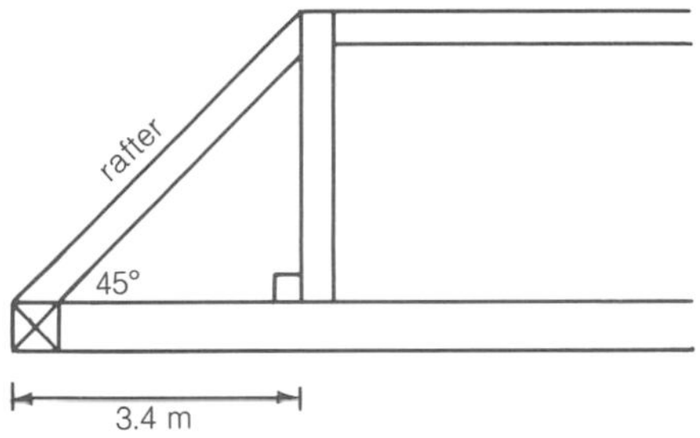


12 Find the length of the pipe "*d*" to the nearest centimetre.

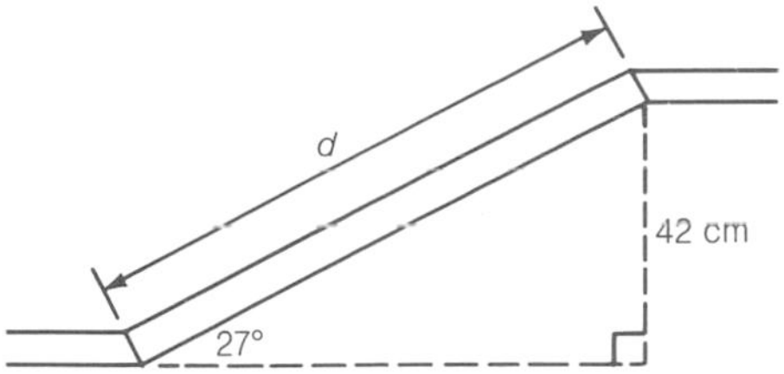


13 A pattern plate has 3 holes as shown in the diagram. Find *k*.

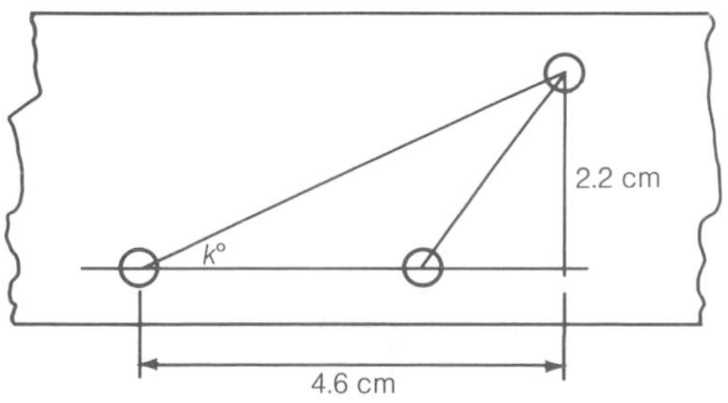


14 Find the taper angle *x* for the shaft shown in the diagram.

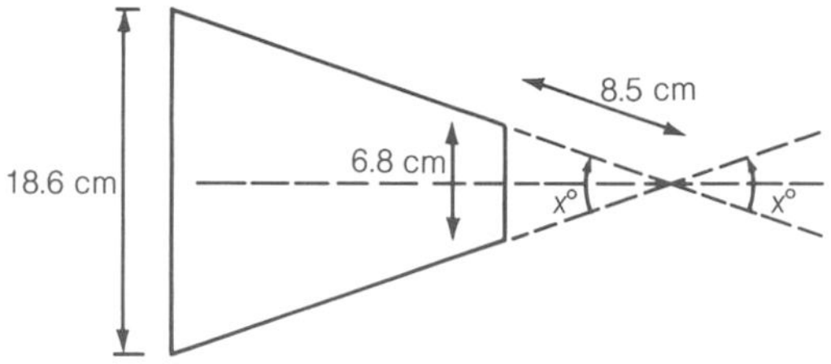


15 For the cutter holder, find the length of AB. All measures are in millimetres.

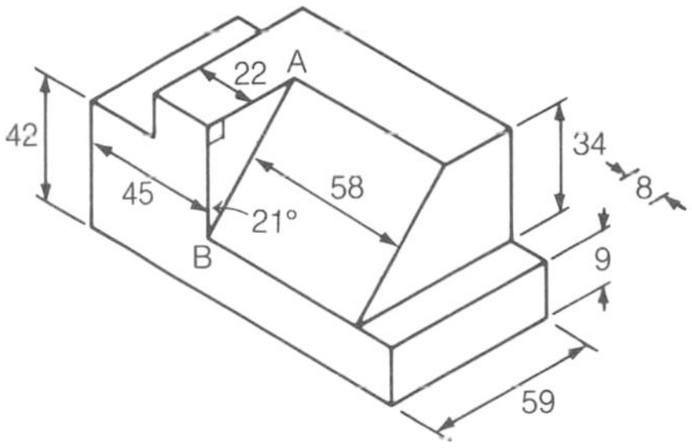


16 (a) In the blueprint design, all lengths shown are in centimetres. Calculate the length of AB.

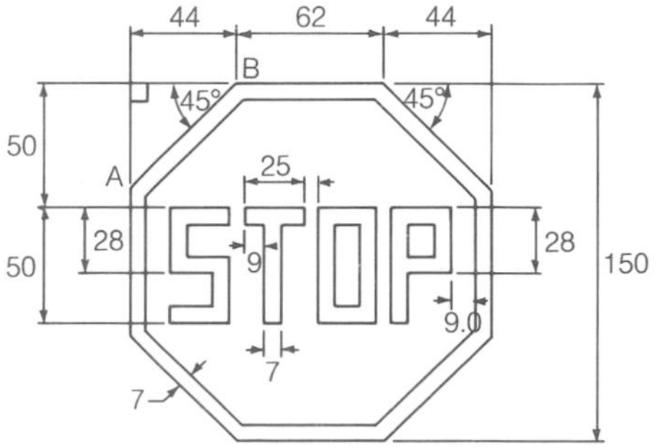


(b) Find your answer in (a) in another way. How do your answers compare?

# 15.8 Solving Problems: Angles of Depression and Elevation

In solving some problems in trigonometry, sightings are made. After the sighting is made, the recorded angle is used to do calculations.

A surveyor sights the top of a tower.

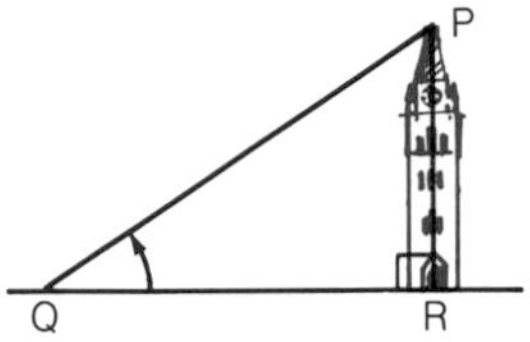


∠PQR is called the angle of elevation.

A rescue mission sights a raft.

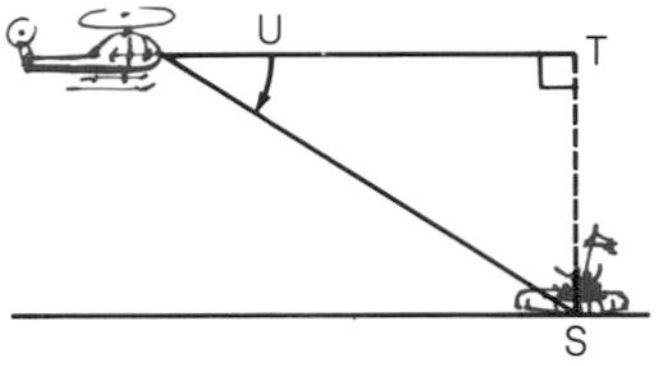


∠SUT is called the angle of depression.

These words occur frequently in problems involving engineers, helicopter pilots, and forest rangers in towers. Remember,

- ▶ the angle of elevation is measured upwards from the horizontal

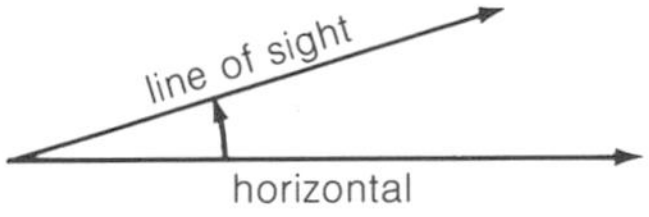


- ▶ the angle of depression is measured downwards from the horizontal

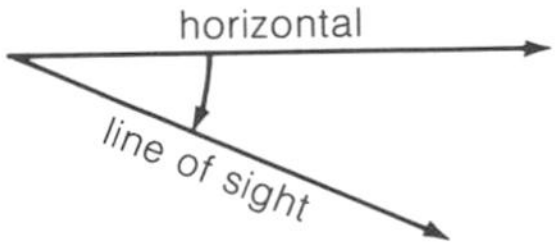


To solve the following problems you must have a clear interpretation of the meaning of elevation and depression.

### Example

From the top of an oil rig, 45 m above sea level, the angle of depression of a ship is 12°. Find the distance of the ship from the base of the oil rig, to the nearest metre.

Remember: sketch the given information on a diagram.

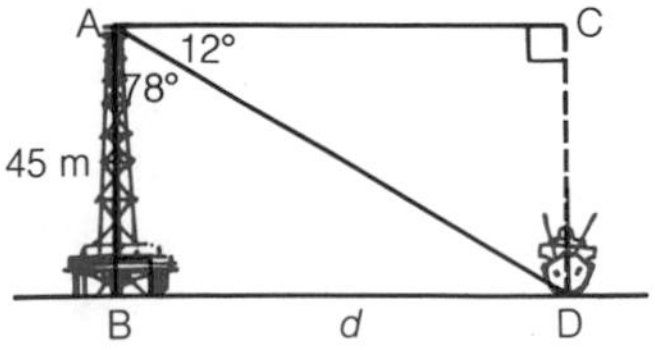


### Solution

Use $d$ to represent the distance of the ship from the oil rig.

In △DBA,

$$\frac{DB}{AB} = \tan 78°$$

$$\frac{d}{45} = \tan 78°$$

∠CAB = 90°
∠BAD = 90° − 12° = 78°

$$d = 45(4.7046)$$
$$= 211.7 \text{ (to 1 decimal place)}$$

The distance of the ship from the oil rig is 212 m, to the nearest metre.

## Try These

For each situation, what equation would you use to find the distance, $d$.

(a) angle of elevation is 32°

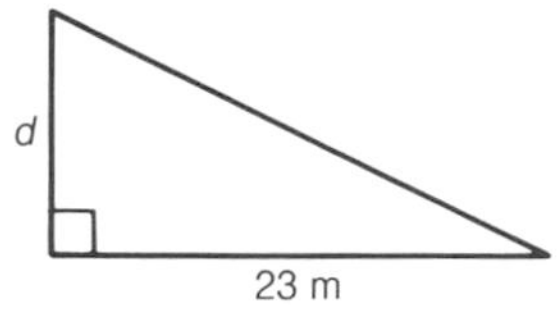


(b) angle of depression is 46°

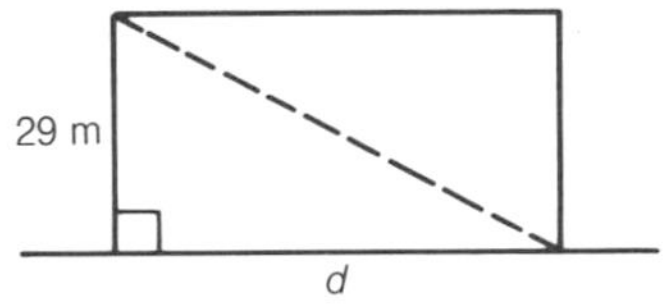


(c) angle of elevation is 62°

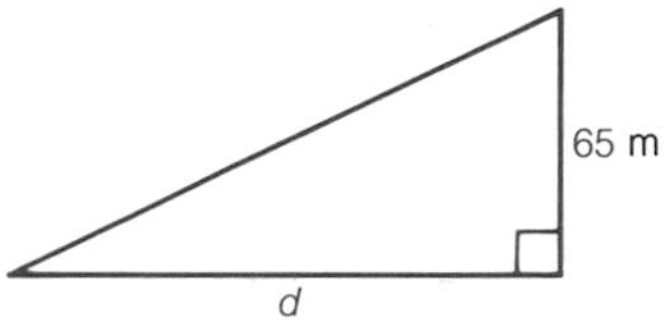


## Written Exercises

**A** Be sure you clearly understand the meaning of the angle of elevation and angle of depression.

1 The angle of elevation of the top of a totem pole is 14°. Use the data in the diagram to calculate the height.

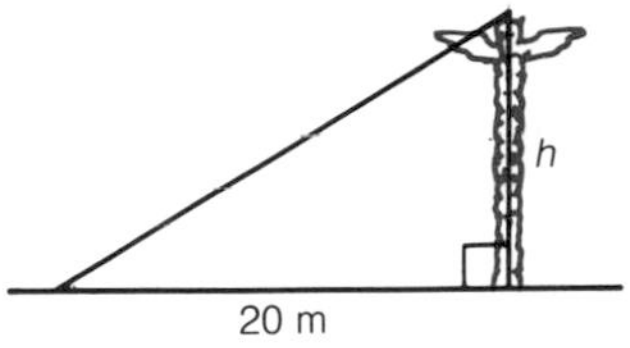


2 How far is the windsurfer from the base of the cliff? The angle of depression is 53°.

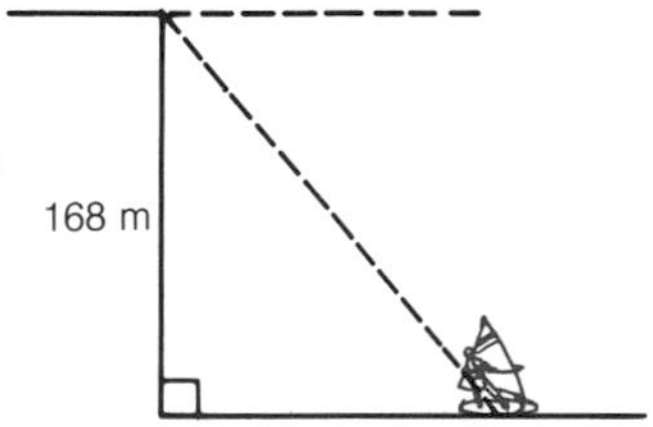


3 How high above the ground is the kite? The angle of elevation is 82°.

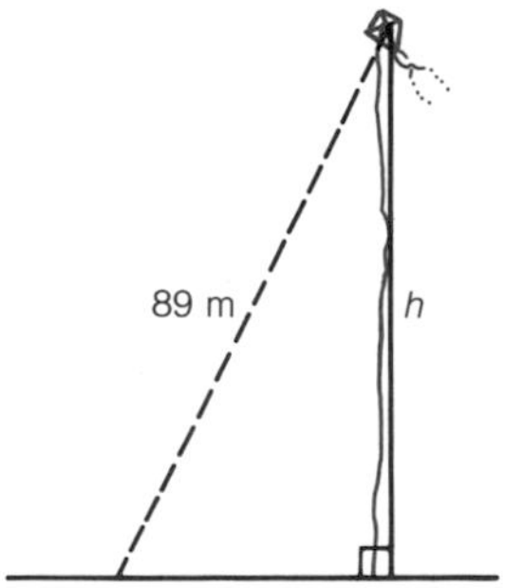


4 From the top of the building, the angle of depression of the fountain is 62°. Find the height of the building.

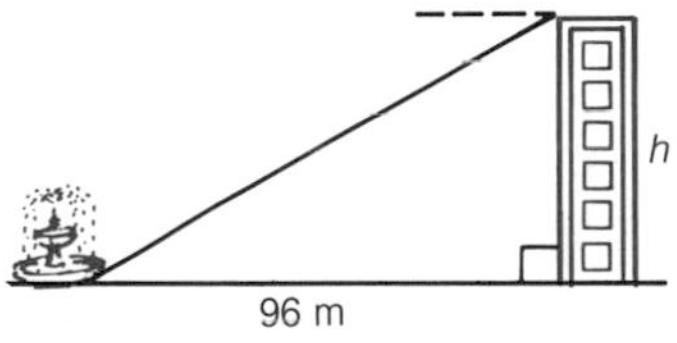


5 Use the data in the diagram. How high is the weather balloon? The angle of elevation is 67°.

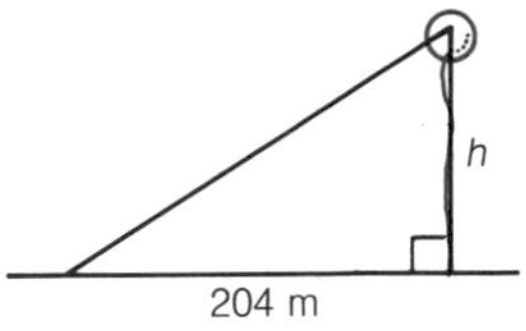


**B** Remember: organize the solution to the following problems. Refer to the *Steps for Solving Problems*. Where possible, use a calculator to do the calculations.

6 A tree casts a shadow 18.6 m long when the angle of elevation of the sun is 47°. How tall is the tree?

7 From a point 56 m above the ground in a control tower, the angle of depression to a helicopter from the observer is 46°. How far is the helicopter from the observer in the control tower?

8 The angle of elevation of the top of a radio tower is 43°. If the observer is 107 m from the base of the tower, find the height of the tower.

9 A boat is 342 m from the base of a cliff. Find the angle of depression of the boat as sighted by an observer on the cliff, which is 174 m high.

10 A fishing captain detects a school of fish at a depth of 60 m. If the angle of depression of the sounding is 13°, how far is the trawler from the school of fish?

For almost four and a half centuries the commercial fisheries, as Canada's first industry, have greatly influenced our history. About 20 000 km of coastline on the Atlantic and 11 500 km on the Pacific contain various species of fish that provide some of the world's best food fishes. More than 80 000 Canadians are employed in fishing related operations.

11 A kite string 61 m long makes an angle of 36° with the ground. Calculate the height of the kite.

12 An observer 2 m tall finds the angle of elevation of the top of a cliff is 63°. If the observer is 34 m from the base of the cliff, find the height of the cliff.

13 A rock dropped from the top of the Leaning Tower of Pisa falls 6 m from the base of the tower. If the height of the tower is 59 m, at what angle does it lean from the vertical?

14 A roadway rises 4.8 m for each 86.0 m along the horizontal. Find the angle of inclination, ∠B, of the roadway.

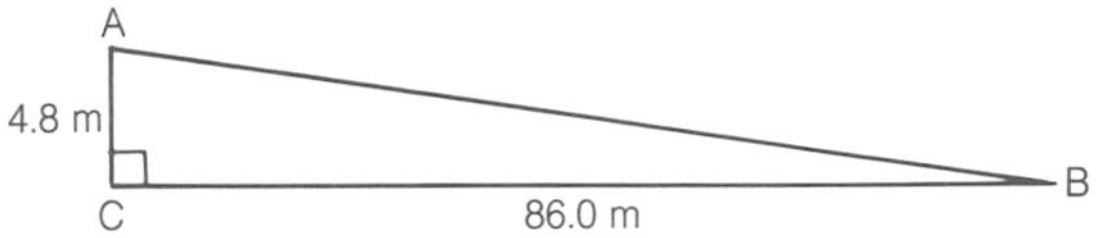


## C

15 An airplane travelling at the rate of 220 km/h is headed North. The wind causes the plane's actual path to be in a direction 39° East of North. (N39°E)

(a) Find the distance travelled in a northerly direction in 1 h.

(b) Find the amount of drift to the East in 1 h.

### Calculator Tip

If you wanted to calculate the height, $h$, of a mountain, as shown, it would be difficult to measure $P_2N$ or $P_2M$.

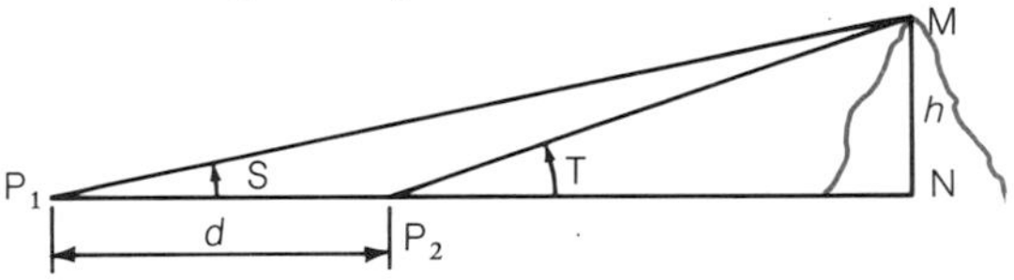


However, you could walk a distance, $d$, and take angle measurements at each point $P_1$ and $P_2$. The following formula is then used to calculate the height.

$$h = \left(\frac{\tan S \tan T}{\tan T - \tan S}\right) d$$

1 Use ∠S = 15.1°, ∠T = 18.3°, $d = 69.8$ m. Find the height, $h$. Use these steps on a calculator. Be sure your calculator is in the degree mode.

[C] 18.3 [Tan] [−] 15.1 [Tan] [=] [MS] 15.1 [Tan]

[×] 18.3 [Tan] [×] 69.8 [=] [÷] [MR] [=] output ?

2 Choose a height to find. Obtain measurements for ∠S, ∠T, and $d$. What is the height?

# 15.9 Extending Skills in Trigonometry

In your earlier work the trigonometric ratios for an angle were introduced.

$$\sin B = \frac{\text{side opposite } \angle B}{\text{hypotenuse}} \qquad \cos B = \frac{\text{side adjacent to } \angle B}{\text{hypotenuse}} \qquad \tan B = \frac{\text{side opposite } \angle B}{\text{side adjacent to } \angle B}$$

In solving problems in trigonometry, it is often convenient to use the reciprocal of these values, namely,

$$\text{cosecant } B = \frac{\text{hypotenuse}}{\text{side opposite } \angle B} \qquad \text{secant } B = \frac{\text{hypotenuse}}{\text{side adjacent to } \angle B} \qquad \text{cotangent } B = \frac{\text{side adjacent to } \angle B}{\text{side opposite to } \angle B}$$

To find the value of cosecant 36°, you can use tables or your calculator. Use the calculator in the degree mode.

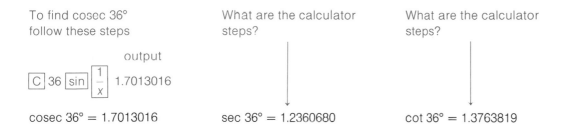

| To find cosec 36° follow these steps | What are the calculator steps? | What are the calculator steps? |
|---|---|---|
| [C] 36 [sin] [$\frac{1}{x}$] output 1.7013016 | ↓ | ↓ |
| cosec 36° = 1.7013016 | sec 36° = 1.2360680 | cot 36° = 1.3763819 |

In some problems, it is convenient to use these reciprocal values.

### Example
A telephone wire is to be placed from A to B. Use the information to calculate the length to the nearest fifty metres.

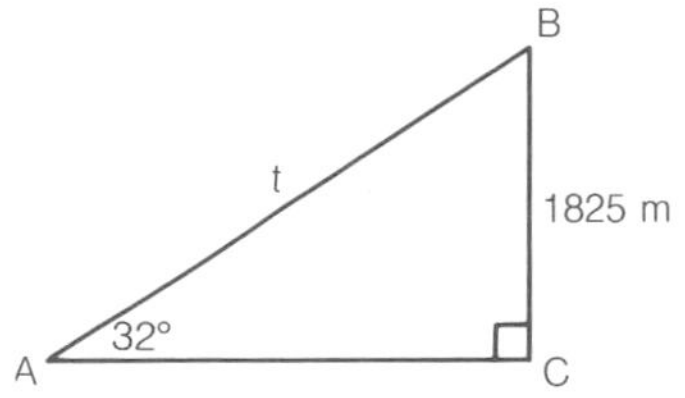


### Solution
Let the length of the wire, in metres, be represented by $t$.
From the diagram

$$\frac{t}{1825} = \text{cosec } 32°$$

$$t = 1825 \times \text{cosec } 32°$$
$$= 3443.9208$$

What are the steps on a calculator? [C] 32 [sin] [$\frac{1}{x}$] [=] [×] 1825 [=] output ?

Thus, the length of the wire is 3450 m.

## Written Exercises

**A** Review the meaning of sine, cosine, tangent, secant, cosecant, cotangent of an angle.

1 Refer to $\triangle PQR$.

(a) Measure PQ, QR, RP.

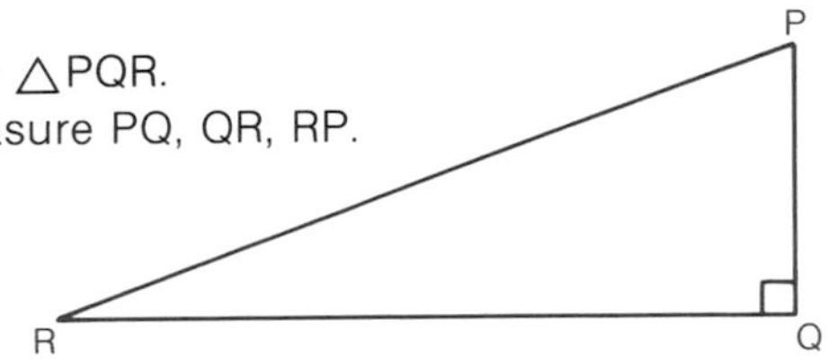


(b) Calculate $\frac{RQ}{PQ}, \frac{RP}{PQ}, \frac{RP}{RQ}$.

(c) Which values in (b) represent sec R, cosec R, cot R?

2 Construct any right triangle.

(a) Measure the angles.

(b) Calculate the secant, cosecant, and cotangent for the acute angles.

3 Construct a triangle for each angle measure. Then, complete the table.

| | ∠A | cosec A | sec A | cot A |
|---|---|---|---|---|
| (a) | 15° | ? | ? | ? |
| (b) | 45° | ? | ? | ? |
| (c) | 60° | ? | ? | ? |
| (d) | 75° | ? | ? | ? |

4 Use your calculator. Find each of the following.

(a) sec 24° (b) cot 13° (c) cosec 56°
(d) cosec 28° (e) sec 53° (f) cot 19°
(g) cot 63° (h) cosec 60° (i) sec 45°
(j) sec 84° (k) cot 4° (l) cosec 79°

5 For each diagram find the missing side. Then, calculate all the reciprocal trigonometric values.

(a)

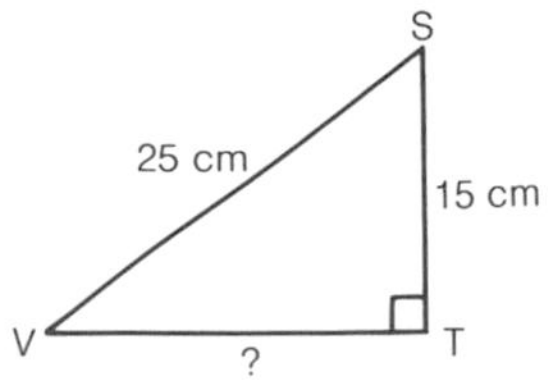


(b)

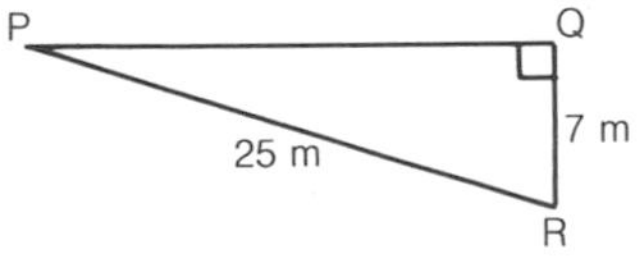


6 Use your calculator. Construct a table of values for

(a) sec A where A is 10°, 11°, 12°, . . . , 20°
(b) cosec B where B is 40°, 41°, . . . , 50°
(c) cot C where C is 60°, 61°, 62°, . . . , 70°

**B** Round your answers to the accuracy needed.

7 For each diagram, find the missing value.

(a)

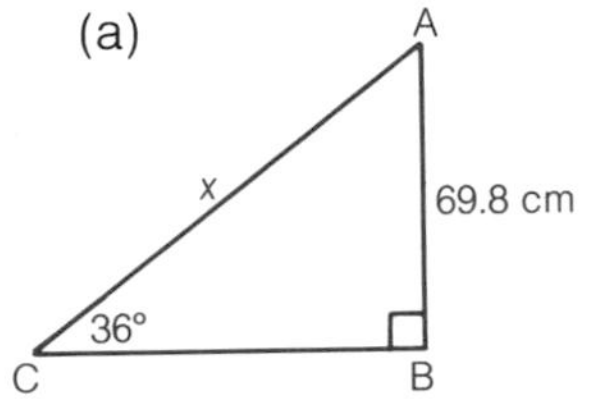


(b)

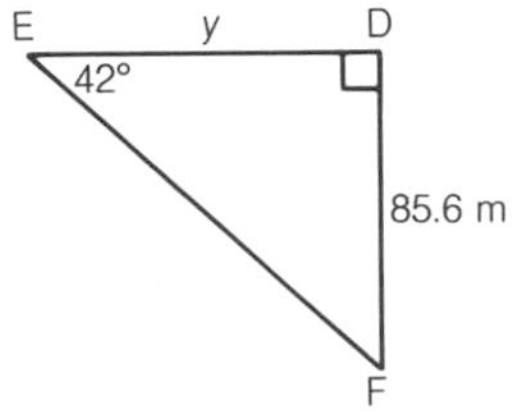


8 (a) Use the diagram to find the diagonal of the land.

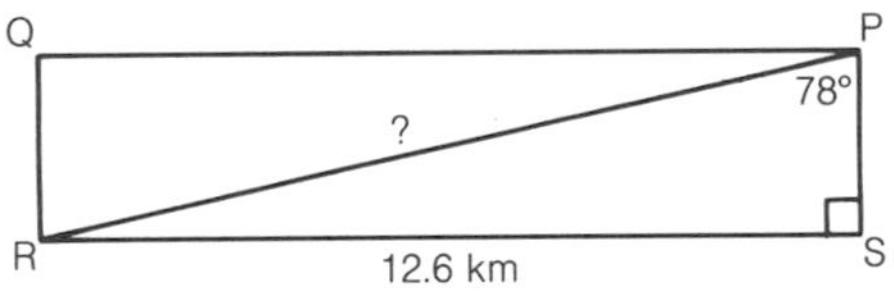

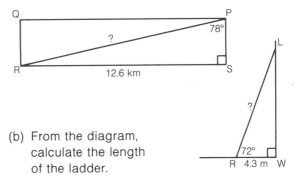

(b) From the diagram, calculate the length of the ladder.

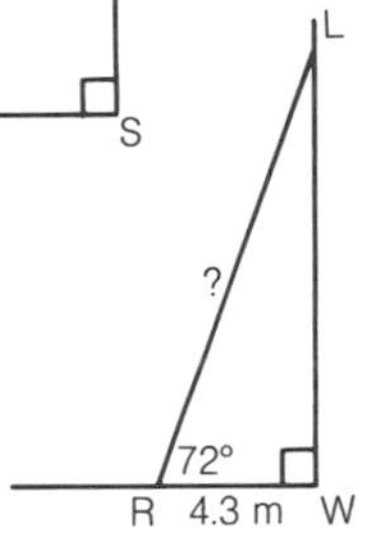


9 A ladder is placed against a building. If the angle of elevation of the ladder is 78° and the foot of the ladder is 5.6 m from the base of the house, how long is the ladder?

10 A cruiser calculates the position of a submarine by measuring the angle of depression to be 39° from the boat. If the submarine is horizontally 720.8 m ahead of the ship, calculate the shortest distance from the submarine to the cruiser.

11 How far are you standing from a weather balloon if it is 45.8 m in the air and its angle of elevation is 36°?

# Index

# Interest Tables $(1 + i)^n$ Compound Amount of 1

| $n$ | 0.25% | 0.5% | 0.75% | 1% | 1.25% | 1.5% | 1.75% | 2% | 2.5% | 3% |
|---|---|---|---|---|---|---|---|---|---|---|
| 1 | 1.002 500 | 1.005 000 | 1.007 500 | 1.010 000 | 1.012 500 | 1.015 000 | 1.017 500 | 1.020 000 | 1.025 000 | 1.030 000 |
| 2 | 1.005 006 | 1.010 025 | 1.015 056 | 1.020 100 | 1.025 156 | 1.030 225 | 1.035 306 | 1.040 400 | 1.050 625 | 1.060 900 |
| 3 | 1.007 519 | 1.015 075 | 1.022 669 | 1.030 301 | 1.037 971 | 1.045 678 | 1.053 424 | 1.061 208 | 1.076 891 | 1.092 727 |
| 4 | 1.010 038 | 1.020 151 | 1.030 339 | 1.040 604 | 1.050 945 | 1.061 364 | 1.071 859 | 1.082 432 | 1.103 813 | 1.125 509 |
| 5 | 1.012 563 | 1.025 251 | 1.038 067 | 1.051 010 | 1.064 082 | 1.077 284 | 1.090 617 | 1.104 081 | 1.131 408 | 1.159 274 |
| 6 | 1.015 094 | 1.030 378 | 1.045 852 | 1.061 520 | 1.077 383 | 1.093 443 | 1.109 702 | 1.126 162 | 1.159 693 | 1.194 052 |
| 7 | 1.017 632 | 1.035 529 | 1.053 696 | 1.072 135 | 1.090 850 | 1.109 845 | 1.129 122 | 1.148 686 | 1.188 686 | 1.229 874 |
| 8 | 1.020 176 | 1.040 707 | 1.061 599 | 1.082 857 | 1.104 486 | 1.126 493 | 1.148 882 | 1.171 659 | 1.218 403 | 1.266 770 |
| 9 | 1.022 726 | 1.045 911 | 1.069 561 | 1.093 685 | 1.118 292 | 1.143 390 | 1.168 987 | 1.195 093 | 1.248 863 | 1.304 773 |
| 10 | 1.025 283 | 1.051 140 | 1.077 583 | 1.104 622 | 1.132 271 | 1.160 541 | 1.189 444 | 1.218 994 | 1.280 085 | 1.343 916 |
| 11 | 1.027 846 | 1.056 396 | 1.085 664 | 1.115 668 | 1.146 424 | 1.177 949 | 1.210 260 | 1.243 374 | 1.312 087 | 1.384 234 |
| 12 | 1.030 416 | 1.061 678 | 1.093 807 | 1.126 825 | 1.160 755 | 1.195 618 | 1.231 439 | 1.268 242 | 1.344 889 | 1.425 761 |
| 13 | 1.032 992 | 1.066 986 | 1.102 010 | 1.138 093 | 1.175 264 | 1.213 552 | 1.252 990 | 1.293 607 | 1.378 511 | 1.468 534 |
| 14 | 1.035 574 | 1.072 321 | 1.110 276 | 1.149 474 | 1.189 955 | 1.231 756 | 1.274 917 | 1.319 479 | 1.412 974 | 1.512 590 |
| 15 | 1.038 163 | 1.077 683 | 1.118 603 | 1.160 969 | 1.204 829 | 1.250 232 | 1.297 228 | 1.345 868 | 1.448 298 | 1.557 967 |
| 16 | 1.040 759 | 1.083 071 | 1.126 992 | 1.172 579 | 1.219 890 | 1.268 986 | 1.319 929 | 1.372 786 | 1.484 506 | 1.604 706 |
| 17 | 1.043 361 | 1.088 487 | 1.135 445 | 1.184 304 | 1.235 138 | 1.288 020 | 1.343 028 | 1.400 241 | 1.521 618 | 1.652 848 |
| 18 | 1.045 969 | 1.093 929 | 1.143 960 | 1.196 147 | 1.250 577 | 1.307 341 | 1.366 531 | 1.428 246 | 1.559 659 | 1.702 433 |
| 19 | 1.048 584 | 1.099 399 | 1.152 540 | 1.208 109 | 1.266 210 | 1.326 951 | 1.390 445 | 1.456 811 | 1.598 650 | 1.753 506 |
| 20 | 1.051 206 | 1.104 896 | 1.161 184 | 1.220 190 | 1.282 037 | 1.346 855 | 1.414 778 | 1.485 947 | 1.638 616 | 1.806 111 |
| 21 | 1.053 834 | 1.110 420 | 1.169 893 | 1.232 392 | 1.289 063 | 1.367 058 | 1.439 537 | 1.515 666 | 1.679 582 | 1.860 295 |
| 22 | 1.056 468 | 1.115 972 | 1.178 667 | 1.244 716 | 1.314 288 | 1.387 564 | 1.464 729 | 1.545 980 | 1.721 571 | 1.916 103 |
| 23 | 1.059 109 | 1.121 552 | 1.187 507 | 1.257 163 | 1.330 717 | 1.408 377 | 1.490 361 | 1.576 899 | 1.764 611 | 1.973 587 |
| 24 | 1.061 757 | 1.127 160 | 1.196 414 | 1.269 735 | 1.347 351 | 1.429 503 | 1.516 443 | 1.608 437 | 1.808 726 | 2.032 794 |
| 25 | 1.064 411 | 1.132 796 | 1.205 387 | 1.282 432 | 1.364 193 | 1.450 945 | 1.542 981 | 1.640 606 | 1.853 944 | 2.093 778 |
| 26 | 1.067 072 | 1.138 460 | 1.214 427 | 1.295 256 | 1.381 245 | 1.472 710 | 1.569 983 | 1.673 418 | 1.900 293 | 2.156 591 |
| 27 | 1.069 740 | 1.144 152 | 1.223 535 | 1.308 209 | 1.398 511 | 1.494 800 | 1.597 457 | 1.706 886 | 1.947 800 | 2.221 289 |
| 28 | 1.072 414 | 1.149 873 | 1.232 712 | 1.321 291 | 1.415 992 | 1.517 222 | 1.625 413 | 1.741 024 | 1.996 495 | 2.287 928 |
| 29 | 1.075 096 | 1.155 622 | 1.241 957 | 1.334 504 | 1.433 692 | 1.539 981 | 1.653 858 | 1.775 845 | 2.046 407 | 2.356 566 |
| 30 | 1.077 783 | 1.161 400 | 1.251 272 | 1.347 849 | 1.451 613 | 1.563 080 | 1.682 800 | 1.811 362 | 2.097 568 | 2.427 262 |
| 31 | 1.080 478 | 1.167 207 | 1.260 656 | 1.361 327 | 1.469 759 | 1.586 526 | 1.712 249 | 1.847 589 | 2.150 007 | 2.500 080 |
| 32 | 1.083 179 | 1.173 043 | 1.270 111 | 1.374 941 | 1.488 131 | 1.610 324 | 1.742 213 | 1.884 541 | 2.203 757 | 2.575 083 |
| 33 | 1.085 887 | 1.178 908 | 1.279 637 | 1.388 690 | 1.506 732 | 1.634 479 | 1.772 702 | 1.922 231 | 2.258 851 | 2.652 335 |
| 34 | 1.088 602 | 1.184 803 | 1.289 234 | 1.402 577 | 1.525 566 | 1.658 996 | 1.803 725 | 1.960 676 | 2.315 322 | 2.731 905 |
| 35 | 1.091 323 | 1.190 727 | 1.298 904 | 1.416 603 | 1.544 636 | 1.683 881 | 1.835 290 | 1.999 890 | 2.373 205 | 2.813 862 |
| 36 | 1.094 051 | 1.196 681 | 1.308 645 | 1.430 769 | 1.563 944 | 1.709 140 | 1.867 407 | 2.039 887 | 2.432 535 | 2.898 278 |
| 37 | 1.096 787 | 1.202 664 | 1.318 460 | 1.445 076 | 1.583 493 | 1.734 777 | 1.900 087 | 2.080 685 | 2.493 349 | 2.985 227 |
| 38 | 1.099 528 | 1.208 677 | 1.328 349 | 1.459 527 | 1.603 287 | 1.760 798 | 1.933 338 | 2.122 299 | 2.555 682 | 3.074 783 |
| 39 | 1.102 277 | 1.214 721 | 1.338 311 | 1.474 123 | 1.623 328 | 1.787 210 | 1.967 172 | 2.164 745 | 2.619 574 | 3.167 027 |
| 40 | 1.105 033 | 1.220 794 | 1.348 349 | 1.488 864 | 1.643 619 | 1.814 018 | 2.001 597 | 2.208 040 | 2.685 064 | 3.262 038 |
| 41 | 1.107 796 | 1.226 898 | 1.358 461 | 1.503 752 | 1.664 165 | 1.841 229 | 2.036 625 | 2.252 200 | 2.752 190 | 3.359 899 |
| 42 | 1.110 565 | 1.233 033 | 1.368 650 | 1.518 790 | 1.684 967 | 1.868 847 | 2.072 266 | 2.297 244 | 2.820 995 | 3.460 696 |
| 43 | 1.113 341 | 1.239 198 | 1.378 915 | 1.533 978 | 1.706 029 | 1.896 880 | 2.108 531 | 2.343 189 | 2.891 520 | 3.564 517 |
| 44 | 1.116 125 | 1.245 394 | 1.389 256 | 1.549 318 | 1.727 354 | 1.925 333 | 2.145 430 | 2.390 053 | 2.963 808 | 3.671 452 |
| 45 | 1.118 915 | 1.251 621 | 1.399 676 | 1.564 811 | 1.748 946 | 1.954 213 | 2.182 975 | 2.437 854 | 3.037 903 | 3.781 596 |
| 46 | 1.121 712 | 1.257 879 | 1.410 173 | 1.580 459 | 1.770 808 | 1.983 526 | 2.221 177 | 2.486 611 | 3.113 851 | 3.895 044 |
| 47 | 1.124 517 | 1.264 168 | 1.420 750 | 1.596 263 | 1.792 943 | 2.013 279 | 2.260 048 | 2.536 344 | 3.191 697 | 4.011 895 |
| 48 | 1.127 328 | 1.270 489 | 1.431 405 | 1.612 226 | 1.815 355 | 2.043 478 | 2.299 599 | 2.587 070 | 3.271 490 | 4.132 252 |
| 49 | 1.130 146 | 1.276 842 | 1.442 141 | 1.628 348 | 1.838 047 | 2.074 130 | 2.339 842 | 2.638 812 | 3.353 277 | 4.256 219 |
| 50 | 1.132 972 | 1.283 226 | 1.452 957 | 1.644 632 | 1.861 022 | 2.105 242 | 2.380 789 | 2.691 588 | 3.437 109 | 4.383 906 |

## Compound Interest

| *n* | 3.5% | 4% | 4.5% | 5% | 5.5% | 6% | 6.5% | 7% | 7.5% | 8% |
|---|---|---|---|---|---|---|---|---|---|---|
| 1 | 1.035 000 | 1.040 000 | 1.045 000 | 1.050 000 | 1.055 000 | 1.060 000 | 1.065 000 | 1.070 000 | 1.075 000 | 1.080 000 |
| 2 | 1.071 225 | 1.081 600 | 1.092 025 | 1.102 500 | 1.113 025 | 1.123 600 | 1.134 225 | 1.144 900 | 1.155 625 | 1.166 400 |
| 3 | 1.108 718 | 1.124 864 | 1.141 166 | 1.157 625 | 1.174 241 | 1.191 016 | 1.207 950 | 1.225 043 | 1.242 297 | 1.259 712 |
| 4 | 1.147 523 | 1.169 859 | 1.192 519 | 1.215 506 | 1.238 825 | 1.262 477 | 1.286 466 | 1.310 796 | 1.335 469 | 1.360 489 |
| 5 | 1.187 686 | 1.216 653 | 1.246 182 | 1.276 282 | 1.306 960 | 1.338 226 | 1.370 087 | 1.402 552 | 1.435 629 | 1.469 328 |
| 6 | 1.229 255 | 1.265 319 | 1.302 260 | 1.340 096 | 1.378 843 | 1.418 519 | 1.459 142 | 1.500 730 | 1.543 302 | 1.586 874 |
| 7 | 1.272 279 | 1.315 932 | 1.360 862 | 1.407 100 | 1.454 679 | 1.503 630 | 1.553 987 | 1.605 781 | 1.659 049 | 1.713 824 |
| 8 | 1.316 809 | 1.368 569 | 1.422 101 | 1.477 455 | 1.534 687 | 1.593 848 | 1.654 996 | 1.718 186 | 1.783 478 | 1.850 930 |
| 9 | 1.362 897 | 1.423 312 | 1.486 095 | 1.551 328 | 1.619 094 | 1.689 479 | 1.762 570 | 1.838 459 | 1.917 239 | 1.999 005 |
| 10 | 1.410 599 | 1.480 244 | 1.552 969 | 1.628 895 | 1.708 144 | 1.790 848 | 1.877 137 | 1.967 151 | 2.061 032 | 2.158 925 |
| 11 | 1.459 970 | 1.539 454 | 1.622 853 | 1.710 339 | 1.802 092 | 1.898 299 | 1.999 151 | 2.104 852 | 2.215 609 | 2.331 639 |
| 12 | 1.511 069 | 1.601 032 | 1.695 881 | 1.795 856 | 1.901 207 | 2.012 196 | 2.129 096 | 2.252 192 | 2.381 780 | 2.518 170 |
| 13 | 1.563 956 | 1.665 074 | 1.772 196 | 1.885 649 | 2.005 774 | 2.132 928 | 2.267 487 | 2.409 845 | 2.560 413 | 2.719 624 |
| 14 | 1.618 695 | 1.731 676 | 1.851 945 | 1.979 932 | 2.116 091 | 2.260 904 | 2.414 874 | 2.578 534 | 2.752 444 | 2.937 194 |
| 15 | 1.675 349 | 1.800 944 | 1.935 282 | 2.078 928 | 2.232 476 | 2.396 558 | 2.571 841 | 2.759 032 | 2.958 877 | 3.172 169 |
| 16 | 1.733 986 | 1.872 981 | 2.022 370 | 2.182 875 | 2.355 263 | 2.540 352 | 2.739 011 | 2.952 164 | 3.180 793 | 3.425 943 |
| 17 | 1.794 676 | 1.947 900 | 2.113 377 | 2.292 018 | 2.484 802 | 2.692 773 | 2.917 046 | 3.158 815 | 3.419 353 | 3.700 018 |
| 18 | 1.857 489 | 2.025 817 | 2.208 479 | 2.406 619 | 2.621 466 | 2.854 339 | 3.106 654 | 3.379 932 | 3.675 804 | 3.996 019 |
| 19 | 1.922 501 | 2.106 849 | 2.307 860 | 2.526 950 | 2.765 647 | 3.025 600 | 3.308 587 | 3.616 528 | 3.951 489 | 4.315 701 |
| 20 | 1.989 789 | 2.191 123 | 2.411 714 | 2.653 298 | 2.917 757 | 3.207 135 | 3.523 645 | 3.869 684 | 4.247 851 | 4.660 957 |
| 21 | 2.059 431 | 2.278 768 | 2.520 241 | 2.785 963 | 3.078 234 | 3.399 564 | 3.752 682 | 4.140 562 | 4.566 440 | 5.033 834 |
| 22 | 2.131 512 | 2.369 919 | 2.633 652 | 2.925 261 | 3.247 537 | 3.603 537 | 3.996 606 | 4.430 402 | 4.908 923 | 5.436 540 |
| 23 | 2.206 114 | 2.464 716 | 2.752 166 | 3.071 524 | 3.426 152 | 3.819 750 | 4.256 386 | 4.740 530 | 5.277 092 | 5.871 464 |
| 24 | 2.283 328 | 2.563 304 | 2.876 014 | 3.225 100 | 3.614 590 | 4.048 935 | 4.533 051 | 5.072 367 | 5.672 874 | 6.341 181 |
| 25 | 2.363 245 | 2.665 836 | 3.005 434 | 3.386 355 | 3.813 392 | 4.291 871 | 4.827 699 | 5.427 433 | 6.098 340 | 6.848 475 |
| 26 | 2.445 959 | 2.772 470 | 3.140 679 | 3.555 673 | 4.023 129 | 4.549 383 | 5.141 500 | 5.807 353 | 6.555 715 | 7.396 353 |
| 27 | 2.531 567 | 2.883 369 | 3.282 010 | 3.733 456 | 4.244 401 | 4.822 346 | 5.475 697 | 6.213 868 | 7.047 394 | 7.988 061 |
| 28 | 2.620 172 | 2.998 703 | 3.429 700 | 3.920 129 | 4.477 843 | 5.111 687 | 5.831 617 | 6.648 838 | 7.575 948 | 8.627 106 |
| 29 | 2.711 878 | 3.118 651 | 3.584 036 | 4.116 136 | 4.724 124 | 5.418 388 | 6.210 672 | 7.114 257 | 8.144 144 | 9.317 275 |
| 30 | 2.806 794 | 3.243 398 | 3.745 318 | 4.321 942 | 4.983 951 | 5.743 491 | 6.614 366 | 7.612 255 | 8.754 955 | 10.062 657 |
| 31 | 2.905 031 | 3.373 133 | 3.913 857 | 4.538 039 | 5.258 069 | 6.088 101 | 7.044 300 | 8.145 113 | 9.411 577 | 10.867 669 |
| 32 | 3.006 708 | 3.508 059 | 4.089 981 | 4.764 941 | 5.547 262 | 6.453 387 | 7.502 179 | 8.715 271 | 10.117 445 | 11.737 083 |
| 33 | 3.111 942 | 3.648 381 | 4.274 030 | 5.003 189 | 5.852 362 | 6.840 590 | 7.989 821 | 9.325 340 | 10.876 253 | 12.676 050 |
| 34 | 3.220 860 | 3.794 316 | 4.466 362 | 5.253 348 | 6.174 242 | 7.251 025 | 8.590 159 | 9.978 114 | 11.691 972 | 13.690 134 |
| 35 | 3.333 590 | 3.946 089 | 4.667 348 | 5.516 015 | 6.513 825 | 7.686 087 | 9.062 255 | 10.676 581 | 12.568 870 | 14.785 344 |
| 36 | 3.450 266 | 4.103 933 | 4.877 378 | 5.791 816 | 6.872 085 | 8.147 252 | 9.651 301 | 11.423 942 | 13.511 536 | 15.968 172 |
| 37 | 3.571 025 | 4.268 090 | 5.096 860 | 6.081 407 | 7.250 050 | 8.636 087 | 10.278 636 | 12.223 618 | 14.524 901 | 17.245 626 |
| 38 | 3.696 011 | 4.438 813 | 5.326 219 | 6.385 477 | 7.648 803 | 9.154 252 | 10.946 747 | 13.079 271 | 15.614 268 | 18.625 276 |
| 39 | 3.825 372 | 4.616 366 | 5.565 899 | 6.704 751 | 8.069 487 | 9.703 507 | 11.658 286 | 13.994 820 | 16.785 339 | 20.115 298 |
| 40 | 3.959 260 | 4.801 021 | 5.816 365 | 7.039 989 | 8.513 309 | 10.285 718 | 12.416 075 | 14.974 458 | 18.044 239 | 21.724 521 |
| 41 | 4.097 834 | 4.993 061 | 6.078 101 | 7.391 988 | 8.981 541 | 10.902 861 | 13.223 119 | 16.022 670 | 19.397 557 | 23.462 483 |
| 42 | 4.241 258 | 5.192 784 | 6.351 615 | 7.761 588 | 9.475 525 | 11.557 033 | 14.082 622 | 17.144 257 | 20.852 372 | 25.339 482 |
| 43 | 4.389 702 | 5.400 495 | 6.637 438 | 8.149 667 | 9.996 679 | 12.250 455 | 14.997 993 | 18.344 355 | 22.416 302 | 27.366 640 |
| 44 | 4.543 342 | 5.616 515 | 6.936 123 | 8.557 150 | 10.546 497 | 12.985 482 | 15.972 862 | 19.628 460 | 24.097 524 | 29.555 972 |
| 45 | 4.702 359 | 5.841 176 | 7.248 248 | 8.985 008 | 11.126 554 | 13.764 611 | 17.011 098 | 21.002 452 | 25.904 839 | 31.920 449 |
| 46 | 4.866 941 | 6.074 823 | 7.574 420 | 9.434 258 | 11.738 515 | 14.590 487 | 18.116 820 | 22.472 623 | 27.847 702 | 34.474 085 |
| 47 | 5.037 284 | 6.317 816 | 7.915 268 | 9.905 971 | 12.384 133 | 15.465 917 | 19.294 413 | 24.045 707 | 29.936 279 | 37.232 012 |
| 48 | 5.213 589 | 6.570 528 | 8.271 456 | 10.401 270 | 13.065 260 | 16.393 872 | 20.548 550 | 25.728 907 | 32.181 500 | 40.210 573 |
| 49 | 5.396 065 | 6.833 349 | 8.643 671 | 10.921 333 | 13.783 849 | 17.377 504 | 21.884 205 | 27.529 930 | 34.595 113 | 43.427 419 |
| 50 | 5.584 927 | 7.106 683 | 9.032 636 | 11.467 400 | 14.541 961 | 18.420 154 | 23.306 679 | 29.457 025 | 37.189 746 | 46.901 613 |

# Compound Interest

| *n* | 8.5% | 9% | 9.5% | 10% | 10.5% | 11% | 11.5% | 12% | 12.5% |
|---|---|---|---|---|---|---|---|---|---|
| 1 | 1.085 000 | 1.090 000 | 1.095 000 | 1.100 000 | 1.105 000 | 1.110 000 | 1.115 000 | 1.120 000 | 1.125 000 |
| 2 | 1.177 225 | 1.188 100 | 1.199 025 | 1.210 000 | 1.221 025 | 1.232 100 | 1.243 225 | 1.254 400 | 1.265 625 |
| 3 | 1.277 289 | 1.295 029 | 1.312 932 | 1.331 000 | 1.349 233 | 1.367 631 | 1.386 196 | 1.404 928 | 1.423 828 |
| 4 | 1.385 859 | 1.411 582 | 1.437 661 | 1.464 100 | 1.490 902 | 1.518 070 | 1.545 608 | 1.573 519 | 1.601 807 |
| 5 | 1.503 657 | 1.538 624 | 1.574 239 | 1.610 510 | 1.647 447 | 1.685 058 | 1.723 353 | 1.762 342 | 1.802 032 |
| 6 | 1.631 468 | 1.677 100 | 1.723 791 | 1.771 561 | 1.820 429 | 1.870 415 | 1.921 539 | 1.973 823 | 2.027 287 |
| 7 | 1.770 142 | 1.828 039 | 1.887 552 | 1.948 717 | 2.011 574 | 2.076 160 | 2.142 516 | 2.210 681 | 2.280 697 |
| 8 | 1.920 604 | 1.992 563 | 2.066 869 | 2.143 589 | 2.222 789 | 2.304 538 | 2.388 905 | 2.475 963 | 2.565 785 |
| 9 | 2.083 856 | 2.171 893 | 2.263 222 | 2.357 948 | 2.456 182 | 2.558 037 | 2.663 629 | 2.773 079 | 2.886 508 |
| 10 | 2.260 983 | 2.367 364 | 2.478 228 | 2.593 742 | 2.714 081 | 2.839 421 | 2.969 947 | 3.105 848 | 3.247 321 |
| 11 | 2.453 167 | 2.580 426 | 2.713 659 | 2.853 117 | 2.999 059 | 3.151 757 | 3.311 491 | 3.478 550 | 3.653 236 |
| 12 | 2.661 686 | 2.812 665 | 2.971 457 | 3.138 428 | 3.313 961 | 3.498 451 | 3.692 312 | 3.895 976 | 4.109 891 |
| 13 | 2.887 930 | 3.065 805 | 3.253 745 | 3.452 271 | 3.661 926 | 3.883 280 | 4.116 928 | 4.363 493 | 4.623 627 |
| 14 | 3.133 404 | 3.341 727 | 3.562 851 | 3.797 498 | 4.046 429 | 4.310 441 | 4.590 375 | 4.887 112 | 5.201 580 |
| 15 | 3.399 743 | 3.642 482 | 3.901 322 | 4.177 248 | 4.471 304 | 4.784 589 | 5.118 268 | 5.473 566 | 5.851 778 |
| 16 | 3.688 721 | 3.970 306 | 4.271 948 | 4.594 973 | 4.940 791 | 5.310 894 | 5.706 869 | 6.130 394 | 6.583 250 |
| 17 | 4.002 262 | 4.327 633 | 4.677 783 | 5.054 470 | 5.459 574 | 5.895 093 | 6.363 159 | 6.866 041 | 7.406 156 |
| 18 | 4.342 455 | 4.717 120 | 5.122 172 | 5.559 917 | 6.032 829 | 6.543 553 | 7.094 922 | 7.689 966 | 8.331 926 |
| 19 | 4.711 563 | 5.141 661 | 5.608 778 | 6.115 909 | 6.666 276 | 7.263 344 | 7.910 838 | 8.612 762 | 9.373 417 |
| 20 | 5.112 046 | 5.604 411 | 6.141 612 | 6.727 500 | 7.366 235 | 8.062 312 | 8.820 584 | 9.646 293 | 10.545 094 |
| 21 | 5.546 570 | 6.108 808 | 6.725 065 | 7.400 250 | 8.139 690 | 8.949 166 | 9.834 951 | 10.803 848 | 11.863 231 |
| 22 | 6.018 028 | 6.658 600 | 7.363 946 | 8.140 275 | 8.994 357 | 9.933 574 | 10.965 971 | 12.100 310 | 13.346 134 |
| 23 | 6.529 561 | 7.257 874 | 8.063 521 | 8.954 302 | 9.938 764 | 11.026 267 | 12.227 057 | 13.552 347 | 15.014 401 |
| 24 | 7.084 574 | 7.911 083 | 8.829 556 | 9.849 733 | 10.982 335 | 12.239 157 | 13.633 169 | 15.178 629 | 16.891 201 |
| 25 | 7.686 762 | 8.623 081 | 9.668.364 | 10.834 706 | 12.135 480 | 13.585 464 | 15.200 983 | 17.000 064 | 19.002 602 |
| 26 | 8.340 137 | 9.399 158 | 10.586 858 | 11.918 177 | 13.409 705 | 15.079 865 | 16.949 096 | 19.040 072 | 21.377 927 |
| 27 | 9.049 049 | 10.245 082 | 11.592 610 | 13.109 994 | 14.817 724 | 16.738 650 | 18.898 243 | 21.324 881 | 24.050 168 |
| 28 | 9.818 218 | 11.167 140 | 12.693 908 | 14.420 994 | 16.373 585 | 18.579 901 | 21.071 540 | 23.883 866 | 27.056 438 |
| 29 | 10.652 766 | 12.172 182 | 13.899 829 | 15.863 093 | 18.092 812 | 20.623 691 | 23.494 768 | 26.749 930 | 30.438 493 |
| 30 | 11.558 252 | 13.267 678 | 15.220 313 | 17.449 402 | 19.992 557 | 22.892 297 | 26.196 666 | 29.959 922 | 34.243 305 |
| 31 | 12.540 703 | 14.461 770 | 16.666 242 | 19.194 342 | 22.091 775 | 25.410 449 | 29.209 282 | 33.555 113 | 38.523 718 |
| 32 | 13.606 663 | 15.763 329 | 18.249 535 | 21.113 777 | 24.411 412 | 28.205.599 | 32.568 350 | 37.581 726 | 43.339 183 |
| 33 | 14.763 229 | 17.182 028 | 19.983 241 | 23.225 154 | 26.974 610 | 31.308 214 | 36.313 710 | 42.091 533 | 48.756 581 |
| 34 | 16.018 104 | 18.728 411 | 21.881 649 | 25.547 670 | 29.806 944 | 34.752 118 | 40.489 787 | 47.142 517 | 54.851 153 |
| 35 | 17.379 642 | 20.413 968 | 23.960 406 | 28.102 437 | 32.936 673 | 38.574 851 | 45.146 112 | 52.799 620 | 61.707 547 |
| 36 | 18.856 912 | 22.251 225 | 26.236 644 | 30.912 681 | 36.395 024 | 42.818 085 | 50.337 915 | 59.135 574 | 69.420 991 |
| 37 | 20.459 750 | 24.253 835 | 28.729 126 | 34.003 949 | 40.216 501 | 47.528 074 | 56.126 776 | 66.231 843 | 78.098 615 |
| 38 | 22.198 828 | 26.436 680 | 31.458 393 | 37.404 343 | 44.439 234 | 52.756 162 | 62.581 355 | 74.179 664 | 87.860 942 |
| 39 | 24.085 729 | 28.815 982 | 34.446 940 | 41.144 778 | 49.105 354 | 58.559 340 | 69.778 211 | 83.081 224 | 98.843 559 |
| 40 | 26.133 016 | 31.409 420 | 37.719 399 | 45.259 256 | 54.261 416 | 65.000 867 | 77.802 705 | 93.050 970 | 111.199 004 |
| 41 | 28.354 322 | 34.236 268 | 41.302 742 | 49.785 181 | 59.958 864 | 72.150 963 | 86.750 016 | 104.217 087 | 125.098 880 |
| 42 | 30.764 439 | 37.317 532 | 45.226 503 | 54.763 699 | 66.254 545 | 80.087 569 | 96.726 268 | 116.723 137 | 140.736 240 |
| 43 | 33.379 417 | 40.676 110 | 49.523 020 | 60.240 069 | 73.211 272 | 88.897 201 | 107.849 788 | 130.729 914 | 158.328 270 |
| 44 | 36.216 667 | 44.336 960 | 54.227 707 | 66.264 076 | 80.898 456 | 98.675 893 | 120.252 514 | 146.417 503 | 178.119 303 |
| 45 | 39.295 084 | 48.327 286 | 59.379 340 | 72.890 484 | 89.392 794 | 109.530 242 | 134.081 553 | 163.987 604 | 200.384 216 |
| 46 | 42.635 166 | 52.676 742 | 65.020 377 | 80.179 532 | 98.779 037 | 121.578 568 | 149.500 932 | 183.666 116 | 225.432 243 |
| 47 | 46.259 155 | 57.417 649 | 71.197 313 | 88.197 485 | 109.150 836 | 134.952 211 | 166.693 539 | 205.706 050 | 253.611 274 |
| 48 | 50.191 183 | 62.585 237 | 77.961 057 | 97.017 234 | 120.611 674 | 149.796 954 | 185.863 296 | 230.390 776 | 285.312 683 |
| 49 | 54.457 434 | 68.217 908 | 85.367 358 | 06.718 957 | 133.275 900 | 166.274 619 | 207.237 575 | 258.037 669 | 320.976 768 |
| 50 | 59.086 316 | 74.357 520 | 93.477 257 | 17.390 853 | 147.269 869 | 184.564 827 | 231.069 896 | 289.002 190 | 361.098 864 |

# UNEMPLOYMENT INSURANCE PREMIUMS

| Remuneration *Rémunération* From-*de* To-*à* | U.I. Premium *Prime d'a.-c.* | Remuneration *Rémunération* From-*de* To-*à* | U.I. Premium *Prime d'a.-c.* | Remuneration *Rémunération* From-*de* To-*a* | U.I. Premium *Prime d'a.-c.* | Remuneration *Rémunération* From-*de* To-*a* | U.I. Premium *Prime d'a.-c.* |
|---|---|---|---|---|---|---|---|
| 214.69 – 215.10 | 5.05 | 245.32 – 245.74 | 5.77 | 275.96 – 276.38 | 6.49 | 306.60 – 307.02 | 7.21 |
| 215.11 – 215.53 | 5.06 | 245.75 – 246.17 | 5.78 | 276.39 – 276.80 | 6.50 | 307.03 – 307.44 | 7.22 |
| 215.54 – 215.95 | 5.07 | 246.18 – 246.59 | 5.79 | 276.81 – 277.23 | 6.51 | 307.45 – 307.87 | 7.23 |
| 215.96 – 216.38 | 5.08 | 246.60 – 247.02 | 5.80 | 277.24 – 277.65 | 6.52 | 307.88 – 308.29 | 7.24 |
| 216.39 – 216.80 | 5.09 | 247.03 – 247.44 | 5.81 | 277.66 – 278.08 | 6.53 | 308.30 – 308.72 | 7.25 |
| 216.81 – 217.23 | 5.10 | 247.45 – 247.87 | 5.82 | 278.09 – 278.51 | 6.54 | 308.73 – 309.14 | 7.26 |
| 217.24 – 217.65 | 5.11 | 247.88 – 248.29 | 5.83 | 278.52 – 278.93 | 6.55 | 309.15 – 309.57 | 7.27 |
| 217.66 – 218.08 | 5.12 | 248.30 – 248.72 | 5.84 | 278.94 – 279.36 | 6.56 | 309.58 – 309.99 | 7.28 |
| 218.09 – 218.51 | 5.13 | 248.73 – 249.14 | 5.85 | 279.37 – 279.78 | 6.57 | 310.00 – 310.42 | 7.29 |
| 218.52 – 218.93 | 5.14 | 249.15 – 249.57 | 5.86 | 279.79 – 280.21 | 6.58 | 310.43 – 310.85 | 7.30 |
| 218.94 – 219.36 | 5.15 | 249.58 – 249.99 | 5.87 | 280.22 – 280.63 | 6.59 | 310.86 – 311.27 | 7.31 |
| 219.37 – 219.78 | 5.16 | 250.00 – 250.42 | 5.88 | 280.64 – 281.06 | 6.60 | 311.28 – 311.70 | 7.32 |
| 219.79 – 220.21 | 5.17 | 250.43 – 250.85 | 5.89 | 281.07 – 281.48 | 6.61 | 311.71 – 312.12 | 7.33 |
| 220.22 – 220.63 | 5.18 | 250.86 – 251.27 | 5.90 | 281.49 – 281.91 | 6.62 | 312.13 – 312.55 | 7.34 |
| 220.64 – 221.06 | 5.19 | 251.28 – 251.70 | 5.91 | 281.92 – 282.34 | 6.63 | 312.56 – 312.97 | 7.35 |
| 221.07 – 221.48 | 5.20 | 251.71 – 252.12 | 5.92 | 282.35 – 282.76 | 6.64 | 312.98 – 313.40 | 7.36 |
| 221.49 – 221.91 | 5.21 | 252.13 – 252.55 | 5.93 | 282.77 – 283.19 | 6.65 | 313.41 – 313.82 | 7.37 |
| 221.92 – 222.34 | 5.22 | 252.56 – 252.97 | 5.94 | 283.20 – 283.61 | 6.66 | 313.83 – 314.25 | 7.38 |
| 222.35 – 222.76 | 5.23 | 252.98 – 253.40 | 5.95 | 283.62 – 284.04 | 6.67 | 314.26 – 314.68 | 7.39 |
| 222.77 – 223.19 | 5.24 | 253.41 – 253.82 | 5.96 | 284.05 – 284.46 | 6.68 | 314.69 – 315.10 | 7.40 |
| 223.20 – 223.61 | 5.25 | 253.83 – 254.25 | 5.97 | 284.47 – 284.89 | 6.69 | 315.11 – 315.53 | 7.41 |
| 223.62 – 224.04 | 5.26 | 254.26 – 254.68 | 5.98 | 284.90 – 285.31 | 6.70 | 315.54 – 315.95 | 7.42 |
| 224.05 – 224.46 | 5.27 | 254.69 – 255.10 | 5.99 | 285.32 – 285.74 | 6.71 | 315.96 – 316.38 | 7.43 |
| 224.47 – 224.89 | 5.28 | 255.11 – 255.53 | 6.00 | 285.75 – 286.17 | 6.72 | 316.39 – 316.80 | 7.44 |
| 224.90 – 225.31 | 5.29 | 255.54 – 255.95 | 6.01 | 286.18 – 286.59 | 6.73 | 316.81 – 317.23 | 7.45 |
| 225.32 – 225.74 | 5.30 | 255.96 – 256.38 | 6.02 | 286.60 – 287.02 | 6.74 | 317.24 – 317.65 | 7.46 |
| 225.75 – 226.17 | 5.31 | 256.39 – 256.80 | 6.03 | 287.03 – 287.44 | 6.75 | 317.66 – 318.08 | 7.47 |
| 226.18 – 226.59 | 5.32 | 256.81 – 257.23 | 6.04 | 287.45 – 287.87 | 6.76 | 318.09 – 318.51 | 7.48 |
| 226.60 – 227.02 | 5.33 | 257.24 – 257.65 | 6.05 | 287.88 – 288.29 | 6.77 | 318.52 – 318.93 | 7.49 |
| 227.03 – 227.44 | 5.34 | 257.66 – 258.08 | 6.06 | 288.30 – 288.72 | 6.78 | 318.94 – 319.36 | 7.50 |
| 227.45 – 227.87 | 5.35 | 258.09 – 258.51 | 6.07 | 288.73 – 289.14 | 6.79 | 319.37 – 319.78 | 7.51 |
| 227.88 – 228.29 | 5.36 | 258.52 – 258.93 | 6.08 | 289.15 – 289.57 | 6.80 | 319.79 – 320.21 | 7.52 |
| 228.30 – 228.72 | 5.37 | 258.94 – 259.36 | 6.09 | 289.58 – 289.99 | 6.81 | 320.22 – 320.63 | 7.53 |
| 228.73 – 229.14 | 5.38 | 259.37 – 259.78 | 6.10 | 290.00 – 290.42 | 6.82 | 320.64 – 321.06 | 7.54 |
| 229.15 – 229.57 | 5.39 | 259.79 – 260.21 | 6.11 | 290.43 – 290.85 | 6.83 | 321.07 – 321.48 | 7.55 |
| 229.58 – 229.99 | 5.40 | 260.22 – 260.63 | 6.12 | 290.86 – 291.27 | 6.84 | 321.49 – 321.91 | 7.56 |
| 230.00 – 230.42 | 5.41 | 260.64 – 261.06 | 6.13 | 291.28 – 291.70 | 6.85 | 321.92 – 322.34 | 7.57 |
| 230.43 – 230.85 | 5.42 | 261.07 – 261.48 | 6.14 | 291.71 – 292.12 | 6.86 | 322.35 – 322.76 | 7.58 |
| 230.86 – 231.27 | 5.43 | 261.49 – 261.91 | 6.15 | 292.13 – 292.55 | 6.87 | 322.77 – 323.19 | 7.59 |
| 231.28 – 231.70 | 5.44 | 261.92 – 262.34 | 6.16 | 292.56 – 292.97 | 6.88 | 323.20 – 323.61 | 7.60 |
| 231.71 – 232.12 | 5.45 | 262.35 – 262.76 | 6.17 | 292.98 – 293.40 | 6.89 | 323.62 – 324.04 | 7.61 |
| 232.13 – 232.55 | 5.46 | 262.77 – 263.19 | 6.18 | 293.41 – 293.82 | 6.90 | 324.05 – 324.46 | 7.62 |
| 232.56 – 232.97 | 5.47 | 263.20 – 263.61 | 6.19 | 293.83 – 294.25 | 6.91 | 324.47 – 324.89 | 7.63 |
| 232.98 – 233.40 | 5.48 | 263.62 – 264.04 | 6.20 | 294.26 – 294.68 | 6.92 | 324.90 – 325.31 | 7.64 |
| 233.41 – 233.82 | 5.49 | 264.05 – 264.46 | 6.21 | 294.69 – 295.10 | 6.93 | 325.32 – 325.74 | 7.65 |
| 233.83 – 234.25 | 5.50 | 264.47 – 264.89 | 6.22 | 295.11 – 295.53 | 6.94 | 325.75 – 326.17 | 7.66 |
| 234.26 – 234.68 | 5.51 | 264.90 – 265.31 | 6.23 | 295.54 – 295.95 | 6.95 | 326.18 – 326.59 | 7.67 |
| 234.69 – 235.10 | 5.52 | 265.32 – 265.74 | 6.24 | 295.96 – 296.38 | 6.96 | 326.60 – 327.02 | 7.68 |
| 235.11 – 235.53 | 5.53 | 265.75 – 266.17 | 6.25 | 296.39 – 296.80 | 6.97 | 327.03 – 327.44 | 7.69 |
| 235.54 – 235.95 | 5.54 | 266.18 – 266.59 | 6.26 | 296.81 – 297.23 | 6.98 | 327.45 – 327.87 | 7.70 |
| 235.96 – 236.38 | 5.55 | 266.60 – 267.02 | 6.27 | 297.24 – 297.65 | 6.99 | 327.88 – 328.29 | 7.71 |
| 236.39 – 236.80 | 5.56 | 267.03 – 267.44 | 6.28 | 297.66 – 298.08 | 7.00 | 328.30 – 328.72 | 7.72 |
| 236.81 – 237.23 | 5.57 | 267.45 – 267.87 | 6.29 | 298.09 – 298.51 | 7.01 | 328.73 – 329.14 | 7.73 |
| 237.24 – 237.65 | 5.58 | 267.88 – 268.29 | 6.30 | 298.52 – 298.93 | 7.02 | 329.15 – 329.57 | 7.74 |
| 237.66 – 238.08 | 5.59 | 268.30 – 268.72 | 6.31 | 298.94 – 299.36 | 7.03 | 329.58 – 329.99 | 7.75 |
| 238.09 – 238.51 | 5.60 | 268.73 – 269.14 | 6.32 | 299.37 – 299.78 | 7.04 | 330.00 – 330.42 | 7.76 |
| 238.52 – 238.93 | 5.61 | 269.15 – 269.57 | 6.33 | 299.79 – 300.21 | 7.05 | 330.43 – 330.85 | 7.77 |
| 238.94 – 239.36 | 5.62 | 269.58 – 269.99 | 6.34 | 300.22 – 300.63 | 7.06 | 330.86 – 331.27 | 7.78 |
| 239.37 – 239.78 | 5.63 | 270.00 – 270.42 | 6.35 | 300.64 – 301.06 | 7.07 | 331.28 – 331.70 | 7.79 |
| 239.79 – 240.21 | 5.64 | 270.43 – 270.85 | 6.36 | 301.07 – 301.48 | 7.08 | 331.71 – 332.12 | 7.80 |
| 240.22 – 240.63 | 5.65 | 270.86 – 271.27 | 6.37 | 301.49 – 301.91 | 7.09 | 332.13 – 332.55 | 7.81 |
| 240.64 – 241.06 | 5.66 | 271.28 – 271.70 | 6.38 | 301.92 – 302.34 | 7.10 | 332.56 – 332.97 | 7.82 |
| 241.07 – 241.48 | 5.67 | 271.71 – 272.12 | 6.39 | 302.35 – 302.76 | 7.11 | 332.98 – 333.40 | 7.83 |
| 241.49 – 241.91 | 5.68 | 272.13 – 272.55 | 6.40 | 302.77 – 303.19 | 7.12 | 333.41 – 333.82 | 7.84 |
| 241.92 – 242.34 | 5.69 | 272.56 – 272.97 | 6.41 | 303.20 – 303.61 | 7.13 | 333.83 – 334.25 | 7.85 |
| 242.35 – 242.76 | 5.70 | 272.98 – 273.40 | 6.42 | 303.62 – 304.04 | 7.14 | 334.26 – 334.68 | 7.86 |
| 242.77 – 243.19 | 5.71 | 273.41 – 273.82 | 6.43 | 304.05 – 304.46 | 7.15 | 334.69 – 335.10 | 7.87 |
| 243.20 – 243.61 | 5.72 | 273.83 – 274.25 | 6.44 | 304.47 – 304.89 | 7.16 | 335.11 – 335.53 | 7.88 |
| 243.62 – 244.04 | 5.73 | 274.26 – 274.68 | 6.45 | 304.90 – 305.31 | 7.17 | 335.54 – 335.95 | 7.89 |
| 244.05 – 244.46 | 5.74 | 274.69 – 275.10 | 6.46 | 305.32 – 305.74 | 7.18 | 335.96 – 336.38 | 7.90 |
| 244.47 – 244.89 | 5.75 | 275.11 – 275.53 | 6.47 | 305.75 – 306.17 | 7.19 | 336.39 – 336.80 | 7.91 |
| 244.90 – 245.31 | 5.76 | 275.54 – 275.95 | 6.48 | 306.18 – 306.59 | 7.20 | 336.81 – 337.23 | 7.92 |

# CANADA PENSION PLAN CONTRIBUTIONS

## WEEKLY PAY PERIOD 203.96–363.95

| Remuneration / Rémunération From-de | To-à | C.P.P. / R.P.C. | Remuneration / Rémunération From-de | To-à | C.P.P. / R.P.C. | Remuneration / Rémunération From-de | To-à | C.P.P. / R.P.C. | Remuneration / Rémunération From-de | To-à | C.P.P. / R.P.C. |
|---|---|---|---|---|---|---|---|---|---|---|---|
| 203.96 | 204.50 | 2.88 | 243.97 | 244.50 | 3.60 | 283.96 | 284.50 | 4.32 | 323.96 | 324.50 | 5.04 |
| 204.51 | 205.06 | 2.89 | 244.51 | 245.06 | 3.61 | 284.51 | 285.06 | 4.33 | 324.51 | 325.06 | 5.05 |
| 205.07 | 205.61 | 2.90 | 245.07 | 245.61 | 3.62 | 285.07 | 285.61 | 4.34 | 325.07 | 325.61 | 5.06 |
| 205.62 | 206.17 | 2.91 | 245.62 | 246.17 | 3.63 | 285.62 | 286.17 | 4.35 | 325.62 | 326.17 | 5.07 |
| 206.18 | 206.72 | 2.92 | 246.18 | 246.72 | 3.64 | 286.18 | 286.72 | 4.36 | 326.18 | 326.72 | 5.08 |
| 206.73 | 207.28 | 2.93 | 246.73 | 247.28 | 3.65 | 286.73 | 287.28 | 4.37 | 326.73 | 327.28 | 5.09 |
| 207.29 | 207.84 | 2.94 | 247.29 | 247.84 | 3.66 | 287.29 | 287.84 | 4.38 | 327.29 | 327.84 | 5.10 |
| 207.85 | 208.39 | 2.95 | 247.85 | 248.39 | 3.67 | 287.85 | 288.39 | 4.39 | 327.85 | 328.39 | 5.11 |
| 208.40 | 208.95 | 2.96 | 248.40 | 248.95 | 3.68 | 288.40 | 288.95 | 4.40 | 328.40 | 328.95 | 5.12 |
| 208.96 | 209.50 | 2.97 | 248.96 | 249.50 | 3.69 | 288.96 | 289.50 | 4.41 | 328.96 | 329.50 | 5.13 |
| 209.51 | 210.06 | 2.98 | 249.51 | 250.06 | 3.70 | 289.51 | 290.06 | 4.42 | 329.51 | 330.06 | 5.14 |
| 210.07 | 210.61 | 2.99 | 250.07 | 250.61 | 3.71 | 290.07 | 290.61 | 4.43 | 330.07 | 330.61 | 5.15 |
| 210.62 | 211.17 | 3.00 | 250.62 | 251.17 | 3.72 | 290.62 | 291.17 | 4.44 | 330.62 | 331.17 | 5.16 |
| 211.18 | 211.72 | 3.01 | 251.18 | 251.72 | 3.73 | 291.18 | 291.72 | 4.45 | 331.18 | 331.72 | 5.17 |
| 211.73 | 212.28 | 3.02 | 251.73 | 252.28 | 3.74 | 291.73 | 292.28 | 4.46 | 331.73 | 332.28 | 5.18 |
| 212.29 | 212.84 | 3.03 | 252.29 | 252.84 | 3.75 | 292.29 | 292.84 | 4.47 | 332.29 | 332.84 | 5.19 |
| 212.85 | 213.39 | 3.04 | 252.85 | 253.39 | 3.76 | 292.85 | 293.39 | 4.48 | 332.85 | 333.39 | 5.20 |
| 213.40 | 213.95 | 3.05 | 253.40 | 253.95 | 3.77 | 293.40 | 293.95 | 4.49 | 333.40 | 333.95 | 5.21 |
| 213.96 | 214.50 | 3.06 | 253.96 | 254.50 | 3.78 | 293.96 | 294.50 | 4.50 | 333.96 | 334.50 | 5.22 |
| 214.51 | 215.06 | 3.07 | 254.51 | 255.06 | 3.79 | 294.51 | 295.06 | 4.51 | 334.51 | 335.06 | 5.23 |
| 215.07 | 215.61 | 3.08 | 255.07 | 255.61 | 3.80 | 295.07 | 295.61 | 4.52 | 335.07 | 335.61 | 5.24 |
| 215.62 | 216.17 | 3.09 | 255.62 | 256.17 | 3.81 | 295.62 | 296.17 | 4.53 | 335.62 | 336.17 | 5.25 |
| 216.18 | 216.72 | 3.10 | 256.18 | 256.72 | 3.82 | 296.18 | 296.72 | 4.54 | 336.18 | 336.72 | 5.26 |
| 216.73 | 217.28 | 3.11 | 256.73 | 257.28 | 3.83 | 296.73 | 297.28 | 4.55 | 336.73 | 337.28 | 5.27 |
| 217.29 | 217.84 | 3.12 | 257.29 | 257.84 | 3.84 | 297.29 | 297.84 | 4.56 | 337.29 | 337.84 | 5.28 |
| 217.85 | 218.39 | 3.13 | 257.85 | 258.39 | 3.85 | 297.85 | 298.39 | 4.57 | 337.85 | 338.39 | 5.29 |
| 218.40 | 218.95 | 3.14 | 258.40 | 258.95 | 3.86 | 298.40 | 298.95 | 4.58 | 338.40 | 338.95 | 5.30 |
| 218.96 | 219.50 | 3.15 | 258.96 | 259.50 | 3.87 | 298.96 | 299.50 | 4.59 | 338.96 | 339.50 | 5.31 |
| 219.51 | 220.06 | 3.16 | 259.51 | 260.06 | 3.88 | 299.51 | 300.06 | 4.60 | 339.51 | 340.06 | 5.32 |
| 220.07 | 220.61 | 3.17 | 260.07 | 260.61 | 3.89 | 300.07 | 300.61 | 4.61 | 340.07 | 340.61 | 5.33 |
| 220.62 | 221.17 | 3.18 | 260.62 | 261.17 | 3.90 | 300.62 | 301.17 | 4.62 | 340.62 | 341.17 | 5.34 |
| 221.18 | 221.72 | 3.19 | 261.18 | 261.72 | 3.91 | 301.18 | 301.72 | 4.63 | 341.18 | 341.72 | 5.35 |
| 221.73 | 222.28 | 3.20 | 261.73 | 262.28 | 3.92 | 301.73 | 302.28 | 4.64 | 341.73 | 342.28 | 5.36 |
| 222.29 | 222.84 | 3.21 | 262.29 | 262.84 | 3.93 | 302.29 | 302.84 | 4.65 | 342.29 | 342.84 | 5.37 |
| 222.85 | 223.39 | 3.22 | 262.85 | 263.39 | 3.94 | 302.85 | 303.39 | 4.66 | 342.85 | 343.39 | 5.38 |
| 223.40 | 223.95 | 3.23 | 263.40 | 263.95 | 3.95 | 303.40 | 303.95 | 4.67 | 343.40 | 343.95 | 5.39 |
| 223.96 | 224.50 | 3.24 | 263.96 | 264.50 | 3.96 | 303.96 | 304.50 | 4.68 | 343.96 | 344.50 | 5.40 |
| 224.51 | 225.06 | 3.25 | 264.51 | 265.06 | 3.97 | 304.51 | 305.06 | 4.69 | 344.51 | 345.06 | 5.41 |
| 225.07 | 225.61 | 3.26 | 265.07 | 265.61 | 3.98 | 305.07 | 305.61 | 4.70 | 345.07 | 345.61 | 5.42 |
| 225.62 | 226.17 | 3.27 | 265.62 | 266.17 | 3.99 | 305.62 | 306.17 | 4.71 | 345.62 | 346.17 | 5.43 |
| 226.18 | 226.72 | 3.28 | 266.18 | 266.72 | 4.00 | 306.18 | 306.72 | 4.72 | 346.18 | 346.72 | 5.44 |
| 226.73 | 227.28 | 3.29 | 266.73 | 267.28 | 4.01 | 306.73 | 307.28 | 4.73 | 346.73 | 347.28 | 5.45 |
| 227.29 | 227.84 | 3.30 | 267.29 | 267.84 | 4.02 | 307.29 | 307.84 | 4.74 | 347.29 | 347.84 | 5.46 |
| 227.85 | 228.39 | 3.31 | 267.85 | 268.39 | 4.03 | 307.85 | 308.39 | 4.75 | 347.85 | 348.39 | 5.47 |
| 228.40 | 228.95 | 3.32 | 268.40 | 268.95 | 4.04 | 308.40 | 308.95 | 4.76 | 348.40 | 348.95 | 5.48 |
| 228.96 | 229.50 | 3.33 | 268.96 | 260.50 | 4.05 | 308.96 | 309.50 | 4.77 | 348.96 | 349.50 | 5.49 |
| 229.51 | 230.06 | 3.34 | 269.51 | 270.06 | 4.06 | 309.51 | 310.06 | 4.78 | 349.51 | 350.06 | 5.50 |
| 230.07 | 230.61 | 3.35 | 270.07 | 270.61 | 4.07 | 310.07 | 310.61 | 4.79 | 350.07 | 350.61 | 5.51 |
| 230.62 | 231.17 | 3.36 | 270.62 | 271.17 | 4.08 | 310.62 | 311.17 | 4.80 | 350.62 | 351.17 | 5.52 |
| 231.18 | 231.72 | 3.37 | 271.18 | 271.72 | 4.09 | 311.18 | 311.72 | 4.81 | 351.18 | 351.72 | 5.53 |
| 231.73 | 232.28 | 3.38 | 271.73 | 272.28 | 4.10 | 311.73 | 312.28 | 4.82 | 351.73 | 352.28 | 5.54 |
| 232.29 | 232.84 | 3.39 | 272.29 | 272.84 | 4.11 | 312.29 | 312.84 | 4.83 | 352.29 | 352.84 | 5.55 |
| 232.85 | 233.39 | 3.40 | 272.85 | 273.39 | 4.12 | 312.85 | 313.39 | 4.84 | 352.85 | 353.39 | 5.56 |
| 233.40 | 233.95 | 3.41 | 273.40 | 273.95 | 4.13 | 313.40 | 313.95 | 4.85 | 353.40 | 353.95 | 5.57 |
| 233.96 | 234.50 | 3.42 | 273.96 | 274.50 | 4.14 | 313.96 | 314.50 | 4.86 | 353.96 | 354.50 | 5.58 |
| 234.51 | 235.06 | 3.43 | 274.51 | 275.06 | 4.15 | 314.51 | 315.06 | 4.87 | 354.51 | 355.06 | 5.59 |
| 235.07 | 235.61 | 3.44 | 275.07 | 275.61 | 4.16 | 315.07 | 315.61 | 4.88 | 355.07 | 355.61 | 5.60 |
| 235.62 | 236.17 | 3.45 | 275.62 | 276.17 | 4.17 | 315.62 | 316.17 | 4.89 | 355.62 | 356.17 | 5.61 |
| 236.18 | 236.72 | 3.46 | 276.18 | 276.72 | 4.18 | 316.18 | 316.72 | 4.90 | 356.18 | 356.72 | 5.62 |
| 236.73 | 237.28 | 3.47 | 276.73 | 277.28 | 4.19 | 316.73 | 317.28 | 4.91 | 356.73 | 357.28 | 5.63 |
| 237.29 | 237.84 | 3.48 | 277.29 | 277.84 | 4.20 | 317.29 | 317.84 | 4.92 | 357.29 | 357.84 | 5.64 |
| 237.85 | 238.39 | 3.49 | 277.85 | 278.39 | 4.21 | 317.85 | 318.39 | 4.93 | 357.85 | 358.39 | 5.65 |
| 238.40 | 238.95 | 3.50 | 278.40 | 278.95 | 4.22 | 318.40 | 318.95 | 4.94 | 358.40 | 358.95 | 5.66 |
| 238.96 | 239.50 | 3.51 | 278.96 | 279.50 | 4.23 | 318.96 | 319.50 | 4.95 | 358.96 | 359.50 | 5.67 |
| 239.51 | 240.06 | 3.52 | 279.51 | 280.06 | 4.24 | 319.51 | 320.06 | 4.96 | 359.51 | 360.06 | 5.68 |
| 240.07 | 240.61 | 3.53 | 280.07 | 280.61 | 4.25 | 320.07 | 320.61 | 4.97 | 360.07 | 360.61 | 5.69 |
| 240.62 | 241.17 | 3.54 | 280.62 | 281.17 | 4.26 | 320.62 | 321.17 | 4.98 | 360.62 | 361.17 | 5.70 |
| 241.18 | 241.72 | 3.55 | 281.18 | 281.72 | 4.27 | 321.18 | 321.72 | 4.99 | 361.18 | 361.72 | 5.71 |
| 241.73 | 242.28 | 3.56 | 281.73 | 282.28 | 4.28 | 321.73 | 322.28 | 5.00 | 361.73 | 362.28 | 5.72 |
| 242.29 | 242.84 | 3.57 | 282.29 | 282.84 | 4.29 | 322.29 | 322.84 | 5.01 | 362.29 | 362.84 | 5.73 |
| 242.85 | 243.39 | 3.58 | 282.85 | 283.39 | 4.30 | 322.85 | 323.39 | 5.02 | 362.85 | 363.39 | 5.74 |
| 243.40 | 243.95 | 3.59 | 283.40 | 283.95 | 4.31 | 323.40 | 323.95 | 5.03 | 363.40 | 363.95 | 5.75 |

# WEEKLY TAX DEDUCTIONS
**Basis — 52 Pay Periods per Year**

| WEEKLY PAY Use appropriate bracket | IF THE EMPLOYEE'S "NET CLAIM CODE" ON FORM TD1 IS | | | | | | | | | | | | |
|---|---|---|---|---|---|---|---|---|---|---|---|---|---|
| | 1 | 2 | 3 | 4 | 5 | 6 | 7 | 8 | 9 | 10 | 11 | 12 | 13 |
| | DEDUCT FROM EACH PAY | | | | | | | | | | | | |
| $197.00 – 198.99 | 20.65 | 18.70 | 15.35 | 12.15 | 8.65 | 5.85 | 4.15 | 1.60 | | | | | |
| 199.00 – 200.99 | 21.20 | 19.25 | 15.85 | 12.65 | 9.15 | 6.30 | 4.65 | 2.05 | | | | | |
| 201.00 – 202.99 | 21.70 | 19.75 | 16.40 | 13.15 | 9.70 | 6.80 | 5.10 | 2.55 | | | | | |
| 203.00 – 204.99 | 22.25 | 20.30 | 16.90 | 13.65 | 10.20 | 7.30 | 5.60 | 3.00 | | | | | |
| 205.00 – 206.99 | 22.80 | 20.85 | 17.40 | 14.15 | 10.70 | 7.85 | 6.05 | 3.50 | | | | | |
| 207.00 – 208.99 | 23.30 | 21.35 | 17.90 | 14.65 | 11.20 | 8.35 | 6.55 | 3.95 | | | | | |
| 209.00 – 210.99 | 23.85 | 21.90 | 18.40 | 15.15 | 11.70 | 8.85 | 7.05 | 4.40 | | | | | |
| 211.00 – 212.99 | 24.40 | 22.45 | 18.90 | 15.65 | 12.20 | 9.35 | 7.55 | 4.90 | 1.30 | | | | |
| 213.00 – 214.99 | 24.90 | 22.95 | 19.45 | 16.15 | 12.70 | 9.85 | 8.05 | 5.35 | 1.80 | | | | |
| 215.00 – 216.99 | 25.45 | 23.50 | 19.95 | 16.65 | 13.20 | 10.35 | 8.55 | 5.85 | 2.30 | | | | |
| 217.00 – 218.99 | 26.00 | 24.05 | 20.50 | 17.15 | 13.70 | 10.85 | 9.05 | 6.30 | 2.75 | | | | |
| 219.00 – 220.99 | 26.50 | 24.55 | 21.05 | 17.65 | 14.20 | 11.35 | 9.55 | 6.85 | 3.25 | | | | |
| 221.00 – 222.99 | 27.05 | 25.10 | 21.55 | 18.15 | 14.70 | 11.85 | 10.05 | 7.35 | 3.70 | | | | |
| 223.00 – 224.99 | 27.60 | 25.65 | 22.10 | 18.65 | 15.20 | 12.35 | 10.55 | 7.85 | 4.20 | | | | |
| 225.00 – 226.99 | 28.10 | 26.15 | 22.65 | 19.20 | 15.70 | 12.85 | 11.05 | 8.35 | 4.65 | | | | |
| 227.00 – 228.99 | 28.65 | 26.70 | 23.15 | 19.75 | 16.20 | 13.35 | 11.55 | 8.85 | 5.15 | 1.25 | | | |
| 229.00 – 230.99 | 29.15 | 27.25 | 23.70 | 20.25 | 16.70 | 13.85 | 12.10 | 9.35 | 5.60 | 1.80 | | | |
| 231.00 – 232.99 | 29.70 | 27.75 | 24.25 | 20.80 | 17.20 | 14.35 | 12.60 | 9.85 | 6.10 | 2.30 | | | |
| 233.00 – 234.99 | 30.25 | 28.30 | 24.75 | 21.35 | 17.75 | 14.85 | 13.10 | 10.35 | 6.55 | 2.75 | | | |
| 235.00 – 236.99 | 30.75 | 28.85 | 25.30 | 21.85 | 18.25 | 15.40 | 13.60 | 10.85 | 7.10 | 3.25 | | | |
| 237.00 – 238.99 | 31.30 | 29.35 | 25.80 | 22.40 | 18.75 | 15.90 | 14.10 | 11.35 | 7.60 | 3.70 | | | |
| 239.00 – 240.99 | 31.85 | 29.90 | 26.35 | 22.90 | 19.25 | 16.40 | 14.60 | 11.85 | 8.10 | 4.15 | | | |
| 241.00 – 242.99 | 32.40 | 30.40 | 26.90 | 23.45 | 19.80 | 16.90 | 15.10 | 12.35 | 8.60 | 4.65 | | | |
| 243.00 – 244.99 | 32.95 | 30.95 | 27.40 | 24.00 | 20.35 | 17.40 | 15.60 | 12.85 | 9.10 | 5.10 | 0.90 | | |
| 245.00 – 246.99 | 33.50 | 31.50 | 27.95 | 24.50 | 20.85 | 17.90 | 16.10 | 13.35 | 9.60 | 5.60 | 1.70 | | |
| 247.00 – 251.99 | 34.50 | 32.45 | 28.90 | 25.45 | 21.80 | 18.75 | 17.00 | 14.25 | 10.45 | 6.45 | 2.50 | | |
| 252.00 – 256.99 | 35.90 | 33.85 | 30.20 | 26.80 | 23.10 | 20.10 | 18.25 | 15.50 | 11.75 | 7.70 | 3.70 | | |
| 257.00 – 261.99 | 37.30 | 35.25 | 31.55 | 28.10 | 24.45 | 21.45 | 19.55 | 16.75 | 13.00 | 8.95 | 4.85 | 0.45 | |
| 262.00 – 266.99 | 38.70 | 36.65 | 32.90 | 29.45 | 25.80 | 22.75 | 20.85 | 18.00 | 14.25 | 10.20 | 6.05 | 2.25 | |
| 267.00 – 271.99 | 40.10 | 38.05 | 34.35 | 30.80 | 27.10 | 24.10 | 22.20 | 19.30 | 15.50 | 11.45 | 7.30 | 3.45 | |
| 272.00 – 276.99 | 41.50 | 39.45 | 35.75 | 32.10 | 28.45 | 25.45 | 23.55 | 20.65 | 16.75 | 12.70 | 8.55 | 4.60 | 1.25 |
| 277.00 – 281.99 | 42.95 | 40.85 | 37.15 | 33.50 | 29.80 | 26.75 | 24.85 | 21.95 | 18.00 | 14.00 | 9.80 | 5.80 | 2.50 |
| 282.00 – 286.99 | 44.35 | 42.30 | 38.55 | 34.90 | 31.10 | 28.10 | 26.20 | 23.30 | 19.30 | 15.25 | 11.10 | 7.05 | 3.70 |
| 287.00 – 291.99 | 45.75 | 43.70 | 39.95 | 36.35 | 32.45 | 29.45 | 27.55 | 24.65 | 20.65 | 16.50 | 12.35 | 8.30 | 4.85 |
| 292.00 – 296.99 | 47.15 | 45.10 | 41.35 | 37.75 | 33.85 | 30.75 | 28.85 | 25.95 | 21.95 | 17.75 | 13.60 | 9.55 | 6.05 |
| 297.00 – 301.99 | 48.55 | 46.50 | 42.75 | 39.15 | 35.30 | 32.10 | 30.20 | 27.30 | 23.30 | 19.05 | 14.85 | 10.80 | 7.30 |
| 302.00 – 306.99 | 49.95 | 47.90 | 44.15 | 40.55 | 36.70 | 33.50 | 31.55 | 28.65 | 24.65 | 20.35 | 16.10 | 12.05 | 8.55 |
| 307.00 – 311.99 | 51.35 | 49.30 | 45.60 | 41.95 | 38.10 | 34.90 | 32.90 | 29.95 | 25.95 | 21.70 | 17.35 | 13.35 | 9.80 |
| 312.00 – 316.99 | 52.75 | 50.70 | 47.00 | 43.35 | 39.50 | 36.30 | 34.30 | 31.30 | 27.30 | 23.00 | 18.65 | 14.60 | 11.10 |
| 317.00 – 321.99 | 54.20 | 52.10 | 48.40 | 44.75 | 40.90 | 37.70 | 35.70 | 32.65 | 28.65 | 24.35 | 19.95 | 15.85 | 12.35 |

# Answers

## CHAPTER 1

### 1.1 Written Exercises, page 9

**1**a)47 b)120 c)4 d)9 **2**a)21.5 b)27 c)6 **3**a)$-5\frac{1}{2}$ b)36 c)$-8\frac{1}{8}$ **4**a)$-4$ b)$-16$ c)$\frac{4}{15}$ d)$2\frac{2}{9}$ **5**a)50 b)29 c)38 d)$-5$ **6**a)405 b)17.898 c)140 d)30 e)8 f)40 **7**a)$w = 44$ b)$R = 8$ c)$a = -9$ d)$t = 11.2$ e)$x = 8$ **8**a)$17.58 b)$11.97 c)$30.46 **9)**6 × (3 + 4) + 7 × (8 + 3) × 5 = 427 **10**a)6, 12, 20, 30 b)$n(n + 1)$ c)110 **11**a)12 b)110 c)2550

### 1.2 Written Exercises, page 12

**1**a)1365 b)5514 c)3767 d)2481 e)7026 **2**a)9728 b)7 468 110 c)152 d)615.344 e)432.463 f)6 **3**a)93 b)52 c)99 d)216 e)1705 f)1695 g)60 h)1056 **4**a)572 b)806 c)$-1428$ d)$-12\,597$ e)57 f)$-6.6$ **5**a)1 b)3 c)2.5 d)17 e)588 **6**a)368 b)82 c)24 d)63 e)350 f)72 g)959 **7**a)A b)A c)B d)A **8**a)35 b)382 c)5287 d)518 e)1975 f)143 **10**a)13 b)4 c)50 **11**a)54 or 24 b)24 or 54 c)20 480 or 5000 **12**a)27 b)32 c)64 d)64 e)0.008 f)0.0625 g)1000 h)100 000

### 1.3 Written Exercises, page 15

**1**a)1666 km b)1731 km c)1031 km **2**a)3394 km b)5652 km c)5862 km **3)**A by 175 km **4)**1796 km **5)**3251 km **6**a)5070 km b)9344 km c)8196 km d)10 876 km **7**a)43.7 h b)104.6 km/h **9**a)6:02 a.m. b)6:17 a.m. c)6:20 a.m. **10**a)8 min b)20 min **11**a)11:02 a.m. b)30 min

### 1.4 Written Exercises, page 19

**1**a)1936.5 b)1200 c)3614.19 d)2319.62 e)4613.4 f)1470 g)13 698.496 h)24 698.932 i)49 000 **2**a)C b)B c)B d)B e)B **3**a)2499 b)4 c)1302 d)2 e)5713 f)8.5 g)12 h)9899 **4**a)6068 b)24 592 c)181 818 d)572.36 e)7.55 f)31 g)104.25 h)10.5 **5**a)14.9 b)3.6 c)0.2375 d)100.637 e)9.525 f)12.925 g)1.898 h)19.51 **6**a)2570 b)6.54 c)872.6 d)5428.76 **7**a)11.336 b)283.823 c)5.129 d)0.013 e)555.556 f)1.013 **8**a)818 b)19.666 c)1.224 d)81.345 **9**a)$187.95 b)$359.91 c)$35.40 d)$17.48 **10**a)B b)B **11**a)$4729.00 b)$14 869.00 c)$28 909.00 **12**a)$435.42 b)$1568.25 c)$4612.50 **13)**172 hours **14)**$708.75 **15**a)$33.81 b)$80.39 c)$92.46 **16)**$7.88 **17)**$763.36 **18)**$90.58 **19**a)1 185 714.29 yen b)$6031.98 (U.S.) **20**a)$556.28 b)$700.00 c)382.85 francs d)466.42 marks e)$15.01 f)$258.73

### 1.5 Written Exercises, page 24

**1**a)2 b)$1\frac{4}{5}$ c)$\frac{2}{7}$ d)2 **2**a)$5\frac{7}{12}$ b)$8\frac{5}{6}$ c)$10\frac{1}{2}$ d)$11\frac{49}{60}$ **3**a)$\frac{3}{8}$ b)$\frac{3}{4}$ c)$5\frac{3}{8}$ d)$6\frac{2}{3}$ **4**a)$2\frac{19}{25}$ b)$6\frac{5}{6}$ c)$20\frac{3}{20}$ d)$51\frac{1}{3}$ **5**a)64 b)$2\frac{1}{10}$ c)$25\frac{3}{5}$ d)2 e)$4\frac{1}{2}$ f)$4\frac{3}{11}$ **6**a)A b)B **7**a)B b)B c)B d)B e)A **8**a)0.3, 3.0, 3.03, 3.30, 3.303, 33.0 b)0.0149, 0.149, 1.49, 14.9, 149.9 c)0.0016, 0.0061, 0.0160, 0.0611, 0.1601 **9**a)0.75 b)0.875 c)0.35 d)0.85 e)0.725 f)0.45 g)0.975 h)1.375 i)0.325 **10**a)1.9 b)1.0 c)0.1 d)0.3 e)3.4 f)2.1 **11**a)3.06 b)9.93 c)1.90 d)3.40 e)0.75 f)1.65 **12**a)2 tanks b)$1\frac{5}{12}$ tanks c)$2\frac{1}{10}$ tanks d)$2\frac{7}{8}$ tanks e)$3\frac{1}{12}$ tanks f)$5\frac{7}{8}$ tanks g)$5\frac{1}{4}$ tanks **13)**$\frac{1}{6}$ **14)**$16\frac{7}{12}$ **15)**6 trips **16)**1.8 sec **17)**$\frac{7}{45}$

### 1.6 Written Exercises, page 26

**1**a)14 b)7 c)0 d)$-8$ e)$-29$ f)$-7$ **2**a)29 b)$-12$ c)$-2$ d)39 **3**a)$-6$ b)24 c)$-9$ d)$-108$ e)27 f)$-52$ **4**a)$-4$ b)4 c)$-5$ d)$-8$ e)$-10$ f)9 **5**a)1 b)$-1$ c)$-6$ d)$-3$ e)$-16$ f)3 g)1 h)216 i)20 j)$-6$ k)$-5$ l)$-1728$ **6**a)$-17$ b)90 c)$-2$ d)$-3$ e)45 f)$-23$ **7**a)16 b)16 c)$-12$ **8**a)17 b)3 c)$-3$ d)$-1$ **9**a)9 b)$-8$ c)$-14$ d)21 e)$-4$ f)6 g)7 h)$-12$ i)$-5$ j)$-96$ k)$-9$ l)$-21$ **10**a)$-8$ b)$-8$ c)$-16$ d)16 e)$-25$ f)25 g)$-125$ h)$-125$ i)9 **11**a)$-13$ b)13 c)$-16$ d)8 **12**a)$-2$ b)$-4$ c)$-3$ d)$-8$ **13**a)0 b)3 **14**a)$-8$ b)$\frac{4}{3}$ c)$-2$ d)$-2.6$ e)2.5 f)$-2\frac{2}{9}$ **15)**$-1.3$°C **16**a)i)8 ii)$-22$ iii)15 iv)9 b)Prince Albert c)Halifax and Victoria; Edmonton and Moncton **17**a)8 b)7 c)$-36$ d)$-6$ e)31 f)$-162$ g)744 h)5 **18**a)1605 b)1745 c)$-3411$ d)$-4701$ e)$-4063$ f)7740 g)$-3618$ **19**a)$-1872$ b)$-30\,976$ c)16 736 281 d)7614 e)$-31\,360$ f)$-334\,488$ **20**a)55 b)$-116.59$ c)239.17 d)$-506.10$ e)$-1325.98$ f)$-235.35$ **21**a)965 b)7184 c)$-75.0$ d)$-734.8$ e)4563 f)$-3.2$ g)$-18.3$ h)$-0.3$

### 1.7 Written Exercises, page 30

**1**a)10% b)60% c)60% d)75% e)24% f)37.5% g)87.5% h)15% i)41.667% j)18% k)125% l)250% m)160% n)375% o)260% **2**a)$\frac{1}{20}$ b)$\frac{1}{10}$ c)$\frac{1}{4}$ d)$\frac{1}{2}$ e)$\frac{3}{5}$ f)$\frac{7}{25}$ g)$\frac{3}{4}$ h)$\frac{11}{25}$ i)$\frac{22}{25}$ j)$\frac{5}{8}$ k)$\frac{7}{8}$ l)$\frac{1}{80}$ m)$\frac{1}{8}$ n)$\frac{23}{250}$ o)1 **3**a)0.5, $\frac{1}{2}$ b)12.5%, $\frac{1}{8}$ c)0.1, 10% d)0.655, $\frac{131}{200}$ e)1.75, 175% f)72.5%, $\frac{29}{40}$ g)1.2, $\frac{6}{5}$ **4**a)30 b)432 c)12.5 g d)32 e)42 f)86 g)133 kg h)48 cm i)94 km j)37.5 m k)0.29 L l)$36.80 **5**a)77.5% b)83.3% c)88.4% d)86.0% e)82.7% f)74.1% g)87.5% h)95% **6)**0.416 L **7**a)16 b)4 **8)**3.978 $m^3$ **9)**3 g, 30 g, 7 g, 185 g, 2 g, 11 g **10**a)307 g b)131 g c)189 g d)741 g e)45 500 g **11)**20%, 15.833%, 29.167%, 21.667%, 9%, 4.333% **12**a)$\frac{2}{5}$ b)33.333% c)96.667% d)$\frac{4}{5}$, 80% **13**a)28.571%, 29.412%, 39.633%, 29.032%, 28.571%, 37.5%, 40.0% b)Igor c)Jack, Jim **14**a)$183.82 **15**a)570 b)90 c)23 d)60 **16**a)30 b)265 **17)**4.5%, 38.7% **18)**16 673 **19**a)1.5% b)9200 c)98.5% **20**a)52 578 b)21 907

### 1.8 Written Exercises, page 34

**1)**8% **2)**$109 444.44 **3**a)88.9% b)11.1% **4**a)1.714 g b)0.403 g c)33.379 g **5)**114 **6)**$161.03 **7**a)0.337% b)0.198% c)97.674% d)96.488% **8)**$327.17 **9)**1029 **10)**$2901.96

### 1.9 Written Exercises, page 36

**1**a)780 b)1246 **2**a)20% b)45% c)125% d)295.1% **3**a)48 b)$1113.33 **4**a)31.2 b)465 c)100.5 d)281.25 **5**a)200 b)650 c)13.25 m **6)**$97.37

**7)**Tina **8)**10.7% **9)**1.0 h **10)**38.2% **11)**\$1.89 **12)**15.3%, 23.6%, 31.5%, 29.6% **13)**\$2.78 **14)**\$366.67 **15)**4.6% **16)**13 **17)**3553 **18)**43.2%

### Review: Practice and Problems, page 37

**1**a)34 b)$-7$ c)92 **2**a)5 b)0 **3**a)$P = 98$ b)$c = 94.2$ c)$u = 43$ d)$t = 10\frac{2}{3}$ **4**a)45 b)2076 c)228 d)$-1$ **5**a)6231 b)23 814 c)260 128 d)361.62 e)8.5 f)13 **6**a)2.88 b)39 c)$\frac{23}{12}$ d)$\frac{23}{6}$ e)$\frac{85}{12}$ f)$\frac{57}{4}$ **7**a)2.0 b)1.4 c)2.2 d)10.1 **8**a)$-8$ b)26 c)$-12$ d)$-34$ e)83 f)102 g)$-27$ h)1 **9**a)$-9.25$ b)$-3$ c)$-3.5$ d)0.25 **10**a)14 865 b)\$328.50 c)\$51.30 **11**a)103 b)8% c)Stereo Mart

## CHAPTER 2

### 2.1 Written Exercises, page 42

**1**a)$4^2$ b)$2^3$ c)$1^{25}$ **2**a)216 b)32 c)121 **3**a)$4^5$ b)$9^3$ c)$52^6$ **4**a)8 b)9 c)25 d)1000 e)625 f)$\frac{1}{27}$ **5**a)$8^8$ b)$2^9$ c)$4^8$ d)$9^6$ e) $(3.5)^{11}$ f)$\left(\frac{2}{5}\right)^4$ g)$3^{10}$ h)$5^9$ **6**a)9 b)$5^3$ c)$7^5$ d) $(2.3)^3$ **7**b)$>$ c)$>$ d)$>$ e)$=$ f)$>$ g)$>$ **8**a)8 b)48 c)40 d)2 e)64 f)0 g)128 h)2 i)137 j)23 **9**a)A b)B c)B d)$=$ e)B **10)**B **11**a)0.01 b)0.001 c)0.04 d)0.125 e)1.21 f)0.000 01 g)0.0009 h)0.000 008 i)0.0144 **12**a)0.729 $cm^3$ c)7.29 $cm^3$ **13**a)4 b)8 c)$2^n$ d)4 **14**a)128 b)531 441 c)32 768 d)20 736 e)19 683 f)50 625 **15**a)0.656 1 b)6.331 625 c)3 936 256 d)31 255.875 e)676.520 1 f)14.19857 **16**a) $(0.6)^4$ b) $(1.7)^3$ c) $(7.2)^2$ d) $(1.01)^2$ **17**a)502 b)2978 c)213 d)52 448 e)195 f)734 812 g)140 520 h)252.9468 **18)**30 watts **19)**257.5 m

### 2.2 Written Exercises, page 45

**1**a)$3^6$ b)$m^6$ **2**a)$m^6$ b)$p^7$ c)$a^6$ d)$y^2$ e)$n^{14}$ f)$k^6$ **3**a)$5^4$ b)$m^4$ **4**a)$m^2$ b)$a^2$ c)$p^2$ d)$x^2$ e)$m^8$ f)$b^5$ **5**a)$2^6$ b)$m^6$ **6**a)$n^{10}$ b)$t^{21}$ c)$d^{16}$ d)$y^{12}$ **7**a)$a^3$ b)$m^3n^3$ c)$m^9$ d)$\frac{x^6}{y^6}$ e)$\frac{p^9}{q^9}$ f)$x^4y^4$ g)$m^{15}$ h)$p^5q^5$ i)$a^7b^7c^7$ j)$a^8$ k)$a^6b^4$ l)$\frac{x^6}{y^8}$ **8**a)$-32$ b)$-64$ c)64 **9**a)18 b)36 c)$-12$ **10**a)8 b)32 c)128 d)8 e)4 f)32 **11**a)36 b)48 c)48 d)108 e)216 f)648 **12**a)$ab^3$ b)$x^2y^5$ c)$m^4n^2$ d)$pq^2$ e)$a^2b$ f)$kt^2m$ **13**a)$m^2n^3$ b)$\frac{p^4}{q}$ c)$a^8b$ d)$a^6bc$ e)$\frac{x^8}{y^5}$ f)$\frac{m^{10}n^6}{p^4}$ **14**a)9 b)$-9$ c)27 d)3 e)$-9$ f)$-9$ **15**a)\$92.16 b)\$200 **16**a)$n^6k^3$ b)125 000 000 **17**a)147.8 kg b)2611.6 kg c)1085.5 kg **18**a)2692.3 kg b)1400 kg c)1166.7 kg d)972.2 kg e)875 kg f)814.0 kg g)shorter is stronger **19**a)$w = \frac{SL}{1.12h^2}$ b)$h = \sqrt{\frac{SL}{1.12w}}$ c)$L = \frac{1.12wh^2}{S}$ **20)**2297.4 kg **21)**137.1 cm **22**a)145.8 kg b)729.2 kg **23)**3 **24)**17.6 cm **25)**9333.3 kg

### 2.3 Written Exercises, page 50

**1**a)1 b)1 c)1 d)1 e)1 f)1 **2**a)$\frac{1}{8}$ b)$\left(\frac{1}{5}\right)^2$ c)$\left(\frac{1}{2}\right)^4$ d)$\left(\frac{1}{a}\right)^3$ e)$\left(\frac{1}{q}\right)^5$ f)$\left(\frac{1}{2x}\right)^1$ **3**a)$\frac{1}{3}$ b)$\frac{1}{125}$ c)1 d)$\frac{1}{10\,000}$ e)$\frac{1}{144}$ f)$\frac{1}{32}$ **4**a)8 b)$\frac{1}{8}$ c)$-\frac{1}{8}$ d)$-8$ e)$-\frac{1}{8}$ f)$-8$ **5**a)$\frac{1}{9}$ b)4 c)4 d)$\frac{1}{8}$ **6**a)1 b)3 c)1 d)5 e)2 f)1 **7**a)$\frac{1}{m^3n^4}$ b)$\frac{a^5}{b^2}$ c)$a^5b^4$ d)$\frac{q^4}{p^3}$ e)$fg^2$ f)$\frac{d^2}{k^2}$ **8**a)$\frac{1}{n^2}$ b)$\left(\frac{1}{k}\right)^8$ c)$\frac{1}{q}$ d)$\frac{1}{p^{32}}$ e)$\frac{1}{n^6}$ f)$z^{12}$ g)$\frac{1}{a^3}$ h)$t^8$ **9**a)$4\frac{1}{4}$ b)$\frac{3}{4}$ c)$\frac{3}{16}$ d)$\frac{1}{1000}$ e)$\frac{1}{8}$ f)$\frac{4}{9}$ g)$\frac{1}{16}$ h)$\frac{8}{9}$ **10**a)2.197 b)0.216 c)1 d)296.296 **11**a)$\frac{1}{m}$ b)$a$ c)$\frac{1}{t}$ d)$\frac{1}{a^2}$ e)$q^2$ f)$\frac{1}{d}$ **12**a)$-\frac{1}{8}$ b)$\frac{1}{4}$ c)$\frac{1}{2}$ d)$\frac{5}{4}$ e)6 f)$-\frac{3}{4}$ g)$\frac{1}{4}$ h)$-16$ **13**a)$\frac{1}{81}$ b)$-12$ c)$\frac{1}{17}$ d)$-\frac{3}{2}$

### 2.4 Written Exercises, page 52

**3**a)$9.6 \times 10^3$ b)0.048 c)0.000 019 d)$2.54 \times 10^4$ e)$8.4 \times 10^{-4}$ **4**a)49 200 b)0.006 05 c)530 000 d)0.000 000 98 e)0.0267 f)140 000 000 g)0.000 08 h)3 010 000 **5**a)$4.98 \times 10^5$ b)0.000 084 c)1.56 08, 156 000 000 d)7.2 $-06$, $7.2 \times 10^{-6}$ e)$5.814 \times 10^{12}$, 5 814 000 000 000 f)1.386 09, $1.386 \times 10^9$ **6**a)1.78E + 04 b)5.6E − 06 c)9.26E − 05 d)7.964E + 09 e)1.82E + 10 f)6.1914E − 05 **7**a)$9.92 \times 10^6$ km b)$4.02 \times 10^{13}$ km c)$2.2 \times 10^{-8}$ cm d)$9.4 \times 10^9$ km e)$1.68 \times 10^{-23}$ g f)$9.46 \times 10^{12}$ km **8**a)$<$ b)$=$ c)$>$ d)$=$ e)$<$ f)$=$ **9**a)$7.98 \times 10^5$ b)$3.551 \times 10^4$ c)$4.818\,73 \times 10^{-10}$ d)$6.068 \times 10^{-3}$ e)$2.0496 \times 10^{-3}$ f)$3.906\,25 \times 10^9$ g)$5.1984 \times 10^{-5}$ **10**a)$2.4 \times 10^3$ b)$4.2 \times 10^{-3}$ c)$6.5 \times 10^{-4}$ d)$4.5 \times 10^{-8}$ **11**a)35 100 000 000 000 000 b)100 320 000 000 c)0.000 141 6 d)0.000 003 5 e)0.045 f)9 280 000 000 g)9 350 000 000 **12)**$6.76 \times 10^6$ **13)**$5.22 \times 10^{-4}$ cm **14)**$8.6 \times 10^4$ km **15)**$7.5 \times 10^8$ $cm^2$ **16)**$6.0 \times 10^7$ Hz **17**a)$1.4175 \times 10^3$ g b)$1.0 \times 10^9$ c)$6.096 \times 10^2$ cm d)$1.0 \times 10^{-6}$ cm **18**a)125 000 b)0.000 11 c)1 000 000 d)64 360 m **19**a)$3.78 \times 10^{19}$ b)37 800 000 000 000 000 000 **20**a)$4.216 \times 10^{10}$ b)$2.1492 \times 10^{10}$ **21)**316.2 km **22)**2.4 times **23**a)162 000 b)1 746 000 **24**a)125 b)$6.25 \times 10^6$

### 2.5 Written Exercises, page 56

**1)**c, e, f, h **2)**a, b, e, h, i **3**a)4 b)2 c)4 d)4 e)4 f)2 g)3 h)3 i)5 j)3 **4**a)2 b)3 c)4 d)3 e)4 f)6 **5**a)$8.15 \times 10^4$ m b)$5.08 \times 10^5$ cm c)$1.4 \times 10^9$ km d)$9.2 \times 10^{-4}$ kg e)$8.08 \times 10^{-3}$ mL f)$5.0 \times 10^{-6}$ m **6**a)514 700 m b)0.7862 g c)1.004 L d)33 080 cm e)0.002 947 kg f)610 000 cm **7**a)9.07 m; 3 b)380 mL; 2 c)0.08 kg; 1 d)9.5 km; 2 **8)**1.7 $m^2$ **9)**260 m **10)**4.2 m **11)**43 000 km **12)**8.3 min **13**a)$3.3 \times 10^{19}$ b)2.8 c)$4.22 \times 10^{13}$ d)$2.66 \times 10^3$ e)$9.9 \times 10^7$ f)$2.93 \times 10^2$ **14**a)$4.66 \times 10^{-6}$ b)$3.31 \times 10^{10}$ c)$5.96 \times 10^{10}$ d)$1.95 \times 10^{-16}$ e)$1.69 \times 10^{14}$ f)$8.255 \times 10^{-23}$ **15**a)$1.53 \times 10^7$ b)$2.25 \times 10^{-6}$ c)$7.67 \times 10^{-6}$ d)$3.91 \times 10^8$ e)$8.38 \times 10^{-5}$ f)$2.34 \times 10^{-29}$ **16)**$1.8 \times 10^{-14}$ cm **17)**$3.6 \times 10^7$ **18)**$2.6 \times 10^{-24}$ $m^3$

### 2.6 Written Exercises, page 61

**1**a)3 b)5 c)6 d)8 e)9 f)10 **2**a)2.24 b)4.58 c)6.63 d)8.19 e)9.43 **3**a)4.796

b)3.742 c)7.280 d)9.165 **4**a)2.588 b)3.962 c)8.961 d)11.832 e)14.142 f)18.974 **5**b)58.997 761 **6**a)12 cm b)8.9 m × 8.9 m **7)**5.3 cm × 5.3 cm **8**a)17.9 m b)26.8 m **9**a)5.23 cm b)2.26 km c)5.45 mm **10**a)6.3 m b)2.1 m **11**a)3.5 b)3.5 s **12**a)35.2 km b)105.0 km c)about 20 km **13**a)3.7 A b)5.3 A c)1.3 A **14**a)3.97 cm b)4.97 m c)0.910 dm **15**a)3.7 cm b)3.0 cm

### 2.7 Written Exercises, page 64

**1**a)3 b)$\frac{1}{2}$ c)3 d)$\frac{1}{3}$ **2**a)5 b)4 c)$\frac{1}{5}$ d)$\frac{1}{3}$ e)6 f)2 g)2 **3**a)1.931 b)1.891 c)2.535 d)1.885 e)2.455 f)1.759 **4**a)2 b)4 c)8 d)2 e)4 f)4 **5**a)4 b)7 c)12 d)2 e)−3 f)4 g)4 h)16 i)−64 j)−8 k)25 l)−2 **6**a)2 b)2 c)−3 d)−5 e)2 f)$\frac{1}{9}$ g)−10 h)−25 i)4 **7**a)0.1 b)0.5 c)0.5 d)0.166 e)0.5 f)0.04 g)0.037 h)0.01 **8**a)16 b)$-\frac{3}{2}$ c)$-\frac{167}{8}$ **9**a)4.92 cm b)3.30 cm c)6.20 cm **10**a)\$238.12 b)\$1193.91

### Review: Practice and Problems, page 65

**1**a)$7^5$ b)$2^{11}$ c)$5^4$ d) $(6.8)^6$ e)$10^3$ f) $(3.8)^2$ g)$\left(\frac{1}{2}\right)^7$ h)$\frac{1}{2}$ **2**a)$m^2$ b)$a^8$ c)$m^8$ d)$r^4$ e)$3^8$ f)$p^{12}$ **3**a)27 b)729 c)9 d)27 e)243 f)2187 **4)**8.6 cm$^2$ **5**a)1 b)$\frac{1}{9}$ c)$\frac{1}{25}$ d)16 e)$\frac{1}{16}$ f)−9 g)16 h)−1 i)1 **6**a)$a$ b)$p^{-2}$ c)$k^{-3}$ d)$m^7$ **7**a)$6.95 \times 10^5$ b)$4.9 \times 10^{-4}$ c)$1.85 \times 10^1$ d)$2.5 \times 10^{-2}$ e)$3.64 \times 10^8$ f)$2.945 \times 10^1$ **8**a)6520 b)0.000 904 c)0.0284 d)50 900 000 **9**a)$1.7 \times 10^{-24}$ g b)$1.5 \times 10^8$ km c)$3.6 \times 10^8$ km d)$5.34 \times 10^3$ mL **10**a)4 b)3 c)4 d)3 e)4 f)4 **11**a)$3.835 \times 10^{19}$ b)$3.241\,35 \times 10^2$ c)$6.1152 \times 10^4$ d)$4.0 \times 10^{-10}$ e)$1.562\,212 \times 10^9$ **12**a)2.98 b)4.393 c)8.044 d)12.53 e)17.481 f)24.271 **13**a)2.9 m b)4.0 m c)4.5 m d)5.8 m

## CHAPTER 3

### 3.1 Written Exercises, page 69

**4**a)$7x$ b)$14ef$ c)$12m$ d)$4p$ e)$-13a$ f)$-3p$ **5**a)3 b)5 c)11 **6**a)8 b)1 c)6 **7**a)7 b)10 c)15 d)32 **8**a)$12d$ b)$3t$ c)$-8q$ d)$3m$ e)$-6y$ f)$10n$ g)$-9d$ h)$-3h$ i)$5k$ j)$-2x^2$ k)$-8a^2$ l)$-11pq$ **9**a)$3p$ b)$11f$ c)$12a + 4d$ d)$7x + 7y$ e)$11n - 17m$ f)$2p - 7q + 9$ **10**a)15 b)−18 c)12 d)−16 e)12 f)−11 g)6 h)18 **11**a)−19 b)−5 c)−5 **12**a)$5x + 5y$ b)$5a + 9b + 3m$ c)$6a + 7b$ d)$5m + 10n$ **13)**B, C, D **14)**C **15)**B **16**a)105 L b)148 L c)112 L d)157.2 L **17**a)\$39 b)\$56.8 c)\$47.85 d)\$59.22

### 3.2 Written Exercises, page 72

**1**a)$8a + 4b$ b)$7x - 3y$ c)$11f - g$ d)$9m + 3n$ e)$6p - 2q$ f)$2n - t$ **2**a)$9a - b$ b)$11m + 4n$ c)$8p - 7q$ d)$2x - 2t$ **3**a)$2m - 3n$ b)$5m - 3n$ c)$2n - 2m$ **4**a)$4x - 7y$ b)$-7p + q$ c)$1 - a$ d)$-3h - 3k$ **5**a)$5x + 3y + z$ b)$-5a - 6b - c$ c)$2h + 2j + 2k$ d)$3m - n + 3$ e)$5 - 9w$ **6**a)$16r + 4t$ b)$12s - 3u$ c)$4k$ d)$3f + g - 4$ e)$-2a + b + 2c$ f)$5d^2 - 8d + 9$ g)$-2.1m + 9.5n$ h)$10.1a - 5.0b$ **7**a)$3x - 7y + 6z$ b)60 **8**a)9.8 b)−79.8 c)17.15 **9)**B **10**a)$24k$ b)72 m **11**a)$25.2t + 2.4$ b)158.64 mm c)118.32 mm **12**a)$10k - 5$ b)\$1995.00 **13**(b) **14**a)$-3a + 3b$ b)$15a - 8b$ c)$-2a + 4b$ **15**a)$8x - 11y$ b)$3a + 3b$ c)$6m - 6$ **16**a)$m - 9n$ b)12 **17**a)$6.1x + 3.5y$ b)$-2.1a - 1.2b$ **18)**15.456 **19)**P

### 3.3 Written Exercises, page 75

**1**a)$4b$ kg b)$bx$ kg c)$5bx$ kg **2**a)$\$8k$ b)$\$4kn$ c)$\$12nk$ **3**a)115¢ b)346¢ **4**a)428¢ b)396¢ **5**a)$mn$ square units b)18 c)$18mn$ square units d)40.5 square units **6**a)$3n$ units b)$6m$ units c)$18mn$ square units d)40.5 square units **7**a)$35pq$ b)$-32xy$ c)$6mn$ d)$-45wt$ e)$40bd$ f)$10hk$ g)$-18fg$ h)$25yz$ i)$18rs$ j)$-12kt$ **8**a)$-24mn$ b)$-24mn$ c)$-24mn$ d)$24mn$ e)$24mn$ f)$24mn$ **9**a)$-15de$ b)$-27pq$ c)$40xy$ d)$24rt$ e)$-7km$ f)$-10mp$ g)$56qtz$ **10**b)$6xyz$ c)$72efg$ d)$6pqr$ e)$-6mpr$ f)$6rtw$ g)$30ktmn$ **11**a)$14ab$ b)$-31cd$ c)$14.1xy$ d)$-30.87uvw$ **12**a)$7n$ b)$10q$ c)$35nq$ **13)**B **14)**B **15**a)$4.5pq$ square units b)16.2 m$^2$ c)11.88 m$^2$ **16**a)$2.25nq$ square units b)18.9 m$^2$ c)9.9 m$^2$ **17**a)$6.72st$ square units b)54.432 m$^2$ c)40.32 m$^2$

### 3.4 Written Exercises, page 79

**1**a)$e^9$ b)$a^{10}$ c)$m^4$ d)$t^{12}$ e)$m^3n^3$ f)$x^3y^5$ g)$a^4b^3$ h)$p^5q^3$ **2**a)$-10x^3$ b)$-24f^3$ c)$30p^5$ d)$2m^2n$ **3**a)$-6m^3$ b)$20w^5$ c)$-24y^5$ d)$56p^9$ e)$8m^3n^4$ f)$-12p^3q^4$ g)$-10r^3s^3$ **4**a)192, 192 b)−6, −6 **5**a)−6, −6 b)−4374 **6**a)$-10d^5$ b)$32x^4$ c)$9y^6$ d)$5m^7$ e)$-28t^3$ f)$k^7$ g)$18d^4$ h)$-35w^5$ **7**a)$-12m^5$ b)$-24t^5$ c)$-5k^4$ d)$15p^4$ e)$14n^5$ f)$-5r^7$ g)$16a^8$ h)$16y^6$ **8**a)$10m^5$ square units b)320 square units **9)**same **10**a)$-2a^3b^4$ b)$-20m^3n^3$ c)$-3k^8r^6$ d)$18p^5q^9$ e)$-12n^3p^4$ f)$49u^6v^4$ g)$-10s^5t^5$ h)$-9c^3d^5$ **11**a)$24p^6$ b)$12m^5$ c)$-2r^6$ d)$30f^6$ e)$-72y^8$ f)$-8h^7$ g)$-3a^4b^4$ h)$-24m^3n^4$ i)$20x^3y^4$ j)$-6a^4b^6$ **12**b)$8a^6b^6$ c)$-27x^3y^6$ d)$m^4n^{20}$ e)$36p^6q^8$ f)$-64h^9k^{12}$ g)$32d^{10}t^5$ **13**a)−64, 36, 16 b)A **14**a)$36a^5b^8$, $-36a^3b^9$ b)A **15)**$9k^5$ **16**a)$10p^4q^3$ square units b)4320 m$^2$ **17**a)$7.5n^2p^3$ b)\$3707 **18**a)$10t^2L^3$ b)6600 **19)**$300k^6$ square units

### 3.5 Written Exercises, page 82

**1**a)$g^2$ b)$m^4$ c)$m^2$ d)$t^4$ e)$m^2n$ f)$x^2$ g)$p^2q$ h)$ab^2$ **2**a)$6n$ b)$5q$ c)$5a$ d)$5m$ e)$-10y$ f)$p$ **3**a)$2n$ b)$-4p$ c)−5 d)$2f$ e)$3ab$ f)$4x$ **4**a)−8, −8 b)−18 **5**a)$-6p$ b)$-3m^2$ c)$-2b^3$ d)$2x^2y^2$ **6**a)$-2n$ b)$4c$ c)$-4q^2$ d)$5pq$ e)$9p$ f)$10ab$ g)$2ab$ h)$p^2q^2$ i)$-5m^2n$ **7**a)−4 b)−6 c)−4 d)−24 e)−10 f)20 **8**a)−15 b)−6 c)15 **9)** (a) **10**a)28.8 b)42 c)43.2 d)14.43 e) (c) **11**a)$3a$ units b)$8p^2q$ units **12**a)$17m$ units b)$6pq^2$ units c)$20m^3$ units **13**a)$50a^2$ b)$7mt$ dollars c)$24n$ dollars/km **14**a)$5pq^2$ hours b)$13dr$ m/s **15**a)$-4pq$ b)$r^2$ c)−30 d)$-p^2q$ e)$24mn^2$ f)$-3x^2y^2$ **16**a)$-2y$ b)$2mn$ c)$-8q^2$ d)$4b^2$

### 3.6 Written Exercises, page 85

**1**a)$3x - 9$ b)$-2y - 12$ c)$16a - 24b$ d)$-6p - 24q$ e)$-15p - 21q$ f)$6a + 4b$ g)$6a - 9b + 12c$ h)$25q - 15r + 10s$ **2**a)$2ab - 2a^2$ b)$-2ap - 2bp$ c)$2pt - tq$ d)$6mp - 12mq$ e)$5ab - 5ac$ f)$2mp - 6mn$ **3**a)$4a^2 + 8a$ b)$2p^2 - 12p$ c)$6m - 6m^2$ d)$12n^2 - 16n$ e)$3p^2 - 2p$ f)$6q - 3q^2$ g)$6y - 4y^2$ h)$12kn - 16k$ **4**a)−9 b)42 c)60 d)−168

**5**a)$16x^3 - 8x^2 + 8x$ b)$6a^3 - 15a^2 + 12a$ c)$16p^4 + 12p^3 - 24p^2$ **6**a)$10m - 6$ b)$6a + 16$ c)$3p - 12$ d)$24x + 12$
**7**a)$-1$ b)9 c)19 d)$-16$
**8**a)$2m + 12$ b)$9a - 12$ c)$2a - 3$ d)$14x - 31$ e)$10x - 24$ f)$m - 4$ g)$14 - 11a$ h)$6 - 3f$ **9**a)17 b)17
**10**a)17 b)24 c)$-56$ **11**a)$-a$ b)$7x + 4y$ c)$-14m$ d)$13k^2 + k$
**12**a)54 b)28 c)$-42$ **13**a)$7k^2 - 12k$ b)$24p - 15p^2$ c)$13p$ d)$63t - 5t^2$ e)$-6m^3 - 32m^2$ **14**a)$21m - 222$ b)$-285$ **15**a)19 b)$-78$ c)$-21$
**16**a)\$820 b)\$777.84 c)\$1009.72
**17**a)19.5°C b)14.3°C c)5.1°C
**18**a)\$302.76 b)\$567.24 c)\$476.62

### 3.7 Written Exercises, page 88

**1**a)$x$ b)$a$, 3 c) $(m - 5)$ d)9, $(9 - x)$
**2**a)$5x$, $x^2$, 25 b)64, $9m^2$, $24m$
**3**a)$x^2 + 6x + 9$ b)$4x^2 + 4x + 1$ c)$x^2 + 6xy + 9y^2$ d)$4m^2 + 12mn + 9n^2$
**4**a)$x^2 + 4x + 4$ b)$y^2 + 10y + 25$ c)$x^2 - 8x + 16$ d)$k^2 - 16k + 64$ e)$9m^2 + 6m + 1$ f)$4a^2 - 4a + 1$
**5**a)$h^2 + 12h + 36$ b)$y^2 - 4y + 4$ c)$y^2 - 16y + 64$ d)$h^2 + 6h + 9$ e)$4h^2 + 4h + 1$ f)$4k^2 - 4k + 1$ g)$9 + 6p + p^2$ h)$9 - 6p + p^2$ i)$4p^2 + 12p + 9$ j)$9a^2 - 12a + 4$
**6**a)$p^2 + 4p + 4$ b)$a^2 - 16a + 64$ c)$9q^2 - 12q + 4$ d)$16m^2 - 24m + 9$ e)$4p^2 - 4pq + q^2$ f)$4p^2 - 8pq + 4q^2$ g)$4a^4 - 12a^2 + 9$ h)$9p^4 - 30p^2 + 25$
**7**b)$2m^2 + 8m + 8$ c)$3p^2 - 12p + 12$ d)$-2y^2 - 4y - 2$ e)$-3k^2 + 18k - 27$ f)$12t^2 - 12t + 3$ g)$-18y^2 - 24y - 8$
**8**a)$3m^3 + 6m^2 + 3m$ b)$2p^3 + 12p^2 + 18p$ c)$-4y^3 + 32y^2 - 64y$ d)$5a^3 - 30a^2 + 45a$ e)$4c^3 + 24c^2 + 36c$ f)$-m^4 + 10m^3 - 25m^2$ g)$p^4 + 12p^3 + 36p^2$ h)$-16t^4 + 32t^3 - 16t^2$ i)$54r^3 + 72r^2 + 24r$ j)$4p^5 - 12p^4 + 9p^3$ **9**a)$2a^2 - 4a + 2$ b)$4a^2 - 4a + 1$

### 3.8 Written Exercises, page 91

**1**a)$y - 6$ b)$k$, $k + 8$ c)$p - 8$, $p - 8$
**2**a)$x^2 + 8x + 15$ b)$x^2 + 12x + 36$
**3**a)$x^2 + 9x + 8$ b)$m^2 + 6m + 8$ c)$n^2 + 8n + 15$ d)$k^2 + 17k + 70$
**4**a)$+2a$ b)$+3m$ c)$+5x$ d)$-k$ e)$2p^2$
**5**a)$a^2 + 5a + 6$ b)$p^2 + 2p - 15$ c)$q^2 - q - 2$ d)$6a^2 - 23a + 21$
**6**a)$a^2 + 7a + 10$ b)$m^2 + 5m + 4$ c)$y^2 + 2y - 24$ d)$y^2 - 3y - 4$ e)$f^2 - f - 6$ f)$y^2 - 64$ **7**a)$x^2 + 9x + 20$ b)$m^2 + 8m - 9$ c)$a^2 + 4a - 32$ d)$w^2 + 2w - 15$ e)$a^2 + a - 56$ f)$p^2 + 4p - 12$ **8**a)$m^2 - 4$ b)$p^2 - 49$ c)$a^2 - b^2$ d)$m^2 - n^2$ **9**a)$9x^2 + 9x + 2$ b)$6p^2 - 12p - 18$ c)$6b^2 + 5b - 6$ d)$6m^2 + 7m + 2$ e)$10s^2 - 29s - 21$ f)$8s^2 - 2s - 15$ g)$6h^2 - 11h + 3$
**10**a)$3m^2 + 3m - 36$ b)$-2y^2 + 18y - 40$ c)$10m^2 - 65m + 100$ d)$-18x^2 - 15x - 3$ e)$2y^3 + 6y^2 - 36y$ f)$9y^3 - 24y^2 + 15y$
**11**a)$-x^2 - 4x + 32$ b)$-5y^2 - 5y + 22$ c)$10a^2 + 5a - 8$ d)$m^2 + 12m - 16$
**12**a)$3x^2 + 12x + 13$ b)$4y^2 - 15y + 17$ c)$-2y^2 + 21y - 57$ d)$2m^2 - 29m + 81$ e) $7p^2 + 33p - 8$ **13**a)$-48$ b)17
**14**a)$-17.5$ b)35.68 c)105.36 **15**a)\$128 b)\$376 c)$-$\$2 d)a loss **16**a)\$30 791 b)\$121 591 c)\$78 071 **17**a)147 mm b)117 mm c)87 mm **18**a)$6x^2 - 7x + 2$ b)35
**19**a)A: $12x^2 + 7x + 1$, B: $12x^2 - 7x + 1$ b)$14x$ **20**a)$8x^2 - 16x + 6$ b)$12x - 10$ c)$4y^2 - 20y + 25$ **21**a)$6p^2 + 7p - 3$ b)$2p^2 + 5p + 2$ c) sum of (a) and (b): $8p^2 + 12p - 1$
**22**a)$24m^2 - 38m + 2$ b)22 c)1
**23**a)$11y^2 - 2y - 9$ b)$16y^2 + 7y + 1$
**24**a)$8x^2 - 14x + 3$, $10x^2 + 14x + 5$ b)7; 73

### Review: Practice and Problems, page 94

**1**a)$21m + n$ b)$-2a + b + 9c$ c)$5.1p + 3.3q$ **2**a)$8m + 11$ b)27 units
**3**a)\$$15p$ b)\$$5pq$ c)\$$15pq$ d)\$$25pqr$
**4**a)$12m^5$ b)$-25x^4$ c)$135y^7$ d)$24r^7$
**5**)$4m$ units **6**a)$12q$ b)$3m$ c)$-4mn$
**7**a)\$1 b)\$870 c)\$7822 **8**a)$x^2 + 8x + 16$ b)$4a^2 - 4a + 1$ c)$16p^2 + 16p + 4$ d)$4a^2 - 12ab + 9b^2$ e)$2m^2 + 4m + 2$ f)$-3a^2 + 24a - 48$ **9**a)A 71, B 126 b)B

## CHAPTER 4

### 4.1 Written Exercises, page 97

**1**a)3 **2**a)10 **3**a)$b - c$ b)$3p + n$ c)$3xy$ d)$6m^2$ **4**a)$b(3 + a)$ b)$n(m + p)$ c)$4(2a + b)$ d)$7(d - 2e^2)$ e)$a(b + 6)$ f)$b(c - 3d)$ g)$p(p + r)$ h)$5x(3x^2 - 2)$
**5**a)$5b(2a - 3c)$ b)$7p(p - 2)$ c)$3m^3(m - 4)$ d)$-12p(q + 4)$ e)$8r^2(r - 3)$ f)$9(f^2 - 3)$ **6**a)0 b)0 c) (b) **7**a)72 b)$-112$ c)$-64$ d)432 e)240 f)$-60$ g)$-192$ h)$-672$
**8**a)$6a(b - 2c)$ b)$-24.96$ **9**a)$-80$ b)$-162$ c)15 600 **10**a)$m$ b)$m(m^2 - 2m + 5)$ **11**a)$a^2 - 3a + 5$ b)$2q - pq + 4$ c)$16a$ d)$4pq$
**12**a)$m(m + 12n - 1)$ b)$4(p^2 - 4p - 3)$ c)$25(a^2 + 3ab + 2b^2)$ d)$4n(2m^2 - mn - 3)$ **13**a)$P(1 + 0.14)$ b)\$421.63 **14)**1688.4 **15**a)$2(l + w)$ b)29.76 units c)i)490 units ii)208.2 units iii)469 units **16**a)$\frac{n(n + 1)}{2}$ b)1275 c)5050 **17**a)3900 b)560 c)8450 d)1437 e)900

### 4.2 Written Exercises, page 100

**4**a) $(m - 5)^2$ b) $(a + 2)^2$ c) $(x - 3)^2$ d) $(x - 3y)^2$ e) $(2a + b)^2$ f) $(3 - 4y)^2$ g) $(3a - 2b)^2$ h) $(x - 6y)^2$ i) $(9 - 2y)^2$ j) $(5p + 2q)^2$ **5**a) $(m + 5)^2$ b) $3(y - 3)^2$ c) $(a + 3b)^2$ d) $a(3x + 2)^2$ e) $x(2x + 1)^2$ f) $(2y - x)^2$ g) $(3a - 4)^2$ h) $y(y - 3)^2$ i) $n(3m - 2n)^2$ j) $(5a - 1)^2$ **6**a)64 b)64
**7**a)7.84 b)7.84 **8**a)81 b)25 c)15.21 d)6.76 **9**a)169 b)30.25 c)25 d)2.0449
**10**a)1 b)2.56

### 4.3 Written Exercises, page 102

**1**a)$-3$, $-5$ b)$-8$, 4 c)3, $-6$ d)$-12$, 8 e)10, $-6$ **2**a)3, 4 b)$-3$, $-2$ c)$-5$, $-4$ d)$-6$, 3 e)$-5$, 8 f)$-6$, $-3$ g)$-7$, 5
**3**a)$-5$, $-4$ b) $(m - 5)(m - 4)$ **4**a)$-7$, 2 b) $(y - 7)(y + 2)$ **5**a)$-5$, 6 b) $(x - 5)(x + 6)$ **6**a) $(x - 6)$ b) $(x - 4)$ c) $(a + 5)$ d) $(p - 1)$ e) $(y + 2)$
**7**a) $(f - 5)(f + 2)$ b) $(d + 3)(d - 2)$ c) $(p + 1)(p - 2)$ d) $(r + 2)^2$ e) $(y + 9)(y + 1)$ f) $(t + 4)(t - 6)$ g) $(t + 8)(t - 6)$ h) $(x - 9)(x - 2)$ i) $(t - 5)(t - 4)$ j) $(h + 6)(h + 2)$ k) $(c + 11)(c + 3)$ l) $(m - 6)(m - 5)$
**8**a) $(5 - p)^2$ b) $(6 - f)(3 - f)$ c) $(9 - d)(1 - d)$ d) $(12 - t)(8 - t)$
**9**a) $(a - 8b)(a - 5b)$ b) $(f - 7g)(f - 4g)$ c) $(x + 5y)(x - 17y)$ d) $(p + 5q)(p - 10q)$ e) $(d - 2e)(d - e)$ f) $(a - 5b)^2$ g) $(m + 3n)(m - 9n)$ h) $(d + 3e)(d - 4e)$
**10**a) $3(m + 2)(m + 1)$ b) $2(x + 2)(x - 1)$ c) $2(a + 2)^2$ d) $3(y + 4)^2$ e) $5(a + 1)^2$ f) $2(y - 5)(y - 4)$ g) $4(x + 5)(x - 1)$ h) $x(x + 6)(x - 8)$ **11**a) $(x + 18)(x - 3)$ b) $(x - 5)(x - 4)$ c) $(m - 7)(m - 6)$ d) $(m + 17)(m - 3)$ e) $(p + 27)(p + 2)$ f) $(f + 6g)(f - 15g)$ g) $(y + 2z)(y - 5z)$ h) $(5 - p)^2$ i) $(6 - a)(3 - a)$ j) $(2f - 1)^2$ k) $(d - 4)(d - 3)$ l) $4(b + 13)(b - 2)$ m) $2(n + 9)(n + 2)$ n) $(10 - g)(2 - g)$
**12**a)$-192$ b)$-192$ **13**a)760.32 b)760.32 **14**a)217 b)868 c)250.25 d)$-1.2975$ **15**a)0 b)$-224$ c)$-42.3$
**16**a) $(b - 7)$ b) $(x + 2)$ c) $(y + 2)$ d) $(x - 15)$ **17**a)$x - 2$ b)$a + 4$

**18**a) $(y+2)$ b) $(h-6)$ c) $(m+11)$ d) $(t+6)$ **19**a) $(a+10)$ b) $(m+9)$ c) $(p+8)$ d) $(f-4)$

### 4.4 Written Exercises, page 105

**1)** squares: (a), (b), (c), (e), (f), (i), (k)
**2**a) 5 b) $2n$ c) $3b$ d) $3m$ e) 4 f) $5b$
**3**a) 7, $6p$ b) $2m$, $9n$ c) $4x$, $6y$ **4**a) $x$, $4y$ b) $(x+4y)(x-4y)$ **5**a) $2a$, $5b$ b) $(2a+5b)(2a-5b)$ **6**a) $x+4m$ b) $5y-x$ c) $a+3b$ d) $4k-1$ e) $2k+3m$ f) $3x-7y$ **7**a) $(x+8)(x-8)$ b) $(y+6)(y-6)$ c) $(a+10b)(a-10b)$ d) $(x+1)(x-1)$ e) $(3k+4m)(3k-4m)$ f) $(1+5n)(1-5n)$ g) $9(n+2x)(n-2x)$ h) $(9+y)(9-y)$ i) $(7m+10h)(7m-10h)$ j) $(4x+5y)(4x-5y)$ **8**a) $2(a+b)(a-b)$ b) $3(m+2n)(m-2n)$ c) $2(p+1)(p-1)$ d) $3(n+4)(n-4)$ e) $2(x+8)(x-8)$ f) $2(7+f)(7-f)$ g) $3(1+5d)(1-5d)$ h) $2(5q+1)(5q-1)$ i) $3(6+y)(6-y)$ j) $2(6+7c)(6-7c)$
**9**a) $(x^2+1)(x+1)(x-1)$ b) $(p^2+4)(p+2)(p-2)$ c) $(f^2+7)(f^2-7)$ d) $(9+n^2)(3+n)(3-n)$ **10**a) 8, $m$ b) i) $(4+p)(4-p)$ ii) $(7+d)(7-d)$
**11**a) $(ab+6)(ab-6)$ b) $(pq+8)(pq-8)$ c) $(10+xy)(10-xy)$ d) $(cd+e)(cd-e)$ e) $(7ab+1)(7ab-1)$ f) $(1+2mn)(1-2mn)$
**12**a) $(a+d)(a-d)$ b) $(3k+1)(3k-1)$ c) $(2p+3q)(2p-3q)$ d) $(p+3m)(p-3m)$ e) $(4p+5y)(4p-5y)$ f) $3(m+4)(m-4)$ g) $2(5a^4-2b^4)$ h) no factors i) $(1+2a)(1-2a)$ j) $3(6+x)(6-x)$ k) $x(x+4)(x-4)$ l) $(5+3y)(5-3y)$ m) $(x^2+1)(x+1)(x-1)$ n) $2(m+6)(m-6)$ o) $(9+y^2)(3+y)(3-y)$ p) no factors q) $(av+h)(av-h)$ r) $(10+ab)(10-ab)$ s) $\left(x+\frac{1}{3}\right)\left(x-\frac{1}{3}\right)$ t) $\left(\frac{x}{2}+5\right)\left(\frac{x}{2}-5\right)$
**13**a) $(a+b+c)(a+b-c)$ b) $(x-y+k)(x-y-k)$ c) $(x+y+p)(x+y-p)$ d) $(x-4y)(x-2y)$ e) $(3x-3y)(x+y)$ f) $-12(4p-9q)(p-4q)$ **14**a) 2.36 m³ b) 3.48 m³ c) 4.10 m³ **15**a) 0.74 m³ b) 2.81 m³ **16**a) 2.32 m² b) 0.53 m³ **17**a) 2.92 cm³ b) 12.10 cm³ c) 17.22 cm³ **18)** 42.3 m²

### 4.5 Written Exercises, page 108

**1)** $3(x+4)$ **2)** $m(m-5)$ **3)** $ab(a+b)$ **4)** $p^2q(p-q)$ **5)** $5(m+2)(m-10)$ **6)** $5(p^2+p+3)$ **7)** $ab(b-1)$ **8)** $r(q+4)(q-4)$ **9)** $4(m+3n)(m-3n)$ **10)** $4(m+2)(m-2)$ **11)** $3(p+5)(p-5)$ **12)** $3(y-6)(y-2)$ **13)** $a(a^2-91)$ **14)** $a(a+5)(a-5)$ **15)** $5(a+1)(a-1)$ **16)** $(k+3)(k-8)$ **17)** $9(x+2)(x-2)$ **18)** $2(x+5)^2$ **19)** $2(a+2)(a-2)$ **20)** $(m+4)(m-2)$ **21)** $2(p-3)^2$ **22)** $3(a+3b)(a-3b)$ **23)** $(x+4)(x+3)$ **24)** $(n-5)(n-2)$ **25)** $(x+4)(x-6)$ **26)** $3(4+x)(4-x)$ **27)** $4(n+4)(n-5)$ **28)** $2(n+5)(n-5)$ **29)** $-(a+b)^2$ **30)** $(5x^2+4y^2)(5x^2-4y^2)$ **31)** $(5m+4n)(5m-4n)$ **32)** $8(x^2-3y^2)$ **33)** no factors **34)** $ab(c+d)$ **35)** $(y+1)(y-3)$ **36)** $(m^2+9)(m+2)(m-2)$ **37)** $(4x-1)^2$ **38)** $(y+2)(y-12)$ **39)** $2y^2(y+4)$ **40)** $x(1+y)(1-y)$ **41)** $(x^2+1)(x+1)(x-1)$ **42)** no factors **43)** $(m+2n)^2$ **44)** $a(a+2b)(a-2b)$

### 4.6 Written Exercises, page 110

**1**a) $\frac{b}{x-y}$ b) $\frac{x+y}{d}$ c) $\frac{a}{b}$ d) $\frac{8}{5(x+y)}$ e) $\frac{m(x+y)}{n}$ f) $\frac{6a}{5(x-a)}$ **2**a) $p-1$ b) $d-4$ c) $x+5$ d) $x-8$ **3**a) $\frac{12x}{5(x+2)}$ b) $\frac{5(m+n)}{2(2m+n)}$ c) $\frac{3x-y}{y+3x}$ d) $\frac{x-2y}{3x+4y}$ **4**a) 3 b) 3 **5**a) 13 b) 13 **6**a) $\frac{x-2}{x-6}$ b) $x-3$ c) $\frac{1}{10+y}$ d) $\frac{x+3}{x-3}$ e) $\frac{x+y}{x-y}$ f) $\frac{3}{a+b}$ **7**a) $\frac{5}{4}$ b) $-\frac{2}{5}$ **8**a) 32 b) 38 c) 9.6 d) 10.9 **9**a) 9 b) 21 c) 9.78 d) 12.69 **10**a) 1.25 b) 6.15 c) 1.17 d) 3.5 **11**a) 0.8 b) 0.8 **12**a) $\frac{(x+2)}{2(x-4)}$, $x \neq -1, 4$ b) $\frac{2+x}{7-x}$, $x \neq 3, 7$ c) $\frac{a(a+b)}{(a-b)}$, $a \neq b$ d) $\frac{x-4}{2(x+4)}$, $x \neq -4, -1$

### 4.7 Written Exercises, page 112

**1**a) $\frac{4}{y}$ b) $\frac{x}{y(x-1)}$ c) $\frac{1}{3(n+1)}$ d) $\frac{1}{x}$ **2**a) $\frac{m(m+5)}{(m+4)(m-4)} \times \frac{m(m-4)}{(m+5)(m-5)}$ b) $\frac{m^2}{(m+4)(m-5)}$ **3**a) $\frac{(a-5)(a-2)}{3(2-a)} \times \frac{9(a+5)}{(a+5)(a-5)}$ b) $-3$ **4**b) $\frac{3x^2y^2(x-2y)}{(x+y)(x-y)}$ **5**b) $\frac{2(x-1)^2(x-6)}{x^2(x-4)}$ **6**a) $\frac{x(x+5)}{x+8}$ b) $\frac{1}{6(p+2)}$ c) $\frac{b(b+a)}{-2a^2}$ d) $\frac{3(a-4b)}{2(a-2b)}$ e) $\frac{x-1}{2x}$ f) $n^2-2$ **7**a) 2 b) 1 c) 2.8 **8**a) A: $\frac{13}{9}$, B: $\frac{7}{5}$ b) A **9**a) A: 5, B: 36 b) A **10**a) 900 b) 92.16 c) 1179.36 d) 7496.28 **11**a) $\frac{5}{2}$ b) $\frac{5}{3}$ c) $\frac{7}{12}$ **12**b) $\frac{a+2}{2a-3}$ **13**a) 1 b) 1 c) $\frac{20x(x+y)}{3y(x+2y)(2x+3y)}$

### 4.8 Written Exercises, page 115

**1**a) $2(x+y)$ b) $\frac{2}{x-y}$ c) 3 d) $\frac{8(x+1)}{3}$ **2**b) $\frac{2(x-3)}{x+3}$ **3**b) $\frac{m+3}{2(m-3)}$ **4**b) 24 **5**a) 1 b) 1 c) $\frac{1}{2(a+3)}$ d) 1 **6**a) $\frac{1}{2}$ b) $\frac{9}{7}$ c) $\frac{26}{5}$ **7**a) 0.3 b) $-0.3$ c) 0.125 d) 0.15 **8**a) 0.12 b) $-0.16$ c) $-0.75$ d) 0.09375 **9**a) A: $-\frac{8}{3}$, B: $-5$ b) A

### Review: Practice and Problems, page 116

**1**a) $14m$ b) $q(p+r)$ c) $6(e-2f^2)$ d) $5m(3m^2-2)$ e) $4p^3(p-4)$ f) $8(r^2-3)$ **2**a) $5m(n-2q)$ b) $-353.4$ c) 4800 **3**a) 34.81 b) 34.81 c) $b$ **4**a) $-7$, 3 b) $(x-7)(x+3)$ **5**a) $(x+1)(x-1)$ b) $(5a+2)(5a-2)$ c) $x(6+7x)(6-7x)$ d) $(7m+9)(7m-9)$ e) $x(4+9x)(4-9x)$ f) $(3a+4)(3a-4)$ g) $4(3p-4q)(3p+4q)$ h) $(10r+9q)(10r-9q)$ i) $(x^2+1)(x+1)(x-1)$ j) $(m^2+5)(m^2-5)$ k) $(10+p^2)(10-p^2)$ l) $(9+r)(9-r)$ **6**a) $m^2(4m+1)$ b) $(x+3y)(x-3y)$ c) $(4a^2+1)(2a+1)(2a-1)$ d) $(ab+1)(ab-1)$ e) $(m-n+5)(m-n-5)$ f) $(y-9)(y-4)$ g) $(x^2+8)(x^2-8)$ h) $(a+7)(a-3)$ i) $2(p+2)(p-3)$ j) $3m(m^2+4)(m^2+1)$ **7)** C **8**a) $r+1$ b) $x^2+9x+14$ c) $2m+n$ d) $6x^2+13xy+6y^2$ **9)** B **10**a) $p+1$ b) $\frac{3}{2}$ c) $\frac{a-7}{a+6}$ d) $\frac{5}{f+6}$ **11**a) $\frac{2}{3}$ b) $\frac{4}{9}$ c) 6

d)$\frac{m}{m+2}$ **12)**A **13**a)$m$ b)$\frac{y-4}{y+8}$ c)$\frac{3}{x}$
d)$\frac{(p+2)^2}{(p+1)^2}$

**Update: A Cumulative Review, page 118**
**1**a)1909 g b)1800 g
**2**a)$-30p^3 + 20p^2 - 5p$
b)$36a^4 - 9a^3 - 15a^2$ c)444
**3**a)32.5%, $\frac{13}{40}$ b)0.75, $\frac{3}{4}$ c)0.125, 12.5%
d)66.6%, $\frac{666}{1000}$ e)1.5, $\frac{3}{2}$ **4**a)4000
b)64 000 c)512 000 **5**a)$-29$ b)$-59$
c)204 d)57 **6**a)$8a - 3b$
b)$-a^2 + 2a + 6$ c)$-2(m-4)$
d)$4p(p-3)$ e)$4(m-n)$ f)$-12a + b$
**7**a)$-6pq$ b)$m^2n$ **8**a)\$1.76 b)\$2228.37
**9**a)$a^2 + a - 20$ b)$a^2 + 10a + 25$
**10**a)$8(x+1)$ b)$7(x-2)$ c) $(x-5)(x-2)$
d) $(x-5)^2$ e)$x(x+3)(x-1)$
f)$3(x^2+4)(x+2)(x-2)$
g) $(3m+4)(3m-4)$ h)$3(a+5)(a-5)$
i) $(p-5)(p+3)$ j)$2(r+5)(r-5)$
**11**a)$3n$ b)$a-5$ c)$\frac{r^2(1+3r)}{(2-r)(r+3)(r-1)}$

## CHAPTER 5

**5.1 Written Exercises, page 122**
**1**a)C b)D c)A d)B **2**a)3 b)24
c)2 d)$-3$ e)6 f)10 g)$-1$ h)$\frac{10}{3}$ **3**a)3
b)$-5$ c)5 d)4 e)6 f)15 g)$-8$
h)$-10$ **4**a)C b)B c)C d)A **5**a)4
b)5 c)$-2$ d)6 e)7 f)$-11$ g)6
h)$-5$ **6**a)$-6$ **7**a)12 **8**a)$\frac{9}{2}$ b)$-8$ c)7
d)$-8$ e)6 f)3 **9**a)9 b)6 c)3 d)9
e)9 f)12 **10**a)8 b)15 c)24 d)8
e)$-12$ f)$-40$ g)$\frac{112}{3}$ h)16 **11**a)$-15$
b)10 c)$-6$ d)2 e)$-4$ f)$-\frac{1}{2}$ g)$-4$
h)$-1$ **12**a)$-2$ b)4 c)1 d)9 e)11
f)8 **13**a)4.5 b)4.6 c)4 **14**a)2 b)20
c)$-13$ d)5 **15)**92 **16)**1839
**17)**290.8 m

**5.2 Written Exercises, page 125**
**1**a)E b)A c)B d)F e)D **2**a)$-6$ b)5
c)16 d)$-60$ e)$-36$ f)$-40$ **3**a)20
b)5 c)40 d)$-8$ **4**a)7 **5**a)3 **6**a)$-16$
b)$-12$ **7**a)20 b)32 c)5 d)6 **8**a)174
b)$-7$ c)$-4$ d)2 **9**a)$\{-6\}$ b)$\{9\}$
c)$\{-13\}$ **10**a)2 b)20 c)$-1$ d)1
e)$-3$ **11)**32 games **12)**72 floors
**13)**156 km/h **14**a)$n = 604$
c)604 adults, 268 students **15**a)29
b)3.0 m, 1.5 m **16**a)\$14.50, \$29.00
b)42, 142 **17)**\$66 **18)**\$63.33
**19)**46 small, 89 large

**5.3 Written Exercises, page 129**
**1**a)20 b)10 c)4 d)1 **2**a)6 b)8 **3**a)8
b)2 **4**a)9 days b)$d = \frac{c-15}{4}$ **5**a)10
b)450 c)325 d)2 e)5 f)3.14 **6**a)225
b)2 c)2 d)12 e)2600 f)3 **7**a)108
b)56 c)78 d)1055.04 e)106 f)195
**8**a)14 b)48 c)$-10$ d)10
**9**a)$m = \frac{y-b}{x}$ b)3, $-2$, 1 **10**a)$s = \frac{t}{3} - P$
b)4.3, 3.5, 7.6, $-1.7$ **11**a)4 b)10 c)6.4
**12**a)$t = \frac{v^2 - u^2}{30}$ b)$n = \frac{s}{180} + 2$ c)$g = \frac{v^2}{2t}$
**13**a)$y = \frac{15-2x}{3}$ b)$t = \frac{I}{pr}$ c)$z = \frac{x-y}{T}$
d)$T = \frac{5H}{2} + 10$ e)$u = \frac{2s}{t} - v$ f)$c = \sqrt{\frac{E}{m}}$
**14**a)270 km b)215 km/h c)$2\frac{1}{2}$ h
**15**a)50 m b)70 km/h **16**a)565.2 cm
b)50 **17**a)1.2 Ω b)24 Ω

**5.4 Written Exercises, page 133**
**1**a)$-2$, $-1$ b)$-1$, 7 c)$-1$, 2 d)1, 5
e)2, 3 f)$-3$, 1 **2**a)$-5$, 5 b)$-6$, 0
c)$-1$, 2 d)$-11$, 3 e)0, 7 f)$-2$, 5
**3**a)$-8$, $-1$ b)1, 2 c)$-6$, 6 d)$-2$, 4
e)$-2$, 3 f)$-3$, 5 g)$-3$, 7 h)$-6$, 7
**4**a)$-3$, $-3$ b)2 **5**a)$-3$, 3 b)2
**6**a)$-1$, $-1$ b)$-2$, 6 c)$-5$, 2 d)2, 6
e)4, 4 f)0, $\frac{1}{2}$ g)$-5$, $-3$ h)$-4$, $-1$
**7**a)$-2$, 6 b)$-9$, 2 c)$-4$, $-1$ d)$-3$, 7
e)$-2$, 4 f)1, 1 g)$-2$, 2 h) 1, 1
**8)**6 cm by 8 cm **9)**\$6.00 **10)** $-1$, 12
**11**a)$-7$, 2 b)$-2$, 9 c)4, 5 d)$-6$, 4
e)$-3$, 4 f)0, 10 g)$-2$, 6 h)$-6$, 1
**12**a)$-5$, 3 b)$-5$, 5 c)1, 3 d)$-8$, 3
**13**a)0, 7 b)7 s c)1 s, 6 s **14**a)1 b)2, 3
c)$-3$ d)$-1$, 1 e)0, 4 f)1, 1
**15)**6 m by 12 m **16)**89 000 000 km
**17)**36 m **18)**18 silver, 10 gold **19)**1957
**20)**1 m or 21 m **21)**1959

**5.5 Written Exercises, page 137**
**1**a)$a \geqq 7$ b)$k < 5$ c)$x < 5$ d)$t \leqq 4$
e)$q > -1$ f)$a < 5$ **2**a)$t > 4$ b)$y \geqq -6$
c)$y < -3$ d)$k > -6$ e)$p < -6$
f)$x \leqq -6$ **3**a)$n > 2$ b)$n \leqq 1$
c)$n < -2$ d)$n \geqq -3$
**4**b)$k \geqq -1$ or $k > -2$ c)$k \leqq 1$ or $k < 2$
d)$k \geqq 2$ or $k > 1$ e)$k \leqq 0$ or $k < 1$
**6**a)$p \geqq 15$ b)$x \leqq \frac{1}{2}$ c)$y > 14$ d)$a \geqq 6$
e)$y > 1$ f)$m < 24$ g)$n \geqq -26$ h)$x > 5$
**7**a)$x \leqq -11$ b)$x \leqq -6$ c)$a \leqq -\frac{3}{2}$
d)$p > \frac{16}{3}$ **8**a)$x < -6$ b)$m < 12$
c)$a \leqq -2$ d)$m \leqq 10$ e)$m \geqq -\frac{19}{5}$
f)$p < 6$ g)$x \leqq 23$ h)$a \leqq -9$
**9**a)$x < 5$ b)$x \leqq 4$ c)$x \geqq 4$ d)$x \leqq -2$

**5.6 Written Exercises, page 139**
**1**a)2 b)3 c)1.5 d)$-1$
**2**a)$-7$ b)5 c)5 d)5 **3**a)1 b)$-12$
c)$\frac{2}{3}$ d)$2\frac{2}{5}$ **4**a)$-2$ b)$-6$ c)$-3$ d)$-2$
**5**a)20 b)$-19$ c)5 d)$-1$ e)$-2$ f)4
g)4 h)11 i)$-8$ j)$-3$ k)$-1$ l)$-2$
**6**a)$\frac{5}{3}$ b)3 c)10 d)$-3$

**Review: Practice and Problems, page 140**
**1**a)8 b)$-2.5$ c)$-3$ d)$12\frac{1}{3}$
**2**a)$t = 3.125$ b)$R = \frac{4}{3}$ c)$z = 3.57$
**3**a)$-3$, $-2$ b)3, 4 c)$-3$, 4 d)$-1$, $+1$
**4**a)2 b)10 **5)**2435 km
**6**a)2 s, 7 s b)up and down

## CHAPTER 6

**6.1 Written Exercises, page 143**
**1**a)73 cm b)206 cm c)15.2 m
d)33.0 cm **2**a)58 cm b)80 cm c)104 cm
d)80 cm **3**a)34.8 cm b)315 m c)27.0 cm
d)183.6 m **4**a)$P = 5y$ b)$P = 6x$
c)$P = 2a + 2b$ d)$P = x + y + z$
e)$P = 8m$ f)$P = 2p + 4q$ **5**a)31.2 cm
b)7.3 cm c)26 cm d)19.6 cm
**6**a)13.7 cm, 79.8 cm b)7.4 cm, 44.8 cm
c)8.8 cm, 73.2 cm **7**a)14.6 m b)12.6 m
**8**a)1080 cm b)48 **9**a)87.3 km
b)17.46 km **10**a)180.2 m b)\$709.99
**11**a)52 m b)\$348.40 c)26 **12**a)51.0 m
b)\$527.00

**6.2 Written Exercises, page 147**
**1**a)37.7 cm b)157 cm c)126 mm d)52.8 cm **2**a)80.7 cm b)83.5 cm c)259 mm d)3.3 km **3**a)48 mm, 150 mm b)18.2 m, 114 m c)12.5 cm, 25.0 cm d)15.2 km, 30.4 km **4**a)23.9 cm b)95.8 cm c)4.71 m d)52.8 km **5)**12.0 m **6**a)8.79 m b)$26.19 **7)**211 000 km **8**a)214 cm b)226 cm **9**a)4926 b)4386 c)201 more **10**a)6.91 m b)51.8 **11)**7.50 cm **12**a)339 m b)314 m c)150 m, 750 m **13**a)7.63 m b)140 cm c)263 cm **14)**16 cm or 27 cm **15**a)144 cm b)9.41 m **16)**3940 m **17)**67.8 m **18)**16 **19)**29 m **20)**38.6 m **21)**76.6 cm, 116 cm, 156 cm, 195 cm, 235 cm

**6.3 Written Exercises, page 152**
**1**a)300 cm² b)625 cm² c)7.1 cm² **2**a)840 cm² b)36 cm² c)13 m² **3**a)60 cm² b)61 m² c)30 cm² **4**a)60 m² b)610 cm² **5**a)2.0 cm² b)230 cm² c)24 cm² d)216 cm² e)14 cm² **6)**B **7**a)260 cm² b)130 cm² c)190 m² d)151 cm² e)160 m² **8**a)8.85 cm² b)7.5 cm² **9**a)120 cm b)78 cm c)19 cm **10)**18 m² **11**a)28.3 m, 14.2 m b)938 m² c)$1585.22 **12**a)2700 cm² b)0.27 m² **13**a)19 m² b)51 m² c)$89.93 **14**a)345 cm² b)1300 cm² c)180 cm² **15)**27 cm²

**6.4 Written Exercises, page 155**
**1**a)314 cm² b)13 m² c)4070 cm² **2)**3.80 m² **3)**491 cm² **4)**240 mm² **5**a)5.0 m, 78.5 m² b)30.0 cm, 707 cm² c)1.95 cm, 3.91 cm d)6.9 m, 13.8 m **6)**804 km² **7)**4.91 m² **8**a)8.0 cm² b)1944 cm² **9)**10 m² **10)**15 cm² **11**a)100 m² b)127 m² c)circle **12)**273 cm² **13**a)70 cm² b)1500 cm² c)65 cm² d)9.2 cm² **14**a)290 cm² b)3770 cm² c)260 cm²

**6.5 Written Exercises, page 159**
**1**a)100 cm² b)EFGH c)200 cm² d)ABFE e)50 cm² f)ADHE g)700 cm² **2**c)25 m² d)15 m² e)85 m² **3**b)5500 cm² **4**a)1700 cm² b)64 cm² c)160 cm² d)1100 cm² **5**a)490 cm² b)460 cm² c)1700 cm² **6**a)2100 mm² b)500 cm² c)942 mm² **7**b)24 cm² c)72 cm², 96 cm², 120 cm² d)336 cm² **8**b)9.5 m² **9)**B **10)**130 cm² **11**a)25 000 cm² b)$4000 **12**a)31 m² b)$209.25 **13**b)46 cm² c)119 cm² d)468 cm² e)505 cm² **14)**700

**6.6 Written Exercises, page 162**
**1)**B **2**a)48 cm² b)24.5 cm by 11.5 cm c)380 cm² **3**a)1000 cm² b)1600 cm² c)620 cm² **4**a)1980 cm² b)3350 cm² c)5330 cm² **5**a)2100 cm² b)1700 cm² c)310 cm² **6**a)2800 cm² b)4100 cm² c)1200 cm² **7)**170 cm² **8)**190 m² **9**a)6.3 m² b)8 cans **10)**B **11)**636 cm² **12**a)3200 mm² b)32 cm² **13**a)93 m³ b)32 L **14)**390 cm² **15)**18 m² **16**a)9.1 cm² b)1.4 cm³

**6.7 Written Exercises, page 165**
**1**a)190 cm³ b)20 cm² c)820 cm³ d)740 cm³ **2**a)60 cm³ b)600 mm³ c)800 cm³ d)3600 mm³ **3**a)60 m³ b)40 cm³ c)52 mm³ d)0.7 km³ **4**a)300 cm³ b)600 m³ c)42 cm³ d)3 m² **5**a)A b)A **6**a)100 cm³ b)15 m² c)3.3 cm d)3.50 m **7)**45 **8)**6.5 m³ **9**a)22.4 L b)16.1 L **10**a)55 000 m³ b)1310 **11**a)2.2 m³ b)1.7 m³ **12)**4900 cm³ **13**a)6000 mm³ b) 3000 mm³ c)9000 mm³ **14**a)5200 cm³ b)7700 cm³ c)9800 cm³ d)390 cm³ **15)**1500 m³ **16)**11.6 cm

**6.8 Written Exercises, page 169**
**1**a)740 cm³ b)640 cm³ c)4670 cm³ **2**b)260 cm³ **3**b)60 m³ **4**a)920 cm³ b)400 cm³ c)120 cm³ d)1120 cm³ **5**b)7980 cm³ **6**a)11 000 cm³ b) 160 000 cm³ c)3600 cm³ **7**a)9200 cm³ b)1630 cm³ c)8990 cm³ **8)**14 000 cm³ **9)**25 mL **10)**24 000 L **11)**9.8 mm³ **12)**4000 g **13)**440 cm³ **14)**9.7 m³ **15)**320 m³ **16)**120 m³ **17)**11 000 cm

**Review: Practice and Problems, page 171**
**1**a)50 cm b)9.5 m **2**a)156 cm b)175 cm **3)**9.4 m **4**a)10 cm², 6.6 cm² b)50, 92 **5)**237 cm² **6**a)130 cm² b)250 cm² c)640 cm² **7**a)576 cm² b)384 cm² c)1536 cm² d)2112 cm² **8)**3200 cm² **9**a)3200 cm³ b)1000 cm³ **10**a)6800 cm³, 2000 cm² b)92 m³, 98 m² c)440 m³, 350 m² **11**a)150 m³ b)25 m³

---

## CHAPTER 7

---

**7.1 Written Exercises, page 175**
**1**a)$77.00 b)$112.50 **2**a)$18.00 b)$105.00 c)$67.50 d)$13.44 **3**a)$444.00 b)$748.00 c)$1326.00 d)$954.13 **4**a)$252.00 b)$93.00 c)$331.70 d)$575.35 **5**a)$237.50 b)$32.50 c)$956.25 d)$4.85 **6**a)$5453.00 b)$885.00 c)$1512.57 **7)**A **8**a)$11.03 b)$132.39 **9)**$1713.60 **10)**$4348 **11**a)6% b)6 months c)$800 d)9% **12)**$972.76 **13)**12.75% **14)**$12.49 **15)**13 years 4 months **16**a)11.3% b)11.3% c)same

**7.2 Written Exercises, page 178**
**1**a)$33.00 b)$4.87 c)$231.82 **2**a)4% b)200(1.04) c)200(1.04)² d)$216.32 **3)**$1782.15 **4)**$1262.48 **5**a)$600 b)$605 c)$5 **6**a)$864.00 b)$865.95 c)$1.95 **7**a)$3850.00 b)$3858.75 c)$3863.35 **8**a)$2531.25 b)$17.61 **9**a)$574.78 b)$17 717.22 c)$7428.36 **10)**b **11**(a)A (b)A **12**a)Karin's b)Daniel's **13**a)$428.49 b)$928.49 c)$994.62 **14)**$330.63 **15)**$74.90

**7.3 Written Exercises, page 181**
**1**a)$221.07 b)$503.13 c)$2304.54 d)$3604.06 e)$11 121.66 f)$28 180.83 **2**a)$80.00, 12%, 5 years b)$250.00, 8%, 5 years c)$175.00, 11%, 3 years d)$58.26, 18%, 1 month e)$656.50, 9%, 3 months **3**a)$759.19 b)$213.22 c)$628.06 d)$3328.74 **4**a)$1163.74 b)$513.64 c)$4917.88 d)$95.30 **5**a)$1043.04, $1076.16, $1093.76, $1105.91 b)D, $62.87 **6)**$1617.72 **7)**$4083.27 **8)**18% **9)**A **10)**Bank **11)**$1188.31 **12**a)9.2% b)9%

**7.4 Written Exercises, page 183**
**1**a)$12.95 b)$2.24 c)$21.36 d)$66.50 **2**a)$15.00 b)$28.54 c)$23.76 **3**a)$2.50 b)$8.00 c)$1498.05 d)$975.29 **4**a)$1.38 b)$20.93 c)$0.91 d)$0.00 e)$49.80 f)$0.73 **5**a)$52.95 b)$8.83 c)$18.08 d)$2304.96 **6**a)B b)A c)B d)A e)B **7**b)$132.65 **8**b)$254.35 **9)**$172.54 **10)**$170.13 **11**a)$296.95 b)$2.69 **12)**$441.29 **13**a)$39.00 b)$47.93 **14)**Newfoundland **15)**$471.70

**7.5 Written Exercises, page 186**
**1**a)$695.94 b)$675.00 c)$1106 d)$1487.20 **2**a)$6719.87 b)$9463.08 c)$14 336.00 d)$16 684.47 **3**a)$9566.50 b)$10 555.55 c)$13 789.00 **4**a)$10 881.90 b)$14 950.95 **5**a)87.5% b)$3745 **6)**$6862 **7**a)$10 312.90 b)$1764.90 **8**a)$4122.50 b)$4369.85 **9**a)$5776.93 b)$5457.00 **10**a)$279.27 b)$80.25

c)$10 610.12 **11**a)$10 280 b)$923.50
**12**a)$10 802.00, $11 529.40, $11 121.60
b)$727.40 **13)**$1244.85 **14**a)$16 541.84
b)$282.56 c)$21 062.88

### 7.6 Written Exercises, page 190

**1)**$3131.11 **2)**$3703.27
**3**a)$308.61 b)$71.22
**4)**used; charged for transmission repair
**5)**public transit, $270.11 per month
**6)**$2703.99 **7)**$450.67
**8)**old vehicle, little value
**9)** < 19, insurance very expensive
**10**a)$3308.31 b)26¢/km **11**a)$1200.10
b)$2576.79 c)$11.81 **12**a)$3579.50
b)other car's insurance **13**a)$10 445
b)$13 602.11 c)$377.84 d)$9476.80
**14**a)$915 b)$794 c)$511
**15**a)$7872.20 b)$6691.37 c)$5118.90
**16)**$8850.63 **17**a)$3675.54 b)$3325.38
c)$3965.58 **18**a)$2625.60
b)$4066.44, $6692.04 d)$1410.00

### 7.7 Written Exercises, page 194

**1**a)1.125 b)1.131 c)1.188 d)1.574
e)1.046 f)1.020 **2**a)2 years b)12%/a
c)annual d)$376.32 e)$336 f)$300
g)$1012.32 **3**b)$4941.04 **4**b)$5256.33
**5)**$755.64 **6)**$55 703.69 **7)**$4101.01
**8)**$1880.92 **9)**$4382.81 **10)**Bonnie **11)**B

### 7.8 Written Exercises, page 197

**1**a)C b)B c)A **2**a)1906.55 b)2309.21
c)3677.67 d)2921.70 **3**a)$635.07
b)$658.16 c)$442.94 d)$401.49
e)$630.05 **4**a)$1409.23 b)$2491.54
c)$4725.40 **5**a)$749.07 b)$1130.32
c)$1942.20 d)$2803.97 e)$3576.13
f)$2595.31 **6**a)$5263.16 b)$4612.09
c)$3541.60 d)$2280.54 **7)**$3478.84
**8)**$2804.78 **9)**$6190.19 **10)**$1034.49
**11)**$2109.56 **12**b)$450.45 c)$405.81
d)$856.26 **13)**$1176.39 **14)**$940.49

### Review Practice and Problems, page 199

**1**a)$435 b)$950 c)$4123.30 **2**a)$167.71
b)$1027.56 c)$2352.61 d)$3279.98
**3**a)$122.27 b)$612.42 c)$1257.25
**4**a)$41.93 b)$139.69 c)$901.31
**5**a)$9410.65 b)$12 657.51 c)$15 081.85
**6**a)$3725.53 b)$901.80 c)$4808.43
d)$9302.00 **7**a)$1609.20 b)$1611.58
c)$1612.82 **8)**$1808.65 **9**a)$1630.56
b)$3354.00 **10)**$6720.41 **11**a)$34.36
b)$346.76 **12)**$13 146.83

## CHAPTER 8

### 8.1 Written Exercises, page 204

**1**a)$108 b)$92.70 c)$121 d)$245.70
**2**a)$166 b)$265.60 c)$332 d)$381.80
e)$456.50 f)$487.63 **3**a)$325 b)$270.10
c)$494.90 d)$363.38 e)$198.90
f)$289.60 **4**a)$272 b)283.20 c)$434.34
d)$613.08 **5)**$349.65 **6)**$620.44
**7**a)$22 464 b)$30 148.80 c)$12 350
d)$24 024 e)$11 892.92 f)$19 240
g)$18 826.60 h)$17 992 **8)**$740.25
**9)**$386.81

### 8.2 Written Exercises, page 207

**1**a)$11.90 b)$27.36 c)$21.72 d)$110.25
**2**a)$39.48 b)$1249.58 c)9.6% d)9.75%
e)$5873.44 **3)**$3492.50 **4)**$33.10 **5)**3%
**6)**$107.29 **7)**$76.20 **8)**$81.40 **9)**$7500
**10)**$192.80 **11**a)$121.86 b)$123.30
**12**a)$75.25 b)$53.14 c)$145.62
d)$252.91 e)$561.83 f)$1033.65
g)$1290.56 h)$1949.61

### 8.3 Written Exercises, page 211

**1**a)$3.22, $5.24 b)$4.54, $6.97
c)$4.96, $7.51 d)$5.25, $7.90
e)$4.73, $7.22 f)$4.38, $6.76 **2**a)$34.35
b)$49.30 c)$23.85 d)$25.80 e)$37.70
**3**a)$3.11, $5.11, $209.02, $21.90, $187.12
b)$4.88, $7.40, $302.80, $49.95, $252.85
c)$4.13, $6.43, $262.93, $32.90, $230.03
d)$3.56, $5.69, $232.75, $29.70, $203.05
e)$4.65, $7.11, $290.95, $36.35, $254.60
**4)**$139.77 **5)**$242.96 **6**a)$218.50
b)$220.68 c)$332.86
**7**a)$7.64, $5.05, $50.70
b)$7.82, $5.20, $54.20
c)$6.96, $4.53, $38.55
**8**a)$200.11 b)$246.01 c)$191.83
**10)**$138.96 **11)**$247.79 **12)**$230.69

### 8.4 Written Exercises, page 215

**2**a)$1520.60 b)$1630.00 c)$244.90
d)$0.00 e)$1773.70 f)$1610.90
**3**a)$1788.30 b)refund, $48.35
**5**a)$1011, $533.30, $1544.30
b)$2340–$2350, $118.10, $264.10
c)$8390–$8400, $1210, $1838.70
d)$12 340–$12 350, $988.90, $2948.90
**6**a)$2380–$2390 b)$8110–$8120
c)$2300–$2310 d)$7220–$7230
e)$12 340–$12 350 f)$8350–$8360
**7)**refund $871.60 **8**a)refund $43.50
b)refund $82.20 c)refund $23.97
d)refund $195.55 **9**a)refund $68.88
b)refund $184.94 c)refund $116.73
d)refund $192.41 e)refund $86.33

### 8.5 Written Exercises, page 224

**3**a)$4140.00 b)$3630.00 c)$710.00
d)$710.00 **4**a)$372.70 b)$241.87
c)$500.00 d)$500.00 **5**a)$379.80
b)$58.70 **6)**$2289.25 **7)**$296.38
**8)**$470.36 **9**a)$562.12 **b)**$129.23
**10**a)$8476.33 b)$7591.30 **11**a)$15 170.25
b)$12 293.03 c)$6751.06 **12**a)$500
b)$10 279.03 **13**a)$500 b)$14 015.02
**14**a)$8842.15 b)$200.09 c)$4502.06
**15**a)$8731.75 b)$6759.99
**16)**refund $665.20

### 8.6 Written Exercises, page 227

**1)**$3027.50 **2)**$3311.40 **3)**$2626.00
**4)**refund $1914.90 **5)**refund $537.41

### 8.7 Written Exercises, page 229

**1**a)$88.40 b)$132.68 c)$202.69
d)$530.15 **2**a)$5.85 b)$22.10 c)$28.54
d)$18.72 e)$1.79 f)$8.57 g)$0.30
**3**a)$41.89 b)$649.28 c)$7447.93
**4**a)$116.78 b)$166.35 **5**a)$36.56
b)$35.85 **6)**39% **7)**23% **8**a)$313.50
b)27% c)21% **9)**A: a)$12.35 b)$5.10
c)$7.25 B: a)$15.80 b)$7.00 c)$8.80
**10**a)$2269.66 b)24% **11**a)$67.57
b)92% **12)**$24.92

### 8.8 Written Exercises, page 233

**1**a)$7.20 b)$0.98 c)$195 d)$380.99
**2**a)$471.20 b)$2.53 c)$591.85
d)$369.35 **3**a)$250 b)$212.50 c)$220.93
d)$322.63 **4**a)$440 b)$461.50 c)$420.48
d)$467.96 **5**a)$195 b)$455
**6**a)$14.85, $34.65 b)$29.95, $89.85
c)$134.51, $762.24 d)$919.65, $8760.85
**7)**$58.47 **8**a)$159.17 b)$170.31
**9)**$198.25 **10)**13.4% **11**a)$49.26
b)$20.38 c)$262.23 d)$8763.69
**12**a)$27.51 b)$39.62 c)$5514.08
**13**a)$47.97 b)$31.98 **14**a)$8901.62
b)$964.13 **15)**$1.56 **16**a)$1109.82
b)23.5%

### Review: Practice and Problems, page 234

**1**a)$267 b)$316.50 **2)**$453.36 **3**a)$8.28
b)$12.89 c)$10.15 d)$10.54 e)$12.41
f)$8.74 **4)**$314.43 **5**a)$1762.10
b)$3364.70 c)$266.80 d)$0 e)$74.60
f)$1590.00 **6)**$13 973.30 **7**a)$6384.24
b)$240.40 **8)**$3364.70 **9)**$4637.50
**10**a)$344.40 b)$39.00 c)$417.33
d)$1299.42 **11**a)$653.23 b)$37 926.78
**12**a)$76.77 b)$72.93 c)$23.03

### Update: A Cumulative Review, page 236

**1**a)0.60 mm b)4.6 m c)9 km
**2)**7.64 years **3)**20 117 **4**a)$5ab^2$

b)$12m^6n^7$ c)$-7b^2$ d)$9a^2$ e)$16p^2q^4$ f)$-4x^3y^7$ **5)**$3(4p^2 + 3p - 10)$ cm² **6**a)101.3 m³ b)18.8 g **7)**1952 **8**a)$\frac{a-2}{5(a-1)}$ b)$\frac{x+2}{2x-3}$ **9**a)3.84 mm b)61.44 mm **10**a)$214.98 b)27% **11)**$\frac{10}{9}$ **12)**$33 381.31 **13)**$7435.56

## CHAPTER 9

**9.1 Written Exercises, page 241**
**2**a)$1.51 b)$0.36 c)$6.84 d)$63.47 **3**a)$994.42 b)$5.01 c)$959.95 **4**a)$0.16 b)$0.08 c)$0.29 d)$2.48 **5**a)$0.20 b)$0.49 **6**a)$1.98 b)$0.00 c)$21.52 d)$78.26 e)$2.67 f)$9.69 **7)**$103.10 **8)**$3003.52 **9)**$814.18 **10**a)$322.12 b)$0.66 **11**a)$4.37 b)$4.47 **12**a)$956.93 b)$4.88 **13**a)$4.37 b)$1044.26

**9.2 Written Exercises, page 245**
**1**a)0.0725 b)0.085 c)0.0875 d)0.095 e)0.1025 f)0.1185 **2**a)$18.63 b)$29.79 c)$8.24 d)$119.29 **3**a)10%, 159 d; $15.90 b)$8\frac{1}{2}$%, 200 d; $44.81 **4**a)$50.95 b)$105.32 c)$252.43 d)$454.93 **5**a)$45.77 b)$53.16 c)$36.50 d)$126.81 e)$620.64 **6**a)$63.38 b)$248.63 c)$212.30 **7)**$35.06 **8)**$994.38 **9**a)$18.34 b)$868.34 **10)**$2250, $56.25 **11**a)term deposit **12)**$2478.40 **13)**10.8% **14)**$8\frac{3}{4}$%

**9.3 Written Exercises, page 247**
**1**a)$24.75 b)$288.30 c)$43.53 d)$8.22 e)$7.44 f)$119.65 **2**a)$256.04 b)$123.52 c)$789.25 **3**a)14.5% b)24.3% c)26.1% **4**a)$5.44 b)$4.13 c)$2.95 d)$2.50 e)$13.88 f)$2.50 **5**a)$198.00 b)$179.31 c)58.0% d)22.1% **6)**65.7% **7)**26.1% **8**a)i)entertainment ii)lunches, clothes, transportation, reading b)11.4% c)$384.43 **9**a)$728.99 b)$485.99 **10**a)$75.24 b)15.0% c)20 **11**a)$38.25 **12**a)C **13**b)24 **14**a)29¢ **15**a)$3.59 b)$1.31

**9.4 Written Exercises, page 250**
**1**a)$11.03 b)$8.10 c)$5.85 d)$2.12 **2**a)$0.64 b)$6.35 c)$14.68 **3**a)$14.48 b)$8.56 c)$10.39 d)$8.65 **4**a)$1.97 b)$5.40 c)$8.91 d)$12.18 **5**a)$2.78, $241.33 b)$5.89, $511.74 c)$404.00, $406.26 **6**a)$45.00 b)$16.50 **7**a)$8.41 b)$25.00 **8**a)$830.20 b)$16.07 c)$889.20 **9**a)$4.05 b)$1.35 c)$2.25 d)$5.55 e)$3.30 f)$5.25 **10**a)$16.00 b)$4.35 **11**a)1.6% b)18.7% **12**a)1.5% b)1.5%

**9.5 Written Exercises, page 254**
**1**a)$691.00 b)$1736.72 c)$3299.68 **2**a)$129.89 b)$344.54 c)$2173.10 **3**a)$179.00 b)$188.20 c)$2864.01 **4**a)$583.20, $52.53 b)$1455.01, $116.87 c)$1127.08, $273.22 **5)**$435.36 **6)**$353.00 **7)**$10.15 **8)**20%/a **9**a)$1341.20 b)382.53 **10**a)$688.60 b)$3334.60 c)26.0% **11**a)$29.30 b)$119.82 c)23.5% **12**a)$1087.81 b)$134.59 **13**a)$4349.69 b)19.3%/a

**9.6 Written Exercises, page 258**
**1**a)$N = 48$, $n = 24$, $P = 700$, $I = 30.5$, $r = 0.167$ b)$N = 52$, $n = 18$, $P = 848.30$, $I = 17.25$, $r = 0.111$ c)$N = 4$, $n = 2$, $P = 1246.50$, $I = 49.75$, $r = 0.106$ d)$N = 24$, $n = 18$, $P = 638.17$, $I = 69.50$, $r = 0.275$ **2**a)$12.80 b)$11.40 **3**a)12 b)12 c)12 d)4 e)2 **4**a)29.5% b)34.6% c)27.7% d)7.4% **5**a)23.8% b)14.0% c)15.3% d)18.5% **6**a)22.0% b)20.8% **7**a)11.4% b)14.9% **8**a)$136.44 b)24.9% **9)**40.1% **10)**12.8% **11)**31.4% **12)**67.3% **13)**3.7% **14**a)the effective interest rate is 28.8% b)14.7% is simple interest rate **15**a)$102.44

**9.7 Written Exercises, page 262**
**1**a)$47.50 b)$104.13 c)$175.50 d)$244.69 **2**a)$41.25 b)$57.50 c)$147.50 d)$168.75 e)$185.00 **3**a)$65.00 b)$293.75 c)$796.25 **4**a)$88.75 b)$43.13 c)$975.00 **5**a)$1000.00 b)discount, $965.00 c)$10\frac{3}{4}$% d)$96\frac{1}{2}$ **6**a)$396.25 b)$1017.00 c)$5425.00 **7**a)$8525.00 b)12.6% **8**a)more b)10.9% **9**a)less b)8.5% **10**a)9.2% b)13% **11)**10.4% **12**a)$1182.00 b)10.6% **13)**9.9% **14**a)9.3% b)9.3% **15)**13.7% **16)**B

**9.8 Written Exercises, page 266**
**1**a)$769.00 b)$1218.75 c)$2331.25 **2**a)$11.40 b)$11.44 c)$57.50 d)$77.36 **3**a)11.28% b)12.05% c)12.06% d)9.35% **4)**11.59% **5)**10.63% **6)**12.60% **7)**9.24% **8)**10.84% **9**a)$282.38 **10**a)$1640.88 b)$178.50 c)$109.39 **11)**A

**Review: Practice and Problems, page 271**
**1**a)$48.40 b)23.85 c)$172.97 d)$479.17 e)$192.23 **2)**$90.51 **3**a)$82.39 b)$86.60 **4)**63% **5**a)$83.98 b)18% **6**a)$6.47 b)$12.19 c)$31.52 d)$37.25 **7**a)$45.00 b)$13.52 **8**a)$298.45 b)$143.30 **9**a)$1585 b)$378.54 c)20.3% **10)**14.5% **11**a)$250 b)13.4%

## CHAPTER 10

**10.1 Written Exercises, page 275**
**5**a)35.6%, 48.0%, 67.3%, 40.5%, 26.5%, 33.7%, 34.2%, 38.8%, 40.5%, 27.0% b)not improving **6)**0%, 0%, 14.3%, 17.4%, 12.5%, 0%, 5%, 0%, 0%, 4.8% **7)**0.6%, 0%, 0%, 1.0%, 1.3%, 0%, 0%, 0.3%, 0.4%, 0% **9**a)60%, 61%, 59.4% b)300 **10**a)40%, 39%, 40.6% c)4000 **11**a)65.2% b)326 c)31.8% d)3480 **12**a)e b)$k$, $z$ c)and

**10.2 Written Exercises, page 278**
**1**a)8, 11, 12, 14, 9, 8, 17, 20, 12 b)8 c)11 **2**a)track and field b)swimming and tennis **3**a)111 b)12.6% c)7.2% **4**a)17 b)14 c)7 **5**a)Cola b)Cream Soda **6**a)30.4%, 25%, 16.1%, 8.9%, 12.5%, 7.1% b)$263.20, $139.39 **8**a)28 b)1 c)10 **9**a)64% b)7% c)6.8 km **10**a)160 b)$647.50 **11)**B **14**a)96 b)64% c)36% **15**a)70.3

**10.3 Written Exercises, page 280**
**1**a)3 b)1 c)1 d)0 **2**a)7 b)11 c)51, 93 **3**a)73.1 b)11, 15 **4**a)39 **5**a)2 b)1 c)2 d)0 **6**a)42 b)13 **8**b)33 **9**a)28 b)19 c)66 **10**a)21.2% b)24.2% **11**b)69.6 **13**b)5 c)21 **14**a)6 b)15.3 s

**10.4 Written Exercises, page 284**
**1**a)28 b)28 c)16 d)20 **2**b)23 **3**a)92 b)5:4 **4**a)60% b)160 c)48 **5**a)30 b)90 c)60 **6**a)Thursday b)Friday c)Saturday **7**a)Wed., Thur., Fri., Sat. b)Thur., Fri., Sat. **8**a)6th, 3 m b)week 6 to 8 c)4.5 m **9**a)crude oil b)uranium **10)**crude oil **11**a)10% b)20% c)40% d)25% **12**a)Sept 9, 21°C b)14 days c)May 13–27 **14**a)8 b)6 **15**a)12:19 b)20:19 **16**a)50% b)50% **17**b)15

**10.5 Written Exercises, page 288**
**1**a)40–50 b)90–100 **2**a)10 b)0–10, 10–20, . . . , 90–100 **3**a)10 b)6 **4**a)5 b)50–60, 60–70, 70–80, 80–90, 90–100 **5**a)2 b)14 **6**a)1:3 b)1:3 c)same **7**a)80–90 b)70–80, 80–90, 90–100 **8**a)120–130 b)90–100 and 150–160; 100–110 and 130–140 c)1 d)100–150 cm **9**b)122.2 cm **12**a)10–20 **16**a)22% b)42% d)3.2

**10.6 Written Exercises, page 291**
**1)**1, 2, 5, 7, 13, 21, 31, 43, 55 **2**a)50 b)24 **3**a)18 b)5 **6**a)9 b)24 **7**a)36 (b)18 **11**a)45–50 b)25–30, 30–35 **12**a)3 b)30 c)3 **14**a)3, 12, 24, 39, 55, 60 **15**a)12 b)21 c)15 **16**a)5%, 15%, 20%, 25%, 27%, 8% b)5%, 20%, 40%, 65%, 92%, 100%

**10.7 Written Exercises, page 295**
**1**a)5 b)41 c)4 d)121 **2**a)33.8 b)11.2 c)127 d)143.4 **3**a)70.5 b)26 c)34 **4**a)$24 666.67, $20 500 b)median **5**a)73 kg, 79.2 kg, 70 kg and 81 kg b)median **6**a)0.275 b)0.274 c)0.275 (d)all very close to same value **7)**192.4, 56, 465, 646 **8)**mode **9**a)40.8, 50.5, 0 c)median **10**a)$69 620.83, $62 250, no mode b)median c)mean **11**a)191 b)180 c)5730 d)Mon, Thurs, Fri **12**a)344 b)A and M Dept. Store **13**a)9442 b)1888 c)Thurs, Fri **15)**25¢ **16)**12% **17)**$26.04 **18)**2.0%

**10.8 Written Exercises, page 299**
**1**a)72 b)76 c)85 **2)**71 **3)**44 **4**a)87 b)88 c)92 d)90 e)87 f)74 **5)**54 **6**a)81st b)70th c)13th d)67th e)66th f)67th **7**a)12th b)88th c)76th **8**a)26.3 b)27.5 c)20.5, 27, 31.5 d)11 **9**a)78th b)50th c)100th **10)**28 **11)**36

**Review: Practice and Problems, page 301**
**2)**32% **3)**20% **4)**32%, 64% **5**a)2, 1, 1 b)3, 8 c)11 **6**a)50% b)band c)1.12 h d)0.64 h **8**a)2.6, 2, 2 and 4 **9**a)93rd b)89th c)89th d)65th **10)**$28 099.07

## CHAPTER 11

**11.1 Written Exercises, page 305**
**1**a)acute b)right c)obtuse d)straight e)right f)acute **3**a)obtuse b)obtuse c)LM, MN d)isosceles **4**a)scalene b)right c)acute **5**a)equilateral b)acute **6**a)acute b)obtuse c)right d)reflex e)right f)obtuse g)reflex h)acute **7**a)right b)right **8**a)equilateral b)equilateral **10**a)△ABD b)△ABC c)△BDC **11**a)△PQR b)△PTQ c)△PSQ, △PST, △RSQ **12**a)△ABC, △ADC b)△ABD, △BCD c)△ABE, △CDE

**11.2 Written Exercises, page 309**
**1**a)straight b)145°, obtuse **2**a)right b)50°, acute **3**a)$x^\circ + 37^\circ + 42^\circ = 180^\circ$ b)101° c)obtuse **4**a)isosceles b)63° c)54° **5**a)123° b)22° c)140° **6**a)115° b)52° c)39° d)25° **7**a)27° b)117° c)63° **8**a)$x^\circ = 55^\circ$, $y^\circ = 76^\circ$ b)$p^\circ = r^\circ = 27^\circ$, $q^\circ = 153^\circ$ c)$a^\circ = 42^\circ$, $b^\circ = 85^\circ$, $c^\circ = 53^\circ$ d)$d^\circ = 42^\circ$, $e^\circ = 96^\circ$, $f^\circ = 138^\circ$, $g^\circ = 22^\circ$ **9**a)70° b)isosceles **10**a)57° b)62° **11)**97° **12**a)46° b)37°, lower **13**a)$4x^\circ + 2x^\circ + 90^\circ = 180^\circ$ b)$x^\circ = 15^\circ$ c)$\angle GHI = 30^\circ$, $\angle HGI = 60^\circ$ **14**a)$p^\circ = 43^\circ$, $q^\circ = 8^\circ$ b)$p^\circ = 10^\circ$, $q^\circ = r^\circ = 130^\circ$ c)$q^\circ = 60^\circ$, $r^\circ = 25^\circ$ d)$p^\circ = 30^\circ$, $q^\circ = 80^\circ$ **15)**24°, 48°, 108°

**11.3 Written Exercises, page 313**
**6**b)45°, isosceles **8**d)square **9**b)equal measures c)all 90° **10**c)rectangle **11**b)equal measures c)opposite angles are equal **13**b)AM = MC; BM = MC **14**b)bisectors are the diagonals c)all 90° **15)**b, c, e **18)**19.2 cm

**11.4 Written Exercises, page 316**
**1**a)8.6 b)14.9 c)8.5 **2**a)9.2 cm b)11.7 cm c)14.2 cm **3**a)9.7 b)18.3 c)6.0 **4)**3.8 m **5)**2.7 m **6)**40.6 cm **7**a)5.7 cm b)2.4 m **8**a)17.6 cm b)1.1 m **9)**14.1 cm **10)**3.9 m **11)**2.2 m **12)**2.4 mm

**11.5 Written Exercises, page 318**
**1**a) (0,3) b) (−7,−2) c) (0,−6) d) (−8,0) e) (5,3) f) (5,−2) g) (−3,4) h) (7,−7) **2**a)P b)R c)V d)Q e)B f)A g)F h)D i)C **3**a) (3,2), (3,7), (3,−3) b)same first co-ordinate **4**a)B, I, P b)V, A **5**a)J, D b)second co-ordinate is 0 **6**a)W, L, V, K b)first co-ordinate is 0 **7)**X, S **8**b)A, C, E, I c)D, F, K d)2nd e)3rd **9**a)rectangle b)parallelogram c)isosceles **10)**P 2nd, Q 4th, R 1st **11**b) (5,−5) **12**b) (7,3) **13**b) (−3,−4) **14)**D, K, J

**11.6 Written Exercises, page 321**
**2**a)0 b)−6 c)5 d)−4 **3**a) (1,4) b) (−3,−4) c) (−2,1) **4**a)10, 5, 0, −5, −10 b)5, 2, 1, 2, 5 c)−7, −5, −3, −1, 1 **6)**b **7**c)yes **8**c)no **9**a)even **10)**all linear **11)**non-linear **12)**linear a, d **13)**linear **14)**linear **15)**non-linear **16)**linear **17)**non-linear **18)**linear **19)**non-linear

**11.8 Written Exercises, page 327**
Some answers may vary.
**1**a)$44, $56 b)3 years, 15 years **2**a)3.2 b)9 c)1.4 d)0.5 and 7.5 **3**a)18 m, 48 m, 128 m b)54 km/h, 79 km/h, 95 km/h **4**b)450 km, 640 km, 310 km c)$2\frac{3}{4}$ h, $6\frac{1}{2}$ h, 11 h **5**b)75 km/h, 60 km/h c)$2\frac{3}{4}$ h, 6 h **6**c)16°C d)15°C e)30 **7**c)48 cm², 432 cm² d)8 cm **8**b)$1.59 c)90 g

**11.9 Written Exercises, page 330**
**1**a)5 b)7 c)$\frac{5}{7}$ **2**a)9 b)−8 c)$-\frac{9}{8}$ **3**a)$\frac{7}{6}$ b)$-\frac{2}{9}$ **4**a)CD, GH, JK b)AB, EF c)AB $-\frac{5}{4}$, CD $\frac{3}{7}$, EF $-\frac{9}{5}$, GH 1, KJ 9 **5**b)$\frac{1}{5}$ **6**a)$-\frac{1}{2}$ b)$\frac{3}{2}$ c)$-\frac{7}{4}$ d)$\frac{7}{8}$ **7**a)0 **8**a)undefined **9**a)$\frac{1}{2}$ b)$\frac{1}{2}$ c)lines are parallel **10**a)$-\frac{4}{5}$ b)$-\frac{4}{5}$ c)lines are parallel

**11.10 Written Exercises, page 332**
**1**a)4 b)11 c)11.7 **2**a)8 b)6 c)10 **3**a)5.8 b)9.2 c)7.6 d)13.2 **4**a)5.8 b)6.3 c)10.0 d)8.1 **5**a)isosceles, AB = BC (4.1) b)scalene

c)scalene **6)**Z **7**a)34.5 b)144
**8**b)both $\sqrt{5}$ **9**a) (2,4.5) b) $(-1,-2)$
c) (1.5,0) d) (1.5,1) **10**b)20 c)7.1
d) $\left(\frac{5}{2},\frac{1}{2}\right)$ **11)**P, **12**a)120 km b)180 km
c)270 km **13**a)no b) (9.5,6.5)

**Review: Practice and Problems, page 334**
**1**b)5.8 cm **2**a)$x = 9.2$ cm, $y = 20$ m
b)13.0 cm × 13.0 cm **3**b)$-\frac{7}{9}$ **4**b) (6,8)
c)10 d) (3,4)

## CHAPTER 12

**12.1 Written Exercises, page 337**
**1**a)5 b)7 c)$\frac{5}{7}$ d)$\frac{5}{7}$ **2**a)5, $-7$, $-\frac{5}{7}$
**3**a)$\frac{2}{3}$ b)$\frac{2}{3}$ **4**a)$\frac{2}{5}$ b)$\frac{2}{5}$ c)$\frac{2}{5}$ d)$\frac{2}{5}$
**5**a)$-\frac{5}{8}$ b)1 c)$-\frac{5}{11}$ d)$-\frac{1}{2}$ e)$-\frac{3.5}{6.4}$
**6**b)2 **7**a)3 b)$\frac{1}{3}$ c)$-2$ d)2 e)$\frac{2}{5}$ f)$\frac{1}{3}$
g)$-3$ h)$\frac{2}{3}$ i)4.2 j)2.5 **8**b)$-\frac{2}{3}$ c)A, C
**9**b)$\frac{3}{2}$ c)P, Q **11)**C **12)**a, b, c **13**a)A
b)no **14**a)$-\frac{1}{2}$ b)you need $\frac{1}{2}$ h less sleep for every year you age, between the ages of 0 and 18 years. **15**a)6 b)she's paid \$6/h. **16**a)6.25, 6.25 km/L b)12, \$12/h c)25, rate is \$25/d d)50, cost is \$50/hundred

**12.2 Written Exercises, page 342**
**1)**$\frac{4}{9}$ **2)**$\frac{3}{2}$ **3)**a, c
**4)**parallel: a; perpendicular: c, e, j **5**a)$-\frac{5}{3}$
b)2 c)$\frac{1}{5}$ **6**a)$\frac{3}{4}$ b)$-1$ **7**a)$\frac{5}{6}$ b)$-\frac{7}{5}$
**8**a)1 b)$-1$ **9**c)$-\frac{1}{2}$, 2, PQ ⊥ RS
**10**c)$-1$, $-1$, AB ∥ CD **11**a)$\frac{1}{10}$ b)2
c)$-2$ d)$-10$ e)none
f)AB ⊥ GH **12**a)4 b)$-\frac{2.5}{7}$ c)4
d)$-\frac{2}{25}$ e)MN ∥ RS f)none **13**a)$-1$
b)$\frac{3}{2}$ c)$-\frac{11}{3}$ d)$\frac{6}{7}$ **14)**no **15)**yes

**12.3 Written Exercises, page 345**
**2**b)2 c) (2,0) **3**b)$-3$ c) $(0,-3)$
**4**b)4 c)$x$:2, $y$:$-8$ d) (2,0), $(0,-8)$
**5**a)i)none ii)$-4$ b)i)5 ii)none **6**a)10
b)5 c)2 d)10 e)4 f)$-3$ g)$-6.5$
h)2.3 **7**a)$-12$ b)$-6$ c)$-5$ d)3
e)11 f)1 g)18 h)$-3.6$ **8**a)$x$:4, $y$:2
b)$x$:3, $y$:$-6$ c)$x$:4, $y$:$-3$ d)$x$:3, $y$:6
e)$x$:1, $y$:$-3$ f)$x$:$-8$, $y$:2 g)$x$:$-8$, $y$:4
h)$x$:6, $y$:$-8$ **9**b)4 c)$-\frac{8}{3}$ **10**b)$-4$
c)$-\frac{16}{3}$ **12**b)6 c)yes **13**b)$-\frac{10}{3}$
c)no **14**b)3 c)yes **15**b)$\frac{3}{4}$ c)yes
**16**a)loss of \$4000 b)year 5

**12.4 Written Exercises, page 348**
**1**a)2 b)$-5$ c)2 d)$-5$ **2**a)$-3$, 1
b)$-3$ c)1 **3**a)$-5$ b)$y = \frac{5}{2}x - 5$
**4**a)$y = 4x - 4$ b)$y = -x + 1$
c)$y = \frac{4}{5}x - 2$ d)$y = \frac{5}{2}$ e)$y = -\frac{1}{2}x$
f)$y = -x - 3.5$ **5**a)1, 1; $y = x + 1$
b)$-\frac{3}{2}$, 3; $y = -\frac{3}{2}x + 3$ c)$-\frac{4}{3}$, 0; $y = -\frac{4}{3}x$
d)$\frac{2}{3}$, $-\frac{5}{3}$; $y = \frac{2}{3}x - \frac{5}{3}$ **7**a)$y = -3x + 4$
b)$-3$ c)4 **8**a)$y = 2x + 3$; 2, 3
b)$y = \frac{2}{3}x + 7$; $\frac{2}{3}$, 7 c)$y = -\frac{2}{5}x + 2$; $-\frac{2}{5}$, 2
d)$y = \frac{3}{2}x - 6$; $\frac{3}{2}$, $-6$ e)$y = \frac{4}{3}x + 5$; $\frac{4}{3}$, 5
f)$y = \frac{2}{5}x - 3$; $\frac{2}{5}$, $-3$ **9**a)$\frac{1}{2}$ b)$y = \frac{1}{2}x + 1$
**10**a)$y = -\frac{3}{5}x - 3$ **11**a)$y = 3x - 5$
b)$y = 3x + 4$ c)$y = 3x$ **12**a)0 b)5
c)$y = 5$ **13**a)$y = 7$ b)$y = -4$ c)$y = -9$
**14**a)undefined b)none c)$x = 3$
**15**a)$x = -5$ b)$x = 2$ c)$x = 0$
**16**a)A: $-3$, B: $\frac{1}{3}$ b)yes; $-3 \times \left(\frac{1}{3}\right) = -1$
**17)**parallel: d; perpendicular: b, c
**18**a)$y = \frac{4}{5}x + 5$, $y = \frac{4}{5}x - 3$ b)yes
**19)**parallel: c and h; perpendicular: c and d, d and h, e and f

**12.5 Written Exercises, page 353**
**1**a)$\frac{2}{5}$, 4, $y = \frac{2}{5}x + 4$
b)$-1$, $-3$, $y = -x - 3$
c)$\frac{3}{2}$, $-5$, $y = \frac{3}{2}x - 5$
d)$-\frac{4}{5}$, 4, $y = -\frac{4}{5}x + 4$
**2**a)$-3x + y + 5 = 0$ b)$x + y = 0$
c)$-2x + 3y - 3 = 0$ d)$3x + 4y + 8 = 0$
e)$-x + 4y + 2 = 0$ f)$-5x + 8y - 20 = 0$
g)$4x - 5 = 0$ h)$3y + 7 = 0$
**3**a)$y = -2x + b$, $-2$ b)5
c)$2x + y - 5 = 0$ **4**b)$\frac{3}{5}$
c)$-3x + 5y + 57 = 0$ **5**a)$\frac{4}{5}$
b)$y = \frac{4}{5}x + \frac{31}{5}$; $\frac{4}{5}$ c)$\frac{31}{5}$
d)$-4x + 5y - 31 = 0$ **6**a)$-\frac{3}{8}$
b)$3x + 8y - 55 = 0$ **7**a)$y = \frac{6}{5}x - 4$
b)$y = -\frac{11}{6}x - \frac{17}{6}$ c)$y = -\frac{2}{5}x - \frac{2}{5}$
d)$y = \frac{5}{3}x$ **8**a)$y = 3x + 15$ b)$y = \frac{2}{3}x - \frac{1}{3}$
c)$y = -4x + 18$ d)$y = -\frac{3}{4}x - \frac{49}{4}$
**9**a)$3x + 5y - 27 = 0$ b)$x + y - 10 = 0$
c)$3x - 2y + 9 = 0$ d)$5x + 8y - 32 = 0$
**10)**$5x - 3y - 81 = 0$ **11)**$7x - 8y - 43 = 0$
**12)**$3x + 4y + 30 = 0$
**13)**$3x + 25y - 170 = 0$ **14**a)$-\frac{A}{B}$ b)$-\frac{C}{B}$

**12.6 Written Exercises, page 356**
**1)**a, b, d, e, f **2**a)A, B b)E, F c)G, I
**3**a) $(5,-2)$ b)$x = 5$, $y = -2$
**4**a)A: $(0,-8)$, (4,0) B: $\left(0,-\frac{4}{3}\right)$, (4,0)
d)$x = 4$, $y = 0$ **5**a)$-3$, 1 b)2, 1
c)no point of intersection, lines are parallel
**6**a) (3,1) b) $(-9,1)$ c) (6,4) d) $(0,-2)$
**7**b) (1,4) **8**b) (1,4) **9**a)$x = 3$, $y = 0$
b)$x = 4$, $y = -3$ c)$x = 3$, $y = 6$
d)$x = 6$, $y = 2$ e)$x = 3$, $y = -1$
f)$x = 8$, $y = 6$ g)$x = 3$, $y = 6$
h)$x = 6$, $y = -2$ **10)** $(2,-1)$ **11)** (9,4)
**12**a) (5,2) **13**a) $(-3,8)$
b)Steve (6,2), Cassie $(-13,-8)$

**12.7 Written Exercises, page 359**
**1**a)$y = x - 1$ b)$y = 2x + 1$ c)$y = 13 - x$
d)$y = 2x + 8$ **2**a)$x = 6 - 3y$ b)$x = 5y + 10$
c)$x = -5y - 12$ d)$x = 4y + 8$ **3**a)5 b)$\frac{1}{3}$
c)$-7$ d)3 **4**a)9 b)21 c)$-13$ d)5
**5**a)$y = -5x - 16$ b)$x = -3$ c)$y = -1$

e) $(-3,-1)$ **6**b) $(5, 2)$ c) $(5,2)$
**7**a)$x = 2, y = -1$ b)$x = 2, y = -1$
**8**b) $(54, -9)$ c) $(54, -9)$ **9**a)$x = 3, y = 6$
**10**a)$x = 8, y = 4$ b) $(8,4)$ **11**a) $\left(\frac{9}{5}, -\frac{6}{5}\right)$
b) $(4,0)$ c) $\left(\frac{12}{5}, \frac{33}{5}\right)$ d) $(-2, -6)$
e) $(2, 1)$ f) $(-2, -4)$ **12**a) $(1,-3)$
b) $(10,2)$ c) $(3,-1)$ d) $(14,9)$
**13**a) $(-4,-2)$ b) $(8,2)$ c) $(4,5)$
d) $(-2,1)$ **14)** $(4,5)$ **15**a) $\left(-\frac{13}{11}, \frac{38}{11}\right)$
b)only if they reach the point of intersection at the same time **16)** $(6,8)$
**17)**21 soft-centred, 11 hard
**18)**reserved 39 000, general 8300

**12.8 Written Exercises, page 362**

**1**a)subtract b)$x = 8, y = 1$ **2**a)add
b)$x = 5, y = 3$ **3**a)$y$ b) $(-2,1)$
**4**b)subtract c)$x = -2, y = -4$
**5**a)$x = 1, y = 1$ b)$x = 1, y = -2$
**6**b)$x = -1, y = -2$ **7**a)$x = -4, y = -1$
b)$x = -3, y = 2$ c)$x = -3, y = 1$
d)$m = 3, n = -1$ e)$x = -5, y = -3$
f)$x = -1, y = 5$ **8**a)$x = 1, y = 1$
b)$p = 1, q = 1$ c)$a = 1, b = 1$
d)$x = 7, y = 4$ e)$x = -9, y = -8$
f)$x = 3, y = 5$ **9**b) $(7,-3)$
**10**b)$x = 2, y = 3$ **11)** $(-84,-65)$
**12)**1 eagle, 2 falcons

**12.9 Written Exercises, page 365**

**1**a)$n + s = 520$ b)$7n + 5s = 485$
c)$7n - 5s = 74$ **2**a)$r + l = 120$
b)$r + 2l = 165$ c)75 regular, 45 large
**3**a)$c + 4p = 16$ b)$c + 5p = 18$
c)person \$2, car \$8
**4)**287 adults, 213 students
**5)**\$5/h, \$1.50 per customer
**6)**hamburger \$1.80, cola \$0.50 **7)**45°, 95°
**8)**rose \$3, carnation \$4
**9)**\$3/h, \$1.50 per person
**10)**carpenter \$180, student \$80
**11)**13 large, 5 small
**12)**\$1200 at 8%, \$4000 at 10%

**Review: Practice and Problems, page 367**

**1**b)$\frac{3}{4}$ c)B, C **2**a)III b)III c)II d)II
**3**b)$\frac{3}{2}$ c)$\frac{10}{3}$, $-5$ **4**a)$x + 9y - 51 = 0$
**5**a)$-3$ b)$y = -3x + 2$ c)$-3$ d)2
**6**a) $\left(\frac{22}{5}, -\frac{18}{5}\right)$ b) $\left(-\frac{37}{5}, \frac{27}{5}\right)$ c) $(6,-2)$
d) $\left(2, \frac{1}{2}\right)$ **7)** $(3,2)$ **8)**18 m by 30 m

**Update: A Cumulative Review, page 368**

**1**a)$a + 14$ b)$m$ c)$9x^2 + 28x - 12$
**2**a)\$1275.00 b)\$90.96 **3**a)16 m³
b)370 m³ c)354 m³ **4)**39.0 m **5)**18.2%
**6**a)$2ab(5 - 12c)$ b) $(10 + p)(10 - p)$
c) $(x + 5)(x + 2)$ d)$2mn(7n - 1)$
e) $(r - 3)^2$ f)$2(3m - 1)(3m + 1)$
g) $(mn + 1)(mn - 1)$ h)$3p^2q(1 - 2q)$
i)$5(m + 6)(m + 5)$ j)$4(2a - 3)(2a + 3)$
k) $(p - 3q - 3r)(p - 3q + 3r)$ **7)**B
**8**a)$2.75 \times 10^{-4}$ b)$7.26 \times 10^{-4}$
c)$3.00 \times 10^4$ **9**a)$\frac{p^2}{(p - 5)(p + 6)}$
b)$\frac{x(x + y)^2}{x(x - y)^2}$ **10)**66.2 years **11)**$\frac{35}{3}$
**12)**\$17 203.20 **13)**\$465.97

## CHAPTER 13

**13.1 Written Exercises, page 372**

**1**a)37:7 b)8:7 c)7:12:37 **2**a)6 b)1
c)30 d)8 **4**a)1:12 b)1:15 c)40:9
d)9:5 e)9:50 f)3:40 g)1:8 h)9:2
**5**a)37:12 b)37:102 c)37:12:102
**6**a)12:5 b)7.2 c)7.5 d)7.5 e)5.625
f)128 **7)**37.5 mL **8**a)200 b)224 **9)**1900
**10)**15.625 cm **11**a)24 b)60 **12**a)40 g, 20 g b)375 g, 25 g **13)**120, \$96
**14)**\$500, \$1750, \$750 **15)**\$1400, \$1750, \$1050 **16)**\$252.85, \$247.15 **17)**\$240, \$504, \$420, \$336 **18)**\$1143.90, \$1032.30

**13.2 Written Exercises, page 375**

**1**a)150 cm b)500 cm c)40 cm **2**a)0.5 m
b)2 cm c)1.4 cm **3**a)2 cm b)0.5 mm
c)0.25 cm **4**a)50 mm b)15 mm c)8 cm
**5**a)20 000 cm b)200 m c)5 cm **6**a)1:50
b)200:1 c)1:75 d)1:20 e)1:300 000
**7**a)40:1 b)0.1 cm c)20 mm
**8**a)25:38 b)25:18 **9**a)1:10 b)8.0 cm
c)7.0 cm d)12.6 cm **10**a)1:70 b)0.2 mm
**11**a)6.2 m b)6.99 m c)0.7 cm
**12**a)144 m² b)F by 24 m² **13**a)200 km
b)666 km **14**a)1:147 b)22.05 m²
c)\$617.57 d)\$77 e)\$694.57 **15**a)6.57 m²
b)7.23 m² c)8 d)\$172.71 **16**a)6.98 m by 0.97 m b)C **17**a)21 cm b)11.7 m
c)\$178.41 d)2.34 m

**13.3 Written Exercises, page 379**

**1)**Arlene **2)**\$5.38 **3)**24 **4)**24 km
**5)**140 km **6**a)\$19 412 b)5.2 cm **7**a)21
b)3500 **8)**80 h **9**a)45 L b)900 m²
**10**a)39.4 kg b)237.4 kg **11**a)693
b)94.2 cm c)653 m d)1.9 km/h
**12)**Halifax **13**a)4.7 cm/h b)34.7 m
**14**a)$1.944 \times 10^{10}$ L b)51 440 h c)2143 d
**15**a)45.6 km/h b)1.9 km/h **16)**28.0 km/h
**17)**5.4 km/h **18**a)4.8 km/h b)10 h
**19**a)1.53 m/s, 1.55 m/s b)91.8 m, 93 m
**20)**22.1 km/h **21**a)14.4 km/h b)4.2 min

**13.4 Written Exercises, page 383**

**1**a)$m = kp$ b)6 **2**a)$t = km$ b)18
**3**a)$t = kv$ b)10 c)1.9 **4**a)$p = kq$ b)17
c)204 **5**a)45 b)30 c)1.25 d)17 **6**a)70
b)14 c)3 **7**a)$\frac{w}{t} = 55$ b)275 c)26 min
**8**a)37.2 kg b)83.4 kg c)184.6 kg
**9**a)8.4 cm b)18.75 cm **10)**22.5 m
**11**a)0.6 Ω b)40 cm **12**a)85 cm²
b)119.5 s **13**a)$1.53 \times 10^5$ cm³ b)33 min
**14)**3727 kPa

**13.5 Written Exercises, page 385**

**1**b)31.25 cm **2**b)8.8 h **3**a)\$20 b)$\frac{4}{3}$
**4**b)11.25 m **5**a)250, 1000 b)800, 2400
**7**a)688 b)10 400 **9**a)76 L b)5.6 h
**11**b)3.6 cm **12**a)6.7 N b)26.6 N

**13.6 Written Exercises, page 388**

**1**a)$mn = k$ b)220 **2**a)$df = k$ b)205
**3**a)$xy = k$ b)100 c)20 **4**a)$pv = k$
b)1200 c)48 **5**a)20 b)8.75 c)150
d)0.9 **6**a)24 b)20 c)9.3 **7**a)$ts = k$
b)100 km/h c)50 km/h **8**a)25 h b)15 h
c)20 h **9**a)96 b)32 **10**a)12 cm b)48
**11**a)2.25 N b)1.13 N **12**a)10% b)\$2666.67

**13.7 Written Exercises, page 390**

**1**b)\$6.67 **2**b)273 **3**a)5 h b)400
**4**b)4.4 h **5**a)12.5 km/L, 9 km/L
b)1125 kg, 1800 kg **6**b)1286 kg
**7**a)7.2 km/L b) 1.4 km/L **8**b)\$1714.29
c)18.5 months **10**a)10.8 m/s b)29.3 s
**12**b)68 min c)150 kPa

**13.8 Written Exercises, page 393**

**1**a)23 b)32 c)65 **2**a)9.3 b)16.5
c)88.5 **3**a)35 b)105 c)5025
**4**a)$C = 300 + 25t$ b)$T = 500 + kn$
c)$f = C + kd$ **5**a)$C = 5.10 + 0.50t$
b)\$6.10 c)\$7.60 d)6 **6**a)$t = 30 + 45m$
c)6 h 7.5 min **7**a)$C = 30 + 15t$ b)\$120
c)3 h **8**a)$C = 3.50 + 0.65t$ b)\$6.75
c)15 min **9**a)$E = 200 + 0.05S$ b)\$240
c)\$2500 **10**a)$C = 32 + 0.08d$ c)\$88.80
**11**a)$C = 530 + 297.50n$ b)297.50 c)\$7670

**13.9 Written Exercises, page 396**

**1**a)$h = kt^2$ b)$\frac{3}{16}$ **2**a)$pq^2 = k$ b)20
**3**a)$m = kn^2$ b)3 c)75 **4**a)$xy^2 = k$
b)600 c)2 **5**a)$Tm^2 = 162$; 4.5 b)9
**6**a)198 m b)8 s **7)**480 g **8)**2.4 s
**9)**25.6 units **10**a)43.75 m b)80 km/h
**11)**$3375 **12)**8.2 km/s **13)**5.12 Ω
**14)**20.0075 m

**Review: Practice and Problems, page 398**
**1**a)420 b)$4900 **2**a)275 cm b)0.64 cm
**3**a)$m = kn$ b)13 c)624 **4**a)$g = kd$
c)108.5 L **5**a)$ED = k$ b)4950 c)123.75
**6**a)$C = 49 + 35(d - 1)$ b)$294

## CHAPTER 14

**14.1 Written Exercises, page 400**
**1**a)acute b)obtuse c)right d)straight
e)reflex **2**a)equilateral b)scalene
c)acute-angled d)right-angled
e)isosceles f)obtuse-angled
**4**a)supplementary angles
b)vertically opposite angles
c)angle sum of triangle
d)isosceles triangle
e)complementary angles **5**a)$x^\circ = 60^\circ$
b)$x^\circ = 160^\circ, y^\circ = 20^\circ$ c)$x^\circ = 50^\circ$
d)$x^\circ = 30^\circ$ **6**a)$x^\circ = 70^\circ$ b)$y^\circ = 30^\circ$
c)$x^\circ = 38^\circ$ d)$x^\circ = 55^\circ, y^\circ = 55^\circ$
e)$a^\circ = 60^\circ, b^\circ = 60^\circ, c^\circ = 60^\circ$ f)$n^\circ = 115^\circ$
**7**a)$x^\circ = 66^\circ, y^\circ = 114^\circ$
b)$a^\circ = 110^\circ, x^\circ = 70^\circ, y^\circ = 70^\circ$
c)$x^\circ = 42^\circ, y^\circ = 84^\circ$ d)$x^\circ = 60^\circ, y^\circ = 60^\circ$
e)$x^\circ = 118^\circ, y^\circ = 31^\circ$
**8**a)$3x^\circ + 60^\circ = 180^\circ$; $x^\circ = 40^\circ$; ∠A = 80°,
∠B = 60°, ∠C = 40°
b)$9x^\circ = 180^\circ$; $x^\circ = 20^\circ$; ∠P = 40°,
∠Q = 60°, ∠R = 80°
c)$6x^\circ + 60^\circ = 180^\circ$; $x^\circ = 20^\circ$; ∠D = 60°,
∠E = 20°, ∠F = 100° d)$x^\circ = 70^\circ, y^\circ = 50^\circ$
e)$a^\circ = 50^\circ, b^\circ = 40^\circ, c^\circ = 50^\circ$
f)$a^\circ = 55^\circ, b^\circ = 35^\circ, c^\circ = 55^\circ$
**10)**unique: a, b, g, i **11**a)A b)C c)A
d)A e)C f)A g)B h)A i)A j)C k)B
l)A m)B **12**a)A b)B c)B d)B
e)A f)A

**14.2 Written Exercises, page 404**
**1**a)PQ = VS, PR = VT, RQ = TS b)SSS
c)∠P = ∠V, ∠Q = ∠S, ∠R = ∠T
**2**a)MP = FD, PN = DE, ∠P = ∠D b)SAS
c)MN = FE, ∠M = ∠F, ∠N = ∠E
**3**a)QR = CB, ∠Q = ∠C, ∠R = ∠B
b)ASA c)∠P = ∠D, PQ = DC, PR = DB
**4**a)PS = AB, ST = BC, ∠T = ∠C
b)Conditions not satisfied **5**a)∠F = 62°
b)TU = 15 cm c)JK = 10 cm
d)QS = 7 mm
**6)**△XYZ ≅ △JHG, △RST ≅ △FED,
△KLM ≅ △ABC
**7)**AB = 7 cm, △ABC ≅ △TSU; MN = 9 cm,
△DEF ≅ △OMN; ∠I = 90°, △JKL ≅ △IHG
**8**a)△DEF ≅ △HGF (SAS)
b)△JKL ≅ △LMJ (SSS)
c)△QRS ≅ △QPS (ASA)
d)△VXW ≅ △ZXY (ASA)
**9**a)△PQR ≅ △RSP (SSS), ∠SPR = 25°
b)△DEF ≅ △GHF (SAS), DE = 9 cm

**14.3 Written Exercises, page 407**
**3**a)AP = AC, BP = BC, AB = AB
b)SSS c)△'s congruent
**4**a)AE = DE, DF = AG, ∠A = ∠D
b)SAS c)△'s congruent
**5**a)QP = SP, RP = RP, ∠RPQ = ∠RPS
b)SAS c)△'s congruent
**6**a)∠S = ∠A, SU = AU, ∠SUV = ∠AUT
b)ASA c)△'s congruent
**7**a)PS = RQ, PQ = RS, SQ = SQ
b)SSS c)△'s congruent
d)∠P = ∠R, ∠PSQ = ∠RQS,
∠PQS = ∠RSQ
**8**a)AB = AC, ∠BAD = ∠CAD, AD = AD
b)SAS c)△'s congruent
d)equal supplementary ∠'s
**11**a)BE = 12 m, △BCE ≅ △DCE (SAS)
b)QR = 15 cm, △OQR ≅ △OPS (SAS)
c)∠AOB = 130°, △AOB ≅ AOC (SSS)
d)WX = 10 cm, ∠W = 50°,
△VWX ≅ △VZY (ASA) **12)**10 m
**13)**48 m

**14.4 Written Exercises, page 410**
**1**a)parallelogram b)square c)trapezoid
d)rhombus e)rectangle f)trapezoid
**2**a)$x^\circ + 240^\circ = 360^\circ$; $x^\circ = 120^\circ$
b)$2x^\circ + 200^\circ = 360^\circ$; $x^\circ = 80^\circ$
c)$x^\circ + 255^\circ = 360^\circ$; $x^\circ = 105^\circ$
d)$2x^\circ + 140^\circ = 360^\circ$; $x^\circ = 110^\circ$
**3**a)60°, 70°, 110°, 120° b)40°, 120°, 80°
c)110°, 100°, 75°, 75° d)135°, 70°, 65°
**4**b)rectangle **5**b)parallelogram
**6**b)trapezoid **7)**120° **8**a)SR ∥ PQ b)45°
**9**a)∠E = 90°, EF = 8.9 cm, FG = 6.9 cm
b)∠P = 80°, PS = 11.5 cm, PQ = 7.2 cm
**11**a)∠D = 105° c)9.7 m

**14.5 Written Exercises, page 413**
**1**a)corresponding b)alternate c)interior
d)corresponding e)corresponding
f)opposite g)alternate h)supplementary
i)opposite **3**a)supplementary,
corresponding b)138° c)138°
**4**a)interior b)$x^\circ = 60^\circ, q^\circ = 60^\circ$
**5**a)∠P + ∠Q + ∠R = 180°, 100°
b)$m^\circ = n^\circ$, 100° c)50°
**6**a)$x^\circ = 148^\circ, y^\circ = 148^\circ, z^\circ = 32^\circ$
b)$a^\circ = 104^\circ, b^\circ = 76^\circ, c^\circ = 104^\circ$
c)$m^\circ = 50^\circ, n^\circ = 130^\circ, p^\circ = 130^\circ$
d)$s^\circ = 72^\circ, t^\circ = 72^\circ$
**7**a)$x^\circ = 30^\circ, y^\circ = 60^\circ$ b)$x^\circ = 5^\circ$
**8**a)$a^\circ = 112^\circ$ b)$x^\circ = 83^\circ, y^\circ = 28^\circ$
c)$a^\circ = 30^\circ, b^\circ = 40^\circ, c^\circ = 110^\circ$,
$d^\circ = 110^\circ$
d)$k^\circ = 50^\circ, m^\circ = 50^\circ, n^\circ = 50^\circ$
e)$p^\circ = 40^\circ, q^\circ = 112^\circ, y^\circ = 28^\circ$
f)$k^\circ = 105^\circ, p^\circ = 77^\circ, x^\circ = 75^\circ$,
$y^\circ = 77^\circ$
**9)**$p^\circ = 48^\circ, x^\circ = 42^\circ, y^\circ = 42^\circ$
**10)**$a^\circ = 109^\circ, b^\circ = 83^\circ, c^\circ = 41.5^\circ$,
$d^\circ = 41.5^\circ, e^\circ = 97^\circ$

**14.6 Written Exercises, page 416**
**1**b)90° **2)**90° **3)**b)90° **4**b)90° **5)**90°
**6**b)equal **7**b)equal **9)**equal
**10**b)∠QOR = 2∠QPR
**11**b)∠QOR = 2∠QPR
**13)**central angle = 2 × inscribed angle
**14)**180°; 180°, equal **16)**supplementary

**14.7 Written Exercises, page 419**
**1**a)OS; OA; OP b)QR c)ST; AV; PQ
d)RQ e)ST; AU; PR f)SOT; VOU; ROP
g)ST; UV; PQ h)∠VUA; ∠PQR
i)∠TOS; ∠VOA; ∠ROP
**2**a)∠UST; ∠UOT b)∠CAB; ∠COB
**3**a)∠P = ∠A b)∠A + ∠P = 180°
c)∠P = 2∠A d)∠A = ∠P
**4**a)subtended by same chord, $m^\circ = 42^\circ$
b)diameter, 90° c)∠POQ, ∠PSQ, 108°
d)∠P + ∠R = 180°, ∠Q + ∠S = 180°,
∠P = 100°, ∠Q = 55°
**5**a)40° b)80° c)200° **6**a)40° b)25°
c)55° **7**a)∠A, ∠C b)∠P, ∠S
c)∠S = ∠R = ∠K, ∠KLS = ∠KMS
**8**a)80° b)80° c)60°
**9**a)∠Q = 40°, ∠S = 50°
b)∠Q = ∠V = 90°
**10**a)$x^\circ = 64^\circ, y^\circ = 101^\circ$
b)$p^\circ = 28^\circ, q^\circ = 38^\circ$ c)$m^\circ = 45^\circ$
d)$f^\circ = 90^\circ$ e)$a^\circ = 104^\circ, b^\circ = 78^\circ$
f)$s^\circ = 42^\circ, t^\circ = 56^\circ$
g)$c^\circ = 90^\circ, d^\circ = 90^\circ$
h)$a^\circ = 50^\circ, b^\circ = 40^\circ$
**11**a)∠P + ∠Q + ∠R = 180°
b)$s^\circ = 54^\circ, t^\circ = 90^\circ$

**12**a) $\angle A$, $\angle B$, $\angle C$, $\angle D$
b) $a^\circ = 46^\circ$, $b^\circ = 46^\circ$, $c^\circ = 46^\circ$
**13**b) $k^\circ = 98^\circ$, $p^\circ = 86^\circ$
**14**a) $r^\circ = 90^\circ$, $w^\circ = 50^\circ$
b) $x^\circ = 39^\circ$, $y^\circ = 39^\circ$, $z^\circ = 39^\circ$
c) $a^\circ = 45^\circ$, $b^\circ = 45^\circ$, $c^\circ = 90^\circ$
d) $p^\circ = 85^\circ$, $x^\circ = 95^\circ$, $y^\circ = 95^\circ$
e) $m^\circ = 62^\circ$
f) $p^\circ = 120^\circ$, $q^\circ = 60^\circ$, $r^\circ = 120^\circ$, $s^\circ = 30^\circ$
g) $k^\circ = 30^\circ$, $p^\circ = 30^\circ$, $s^\circ = 150^\circ$, $t^\circ = 30^\circ$, $r^\circ = 150^\circ$
h) $x^\circ = 64^\circ$, $y^\circ = 36^\circ$, $z^\circ = 80^\circ$
**15**a) $90^\circ$ b) $60^\circ$ c) $45^\circ$ d) $30^\circ$ e) $135^\circ$
f) $120^\circ$ g) $270^\circ$ h) $360^\circ$ **16**a) $\frac{\pi}{6}$
b) $\frac{\pi}{3}$ c) $\frac{\pi}{2}$ d) $\frac{\pi}{4}$ e) $\frac{13\pi}{45}$ f) $\frac{13\pi}{36}$
g) $\frac{251\pi}{600}$ h) $\frac{143\pi}{180}$ **17**a) $86^\circ$
b) $37^\circ$ c) $26^\circ$ d) $132^\circ$ **18**b) $10\pi$ rad/s
**19**a) $20\pi$ rad/s b) $10.6\pi$ rad/s
c) $320\pi$ rad/s

### 14.8 Written Exercises, page 423

**1**c) centre **2**c) centre
**3)** passes through centre of circle
**4)** equal
**6)** A line drawn perpendicular to a chord from the centre bisects the chord
**7)** $\angle OMC = \angle OMD = 90^\circ$
**9)** A line drawn from the centre of a circle to the midpoint of the chord is perpendicular to the chord

### 14.9 Written Exercises, page 425

**1**c) CM = DM, 2.5 cm d) II
**2**c) $\angle SCO = \angle TCO = 90^\circ$ d) III **3)** 24 cm
**4)** 18 cm **5**b) centre of circle **7)** 48 cm
**8**a) 31.2 cm b) 12.7 cm c) 7.6 cm
d) 19.2cm **9)** 5.1 cm **10)** 8.4 cm
**11)** 7.1 cm **12)** 14.2 cm

### Review: Practice and Problems, page 327

**1**a) $x^\circ = 70^\circ$ b) $x^\circ = 38^\circ$
c) $x^\circ = 58^\circ$, $y^\circ = 116^\circ$, $z^\circ = 64^\circ$
d) $x^\circ = 55^\circ$ e) $x^\circ = 30^\circ$ **3**a) 42 cm
b) 10.4 cm 6) $x^\circ = 40^\circ$ **8**a) $x^\circ = 20^\circ$
b) $x^\circ = 28^\circ$ **10**a) $x^\circ = 42^\circ$ b) $y^\circ = 47^\circ$
**11)** 34 cm **12)** 11 cm

## CHAPTER 15

### 15.1 Written Exercises, page 433

**1**a) DE, EF, DF b) $\angle P$, $\angle Q$, $\angle N$
**2**a) $\angle S = \angle P$, $\angle T = \angle U$, $\angle U = \angle R$
b) $\frac{ST}{PQ} = \frac{TU}{QR} = \frac{US}{RP}$ **3)** (a), (c) **4**a) 48
b) $33\frac{1}{3}$ **5**a) $\triangle CAB \sim \triangle CED$ b) 30
**6**a) $\triangle PQR \sim \triangle PST$ b) 5
**7**a) $\triangle ABC \sim \triangle DBE$ b) 5
**8**a) $\triangle ADE \sim \triangle CBE$ b) 24 **9**a) 15 b) 45
c) 10.5 d) 5 **10**b) 19.5 m **11**a) 13.5 m
b) 12.8 m c) 11.9 m

### 15.2 Written Exercises, page 436

**1**a) $\triangle ABC \sim \triangle DEF$ b) $\frac{h}{1.9} = \frac{18.0}{3.8}$ c) 9.0
d) 9.0 m **2**a) $\triangle ABD \sim \triangle ACE$
b) $\frac{w}{20.8 + w} = \frac{8.2}{19.6}$ c) 14.96 d) 15.0 m
**3**a) $\triangle SPT \sim \triangle VUT$ b) $\frac{y}{16.2} = \frac{18.6}{3.6}$
c) 83.7 d) 83.7 m **4)** 5 m **5)** 43.3 m
**6)** 44.8 m **7)** 19.2 m **8)** 14.1 m **9)** 7.0 m
**10)** 6.9 m **11)** 261.3 m **12)** 850 m

### 15.3 Written Exercises, page 438

**1**b) 0.58, 0.50, 0.87 **3**c) 0.58, 0.50, 0.87
**4**a) 0.70, 0.57, 0.82 **5**a) 1.19, 0.77, 0.64
c) 1.19, 0.77, 0.64 **6**a) 0.18, 0.17, 0.98
b) 0.84, 0.34, 0.94 c) 0.47, 0.42, 0.91
d) 0.58, 0.50, 0.87 e) 0.70, 0.57, 0.82
f) 0.84, 0.64, 0.77 g) 1.00, 0.71, 0.71
h) 1.19, 0.77, 0.64 i) 1.73, 0.87, 0.50
j) 2.75, 0.94, 0.34 k) 5.67, 0.98, 0.17

### 15.4 Written Exercises, page 441

**1)** 6.7 m **2**a) 14.6 m b) 1.6 m c) 160.6 m
d) 94.0 m e) 0.8 m **3)** 16.8 m **4)** 79.4 m
**5)** 75.5 m **6)** 4.5 m **7)** 13.5 m **8)** 10.3 m
**9)** 90.4 m **10)** 0.7 km

### 15.5 Written Exercises, page 445

**1)** c **2)** a, b, d **4**a) $\frac{a}{c}$ b) $\frac{b}{c}$ c) $\frac{b}{c}$ d) $\frac{a}{c}$
e) $\frac{a}{b}$ f) $\frac{b}{a}$ **5**a) $\frac{4}{5}$ b) $\frac{15}{8}$ **6**a) 20, $\sin A = \frac{15}{25}$
b) 12, $\sin A = \frac{12}{20}$ c) 9, $\sin A = \frac{12}{15}$
d) 24, $\sin A = \frac{7}{25}$ **8**b) $\frac{5}{13}$ c) $\frac{5}{13}$
**9**a) $\sin P = \frac{12}{13}$, $\cos P = \frac{5}{13}$, $\tan P = \frac{12}{5}$,
$\sin R = \frac{5}{13}$, $\cos R = \frac{12}{13}$, $\tan R = \frac{5}{12}$
b) $\sin M = \frac{15}{25}$ c) $\sin Y = \frac{8}{17}$ **10**a) 24 m
b) 119 m c) 39 m d) 38 m **11)** 45.5 m
**12)** 118 m **13)** 176 m **14)** 1.1 km
**15)** 11.7 m **16)** 89.1 m

### 15.6 Written Exercises, page 449

**4)** 0.2079, 0.3090, 0.5878, 0.6428, 0.9397, 0.9962
**5)** 0.9903, 0.9659, 0.8988, 0.7880, 0.6018, 0.4695, 0.3420
**6**a) $\angle A = 51^\circ$, $\angle B = 39^\circ$
b) $\angle A = 56^\circ$, $\angle B = 34^\circ$ **7**a) 18.8 cm
b) 43.7 km c) 229.6 m d) 3.5 m **8)** 58.9 m
**9)** 0.3 km **10)** 104.6 m **11)** 7.3 m

### 15.7 Written Exercises, page 451

**1**a) 22.5 b) 20.8 c) 25.3 d) 90.2 e) 42.4
f) 17.0 **2**a) $42^\circ$ b) $22^\circ$ c) $38^\circ$ d) $16^\circ$
e) $12^\circ$ **3**a) $\angle A = 50^\circ$, AC = 5.8, BC = 6.9
b) $\angle P = 45^\circ$, $\angle R = 45^\circ$, PR = 9.9
c) $\angle M = 49^\circ$, $\angle L = 41^\circ$, MN = 10.6
d) $\angle P = 39^\circ$, PQ = 24.9, QR = 20.1
e) $\angle C = 52^\circ$, BC = 55.2, AB = 43.5
f) $\angle G = 35^\circ$, $\angle K = 55^\circ$, GK = 71.0
**4**a) $\angle P = 28^\circ$, QR = 4.3 cm, PR = 9.1 cm
b) $\angle P = 44^\circ$, QR = 11.6 m, PQ = 16.7 m
c) $\angle R = 13^\circ$, PQ = 0.9 mm, QR = 4.1 mm
d) $\angle R = 65^\circ$, PQ = 32.2 cm, PR = 35.5 cm
**5)** $83^\circ$ **6**a) $52^\circ$ b) 2.4 m **7)** $35^\circ$ **8)** 16.9 m
**9)** $\angle B = 19^\circ$, 15.1 m **10)** 1.0 km **11)** 4.8 m
**12)** 92.5 cm **13)** $26^\circ$ **14)** $47^\circ$ **15)** 36 mm
**16)** 62 cm

### 15.8 Written Exercises, page 454

**1)** 5 m **2)** 127 m **3)** 88 m **4)** 181 m
**5)** 481 m **6)** 19.9 m **7)** 78 m **8)** 100 m
**9)** $27^\circ$ **10)** 260 m **11)** 36 m **12)** 69 m
**13)** $6^\circ$ **14)** $3^\circ$ **15**a) 171 km b) 138 km

### 15.9 Written Exercises, page 458

**7**a) 118.8 cm b) 95.1 m **8**a) 12.9 km
b) 13.9 m **9)** 26.9 m **10)** 927.5 m
**11)** 77.9 m